Marine Community Ecology

Marine
Community
Ecology

Edited by

Mark D. Bertness
Brown University

Steven D. Gaines
University of California at Santa Barbara

Mark E. Hay
Georgia Institute of Technology

Sinauer Associates, Inc. • Publishers
Sunderland, Massachusetts

ABOUT THE COVER

A diverse coral reef community at Manado, Indonesia.
Photograph by Mike Severns/Tom Stack & Associates.

MARINE COMMUNITY ECOLOGY

Sinauer Associates, Inc.
P.O. Box 407
Sunderland, MA 01375-0407 U.S.A.

Fax: 413-549-1118
publish@sinauer.com
http://www.sinauer.com

Library of Congress Cataloguing-in-Publication Data

Marine community ecology / Mark D. Bertness, Steven D. Gaines, & Mark Hay.
    p. cm.
  Includes bibliographical references (p.).
  ISBN 0-87893-057-4 (alk. paper)
  1. Marine ecology. I. Bertness, Mark D. II. Gaines, Steven D. (Steven Dean).
III. Hay, Mark E.

QH541.5.S3 M256 2000
577.7—dc 21

00-052650

10 9 8 7 6 5 4 3 2 1

We dedicate this book to the pioneering careers of
Joseph H. Connell and Robert T. Paine

Contents

Preface

*I*n recent decades, marine ecologists have fundamentally advanced our understanding of the processes and interactions affecting population regulation and community organization, both in the sea and on land. Our purpose is to provide an overview of the recent history and present status of marine ecology, to provide students with an extensive introduction to the primary literature in this area, to convey the intellectual excitement of discovery that is propelling the field forward, and to stimulate students to prepare for the challenges and opportunities that we think marine ecologists will face in the future.

Just within the last 20 years, our understanding of marine communities has changed dramatically:

- **Deep-sea hydrothermal vent communities were discovered,** populated by organisms that use geochemical energy rather than photosynthesis. The discovery of these communities has fundamentally enlarged both the search for the origins of life on Earth and the search for new life forms on Earth, below Earth's surface, and on other planets.

- **No part of the ocean remains unaffected by human activity.** With fisheries, aquaculture, introductions of non-native species, modification or destruction of critical habitats, and additions of nutrients and chemical pollutants such as estrogen mimics, humans have fundamentally affected marine ecosystems worldwide. Coastal oceans are being affected more profoundly and more rapidly by human population increases than by global climate change. Ocean ecology can no longer be understood without reference to these perturbations to the ecosystem.

- **We now know that complex, indirect effects among species can profoundly affect food-web interactions and can structure entire communities over large areas.** These indirect effects can cause nonlinear responses of populations or communities to natural or anthropogenic change, resulting in ecosystems that rapidly switch from one state to another with little warning of impending change.

We suspect that even more drastic changes are in store for marine ecology over the next few decades. Marine ecologists must provide better stewardship of marine resources and ecosystems, by understanding which perturbations and food-web alterations will cause collapses of marine communities and the ecosystem services that they provide; predicting and mitigating the effects of these disturbances; and understanding and predicting interactions among global climate, marine geochemical processes, and marine biota.

Meeting these challenges will require better understanding of the causes and consequences of change on scales from hours and centimeters to millennia and thousands of kilometers. In the next two decades, new marine reserves will be started and entire estuaries manipulated within management strategies. It is critical that we learn from these manipulations rather than simply celebrate or bemoan ensuing changes. Doing so will require that we dismantle the artificial intellectual barriers that currently separate ecosystem and community perspectives on marine systems. These approaches need to complement one another to solve the problems at hand, and marine community ecology needs to shift its status from that of a highly successful, but almost purely exploratory, science to a predictive science capable of dealing with pressing current and future applied problems. This shift will be a formidable test of our understanding of marine systems. With this book, we hope to help prepare students to meet the challenges and opportunities of the coming decades.

MARK D. BERTNESS
STEVEN D. GAINES
MARK E. HAY

Contributors

Mark D. Bertness, Department of Ecology and Evolutionary Biology, Brown University, Providence, RI 02912 U.S.A.

George M. Branch, Zoology Department, University of Cape Town, Rondebosch 7701 South Africa

John F. Bruno, Department of Marine Sciences, University of North Carolina, Chapel Hill, NC 27599 U.S.A.

James T. Carlton, The Maritime Studies Program, Williams College and Mystic Seaport, Mystic, CT 06355 U.S.A.

C. W. Cunningham, Department of Biology, Duke University, Durham, NC 27708 U.S.A.

Paul K. Dayton, Scripps Institution of Oceanography, University of California at San Diego, La Jolla, CA 92093 U.S.A.

Mark Denny, Hopkins Marine Station, Stanford University, Pacific Grove, CA 93950 U.S.A.

J. Emmett Duffy, School of Marine Science, The College of William and Mary, Gloucester Point, VA 23062 U.S.A.

Aaron M. Ellison, Department of Biological Sciences, Mount Holyoke College, South Hadley, MA 01075 U.S.A.

James A. Estes, U.S. Geological Survey, Biological Resources Division, University of California, Santa Cruz, CA 95064 U.S.A.

Ron J. Etter, Biology Department, University of Massachusetts, Boston, MA 02125 U.S.A.

Elizabeth J. Farnsworth, New England Plant Conservation Program, New England Wild Flower Society, Framingham, MA 01701 U.S.A.

Rick Grosberg, Center for Population Biology, University of California, Davis, CA 95616 U.S.A.

Mark E. Hay, School of Biology, Georgia Institute of Technology, Atlanta, GA 30332 U.S.A.

Kenneth L. Heck, Jr., Dauphin Island Sea Laboratory, Dauphin Island, AL 36528 U.S.A.; and University of South Alabama, Mobile

Jeremy B. C. Jackson, Scripps Institution of Oceanography, University of California at San Diego, La Jolla, CA 92093 U.S.A.; and Smithsonian Tropical Research Institute, Balboa, Republic of Panama

Michael J. Keough, Department of Zoology, University of Melbourne, Parkville, Vic 3052 Australia

Nancy Knowlton, Scripps Institution of Oceanography, University of California at San Diego, La Jolla, CA 92093 U.S.A.; and Smithsonian Tropical Research Institute, Balboa, Republic of Panama

Hunter S. Lenihan, Institute of Marine Sciences, University of North Carolina at Chapel Hill, Morehead City, NC 28557 U.S.A.

Bruce A. Menge, Department of Zoology, Oregon State University, Corvallis, OR 97331 U.S.A.

Fiorenza Micheli, Hopkins Marine Station, Stanford University, Pacific Grove, CA 93950 U.S.A.

Steven G. Morgan, Bodega Marine Laboratory, University of California, Bodega Bay, CA 94923 U.S.A.

Lauren S. Mullineaux, Woods Hole Oceanographic Institution, Woods Hole, MA 02543 U.S.A.

Stephen R. Palumbi, Department of Organismic and Evolutionary Biology, Harvard University, Cambridge, MA 02173 U.S.A.

Steven G. Pennings, University of Georgia Marine Institute, Sapelo Island, GA 31327 U.S.A.

Charles H. Peterson, University of North Carolina at Chapel Hill, Institute of Marine Sciences, Morehead City, NC 28557 U.S.A.

Wayne P. Sousa, Department of Integrative Biology, University of California, Berkeley, CA 94720 U.S.A.

Robert S. Steneck, School of Marine Sciences, University of Maine, Darling Marine Center, Walpole, ME 04573 U.S.A.

A. J. Underwood, Centre for Research on Ecological Impacts of Coastal Cities, Marine Ecology Laboratories A11, University of Sydney, N.S.W. 2006, Australia

Geerat J. Vermeij, Department of Geology, University of California, Davis, CA 95616 U.S.A.

David Wethey, Department of Biological Sciences and Marine Science Program, University of South Carolina, Columbia, SC 29208 U.S.A.

Susan L. Williams, Bodega Marine Laboratory, University of California at Davis, Bodega Bay, CA 94923 U.S.A.

Jon D. Witman, Department of Ecology and Evolutionary Biology, Brown University, Providence, RI 02912 U.S.A.

part I

Processes Influencing Pattern in Marine Communities

chapter 1

Physical Processes That Generate Patterns in Marine Communities

Mark Denny and David Wethey

As with all assemblages of plants and animals, marine communities respond to their environment. A wide variety of physical factors contribute to the pattern of this response. For example, there is a vertical zonation of marine algae in response to the attenuation of light by seawater. As depth increases, primary productivity decreases, the diversity of algal species declines, and below a critical depth algae are no longer found. Similar broad-scale patterns are found in response to changes in salinity (e.g., the depauperate fauna of the Baltic Sea, a function at least in part of low salinity), temperature (e.g., the absence of coral reefs from waters in which the average temperature falls below about 20°C), and oxygen concentration (e.g., the exclusion of many midwater species from the oceanic oxygen-minimum zone).

It would be impossible to introduce (much less explore) all of these factors in this single chapter, and we will not attempt to do so. Instead, we focus on a particular subset of physical factors that has been shown to exert a strong influence on the small-scale pattern of nearshore marine communities—processes that are driven by the movement of fluids relative to organisms. Examples include the effects of water motion on external fertilization (e.g., Levitan 1995; Serrão et al. 1996; Pearson and Brawley 1998), the recruitment of planktonic larvae (e.g., Wing et al. 1995, 1998), the delivery of nutrients to macroalgae (e.g., Koehl and Alberte 1988), and the flux of particulate matter to suspension feeding animals (e.g., Shimeta and Jumars 1991). "Wave exposure," a complex of factors related to wave-induced water motion, is another example; it is a strong influence on community dynamics and species composition on wave-swept intertidal shores (e.g., Lewis 1964, 1968; Dayton 1971; Newell 1979; Sousa 1984, 1985; Ricketts et al. 1985, McQuaid and Branch 1985; Leigh et al. 1987). Similarly, the vertical zonation of littoral algae, plants, and animals is governed in large part by tidal fluctuations in water level (e.g., Stephenson and Stephenson 1972; Denny and Paine 1998), and when the tide is out, the temperature and osmotic balance of intertidal organisms are influenced by the flow of air (e.g. Bell 1993; Helmuth 1999). In addition to these direct effects, the movements of both air and water have secondary effects on community patterns through their influence on predation and competition for space (e.g., Menge 1978; Paine 1979; Paine and Levin 1981).

As disparate as these effects may seem, the physics by which each is governed is similar. In the language of engineering, each of the effects of flow mentioned above is an example of a **transport process** in which it is heat, mass, or momentum that is being transported. This chapter, then, is an exposition of the principles of transport phenomena as applied to marine communities. Our goal is to describe in broad strokes how these phenomena can affect patterns in community ecology, and to provide the reader with the basic tools and vocabulary required to approach the technical literature on the subject.

A Primer on the Physics of Flow

Introductory texts on biological aspects of fluid flow include Vogel (1994), Mann and Lazier (1991), and Denny (1988, 1993), and these should be the starting point for any practical exploration of the effects of transport processes in marine ecology. What follows here is a drastically condensed overview of the subject. The reader is hereby warned that when it comes to fluid dynamics, a little knowledge can be a dangerous thing, and the information presented here should be used only as a stepping stone towards a more thorough understanding.

A List of Symbols Used in This Chapter

a	acceleration
A	area
A_{conv}	area over which convective heat transfer occurs
A_{dif}	area exposed to diffuse solar radiation
A_{evap}	area over which evaporation occurs
A_F	frontal area
$A_{lw,ground}$	area exposed to long-wave radiation from the substratum
$A_{lw,sky}$	area exposed to long-wave radiation from the sky
A_{MAX}	maximum projected area of an alga
A_P	planform area
A_{sol}	area exposed to direct solar radiation
C	conncentration
C_A	added mass coefficient
C_D	drag coeffcient
C_M	inertia coefficient
d	depth of the water column
d_B	depth at wave breaking
d_d	damping depth (thermal conduction)
D	molecular diffusion coefficient
D_H	diffusivity of heat
E	wave energy per surface area
F	force
F_{AM}	added mass force
F_D	drag
F_I	inertial force
F_L	lift
F_{VB}	virtual buoyancy
g	acceleration due to gravity
h_C	convective heat transfer coefficient
H	wave height
H_B	wave height at breaking
H_{MAX}	maximum wave height
H_S	significant wave height
I	light intensity
I_{dif}	diffuse light intensity
I_{emit}	intensity of emitted light
I_{sol}	intensity of direct solar radiation
I_{surf}	intensity of direct solar radiation on a surface
J_z	amplitude of temperature fluctuations at depth z
J_0	amplitude of temperature fluctuations at the surface
k	wave number ($2p/l$)
K_z	turbulent diffusivity
L_C	characteristic length
L	linear dimension
m	mass
m_A	added mass
p	pressure
P	probability
Pr	Prandtl number
q	specific heat capacity
Q	net heat flux
Q_{cond}	heat flux due to conduction
Q_{conv}	heat flux due to convection
Q_{evap}	heat flux due to evaporation or condensation
$Q_{lw,ground}$	heat flux due to long-wave radiative transfer with the substratum

$Q_{lw,sky}$	heat flux due to long-wave radiative transfer with the sky
Q_{metab}	heat flux due to metabolism
Q_{sol}	heat flux due to direct solar radiation
Re	Reynolds number
s	distance above the substratum
Sc	Schmidt number
S_D	shape coefficient of drag
S_L	shape coefficient of lift
t	time
T	wave period
Te	temperature
Te_{air}	air temperature
Te_{fluid}	fluid temperature
Te_{ground}	substratum temperature
Te_{sky}	effective sky temperature
u	horizontal velocity
u_C	velocity of water at the wave crest
$u_{C,MAX}$	maximum velocity of water at the wave crest
u_{MAX}	maximum horizontal velocity
u_R	relative velocity
u_0	mainstream velocity
u_*	friction velocity
U	phase speed of a wave form
v	latent heat of vaporization
V	volume
w	vertical velocity
w_{MAX}	maximum vertical velocity
x	distance along the (horizontal) x-axis
z	distance along the (vertical) z-axis
α	absorptivity
β_D	shape exponent of drag
β_L	shape exponent of lift
δ	boundary-layer thickness
δ_C	thickness of a concentration boundary layer
δ_M	thickness of a momentum boundary layer
δ_T	thickness of a thermal boundary layer
δ_{VS}	thickness of the viscous sublayer
$\varepsilon(\lambda)$	emissivity at wavelength λ
ε_{ground}	emissivity of the substratum
ε_{org}	emissivity of an organism
ε_{sky}	effective emissivity of the sky
θ	angle of incidence
κ	diffusivity of heat
$\mathcal{K}$	conductivity of heat
λ	wavelength
λ_{MAX}	wavelength of most intense radiation
μ	dynamic viscosity
ν	kinematic viscosity
ρ	mass density
ρ_A	density of air
ρ_K	density of kelp body tissue
ρ_W	density of water
σ	Stephan-Boltzmann constant
τ	shear stress
τ_B	boundary shear stress
ω	wave frequency ($2\pi/T$)

Density

We begin with density, the mass of a substance found in a given volume. At a typical salinity of 35 grams per liter, the density of seawater, ρ_W, is approximately 1025 kg m^{-3}, a value that varies slightly with temperature (Denny 1993). At 0°C, ρ_W is 1028 kg m^{-3}, at 30°C density is 0.6% less (1022 kg m^{-3}). The density of air at sea level, ρ_A, is about 830 times less that that of seawater; it varies from 1.29 kg m^{-3} at 0°C to 1.17 kg m^{-3} at 30°C, a variation of 9.3%.

A Coordinate System

To facilitate our discussion of fluid flows and forces, we need to specify how we are going to locate objects in space. A standard Cartesian coordinate system serves well for our purposes. We let the *x*-axis be horizontal, and in most cases we align it with the major axis of flow. Velocity along the *x*-axis is denoted by *u*. The *y*-axis is also horizontal, but, for the simple situations we deal with in this chapter, flows in this direction are not encountered. The *z*-axis is vertical, and flow along it is denoted by *w*. Depending on the circumstances, the origin of the coordinate system is located either at the air–water interface or at the substratum.

Momentum

The mass of any object is a measure of the object's **inertia**, the resistance of the object to change in its state of motion. If an initially stationary mass is to be moved, a net force *F* must be applied. (This is Newton's first law of motion.) Similarly, if the mass is already moving, a net force is required to make it move faster or slower. If we define **momentum** as the product of velocity (*u*) and mass (*m*), the relationship between net force and the state of motion of a mass can be expressed as Newton's second law of motion:

$$F = \frac{d(mu)}{dt} \qquad \text{Eq. 1}$$

where *t* is time. That is, net force is equal to the rate of change of momentum.

If the mass of the object is constant, *m* can be brought outside the derivative. Noting that the rate of change of velocity is acceleration (*a*), we arrive at an equivalent relationship between net force and the state of motion of a constant mass:

$$F = m\frac{du}{dt} = ma \qquad \text{Eq. 2}$$

Thus, force is equal to mass times acceleration. With mass measured in kilograms, length in meters, and time in seconds, force has the units of kg m s^{-2}, termed newtons, N.

When dealing with solid objects (such as baseballs or Mack trucks) we can easily think of discrete masses moving with defined velocities, and the application of Equations 1 and 2 is straightforward. Fluids, however, are less discrete, and in fluid dynamics it is sometimes inconvenient to divide a gas or liquid into distinct, separate masses. As a practical al-ternative, we often deal with fluid forces in terms of the mass per volume of a fluid (its density, ρ) and the momentum per volume, ρu.

Momentum Flux

Similarly, when dealing with fluids, it is often advantageous not to follow the changes in momentum of an individual fluid particle, but rather to calculate at a fixed location a quantity known as **momentum flux**, the rate per area at which momentum is transported by the fluid. For example, consider the following situation. A fluid of constant density ρ flows at velocity *u*. If we define an area *A* perpendicular to the direction of flow, the volume of fluid transported through this area per time is *uA*. Multiplying volume by density, we see that the mass per time moving through area *A* is ρuA. This mass has velocity *u*, so the rate at which momentum (the product of mass and velocity) is transported through *A* is $\rho u^2 A$. The momentum flux (rate of momentum transport per area) is thus

$$\text{Momentum flux} = \rho u^2 \qquad \text{Eq. 3}$$

In essence, this is a force per area, or a **pressure**. The message here is that in the process of transporting momentum, fluids are capable of exerting pressure. This pressure is proportional to the density of the fluid and the square of its velocity. Newton's third law of motion (for every action there is an equal and opposite reaction) allows us to turn this relationship around. By imposing a spatially varying pressure on a fluid, the fluid can be coaxed to transport momentum. In this light, fluid-dynamic forces are revealed as transport phenomena: The pattern in which momentum is transported affects (and is affected by) the force experienced by an object of a given size.

Viscosity

Fluids, both gases and liquids, are distinguished from solids by their ability to flow. Whereas a constant **stress** (force per area) applied to a solid results in a fixed deformation, a constant stress applied to a fluid results in a fixed *rate* of deformation (Vogel 1994; Denny 1993). The proportionality constant between the **shear stress**, τ, (the stress that tends to slide one fluid layer parallel to another) and the rate of the consequent deformation is the fluid's **dynamic viscosity**, μ:

$$\tau = \mu \frac{du}{dz} \qquad \text{Eq. 4}$$

In Equation 4 *u* is the velocity of the fluid at position *z*, and du/dz (the **velocity gradient** along the *z*-axis) is a measure of the rate at which the fluid is deformed. It is worth dwelling on this equation for a moment; it embodies an important message: Whenever there is a velocity gradient in a viscous fluid, there must be an accompanying shear stress.

With shear stress measured in N m^{-2} (known as pascals, Pa) and velocity in m s^{-1}, dynamic viscosity has units of Pa s.

Seawater has a dynamic viscosity of 1.8×10^{-3} Pa s at 0°C, a value that decreases drastically with increasing temperature; μ is only 0.87×10^{-3} Pa s at 30°C (Denny 1993). Air is about 100 times less viscous than water, and (in contrast with water) its viscosity rises with temperature. The dynamic viscosity of dry air is 1.72×10^{-5} Pa s at 0°C and 1.87×10^{-5} Pa s at 30°C (Denny 1993).

In fluid dynamics it is often the ratio of viscosity to density that is important, and to streamline the notation this ratio is given a name—**kinematic viscosity**, ν:

$$\nu \equiv \frac{\mu}{\rho} \qquad \text{Eq. 5}$$

Kinematic viscosity has units $m^2 \, s^{-1}$. The kinematic viscosity of seawater is $1.84 \times 10^{-6} \, m^2 \, s^{-1}$ at 0°C, decreasing to $0.85 \times 10^{-6} \, m^2 \, s^{-1}$ at 30°C. The kinematic viscosity of air is greater than that of water (relative to its density, air is more viscous than water), with a value of $13.3 \times 10^{-6} \, m^2 \, s^{-1}$ at 0°C and $16.0 \times 10^{-6} \, m^2 \, s^{-1}$ at 30°C (Denny 1993).

The definition of kinematic viscosity allows for a useful rearrangement of Equation 4. Multiplying the right-hand side of the equation by 1 in the guise of ρ/ρ, we see that:

$$\tau = \nu \frac{d(\rho u)}{dz} \qquad \text{Eq. 6}$$

In other words, shear stress is equal to the product of kinematic viscosity and the spatial gradient in momentum per volume. We will make use of this form of Equation 4 when we deal with boundary layers.

Reynolds Number

In a fluid, the transport of momentum (a force) depends on the pattern of flow, and there are two counteracting factors that prove valuable in predicting this pattern. The inertia of a fluid can result in a force that tends to keep the fluid in continued motion. In contrast, the viscous forces acting on the fluid provide a tendency for motion to grind to a halt. For reasons we will not delve into here (see Vogel 1994), it is the *ratio* of these two forces (inertial and viscous) that is useful in predicting the pattern of flow. The ratio of inertial to viscous forces is the **Reynolds number**, *Re*:

$$Re \equiv \frac{\rho u L_C}{\mu} = \frac{u L_C}{\nu} \qquad \text{Eq. 7}$$

L_C is a characteristic length of the object in question, here taken as the maximum length in the direction of flow. As the ratio of two forces, the Reynolds number is dimensionless.

Reynolds numbers in aquatic environments vary over a large range. For a large intertidal kelp ($L_C = 1$ m) and the rapid water motion found in breaking waves (10 m s^{-1}), *Re* is 10^7. For a small organism ($L_C = 0.01$ m) and slow, subtidal flows (0.1 m s^{-1}), *Re* is ten-thousandfold smaller, approximately 1,000. Even in this case, however, *Re* greatly exceeds 1,

implying that in most situations relevant to our discussion the inertial forces in water far outweigh the viscous forces. Only for very small objects (such as larvae and gametes) capable of moving with the ambient flow does the Reynolds number fall below 1 in the nearshore environment. In air, Reynolds numbers are approximately 15-fold smaller than those in water for the same size of organism and the same relative velocity.

Bernoulli's Principle

As fluid flows relative to an organism, it often changes velocity, and these changes in speed are tied to changes in pressure. The specifics of this relationship (known as **Bernoulli's principle**) are beyond the purview of this chapter (see Vogel 1994 for a discussion), but the general message is relevant: An increase in velocity as fluid flows along a steady path is accompanied by a decrease in pressure, and vice versa.

The No-Slip Condition

The interaction between fluid dynamics and biology inevitably involves the interface between a fluid and the solid surface of a plant, animal, or the substratum. At this interface there is no motion of the fluid relative to the surface. This fact (known as the **no-slip condition**) is a basic tenet in much of our understanding of the pattern of flow around organisms, and we make use of it in our discussion of boundary layers later in this chapter.

Fick's First Law of Diffusion

Random motion has the tendency to disperse objects. For example, the random thermal motion of an initially concentrated group of molecules results in the gradual spread of the molecules in the process known as molecular diffusion. On a larger scale, the "random" motions of a turbulent fluid can result in the diffusive transport of both molecules and macroscopic particles suspended in the fluid (gametes and larvae, for instance) as well as the transport of heat and momentum as the fluid itself is mixed. The flux of mass, heat, or momentum by random motion is often described using **Fick's first law of diffusion** (shown here in generic form):

$$\text{Flux along the } z\text{-axis} = -X \frac{dY}{dz} \qquad \text{Eq. 8}$$

Here flux is the rate per area at which the quantity in question is transported. For example, when dealing with molecular diffusion, flux is commonly measured in moles per m^2 per second. In this case Y is a measure of concentration (moles or mass per m^3) and X is the **molecular diffusivity**, also known as the **diffusion coefficient** (with units $m^2 \, s^{-1}$). When dealing with turbulent "diffusion" (turbulent mixing), Y is again concentration and X is the **turbulent diffusivity** (also known as the **eddy diffusivity**), again with units of $m^2 \, s^{-1}$. When we consider laminar boundary layers, we will concern ourselves with the diffusive transport of momentum. In this case, the appropriate diffusivity turns out to be the kinematic viscosity, v, and Y is the momentum per volume (see Equation 6). Each of these various forms of the generic Fick's law is discussed in greater detail later in this chapter.

TRANSPORT OF MOMENTUM: HYDRODYNAMIC FORCES

We now turn our attention to the forces that can be imposed on organisms by moving fluids. These forces can serve both as selective factors in the evolution of morphology and as agents of disturbance. Both air and water can exert forces on plants and animals, but because water is roughly 830 times as dense as air, these forces are generally much larger in water than in air, and in the discussion here we limit ourselves to hydrodynamic forces. In the marine environment, there are three general forces associated with the movement of water: *drag*, *lift*, and the *accelerational force*. The last of these, the accelerational force, is itself composed of two forces: *virtual buoyancy*, and the *added mass force*. Each of these forces will be treated in turn.

Drag

Consider the situation shown in Figure 1.1. Water flows relative to an organism with a mainstream velocity u_R, and the pattern of flow is affected by the organism's presence. Near the upstream face of the object, water slows down, and it may actually be brought to halt at one spot (the stagnation point). Water that is not brought to a complete standstill is redirected laterally. As water moves around the sides of the organism, it speeds up, often attaining a speed twice that of the mainstream. Downstream of the organism, the speed of the water is reduced, but before the flow can be brought to a halt, it separates from the object, forming a turbulent wake. The average speed of water in the wake is less than that in the mainstream.

The net result of all this speeding up and slowing down is that the overall momentum flux downstream of the organism (measured in a plane perpendicular to flow) is less than that measured in a plane upstream of the organism (Vogel 1994). When summed across area, this change in momentum flux is (by definition) a force, and it acts to push the organism downstream. This force is termed **drag**.

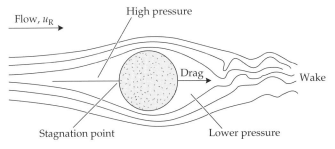

Figure 1.1 Fluid-dynamic drag. The pattern of flow around an object is associated with a relatively high pressure on the object's upstream face and a relatively low pressure downstream in the turbulent wake. This upstream–downstream difference in pressure results in drag, a force tending to push the object in the direction of flow.

The proximal mechanism by which the momentum flux is reduced as fluid flows around an object is a pressure difference that results from the pattern of flow. As water slows near the upstream face of an organism, its pressure is increased (due to Bernoulli's principle), and at a stagnation point the pressure is increased above ambient hydrostatic pressure by an amount known as the **dynamic pressure**:

$$\text{Dynamic pressure} = \frac{1}{2}\rho_W u_R{}^2 \qquad \text{Eq. 9}$$

Note the similarity of this expression for the dynamic pressure to that for momentum flux we calculated earlier. Water in the wake is at a higher pressure than ambient, but lower than that on the upstream face of the object. The resulting upstream–downstream difference in pressure acts over the area of the organism to impose drag. The pertinent area in this case is A_F, the **frontal area**, the area projected in the direction of flow. The exact magnitude of drag depends on the precise pattern of flow.

This description of the origin of drag is embodied in a standard equation:

$$F_D = \frac{1}{2}\rho_W u_R^2 A_F C_D \qquad \text{Eq. 10}$$

with the implicit understanding that the direction of drag is the same as that of the relative flow. In other words, drag is equal to the product of dynamic pressure and frontal area, tempered by the dimensionless **drag coefficient, C_D**. Equation 10 serves as a definition of C_D:

$$C_D = \frac{2F_D}{\rho_W u_F^2 A_F} \qquad \text{Eq. 11}$$

Note that C_D need not be constant. In fact, the drag coefficient commonly varies substantially as a function of Reynolds number and the shape of the organism. For flexible organisms, C_D may also vary with drag itself as the organism reconfigures in flow. In all but a few simple cases it is not yet possible to predict C_D from first principles. In practice, C_D is estimated empirically by measuring the drag exerted on an organism of known projected area at a known water velocity (see Denny 1988).

In as much as it is a function of Reynolds number, the drag coefficient varies with kinematic viscosity, velocity, and length. Relative to the variation in water velocity, the variation in kinematic viscosity in the marine environment is small. As a result, for an organism of a given shape and length, the drag coefficient is a function primarily of water velocity. In this instance, an alternative model of drag has some advantages (Gaylord et al. 1994; Denny 1995):

$$F_D = \frac{1}{2}\rho_W u_R^{B_D} A_F S_D \qquad \text{Eq. 12}$$

Here, the Reynolds-number dependence (and any dependence on reconfiguration) of the drag coefficient has been subsumed into the **velocity exponent of drag**, β_D, and S_D, the **shape coefficient of drag**, is a constant for objects of a given shape. By separating the effects of water velocity and shape, this expression provides a more intuitive presentation of the factors that govern drag in nearshore environments. Note, however, that the shape coefficient has units $m^{(2-\beta_D)}s^{-(2-\beta_D)}$. Thus, the shape coefficient is dimensionless only when $\beta_D = 2$.

For marine organisms, the velocity exponent follows one of two typical patterns. For so called "bluff objects," β_D is approximately 2. Note that in this case, the shape coefficient is approximately equal to the drag coefficient. Bluff objects are characterized by: (1) the lack of a streamlined shape and (2) the inability to change their shape under the influence of flow. Acorn barnacles and massive coral heads are excellent examples of biological bluff bodies. In contrast, most fish (due to their streamlined shape) and marine algae (due to their flexibility and the consequent ability to change shape) are not bluff.

For organisms that are inherently streamlined (or flexible enough to become streamlined in flow), the velocity exponent is less than 2 and varies from about 0.5 to 1.5 (Gaylord et al. 1994). In other words, for streamlined objects drag does not increase as rapidly with velocity as it does for a bluff object.

In this discussion, we have implicitly relied on the reader's intuition to recognize a "streamlined" shape, but this is seldom problematic. By using fast cars and airplanes as archetypical streamlined shapes, most people are innately adept at recognizing the characteristics of objects that have small velocity exponents. In a more technical definition, a streamlined shape is one that reduces the size of the turbulent wake. This involves a gently curving outline to the object and a tapered downstream end that reduces the tendency for the flow to separate.

As mentioned above, the flexibility of organisms such as kelps and other marine algae allows them to reconfigure in flow, assuming a streamlined shape and resulting in a small velocity exponent. This is not a certain recipe for drag reduction, however. Flags are quite flexible, and they continuously reconfigure in flow, but the resulting flapping can actually *increase* drag (Hoerner 1965). A flag of a given area experiences much higher drag than a rigid thin plate of the same area (assuming, of course, that the plate is held parallel to flow).

Lift

Consider the situation shown in Figure 1.2A. Water flows past an asymmetrical object with a mainstream velocity u_R, and (as we have seen) the pattern of flow is affected by the object's presence. In this case, because the object is asymmet-

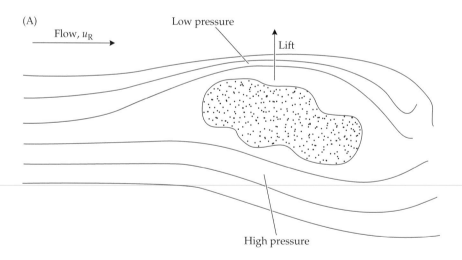

(A)

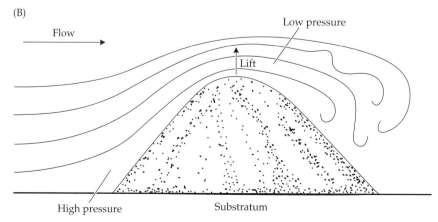

(B)

Figure 1.2 Fluid-dynamic lift. (A) If an object is not symmetrical with respect to the axis of flow, the pressure on one lateral face may be different from that on the opposite face. This lateral difference in pressure results in lift, a force perpendicular to the direction of flow. (B) Lift may be enhanced for an object in contact with a solid substratum. For example, the presence of the seafloor results in a high average pressure near the base of the limpet shell shown here. Coupled with the low pressure over the apex of the shell, this high pressure results in a substantial lift.

rical, the pattern of flow on one side of the object differs from that on the other. As a consequence, the application of Bernoulli's principle tells us that pressures on the two sides of the object are different. This lateral difference in pressure applied over the area of the object results in **lift**, a force acting at right angles to the direction of flow. Note that lift is not constrained to act upwards against gravity. Depending on the orientation of an object's asymmetry, lift can act in any direction, even downward.

Because the mechanism of lift is similar to that of drag (in that it entails a difference in pressure between two faces of an organism), the standard equation describing lift is similar to that for drag:

$$F_L = \frac{1}{2}\rho_W u_R^2 A_P C_L \qquad \text{Eq. 13}$$

Here A_P is the **planform area**, the area that one would trace around if the organism were laid in its natural posture on a piece of paper. Note that for most organisms planform area is different from the frontal area used to calculate drag. C_L is the **lift coefficient**, a dimensionless value akin to the drag coefficient. As with the drag coefficient, C_L is a function of Reynolds number and the shape of the organism. Equation 13 serves as a definition for the lift coefficient:

$$C_L \equiv \frac{2F_L}{\rho_W u_R^2 A_P} \qquad \text{Eq. 14}$$

An alternative model for lift, similar to that for drag, can also be used:

$$F_L = \frac{1}{2}\rho_W u_R^{B_L} A_P S_L \qquad \text{Eq. 15}$$

Here β_L is the **velocity exponent of lift** and S_L is the **shape coefficient of lift**. As with Equation 12 for drag, Equation 15 has the advantage of specifically separating the effects of velocity and shape, but has the disadvantage that unless $\beta_L = 2$, the shape coefficient has dimensions.

Lift has received far less attention than drag for marine organisms, and as a result less is known of its typical behavior. From the few measurements made to date (see Denny 1995 for a compilation) it appears that β_L is very nearly 2 for most organisms (both bluff and streamlined).

The magnitude of lift can be strongly affected by the presence of nearby objects. Benthic organisms provide a prime example (Figure 1.2B). In this case, the presence of the substratum prevents flow beneath the organism and (on average) slows the flow around the base of the organism. This reduction in flow results in a relatively high pressure beneath the organism. As flow is forced over the top of the plant or animal, it speeds up and its pressure is reduced. The net affect is a high pressure below the organism, a low pressure above, and a substantial lift. Even symmetrical objects (such as spheres) can experience large lifts when placed on a solid substratum.

Note that "lift" and "drag" are, in a sense, computational fictions. In reality, the pattern of flow around a plant or animal results in a distribution of pressures acting on the organism. If the pressure differs among exposed portions of the organism's body, a net force may be applied, acting at some angle to the mainstream flow. The component of this net force that lies parallel to flow we call drag, the component perpendicular to flow we call lift, but to the organism there is simply one force:

$$\text{Net velocity-induced force} = \sqrt{\text{drag}^2 + \text{lift}^2} \qquad \text{Eq. 16}$$

This force is proportional to the velocity of the fluid (raised to some positive exponent) and to the exposed area of the organism. Its direction may change as a function of velocity as the relative magnitude of lift and drag changes:

$$\text{Angle of force (relative to the direction of flow)} = \arctan\left(\frac{F_L}{F_D}\right) \qquad \text{Eq. 17}$$

Accelerational Forces

Additional hydrodynamic forces are placed on plants and animals if either the water or the organism accelerates. Consider, for instance, the situation shown in Figure 1.3A. Because a column of water is acted upon by the acceleration of gravity g, hydrostatic pressure p increases with depth. Following the tradition of nearshore engineers, we measure depth on a vertical axis (the z-axis) with its origin at the water's surface and positive values extending upward. In this case, it can be calculated that $p = -\rho_W g z$, where g is the acceleration due to gravity (9.81 m s^{-2}; Denny 1993). As a result, an object suspended in water has a larger force applied to its lower surface than its upper surface, and it feels a buoyant force pushing it up. The magnitude of this buoyant force is $\rho_W V g$, where V is the volume of fluid displaced by the object, and ρ_W is again the density of the water.

An analogous situation occurs if, rather than being stationary, the water accelerates. For example, in Figure 1.3B, water is shown accelerating horizontally. In order for the water to accelerate in this fashion, there must be a horizontal gradient in pressure, with pressure decreasing in the direction of acceleration. It is this pressure gradient that provides the net force necessary to accelerate the fluid. But if there is a pressure gradient, an object suspended in flow will feel a buoyant force, analogous to that felt by the object in Figure 1.3A. This acceleration-induced buoyant force is traditionally called the **virtual buoyancy**, F_{VB}, and it acts along the direction of acceleration (Batchelor 1967). By analogy to hydrostatic buoyancy:

$$F_{VB} = \rho_W V \frac{du}{dt} \qquad \text{Eq. 18}$$

(A)

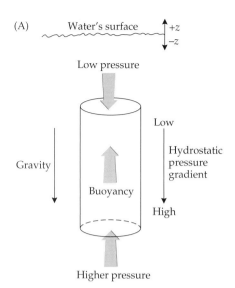

(B)

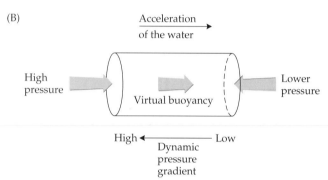

Figure 1.3 Buoyancy and virtual buoyancy. (A) The acceleration of gravity results in a gradient in hydrostatic pressure in a still fluid: pressure increases with increasing depth. As a result, the deep end of a submerged object feels a greater pressure than the shallow end, and a vertical buoyant force is imposed. (B) The horizontal acceleration of a fluid results in a dynamic pressure gradient and a horizontally directed virtual buoyancy.

Whereas the virtual buoyancy acts only when water accelerates relative to the stationary substratum, a second force acts when an object accelerates relative to the water. As a solid object accelerates relative to a fluid, the pattern of flow in the fluid is continuously changed, and the momentum of the fluid is affected. This change in momentum is (by definition) a force. From Newton's third law of motion, we know that if (by changing fluid's momentum) an object places a force on the fluid, the fluid imposes an equal force on the object. Now, the effect of a moving object on the fluid's momentum is distributed throughout the fluid, varying from place to place. However, if these distributed effects are summed over the entire fluid, we find that they act *as if* there is a mass of fluid (called the **added mass**, m_A) that accelerates at the same rate as the solid object. As a result, the change in momentum in the fluid can be calculated as the product of this (fictitious) added mass and the object's acceleration relative to the fluid. The **added-mass force** is thus:

$$F_{AM} = m_A \frac{du_R}{dt}$$ Eq. 19

where du_R/dt is the relative acceleration between the object and the fluid. Traditionally, the added mass is expressed in terms of a volume of fluid:

$$m_A = \rho_W C_A V$$ Eq. 20

where V is again the volume displaced by the solid object and C_A is the dimensionless **added-mass coefficient**. In other words, if $C_A = 1$, the accelerating object behaves as if there were a volume of fluid equal to the object's volume that is accelerated along with the object.

The overall hydrodynamic accelerational force acting on an object is the sum of virtual buoyancy and the added mass force:

$$F_A = \rho_W V \frac{du}{dt} + C_A \rho_W V \frac{du_R}{dt}$$ Eq. 21

Note that if the object is stationary, $du_R/dt = du/dt$ and

$$F_A = (1 + C_A)\rho_W V \frac{du}{dt} \text{(object stationary)}$$ Eq. 22

The sum $(1 + C_A)$ is sometimes referred to as the **inertia coefficient**, C_M.

If the water is stationary and only the object accelerates, there is no virtual buoyancy, $du_R/dt = d^2x/dt^2$ (the acceleration of the object relative to the substratum), and the overall hydrodynamic accelerational force is:

$$F_A = C_A \rho_W V \frac{d^2x}{dt^2}$$ Eq. 23

(The separate force required to accelerate the mass of the object itself is considered below.)

Note that regardless of whether the fluid or the object accelerates, the accelerational force is proportional to the volume of fluid displaced by an organism. This is in contrast to lift and drag, in which force is proportional to the area exposed to flow. The consequences of this difference are discussed below.

Both the accelerational force and drag act along the direction of fluid motion relative to an organism. They need not act in the same direction, however. For example, if water is moving relative to a benthic organism, but is slowing down, the direction of acceleration is opposite that of velocity. In this situation the accelerational force tends to counteract drag.

As with lift and drag coefficients, added mass coefficients for plants and animals must be measured empirically. The methods by which this is accomplished are not entirely straightforward, and the interested reader is urged to consult Sarpkaya and Isaacson (1984), Gaylord et al. (1994), Denny and Gaylord (1996), and Gaylord (1997). Perhaps because of the practical difficulties in measuring C_A, it has been accomplished for only a few marine organisms (limpets, barnacles, sea urchins, and a variety of algae), and few generalities are available. The added mass coefficients for bluff objects (an acorn barnacle, for instance) are in the range of theoretical values predicted for cylinders ($C_A = 1$) and spheres ($C_A = 0.5$). In contrast, Gaylord et al. (1994) and Gaylord (1997) found very high added-mass coefficients for kelps (C_A of 6–9). These flexible, often bushy plants tend to affect a large volume of water for the volume that they actually displace.

The Morison Equation

Organisms exposed to real-world flows simultaneously experience drag, lift, and accelerational forces. Predicting how these forces combine has been the subject of controversy among engineers for decades. For example, drag and lift coefficients are typically measured by exposing an organism to a steady velocity and noting the resulting force. In an accelerating flow, the same velocity may be transiently obtained, but the pattern of flow around the organism could be different because the velocity is not constant. Thus, the drag coefficient corresponding to a particular velocity might be different in an accelerating flow than in a steady flow. This effect could be particularly important in cases where the flow changes direction as well as velocity, for instance in wave-induced oscillatory flow.

Despite the many reasons for concern regarding the summation of hydrodynamic forces, a simple approach to the calculation of the overall force appears to work reasonably well. As proposed by Morison et al. (1950), drag (calculated using Equation 10) and the accelerational force (Equation 21) are summed to estimate the inline hydrodynamic force, and lift

(Equation 13) is added via the Pythagorean theorem. Thus the overall hydrodynamic force applied by the fluid is:

$$F = \sqrt{\left(F_A + F_D\right)^2 + F_L^2} \qquad \text{Eq. 24}$$

This expression is known as the **Morison equation**.

AN INERTIAL FORCE

The forces examined so far have been external forces, those applied by the fluid to a plant or animal. In some situations it is possible for a marine organism to apply a force to itself (Denny et al. 1998). Consider, for example, Figure 1.4. The hydrodynamic forces imposed upon a large kelp plant have caused the plant to move, and as a result, the frond mass of the kelp has acquired considerable momentum. What happens when the kelp's motion brings it to the end of its tether? As soon as the tether (the stipe of the kelp) is extended to its full length it begins to apply an elastic force to the moving frond mass, tending to tug the mass to a halt. From Newton's second law (Equation 2), we know that the magnitude of this **inertial force** is determined by the deceleration of the effective mass of the kelp. In this case, the effective mass is the sum of the mass of the kelp itself ($\rho_K V$, where ρ_K is the density of the kelp and V is the volume of the moving portions of the alga) and the added mass that acts as if it were attached to the plant. As a result, the inertial force, F_I is:

$$F_I = \left(C_A \rho_W + \rho_K\right) V \frac{d^2 x}{dt^2} \qquad \text{Eq. 25}$$

The term $(C_A \rho_W + \rho_K) V$ is the **effective mass** of the kelp.

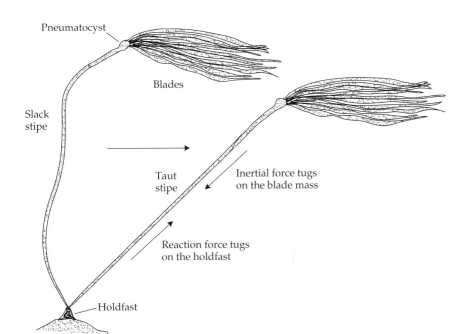

Pneumatocyst

Blades

Slack stipe

Taut stipe

Inertial force tugs on the blade mass

Reaction force tugs on the holdfast

Holdfast

Figure 1.4 The blade mass of a bull kelp (*Nereocystis luetkeana*) is attached to the substrate by a ropelike, flexible stipe. As the bade mass moves with the flow, it may abruptly come to the end of its "tether." The resulting deceleration can apply a substantial inertial force to the stipe.

Here we have presented the inertial force in terms of an applied elastic force because that is the most common situation among benthic organisms. Equation 25 is quite generally applicable, however. If a stationary fish applies a thrust to its body by swishing its tail, the magnitude of the thrust can be calculated as the product of the fish's acceleration and its effective mass as given by Equation 25.

SCALING HYDRODYNAMIC FORCES

As we noted above, lift and drag are proportional to the area an organism presents to flow, while the accelerational force is proportional to the volume of fluid displaced. As a result, the relative importance of lift, drag, and accelerational force depends on the size of the organism. If we assume that organisms stay the same shape as they grow, the area exposed to flow is proportional to L^2, where L is some linear dimension of the organism. Thus, the ratio of lift to drag is

$$\frac{\text{Lift}}{\text{Drag}} \propto \frac{\frac{1}{2}\rho_W u_R^2 L^2 C_L}{\frac{1}{2}\rho_W u_R^2 L^2 C_D} = \frac{C_L}{C_D} \qquad \text{Eq. 26}$$

For a given Reynolds number, this expression is independent of size. Thus, although the ratio of lift to drag may vary drastically among shapes (shape affects both the ratio of planform to frontal area and the force coefficients), for a given shape the ratio does not depend on how large the organism is.

Note, however, that volume is proportional to L^3 rather then L^2. As a result, the ratio between accelerational force (here calculated for a stationary organism) and velocity-induced force (here, drag) is:

$$\frac{\text{Accleration force}}{\text{Velocity-induced force}} \propto \frac{(1+C_A)\rho L^3 a}{\frac{1}{2}\rho u_R^2 L^2 C_D} = L\left(\frac{1+C_A}{C_D}\frac{2a}{u_R^2}\right)$$

$$\text{Eq. 27}$$

Thus, for a given flow regime (which sets the acceleration and velocity), the larger an organism is (that is, the larger L is), the larger the accelerational force is relative to drag. The same conclusion applies when accelerational force is compared to lift. The message of this equation is that accelerational forces are likely to be of biological importance only for relatively large organisms (massive corals, for example; see Massel and Done 1993; Massel 1996).

For any given size, the ratio of accelerational force and velocity-induced force is set by the term in parentheses in Equation 27. This term varies widely depending on the environmental circumstances. For example, in a tidal current, flow is nearly steady over periods of many minutes and acceleration is very small compared to the square of velocity. In this situation, the accelerational force is small compared to drag or lift regardless of the size of the organism. In contrast, in the turbulent flows found in blind-ended surge channels, accelerations may be high at times when the velocity is quite low. In this case, the accelerational force can potentially be large compared to the velocity-induced force even for small organisms.

PATTERNS OF HYDRODYNAMIC FORCES: OCEAN WAVES

The principles that underlie hydrodynamic forces can be applied to the study of pattern in community ecology in a variety of ways. Here we explore the role of water motion as a potential mechanism of disturbance. Knowledge of the pattern in which disturbance varies in the environment (both through space and through time) provides insight into the spatial and temporal variation in species composition, the rate of turnover within a population, and the maximal size of plants and animals. In the nearshore environment these patterns are governed in large part by the nature of ocean waves and the flows that they induce. As we will see, hydrodynamic theory will allow us to predict and *quantify* these effects.

As wind blows over the ocean, energy is transferred to seawater and is embodied partially in the form of waves. Energy within a wave is evenly split between gravitational potential energy (due to water being displaced above or below average sea level) and kinetic energy (the energy of water in motion beneath the wave). Once formed, waves propagate across the sea, and as they approach shore the horizontal and vertical motions of water beneath the waves interact with benthic algae and animals.

The terminology of the nearshore is shown in Figure 1.5. The depth of the water, d, is measured from the **still-water level** of the ocean (its level in the absence of waves) and varies with distance from the shore depending on the slope of the sea floor. The intersection of the still-water level and the sea floor defines the **shoreline**. As waves move toward shore they encounter ever-shallower water, and (as discussed below) at a critical depth they break. For our purposes, the ocean outside of this breaking point is referred to as the **offshore** area, and the area between the break point and the shore line is the **surf zone**. Above the shore line is an area of the coast that is occasionally subjected to wave-induced flows, the **run-up** or **swash zone**.

Ocean waves have been the subject of intense study by fluid dynamicists and engineers, and as a consequence the bulk water motions that they cause can be accurately described. The simplest practical description is provided by **linear wave theory**. For a thorough introduction to linear wave theory, the reader should consult Kinsman (1965) or Denny (1988), but the relevant concepts and equations are summarized here.

The morphology of a deep-water ocean wave is shown in Figure 1.6. Each wave is approximately sinusoidal, with a distinct **crest** and **trough**. The vertical distance between crest and trough is the **wave height**, H, and the horizontal distance between two successive crests (or troughs) is the **wavelength**,

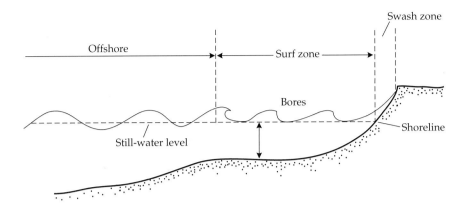

Figure 1.5 The nomenclature of the nearshore. Waves "peak up" and break as they move inshore. The surf zone extends from the breaking point to the shoreline (the intersection of still-water level with the shore). Waves may continue their motion in the swash zone, shoreward of the shoreline. (After Denny 1988.)

λ. The wave form travels at a **phase speed**, *U* (also known as the **celerity**). The time it takes for a wave form to travel one wavelength is the **wave period**, *T*:

$$T = \frac{\lambda}{U} \qquad \text{Eq. 28}$$

The period of ocean waves varies greatly. Locally produced **seas** often have a period of 4–6 seconds. **Swell** (waves that have traveled from a distant source) commonly have periods of 8–20 seconds. As we will see, the wavelength depends on the wave period, but is independent of the wave height. The morphology shown above applies primarily to waves in **deep water**, water in which the depth is greater than half the wavelength. The logic behind this definition of deep water is discussed below.

When dealing with ocean waves it is important to distinguish between the motion of the wave form and the motion of the water itself, a distinction best grasped through an example. Imagine yourself in a small boat floating on the ocean. You and your boat move with the water, and we follow these motions in the presence of waves. The first thing to notice is that the wave form moves relative to your boat. As you look out to sea, it is easy to spot a particular wave crest as the crest approaches and then passes by. In other words, ocean waves

are traveling waves—unless acted upon by the vagaries of shoreline topography they move at a constant rate in a fixed direction. In contrast, the motion of your boat is cyclical. As a wave approaches from the west, your boat (and the water in which it is embedded) initially moves upward and westward. As you near the wave crest, your velocity is upward and eastward. As the wave retreats, your boat moves downward and eastward, and finally, downward and westward. The result is that you, your boat, and the water have moved through a circular orbit (much as a chair on a Ferris wheel moves) and arrive back at the point from which you started. In other words, while the wave form travels, the water beneath a wave has no net displacement. (This is not strictly true. There is a small net displacement associated with deep-water wave motion, but the effect is negligible for our purposes.)

The rate and direction in which the waveform and the water move in a linear wave are embodied in a compact set of equations. Here motion is measured relative to a set of stationary Cartesian axes. The origin is located at still-water level, and the positive *x*-axis is aligned with the direction of wave-form propagation. As before, the *z*-axis is vertical, with positive values above still-water level and negative values below. The seafloor lies at a depth $z = -d$ below still-water level. It is often more convenient to locate a vertical position in the water column relative to the sea floor rather than rela-

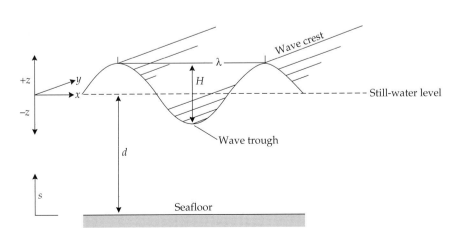

Figure 1.6 The nomenclature of a sinusoidal wave form. Wave length is the distance between two wave crests along the direction of wave travel. Wave height is the vertical distance between a wave crest and the adjacent wave trough. The depth of the water column is measured with respect to still-water level. (After Denny 1988.)

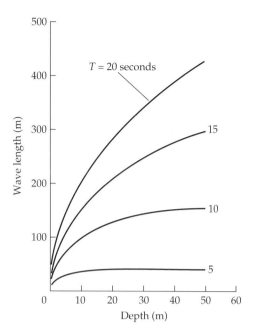

Figure 1.7 Wave length as a function of wave period and water-column depth (Equation 30).

tive to the water's surface. This is done using the variable $s = d + z$. Thus, s equals 0 at the bottom and d at the surface. Waves are assumed to have infinitely long crests, so that the wave form looks the same in any x-z plane. In other words, linear waves are assumed to be two-dimensional and therefore do not vary along the y-axis.

The equations of linear wave motion utilize the following terms. The **wave number**, k, is defined as:

$$k \equiv \frac{2\pi}{\lambda} \qquad \text{Eq. 29}$$

To calculate k, one must know the wavelength, λ. An approximate expression for λ is given by Eckart (1951):

$$\lambda \cong \frac{gT^2}{2\pi} \sqrt{\tanh\left(\frac{4\pi^2 d}{T^2 g}\right)} \qquad \text{Eq. 30}$$

This estimate is accurate to within about 5%. The hyperbolic tangent function is:

$$\tanh(x) = \frac{\sinh(x)}{\cosh(x)} = \frac{\frac{1}{2}\left(e^x - e^{-x}\right)}{\frac{1}{2}\left(e^x + e^{-x}\right)} \qquad \text{Eq. 31}$$

Equation 30 is graphed in Figure 1.7. At any given depth, wavelength increases approximately as the square of wave period. As waves move into shallower water, their wavelength decreases.

The **wave frequency**, ω, is defined as:

$$\omega \equiv \frac{2\pi}{T} \qquad \text{Eq. 32}$$

where T is again the wave period.

With this nomenclature in place, we can now describe various quantities associated with ocean waves. First we quantify the wave energy:

$$\text{Wave energy} = E = \frac{\rho g H^2}{8} \qquad \text{Eq. 33}$$

Here g is again the acceleration due to gravity and E is the average wave energy contained in a square meter of ocean surface. This energy can be substantial. For example, when $H = 2$ meters (a common value for ocean swell), there are 5028 joules of wave energy in each square meter of ocean surface. This is enough energy to lift a metric ton (1000 kg) half a meter.

The wave's phase speed (the speed of the wave form) depends on the water's depth and the wave number (and hence on the wavelength):

$$U = \sqrt{\frac{g \tanh(kd)}{k}} \qquad \text{Eq. 34}$$

This expression is graphed in Figure 1.8. As waves move into shallow water, their phase speed decreases. Note that according to linear wave theory phase speed is independent of wave height; it depends solely on wave number (and thereby on wave length) and the depth of the water column. Note

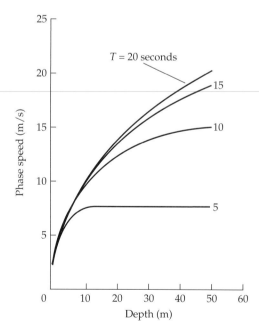

Figure 1.8 Phase speed (the speed of the wave form) as a function of wave period and water-column depth (Equation 34). Note that at very shallow depths, phase speed is nearly independent of wave period.

also that in very shallow water, phase speed is independent of wave period.

The horizontal velocity of the water beneath a wave, u, is

$$u = \frac{\pi H}{T} \cos(kx - \omega t) \frac{\cosh(ks)}{\sinh(kd)} \qquad \text{Eq. 35}$$

where t is time. The expression containing the hyperbolic sine and cosine adjusts the equation to account for the effects of depth (d) and vertical location in the water column (s).

A similar equation describes the water's vertical velocity:

$$w = \frac{\pi H}{T} \sin(kx - \omega t) \frac{\sinh(ks)}{\sinh(kd)} \qquad \text{Eq. 36}$$

The vertical velocity is 90° out of phase with the horizontal velocity. In other words, when the water is at its maximum or minimum horizontal velocity, its vertical velocity is zero; when it is at its maximum or minimum vertical velocity, the horizontal velocity is zero. Note that $\sinh(0) = 0$. As a consequence, vertical velocity is 0 at the substratum (where $s = 0$).

Taking the derivative of Equations 35 and 36 with respect to time, we can calculate the water's wave-driven acceleration:

$$\frac{\partial u}{\partial t} = \frac{2\pi^2 H}{T^2} \sin(kx - \omega t) \frac{\cosh(ks)}{\sinh(kd)} \qquad \text{Eq. 37}$$

$$\frac{\partial w}{\partial t} = \frac{-2\pi^2 H}{T^2} \cos(kx - \omega t) \frac{\sinh(ks)}{\sinh(kd)} \qquad \text{Eq. 38}$$

Note the flexibility of Equations 35–38. For instance, given the wave height and period (H and T) and the water's depth (d), Equation 34 can be used to calculate the horizontal water velocity at any point in space (x, s) and any time (t).

Often we do not need to know how water velocity or acceleration vary through time; it is sufficient to know their maximal value. In this case, time or position on the x-axis can be chosen such that the sine or cosine term in Equations 35–38 is at its maximal value ($= 1$), and the maximal values for velocity and acceleration can be calculated:

$$u_{\text{MAX}} = \frac{\pi H}{T} \frac{\cosh(ks)}{\sinh(kd)} \qquad \text{Eq. 39}$$

This expression is graphed in Figure 1.9 as a function of depth for flow at the substratum ($s = 0$). Maximum vertical velocity is:

$$w_{\text{MAX}} = \frac{\pi H}{T} \frac{\sinh(ks)}{\sinh(kd)} \qquad \text{Eq. 40}$$

Maximum horizontal acceleration is:

$$\frac{\partial u}{\partial t}\Big|_{\text{MAX}} = \frac{2\pi^2 H}{T^2} \frac{\cosh(ks)}{\sinh(kd)} \qquad \text{Eq. 41}$$

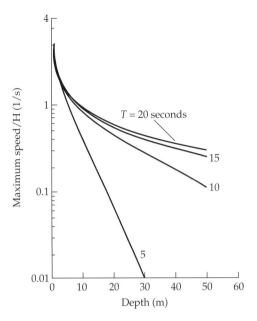

Figure 1.9 Maximum horizontal water velocity at the substratum ($s = 0$) as a function of wave period and water-column depth (Equation 39). Here speed has been normalized to wave height. Note the logarithmic ordinate.

This expression is graphed in Figure 1.10 as a function of depth for flow at the substratum. And finally, maximum vertical acceleration is:

$$\frac{\partial w}{\partial t}\Big|_{\text{MAX}} = \frac{-2\pi^2 H}{T^2} \frac{\sinh(ks)}{\sinh(kd)} \qquad \text{Eq. 42}$$

The equations of linear wave theory can be used to explain a wide variety of the biological patterns found in nearshore communities. For example, it is evident from Equations 39–42 that both the maximum velocity and maximum acceleration of water under linear waves are linearly proportional to wave height, H. As a result, the maximal lift and drag imposed on stationary, benthic organisms (which are proportional to the square of velocity) are predicted to vary as the square of wave height. Thus, in those areas of the shore subjected to large waves, organisms will be subjected to very large wave-induced forces. Similarly, water acceleration is proportional to wave height, and the accelerational forces will be largest where the waves are highest.

The fact that large waves lead to large wave forces is likely to be intuitive to anyone who has spent time on a wave-swept shore. The value of linear wave theory in this case is that it allows one to *quantify* one's intuition. For example, if one knows enough about the size and shape of an organism to estimate its drag, lift, and added mass coefficients (or if one can measure C_D, C_L, and C_A empirically), linear wave theory allows one to predict quantitatively the maximal force imposed on the organism as a function of wave height.

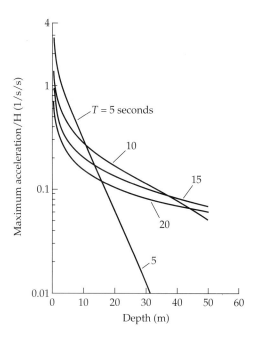

Figure 1.10 Maximum horizontal water acceleration at the substratum (*s* = 0) as a function of wave period and water-column depth (Equation 41). Here acceleration has been normalized to wave height. In very shallow water, the highest accelerations are associated with the shortest wave period, but this order reverses as water column depth increases. Note the logarithmic ordinate.

In addition, wave theory allows one to quantify aspects of flow that are nonintuitive. For example, the hyperbolic cosine term in Equations 35 and 37 shows that the horizontal velocity and acceleration decrease as one approaches the substratum. This effect is particularly evident when the water column is deep relative to the wavelength. For example, if λ = 100 m (a common value for ocean waves) and *d* = 50 m, the maximal horizontal water velocity at the sea floor is only about 4% of that at the surface. Thus, when the water column is sufficiently deep, depth can provide a refuge from wave-induced water motion. The fact that water velocity decreases with increasing depth provides the logic behind the functional definition of deep water cited earlier (*d* > λ/2). When *d* > λ/2, water motion at the sea floor is negligible, and as a consequence the sea floor does not appreciably affect wave motion at the surface.

The effect of depth on wave-induced water motion is not as strong in shallow water. When *d* < λ/20 (the formal definition of **shallow water**), the term cosh(*ks*)/sinh(*kd*) in Equations 35 and 37 is approximately equal to 1/(*kd*). In other words, in shallow water the horizontal velocity and acceleration are virtually independent of *s* (the distance from the substratum), and there is no refuge from the flow. Note also that as *d* becomes small, 1/(*kd*) becomes very large (see Figure 1.9). Not only is there no spatial refuge from the flow in intermediate and shallow water, but the magnitude of the flow [which in shallow water is proportional to 1/(*kd*)] actually increases. In essence, Equations 35 and 37 imply that the flow regime of

benthic organisms becomes increasingly severe as the water depth decreases, a prediction that can account for much of the gross pattern of species distributions along a depth gradient on wave-swept shores. For example, on coral reefs the distribution of morphologies changes in a predictable fashion as a function of depth—the shallower the water, in general the more structurally robust the coral (Nybakken 1988).

Note that water is "deep" if *d* > λ/2, and "shallow" if *d* < λ/20. There is thus a gap between these two depths, and it is referred to as water of **intermediate depth.**

WAVE REFRACTION

Equation 34 shows that the phase speed of a wave depends on the depth of the water—the shallower the water, the slower the wave. As a result, waves have a tendency to **refract** as they approach shore. The process is shown in Figure 1.11. A series of wave crests moves at an oblique angle toward shore. Because the water is shallower near the shore, the shoreward portion of the wave crests moves slower than the seaward portion. The result is that the crests change direction to become more nearly parallel to the shoreline. The effect is simi-

(A)

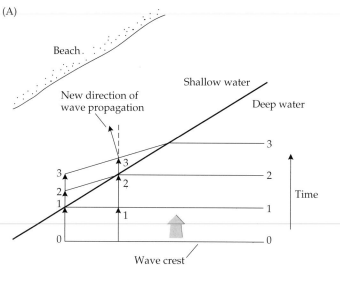

(B)

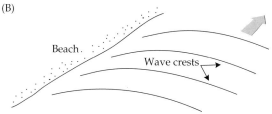

Figure 1.11 Wave refraction. (A) Waves move at an oblique angle over a sea floor that contains an abrupt change in depth. As the waves encounter shallow water, their phase speed is reduced (Equation 34; Figure 1.8). As a result, the direction of wave propagation is shifted to become more nearly perpendicular to the shoreline. (B) On a more typical beach with a gently sloping bottom, waves continually refract as they move inshore. (After Denny 1988.)

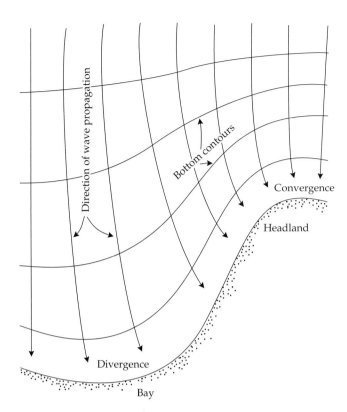

Figure 1.12 The refraction of waves focuses wave energy on headlands. As a result, waves are higher near headlands than in the adjacent bays. (After Denny 1988.)

lar to the refraction of light by media of differing refractive index. For instance, as light moves obliquely into a region of higher refractive index (a glass lens, for instance), its velocity decreases and its direction of travel is bent.

The biological importance of refraction concerns its ability to affect wave energy (Figure 1.12). As waves approach a headland, the slope of the sea floor focuses the waves. The effect is to concentrate wave energy in the vicinity of the headland, thereby increasing the local wave height (see Equation 33). Higher waves translate to larger hydrodynamic forces, with a wide variety of biological consequences. Embayments have the opposite effect of headlands—wave energy is diffused, and wave heights are reduced. In this fashion, the physics of wave motion interacts with the topography of the shoreline to impose a spatially varying pattern of hydrodynamic forces.

The pattern in which waves refract can be accurately predicted from information concerning the topography of the coastal sea floor. Although the methodology is straightforward, an explanation is beyond the purview of this chapter and the interested reader is urged to consult the Shore Protection Manual published by the U. S. Army Corps of Engineers (1984).

BREAKING AND BROKEN WAVES

As useful as linear wave theory is for predicting the pattern of water velocities and accelerations in nearshore environ-

ments, it has its limitations. The primary limitation concerns the process of wave breaking. As waves move inshore, their phase speed and wavelength decrease (Equations 34 and 30, respectively), but the rate at which they transport energy remains constant. As a consequence, the height of waves changes as they move into shallower water. In general, the height increases as the depth decreases. Increasing height accompanied by a decreasing wavelength means that waves become ever steeper as they approach a shore. At some point, this steepness is such that the wave form becomes unstable and the wave breaks; the wave crest pitches over the shoreward slope of the wave, producing the turbulent "white water" that is characteristic of surf. After a wave breaks, it continues to travel shoreward, but its form has been converted to that of a **turbulent bore** with a steep leading face and a gradually sloping trailing face. On a beach with a gradual slope, most of the energy of a broken wave is dissipated as heat by the time the bore reaches the shoreline. If sufficient residual energy is available, the wave may travel beyond and above the shoreline as a **run-up** or **swash**. This effect is most evident on steep rocky shores where waves break very near the shoreline.

The process of wave breaking depends on a number of factors, including the wave period, the wave height, and the slope of the bottom (see U. S. Army Corps of Engineers 1984). When the bottom slope is very gradual, waves break when their height is equal to approximately 80% of the water's depth. In general, the steeper the slope of the shore, the higher the wave is when it breaks, and on very steep shores waves may reach a height equal to 140% of the local still-water depth. The longer the wave period, the higher the breaker. As a general rule of thumb, we assume here that waves break on a planar beach when their height is approximately equal to the depth of the water.

Wave breaking is a complex process, one that is not yet fully described by theory, but the relevant events are as follows. At the instant of breaking, the water at the wave crest moves just as fast as the wave form itself. As the wave continues to move inshore, the wave form slows down (see Equation 34), but the water at the crest does not, with the result noted above—water at the wave crest arches over the front of the wave form and the wave degenerates into a turbulent bore. The velocities associated with broken waves depend on the nature of the shore. If the bottom slope is gradual, waves break far seaward of the shoreline, and a well-defined surf zone exists. In this case, the height of the bores gradually decreases as they approach shore. If the wave breaks on a steep shore, the arching crest may still be in flight when it intersects with the substratum, and the crest velocity at breaking can be imposed directly on intertidal organisms. In this case, the crest velocity provides an estimate of the maximal water velocity to which intertidal organisms are subjected.

The equations of linear wave theory become increasingly unreliable as waves approach their breaking point. In practice, Equations 34–42 can be used cautiously to estimate the wave-induced flow regime up to the point at which waves break, but should not be used to predict flows in waves that have broken. In the surf zone, the predictions from another theory [solitary wave theory; Munk (1949)] are commonly used to estimate water velocities. According to this theory, the crest velocity in a breaking or broken wave is estimated to be:

$$u_C = \sqrt{g(d + H)} \qquad \text{Eq. 43}$$

Here d is the depth below still-water level at the position of the crest and H is again wave height. In a breaking or broken wave, u_C is equal to the phase speed of the wave form.

As noted above, this crest velocity interacts with benthic organisms only on shores that are quite steep. If the slope of the sea floor is gradual, a wave breaks well seaward of the shoreline, and organisms are subjected to the slower flows present below the passing bore. At the substratum, the maximal velocity beneath a bore is (according to solitary wave theory) approximately

$$u_{MAX} \cong 0.3\sqrt{g(d + H)} \qquad \text{Eq. 44}$$

30% of that at the crest. This decrease in horizontal water velocity with depth is at odds with the predictions of linear wave theory, and this is one reason why linear wave theory is not used to estimate velocities in the surf.

As we have noted, the energy of a turbulent bore is rapidly converted to heat through the action of viscosity. As a consequence, as a broken wave moves inshore through the surf zone its height (and thereby its phase velocity, Equation 43) decreases. This effect is most evident as broken waves move over a beach with a gentle slope. In this case, the energy of even large storm waves is largely dissipated by the time waves near the shoreline, and algae, plants, and animals in the shallows are protected from extreme hydrodynamic forces.

Note that by limiting the maximal height of waves, the process of breaking limits the maximal velocity to which organisms are subjected. Using the rough rule of thumb that maximal wave height (H_B) is equal to the depth at breaking (d_B), we see that the maximal crest velocity is

$$u_{C,MAX} \cong \sqrt{2gd_B} \qquad \text{Eq. 45}$$

or equivalently:

$$u_{C,MAX} \cong \sqrt{2gH_B} \qquad \text{Eq. 46}$$

Maximal velocities at the substratum are about 30% of these crest values.

The utility of Equation 45 becomes apparent when dealing with a shore with a known bottom topography. For example, if one knows that the sea floor slopes down 2 m for each 10 m one moves out from the shoreline, one need only note roughly how far from shore the waves are breaking to estimate

$u_{C,MAX}$. A wave breaking 5 m from the shoreline breaks at a depth of about 1 m and has a crest velocity of approximately 4.5 m s^{-1}. This result must be taken with a large grain of salt, however. The velocity calculated here is that of the wave crest before it interacts with the local small-scale topography of the shore, and these interactions can act to either decrease or increase the water's velocity.

As we have seen, the loss of wave energy to heat steadily decreases wave height as bores move through the surf zone, suppressing extreme flows, and this effect is most evident on shores with gradual slopes. In contrast, on steep rocky shores where the crest may directly strike the substratum, the small-scale topography of the rock can initially augment water velocities in breaking waves. For example, recent empirical measurements on rocky shores have shown that Equations 45 and 46 provide a reasonable estimate of the maximal velocity that impinges on horizontal surfaces subjected to swash (Gaylord 1997). On vertical surfaces, however, flow often interacts with the local topography of the shore to increase the velocity. Hibberd and Peregrine (1979) estimate that swash can initially accelerate water to twice the phase speed of the bore impinging on the shore, and a funnel-shaped surge channel can "squeeze" the flow of a breaking wave, increasing the water's velocity in much the same fashion as one increases the velocity of water emerging from a garden hose by restricting the outlet with one's thumb. The process by which eddies (technically, irrotational vortices) are formed in the lee of boulders can cause water velocities to be locally augmented, and there are a wide variety of small-scale wave–wave interactions that can initially increase the water velocity above that calculated using Equations 45 or 46. Eventually, the dissipation of energy through turbulence and viscosity reduces the velocity associated with swash in the same fashion as for bores in the surf zone, with the result that the farther an organism lives shoreward of the break point, the lower the velocity it is likely to encounter.

Given that local topography can either augment or suppress wave-induced velocities, how should an ecologist cope? At present there is no substitute for direct observation and careful fine-scale measurement. Recording dynamometers such as that shown in Figure 1.13 (Bell and Denny 1994) have proven to be a low-cost, reliable means for estimating maximal water velocities on wave-swept shores, and appropriately designed electronic transducers can be used to measure wave forces continuously at a site to determine the wave-by-wave variation in drag (e.g., Gaylord 1999, 2000).

SPATIAL SCALES OF FLOW VARIATION

As we have seen, the maximum water velocity and acceleration at a particular location (and thereby the maximum hydrodynamic force) are functions of wave height and the depth of the water column. Because H and d differ from place to place, we should explore the spatial scales at which the flow varies. For our purposes here, the term "spatial scale" is loosely defined to be the distance one would have to travel

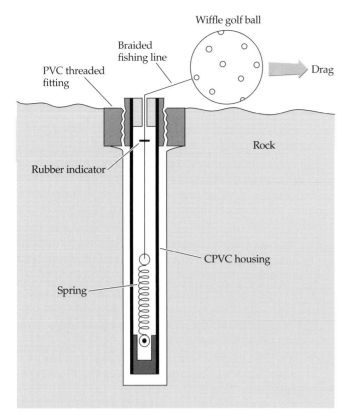

Wiffle golf ball

Braided
fishing line

PVC threaded
fitting

Drag

Rock

Rubber indicator

CPVC housing

Spring

Figure 1.13 A recording dynamometer for use on wave-swept rocky shores. A CPVC tube houses a stainless steel spring that is attached by fishing line to a drag element (a practice golf ball). The tube is inserted into a hole drilled in the rock, and is held in place by a threaded PVC fitting glued to the rock. As wave-induced velocities impose drag on the practice golf ball, the spring is extended by an amount proportional to the applied force. The maximum excursion of the spring is recorded by a piece of rubber threaded onto the fishing line. To read the device, the tube is unscrewed from its fitting and the displacement of the rubber is noted through a slot milled into the side of the tube (not shown here). For more details on the construction and theory of the device, consult Bell and Denny (1994).

before flow conditions change enough to affect the structure or function of the local community. Given that conditions vary continuously through space and that the response of communities to flow is often not well understood, it is difficult to quantify spatial scale unambiguously. Despite this lack of precision, the concept has heuristic value, and we cautiously employ it here.

The waves that crash on shore are produced by winds at sea, and the storms that produce large waves often act over tens of thousands of square kilometers, sending waves in all directions. As a result, the offshore (deep-water) heights of waves are often consistent along a coastline over the scale of tens of kilometers. It is this large-scale consistency of wave heights that allows the weather service to provide useful surf warnings. Within a stretch of coastline subjected to the same height of deep-water waves, the scale of the local variation in water velocities depends on the topography of the sea floor.

These topographically governed variations can be followed either on a shoreward–seaward axis (a deep-to-shallow axis) or on an axis parallel to shore.

Deep to Shallow

As we have seen, the equations of linear wave theory can be used to predict how velocity and acceleration at the substratum ($s = 0$) vary as a function of the depth of the water column (see Figures 1.9 and 1.10). As a result, if critical values of velocity or acceleration can be identified for a particular species or community, the ecologically relevant spatial scale of onshore-offshore variation in flow can be estimated. For example, a hypothetical species of coral is subjected to both predation by starfish and breakage by hydrodynamic forces. Predation is in turn limited by the maximum water velocity in which the starfish can forage, and this velocity is lower than that required to break the corals. In this hypothetical scenario, the coral is confined to a depth band with a lower edge set by predation and an upper edge set by breakage. The spatial scale of this band (distance along the substratum) can be calculated directly from Figures 1.9 and 1.10 and information regarding the slope of the sea floor. The more gradual the slope, the more gradual the spatial variation in velocity and acceleration, and the larger the onshore–offshore width of viable coral habitat. This approach has been applied, for instance, to predict the distribution of sea urchins (Kawamata 1998).

Alongshore

Alongshore variation in wave height (within a stretch of coast exposed to the same offshore waves) is driven primarily by the pattern of refraction. As a result, the spacing of headlands and bays determines the scale of variation in nearshore wave height. Reasonable estimates of this variation can be obtained by applying the theory of refraction to the shore's known bottom topography. The alongshore variation in wave-induced flow can then be calculated for any specific depth, and the scale of variation determined as outlined above.

The Surf Zone

As we have noted, the equations of linear wave theory apply only up to the point at which waves break. As a consequence, this theory can be used to estimate spatial scales only outside of the surf zone. However, the scale of the surf zone itself (its onshore–offshore width) provides another useful metric for nearshore communities. The surf zone extends from the shoreline out to the depth at which waves break, a depth roughly equal to the incident wave height. Thus, the more gentle the bottom slope, the wider the surf zone for a given offshore height of waves, the larger the habitat available to surf-zone communities, and the more gentle the gradient in flow within the surf-zone habitat. In addition, the refraction-driven alongshore variation in wave height affects the height of waves as they enter the surf zone, and thereby can interact with the bottom slope to determine the width of the surf zone.

On steep rocky shores the surf zone typically begins at (or very near) the shoreline, and water velocities and accelerations are characterized by swash conditions. In this case, the relevant spatial variation in water velocity and acceleration is driven both by small-scale variation in rock topography and the spatial scale of turbulence in the flow. Unfortunately, these fine-scale variations must be determined on a site-by-site basis. Current research (M.W. Denny unpub. data) suggests that in the swash zone maximal water velocities at the substratum can vary substantially over very small distances (less than a meter).

The Scale of Acceleration

The spatial scale of acceleration is of particular interest because of the manner in which the accelerational force potentially limits the size of wave-swept organisms (see Equation 27). Denny et al. (1985) and Gaylord et al. (1994) suggest that the imposition of accelerations of several hundred m s^{-2} could set the optimal size of intertidal organisms. Field experiments by Denny et al. (1985) and Gaylord (1997, 2000) show that water acceleration in broken waves can indeed reach values in excess of 400 m s^{-2}, but that these extreme accelerations are present over distances of a centimeter or less (Gaylord 1997, 2000). For example, in the surf zone the acceleration imposed on a sea urchin (with a diameter of, say, 8 cm) would vary drastically from place to place on the urchin's test, and the equations describing the accelerational force (which assume that acceleration is constant across an organism) would vastly overestimate the accelerational force. In this case, information about the spatial scale of flow is of critical importance in determining how the theory of fluid dynamics should be applied to life on wave-swept shores.

Note that outside the swash and surf zones the spatial scale of acceleration is comparable to the wave length and therefore much larger than the size of benthic organisms. In this case, accelerational forces may still be of importance in determining ecological patterns (see Massel and Done 1993; Massel 1996).

TEMPORAL SCALES OF VARIATION IN HYDRODYNAMIC FORCES

Anyone who has spent time working or playing in the surf can attest to the fact that the heights of individual waves are unpredictable. Precise information regarding the height of one wave does not provide a useful basis for predicting the height of subsequent waves. Despite the short-term stochastic nature of wave heights (in fact, *because* of this random behavior), the long-term behavior of waves is predictable. In two seminal papers, Longuet-Higgins (1952, 1980) showed that the distribution of heights in deep-water ocean waves follows a Rayleigh distribution such that the probability that a wave height chosen at random is greater than a value H is:

$$P(x \geq H) = \exp\left[-2.338\left(\frac{H}{H_S}\right)^2\right] \qquad \text{Eq. 47}$$

Here H_S is the significant wave height, a measure of the "waviness" of the ocean:

$$H_S = 1.41\sqrt{\frac{1}{n}\sum_{i=1}^{n}H_i^2} \qquad \text{Eq. 48}$$

where H_i is the height of an individual wave. Theory shows that the significant wave height is the average height of the highest third of the waves present at a given time, and it corresponds roughly to visually estimated wave heights.

Although significant wave height can be estimated by sight (given an experienced and "calibrated" observer), it is best measured more directly. Wave-rider buoys measure the variation in ocean surface elevation by measuring the acceleration of the buoy as it moves up and down. The National Data Buoy Center (www.ndbc.noaa.gov) archives wave records from buoys scattered along the coasts of the United States. Alternatively, nearshore wave heights can be measured using a bottom-mounted pressure transducer. As a wave crest passes overhead, the pressure at the bottom reaches a maximum; as a trough passes, the pressure falls to a minimum. This pressure signal is attenuated with depth, but a time series of variations in pressure at the sea floor can be used to calculate the variation in elevation at the surface [see Denny (1988) for a more thorough explanation]. This approach can be used where it is feasible to mount the pressure transducer rigidly at a depth of less than $\lambda/4$ or so. To facilitate logging data, commercial instruments couple a stable pressure transducer to an onboard computer in a waterproof housing. These self-contained devices could be purchased for about $10,000 in 2000.

Because waves typically follow the Rayleigh distribution of heights, it is possible to use H_S to calculate the highest wave that can be expected in a given interval of time:

$$H_{MAX} = 0.654H_S\left\{\left[\ln\left(\frac{t}{T}\right)\right]^{1/2} + 0.2886\left[\ln\left(\frac{t}{T}\right)\right]^{-1/2}\right\}$$

$$\text{Eq. 49}$$

In this expression T is again a measure of the wave period, but in this case it is the *average* period of the waves in the interval, a value that recognizes the fact that the period of real ocean waves varies from wave to wave. Given the average wave period and the significant wave height, Equation 49 allows one to predict the highest deep-water wave that will impinge on a shore. This relationship is shown in Figure 1.14. The longer one waits, the higher the highest wave one encounters. Notice, however, that this relationship has been plotted on a logarithmic scale. In the course of a day, the largest wave will have a height roughly twice the significant wave height. In the course of a year, the highest wave will be only slightly higher, about $2.5H_S$.

The primary problem with the application of Equation 49 is that significant wave height varies through time. As an index

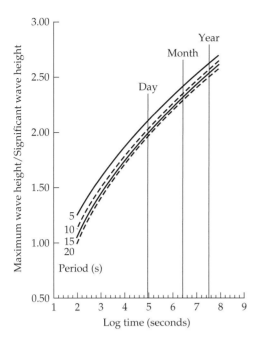

Figure 1.14 The maximum wave height encountered on a shore increases with time for a given "waviness" of the ocean (Equation 49). Here the maximum wave height has been normalized to the significant wave height (Equation 48), an index of the average height of waves. Note the logarithmic abscissa. The highest wave encountered in a year is only slightly higher than the highest wave encountered in a day (assuming a constant significant wave height). The shorter the wave period, the more waves arrive at the shore in a given interval, and the higher the maximum wave.

of the "waviness" of the sea, H_S is large during storms and is small during periods of calm weather. Thus, the temporal pattern of extreme wave heights depends largely on the temporal variation in ocean waviness. This variation has been quantified, but may prove difficult to predict. For example, Figure 1.15 shows the temporal variation in significant wave height at the Farallon Islands off the coast of California. Significant wave heights were measured four times per day and averaged daily for a period of 13 years (Figure 1.15A). Through the use of the Fourier transform, the overall variance in significant wave height has been subdivided into the components of that variance that are associated with different periodicities. These components (technically, estimates of the power spectral density) are plotted in Figure 1.15B as a function of frequency, where frequency is the inverse of the period in question.

This analysis shows that most of the variation in significant wave heights is associated with low frequencies (= long periods). There is a discernable peak at the frequency corresponding to a period of a year, indicating that there is (on average) a yearly cycle to the variation in significant wave height. Nonetheless, there is more variation across years (that is, at very low frequencies) than there is within years.

Given this pattern of variation in significant wave height, it is difficult (and perhaps impossible) to specify the temporal scale of maximal wave-induced hydrodynamic forces. Clearly there is some predictability to the pattern of variation with-

in a year—winter storms cause large waves, and summer calm is typically associated with small waves. This seasonal fluctuation (while, on average, predictable) is likely to be small compared to the longer-term variation. Occasionally, large waves are encountered in the summer and small waves in winter. These longer-term (and as yet unpredictable) variations are likely to have a strong effect on the pattern of nearshore communities. Unfortunately, reliable wave-height measurements have been conducted in only a few locations and then only for the past few decades. As a result, we do not yet have the diverse set of centuries-long time series that would be required to analyze accurately the temporal pattern of variation in wave heights.

AN EXAMPLE

As an example of the manner in which hydrodynamic theory can be used to predict pattern in nearshore communities, we consider the female gametophytes of *Mastocarpus papillatus*, a red alga found commonly on intertidal shores on the west coast of temperate North and South America. The morphology of the plant is highly variable, but has the following general pattern (Figure 1.16). A short stipe is attached to the substratum by a crustose holdfast. Several stipes may emerge from the same holdfast, and each stipe supports a frond that branches dichotomously. Fronds are covered with small papillae, each of which is a reproductive structure. The spatial density of papillae varies from one frond to another, but for an individual frond, the density of papillae is approximately independent of the size of the frond. In other words, the larger the frond, the more papillae it has, and the larger the potential reproductive output.

Unless tattered by wave forces, a frond continues to grow throughout the year. In contrast, after the frond has reached some minimal size, the stipe does not increase in cross-sectional area. As a result, the force required to dislodge a frond from the substratum (which depends on the cross-sectional area of the stipe) does not increase as the frond's area increases.

In a ground-breaking study, Carrington (1990) measured the drag on 139 *M. papillatus* fronds. Surprisingly, she found that drag at a given water velocity was virtually independent of the branching morphology and papillar density of the frond, and depended primarily on the frond's area. Averaged across the 139 fronds, $\beta_D = 1.623$ and $S_D = 0.155$. Thus (from Equation 12)

$$F_D = 79.44 u_R^{1.623} A_{MAX} \qquad \text{Eq. 50}$$

where A_{MAX} is the maximal projected area of the frond (approximately half the wetted area) and we have used a water density of 1025 kg m^{-3}. The average force required to break a stipe was 4.8 N.

Setting drag equal to the average breaking force, we can solve for frond area as a function of water velocity:

$$A_{MAX} = \frac{0.06}{u_R^{1.623}} \qquad \text{Eq. 51}$$

Figure 1.15 The temporal variation in significant wave height at the Farallon Islands off of central California (data from the Coastal Data Information Program). Significant wave height is measured four times per day, and these values have been averaged to provide the daily average significant wave heights shown in (A). Annual fluctuation in wave heights is evident, but is coupled with substantial interannual variation. (B) The power spectrum of the time series shown in (A). The power spectral density is a measure of the component of overall variation that occurs at a particular frequency. A discernable peak is present at the frequency corresponding to an annual cycle, but the largest variation is associated with still lower frequencies.

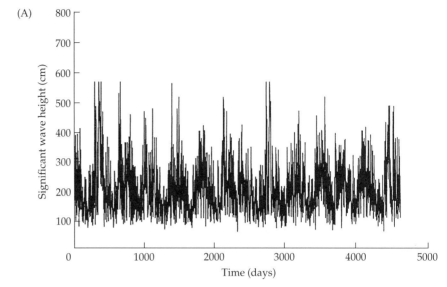

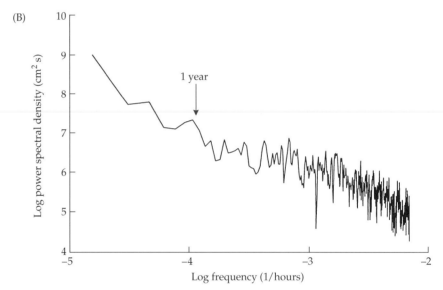

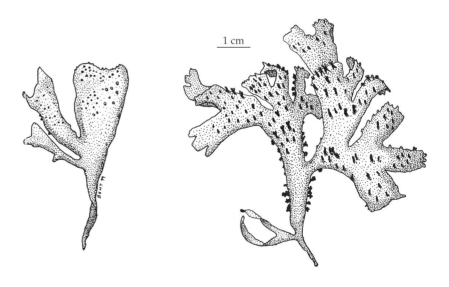

Figure 1.16 Female gametophytes of *Mastocarpus papillatus*, a red alga.

If we take the crest velocity at breaking (Equation 46) as an estimate of maximal water velocity imposed on *M. papillatus*, we can rewrite this equation as a function of wave height:

$$A_{MAX} = \frac{0.06}{(gH_S)^{0.812}} \qquad \text{Eq. 52}$$

This expression is graphed in Figure 1.17. As the breaking wave height increases, the maximal size of *M. papillatus* fronds rapidly decreases. As noted above, the reproductive output of the plants is presumably proportional to their frond area, so the predictions of area made here could potentially be translated into predictions of reproductive output as a function of wave height.

The calculations made so far assume that fronds grow to the size allowed by the prevailing waves. If the wave height changes through the year, this could lead to frond mortality in the plants. Fronds that have grown large in a period of calm may be broken by the re-imposition of large waves. Given an independent measurement of the growth rate of *M. papillatus* (approximately 0.12×10^{-4} m²/day; Bell 1992), we can predict from the historical record of significant wave heights (Figure 1.15) what the wave-mediated pattern of growth and breakage would be for this plant. This calculation is shown in Figure 1.18, in which we have assumed that $H_B = H_S$.

The calculation begins in January 1984 with plants of 0 area. A biannual pattern of plant size is evident through the first 5 years of the record. Due to their small initial size, the plants are not dislodged during the first winter, but are bro-

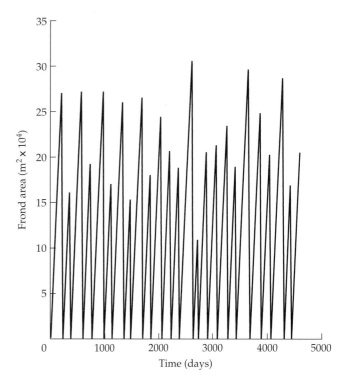

Figure 1.18 Predicted maximum frond area in *M. papillatus*. The fluctuation in size seen here is driven by the variation in wave heights shown in Figure 1.15A. Through the first five years of this model, there is a strict alternation between growth to a large size in summer (before breakage by autumn storms) and growth to a smaller size in winter (before breakage by winter or spring storms). This alternation breaks down in subsequent years, however, due to long-term variations in the pattern of wave heights.

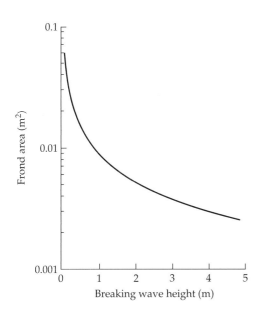

Figure 1.17 The predicted maximum frond area of *M. papillatus* decreases with increasing wave height (Equation 52). Note the logarithmic ordinate.

ken during one of the rare stormy days in summer. A new bout of growth begins, but the plants are broken at a relatively small size by the first storm of the autumn. The pattern is then repeated, but not indefinitely. Year-to-year variation in the time series of significant wave heights eventually results in an unpredictable pattern of size limitation in this hypothetical alga, and the long-term (interannual) variation in size is large compared to the seasonal alternation in size. (The results are virtually the same if the numerical experiment is begun at other times through the year.)

Given information on the fine-scale spatial variation in wave-induced water velocity, one could use this approach to predict the fine-scale (both spatial and temporal) pattern of growth, survivorship, and reproductive output of *M. papillatus* along a given shore. Furthermore, one could predict how this pattern would change if there were a change in the "waviness" of the ocean. For example, El Niño/ Southern Oscillation (ENSO) events may be accompanied by unusually high waves (Seymour et al. 1984; Seymour 1996), and some models for global climate change predict that ENSO events will become more common in the future. The calculations outlined above would allow us to predict how this shift in the frequency and severity of ENSO events will affect the survivorship and reproductive output of *M. papillatus*.

The example presented here (Figure 1.18) is not intended to be an accurate prediction. At present there are several aspects of the biology and ecology of *M. papillatus* that have not been sufficiently studied to allow such a prediction to be made. For example, the shape coefficient of drag for *M. papillatus* has been measured only up to a water velocity of about 4 m s^{-1}, much lower than that predicted for the field, and there is much work to be done before the site-specific predictions of surge-zone flows can be trusted even within a factor of two. There is substantial variation among individuals as to the strength of their stipes, and some of this variation may be caused by herbivory. Thus, there is the possibility for biological mediation of the wave-induced limit to size in this alga. Furthermore, the growth rate of *M. papillatus* varies through the year, and plants may tatter rather than catastrophically break; neither effect has been included in our calculations. Despite these current limitations, the mechanistic approach to predicting the pattern of survivorship in wave-swept organisms appears to have great potential, and it is an area of active research.

In this brief introduction we have only scratched the surface of the complex topic of ocean waves, wave-induced hydrodynamic forces, and their biological effects. For a more thorough discussion, the interested reader should consult Kinsman (1965), Denny (1988, 1995), Gaylord (1997), Massel (1996), or Sarpkaya and Isaacson (1984).

To this point, we have focussed our exploration on the transport of momentum and the associated forces imposed on wave-swept plants and animals. We now shift our attention to the transport of heat and mass and the resulting effects on the temperature of intertidal organisms. This shift is accomplished in two steps. First we set the stage by discussing the effect of a solid substratum on the local transport of momentum, mass, and heat. This is the topic of boundary layers. Although boundary layers are important in their own right, our discussion of them will be brief, and serves primarily as a segue to a more general exploration of the factors that govern the temperature of intertidal organisms.

BOUNDARY LAYERS

The presence of a solid surface can affect the motion of the fluid nearby, and thereby can affect the local transport of momentum, mass and heat. In each case, the effect of the surface is confined to a layer of fluid in close proximity, and it is this **boundary layer** that is our topic in this section. The size and properties of the boundary layer depend on the type of transport being examined. Thus, at any solid surface in contact with a moving fluid there is a **momentum** (or **velocity**) **boundary layer**, and there can also be a boundary layer that governs the transport of mass (the **concentration boundary layer**) and a boundary layer that affects the transport of heat (the **thermal boundary layer**). We discuss each of these in turn.

Momentum Boundary Layers

We have noted previously that the fluid in contact with a solid surface does not move relative to that surface. As a result of this no-slip condition, whenever fluid (either air or water) moves over the substratum, a velocity gradient is necessarily created. In turn, wherever there is a velocity gradient in a viscous fluid, a shear stress is imposed between the substratum and the moving air or water (see Equation 4). This shear stress is one form of drag (friction or viscous drag), and because the solid surface exerts drag on the fluid, the fluid slows down. The net result is a transfer of momentum from the fluid to the substratum. In essence, momentum diffuses down the velocity gradient from the fast flowing mainstream, through the momentum boundary layer (the velocity gradient itself), to the still fluid at the substratum.

For simplicity, we here describe boundary layers as they occur over a horizontal substratum. In this case, the mainstream flow is also horizontal, directed along the *x*-axis. The boundary layer in this scenario is therefore a horizontal layer of fluid, and any cross-stream transport of heat, mass, or momentum is vertical, along the *z*-axis. This arrangement is for convenience only; the same physics apply for solid surfaces in other orientations. For example, if a fluid flows vertically past a vertical surface, cross-stream transport can occur along the *x*-axis.

In measuring the thickness of the boundary layer, we follow the tradition used by biologists (Vogel 1994). The top of the boundary layer is defined to be the distance away from the substratum at which the average velocity of the fluid is equal to 99% of that in the mainstream. Other definitions are used by fluid dynamicists (Schlichting 1979), and one must be careful to note which definition is in effect when delving into the literature.

The thickness of a momentum boundary layer depends on whether momentum is transported solely by viscosity (resulting in a **laminar boundary layer**) or by a combination of viscosity and turbulence (resulting in a **turbulent boundary layer**). The effects of these two transport mechanisms are substantially different, and the two types of boundary layer are discussed separately.

Laminar boundary layers exist when and where the viscous interaction of the fluid with the substratum are sufficient to damp out any "swirl" in the flow. This commonly occurs when the flow is slow and sizes of objects are small; that is, when the Reynolds number of the flow (Equation 7) is low. Examples include the flow within the gills of clams and around the feeding apparatus of zooplankton. Because in a laminar boundary layer, momentum is transported solely by viscosity (which is a relatively ineffective process), the velocity changes relatively slowly with elevation above the substratum (Figure 1.19).

How thick are laminar boundary layers? Thickness depends on two factors: (1) the intrinsic tendency for momentum to diffuse down a velocity gradient and (2) the time over which diffusion is allowed to occur. As we have seen (Equation 6), the intrinsic diffusivity of momentum in a fluid is

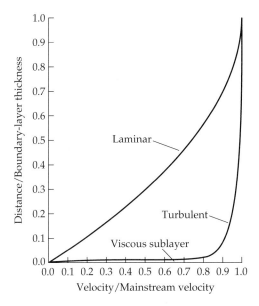

Figure 1.19 Velocity profiles for laminar and turbulent boundary layers. In each case, the velocity at any point in the boundary layer has been divided by the mainstream velocity. The absolute magnitude of flow in a turbulent boundary layer is typically larger than that in a laminar boundary layer. Similarly, the distance from the substrate has in each case been divided by the total boundary-layer thickness. In general, the absolute thickness of a turbulent boundary layer is larger than that of a laminar boundary layer. In the turbulent boundary layer, note that most of the velocity gradient is confined to the viscous sublayer.

quantified by the fluid's kinematic viscosity, ν. The higher ν is, the faster momentum diffuses, and the thicker the boundary layer will be. Similarly, the longer the time available, the farther momentum will diffuse, and the thicker the boundary layer. These effects are embodied in a standard estimate for laminar boundary-layer thickness (Vogel 1994):

$$\delta \cong 5\sqrt{\nu t} \qquad \text{Eq. 53}$$

Here δ is the boundary-layer thickness (in m) and t is the time for which the fluid has been in motion at a constant speed (measured in seconds). For example, in water (where ν is approximately $1 \times 10^{-6}\,\text{m}^2\,\text{s}^{-1}$) if the flow has been constant for a minute, the boundary layer is about 4 cm thick. In air, (where ν is approximately $15 \times 10^{-6}\,\text{m}^2\,\text{s}^{-1}$), the boundary layer is about 15 cm thick.

In many cases in the marine environment, water flows in an oscillatory fashion under the influence of surface waves. In these cases,

$$\delta = \frac{\sqrt{\pi}}{2}\sqrt{\nu T} \qquad \text{Eq. 54}$$

where T is the period of the oscillation (Denny 1993). For waves with a period of 10 s, the boundary-layer thickness in water is about 3 mm.

Alternatively, we can calculate the boundary thickness as a function of the distance over which the fluid has interacted with a solid surface. If x is the distance in the direction of flow from the leading edge of an object and u_0 is mainstream fluid velocity, $t \cong x/u_0$ and

$$\delta \cong 5\sqrt{\frac{\nu x}{u_0}} \qquad \text{Eq. 55}$$

For example, if u_0 is 10 cm s^{-1} and x is 10 cm, a laminar boundary layer in water is 5 mm thick. In air under the same conditions, the boundary layer is about 2 cm thick.

Equation 55 implies that as distance from a leading edge gets large, the thickness of a laminar boundary layer should increase without bound. In reality, this is not the case. As x increases, the effective Reynolds number of the flow increases as well, and a point is reached at which the effect of viscosity can no longer damp out the potential for swirl in the fluid. At this point turbulence develops in the boundary layer (Figure 1.20).

Turbulent boundary layers are common wherever flow is rapid and objects are large. Given that the sea bottom is a very large object, most flows in the benthic marine environment are turbulent. Intertidal rocks are often large and the flow of air over them is sufficiently rapid that most boundary layers in the intertidal zone are turbulent as well. Because turbulent boundary layers are so pervasive, we are motivated to describe the effects of turbulence in some detail.

Large eddies form in the outer regions of a turbulent boundary layer, and these eddies break up into smaller and smaller eddies close to surfaces. As a result of this **turbulent mixing**, fast-moving fluid can be delivered from the mainstream to points quite near the solid substratum. Consequently, the outer regions of a turbulent boundary layer are characterized by a weak gradient in velocity (the velocity is "well mixed"), and average velocities close to the substratum are greater than they would be in a laminar boundary layer (Figure 1.19).

The effective transport of momentum by turbulence does not negate the effect of the no-slip condition, however. In a

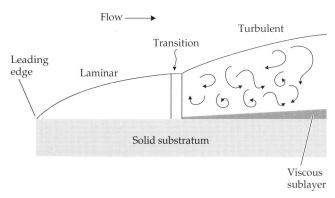

Figure 1.20 Boundary layers get thicker as flow moves downstream from a leading edge. At some point, turbulent eddies form and the boundary layer changes from laminar to turbulent.

turbulent boundary layer, the velocity of fluid directly at the substratum is still zero, and (given that fluid away from the substratum is moving) a velocity gradient must still exist. In this regard, the effect of turbulent mixing is to confine the velocity gradient to a thin layer very close to the substratum. In this **viscous sublayer** (Figures 1.19, 1.20), viscosity is able to preclude the presence of turbulent eddies, and momentum is transported by the action of viscosity alone. Because in a turbulent boundary layer virtually all the change in velocity is confined to the thin viscous sublayer, the velocity gradient in the sublayer is very steep and the shear stress imposed on the substratum is large, in many cases larger than that imposed by a laminar boundary layer.

Turbulent boundary layers differ from laminar boundary layers in another respect as well. In a laminar boundary layer, the flow is orderly. As long as the mainstream velocity is constant, the velocity at any height in the boundary layer is constant and approximately parallel to the flow in the mainstream. Not so in a turbulent boundary layer. At any distance from the substratum, velocity varies through time as eddies swirl by, and this fluctuation is present even when the mainstream flow is constant. Furthermore, the direction of flow varies. The passage of an eddy can cause flow to be directed either towards or away from the substratum, and it is this flow perpendicular to the substratum that results in the transport of momentum.

The rate of momentum transport in either a laminar or turbulent boundary layer is often quantified by measuring τ_B, the shear stress imposed on the substratum. In a turbulent boundary layer, this **boundary shear stress** is useful to us in two ways. First, we can use it in an analogue to Equation 6:

$$\tau_B = K_z \frac{d(\rho u)}{dz} \qquad \text{Eq. 56}$$

The quantity K_z is the **turbulent mixing coefficient**, or **turbulent diffusivity**, a turbulence analogue of kinematic viscosity. Like the molecular diffusion coefficient and kinematic viscosity, K_z has the units $m^2\ s^{-1}$. In practice, this equation is used as a working definition of K_z. If one can empirically measure both the boundary shear stress and the velocity gradient near the substratum, and if the density of the fluid is constant and known, K_z can be calculated. This is important because, as we will see in a moment, the turbulent mixing coefficient for momentum is used as an estimate of the turbulent mixing coefficient for both mass and heat as well.

The boundary shear stress can also be used to calculate the **friction velocity**, u_*, an index of boundary layer turbulence:

$$u_* \equiv \sqrt{\frac{\tau_B}{\rho}} \qquad \text{Eq. 57}$$

The friction velocity has the units $m\ s^{-1}$, and it is for this reason that it is referred to as a velocity. It should be kept in mind, however, that the friction velocity's value is primarily as an index of turbulence—the larger the friction velocity, the

more turbulent the flow. The magnitude of the friction velocity typically varies between 5% and 15% of the mainstream velocity, and $u_* = 0.1u_0$ can serve as a reasonable rule of thumb when a value of u_* is needed in a calculation. The friction velocity is an important ingredient of theoretical models of boundary-layer transport.

Having briefly examined the physics of turbulent boundary layers, we now return to their biological consequences by asking an important question—how thick is the viscous sublayer? In particular, how thick is the viscous sublayer relative to the size of rigid organisms (e.g., barnacles, snails, corals, coralline algae) that are attached to the substratum? The question of the relative size of the viscous sublayer and the size of organisms is of interest when we need to know whether a plant or animal is small enough to be enclosed in the orderly world of the sublayer, or whether it extends out into the chaotic flow of the rest of a turbulent boundary layer. To a first approximation, the thickness of the viscous sublayer is

$$\delta_{VS} = \frac{5\nu}{u_*} \qquad \text{Eq. 58}$$

As we noted above, u_* is often approximately ten percent of the mainstream velocity, u_0, implying that the thickness of the viscous sublayer (δ_{VS}) is

$$\delta_{VS} = \frac{50\nu}{u_0} \qquad \text{Eq. 59}$$

For example, if the mainstream velocity is 10 cm s^{-1}, the viscous sublayer is 0.5 mm thick. If the mainstream velocity is 1 m s^{-1}, the viscous sublayer is only 50 μm thick. In either case, the sublayer is small compared to most benthic organisms.

Equation 58 provides a conservative estimate of the thickness of the sublayer; it includes only the deep sublayer into which eddies seldom if ever intrude. If one is willing to accept a more daring approach and include in the sublayer portions of the boundary layer in which eddies occasionally appear, the sublayer thickness may extend out to $70\nu/u_*$. Given this more liberal estimation, the viscous sublayer in a mainstream flow of 10 cm s^{-1} might be 7 mm thick.

Note that in this discussion we have characterized only the thickness of the viscous sublayer. How thick is the overall turbulent boundary layer? A variety of equations are available to calculate turbulent boundary layer thickness (see Denny 1988, 1993; Vogel 1994), but they are likely to be misleading. For present purposes, momentum boundary layers (either turbulent or laminar) are of importance to ecologists primarily because they may provide a refuge from the hydrodynamic forces imposed by mainstream flows. The thickness of a turbulent boundary layer (as calculated by most authors) includes the outer regions in which turbulent eddies are present. Although the *average* velocity in this region is lower than that of the mainstream, large hydrodynamic forces will nonetheless be periodically encountered as eddies swirl by. It is only in the viscous sublayer that organisms can effectively hide from the flow. Therefore, for our purposes here, Equation 58 is the most relevant measure of the effective boundary-layer thickness for turbulent boundary layers.

Concentration Boundary Layers

When materials dissolve or evaporate into a moving fluid, their subsequent transport in the fluid is by advection (the bulk movement of the fluid) and by diffusion. An example is the transport of water vapor from the wet surface of an emersed alga in the intertidal zone. As water evaporates, it diffuses into the air, and if the alga is exposed to wind, the vapor is subsequently advected through the atmospheric boundary layer. Conversely, when dissolved materials are absorbed by a solid surface, their transport to the surface is likewise brought about by advection and diffusion. An example here is the uptake of dissolved carbon dioxide or bicarbonate by a submerged alga as it photosynthesizes.

As matter diffuses toward or away from a surface, a **concentration boundary layer** develops, analogous to the momentum boundary layer we explored above. In this case it is mass that is transported (rather than momentum), and it is transported along a concentration gradient (rather than a velocity gradient).

In laminar flow, molecular diffusion is the only mechanism available to transport material down a concentration gradient, and as a result, transport perpendicular to the substratum (along the z-axis in our case) is relatively slow. As we have seen, the diffusive flux of mass along the z-axis can be calculated by Fick's first equation:

$$\text{Flux along the } z\text{-axis} = -D\frac{dC}{dz} \qquad \text{Eq. 60}$$

where D is the molecular diffusion coefficient and C is concentration (mass per volume or moles per volume). This equation can be used to describe the mass flux across a laminar concentration boundary layer. The diffusion coefficient for small molecules is about 10^{-5} m^2 s^{-1} in air, and 10,000-fold smaller (10^{-9} m^2 s^{-1}) in water (Denny 1993).

Although the velocity of the fluid does not appear explicitly in Equation 60, it is present implicitly through its effect on the concentration gradient. Consider, for instance, the situation in which carbon dioxide is taken up by the blade of an alga. The concentration of CO_2 in the mainstream flow is high, but (due to the absorption of carbon dioxide by the blade) the concentration of CO_2 at the blade's surface is low. A concentration gradient is thereby established across the boundary layer. Where flow is rapid, a laminar boundary layer is thin (Equation 53), the concentration gradient between the solid surface and mainstream is consequently steep, and flux is rapid. When flow is slow, the boundary layer is thick, and flux is reduced. For a more thorough exploration of the effects of flow on transport, see Bird et al. (1960) or Denny (1993).

In contrast, in a turbulent boundary layer, the flux of mass down a concentration gradient is not by molecular diffusion alone, but instead is controlled primarily by turbulent eddies

(Bird et al. 1960, Schlichting 1979). This leads to a turbulent equivalent of Fick's first law of diffusion

$$\text{Flux along the } z\text{-axis} = -K_z\frac{dC}{dz} \qquad \text{Eq. 61}$$

Again, velocity is not explicitly present in this equation, but in this case it is implicitly present in two ways. First, the more rapid the flow, the more intense the turbulence, and the larger the turbulent mixing coefficient, K_z. The larger K_z is, the more rapid the flux for a given concentration gradient. Second, in a turbulent boundary layer the limiting factor in the rate of mass transport to or from the substratum is the diffusive transport across the viscous sublayer. As with a laminar boundary layer, transport in the viscous sublayer is due to molecular diffusion alone. The higher the mainstream velocity, the thinner the viscous sublayer (Equation 59), and the steeper the concentration gradient. Again we should expect that the higher the velocity, the more rapid the transport of mass in a turbulent boundary layer.

Note that the diffusion of mass in a turbulent boundary layer is governed by the same diffusion coefficient (K_z) as that for the diffusion of momentum in a velocity boundary layer. This is due to the fact that the physical mixing of the fluid is due to the bulk motion of eddies. If a small bit of fluid is bodily moved up or down by a large eddy, it can carry with it dissolved matter just as it can carry with it its horizontal velocity. Thus, in a turbulent flow, mass and momentum are (to a first approximation) transported equally well and by the same mechanism, and the use of a single, all-purpose diffusivity is appropriate.

In a laminar boundary layer, the relative thickness of the momentum boundary layer and the concentration boundary layer is determined by the dimensionless **Schmidt number**:

$$Sc = \frac{\nu}{D} \qquad \text{Eq. 62}$$

The Schmidt number is the ratio of the diffusivity of momentum (the kinematic viscosity) to molecular diffusivity. For example, in water at 20°C the Schmidt number for oxygen ($D = 2 \times 10^{-9}$ m^2 s^{-1}, $\nu = 1 \times 10^{-6}$ m^2 s^{-1}) is approximately 500; in air the Schmidt number of oxygen ($D = 20.1 \times 10^{-6}$ m^2 s^{-1}, $\nu = 15.3 \times 10^{-6}$ m^2 s^{-1}) is approximately 0.75 (Denny 1993). The ratio of the concentration boundary layer thickness, δ_C, to that of momentum, δ_M, is (Bird et al. 1960):

$$\frac{\delta_C}{\delta_M} = Sc^{-1/3} \qquad \text{Eq. 63}$$

In other words, in water, laminar concentration boundary layers are only about 13% as thick as momentum boundary layers, whereas in air the two types of boundary layer are approximately the same thickness (δ_C is about 10% greater than δ_M).

As we noted above, in a turbulent boundary layer, momentum and mass are both transported primarily by eddies. Therefore, their respective boundary layers are (to a first approximation) equally thick. In essence, the turbulent Schmidt number for both air and water is 1.

We will not explore the biological consequences of concentration boundary layers here. You may wish to consult Nobel (1991) for terrestrial examples or Hurd (2000) for examples involving marine plants.

Thermal Boundary Layers

When an object is warmer or cooler than its surrounding fluid, heat is transferred between the object and the fluid. If the fluid is still, this transfer is solely by **conduction**, the thermal equivalent of molecular diffusion. If the fluid is moving, however, heat transport can be augmented by either free or forced **convection** (Bird et al. 1960, Gates 1980). In **free convection**, the fluid moves past the object as a result of changes in the density of the fluid as it is warmed or cooled by the object. A common household example is the current of cold air that moves downward past an uninsulated window in winter, or the current of hot air that rises from a cup of hot tea or soup. In **forced convection**, the fluid moves past the object as a result of external forces, such as wind or water currents.

If heat is transported by convection (either free or forced), a **thermal boundary layer** develops, analogous to the momentum and concentration boundary layers described above. In this case, transport is down a gradient in temperature. As with other types of boundary layers, the thermal boundary layer can be either laminar or turbulent.

In a laminar thermal boundary layer, the flux of heat perpendicular to the solid substratum is due to conduction alone, as described by the thermal equivalent of Fick's first law:

$$\text{Heat flux along } z\text{-axis} = -\mathcal{K}\frac{d(Te)}{dz} \qquad \text{Eq. 64}$$

Here heat flux is measured in W m^{-2}, $\mathcal{K}$ is the thermal conductivity of the fluid (with units of watts per meter per kelvin), and Te is the absolute temperature. Recall that the absolute temperature scale (measured in kelvins) is the same as the Celsius scale, except that there is a different zero point. Zero kelvin equals –273.15 degrees Celsius. The thermal conductivity of water (at 20°C) is 0.6 W m^{-1} K^{-1}, approximately 23 times that of air (0.026 W m^{-1} K^{-1}; Denny 1993).

Fluid flow is not explicitly present in Equation 64, but (as for the transport of mass) it is implicitly present in that it affects the steepness of the thermal gradient. Where laminar flow is fast, the boundary layer is thin, and the gradient in temperature is consequently steep. Thus, fast flow augments the transport of heat in a laminar boundary layer.

The relative thickness of the momentum boundary layer and the thermal boundary layer is a function of a dimensionless number analogous to the Schmidt number. In this case it is the **Prandtl number**, Pr, the ratio of the diffusivity of momentum (the kinematic viscosity) to thermal diffusivity:

$$Pr = \frac{\nu}{D_{\mathrm{H}}} \qquad \text{Eq. 65}$$

D_{H} (the diffusivity of heat) is in turn related to the thermal conductivity:

$$D_{\mathrm{H}} = \frac{\mathcal{K}}{\rho q} \qquad \text{Eq. 66}$$

Here ρ is again the mass density of the fluid and q is its **specific heat capacity**. Specific heat capacity is the number of joules of heat energy required to raise the temperature of one kilogram of the fluid one degree Celsius, and it will be discussed in greater depth below. The thermal diffusivity of water is 0.14×10^{-6} m^2 s^{-1} and the thermal diffusivity of air is about 150 times larger (21.5×10^{-6} m^2 s^{-1}; Denny 1993). The Prandtl number of water is 6–14 depending on the temperature (it is high at low temperature), whereas the Prandtl number of air is approximately 0.7, with very little variation with temperature.

The relative thickness of a laminar thermal boundary layer, δ_{T}, and the co-occurring momentum boundary layer, δ_{M}, is:

$$\frac{\delta_{\mathrm{T}}}{\delta_{\mathrm{M}}} = Pr^{-1/3} \qquad \text{Eq. 67}$$

Thus, in air ($Pr = 0.7$) a laminar thermal boundary is roughly the same thickness as the co-occurring momentum boundary layer, while in water, a thermal boundary layer is only about 45% as thick as the co-occurring momentum boundary layer.

As with the transport of momentum and mass, in a turbulent thermal boundary layer the flux of heat through the bulk of the boundary layer is controlled by turbulent mixing:

$$\text{Heat flux along } z\text{-axis} = -\mathcal{K}_z\frac{d(Te)}{dz} \qquad \text{Eq. 68}$$

Note that the turbulent diffusivity of heat ($\mathcal{K}_z$) is the same as the turbulent diffusivity of momentum and mass. Again, this is due to the fact that heat is transported by the bulk movement of water in eddies rather than by some property of the fluid itself (i.e., its thermal conductivity). As with concentration boundary layers, to a first approximation the relative thickness of turbulent momentum and thermal boundary layers is 1.

The velocity of the fluid is not explicitly present in Equation 68, but it is implicitly present in that flow affects both the intensity of turbulence (and thereby $\mathcal{K}_z$) and the thickness of the viscous sublayer. The faster the mainstream flow, the thinner the viscous sublayer, and the steeper the temperature gradient across the sublayer. Because heat in the viscous sublayer can be transported solely by conduction, a steep temperature gradient results in an augmented rate of heat transport.

We have only scratched the surface of the important and complex subject of boundary layers. For more complete discussions of the properties of boundary layers, see Bird et al. (1960), Schlichting (1979), Middleton and Southard (1984), Sleath (1984), Denny (1988), Monteith and Unsworth (1990), and Mann and Lazier (1991).

A Primer on the Physics of Heat Transport

The physics of a thermal boundary layer serves nicely to set the stage for the last topic we cover in this introductory chapter—the transport of heat in general. The temperature of an organism affects its life in many ways, and extremes of temperature may be responsible for its death. The object here is to provide a brief overview of the factors that determine the temperature of intertidal organisms.

Temperature is a measure of the average thermal energy of molecules in an object (see Denny 1993). As heat energy is added to or taken away from an object, its temperature rises or falls. The proportionality between heat energy and temperature is set by a property we have briefly touched on before, the **specific heat capacity**, q. For example, the specific heat capacity of water is very high, approximately 4200 J kg^{-1} K^{-1} (Denny 1993). In other words, one would have to add 4000 joules of heat energy to a kilogram of water to raise its temperature by one degree Celsius. In contrast, air has a specific heat capacity of only about 1000 J kg^{-1} K^{-1} (Denny 1993), and we would have to add only a quarter as much energy to a kilogram of air to get its temperature to increase by one degree as we would have to add to a kilogram of water. Because plants and animals are largely made of water, their specific heat capacity is typically high, near that of water.

Given the specific heat capacity of an organism, if we desire to predict how its temperature changes through time, we simply need to specify how much net heat energy it gains or loses. Although this is simple in principle, it is a bit complicated in practice, primarily because there is a wide variety of ways in heat energy can be transported (Figure 1.21). We have dealt with two of these so far in our discussion of thermal boundary layers. First, heat can be transported by conduction to or from other objects in the environment. For example, an intertidal limpet could be heated by the inward conduction of thermal energy from the hot air surrounding it. At the same time, it could be cooled by the outward conduction of heat energy to the cold rock beneath it. We denote the flux of heat by conduction with the symbol Q_{cond}. Q_{cond}, as with all other forms of heat flux, has the units of watts. Second, we have seen that heat can be transported by convection (either free or forced). We denote convective heat transport by the symbol Q_{conv}.

In addition to these mechanisms of heat transport, there are four others of importance to intertidal organisms. (1) Heat can flow into an organism when solar radiation is absorbed, a flux denoted as Q_{sol}. (2) Heat can also be transported to or from an organism through the absorption or radiation of long-wave (infrared) light. This flux, Q_{rad}, is described in greater detail below. (3) If water evaporates from or condenses on an organism, the organism is cooled or heated (respectively), a flux of energy denoted by Q_{evap}. (4) And finally, the organism's metabolism can release chemical energy in the form of heat, and this flux is given the symbol Q_{metab}.

Given this list of the various ways in which an organism can gain or lose heat, it is a simple process to calculate the net energy gain or loss, Q. The net rate of energy transfer is simply the sum of the individual fluxes:

$$Q = Q_{sol} + Q_{rad} + Q_{cond} + Q_{conv} + Q_{evap} + Q_{metab} \qquad \text{Eq. 69}$$

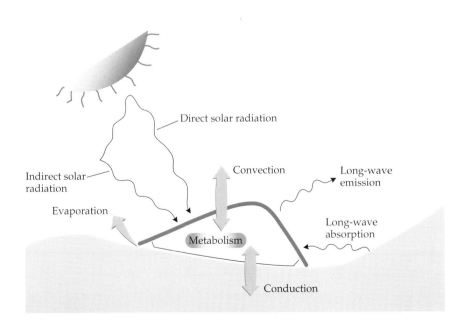

Figure 1.21 There are a variety of mechanisms by which heat energy can be transported to and from a benthic organism (exemplified here by a limpet). The double-headed arrows for convection and conduction express the fact that heat can flow either into or out of the organism, depending on the direction of the temperature gradient between the organism and either the air or the substrate.

The convention here is that a flux is positive if it transports energy into an organism and negative if it transports energy out. The relation between the energy gains or losses of an object, Q, and the rate of change of body temperature, Te_B, is quantified by the **transient heat equation**:

$$\frac{d(Te)}{dt} = \frac{Q}{mq} \qquad \text{Eq. 70}$$

In other words, the temporal rate of change of an organism's temperature is proportional to the net heat influx and inversely proportional to the organism's mass (m) and specific heat capacity (q).

We will not delve into the details, but the rate of heat efflux from an object generally increases as the object's temperature increases. As a result, while Q_{sol} stays constant, Q_{rad}, Q_{cond}, Q_{conv}, and Q_{evap} become increasingly negative as the body temperature of an organism increases. As a result, at some temperature, the energy gained from the environment and metabolism is just offset by the energy lost to the environment. At this temperature, the net heat flux is zero, and the temperature of the organism stays constant. Under these conditions, the organism is in **thermal equilibrium**. For many small organisms, this equilibrium is reached quickly.

Physiological ecologists often refer to a quantity called the **operative temperature** of the environment, which is the temperature that the organism would have at thermal equilibrium. The operative temperature is often measured with a hollow model of the organism, which has very low specific heat and mass, and thereby equilibrates very quickly to changes in the rates of heat exchange (Bakken 1976).

The transient heat equation (Equation 70) is a very useful tool. In essence, it allows us to predict the temperature of an intertidal plant or animal from a knowledge of its thermal environment. To make this prediction, however, one needs to know some of the details that govern each form of heat flux, and it is to these details that we turn next. The presentation here is but a brief introduction to heat transport. For further information, see engineering transport texts such as Bird et al. (1960) or Holman (1986), or biophysical ecology sources such as Gates (1980), Woodward and Sheehy (1983), Campbell and Norman (1998), or Monteith and Unsworth (1990).

Solar Radiation

The flux of energy to a plant or animal from direct solar radiation depends on three factors: the intensity of the sunlight, the angle of the organism's surface relative to the incoming light, and the tendency of the organism's surface to absorb radiation.

The intensity of **direct solar radiation** (I_{sol}, in watts per square meter) varies with the time of day, the time of year, and the clarity of the atmosphere. Fortunately, light intensity is easily measured by simple devices known as pyranometers. The energy incident on a surface (I_{surf}) is proportional to the cosine of the **angle of incidence**, θ

$$I_{surf} = I_{sol}\cos(\theta) \qquad \text{Eq. 71}$$

Here the angle of incidence is measured as shown in Figure 1.22. Since the primary source of radiant energy is the sun, which moves through the sky, the angle of incidence changes continuously as a function of the hour of the day, day of the year, and geographic location. In the northern hemisphere, surfaces that face north receive less intense solar radiation than those that face south, and the opposite is true in the southern hemisphere. The precise geometry that dictates the instantaneous angle of incidence is well and thoroughly described in Gates (1980).

The **absorptivity** of a surface $\alpha(\lambda)$ is the fraction of incident radiation absorbed at wavelength λ. If the object absorbs all radiation that hits it, it has an absorptivity of 1 and is said to be a **black body**. Objects not only absorb light energy, they radiate it as well, at a rate that depends on their temperature. The higher the temperature of the body, the more light is emitted. The **emissivity** of an object, $\varepsilon(\lambda)$, is the ratio of actual emitted radiation to the theoretical radiation of a black body. The emissivity and absorptivity of an object are always equal (see Bird et al. 1960).

The absorptivities of natural surfaces vary greatly, and when dealing with a particular plant or animal it is wise to measure absorptivity directly. The absorptivity of surfaces as a function of wavelength can be measured using a scanning spectroreflectometer, which consists of a light source, an adjustable monochromator (to illuminate the specimen with a narrow band of wavelengths), and an integrating sphere within which the sample is placed (Porter and Gates 1969).

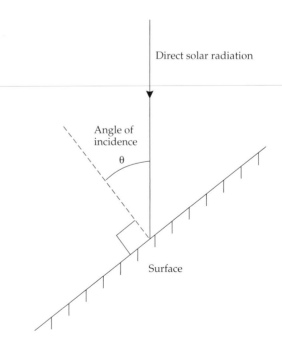

Figure 1.22 The angle of incidence, θ, for direct solar radiation is measured relative to a line perpendicular to the surface on which light impinges (Equation 71).

Diffuse radiation is solar radiation scattered by atmospheric clouds and dust. On sunny days, it is a minor component of the total radiation, but in shaded locations and on fully overcast days it represents 100% of the incoming solar radiation. As with direct solar radiation, diffuse radiation is easily measured with a pyranometer.

The total solar radiation absorbed by a surface is the sum of the direct and diffuse components:

$$Q_{sol} = \alpha \left(A_{sol} I_{surf} + A_{dif} I_{dif} \right) \qquad \text{Eq. 72}$$

where I_{surf} is the direct solar radiation flux, taking into account the slope and orientation of the animal surface (Equation 71), A_{sol} is the area of the organism projected in the direction of solar radiation (which depends upon the organism's position and the location of the sun in the sky), A_{dif} is the total area of the organism exposed to diffuse radiation, and I_{dif} is the diffuse radiation flux.

Long-Wave Radiation

As we noted above, objects emit radiation as well as absorb it. The spectral distribution of radiation emitted by a black body depends upon its temperature, and the wavelength at which light is most intense, λ_{MAX}, is described by Wien's displacement law:

$$\lambda_{MAX} = 2897 (\mu m \text{ kelvin}) / Te_B \qquad \text{Eq. 73}$$

where λ_{MAX} is measured in micrometers, and Te_B is the absolute temperature of the radiating body. Thus, the sun (whose surface is very hot, about 5800°K) emits primarily short-wave radiation ($\lambda_{MAX} = 0.5\ \mu m$), and objects at environmental temperatures ($Te_B = 300°K$) emit long wave or infrared radiation ($\lambda_{MAX} = 9.7\ \mu m$).

The intensity of radiation emitted from the surface of a black body is proportional to the fourth power of its absolute temperature:

$$I = \sigma Te_B^4 \qquad \text{Eq. 74}$$

where σ is the Stefan-Boltzman constant (5.67×10^{-8} W m^{-2} K^{-4}), and I is a flux measured in watts per meter squared. Therefore, the radiation emitted from a surface of emissivity ε is

$$I_{emit} = \varepsilon \sigma Te_B^4 \qquad \text{Eq. 75}$$

A plant or animal at ambient environmental temperature emits long-wave radiation, and at the same time is absorbing long wave radiation from the ground and from the sky. The net flux of energy from long-wave radiation with respect to the sky and ground is:

$$Q_{lw,sky} = \sigma A_{lw,sky} \left(\varepsilon_{org} Te_B^4 - \varepsilon_{sky} Te_{sky}^4 \right) \qquad \text{Eq. 76}$$

$$Q_{lw,ground} = \sigma A_{lw,ground} \left(\varepsilon_{org} Te_B^4 - \varepsilon_{ground} Te_{ground}^4 \right) \qquad \text{Eq. 77}$$

where ε_{org} is the emissivity of the organism, ε_{sky} is the emissivity of the sky, and ε_{ground} is the emissivity of the substratum. $A_{lw,sky}$ is the area of the organism exposed to diffuse radiation from the sky, and $A_{lw,ground}$ is the area of the organism exposed to radiation from the substratum. Te_b is the body temperature of the organism, Te_{sky} is the effective temperature of the sky, and Te_{ground} is the temperature of the substratum.

Swinbank (1963) measured clear sky radiation in relation to air temperature at the ground. The sky temperature and emissivity of the sky can be estimated as (Monteith and Unsworth 1990):

$$Te_{sky} = \left(Te_{air} - 21 \right) + 0.2 Te_{air} \qquad \text{Eq. 78}$$

$$\varepsilon_{sky} = 1.20 - 171 / \sigma Te_{air}^4 \qquad \text{Eq. 79}$$

where Te_{air} is the temperature of the air near the organism.

The net energy transport due to long-wave radiation is:

$$Q_{rad} = Q_{lw,sky} + Q_{lw,ground} \qquad \text{Eq. 80}$$

Conduction

Transfer of heat between two solids (or between a solid and a stationary fluid) occurs by **conduction**. Conduction of heat occurs at a rate proportional to the gradient in temperature.

$$\frac{Q_{cond}}{A_{cond}} = \mathcal{K} \frac{d(Te)}{dz} \qquad \text{Eq. 81}$$

where $\mathcal{K}$ is again the thermal conductivity. Note that this is analogous to the equation relating shear stress (force per area) to a velocity gradient in a fluid (Equation 4), and Fick's equation relating molecular diffusion to a concentration gradient (Equation 60). [The sign of the right-hand side of the equation has been adjusted to match the tradition that a positive heat flux represents heat flowing into an organism (in this case heat flowing down a temperature gradient that increases with distance away from the plant or animal).] Here, the proportionality constant between heat flux and the temperature gradient is the thermal conductivity of the material, $\mathcal{K}$. The temperature gradient is measured in °C m^{-1}. Note that Q_{cond} depends on the *gradient* of temperature, not just the temperature difference between an object and its surroundings. The thermal conductivity of animal tissue is about 75% of that of free water (Denny 1993).

In the analysis of heat transfer it is often the ratio of thermal conductivity to the product of specific heat and density that is important. This ratio is given the name **thermal diffusivity**, κ:

$$\kappa = \frac{\mathcal{K}}{\rho q} \qquad \text{Eq. 82}$$

where ρ is the density of the material (kg m^{-3}) and q is again the specific heat (J kg^{-1}). As with all diffusivities, thermal diffusivity has units of m^2 s^{-1}.

As we have seen, air conducts heat less well than water. Thermal properties of many materials are published in Touloukian (1970), Touloukian and Buyco (1970), and Touloukian and DeWitt (1972).

Convection

When an organism is surrounded by a moving fluid, **convective heat transfer** occurs. The rate of transfer depends on the velocity of the fluid and the temperature difference between the object and the fluid. In newspaper meteorology, this relationship is called the **wind chill**, but it applies to water as well as air. In more formal terms, Q_{conv} is calculated according to **Newton's law of cooling**:

$$Q_{conv} = h_C A_{conv} \left(Te_{fluid} - Te_B \right) \qquad \text{Eq. 83}$$

Here, h_C is the **convective heat transfer coefficient**, A_{conv} is the surface area over which convection occurs, and Te_{fluid} is the temperature of the fluid. When the temperature of the fluid is higher than that of the body, heat energy is transported into the body. When the temperature of the body is higher than that of the fluid, heat energy is lost to the fluid. The convective heat transfer coefficient is proportional to the fluid velocity and is influenced by the size and shape of the organism. In most cases, h_C must be determined empirically.

The heat transfer coefficient of an object is usually measured using a polished metal model whose thermal emissivity is near to zero, so that convection is the dominant mode of heat transport. Such models are made by lost-wax casting, in which a rubber mold of the organism is filled with hot wax. The wax is then embedded in fine plaster, which is subsequently baked at 500°C to burn off the wax. The resulting plaster mold is filled with molten metal in a centrifuge. The equipment for this process is readily available in the jewelry fabrication shops of university art departments. Thermocouples are soldered or welded into holes drilled into the metal models so that their temperatures can be measured. The models are heated with a heat-gun, placed in a wind tunnel, and their rate of cooling is measured as a function of wind speed and air temperature.

The model's temperature declines exponentially with time, approaching as an asymptote the ambient air temperature. If we know the specific heat capacity of the material

from which the model is made, we can use the rate of change in temperature of the model to calculate Q_{conv}, the convective rate of energy transport. Because we have also measured body and air temperature, we know $Te_{fluid} - Te_B$ and can then calculate h_c from Equation 83. Alternatively, the entire curve of cooling through time can be used to estimate the convective heat transfer coefficient. It can be calculated that

$$\frac{\ln\left(\dfrac{Te_t - Te_\infty}{Te_0 - Te_\infty} \right) mq}{A_{conv}} = -h_C t \qquad \text{Eq. 84}$$

where Te_t is the temperature of the object at time t, Te_∞ is the temperature of the air (the temperature to which the object eventually asymptotes), Te_0 is the initial temperature of the model, and A_{conv} is the surface area over which convection occurs. A plot is constructed of the scaled temperature (the left-hand side of Equation 84) versus time, and the slope of the resulting line is $-h_C$.

In yet another alternative, we can use the relationships measured by others to estimate h_C. For example, for spheres in the range $Re = 50 - 1.5 \times 10^5$, $h_C = 0.34 \, \mathcal{K} \, Re^{0.6} / L_C$, where L_C is the sphere's diameter. For cylinders broadside to flow in the range $Re = 10^3 - 5 \times 10^4$, $h_C = 0.24 \, \mathcal{K} \, Re^{0.6} / L_C$, where L_C is the cylinder's diameter and $\mathcal{K}$ is the thermal conductivity of the fluid (Monteith and Unsworth 1990).

Evaporation

At the interface between water and air, a water molecule occasionally gains sufficient kinetic energy to break the hydrogen bonds that attach it to other water molecules, and the energetic molecule escapes into the air. This is the process of evaporation. Now, it takes energy to break these hydrogen bonds, and during evaporation this energy is supplied by the thermal energy of the water itself. As a result, when a water molecule evaporates, it takes with it a bit of the thermal energy of the liquid, and the remaining liquid water is cooled. Just the opposite occurs when water vapor in the air condenses back to liquid water. As each molecule of vapor condenses, new hydrogen bonds are formed, and heat is released into the liquid. This exchange of heat energy during evaporation or condensation is know as the **latent heat of vaporization**, v, and for water its value is quite high, about 2.6 MJ per kilogram (Denny 1993).

The latent heat of vaporization can be used to calculate the evaporative energy flux:

$$Q_{evap} = v \, h_M A_{evap} \left(\rho_{v,air} - \rho_{v,body} \right) \qquad \text{Eq. 85}$$

Where h_M is the **convective mass transfer coefficient**, and ρ_v is the water vapor density (kg m^{-3}) either in the air or at the surface of the organism.

Unless the organism is in a confined space, the water vapor density of the surrounding air is largely independent of the temperature of the organism or its rate of evaporation, and we

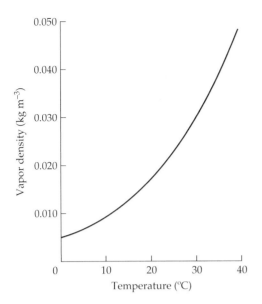

Figure 1.23 The saturation water vapor density increases rapidly with increasing temperature. Data from Weast (1978).

can treat $\rho_{v,air}$ as a constant. In contrast, the water vapor density at the organism's surface is sensitive to the organism's temperature. If the surface of the body is wet (as it often is for intertidal organisms), the air at the surface is saturated with water vapor. Saturation water-vapor density is very sensitive to temperature; it increases rapidly as the temperature goes up (Figure 1.23). Furthermore, the air at the surface of an organism is at body temperature. As a result, $\rho_{v,body}$ increases as body temperature increases, and the evaporative heat loss from an organism increases in proportion (Equation 85).

The convective mass transfer coefficient, h_M, is analogous to the heat transfer coefficient. Its magnitude depends on the size and shape of the object from which mass is transported, and on wind speed. As with the convective heat transfer coefficient, the convective mass transfer coefficient is typically measured empirically. In this case, the relevant equation is:

$$\frac{dm}{dt} = h_M A_{evap}\left(\rho_{v,body} - \rho_{v,air}\right) \qquad \text{Eq. 86}$$

where dm/dt is the rate at which mass is lost through evaporation and A_{evap} is the area over which evaporative mass exchange occurs. The rate of mass exchange at a given wind speed can be determined in a wind tunnel by measuring the weight loss of a wet plaster model of the plant or animal in question. The time course of mass loss is exponential, analogous to the cooling of a heated object in wind (Equation 84).

CONSEQUENCES OF HEAT TRANSPORT

Rocky Shores

The intertidal zone experiences terrestrial conditions for part of the tidal cycle and marine conditions for the remainder. As a result, there are dramatic fluctuations in heat transport and

temperature. When submerged, the organism quickly reaches thermal equilibrium, because of the very high convective heat transfer coefficients in water. If the tide recedes while the sun is up, the organism begins to warm. During the day, as the sun moves through the sky, the air and ground temperature, wind speed, and relative humidity change, and the organism constantly changes temperature. It is very common during sunny conditions for intertidal organisms in direct sunlight to reach temperatures well above those of ambient air (Davies 1970, Vermeij 1973, Wolcott 1973, Johnson 1975, Thomas 1987, Etter 1988, Bertness 1989, Hayworth and Quinn 1990, Davey 1992, Gomez-Cornejo 1994, Helmuth 1998). Then as the tide covers the shore, the organisms may drop 20°C within less than a minute. As we have noted, hot organisms experience higher rates of water loss than do cooler individuals.

All of these effects are mediated by the effects the organisms have on their own habitat. Much as trees modify the rates of transport of heat, mass, and momentum within canopies, so do marine macroalgae (e.g., Eckman et al. 1989, Leonard 2000). Organisms in aggregations also modify transport rates. For example, aggregations of barnacles and mussels experience narrower temperature ranges than do adjacent solitary individuals (Thomas 1987, Bertness 1989, Helmuth 1998).

One of the major consequences of the thermal extremes in the rocky intertidal is to limit the local distribution of organisms on shores. The upper limits of local distribution in the intertidal zone are often limited by intolerance of high temperatures, desiccation, or both (e.g., Hatton 1938, Connell 1961, Lewis 1964, Newell 1979, Wethey 1984, Stillman and Somero 1996, Leonard 2000). The influence of the radiation environment is particularly obvious on boulder-covered shores, where the upper limits of distribution of some species vary as a function of the slope and azimuth of the substratum (Wethey 1983) or presence of algal canopies (Leonard 2000). Local microhabitat variation in thermal conditions can also cause genetic changes in intertidal populations after larval settlement, as a result of the action of natural selection on particular genotypes (Schmidt and Rand 1999, Schmidt et al. 2000).

The geographic distribution of some species is also correlated with the thermal environment (Hutchins 1947, Lewis 1964, 1986). Hutchins (1947) made the point eloquently that both the lower and upper thermal limits of species are likely to influence their geographic distribution through the effects on survival and reproduction. He argued that the minimum temperature at which a species could survive would be associated with the winter poleward boundary of the species, whereas the minimum temperature at which a species could repopulate a shore through recruitment would set the summer poleward boundary. Similarly, the maximum temperature at which a species could recruit would set the winter equatorward boundary and the maximum temperature at which a species could survive would set the summer equatorward boundary. Hutchins related the geographic distributions of several intertidal species (including barnacles and mussels) to maximum and minimum sea surface temperature. In this respect, Hutchins (1947) presentation is a very important framework for considering biogeography.

The examples presented by Hutchins are flawed by his assumption that the submerged temperature conditions are dominant in intertidal organisms. From our presentation above, it is clear that the thermal conditions for epibiotic organisms at low tide are much more extreme than those in submersion, because of the rapid heating caused by direct solar radiation. However, the idea of the interaction between the thermal environment and the geographic range of species is sound. Lewis (1964, 1986, 1993) has examined this idea in relation to the distribution of many intertidal species in Europe and has found in several cases that failure of recruitment in low-temperature conditions sets the poleward boundary. Wethey (1984) demonstrated experimentally that a poleward boundary was set by the same thermally mediated biological factors that limited local vertical distribution in the intertidal zone. From long-term studies, there is evidence that both local population densities and geographic limits of species are changing on decadal to 50-year time scales, correlated with changes in the thermal environment (e.g., Southward 1991, Southward et al. 1995, Sagarin et al. 1999).

Sedimentary Shores

To this point we have dealt with organisms living *on* the substratum. On sedimentary shores, animals also live *in* the substratum, and the thermal environment of these infauna is less extreme than for epibiota. At low tide the surface layers of sediments are heated to temperatures well above ambient air temperature (Johnson 1965, Harrison 1984, Harrison and Phizacklea 1987). The amplitude of the temperature variation depends upon grain size and percent saturation of the sediment (Tuller 1972, Monteith and Unsworth 1980, Campbell and Norman 1998). Sediments themselves offer a refuge from the extreme thermal conditions on the surface. Heat is conducted into sediments (Equation 81), but J_z, the amplitude of the temperature fluctuations at depth z, decreases exponentially with depth (Porter et al. 1973, Arya 1988, Campbell and Norman 1998):

$$J_z = J_0 \exp(z/d_\mathrm{d})$$ Eq. 87

Here J_0 is the amplitude of temperature fluctuations at the sediment surface. The damping depth, d_d, is related to the period, T, of fluctuations at the surface, and to the thermal diffusivity of the sediment, κ:

$$d_\mathrm{d} = \sqrt{\frac{T\kappa}{\pi}}$$ Eq. 88

We have made measurements that show that moving cloud cover over salt marshes can result in thermal "waves" with a period of 2 hours (Gomez-Cornejo and Wethey, unpub. data). These measurements indicate a thermal diffusivity for these muddy sediments of 1.4×10^{-6} m^2 s^{-1}, and a damping depth of 5 cm. For diurnal thermal waves, the damping depth is 20 cm. Other estimates of the thermal diffusivity are: mud $0.47 \times$

$10^{-6} - 0.81 \times 10^{-6}$ m^2 s^{-1} (Harrison 1984, Harrison and Phizacklea 1987), and dry sand 0.25×10^{-6} m^2 s^{-1} (Harrison and Phizacklea 1987). For diurnal thermal waves the corresponding damping depths are 11–15 cm (mud) and 9 cm (sand). At the damping depth, the amplitude of the temperature fluctuations is 37% of the surface amplitude. Therefore, for a burrowing organism, there is a thermal refuge within a few centimeters of the surface.

In general, the subtidal thermal environment has small-scale thermal fluctuations on a diurnal cycle, and larger-scale fluctuations on a yearly cycle. The large volume of overlying water with its high specific heat and large amount of mixing tends to average temperature changes over long time periods. In some cases, however, tidal forces can cause the themocline to oscillate up and down. These internal waves are associated with rapid fluctuations in temperature on some coral reefs (Leichter and Miller 1999).

CONSEQUENCES OF MASS TRANSPORT

Why the Schmidt Number Matters

Crisp and Meadows (1962) use the relative thickness of the velocity and concentration boundary layers (proportional to the $Sc^{1/3}$) to make the argument that a diffusible chemical cue from a flat surface (within the viscous sublayer) reaches near zero concentration at distances of a only few millimeters above the bottom. They go on to argue that a "soluble pheromone would be diluted to extinction within a very short distance of the surface to which larvae were being attracted" (Crisp 1974). For this reason, they argue that such diffusible attractants would only be effective if the source of the cue covers very large areas (mud for *Ilyanassa*: Scheltema 1961; oyster reefs: Zimmer-Faust and Tamburri 1994, Tamburri et al. 1996). As a consequence, adsorbed or surface active cues are more likely than dissolved cues to be effective in areas where there is intense mixing (barnacles responding to each other: Crisp and Meadows 1962) or small-sized sources (abalone responding to coralline algae: Morse and Morse 1984). However, there is evidence that settling larvae of infauna can respond to short-lived diffusible cues associated with small-scale sediment disturbance (Woodin et al. 1993, 1995, 1998). The larvae are able to detect diffusible cues only when they are in direct contact with the bottom, when their epidermis is within the viscous sublayer. Worm larvae lie prostrate on the surface for several seconds while they are deciding whether to burrow or not. During this time they presumably are detecting diffusible cues through their ventral surface.

The metabolic mass exchange (O$_2$, CO$_2$) rates of organisms are influenced by boundary layer thickness. For oxygen and carbon dioxide, the Schmidt number for water is around 500 (Patterson 1992), so the velocity boundary layer is much thicker than the concentration boundary layer (Equation 63). Metabolism in coral reef assemblages is mass transfer limited (e.g., Thomas and Atkinson 1997, Williams and Carpenter 1998), and concentration boundary layer thickness varies as a function of flow speed and organism morphology (e.g., Patterson 1992, Shashar et al. 1993, Kühl et al. 1995, Gardella and Edmunds 1999). The size scale of surface topography and its interaction with flow determines boundary layer structure, which in turn determines the extent exposure of organisms to water from outside the concentration boundary layer (e.g., Lesser et al. 1994, Shashar et al. 1996, Helmuth et al. 1997, Bruno and Edmunds 1998).

Some predators find their prey using the plumes of odor released into free-stream flow by their prey. Since the Schmidt number for biological molecules is large, the mixing of odor is largely by turbulence and there is very little molecular diffusion. As a result, the distribution of odors in plumes is very heterogeneous, with high concentration odor filaments being transported long distances downstream (Zimmer-Faust et al. 1995, Finelli et al. 1999a,b). This movement increases the detectability of odors in plumes at long distances downstream from the source.

A Note at the End

The reader is reminded that the transport of heat, mass, and momentum, although of undoubted importance in determining ecological patterns, are only three of the many factors that effect the distribution and abundance of marine plants and animals. It is typically the *interaction* of these transport phenomena with the morphology, physiology, and behavior of organisms that is important in ecology. Put simply, physics can take an ecologist only so far. The rest of the journey is the subject of the rest of this book.

Acknowledgments

We thank Brian Gaylord, Ben Hale, and Brian Helmuth for helpful comments on the manuscript. Brianna Timmerman lent her artistry to Figure 1.16.

Literature Cited

Arya, S. P. 1988. *Introduction to Micrometeorology.* Academic Press, San Diego.

Bakken, G. S. 1976. A heat transfer analysis of animals: Unifying concepts and the application of metabolism data to field ecology. *J. Theoret. Biol.* 60: 337–384.

Batchelor, G. K. 1967. *An Introduction to Fluid Dynamics.* Cambridge University Press, Cambridge, U.K.

Bell, E. C. 1992. Consequences of morphological variation in an intertidal macroalga: Physical constraints on growth and survival of *Mastocarpus papillatus* Kützing. PhD. Thesis, Stanford University, Stanford, CA.

Bell, E. C. 1993. Photosynthetic response to temperature and desiccation of the intertidal alga *Mastocarpus papillatus. Mar. Biol.* 117: 337–346.

Bell, E. C. and M. W. Denny. 1994. Quantifying "wave exposure": A simple device for recording maximum velocity and results of its use at several field sites. *J. Exp. Mar. Biol. Ecol.* 181: 9–29.

Bertness, M. D. 1989. Intraspecific competition and facilitation in a northern acorn barnacle population. *Ecology* 70: 257–268.

Bird, R. B., W. E. Stewart and E. N. Lightfoot. 1960. *Transport Phenomena.* Wiley, New York.

Bruno, J. F. and P. J. Edmunds. 1998. Metabolic consequences of phenotypic plasticity in the coral *Madracis mirabilis* (Duchassaing and Michelotti): The effect of morphology and water flow on aggregate respiration. *J. Exp. Mar. Biol. Ecol.* 229: 187–195.

Campbell, G. S. and J. M. Norman 1998. *An Introduction to Environmental Biophysics*, 2nd ed. Springer-Verlag, New York.

Carrington, E. 1990. Drag and dislodgment of an intertidal macroalga: Consequences of morphological variation in *Mastocarpus papillatus* Kützing. *J. Exp. Mar. Biol. Ecol.* 139: 185–200.

Connell, J. H. 1961. The influence of interspecific competition and other factors on the distribution of the barnacle *Chthamalus stellatus. Ecology* 42: 710–723.

Crisp, D. J. 1974. Factors influencing the settlement of marine invertebrate larvae. pp 177–265. In P. T. Grant and A. M. Mackie (eds.), *Chemoreception in Marine Organisms.* Academic Press, London.

Crisp, D. J. and P. S. Meadows. 1962. The chemical basis of gregariousness in cirripedes. *Proc. Roy. Soc. Lond.* B 158: 364–387.

Davey, P. 1992. Effect of microclimate on the distribution of the mussel *Brachidontes exustus.* MS Thesis, University of South Carolina, Columbia.

Davies, P. S. 1970. Physiological ecology of *Patella*. IV. Environmental and limpet body temperatures. *J. Mar. Biol. Ass. U. K.* 50: 1069–1077.

Dayton, P. K. 1971. Competition, disturbance, and community organization: The provision and subsequent utilization of space in a rocky intertidal community. *Ecol. Monogr.* 45: 137–159.

Denny, M. W. 1988. *Biology and the Mechanics of the Wave-Swept Environment.* Princeton University Press, Princeton, NJ.

Denny, M. W. 1993. *Air and Water.* Princeton University Press, Princeton, NJ.

Denny, M. W. 1995. Predicting physical disturbance: Mechanistic approaches to the study of survivorship on wave-swept shores. *Ecol. Monogr.* 65: 371–418.

Denny, M. and B. Gaylord. 1996. Why the urchin lost its spines: Hydrodynamic forces and survivorship in three echinoids. *J. Exp. Biol.* 199: 717–729.

Denny, M. W. and R. T. Paine. 1998. Celestial mechanics, sea-level changes, and intertidal ecology. *Biol. Bull.* 194: 108–115.

Denny, M. W., T. L. Daniel and M. A. R. Koehl. 1985. Mechanical limits to size in wave-swept organisms. *Ecol. Monogr.* 51: 69–102.

Denny, M., B. Gaylord, B. Helmuth and T. Daniel. 1998. The menace of momentum: Dynamic forces on flexible organisms. *Limnol. Oceanogr.* 43: 955–968.

Eckart, C. 1951. Surface waves on water of variable depth. Ref. No. 51–12. Scripps Institute of Oceanography, La Jolla, CA.

Eckman, J. E., D. O. Duggins and A. T. Sewell. 1989. Ecology of understory kelp environments. I. Effects of kelps on flow and particle transport near the bottom. *J. Exp. Mar. Biol. Ecol* 129: 173–187.

Etter, R. J. 1988. Physiological stress and color polymorphism in the intertidal snail *Nucella lapillus. Evolution* 42: 660–680.

Finelli, C. M., N. D. Pentcheff, R. K. Zimmer-Faust and D. S. Wethey. 1999. Odor transport in turbulent flow: Constraints on animal navigation. *Limnol. Oceanogr.* 44: 1056–1071.

Finelli, C. M., N. D. Pentcheff, R. K. Zimmer and D. S. Wethey. 2000. Physical constraints on ecological processes: The effects of prey odor and flow speed on foraging. *Ecology* 81: 784–797.

Gardella, D. J. and P. J. Edmunds. 1999. The oxygen microenvironment adjacent to the tissue of the scleractinian *Dichocoenia stokesii* and its effects on symbiont metabolism. *Mar. Biol.* 135: 289–295.

Gates, D. M. 1980. *Biophysical Ecology.* Springer-Verlag, New York.

Gaylord, B. 1997. Consequences of wave-induced water motion to nearshore macroalgae. PhD. Dissertation, Stanford University, Stanford, CA.

Gaylord, B. 1999. Detailing agents of physical disturbance: Wave-induced velocities and accelerations on a rocky shore. *J. Exp. Mar. Biol. Ecol.* 239: 85–124.

Gaylord, B. 2000. Size, scaling, and compliant design in intertidal organisms: Implications of fine-scale features of surf-zone flows. *Limnol. Oceanogr.* 45: 174–188.

Gaylord, B., C. A. Blanchette and M. W. Denny. 1994. Mechanical consequences of size in wave-swept algae. *Ecol. Monogr.* 64: 287–313.

Gomez-Cornejo, E. 1994. Effect of microclimate on the behavioral ecology of the salt marsh periwinkle *Littoraria irrorata* (Say).

PhD Dissertation, University of South Carolina, Columbia.

Harrison, S. J. 1984. Heat exchanges in muddy intertidal sediments: Chichester Harbour, West Sussex, England. *Estuar. Coastal Mar Sci.* 20: 477–490.

Harrison, S. J. and A. P. Phizacklea. 1987. Vertical temperature gradients in muddy intertidal sediments in the Forth estuary, Scotland. *Limnol. Oceanogr.* 32: 954–963.

Hatton, H. 1938. Essais de bionomie explicative sur quelques espèces intercotidales d'algues et d'animaux. *Ann. Inst. Océanogr. Monaco* 17: 241–348.

Hayworth, A. M. and J. F. Quinn. 1990. Temperature of limpets in the intertidal zone: Effects of caging and substratum. *Limnol. Oceanogr.* 35: 967–970.

Helmuth, B. T. 1998. Intertidal mussel microclimates: Predicting the body temperature of a sessile invertebrate. *Ecol. Monogr.* 68: 51–74.

Helmuth, B. 1999. Thermal biology of rocky intertidal mussels: Quantifying body temperature using climatological data. *Ecology* 80: 15–34.

Helmuth, B. S. T., K. P. Sebens and T. L. Daniel. 1997. Morphological variation in coral aggregations: Branch spacing and mass flux to coral tissues. *J. Exp. Mar. Biol. Ecol.* 209: 233–259.

Hibberd, S., and D. H. Peregrine. 1979. Surf and run-up on a beach: A uniform bore. *J. Fluid Mech.* 95: 323–345.

Hoerner, S. 1965. *Fluid-Dynamic Drag.* Hoerner Press, Bricktown, NJ.

Holman, J. P. 1986. *Heat Transfer.* McGraw-Hill, New York.

Hurd, C. L. 2000. Water motion and marine macroalgal physiology and production. *J. Phycol.* 36: 453–472.

Hutchins, L. W. 1947. The bases for temperature zonation in geographical distribution. *Ecol. Monogr.* 17: 325–335.

Johnson, R. G. 1965. Temperature variation in the infaunal environment of a sand flat. *Limnol. Oceanogr.* 10: 114–120.

Johnson, S. E. 1975. Microclimate and energy flow in the marine intertidal. In D. Gates and R. B. Schmerl (eds.), *Perspectives on Biophysical Ecology*, pp. 559–587. Springer-Verlag, New York.

Kawamata, S. 1998. Effect of wave-induced oscillatory flow on grazing by a subtidal sea urchin *Strongylocentrotus nudus* (A. Agassiz). *J. Exp. Mar. Biol. Ecol.* 224: 31–48.

Kinsman, B. 1965. *Wind Waves.* Prentice-Hall, Englewood Cliffs, NJ.

Koehl, M. A. R. and R. S. Alberte. 1988 Flow, flapping, and photosynthesis of *Nereocystis luetkeana*: A functional comparison of undulate and flat blade morphologies. *Mar. Biol.* 99: 435–444.

Kühl, M., Y. Cohen, T. Dalsgaard, B. B. Jørgensen and N. P. Revsbech. 1995. Microenvironment and photosynthesis of zooxanthellae in scleractinian corals studied with microsensors for O_2, pH and light. *Mar. Ecol. Prog. Ser.* 117: 159–172.

Leichter, J. J. and S. L. Miller. 1999. Predicting high-frequency upwelling: Spatial and temporal patterns of temperature anomalies on a Florida coral reef. *Cont. Shelf Res.* 19: 911–928.

Leigh, E. G., R. T. Paine, J. F. Quinn and T. H. Suchanek. 1987. Wave energy and intertidal productivity. *Proc. Natl. Acad. Sci. USA* 84: 1314–1318.

Leonard, G. H. 2000. Latitudinal variation in species interactions: A test in the New England rocky intertidal zone. *Ecology* 81: 1015–1030.

Lesser, M. P., V. M. Weis, M. R. Patterson, and P. L. Jokiel. 1994. Effects of morphology and water motion on carbon delivery and productivity in the reef coral, *Pocillopora damicornis* (Linnaeus): Diffusion barriers, inorganic carbon limitation, and biochemical plasticity. *J. Exp. Mar. Biol. Ecol.* 178: 153–179.

Levitan, D. R. 1995. The ecology of fertilization in free-spawning invertebrates. In L. M. McEdwards (ed.), *Ecology of Marine Invertebrate Larvae*, CRC Press, Boca Raton, FL.

Lewis, J. R. 1964. *The Ecology of Rocky Shores.* English Universities Press, London.

Lewis, J. R. 1968. Water movements and their role in rocky shore ecology. *Sarsia* 34: 13–36.

Lewis, J. R. 1986. Latitudinal trends in reproduction, recruitment and population characteristics of some rocky littoral mollusks and cirripedes. *Hydrobiologia* 142: 1–13.

Lewis, J. R. 1993. Rationale, methods and problems involved in the assessment and causes of recruitment fluctuations of some rocky shore species. In B. F. Keegan (ed.), *Space and Time Series Data Analysis in Coastal Benthic Ecology*, pp. 439–480. Commission of European Communities, Brussels.

Longuet-Higgins, M. S. 1952. On the statistical distribution of the heights of sea waves. *J. Mar. Res.* 11: 245–266.

Longuet-Higgins, M. S. 1980. On the distribution of heights of sea waves: Some effects of nonlinearity and finite bandwidth. *J. Geophys. Res.* 85(C3): 1519–1523.

Mann, K. H. and J. R. N. Lazier. 1991. *Dynamics of Marine Ecosystems.* Blackwell Scientific, London.

Massel, S. R. 1996. *Ocean Surface Waves: Their Physics and Prediction.* World Scientific, London.

Massel, S. R. and T. J. Done. 1993. Effects of cyclone waves on massive coral assemblages on the Great Barrier Reef: Meteorology, hydrodynamics, and demography. *Coral Reefs* 12: 153–166.

McQuaid, C. D. and G. M. Branch. 1985. Trophic structure of rocky intertidal communities: Response to wave action and implications for energy flow. *Mar. Ecol. Prog. Ser.* 22: 153–161.

Menge, B. A., 1978. Predation intensity in a rocky intertidal community: Relation between predator foraging activity and environmental harshness. *Oecologia* 34: 1–16.

Middleton, G. V. and J. B. Southard. 1984. *Mechanics of Sediment Movement.* Society of Economic Paleontologists and Mineralogists, Tulsa, OK.

Monteith, J. L. and M. H. Unsworth. 1990. *Principles of Environmental Physics.* Edward Arnold, London.

Morison, J. R., M. P. O'Brien, J. W. Johnson and S. A. Schaaf. 1950. The forces exerted by surface waves on piles. *Petroleum Trans. AIME* 189: 149–157.

Morse, A. N. C. and D. E. Morse. 1984. Recruitment and metamorphosis of *Haliotis* larvae induced by molecules uniquely available at the surfaces of crustose red algae. *J. Exp. Mar. Biol. Ecol.* 75: 191–215.

Munk, W. H., 1949. The solitary wave theory and its application to surf problems. *Ann. New York Acad. Sci.* 51: 376–424.

Newell, R. C. 1979. *Biology of Intertidal Organisms*, 3rd ed. Marine Ecological Surveys, Faversham, U.K.

Nobel, P. S. 1991. *Physicochemical and Environmental Plant Physiology.* Academic Press, New York.

Nybakken, J, W. 1988. *Marine Biology: An Ecological Approach*, 2nd ed. Harper & Row, New York.

Paine, R. T., 1979. Disaster, catastrophe, and local persistence of the sea palm, *Postelsia palmaeformis. Science* 205: 685–687.

Paine, R. T. and S. A. Levin. 1981. Intertidal landscapes: Disturbance and the dynamics of pattern. *Ecol. Monogr.* 51: 145–178.

Patterson, M. R. 1992. A chemical engineering view of cnidarian symbiosis. *Amer. Zool.* 32: 566–582.

Pearson, G. A. and S. H. Brawley. 1998. Sensing hydrodynamic conditions via carbon acquisition: Control of gamete release in fucoid seaweeds. *Ecology* 79: 1725–1739.

Porter, W. P. and D. M. Gates. 1969. Thermodynamic equilibria of animals with environment. *Ecol. Monogr.* 39: 227–244.

Porter, W. P., J. W. Mitchell, W. A. Beckman and C. B. DeWitt. 1973. Behavioral implications of mechanistic ecology. Thermal and behavioral modeling of desert ectotherms and their microenvironment. *Oecologia* 13: 1–54.

Ricketts, E. F., J. Calvin, J. W. Hedgpeth and D. W. Phillips. 1985. *Between Pacific Tides*, (5th ed.) Stanford University Press, Stanford, CA.

Sagarin, R. D., J. P. Barry, S. E. Gilman and C. H. Baxter. 1999. Climate-related change in an intertidal community over short and long time scales. *Ecol. Monogr.* 69: 465–490.

Sarpkaya, T. and M. Isaacson. 1984. *Mechanics of Wave Forces on Offshore Structures.* Van Nostrand Reinhold, New York.

Scheltema, R. S. 1961. Metamorphosis of the veliger larvae of *Nassarius obsoletus* (Gastropoda) in response to bottom sediment. *Biol. Bull.* 120: 92–109.

Schlichting, H. 1979. *Boundary Layer Theory.* McGraw-Hill, New York.

Schmidt, P. S. and D. M. Rand. 1999. Intertidal microhabitat and selection at *Mpi*: Interlocus contrasts in the northern acorn barnacle, *Semibalanus balanoides. Evolution* 53: 135–146.

Schmidt, P. S., M. D. Bertness and D. M. Rand. 2000. Environmental heterogeneity and balancing selection in the acorn barnacle *Semibalanus balanoides. Proc. Roy. Soc. Lond.* B 267:379–384.

Serrão, E. A., G. A. Pearson, L. Kautsky and S. H. Brawley. 1996. Successful external fertilization in turbulent environments. *Proc. Natl. Acad. Sci. USA* 93: 5286–5290.

Seymour, R. 1996. Wave climate variability in southern California. *J. Waterway, Port, Coastal, and Ocean Engineering*

Seymour, R., R. R. Strange, D. R. Cayan and R. A. Nathan. 1984. Influence of El Niño on California's wave climate. In *Proceedings of the 19th International Coastal Engineering Conference*, pp. 577–592. American Society of Civil Engineers, New York.

Shashar, N., Y. Cohen and Y. Loya. 1993. Extreme diel fluctuations of oxygen in diffusive boundary layers surrounding stony corals. *Biol. Bull.* 185: 455–461.

Shashar, N., S. Kinane, P. L. Jokiel and M. R. Patterson. 1996. Hydromechanical boundary layers over a coral reef. *J. Exp. Mar. Biol. Ecol.* 199: 17–28.

Shimeta, J. and P. A. Jumars. 1991. Physical mechanisms and rates of particle capture by suspension feeders. *Oceanogr. Mar. Biol. Annu. Rev.* 29: 191–257.

Sleath, J. F. A. 1984. *Sea Bed Mechanics.* Wiley, New York.

Sousa, W. P. 1984. The role of disturbance in natural communities. *Annu. Rev. Ecol. Syst.* 15, 353–391.

Sousa, W. P. 1985. Disturbance and patch dynamics on rocky intertidal shores. In S. T. A. Pickett and P. S. White (eds.), *The Ecology of Natural Disturbance and Patch Dynamics*, pp. 101–124. Academic Press, Orlando.

Southward, A. J. 1991. Forty years of changes in species composition and population density of barnacles on a rocky shore near Plymouth. *J. Mar. Biol. Ass. U. K.* 71: 495–513.

Southward, A. J., S. J. Hawkins and M. T. Burrows. 1995. Seventy years' observations of changes in distribution and abundance of zooplankton and intertidal organisms in the western English Channel in relation to rising sea temperature. *J. Thermal Biol.* 20: 127–155.

Stephenson, T. A. and A. Stephenson. 1972. *Life Between Tide Marks on Rocky Shores.* Freeman, San Francisco.

Stillman, J. H. and G. N. Somero. 1996. Adaptation to temperature stress and aerial exposure in congeneric species of intertidal porcelain crabs (genus *Petrolisthes*): Correlation of physiology, biochemistry and morphology with vertical distribution. *J. Exp. Biol.* 199: 1845–1855.

Swinbank, W. C. 1963. Long wave radiation from clear skies. *Q. J. Roy. Met. Soc.* 89: 339–348.

Tamburri, M. N., C. M. Finelli, D. S. Wethey and R. K. Zimmer-Faust. 1996. Chemical induction of larval settlement behavior in flow. *Biol. Bull.* 191: 367–373.

Thomas, F. I. M. 1987. The hot and cold of life on the rocks: Determinants of body temperature of the northern rock barnacle *Semibalanus balanoides*. MS Thesis, Brown University, Providence, RI.

Thomas, F. I. M. and M. J. Atkinson. 1997. Ammonium uptake by coral reefs: Effects of water velocity and surface roughness on mass transfer. *Limnol. Oceanogr.* 42: 81–88.

Touloukian, Y. S. 1970. *Thermal Diffusivity.* IBI/Plenum, New York.

Touloukian, Y. S. and E. H. Buyco. 1970. *Specific Heat.* IBI/Plenum, New York.

Touloukian, Y. S. and D. P. DeWitt. 1972. *Thermal Radiative Properties.* IBI/Plenum, New York.

Tuller, S. E. 1972. Energy balance microclimatic variations on a coastal beach. *Tellus* 24: 260–270.

U. S. Army Corps of Engineers. 1984. *Shore Protection Manual*, 4th ed. U. S. Government Printing Office, Washington, DC.

Vermeij, G. J. 1973. Morphological patterns in high intertidal gastropods: Adaptive strategies and their limitations. *Mar. Biol.* 20: 319–346.

Vogel, S. 1994. *Life in Moving Fluids* (2nd ed.). Princeton University Press, Princeton, NJ.

Weast, R. C. 1978. *CRC Handbook of Chemistry and Physics*. CRC Press, Cleveland, Ohio.

Wethey, D. S. 1983. Geographic limits and local zonation: The barnacles *Semibalanus (Balanus)* and *Chthamalus* in New England. *Biol. Bull.* 165: 330–341.

Wethey, D. S. 1984. Sun and shade mediate competition in the barnacles *Chthamalus* and *Semibalanus*: A field experiment. *Biol. Bull.* 167: 176–185.

Williams, S. L. and R. C. Carpenter 1998. Effects of unidirectional and oscillatory flow on nitrogen fixation (acetylene reduction) in coral reef algal turfs, Kaneohe Bay, Hawaii. *J. Exp. Mar. Biol. Ecol.* 226: 293–316.

Wing, S. R., L. W. Botsford and J. F. Quinn. 1995. Settlement and transport of benthic invertebrates in an upwelling region. *Limnol. Oceanogr.* 40: 316–329.

Wing, S. R., L. W. Botsford, S. V. Ralston and J. L. Largier. 1998. Meroplanktonic distribution and circulation in a coastal retention zone of the northern California upwelling system. *Limnol. Oceanogr.* 43: 1710–1721.

Wolcott, T. G. 1973. Physiological ecology and intertidal zonation in limpets (*Acmaea*): A critical look at "limiting factors." *Biol. Bull.* 145: 389–422.

Woodin, S. A., R. L. Marinelli and D. E. Lincoln. 1993. Allelochemical inhibition of recruitment in a sedimentary assemblage. *J. Chem. Ecol.* 19: 517–530.

Woodin, S. A., S. M. Lindsay, and D. S. Wethey. 1995. Process-specific recruitment cues in marine sedimentary systems. *Biol. Bull.* 189: 49–58.

Woodin, S. A., R. L. Marinelli and S. M. Lindsay. 1998. Process-specific cues for recruitment in sedimentary systems: Geochemical signals? *J. Marine Research* 56: 535–558.

Woodward, F. I. and J. E. Sheehy. 1983. *Principles and Measurements in Environmental Biology.* Butterworths, London.

Zimmer-Faust, R. K. and M. N. Tamburri. 1994. The chemical identity and ecological implications of a waterborne larval settlement cue. *Limnol. Oceanogr.* 39: 1075–1087.

Zimmer-Faust, R. K., C. M. Finelli, N. D. Pentcheff and D. S. Wethey. 1995. Odor plumes and animal navigation in turbulent water flow: A field study. *Biol. Bull.* 188: 111–116.

chapter 2

Community Assembly in the Sea
Geologic History of the Living Shore Biota

Geerat J. Vermeij

The communities and ecosystems of nature owe much of their aesthetic and intellectual appeal to the diversity of their component species and interactions. Somehow, despite all the scrambling for resources among members, species coexist with and accommodate one another until some catastrophic event disrupts populations to the point of extinction. Where does all this richness come from? How are communities and ecosystems assembled? These are the questions to which I shall address myself in this chapter. I do so in the context of shallow-water ecosystems on the sea bottom in the North Pacific, North Atlantic, and tropical oceans. From taxonomic, stratigraphic, and phylogenetic evidence, I shall piece together historical accounts of the assembly and composition of the nearshore marine ecosystems whose structure and dynamics have been the subject of extensive scrutiny by ecologists.

From an ecological point of view, it is perhaps most interesting to ask when, where, and under what circumstances species with disproportionately large effects in ecosystems appeared. Species of large effect fall into two general categories: (1) structural or foundation species, which provide most of the three-dimensional architecture in which other species find shelter and food; and (2) keystone species (Paine 1966, 1969), which, by virtue of their high rates of consumption and their generalized diets, exercise disproportionate control over the distributions, population sizes, activities, and adaptive characteristics of many other species. These ecologically "important" species contrast with the so-called "ornamental" species of small effect (Birkeland 1996), which play subordinate roles but which nonetheless contribute much of the stunning diversity that draws me and so many other naturalists to the study of life in the wild.

SOURCES OF HISTORICAL DATA

Fossils provide the most direct evidence of the distribution of taxa in space and time. Not only do they document when, where, and for how long a species existed, but they offer the only evidence that a living taxon once occupied regions outside its current distributional range. Fossils also chronicle changes in adaptive morphology through time.

The rocks or sediments in which fossils are preserved represent specific time intervals. Inferences about the ages of fossils rest on radiometrically determined dates and on stratigraphic correlations, which are established by the occurrence either of widespread geochemical markers or of short-lived, widely distributed planktonic species. Refinements in stratigraphy continue to be made, but uncertainties persist about how rock sequences and fossils in one part of the world relate temporally to those elsewhere. Local stage names are therefore sometimes preferable to the standard, internationally recognized stages because they indicate that a precise correspondence remains uncertain.

Most of the plants and animals living on the world's shores evolved during the Cenozoic era, which began 65 million years ago (Mya) after the end-Cretaceous mass extinction. In particular, it is the latter half of the Cenozoic—the last 32 million years (my), beginning with the Oligocene epoch—with which this chapter is occupied. The Cenozoic stage nomenclature and time scale I adopt is that of Berggren et al. (1995) (see Table 2.1).

Although the marine fossil record of the Cenozoic era is more complete and geographically more representative than that of any other era, some intervals of time and some habitats are not well chronicled. Such preservational biases obvi-

TABLE 2.1   The Cenozoic time scale.

Stage	Mya
PALEOGENE PERIOD	
Paleocene epoch	
Danian (early Paleocene)	65–61
Selandian-Thanetian (late Paleocene)	61–55
Eocene epoch	
Ypresian (early Eocene)	55–49
Lutetian (middle Eocene)	49–41
Bartonian (middle Eocene)	41–37
Priabonian (late Eocene)	37–34
Oligocene epoch	
Rupelian (early Oligocene)	33.7–28.5
Chattian (late Oligocene)	28.5–23.8
NEOGENE PERIOD	
Miocene epoch	
Aquitanian (early Miocene)	23.8–20.5
Burdigalian (early Miocene	20.5–16.4
Langhian (early middle Miocene)	16.4–14.8
Serravallian (late middle Miocene)	14.8–11.2
Tortonian (late Miocene)	11.2–7.1
Messinian (late Miocene)	7.1–5.3
Pliocene epoch	
Zanclian (early Pliocene)	5.3–3.5
Piacenzian (late Pliocene)	3.5–1.6
Pleistocene epoch	1.6–0.12

Source: After Berggren et al. 1995.

ously affect the way in which we interpret history, and we must be aware of them at all times when drawing conclusions from the fossil record. For example, strata of Oligocene age have yielded large and well-preserved faunas from the North Pacific, Europe, southeastern North America, southeastern Australia, New Zealand, and the Indian subcontinent; but deposits of this age are either entirely missing or yield poorly preserved fossils in tropical America, Africa, and Indonesia. The tropical eastern Pacific fossil record is substantially less complete, less well preserved, and geographically less representative than the record in the western Atlantic. Finally, we know less about the history of the Indo-West Pacific region than about the recent past in the cool-temperate Northern and Southern Hemispheres or tropical America.

Some biases are more subtle. Because fossils tend to be preserved in sediments, habitats where sediments do not accumulate are poorly represented in the fossil record. The rocky intertidal zone is a prime example. Unusual cases of preservation of rocky shore assemblages are known (Johnson 1988; Lee et al. 1983; Lindberg and Lipps 1996), but rocky shores are typically not sites of sedimentary deposition. For-tunately, the great majority of rocky shore species also occur below the tidal zone, and others are transported after death to subtidal settings, where opportunities for preservation are greater. As a result, we have a reasonable, if sparse, record of intertidal molluscs, barnacles, and other organisms with hard parts found in rocky habitats.

A less recognized bias is toward the preservation of fossils in highly productive communities. Extensive runoff from the land is associated not only with high rates of sedimentation, which promotes fossilization, but also with enhanced primary productivity and therefore with abundance. Chemical weathering and physical erosion introduce nutrients into nearshore marine ecosystems and sustain high levels of biomass production. Habitats with low primary planktonic productivity, such as blue-water coral reefs, are often preserved in the geologic record, but many of their inhabitants do not enter the fossil record, because the calcium carbonate skeletons of the relatively unstable aragonitic morph rapidly dissolve or recrystallize. As a result, we know relatively little about the biological history (especially that of mobile animals) of oceanic islands and of shores far from river mouths or landslides.

Evidence from phylogeny complements and refines data from the stratigraphic record. By working out the pattern and order of evolutionary branching events, we can infer the time and place of origin of species, even in the absence of fossil specimens, and identify conditions favorable to rapid adaptive diversification. A phylogeny is, of course, only as good as the taxonomy and understanding of characters it is based upon. For Cenozoic groups, with which this chapter is concerned, so many members are still living that phylogenetic analysis of molecular sequences offers a powerful line of evidence that can be used in conjunction with morphological characters and the stratigraphic record to produce robust hypotheses about the distributional and adaptive history of many clades.

History is much more than names and dates. It must also come to grips with the context of life and with interactions among species. Although we cannot expect to reconstruct all the subtleties of interaction observable in living ecosystems, the fossil record does provide important clues to the evolutionary importance of such interactions as predation involving the destruction of hard parts. Functional morphology coupled with careful observations of the environments in which fossil organisms lived are essential to the telling of biological history. Much of the evidence discussed in this chapter is drawn from molluscs and barnacles. This is so not only because of my own familiarity with these groups, but also because of the extensive work that has been done on their taxonomy, distributions, fossil record, and phylogeny. Even for these well-studied groups, however, information is far from complete. I have therefore had to resort to lists of examples instead of providing robust, quantitative estimates of phenomena and events. I hope that the synthesis that follows will spur others to intensify the historical research necessary to establish a more rigorous account.

THE NORTH PACIFIC BIOTA

Living cool-temperate communities of benthic organisms extend around the North Pacific from central California northward to Alaska and thence southward to Cape Inubo and Shimane Prefecture in Japan (Briggs 1974; Kussakin 1990; Kafanov and Volvenko 1997). I think it is fair to say that we understand broadly how shallow-water benthic ecosystems of the North Pacific work, both at the local scale of communities and at the larger scale of geographic biotas. Predators such as the sea stars *Pisaster ochraceus* and *Pycnopodia helianthoides*, the sea otter *Enhydra lutris*, and the oystercatcher *Haematopus bachmani* exercise strong top-down control over the vertical distributions, abundances, size distributions, and competitive relationships of major space occupiers (mussels, barnacles, and seaweeds) as well as low-level mobile consumers such as gastropods, crustaceans, chitons, and echinoderms (Paine 1966, 1974, 1980; Estes and Palmisano 1974; Dayton 1971, 1975a,b; Estes et al. 1989, 1998; Simenstad et al. 1978; Lindberg et al. 1998). Regional variation in prey eaten by these generalist predators (Paine 1980; Ostfeld 1982; Duggins 1983; Lindberg et al. 1998) is superimposed on spatial variation in larval recruitment, nutrient availability, and primary productivity, which in turn are determined by onshore and offshore transport of water masses and by wave-induced turbulence (Gaines and Roughgarden 1987; Leigh et al. 1987; Roughgarden et al. 1988; Menge and Farrell 1989; Menge 1992, 1995; Connolly and Roughgarden 1998). There is thus both bottom-up control by physical factors in the ocean and atmosphere and top-down control by species of large economic effect.

The cool-temperate ecosystems of the North Pacific were not assembled overnight. Instead, they have a long history stretching back more than 30 million years to the early Oligocene or perhaps late Eocene, when the first significant episode of cooling established the first large-scale cold-water habitats in the post-Cretaceous Northern Hemisphere.

The biotic history of the cool-temperate North Pacific has until recently been reconstructed mainly from a stratigraphic perspective. Important regional studies of strata and their successive faunas have been carried out in Russia (Gladenkov 1988, 1990a,b; Gladenkov et al. 1988, 1991; Fotyanova and Serova 1987; Barinov and Gladenkov 1998; Kafanov and Volvenko 1997), Japan (Chinzei 1978, 1986; Ogasawara 1981, 1986; Tsuchi and Shuto 1984; Tsuchi and Ibaraki 1988; Tsuchi 1990a,b; Amano 1986; Honda 1991, 1994), Alaska (Allison 1978; Marincovich 1988, 1990; Marincovich and Moriya 1992; Marincovich and Wiggins 1991), and the northwestern continental United States (Addicott 1976, 1977; Armentrout 1981; Armentrout et al. 1983, 1984; Barron 1981; Marincovich 1984; Moore 1984; Moore and Addicott 1987). There have also been international efforts to correlate faunas as well as rock sequences around the North Pacific and to identify basin-wide faunistic changes (Kafanov 1978, 1984; Addicott 1969; Gladenkov 1979, 1990b; Marincovich 1984; Tsuchi 1990b; Titova 1994a; Kafanov and Volvenko 1997). In spite of this considerable body of work, important aspects of biotic history in the

North Pacific have gone unrecognized or underappreciated. The following account is based on my synthesis of the primary systematic and stratigraphic literature and on my evolutionary studies of several gastropod clades.

Origins and Early Distribution

The genesis of the cool-temperate North Pacific ecosystem can be found in the latest Eocene or early Oligocene. Rocks representing this first distinctly cool interval of the Cenozoic in the Northern Hemisphere contain the earliest known members of many clades that later became fixtures of North Pacific communities.

A large number of these clades originated in the northwestern Pacific. They include buccinid gastropods of the Buccininae and several other subfamilies derived from it (Goryachev 1987; Gladenkov et al. 1988; Titova 1993, 1994a); turritellid gastropods of the Turritellinae and Tachyrhynchinae (Titova 1994b,c); the predatory ranellid gastropod *Fusitriton* (Smith 1970; Beu 1988); the volutid gastropod genus *Arctomelon* (Oleinik 1996); various clades of protobranchs, including *Megayoldia* and *Cnesterium* (Kafanov and Savizky 1995); cockles of the cardiid subfamily Clinocardiinae (Kafanov 1980; Kafanov and Savizky 1982; Schneider 1998); the glossy venerid bivalve *Liocyma*; the large tellinid bivalve genus *Macoma* (Coan 1971); the razor clam genera *Siliqua* and *Ensisolen*; the large hiatellid bivalve *Panomya* (Strauch 1972); and the soft-shelled clam *Mya* (MacNeil 1965; Strauch 1972). Other clades that may have originated in the northwestern Pacific but whose place of origin is less secure include fulgorariine volutids (Oleinik 1993), turrid gastropods of the *Aforia* group (Sysoev and Kantor 1987), trochid gastropods including *Solariella* and the subfamily Margaritinae (see Hickman 1980; Squires and Goedert 1991), protobranch bivalves including *Acila* and the sulfide-associated *Acharax* (Schenck 1936), the mussel *Mytilus* (Kafanov 1987), and the *Cyclocardia* group of carditid bivalves (Popov 1983).

The clades that made their first appearance in the northwestern Pacific during the latest Eocene or early Oligocene spread to the northeastern Pacific (Alaska to Washington, Oregon, and California) gradually, beginning in the Oligocene. Interestingly, most of these clades have remained more species-rich in the northwestern Pacific. This is notably the case for the northern buccinids, which are represented by at least 200 living cool-temperate species in the northwestern Pacific and by about 100 in the northeastern Pacific, mainly in Alaska.

Still other taxa originated during the latest Eocene or earliest Oligocene on the American side of the Pacific. Examples include the moon snail genera *Glossaulax*, *Euspira*, and *Cryptonatica* (Marincovich 1977; Majima 1989; Noda 1992); the extinct helmet-shell genus *Liracassis* (Kanno 1973; Moore 1984); the limpets *Puncturella* and *Erginus* (Lindberg 1988a); and the bivalves *Crenomytilus* (Kafanov 1987), *Nuttallia*, *Megangulus* (Matsukuma et al. 1988), *Mactromeris*, *Heteromacoma*, and *Pseudocardium*.

Where did these cold-water clades came from? There are at least four possible sources: (1) the tropical or warm-temperate western Pacific, (2) the tropical to warm-temperate coasts of the Americas, (3) the cool-temperate Southern Hemisphere, and (4) the deep sea. A potential fifth source, the Arctic-Atlantic basin, was separated from the North Pacific by an impenetrable land barrier until the late Miocene.

We know or can infer the place of origin for only a few of the North Pacific clades that adapted to cool conditions during the Eocene and early Oligocene. Turritelline gastropods of the *Hataiella–Neohaustator* group evidently arose from warm-water groups that were already present in the warm North Pacific during and before the late Eocene (Titova 1994a,b,c). The volutid genus *Arctomelon* (known from the middle Eocene to the Recent) is a member of the subfamily Zidoninae, and may represent a case of invasion from cold southern latitudes, where the subfamily evolved and is still most diverse (Oleinik 1996). There may be Southern Hemisphere connections for the turrid *Aforia* and for the *Yoldia* group of protobranch bivalves, which occur in cold northern and southern waters but not in the tropics. Phylogenetic studies of these and most other taxa mentioned in the two paragraphs above have not been conducted, however, so a scenario of northward invasion must remain speculative. It is interesting to note in passing that the cool-water fauna of the Southern Hemisphere substantially predates that of the North Pacific. Cool-water clades are known from the Antarctic region and from the nearby land masses of Australia, New Zealand, and South America since at least late Cretaceous time (Zinsmeister and Camacho 1980; Zinsmeister 1982; Darragh 1985; Crame 1986, 1992, 1993; Beu 1990).

A noteworthy characteristic of the early (Eocene and early Oligocene) North Pacific cold-water fauna is that its living descendants occupy mainly subtidal and sandy or muddy intertidal habitats. For example, the cool-water buccinids occur chiefly on sublittoral bottoms, save for a few rocky intertidal species of *Buccinum*, *Volutharpa*, *Neptunea*, and *Barbitonia* in northeastern Asia and Alaska. Species of *Cryptonatica*, *Euspira*, *Macoma*, *Megangulus*, *Nuttallia*, *Mactromeris*, *Pseudocardium*, *Macoma*, *Siliqua*, *Cyclocardia*, *Clinocardium*, and *Mya* are familiar elements in the intertidal sand around the North Pacific rim. A few clades (*Mytilus*, *Crenomytilus*, *Puncturella*, and *Erginus* and maritime trochids) are common in sublittoral rocky habitats, but only *Mytilus* and the margaritine *Valvatella* extend into the rocky intertidal zone.

Cold-Water Adaptation and Patterns of Invasion during the Neogene

Much of the biota of the cold-water coastal North Pacific comprises species in clades that became cold-adapted during or after the late Oligocene. This new wave of taxa, which includes the great majority of clades on rocky shores, overwhelmingly originated on the American side from warm-water ancestors, not on the Asian side of the Pacific. Large-scale invasions during the Miocene led to a homogenization of the North Pacific biota. These aspects of North Pacific history, which have gone largely unnoticed by previous authors, are documented briefly below.

Most of the rocky shore fauna of molluscs and barnacles in the northeastern Pacific apparently originated there in latest Oligocene to early Miocene ("Juanian" to "Pillarian") time. Phylogenetically documented cases include periwinkles of the genus *Littorina* (Reid 1989, 1990, 1996), the drilling muricids *Nucella* (Amano et al. 1993; T. M. Collins et al. 1996) and *Ceratostoma* (Amano and Vermeij 1998; Marko and Vermeij 1999), and the trochid top-shells of the Tegulinae (Hellberg 1998). Other examples, based mainly on stratigraphic evidence, include the slipper limpet *Grandicrepidula* (Hoagland 1977; McLean 1995), the buccinid *Lirabuccinum* (Vermeij 1991b), the oyster *Crassostrea*, and barnacles (*Balanus* and the balanid subfamily Concavinae) (Newman and Ross 1976; Zullo and Marincovich 1990; Zullo 1992). Lottiid limpets probably also belong in this group (Lindberg 1988b), as do cancrid rock crabs (Nations 1975, 1979; Berglund and Goedert 1996). The North Pacific clade of large abalones (family Haliotidae) may also have originated in the northeastern Pacific. This clade is evidently most closely related to small tropical American species rather than to warm-water types from the western Pacific (see Itoigawa and Tomida 1982; Lindberg 1992; Brown 1993; Geiger 1998; Geiger and Groves 1999).

Another ecologically important clade for which a latest Oligocene or earliest Miocene origin in the northeastern Pacific seems likely is the Laminariales, the brown algae known as kelps. Estes and Steinberg (1988) postulated that kelps originated during the middle to late Miocene, at about the same time that marine mammals capable of eating sea urchins (the main invertebrate consumers of seaweeds in the North Pacific) arose. Domning (1989), however, suggested that kelps originated earlier, no later than the late Oligocene, because several of the herbivorous desmostylian mammals of that age exhibit dental features consistent with a diet of seaweeds. The time and place of first appearance of kelps may never be known with certainty owing to the paucity of fossils, but phylogeny as well as the geographic pattern of kelp diversity to me imply a post-Eocene and pre-late Miocene origin in the northeastern Pacific (Druehl 1981).

In addition to these clades of sublittoral and intertidal hard surfaces, several rock-boring and soft-sediment groups also made their first appearance in the cool-temperate North Pacific on the American side during the late Oligocene to early Miocene. The borers include the bivalves *Platyodon* and *Penitella* (Adegoke 1967). Among the sand and mud dwellers are the venerid clams *Protothaca*, *Saxidomus*, *Securella*, and the *Dosinia* group; the tellinid *Rexithaerus* (Matsubara 1994; Amano et al. 1999); turrid gastropods of the *Antiplanes* group (Kantor and Sysoev 1991); and the sand dollar genus *Echinarachnius* (Nisiyama 1968; Wagner 1974). The large venerid *Securella*, now confined to the western Pacific, evidently arose from a warm-water early Oligocene species in the southeastern United States related to or congeneric with *Mercenaria*, and not, as Harte (1998) thought, from an Eocene tropical western Pacific species of *Placamen*. Given Harte's hypothesis, there would be an unexplained temporal gap between the

Eocene *Placamen* and the first appearance of *Securella* in Japan during the early middle Miocene. In the Americas, *Securella* is known from the Pacific coast.

Many clades with an Oligocene to early Miocene origin in North America expanded westward in the North Pacific and reached temperate coasts of Japan by early middle Miocene time. The colonization of northeast Asian shores by clades from America was recognized previously for individual clades such as *Nucella* (Amano et al. 1993), *Rexithaerus* (Matsubara 1994), *Littorina* (Reid 1996), several groups of moon snails (Marincovich 1977; Majima 1989), *Liracassis* (Kanno 1973; Moore 1984), and *Lirabuccinum* (Vermeij 1991b), but the general pattern was not recognized until Amano and Vermeij (1998) studied the spread of *Ceratostoma* and noted historical similarities with many of the above-mentioned clades. The expansion apparently coincided with an episode of maximal Neogene warmth in the North Pacific, when relatively warm-water genera such as *Ficus*, *Hataiella*, and *Dosinia* reached the Gulf of Alaska (Marincovich and Moriya 1992).

The consumers with potentially the greatest effects on North Pacific marine ecosystems—the mammals and birds—also conform to the pattern of eastern origins and westward spread in the North Pacific from late Oligocene time onward. As herbivores and high-level predators with voracious appetites, they exercise a profound influence on the distributions and characteristics of many species. Herbivorous desmostylian mammals were part of the shore ecosystem on both sides of the North Pacific from the late Oligocene to the late Miocene (Domning et al. 1986; Domning 1989). In the middle Miocene, they were joined in the eastern Pacific by hydrodamaline dugongid sirenians (sea cows), to which the late Miocene to Recent Steller's sea cow (*Hydrodamalis*) of the cool-temperate North Pacific belongs (Domning 1978; Takahashi et al. 1986). Steller's sea cow (*H. gigas*) was evidently a major consumer of littoral and canopy kelps before it was exterminated by people in the eighteenth century (Dayton 1975a,b; Estes et al. 1989; Domning 1978, 1989). Carnivorous seals (Pinnipedia) arose in latest Oligocene or earliest Miocene time in warm-temperate California. By early middle Miocene time they had spread westward to Japan and eastward to the North Atlantic (see Wyss 1987, 1988; Berta et al. 1989). A second group of marine predatory mammals, the otters (*Enhydritherium*), appeared during the late Miocene in California, and in late Pliocene or early Pleistocene time gave rise to the North Pacific sea otter *Enhydra lutris* (Repenning 1976b; Berta and Morgan 1985; Riedman and Estes 1988). Oystercatchers (*Haematopus*) and marine gulls (*Larus*) did not make their appearance until the Pliocene (Olson 1985; Warheit 1992). Seals feeding on benthic invertebrates appeared in the late Miocene, and gray whales (*Eschrichtius robustus*), which together with walruses (*Odobenus odobenus*) are the most important agents of disturbance on the sea bottom in the Bering Sea, arose only during the Pleistocene (Repenning et al. 1976a; Mead and Mitchell 1984). Although seals, otters, and sirenians evidently made their first appearance in the North Pacific on the American side and subse-

quently spread westward, it is not clear on which side of the North Pacific desmostylians, marine gulls, benthic-feeding seals, and gray whales originated.

Sea urchins of the genus *Strongylocentrotus* have a very spotty fossil record from the Miocene onward in Japan (Nisiyama 1966). The time and place of origin of this group of important consumers unfortunately remain obscure.

Evidence from molluscs and barnacles strongly implies that, whereas the direction of invasion was overwhelmingly if not exclusively from east to west during the early middle Miocene, it became predominantly west to east during and after late Miocene time. My preliminary data for molluscs show that 41 taxa invaded from west to east, whereas only 9 invaded from east to west during this time (Vermeij 1991c). Most of the eastward invaders were species belonging to clades that had previously spread westward from North America to Asia. This pattern is well exemplified also by several barnacles, including *Balanus balanus* and *Semibalanus balanoides* (see Zullo and Marincovich 1990).

Several ecologically important cool-water clades evidently entered or originated in the northeastern Pacific during the Miocene and did not spread to the northwestern Pacific. These include the large cemented scallop *Crassadoma* (Waller 1993); cool-water species of the cemented oysterlike bivalve *Chama*; the drilling muricid gastropod *Ocinebrina* (Marko and Vermeij 1999); the large suspension-feeding sand dollar *Dendraster*; the boring or nestling bivalves *Cooperella*, *Semele*, and *Cumingia* (see Beadle 1991, 1995; Coan 1988, 1997); and the columbellid gastropod *Amphissa*.

All members of the northeastern Pacific contingent, including both the groups that expanded westward and those that did not, adapted to cold conditions on the American side. Their ancestors were warm-water species with origins in the warm-temperate or tropical Atlantic or eastern Pacific. Much of the cold adaptation seems to have taken place during or after the late Miocene (see Amano et al. 1993; T. M. Collins et al. 1996).

It is remarkable that, in contrast to the large number of clades that gave rise to cold-adapted species in the northeastern Pacific, relatively few warm-water clades in the western Pacific contain species adapted to cool-temperate conditions. Possible examples are the ark shell *Arca bouchardi*, the venerid bivalve *Ezocallista*, the mactrid bivalve *Mactra*, the venerid *Ruditapes philippinarum* (introduced by humans to the west coast of North America), the semelid bivalve *Theora*, and the gastropod genera *Suchium* (button shells), *Batillaria* (also introduced to the west coast of North America), *Hima*, and *Indomitrella*. The cold-water derivatives in these groups usually comprise single species that were restricted to the low-boreal coasts of eastern Asia before humans introduced some of them to North America. The small number of examples is especially noteworthy in view of the hundreds of essentially tropical clades that contain warm-temperate species in Japan. Evidently, there is an effective barrier between the warm-temperate and cool-temperate zones in eastern Asia, a barrier that does not exist to the same degree in western North

America. Perhaps the much more gradual temperature gradient in the eastern Pacific as compared with the western Pacific accounts for this previously unrecognized asymmetry in the origin of cool-temperate North Pacific taxa. There is a sharp, though fluctuating, boundary between warm and cold water masses in eastern Asia, whereas in the eastern Pacific the transition from cool-temperate to tropical waters extends over more than a thousand kilometers. Most of the cool-water species in warm-water clades of the western Pacific occur in sheltered environments, which even at high latitudes can become quite warm during the summer months but in winter are subject to freezing.

By the late Miocene, the major components of the North Pacific shore biota had become established and had adapted to cool-water conditions. Only a few clades were added later. The most important of these were the sea otter, which arose in the Pliocene or earliest Pleistocene, and our own species, which reached the North Pacific during late Pleistocene time. A very small additional contingent of intertidal species, including the kelp-associated limpet *Discurria insessa* and the columbellid gastropod *Alia carinata*, may have entered the northeastern Pacific as Pliocene trans-equatorial invaders from temperate western South America (Lindberg 1991). Finally, some taxa entered the North Pacific beginning in latest Miocene or earliest Pliocene time from the Arctic-Atlantic basin (Marincovich and Gladenkov 1999). These include the bivalve genera *Astarte*, *Tridonta*, and *Cyrtodaria*, as well as ecologically important consumers such as cod (genus *Gadus*), herring (genus *Clupea*), and the walrus (*Odobenus odobenus*) (see Ray 1976; Repenning et al. 1979; Grant and Stahl 1988; Grant 1986; Vermeij 1991a). The invading South American and Arctic-Atlantic molluscs did not achieve wide penetration of the North Pacific, but the North Atlantic fish and mammals did disperse widely and, in the case of the walrus in the Bering Sea, became important agents of bottom disturbance.

Evolution of the Biotic Environment

Astonishingly little information is available about the biotic environment during the various phases of development of the North Pacific biota. Indirect evidence for unusually intense predation by shell breakers is provided by the occurrence of strikingly thick-shelled molluscs during the early middle Miocene and early Pliocene, especially in the northwestern Pacific. Massive oysters occurred in the early middle Miocene of Japan (*Crassostrea gravitesta*) and in the Miocene of California (*C. titan*). Thick-shelled large mussels (*Plicatomytilus* and *Tumidimytilus*) were widespread throughout the North Pacific during the Miocene (Allison and Addicott 1976; Kafanov 1987). Other notably thick-shelled groups include the middle Miocene to Recent bivalve *Crassicardia*, known mainly from the Asian side (Popov 1983); the sedentary scallop *Fortipecten* of the early Pliocene of the northwestern Pacific (Hayami and Hosoda 1988), and the Japanese venerid bivalves of the *Pseudamiantis-Neogenella* group (early middle Miocene to early Pleistocene). A combination of high planktonic primary productivity and relatively high temperatures

may have made the evolution of such groups possible, and may also have permitted the establishment and maintenance of other abundant, large-bodied suspension feeders such as the huge tall barnacles of the late Miocene and Pliocene of California (Zullo 1979, 1992; Zullo and Guruswami-Naidu 1982), large pectinid scallops from the late Oligocene onward in California and the early middle Miocene onward in Japan (Addicott 1974; Kafanov 1986; Smith 1991; Waller 1991), oversized calyptraeid slipper limpets in the Miocene and Pliocene of California (Hoagland 1977; Vermeij 1989b; McLean 1995); and the late Miocene to Recent eastern Pacific sand dollar *Dendraster* (Beadle 1991, 1995). Large predaceous sea stars such as *Pisaster*, *Pycnopodia*, and *Orthasterias* and large-clawed cancrid crabs also evolved in the North Pacific Miocene. Evidence for predation and for other biological activity is easily obtained from the abundant fossil record in the North Pacific, but has not so far been systematically collected. From the morphology of predators and prey, however, I would guess that the intensity of shell-breaking and shell-entering predation has been substantially higher in the North Pacific, especially during Miocene and Pliocene time, than elsewhere in the cool-temperate Northern Hemisphere. This hypothesis needs to be tested.

Extinction

Extinction has played a relatively minor role in the post-Eocene history of the North Pacific biota. On the American side, some warm-water taxa made their last appearances during the "Juanian" local stage, probably corresponding to the latest Oligocene (Addicott 1976, 1977). Another contingent of warm-water taxa disappeared at the end of "Newportian" time, 14.5 to 15.0Mya, during the middle Miocene (see also Marincovich 1984; Marincovich and Moriya 1992). As was true elsewhere in the Northern Hemisphere, there were extinctions of relatively warm-water taxa during the Pliocene and early Pleistocene (see Stanley 1986b; Lindberg and Lipps 1996; Table 2.2), but the overall magnitude of extinction was low. In the Empire Formation of latest Miocene to early Pliocene age in Oregon, Weaver (1945) recorded about 105 species of molluscs, of which, by my calculation, 40% survive today. On the Asian side of the Pacific, the history of extinction is broadly similar. Of the 50 species in the earliest Pliocene Atsuga Formation of Hokkaido, Japan (Uozumi et al. 1986), as many as 72% survive, and only 28% have become extinct. Stanley (1986b) argued that the proportion of late Pliocene species still living is about 70% on both sides of the North Pacific, though questions remain about the precise ages of the assemblages he surveyed. Indeed, all the estimates given above should be viewed as provisional. More reliable data on ages and taxonomy may change our perception of the magnitude of extinction somewhat, although it is clear that extinction was dramatically smaller in magnitude in the Pacific than in the Atlantic.

Several taxa present during late Neogene time on both sides of the North Pacific now live only on one side or the other. Most of the geographic restriction has been to the

TABLE 2.2   Preliminary estimates of the magnitude of extinction in early to middle Pliocene molluscan assemblages.

Assemblage	Number of species	Percentage extinct species
NORTH PACIFIC		
Empire Formation, Oregon	105	60%
Atsuga Formation, Hokkaido	50	28%
NORTH ATLANTIC		
Yorktown Formation zone 2, Virginia	444	82%
Oorderen Member, Lillo Formation, Belgium	115 (gastropods)	71%
Kruisschans Member, Lillo Formation, Belgium	135	68%
TROPICS		
Melajo Clay, Trinidad	121	79%
Esmeraldas beds, Ecuador	156	72%
Pinecrest beds, Florida	700+	71%
Shinzato Formation, Okinawa	191	57%

Asian side (Vermeij 1989b). Examples include the slipper limpet *Grandicrepidula* (see also McLean 1995), periwinkles of the *Littorina squalida–petricola* group (see also Reid 1996), the turritellid gastropod *Neohaustator* (Titova 1994c), the moon snail *Cryptonatica* (Marincovich 1977; Majima 1989), the buccinid *Pseudoliomesus* (Gladenkov et al. 1988), the volutid subfamily Fulgorariinae (Oleinik 1993), the protobranch *Acila* s.s. (Schenck 1936), the mussel *Crenomytilus* (Kafanov 1987), several scallops, including *Swiftopecten* (Masuda 1972, 1978, 1986; Smith 1991; Waller 1991), the venerid bivalve *Securella* (Harte 1998), and the mactrid *Pseudocardium*. The *Mya arenaria* group of soft-shelled clams became extinct on the American west coast as well, but *M. arenaria* has been reintroduced by humans. Large, often thick-shelled suspension feeders are prominently represented in the above list, perhaps implying that the high planktonic primary productivity that characterized parts of the northeastern Pacific during the Neogene and Recent was greatly reduced or interrupted at some time during the Pliocene, whereas it remained high in the western North Pacific (Vermeij 1989b).

A smaller number of taxa with members on both sides of the North Pacific during the Miocene are now restricted to the eastern Pacific. These include the venerid clams *Compsomyax* and *Humilaria* and the boring myid bivalve *Platyodon* (Amano 1998), as well as perhaps the subgenus *Mytilus* (*Tumidimytilus*), which contains the well-known California mussel *Mytilus californianus* (Kafanov 1987; Vermeij 1989b).

Still other taxa have eastern and western North Pacific representatives separated by a large northern geographic disjunction, whose existence implies the extinction of northern populations, possibly as a result of cooling (Keen 1941; Vermeij 1989b). Well-known examples include the abalone *Haliotis*, the star shell *Pomaulax*, the top shell *Tegula* (*Chlorostoma*) (Hellberg 1998), the buccinid *Lirabuccinum* (Vermeij 1991b), the drilling muricid *Ceratostoma* (Amano and Vermeij 1998),

the cockle *Keenaea*, the deep-burrowing clams *Tresus* and *Panopea*, the boring mussel *Adula*, the razor clam *Ensisolen*, and the large sanguinolariid clam *Nuttallia*.

Summary of North Pacific History

It is evident from the foregoing review that the basic cold-water North Pacific biota was established by late Miocene time, and that this biota is still largely intact, albeit with some subsequent extinctions and invasions. The most interesting finding to come out of this study is that the great majority of clades becoming cool-adapted during or after the late Oligocene originated in, or first entered, the North Pacific on its eastern (that is, North American) side. Large-scale westward invasion during the early middle Miocene, and generally eastward invasion since then, have helped to homogenize the North Pacific biota, although regional differences remain and in fact have become accentuated somewhat by regional extinctions. Whether and how the intensities of ecological interactions have varied over time is not yet clear. The prevalence of thick shells and large body sizes, especially in the Miocene and Pliocene of Japan and, to a lesser extent, California, may imply that shell-breaking predation as well as competition were intense during this interval, perhaps more so than today. Extinction may have been particularly severe among the most highly armored prey species and their predators, perhaps because their high investment in defense and offense compromised the ability of these populations to recover from the sharp reductions in size that would be expected at times of crisis. Tests of this hypothesis will require data on frequencies of successful and unsuccessful attempts at shell damage through time, as well as on the characters of would-be predators. Unfortunately, although predators are often preserved as fossils, their mouthparts or other feeding organs that would aid in the interpretation of performance levels are often missing.

THE NORTH ATLANTIC

The biota of the cool-temperate North Atlantic offers a striking historical contrast to that of the climatically comparable North Pacific. The timing and magnitude of extinction and invasion events differ from those in the North Pacific, and the cohesiveness and cumulative nature of communities have been much more profoundly compromised in the Atlantic.

Historical reconstructions of the North Atlantic and Arctic biota are hampered by the highly uneven temporal and spatial distributions of well-dated fossiliferous deposits. A few scattered cool-water faunas are known from the Paleocene of North Dakota, northern Alaska, Arctic Canada, Greenland, and Spitsbergen (see, e.g., Kollmann and Peel 1983; Marincovich and Zinsmeister 1991; Marincovich 1993). Neogene deposits in the Arctic are also very scarce, being limited to a few late Miocene and Pliocene formations in northern Alaska, Arctic Canada, and Greenland (see Hopkins and Marincovich 1984; Carter et al. 1986; Brouwers and Marincovich 1988; Brigham-Grette et al. 1987; Brigham-Grette and Carter 1992; Bennike 1989; Funder et al. 1985; Marincovich et al. 1990; Fyles et al. 1991). There is an important Plio-Pleistocene sequence in the Tjörnes beds of Iceland, chronicling the arrival and evolution of invaders from the Pacific (Einarsson et al. 1967; Gladenkov et al. 1980; Eiríksson 1981; Cronin 1991). In the North Sea basin of Europe, there is a nearly continuous sequence of fossil-bearing sediments from the Danian (early Paleocene) to the Pleistocene. At least some of these deposits represent mild- to cool-temperate conditions (for reviews see de Meuter and Laga 1976; Curry et al. 1978; Pomerol 1981; Gramann 1990; Hinsch 1990; Steurbaut 1998). In the northwestern Atlantic, the Chesapeake Group on the coastal plain from New Jersey to North Carolina contains rich biotas extending discontinuously from the Danian to the Pleistocene. Although some of these biotas are warm-temperate or even subtropical, a few apparently existed in mild- to cool-temperate conditions (see Ward 1992; Ward and Blackwelder 1980; Blackwelder 1981; Kidwell 1984; Krantz 1991; Cronin 1990; Petuch 1988, 1993, 1997; Campbell 1993; Miller et al. 1996). No pre-Pleistocene record is available for Scandinavia or the American coast north of New Jersey.

Origins and Pre-Pliocene Patterns of Invasion

Cold-water clades in the North Atlantic often originated substantially before their North Pacific counterparts. Astartid, hiatellid, nuculid, and arcticid bivalves, as well as aporrhaid and naticid gastropods, survived the end-Cretaceous extinctions at high latitudes in the Atlantic (Heinberg 1979; Kollmann 1979; Roy 1994). These ancient clades tend to occupy sublittoral sandy and muddy bottoms on both sides of the Atlantic. Throughout the Cenozoic until the latest Miocene or early Pliocene, cool-temperate biotas of the Atlantic developed in isolation from those of the North Pacific. Strong similarities at the level of the genus between the faunas of northern Europe and northern America imply intermittent contact across the Atlantic, but the nature, extent, and timing of such connections remain poorly studied. Waller (1991, 1993)

showed in his phylogenetic studies of scallops that European clades periodically expanded westward, where they gave rise to such endemic eastern North American genera as the extinct *Carolinapecten*, *Chesapecten*, and *Dimarzipecten* and the living *Argopecten* and *Placopecten*. These expansions occurred discontinuously in the Oligocene, middle Miocene, and Pliocene. Some trans-Atlantic expansions, however, evidently proceeded from west to east. Probable examples include one clade of glycymeridid bivalves (Maestrati and Lozouet 1996) and the extinct drilling muricid *Ecphora* (see Kadolsky 1988; Vermeij 1995; Petuch 1997), both of which invaded Europe during or before the late Oligocene. Unfortunately, the paleontological study of North Atlantic fossil taxa has been decidedly provincial, with American and European work proceeding on independent tracks, with the result that we do not know whether and to what extent evolution on the two sides of the Atlantic occurred in distinctly eastern and western clades or whether there was some exchange. Taxonomic data imply that separate western and eastern lineages often diverged in the Oligocene and did not cross the ocean subsequently. Examples include the *Scalaspira* group of buccinids (Tembrock 1968; Petuch 1993), razor clams of the genus *Ensis* (van Urk 1971, 1972), anadarine arcid bivalves, and the strongly coiled clam genus *Glossus*, among others. Groups that today occur on both sides of the Atlantic but about whose geographic history we know little include homarid lobsters (Feldmann 1981), gadid fishes (Grant and Stahl 1988; Howes 1991), and probably fucoid algae (Clayton 1984).

Some clades evidently developed only on one or the other side of the Atlantic with no corresponding sister group in the North Atlantic. American examples include the slipper limpets *Crepidula* and *Dispotaea*, the muricid oyster drill *Urosalpinx*, whelks of the family Busyconidae, the nassariid mud snails *Ilyanassa* and *Bulliopsis*, and the bivalves *Carditamera*, *Planicardium*, *Marvacrassatella*, *Ceronia*, *Stewartia*, and *Mercenaria* (see, e.g., Beu and de Rooij-Schuiling 1982; Saul 1989; Allmon 1990; Ward 1992; Petuch 1993). The peculiar ribbed mussel (*Geukensia demissa*) so characteristic of eastern North American salt marshes has no fossil record, and appears to have no close phylogenetic relationships with other mytilids. Unique European clades without apparent American sister groups include patellid limpets (Ridgway et al. 1998), gibbuline trochid top shells, the ascidian-associated cowrie *Trivia*, the extinct muricids *Pterynopsis* (Vokes 1972) and *Spinucella* (Vermeij 1993), the *Euthria–Searlesia* complex of buccinids (Vermeij 1991b), the extinct *Streptochetus* complex of fasciolariids (Cadée and Janssen 1994), the littorinid periwinkle genus *Melarhaphe* (Reid 1989), various cockles (*Parvicardium*, *Cerastoderma*, and the extinct *Habecardium*) (Schneider 1998), the deep-burrowing mactrid *Lutraria* (van Urk 1980), the portunid green crab *Carcinus*, the sea urchins *Echinus* and *Paracentrotus*, and the sea star *Marthasterias*.

Most of the clades that are known to have originated or appeared in the temperate North Atlantic during Oligocene or Miocene time have close relatives in, and probably are derived from ancestors in, the tropics. Adaptation to cool conditions was therefore in situ, as it was during the same time interval in the northeastern Pacific, rather than by invasion. I know of only two possible exceptions to this generalization. One is the mesodesmatid bivalve *Ceronia*, endemic to the northwestern Atlantic, close relatives of which are known only from the Southern Hemisphere temperate zone (see Beu and de Roooij-Schuiling 1982; Saul 1989). The other is the lobster *Homarus*, whose two North Atlantic species are related to a third species in South Africa (Holthuis 1974).

Biotic Conditions

As is true for the North Pacific, we know relatively little about the conditions of life during the Cenozoic in the North Atlantic. Using the Chesapeake Group of Maryland, Kelley (1989, 1991a,b, 1992) has carefully documented the intensity and effectiveness of drilling predation by gastropods (mainly naticids) on bivalves from early middle Miocene (Langhian) time in the Calvert Formation to late Miocene (Tortonian) time in the St. Marys Formation. Although some lineages of bivalves did not respond in any obvious way to drilling, several initially thick-shelled bivalves became thicker-shelled and larger, and the incidence of unsuccessful drilling of their valves increased through time. Moon snails of the genera *Euspira* and *Glossaulax* likewise became thicker, and their apertures increased in relative size. These temporal patterns are generally consistent with a model in which both moon snails and bivalves are responding evolutionarily to their enemies (Vermeij 1994; Kelley 1992). In a more limited but very interesting study, Dietl and Alexander (1998) showed that an increase in shell lip thickness in busyconine whelks between the early Miocene (Kirkwood Formation, New Jersey) and the present day (New Jersey) is associated with a sharp rise in the number of repaired breaks at the lip, probably caused either by predatory crabs or by the whelks' attempts to wedge open the thick-shelled bivalves on which they prey.

Certain time intervals are characterized by conspicuously large suspension-feeding bivalves, whose rapid growth rates may imply high levels of planktonic primary productivity. For the western Atlantic, one such interval is that represented by the St. Marys Formation of Maryland (late Miocene, Tortonian), whereas in the North Sea basin the early Pliocene (Kattendijk and part of the Lillo Formation of Belgium) may have been a particularly productive interval. Phosphatic deposits characterize episodes of late Oligocene, early to middle Miocene, and Pliocene high productivity in the Chesapeake Group (Riggs 1984; Compton et al. 1990; Mallinson and Compton 1997), whereas they characterize the middle Miocene and earliest Pliocene in the North Sea basin (de Meuter and Laga 1976; Humphreys and Balson 1985; Balson 1987).

Extinction

Extinctions during the Pliocene took a heavy toll on the Atlantic biota (Raffi et al. 1985; Stanley 1986a; Vermeij 1989a, 1991a). Although we have few suitable data for the cool-temperate faunas of the North Atlantic, recent taxonomic revisions of the molluscs of two very rich deposits permit new estimates of the magnitude of extinction in warm-temperate assemblages. In zone 2 of the Yorktown Formation of Virginia, which ranges in age from approximately 3.9 to 3.2 Mya, Campbell (1993) identified 444 species of molluscs (175 bivalves, 3 scaphopods, 1 chiton, and 265 gastropods). Only 52 of these species (12%) are still extant, the others having become extinct or having evolved anagenetically during several episodes in the middle and late Pliocene and early Pleistocene. In the Oorderen Sand Member of the Lillo Formation of Belgium, laid down about 3.5 Mya, Marquet (1995, 1997a,b,c) identified 115 gastropod species, among which I count 33 (29%) as still living. The overlying and therefore slightly younger Pliocene Kruisschans Member contains 69 bivalves (Marquet 1993), of which 28 (41%) still live. It also contains 66 gastropods (Marquet 1995, 1997a,b,c), among which I count 16 (24%) extant species. These data confirm earlier impressions that the magnitude of Pliocene extinction was even higher on the American than on the European side of the warm-temperate Atlantic, and that extinction throughout the Atlantic was substantially greater than in the North Pacific (see also Raffi et al. 1985; Vermeij 1991c). In Iceland, the *Mactra* zone (roughly correlated with the Oorderen Sand) contains a molluscan fauna of 29 species, of which about 48% are still living (Gladenkov et al. 1980; Vermeij 1989a).

Although the evidence indicates that the magnitude of extinction since mid-Pliocene time was generally higher in the western than in the eastern North Atlantic, the pattern may have been reversed for the most recent (and rather minor) Pleistocene episode of extinction (Vermeij 1989a). A number of clades known or inferred to have been present on both sides of the North Atlantic during the late Neogene survived longer (usually into the Recent) on the American side. These taxa include the twisted burrowing clam *Cyrtodaria*, the wentletrap *Acirsa*, the protobranch bivalve *Yoldia myalis*, the extinct buccinid gastropod *Atractodon*, and the soft-shelled clam *Mya arenaria*. In the case of *M. arenaria*, European occurrences in the living fauna evidently represent reintroduction of this species from the western Atlantic during the sixteenth century (Petersen et al. 1992).

The Trans-Arctic Interchange

Biotas of the North Atlantic and Arctic underwent a dramatic transformation during the Pliocene, beginning about 3.5 Mya. Following the extinctions of the late Miocene and early to mid-Pliocene, a flood of invading species from the North Pacific entered the Arctic and Atlantic oceans through the Bering Strait. Throughout most of the Cenozoic era, there was a dryland connection between Asia and North America that formed an impenetrable barrier to marine species. The Bering Strait may have opened during latest Miocene or earliest Pliocene time, 5.5 to 4.8 Mya (Marincovich and Gladenkov 1999), or even as early as the middle Miocene (for a review see Sher 1999), but the earliest molluscan and ostracodan invaders of the North Atlantic are recorded from the *Mactra* zone in the Tjörnes beds of Iceland, dated at about 3.5 Mya (see Durham and MacNeil 1967; Einarsson et al. 1967; Gladenkov et al. 1980; Vermeij 1991a; Cronin 1991). Some of these invaders penetrated rapidly into warm-temperate parts of the North Atlantic. Among the 444 molluscan species in zone 2 of the Yorktown Formation of Virginia (Campbell 1993), I recognize 3 or 4 Pacific invaders or their descendants: *Macoma cookei* (related to the living *M. balthica*), *Mya arenaria*, *Mytilus edulis*, *Cyclocardia granulata* (a possible forerunner of the living *C. borealis*), and perhaps *Buccinum undatum*. In the more or less contemporaneous Oorderen Sands of Belgium, there are 5 early Pacific invaders among the 115 gastropods. The numbers of invaders increase sharply in the Kruisschans Member of the Lillo Formation and in the Merksem Formation of Belgium, as well as in the *Serripes* zone of the Tjörnes beds of Iceland and the Red Crag of England, all of late Pliocene age.

The effect of this invasion was especially great on the American side of the North Atlantic. Some 83% of rocky intertidal molluscs, and 50% of molluscs from sandy and muddy shores, in New England and the Canadian Maritime Provinces arrived from the Pacific or are the derived descendants of Pacific invaders (Vermeij 1991a). Invaders living on both sides of the Atlantic include the periwinkles *Littorina saxatilis* and *L. obtusata*, both derived from a common ancestor in the subgenus *Neritrema* (Reid 1996); the limpets *Tectura*, *Erginus*, and *Puncturella* (Lindberg 1988a,b); margaritine trochids in several genera; velutinids and perhaps other lamellarioid gastropods; sedentary trichotropine capulid gastropods (Golikov 1986); the wentletrap *Epitonium greenlandicum* (Durham 1937); the muricids *Nucella* (dog whelk) and *Boreotrophon* (see T. M. Collins et al. 1996); buccinids of the genera *Buccinum*, *Beringius*, *Volutopsius*, *Neptunea*, *Plicifusus*, and others (Goryachev 1987; Gladenkov et al. 1988; Kantor 1990; Titova 1994a); species of the protobranch genus *Yoldia*; mytilid mussels of the genera *Mytilus*, *Modiolus*, and *Musculus*, among others (Kafanov 1987; Seed 1992); the cockles *Ciliatocardium* and *Serripes* (Kafanov 1980); the tellinid *Macoma* (Coan 1971); the soft-shelled clam *Mya* (MacNeil 1965; Strauch 1972); barnacles of the genera *Balanus*, *Chirona*, and *Semibalanus* (Zullo and Marincovich 1990); sea urchins of the genus *Strongylocentrotus* (Palumbi and Wilson 1990; Palumbi and Kessing 1991); auks (Alcidae) and several other groups of seabirds (Olson 1985); the eelgrass *Zostera marina* (den Hartog 1970); and many seaweeds, including kelps (Laminariales) and the red algae *Chondrus* and *Phycodrys* (Lüning et al. 1987; Estes and Steinberg 1988; van Oppen et al. 1995). Molecular data imply that rock crabs of the genus *Cancer*, represented by distinct sets of species on the American and European sides of the Atlantic, invaded from the North Pacific during the late Miocene (Harrison and Crespi 1999). Patterns of diversity in the Atlantic and Pacific support the further interpretation that the sea star genera *Asterias*, *Crossaster*, *Henricia*, *Leptasterias*, and *Solaster* also took part in the invasion (Franz et al. 1981). Several invaders may always have been limited to the western Atlantic. They include the bivalves *Cyclocardia* (Popov 1983), *Siliqua*, the recently extinct limpet *Lottia alveus* (Carlton et al. 1991), the bivalve *Liocyma*, and the sand dollar *Echinarachnius* (Wagner 1974).

In northern Europe, the effect of invaders from the Pacific is smaller. About 40% of rocky shore molluscs, and only 20% of those on sandy and muddy shores, have Pacific origins (Vermeij 1991a). Not only was the magnitude of extinction prior to invasion smaller in Europe than in eastern North America, but fewer invaders settled and diversified there. One of the very few invaders from the Pacific that occupied mainly or exclusively European shores is the *Littorina squalida–littorea* group (Reid 1996). The common periwinkle, *L. littorea*, greatly expanded onto North American shores during the middle of the nineteenth century, either as the result of introduction by humans from Europe or by the expansion of a population that may have occupied North America since Viking times, or even since the late Pleistocene (Reid 1996).

For the native Atlantic species that survived the Pliocene extinctions, the arrival of so many invaders must have ushered in an entirely new ecological and evolutionary environment. This interesting subject, which has important implications for the effects of human transport of species around the world in ever-increasing numbers today, has received little attention. One interesting ramification of the invasions has been the specialization of several herbivorous molluscs on particular algal hosts. *Littorina obtusata* and *L. fabalis*, sister species descended from a Pacific invader (Reid 1996), have become specialized to eat and live on fucoid brown algae, which are apparently native to the Atlantic (Vermeij 1992). The European limpet *Patella pellucida*, which I had previously regarded as an invader from southern Africa, is a member of a northern European clade (Ridgway et al. 1998). Unlike other members of this clade of *Patella*, *P. pellucida* has become more or less specialized on a diet and habitat of kelp, which arrived from the Pacific (Vermeij 1992).

THE TROPICS

The greatest exuberance of marine biological diversity occurs in the shallow-water tropics. In today's oceans, the tropics are divided into four biogeographically distinct regions: the Indo-West Pacific (Indian and western Pacific oceans east to Polynesia), the eastern Pacific (western America from central Baja California, Mexico, to northern Peru), the western Atlantic (southeastern Florida and the Yucatan Peninsula of Mexico through the Caribbean Sea to southern Brazil), and the eastern Atlantic (West Africa from Senegal to southern Angola).

Origin and Early Differentiation

Some of the elements of the modern tropical biotas were already in place during the Eocene. At this time, the center of known maximum diversity was in the Paris Basin of France, where as many as 1200 species of molluscs may have occurred during the Lutetian (middle Eocene) stage, 49–41 Mya. Many species of large effect have histories dating back to Eocene time. These include herbivorous sirenian mammals, most of the major groups of advanced teleost fishes and brachyuran crabs, chelonian sea turtles, and sea urchins.

Seagrasses, reef-building corals, and mangroves also had achieved wide distributions by the Eocene.

Distinctions among the tropical biotas of the Paleogene were generally much smaller than those in the Neogene. For example, the Eocene biotas of the Gulf coastal plain of the southeastern United States have many genera in common with those in Europe. The nature and extent of these connections and similarities, as well as the timing and direction of invasion events, remain poorly documented. Extinctions near the close of the Eocene greatly impoverished the Paleogene biotas, especially in America (Dockery 1986; Hansen 1987; Haasl and Hansen 1996), and set the stage for the events that culminated in the biotas of today's tropics.

An intriguing but scattered body of evidence indicates that there was a west-to-east pattern of expansion of clades at some time during the early Oligocene, which brought clades that originated in late Eocene time in tropical America to Europe and thence to the region we now know as the Indo-West Pacific. This pattern of invasion has been noted piecemeal for the gastropods *Bursa* (Beu 1988), *Oliva* (Petuch and Sargent 1986), *Chicoreus* (Vokes 1990), *Turbinella* (Vokes 1964), *Vasum* (Vokes 1966), *Phos* (my own data), and the family Coralliophilidae (Lozouet and Le Renard 1998). Unpublished observations by D. Haasl imply a similar pattern of expansion for nassariid gastropods.

What makes this pattern particularly interesting is the implication that the modern shallow-water biota of the Indo-West Pacific may have its origins in the Americas, rather than in Europe or in the Indo-West Pacific region itself. The few monographs on Eocene molluscs from the Indo-West Pacific document the presence of many unique clades that became globally extinct before Oligocene time, and of many other clades that have persisted in today's Indo-West Pacific biota in deep waters. The origins of the modern Indo-West Pacific biota need much more investigation, but if the American connection proves to be as important as the preliminary date imply it is, the eastward invasion to the Indo-West Pacific may be one of the most far-reaching marine biogeographic events of the Cenozoic era.

The predominant historical trend in the tropical ocean over the past 25 million years has been geographic differentiation. During the Paleogene, the tropical ocean extended more or less continuously around the world. Though by no means identical, tropical faunas of the early Oligocene showed great taxonomic similarities to one another. This situation began to change in the early Miocene. In the Burdigalian (19–20 Mya), a barrier between the Indian Ocean and the Mediterranean Sea became established in the Middle East (Rögl and Steininger 1984). Por (1989) has suggested that intermittent lagoonal or shallow-water connections persisted until the late Miocene, but a very large number of clades with early Miocene origins have histories confined either to the Indo-West Pacific or to the Mediterranean-Atlantic basins. Farther east in the Indo-Malayan region of the Indo-West Pacific, northward motion of the plate carrying New Guinea and Australia began to constrict oceanic circulation between

the Pacific and Indian oceans beginning in early to middle Miocene time (Kennett et al. 1985; Grigg and Hey 1992). Although marine connections there continue to this day, phylogenetic separation between Indian Ocean and Pacific Ocean clades may in some cases extend back to the Miocene (Pandolfi 1992). Differentiation into Indian and Pacific Ocean branches has probably affected nearly all shallow-water Indo-West Pacific clades, but it has been particularly well documented at the molecular level in tridacnid bivalves (giant clams) (Benzie and Williams 1997), the sea star *Linckia laevigata* (Williams and Benzie 1998), and chaetodontid butterfly fishes (McMillan and Palumbi 1995). Some of these divergences occurred within the last 1 to 3 million years.

The tropical American biota developed in general isolation from that of the Indo-West Pacific during the Miocene. Although the Central American barrier was not in place until the mid-Pliocene and the biotas of the eastern Pacific and western Atlantic were in communication, these biotas were by no means identical during the Miocene (Vermeij 1993, 1997; Knowlton et al. 1993). Divergence between apparent sister taxa on the two coasts may have begun as early as 12 Mya if estimates of molecular evolution in snapping shrimps are reliable. Moreover, some widespread taxa in the western Atlantic sector evidently never existed in the eastern Pacific. The nature of the barriers to dispersal before the formation of the Central American isthmus remains a deep mystery.

Constriction of seaways in Indonesia may also have initiated, or caused the intensification of, El Niño events in the eastern Pacific, in which the normal regime of upwelling of nutrient-rich deep water is replaced from time to time by warm oceanic waters flowing from the west (Kennett et al. 1985; Grigg and Hey 1992). Such climatic oscillations may have become even more pronounced in the eastern Pacific as the seaway between the Atlantic and Pacific oceans began to shoal during the middle Miocene (Duque-Caro 1990).

The history of a continuous land bridge connecting North and South America and creating an impenetrable barrier for marine organisms is complex (Coates et al. 1992; Keller et al. 1989; Cronin and Dowsett 1996; L. S. Collins et al. 1996a,b; Vermeij 1997). An isthmus may have become established by 3.1–3.6 Mya, during the mid-Pliocene, then breached, and then perhaps formed again about 1.8 Mya at the end of the Pliocene.

Dispersal among Tropical Regions

Despite the establishment of these impediments to dispersal, some biotic connections between marine tropical regions became intermittently stronger during the Neogene. Eastward dispersal of many reef-associated and reef-forming animals from the central Pacific to the eastern Pacific evidently began during the Pleistocene, after closure of the Central American seaway (Vermeij 1987; Richmond 1990; Grigg and Hey 1992). This movement was facilitated not only by more vigorous west-to-east currents (Kennett et al. 1985; Grigg 1988), but also by the northward motion of the Line Islands directly into the path of the eastward-flowing surface currents (Grigg and

Hey 1992). There is evidence that dispersal of planktonic larvae from the western Pacific replenishes and perhaps even maintains eastern Pacific populations, particularly during El Niño years, when easterly flow across the 5400 km between the Line Islands and Clipperton Island is faster (Richmond 1990; Grigg and Hey 1992; Lessios et al. 1996). In the tropical Atlantic, invasions from east to west occurred in various clades (including pectinids and muricids) during the Miocene (see Vermeij and Rosenberg 1993 for a review). Following the emergence of the Central American isthmus, a number of Indo-Pacific clades dispersed around southern Africa during warm intervals of the Pleistocene, and became established in the western Atlantic and West Africa (Vermeij and Rosenberg 1993). There is also substantial dispersal of planktonic larvae across the Atlantic, perhaps in both directions (Scheltema 1971; Vermeij and Rosenberg 1993).

Neogene Diversification

As was the case in the cool-temperate Northern Hemisphere, the late Oligocene to early Miocene interval in the tropics witnessed dramatic diversification. This proliferation of species, which was associated with a general rise in sea level and an expansion of tropical and subtropical zones to relatively high latitudes (Savin et al. 1985; Marincovich 1988; Kafanov and Volvenko 1997), culminated in extraordinarily rich faunas, such as that of the Burdigalian (early Miocene) Cantaure Formation of Venezuela (600 molluscs) and the Chipola Formation of Florida (perhaps 1000 species). Stratigraphic and phylogenetic evidence points to lesser episodes of diversification during the late Miocene (9–10 Mya) and early Pliocene (3.5–5 Mya), with additional species arising after extinctions at the end of the Pliocene (see Jackson et al. 1993, 1996; Fortunato 1998). Among molluscs, the proliferation of species was greatest among groups with exceptionally well-armored shells. Families such as the Muricidae, Columbellidae, Costellariidae, Mytridae, Conidae, Cypraeidae, Strombidae, Marginellidae, Olividae, Nassariidae, Bursidae, Ranellidae, and Terebridae, which are characterized by shells with small or narrow apertures, fortified adult apertural lips, and crack-resistant microsculpture and external ornamentation, diversified enormously (Vermeij 1974, 1978, 1989a). In general, Neogene tropical gastropod faunas show much higher incidences of armor and of repaired breaks than do Paleogene ones (Vermeij 1987).

We know very little about the Neogene history of the Indo-West Pacific region, biologically by far the richest biogeographic marine province of the living biota. The published stratigraphic information is outdated, and most of the basic descriptive taxonomy was done 50 to more than 100 years ago, based on relatively small collections of large invertebrate fossils. Despite these inadequacies, some robust conclusions can be drawn from the available data.

Wilson and Rosen (1998) have made a strong case for the hypothesis that Southeast Asia, the geographic center of what is now the Indo-West Pacific region, was an area of surprisingly low coral diversity during the Paleogene. There were no more than 12 co-occurring genera of probable reef-forming corals during the Eocene, and these formed few reefs. At that time, the center of coral diversity lay in the Mediterranean region, with a secondary center in the Caribbean (see also Budd et al. 1992). Molluscs show a similar pattern. Whereas the middle Eocene was a time of astonishingly high diversity of molluscs in the Paris Basin (with perhaps 1200 species) and the Gulf coastal plain of the southern United States, known middle Eocene molluscan faunas from Java comprise fewer than 200 species. Beginning in the late Oligocene, there was a major episode of diversification among corals, leading to a fivefold increase in diversity. The imperfect evidence from molluscs indicates a similar bout of proliferation in that group during the early Neogene in the Indo-Malayan area.

Among biogeographic provinces, the Indo-West Pacific may be unique in having received almost no invaders from other regions during the Neogene (Vermeij and Rosenberg 1993). The Indo-West Pacific biota is therefore composed of clades that, over the course of the Cenozoic, either became restricted to the Indo-West Pacific after having had a wider distribution or evolved in situ. In the former category belong numerous molluscs and corals, as well as mangroves, that previously also occurred in Europe and in tropical America (Vermeij 1986, 1998; Ricklefs and Latham 1993; Edinger and Risk 1995; Johnson et al. 1995). Most of these relicts occur in the Indian Ocean and in the Indo-Malayan region, but others persist in fringe regions such as New Caledonia and, in the bizarre case of the fasciolariid gastropod *Cyrtulus*, in the Marquesas Islands at the far eastern limit of the province.

The in situ proliferation of shallow-water marine clades in the Neogene Indo-West Pacific has produced a wealth of biologically sophisticated and often highly specialized species. For example, armor and specialization for rapid locomotion have been carried further among Indo-West Pacific molluscs than in those from any other part of the world (see Vermeij 1989b for a review). Phylogenetic evidence implies that cone snails (Conidae) and rapanine muricids evolved diets and modes of feeding in the Indo-West Pacific that are unknown elsewhere. For example, predation on molluscs among Conidae is unique to the Indo-West Pacific genus *Cylinder*, although one species (*C. dalli*) is an eastern Pacific offshoot from a recent invader from the western Pacific. Rapanines in the western Pacific and Indian Ocean, but nowhere else, have evolved specialized diets of sipunculans, corals, and polychaetes, food sources that were already being exploited by other Indo-West Pacific gastropods when rapanines evolved these habits.

Some of the specializations that typify the living Indo-West Pacific biota were geographically more widely distributed before the Pliocene. Coralliophilid gastropods are distributed throughout the tropics, but only in the western Pacific and Indian oceans do they bore into their coral hosts. The fossil record shows that this boring habit occurred as early as the early Oligocene in southern Europe, and that it was present in Florida as late as the mid-Pliocene (see Lozouet and Le Renard 1998). The Indo-West Pacific hipponicid gastropod *Sabia conica*, which lives in a self-made excavation on the shells of gastropod and hermit crab hosts, has a more or less similar history. Although *Sabia* is restricted to the Indo-West Pacific today, fossil evidence demonstrates that *Sabia* and its excavations occurred in tropical America until early Pliocene time. Extinction eliminated both of these rather specialized habits in the western Atlantic, but not in the Indo-West Pacific (Vermeij 1998).

Extinction

The role of the Indo-West Pacific as a biogeographic refuge for taxa is consistent with the relatively small magnitude of extinction there. The early Pliocene Shinzato Formation of Okinawa, Japan, contains 133 gastropod and 58 bivalve species (Noda 1988). Of these, 52 gastropods (39%) and 31 bivalves (23%) are still living. In Paulay's (1996) analysis of Pliocene bivalves from Niue, in the Cook Islands of Polynesia, he found that 72% survive somewhere in the Indo-West Pacific, though not always in the Cook Islands.

Extinction during the late Neogene took a heavy toll on the tropical American fauna, especially in the western Atlantic. Of the 121 described molluscs in the Melajo Clay fauna (early Pliocene) of Trinidad (Jung 1969), only 21% survive today. Approximately 29% of the more than 700 molluscan species in the early to mid-Pliocene Pinecrest beds of Florida survive today (Allmon et al. 1993, 1996; Stanley 1986a). My calculations for the more or less contemporaneous Esmeraldas fauna of Ecuador in the eastern Pacific (see Olsson 1964; Vokes 1988; Pitt and Pitt 1992; Groves 1997) show that about 28% of the 156 species are still living in tropical America. In the Atlantic, the extinctions fell most heavily on large suspension feeders, including large barnacles and venerid bivalves as well as turritellid and calyptraeid gastropods (Vermeij 1978; Allmon 1992; Zullo 1992; Roopnarine 1996). This pattern, together with the fact that large suspension feeders survived in the eastern Pacific, where waters tend to be rich in nutrients, points to the likelihood that reduced planktonic primary productivity was responsible for many of the extinctions in the western Atlantic (Vermeij 1978, 1986; Allmon 1992; Vermeij and Petuch 1986). Roopnarine's (1996) data on chionine venerid bivalves support Petuch's (1995) thesis that there have been at least two late Neogene episodes of extinction, one between early and mid-Pliocene time, affecting the Caribbean and eastern Pacific about equally (54% and 57% extinction respectively) but affecting Florida much less (18% extinction), and a late Pliocene extinction affecting Florida and the Caribbean much more (50% and 58% extinction respectively) than the eastern Pacific (11% extinction). After these extinctions, the eastern Pacific became a refuge for hundreds of clades that had previously occupied both coasts of tropical America (Woodring 1966; Vermeij 1978, 1986). Only about one-eighth as many clades have a refugial distribution in the Caribbean, usually along the nutrient-rich coasts of Central and South America (see also Vermeij and Petuch 1986).

Although speciation has replenished some of the losses due to extinction, especially in the eastern Pacific (Fortunato 1998), the tropical American marine fauna as a whole remains smaller, and has achieved a lower level of biological sophistication, than is seen in the Indo-West Pacific. Despite the fact that levels of extinction in the tropical western Atlantic are comparable to those in the temperate northwestern Atlantic, the American tropics have been less affected by invasion than has the North Atlantic (Vermeij and Rosenberg 1993).

THE HISTORICAL PERSPECTIVE

Despite the obvious shortcomings and incompleteness of the preceding account, it is clear that patterns of community assembly and cohesiveness differ greatly from region to region. The Indo-West Pacific, and to a lesser extent the North Pacific and tropical America, is characterized by ecosystems that have accumulated species and that have remained relatively cohesive over the last 20 to 30 million years, with extinction and invasion playing comparatively minor roles. The North Atlantic (including the tropical western portion), by contrast, conformed to this pattern until the Pliocene, when widespread extinctions and invasions altered the status quo dramatically.

Besides the obvious need to quantify and further document many of these patterns, many important questions remain. How do the arrival and disappearance of structural and keystone species affect the pattern of selection to which resident species of an ecosystem are exposed? If incumbents generally keep out invaders and thwart in situ evolution, how do they do it? Do ecosystems and communities whose cohesion has been disrupted by extinctions and invasions differ in measurable emergent properties from those whose members have lived together for millions of years? What factors affect the location and timing of major ecological transitions, such as those from warm to cold climates? Why have no cool-water clades successfully invaded tropical waters during Neogene times?

Adaptation and Incumbency

These questions revolve around a common theme: the relationship between adaptation and incumbency. The most important reason why incumbents are difficult for invaders to displace is that incumbents are well adapted to the conditions in which they live, whereas invaders are adapted to the conditions from which they came, or to disturbed environments in which incumbents are absent. When events decimate or eliminate incumbents, opportunities for invasion are therefore greatly enhanced. I suspect that the crises at the end of the Eocene, during or near the end of the late Oligocene, during the middle Miocene, and during the Plio-Pleistocene account for the large-scale establishment of invaders. A warming climate, which brought about a broadening of tropical and subtropical climatic belts and a poleward spread of many warm-water species, may have greatly aided the invasion of colder regions by warm-adapted species during the late Oligocene to early Miocene interval and the westward spread of species in the North Pacific during the early middle Miocene thermal maximum. Patterns of oceanic and atmospheric circulation may also have affected the direction of invasion. Thus, the westward spread of taxa in the North Pacific during the early middle Miocene may reflect prevailing flows of ocean currents or surface winds. If so, then there should have been a reversal during and after late Miocene time, when the predominant direction of invasion in the North Pacific was eastward. Similarly, the highly asymmetrical trans-Arctic interchange of the Pliocene and Pleistocene may reflect a net northward flow of Pacific water through the Bering Strait at the time when the great Pacific-to-Atlantic invasion began, about 3.5 Mya. At present, the relative contributions of extinction and oceanic circulation to invasion cannot be definitively ascertained. In the case of the trans-Arctic interchange, for example, it is possible that the onset of Pliocene extinctions, which would have increased opportunities for invasion, coincided with a change in the direction of flow through the Bering Strait.

Tropical biotas have rarely been invaded by species from higher latitudes. Even when extinctions deplete tropical diversity, as during the Pliocene in the Atlantic, the surviving taxa may offer enough resistance to prevent the establishment of temperate populations, whose members would typically experience much less intense predation than is usual in tropical marine environments. Only the most devastating crises, such as the end-Cretaceous extinction event, may enable temperate (and perhaps deep-sea) clades to penetrate shallow-water equatorial regions.

Where do species of large effect—the keystone consumers and the species that impart three-dimensional structure—come from, and how do they invade? Invasion from other regions or habitats is one possibility. Marine mammals and birds, seagrasses and mangroves, and humans are examples of species of large effect that entered the sea from the land. A review of the fossil record of such transitions (Vermeij and Dudley 2000) reveals that land-to-sea invasions by species of large effect occurred at times and sites of high marine planktonic productivity. For these invaders, the presence of incumbents was probably not a significant impediment, because the invaders already possessed either the adaptive flexibility or the competitive ability to cope effectively with native marine species and to exploit marine habitats. Metabolically active tetrapod vertebrates in particular are able to consume food, and therefore to be potent competitors, in their new marine surroundings because they do not shut down their metabolic machinery when in the water. From this perspective, it is interesting that sea otters and marine gulls were able to enter the North Pacific ecosystem during the late Neogene, when diversity and the biological sophistication of native marine incumbents were already high. Similarly, the evolution of benthic-feeding seals and whales from fish-eating ancestors took place in highly productive, diverse, and competitively rigorous communities.

It is surprising that these high-intensity consumers had so little effect on the adaptive characteristics of the marine incumbents whose communities they invaded. Sea otters, walruses, gray whales, sea cows, and marine birds profoundly affect the abundances and distributions of the marine organisms they eat, and they must exercise strong selection on the morphology of many species. At this point in our knowledge, however, noteworthy evolutionary responses to these consumers are not obvious within most clades. I noted a few examples of responses to Pacific invaders in the North Atlantic, but these responses were to native marine invaders and not to the arrival of high-intensity land-derived consumers. Even so, the invading consumers may be responsible for trophic and habitat specialization among native marine clades. I suspect that much of the remarkable Neogene diversification observed in tropical as well as temperate marine clades was driven by selection in favor of such specialization as a means of minimizing competition and predation, and that this selection is exercised mainly by high-intensity consumers, both marine and land-derived. Some of this diversification may have proceeded by sympatric speciation, the likelihood of which increases as the difference in potential fitness among adjacent habitats increases with rising pressure from consumers. The role of biotic interactions, as well as the timing and mode of speciation, should be explored further in a phylogenetic context.

Limits on specialization and on competitive ability may be imposed directly by disturbances, extreme forms of which lead to extinction. The greatest habitat specialization (host specificity, exploitation of the upper shore, and novel sources of food) in the modern biota is seen in the Indo-West Pacific, the region in which extinction has been least severe during the Neogene. It is therefore important to consider briefly the selectivity, causes, consequences, and scale of extinction.

Extinction and the Role of Spatial Scale

Extinction is a selective process, falling most heavily on species with the narrowest habitat requirements or the greatest energetic investments in defense. During a productivity crisis, for example, the probability that a species will survive is dictated not only by the ability of individuals at some point in the life cycle to withstand the adverse conditions, but also by the ability of populations to recover rapidly before another calamity strikes. Per capita fecundity, which in part determines a population's potential rate of increase, is compromised by high levels of investment in defense and away from reproduction. Habitat specialization may limit potential population size or the capacity of individuals to find mates if the habitat is widely dispersed, and could therefore adversely affect a species during times of crisis. The degree of biological sophistication in terms of defense, competition, and trophic and habitat specialization therefore depends in part on the magnitude of extinction, which has varied greatly from place to place in recent earth history.

Why did extinction plague some biotas more than others during the Pliocene? On the spatial scale of biogeographic provinces, extinction was much less severe in the Indo-West Pacific and the North Pacific regions than in the tropical and temperate Atlantic.

In general, extinction occurs either because no member of a population can survive or because the population cannot recover from a rare event. Whether a rare event will result in extinction depends on the spatial scale of that event relative to the spatial distribution of a population. In other words, as long as there are refuges—places where populations persist—there will be no global extinction. Analysis of the geography of extinction during the Pliocene leads me to believe that a dramatic, perhaps short-lived, reduction in primary planktonic productivity was responsible for extinction and geographic restriction. Geographic refuges such as those in the tropical eastern Pacific, the mainland coasts of Atlantic Central and South America, the seas of the Indonesian and Philippines archipelagoes, and the cool-temperate northwestern Pacific (among others) are characterized by continuously high planktonic productivity (Vermeij 1978, 1986, 1989a,b). The high magnitude of extinction observed during the Pliocene and Pleistocene in Peru and Chile (Herm 1969), where upwelling today and at times in the geologic past is associated with very high productivity, may therefore be explained by a reduction in the availability of plankton, a reduction that lasted long enough to eliminate many species. A similar explanation may apply to the northeastern Pacific, another area where upwelling is linked to high productivity today. Other potential explanations—cooling associated with the onset of glaciation, coastal uplift and the disappearance of shallow embayments, and changes in circulation in the world ocean brought about by the opening of the Bering Strait and the formation of the Central American isthmus—may also have contributed to extinction during the Pliocene. In fact, oceanographic changes in circulation may well have brought about the reductions in productivity that I believe are primarily responsible for the extinctions. Regional differences in the magnitude of extinction therefore arise because reductions in productivity did not affect all parts of such biogeographic provinces as the Indo-West Pacific, whereas they did affect most or all parts of such other provinces as the Atlantic coast of North America.

Implications for the Human-Dominated Biosphere

In ways that no other species ever has before, humans are exploiting species and altering habitats worldwide. Although our effects may still be less in the sea than they are on land, they are nonetheless profound in all nearshore and intertidal environments on earth. From a biological point of view, the most important consequence of human activity is a reduction in the abundance of incumbent species. Such disturbance inevitably leads to a greater likelihood that casual invaders, many of them introduced by humans, will become established (see also Vermeij 1991c).

Another important consequence of human activity is that the populations of most species other than those thriving in disturbed environments are shrinking. From an evolutionary point of view, this means that the ability of species to adapt to the rapidly changing conditions of the human-dominated biosphere is greatly stunted. The regime of selection may be intense and rapidly changing, but the ability of populations to respond is declining. Diversification and adaptation generally require circumstances that allow populations of many species to increase in numbers of individuals and in spatial range. In today's world, the fate of most populations is a reduction in numbers and distribution. History teaches that the inability to respond adaptively will have serious long-term deleterious consequences not only for individual species, but also for the communities and ecosystems they constitute.

The time scales and spatial scales with which I have dealt in this chapter are larger than those to which experimental ecologists are accustomed. Although experimental manipulation is not a reasonable option in the study of large-scale phenomena, the interactions that experimental ecologists study have causes and effects at many scales of analysis. The power of the study of history lies in putting the ecological lives of individuals in communities into the larger context of climate, disturbance, and the supply-and-demand marketplace of resources and competitors. Progress in comprehending these links and applying their implications to human-dominated ecosystems hinges on the integration of experimental ecology with systematics, oceanography, paleobiology, and biological economics.

Acknowledgments

The research on which this chapter is based was made possible by grants from the National Science Foundation. I am grateful to Kazutaka Amano and two anonymous reviewers for extremely helpful comments on the manuscript, and to Janice Cooper for technical assistance.

Literature Cited

Addicott, W. O. 1969. Tertiary climatic change in the marginal northeastern Pacific Ocean. *Science* 165: 583–586.

Addicott, W. O. 1974. Giant pectinids of the eastern North Pacific margin: Zoogeography and chronostratigraphy. *J. Paleontol.* 48: 180–194.

Addicott, W. O. 1976. Neogene molluscan stages of Oregon and Washington. In Neo-gene Symposium, Pacific Section, Annual Meeting, SEPM, San Francisco, 1976, 95–115.

Addicott, W. O. 1977. Neogene chronostratigraphy of nearshore marine basins of the eastern North Pacific. Proceedings of the First International Congress on Pacific Neogene Stratigraphy, Tokyo, 1976: 151–175.

Adegoke, O. S. 1967. Earliest Tertiary West American species of *Platyodon* and *Penitella*. Proceedings of the California Academy of Science (4th series) 35: 1–22.

Allison, R. C. 1978. Late Oligocene through Pleistocene molluscan faunas in the Gulf of Alaska region. *Veliger* 21: 171–188.

Allison, R. C. and W. O. Addicott. 1976. The North Pacific Miocene record of *Mytilus* (*Plicatomytilus*), a new subgenus of Bivalvia. U.S. Geological Survey Professional Paper 962: 1–22.

Allmon, W. D. 1990. Review of the *Bullia* group (Gastropoda: Nassariidae) with comments on its evolution, biogeography, and phylogeny. *Bull. Am. Paleontol.* 99: 1–179.

Allmon, W. D. 1992. Role of temperature and nutrients in extinctions of turritelline gastropods: Cenozoic of the northwestern Atlantic and northeastern Pacific. *Palaeogeogr. Palaeoclimatol. Palaeoecol.* 92: 41–54.

Allmon, W. D., G. Rosenberg, R. W. Portell and K. S. Schindler. 1993. Diversity of Atlantic Coastal Plain mollusks since the Pliocene. *Science* 260: 1626–1629.

Allmon, W. D., S. D. Emslie, D. S. Jones and G. S. Morgan. 1996. Late Neogene oceanographic change along Florida's west coast: Evidence and mechanisms. *J. Geol.* 104: 143–162.

Amano, K. 1986. Age and characteristics of the so-called "Atsunai-Togeshita fauna" in Hokkaido. Palaeontological Society of Japan Special Paper 29: 187–198.

Amano, K. 1998. First discovery of fossil *Humilaria* (Bivalvia: Veneridae) from Japan. *Venus* 57: 271–280.

Amano, K. and G. J. Vermeij. 1998. Origin and biogeographic history of *Ceratostoma* (Gastropoda: Muricidae). *Venus* 57: 209–223.

Amano, K., G. J. Vermeij and K. Narita. 1993. Early evolution and distribution of the gastropod genus *Nucella*, with special reference to Miocene species from Japan. Transactions and Proceedings of the Palaeontological Society of Japan 171: 237–248.

Amano, K., K. A. Lutaenko and T. Matsubara. 1999. Taxonomy and distribution of *Macoma* (*Rexithaerus*) (Bivalvia: Tellinidae) in the northwestern Pacific. *Palaeontol. Res.* 3: 95–105.

Armentrout, J. M. 1981. Correlation and ages of Cenozoic chronostratigraphic units in Oregon and Washington. Geological Society of America Special Paper 184: 137–148.

Armentrout, J. M., D. A. Hull, J. D. Beaulieu and W. W. Rau. 1983. Correlation of Cenozoic stratigraphic units of western Oregon and Washington. State of Oregon Department of Geology and Mineral Industries, Oil and Gas Investigations 7: 1–90.

Armentrout, J. M., R. J. Echols and J. C. Ingle, Jr. 1984. Neogene biostratigraphic-chronostratigraphic scale for the northeastern Pacific margin. In N. Ikebe and R. Tsuchi (eds.), *Pacific Neogene Dating Planes: Contributions to Biostratigraphy and Chronology*, pp. 171–177. University of Tokyo Press, Tokyo.

Balson, P. S. 1987. Authigenic phosphorite concretions in the Tertiary of the southern North Sea Basin: An event stratigraphy. *Mededelingen van de Werkgroep voor Tertiaire and Kwartaire Geologie* 24: 79–94.

Barinov, K. B. and Yu. B. Gladenkov. 1998. Subdivision of Oligocene and Lower Miocene sediments of northern Sakhalin evidenced by mollusks. *Stratigraphy and Geological Correlation* 6: 280–292.

Barron, J. A. 1981. Late Cenozoic diatom biostratigraphy of the middle-latitude eastern North Pacific, Deep Sea Drilling Project Leg 63. Initial Reports of the Deep Sea Drilling Project 63: 507–538.

Beadle, S. C. 1991. The biogeography of origin and radiation: Dendrasterid sand dollars in the northeastern Pacific. *Paleobiology* 17: 325–339.

Beadle, S. C. 1995. Retrodisplacement of the oral and anal openings in dendrasterid sand dollars. *Evolution* 49: 1203–1214.

Bennike, O. 1989. *Trichotropis bicarinata* (Gastropoda) from the Plio-Pleistocene Kap Köbenhavn Formation, new to the fossil fauna of Greenland. *Mededelingen van de Werkgroep voor Tertiaire en Kwartaire Geologie* 26: 137–143.

Benzie, J. A. H. and S. T. Williams. 1997. Genetic structure of giant clam (*Tridacna maxima*) populations in the western Pacific is not consistent with dispersal by present-day ocean currents. *Evolution* 51: 768–783.

Berggren, W. A., D. V. Kent, C. C. Swisher III and M.-P. Aubry. 1995. A revised Cenozoic geochronology and chronostratigraphy. In W. A. Berggren, M.-P. Aubry and J. Hardenbol (eds.), *Geochronology, Time Scales and Global Stratigraphic Correlation*, pp. 129–212. Special Publication 54, SEPM, Tulsa, OK.

Berglund, R. E. and J. L. Goedert. 1996. A new crab (Brachyura: Cancridae) from Lower Miocene rocks of the northwestern Olympic Peninsula, Washington. *J. Paleontol.* 70: 830–838.

Berta, A. and G. S. Morgan. 1985. A new sea otter (Carnivora: Mustelidae) from the late Miocene and early Pliocene (Hemphillian) of North America. *J. Paleontol.* 59: 809–819.

Berta, A., C. E. Ray and A. R. Wyss. 1989. Skeleton of the oldest known pinniped, *Aliarctos nealsi*. *Science* 244: 60–62.

Beu, A. G. 1988. Taxonomy of gastropods of the families Ranellidae (= Cymatiidae) and Bursidae. Part 5. Early history of the families, with four new genera and recognition of the family Personidae. Saito Ho-On Kai Special Publication 2: 69–96.

Beu, A. G. 1990. Molluscan generic diversity of New Zealand Neogene stages: Extinction and biostratigraphic events. *Palaeogeogr. Palaeoclimatol. Palaeoecol.* 77: 279–288.

Beu, A. G. and L. A. de Rooij-Schuiling. 1982. Subgeneric classification of New Zealand and Australian species of *Paphies* Lesson (Bivalvia: Mesodesmatidae), and names for the two species of tuatua in New Zealand. *NZ J. Zool.* 9: 211–230.

Birkeland, C. 1996. Why some species are especially influential on coral-reef communities and others are not. *Galaxea* 13: 77–84.

Blackwelder, B. W. 1981. Late Cenozoic stages and molluscan zones of the U.S. Middle Atlantic Coastal Plain. Paleontological Society Memoir 12, supplement to *J. Paleontol.* 55: 1–34.

Briggs, J. C. 1974. *Marine Zoogeography.* McGraw Hill, New York.

Brigham-Grette, J. and L. D. Carter. 1992. Pliocene marine transgressions of northern Alaska: Circumarctic correlations and paleoclimatic interpretations. *Arctic* 45: 74–89.

Brigham-Grette, J., J. V. Matthews, Jr. and L. Marincovich, Jr. 1987. Age and paleoenvironmental significance of *Arctica* in the Beaufort Formation on Meighen Island,

Queen Elizabeth Islands, Canada. Abstracts, 16th Arctic workshop (Research on the roof of the world), Edmonton, Alberta, April 30 to May 2, 1987, Boreal Institute for Northern Studies, University of Alberta, Edmonton: 12–14.

Brouwers, E. M. and L. Marincovich, Jr. 1988. Ostracode and molluscan assemblages from the Late Neogene Nuwok Member of the Sagavanirktok Formation, North Slope. U.S. Geological Survey Circular 1016: 24–26.

Brown, L. D. 1993. Biochemical genetics and species relationships within the genus *Haliotis* (Gastropoda: Haliotidae). *J. Molluscan Stud.* 59: 429–443.

Budd, A. F., T. A. Stemann and R. H. Stewart. 1992. Eocene Caribbean reef corals: A unique fauna from the Gatuncillo Formation of Panama. *J. Paleontol.* 66: 570–594.

Cadée, M. C. and A. W. Janssen. 1994. A taxonomic revision of NW European Oligocene and Miocene Fasciolariidae traditionally included in the genus *Streptochetus* (Mollusca, Gastropoda). *Contrib. Tert. Quat. Geol.* 31: 31–107.

Campbell, L. D. 1993. Pliocene molluscs from the Yorktown and Chowan River Formations in Virginia. Virginia Division of Mineral Resources Publication 127: 1–259.

Carlton, J. T., G. J. Vermeij, D. R. Lindberg, D. A. Carlton and E. C. Dudley. 1991. The first historical extinction of a marine invertebrate in an ocean basin: The demise of the eelgrass limpet *Lottia alveus*. *Biol. Bull.* 180: 72–80.

Carter, L. D., J. Brigham-Grette, L. Marincovich, Jr., V. L. Pease and J. W. Hillhouse. 1986. Late Cenozoic Arctic Ocean sea ice and terrestrial paleoclimate. *Geology* 14: 675–678.

Chinzei, K. 1978. Neogene molluscan faunas in the Japanese islands: An ecologic and zoogeographic synthesis. *Veliger* 21: 155–170.

Chinzei, K. 1986. Faunal succession and geographic distribution of Neogene molluscan faunas in Japan. Palaeontological Society of Japan Special Paper 29: 17–32.

Clayton, M. N. 1984. Evolution of the Phaeophyta with particular reference to the Fucales. *Prog. Phycol. Res.* 3: 11–46.

Coan, E. V. 1971. The northwest American Tellinidae. *Veliger* 14 (Suppl.): 1–63.

Coan, E. V. 1988. Recent eastern Pacific species of the bivalve genus *Semele*. *Veliger* 31: 1–42.

Coan, E. V. 1997. Recent species of the genus *Petricola* in the eastern Pacific (Bivalvia: Veneroidea). *Veliger* 40: 298–340.

Coates, A. G., J. B. C. Jackson, L. S. Collins, T. M. Cronin, H. J. Dowsett, L. M. Bybell, P. Jung and J. A. Obando. 1992. Closure of the Isthmus of Panama: The near-shore marine record of Costa Rica and western Panama. *Geol. Soc. Am. Bull.* 104: 814–828.

Collins, L. S., A. F. Budd and A. G. Coates. 1996a. Earliest evolution associated with closure of the tropical American seaway. *Proc. Natl. Acad. Sci. USA* 93: 6069–6072.

Collins, L. S., A. G. Coates, W. A. Berggren, M.-P. Aubry and J. Zhang. 1996b. The Late

Miocene Panama isthmian strait. *Geology* 24: 687–690.

Collins, T. M., K. Frazier, A. R. Palmer, G. J. Vermeij and W. M. Brown. 1996. Evolutionary history of northern hemisphere *Nucella* (Gastropoda, Muricidae): Molecular, morphological, ecological, and paleontological evidence. *Evolution* 50: 2287–2304.

Compton, J. S., S. W. Snyder and D. A. Hodell. 1990. Phosphogenesis and weathering of shelf sediments in the southeastern United States: Implications for Miocene $\delta^{13}C$ excursions and global cooling. *Geology* 18: 1227–1230.

Connolly, S. R. and J. Roughgarden. 1998. A latitudinal gradient in northeast Pacific intertidal community structure: Evidence for an oceanographically based synthesis of marine community theory. *Am. Nat.* 151: 311–326.

Crame, J. A. 1986. Polar origins of marine invertebrate faunas. *Palaios* 1: 616–617.

Crame, J. A. 1992. Evolutionary history of the polar regions. *Histor. Biol.* 6: 37–60.

Crame, J. A. 1993. Bipolar molluscs and their evolutionary implications. *J. Biogeogr.* 20: 145–161.

Cronin, T. M. 1990. Evolution of Neogene and Quaternary marine Ostracoda, United States Atlantic Coastal Plain: Evolution and speciation in Ostracoda, IV. U.S. Geological Survey Professional Paper 1367-C: 1–43.

Cronin, T. M. 1991. Late Neogene marine Ostracoda from Tjörnes, Iceland. *J. Paleontol.* 65: 767–794.

Cronin, T. M. and H. J. Dowsett. 1996. Biotic and oceanographic response to the Pliocene closing of the Central American isthmus. In J. B. C. Jackson, A. F. Budd and A. G. Coates (eds.), *Evolution and Environment in Tropical America*, pp. 76–104. University of Chicago Press, Chicago.

Curry, D., C. G. Adams, M. C. Boulter, F. C. Dilley, F. E. Eames, B. M. Funnell and M. K. Wells. 1978. A correlation of Tertiary rocks in the British Isles. Geological Society of London Special Report 12: 1–72.

Darragh, T. A. 1985. Molluscan biogeography and biostratigraphy of the Tertiary of southeastern Australia. *Alcheringa* 9: 83–116.

Dayton, P. K. 1971. Competition, disturbance, and community organization: The provision and subsequent utilization of space in a rocky intertidal community. *Ecol. Monogr.* 41: 351–389.

Dayton, P. K. 1975a. Experimental evaluation of ecological dominance in a rocky intertidal algal community. *Ecol. Monogr.* 45: 137–159.

Dayton, P. K. 1975b. Experimental studies of algal canopy interactions in a sea otter-dominated kelp community at Amchitka Island, Alaska. *Fisheries Bull.* 73: 230–237.

de Meuter, F. J. and P. G. Laga. 1976. Lithostratigraphy and biostratigraphy based on benthonic Foraminifera of the Neogene deposits of northern Belgium. *Bulletin de la Société Belge de Géologie* 85: 133–152.

den Hartog, C. 1970. *The Sea-Grasses of the World*. North-Holland, Amsterdam.

Dietl, G. P. and R. R. Alexander. 1998. Shell repair frequencies in whelks and moon snails

from Delaware and southern New Jersey. *Malacologia* 39: 151–165.

Dockery, D. T. 1986. Punctuated succession of Paleogene mollusks in the northern Gulf Coastal Plain. *Palaios* 1: 582–589.

Domning, D. P. 1978. Sirenian evolution in the North Pacific Ocean. University of California Publications in Geological Sciences 118: 1–176.

Domning, D. P. 1989. Kelp evolution: A comment. *Paleobiology* 15: 53–56.

Domning, D. P., C. E. Ray and M. C. Mackenna. 1986. Two new Oligocene desmostylians and a discussion of tethytherian systematics. Smithsonian Contributions to Paleobiology 59: 1–56.

Druehl, L. D. 1981. The distribution of Laminariales in the North Pacific with reference to environmental influences. In G. G. E. Scudder and J. L. Reveal (eds.), *Evolution Today: Proceedings of the Second International Congress of Systematic Evolutionary Biology*, pp. 55–67. Hunt Institute of Botanical Documentation, Carnegie-Mellon University, Pittsburgh.

Duggins, D. O. 1983. Starfish predation and the creation of mosaic patterns in a kelp-dominated community. *Ecology* 64: 1610–1619.

Duque-Caro, H. 1990. Neogene stratigraphy, paleoceanography and the paleobiogeography in northwest South America and the evolution of the Panama seaway. *Palaeogeogr. Palaeoclimatol. Palaeoecol.* 77: 203–234.

Durham, J. W. 1937. Gastropods of the family Epitoniidae from Mesozoic and Cenozoic rocks of the west coast of North America, including one new species by F. E. Turner and one by R. A. Bramkamp. *J. Paleontol.* 11: 479–512.

Durham, J. W. and F. S. MacNeil. 1967. Cenozoic migrations of marine invertebrates through the Bering Strait region. In D. M. Hopkins (ed.), *The Bering Land Bridge*, pp. 326–349. Stanford University Press, Stanford, CA.

Edinger, E. N. and M. J. Risk. 1995. Preferential survivorship of brooding corals in a regional extinction. *Paleobiology* 21: 200–219.

Einarsson, T., D. M. Hopkins and R. R. Doell. 1967. The stratigraphy of Tjörnes, northern Iceland, and the history of the Bering land bridge. In D. M. Hopkins (ed.), *The Bering Land Bridge*, pp. 312–325. Stanford University Press, Stanford, CA.

Eiríksson, J. 1981. Lithostratigraphy of the upper Tjörnes sequence, north Iceland: The Breidavík Group. *Acta Naturalia Islandica* 29: 1–37.

Estes, J. A. and J. P. Palmisano. 1974. Sea otters: Their role in structuring nearshore communities. *Science* 185: 1058–1060.

Estes, J. A. and P. D. Steinberg. 1988. Predation, herbivory, and kelp evolution. *Paleobiology* 14: 19–36.

Estes, J. A., D. O. Duggins and G. B. Rathbun. 1989. The ecology of extinctions in kelp forest communities. *Conserv. Biol.* 3: 252–264.

Estes, J. A., M. T. Tinker, T. M. Williams and D. F. Doak. 1998. Killer whale predation on sea otters linking oceanic and nearshore ecosystems. *Science* 282: 473–476.

Feldmann, R. M. 1981. Paleobiogeography of North American lobsters and shrimps (Crustacea: Decapoda). *Géobios* 14: 440–468.

Fortunato, H. 1998. Reconciling observed patterns of temporal occurrence with cladistic hypotheses of phylogenetic relationship. *Am. Malacol. Bull.* 14: 191–200.

Fotyanova, L. I. and M. Y. Serova. 1987. Late Miocene climatic optimum in the northeast Pacific Province. *Int. Geol. Rev.* 29: 515–528.

Franz, D. R., E. K. Worsley and A. S. Merrill. 1981. Distribution patterns of common seastars of the middle Atlantic continental shelf of the northwest Atlantic (Gulf of Maine to Cape Hatteras). *Biol. Bull.* 160: 394–418.

Funder, S., N. Abrahamsen, O. Bennike and R. W. Feyling-Hanssen. 1985. Forested Arctic: Evidence from north Greenland. *Geology* 13: 542–546.

Fyles, G. J., L. Marincovich, Jr., J. V. Matthews and R. Barendrecht. 1991. Unique mollusc find in the Beaufort Formation (Pliocene) on Meighen Island, Arctic Canada. Current Research, Part B, Geological Survey of Canada, Paper 91–1B: 105–112.

Gaines, S. D. and J. Roughgarden. 1987. Fish in offshore kelp forests affect recruitment to intertidal barnacle populations. *Science* 235: 479–481.

Geiger, D. L. 1998. Recent genera and species of the family Haliotidae Rafinesque, 1815 (Gastropoda: Vetigastropoda). *Nautilus* 111: 85–116.

Geiger, D. L. and L. T. Groves. 1999. Review of fossil abalone (Gastropoda: Vetigastropoda: Haliotidae) with comparison to Recent species. *J. Paleontol.* 73: 872–885.

Gladenkov, Yu. B. 1979. Cenozoic molluscan assemblages in northern regions of the Atlantic and Pacific Oceans. *Int. Geol. Rev.* 21: 880–890.

Gladenkov, Yu. B. 1988. The North Pacific Holarctic Neogene from an ecostratigraphic point of view. Saito Ho-On Kai Museum Special Publication 2: 33–45.

Gladenkov, Yu. B. 1990a. Ecostratigraphy of the North Pacific Neogene Holarctic. *Palaeogeogr. Palaeoclimatol. Palaeoecol.* 77: 195–197.

Gladenkov, Yu. B. 1990b. System of the Neogene regional divisions of Kamchatka and Sakhalin: Horizons, zones and beds. *Palaeogeogr. Palaeoclimatol. Palaeoecol.* 77: 199–201.

Gladenkov, Yu. B., Norton, P. and G. Spaink. 1980. Verkhnii Kainozoi Islandii. Akademia Nauk SSSR Geological Institute 345: 1–114.

Gladenkov, Yu. B., G. M. Brattseva and V. N. Sinelnikova. 1988. Subdivision of Oligocene-Lower Miocene sequences of eastern Kamchatka: The Korf Bay section. *Int. Geol. Rev.* 30: 931–944.

Gladenkov, Yu. B., K. B. Barinov, A. E. Basilyan and T. M. Cronin. 1991. Stratigraphy and paleoceanography of Pliocene deposits of Karaginsky Island, eastern Kamchatka, U.S.S.R. *Quat. Sci. Rev.* 10: 239–245.

Golikov, A. N. 1986. Trichotropidae in the temperate and cold waters of the northern hemisphere. USSR Academy of Sciences, Proceedings of the Zoological Institute 152: 11–29.

Goryachev, V. N. 1987. K istorii formirovaniya fauny *Neptunea* (Gastropoda, Buccinidae) severnoipatsifiki. In *Fauna i raspredelenie mollyuskov: Severnaya patsifika i polyarnui bassein*, pp. 57–64. Akademiya Nauk SSSR, Vladivostok.

Gramann, F. 1990. Eocene/Oligocene boundary definitions and the sequence of strata in NW Germany. *Tert. Res.* 11: 73–81.

Grant, W. S. 1986. Biochemical genetic divergence between Atlantic, *Clupea harengus*, and Pacific, *C. pallasi*, herring. *Copeia* (1986): 714–719.

Grant, W. S. and G. Stahl. 1988. Evolution of Atlantic and Pacific cod: Loss of genetic variation and gene expression in Pacific cod. *Evolution* 42: 138–146.

Grigg, R. W. 1988. Paleoceanography of coral reefs in the Hawaiian-Emperor chain. *Science* 240: 1737–1743.

Grigg, R. W. and R. Hey. 1992. Paleoceanography of the tropical eastern Pacific Ocean. *Science* 255: 172–178.

Groves, L. T. 1997. A review of cypraeiform gastropods from Neogene strata of northwestern Ecuador, with the description of two new species. Tulane Studies in Geology and Paleontology 30: 147–157.

Haasl, D. M. and T. A. Hansen. 1996. Timing of latest Eocene molluscan extinction patterns in Mississippi. *Palaios* 11: 487–494.

Hansen, T. A. 1987. Extinction of Late Eocene to Oligocene molluscs: Relationship to shelf area, temperature changes, and impact events. *Palaios* 2: 69–75.

Harrison, M. K. and B. J. Crespi. 1999. Phylogenetics of Cancer crabs (Crustacea: Decapoda: Brachyura). *Mol. Phylogenet. Evol.* 12: 186–199.

Harte, M. E. 1998. The evolution of *Mercenaria* Schumacher, 1817 (Bivalvia: Veneridae). In P. A. Johnston and J. W. Haggart (eds.), *Bivalves: An Eon of Evolution. Paleobiological Studies Honoring Norman D. Newell*, pp. 305–315. University of Calgary Press, Calgary.

Hayami, I. and I. Hosoda. 1988. *Fortipecten takahashii*, a reclining pectinid from the Pliocene of North Japan. *Palaeontology* 31: 419–444.

Heinberg, C. 1979. Bivalves from the latest Maastrichtian of Stevns Klint and their stratigraphic affinities. In T. Birkelund and R. C. Bromley (eds.), *Cretaceous-Tertiary Boundary Events*. I. *The Maastrichtian and Danian of Denmark*, pp. 58–64. University of Copenhagen, Copenhagen.

Hellberg, M. E. 1998. Sympatric sea shells along the seas' shore: The geography of speciation in the marine gastropod *Tegula*. *Evolution* 52: 1311–1324.

Herm, D. 1969. Marines Pliozän und Pleistozän in Nord- und Mittel-Chile unter besonderer Berücksichtigung der Entwicklung der Mollusken-Faunen. *Zitteliana* 2: 1–159.

Hickman, C. S. 1980. Paleogene marine gastropods of the Keasey Formation in Oregon. Bulletins of American Paleontology 78: 1–112.

Hinsch, W. 1990. Subdivision and paleogeography of the Gramian and Syltian stages (late Miocene) in Schleswig-Holstein and Wursten (NW Germany). *Tert. Res.* 11: 159–177.

Hoagland, K. E. 1977. Systematic review of fossil and Recent *Crepidula* and discussion of evolution of the Calyptraeidae. *Malacologia* 16: 353–420.

Holthuis, L. B. 1974. The lobsters of the superfamily Nephropidea of the Atlantic Ocean (Crustacea: Decapoda). *Bull. Mar. Sci.* 24: 723–784.

Honda, Y. 1991. Paleogene molluscan biogeography of Japan. Saito Ho-On Kai Special Publication 3: 489–506.

Honda, Y. 1994. History of the Paleogene molluscan fauna of Japan: A paleobiogeographic approach. *Palaeogeogr. Palaeoclimatol. Palaeoecol.* 108: 295–309.

Hopkins, D. M. and L. Marincovich, Jr. 1984. Whale biogeography and the history of the Arctic basin. University of Groningen, Works of the Arctic Center 8: 7–24.

Howes, G. J. 1991. Biogeography of gadoid fishes. *J. Biogeogr.* 18: 595–622.

Humphreys, B. and P. S. Balson. 1985. Authigenic glaucony in the East Anglian crags. *Proc. Geol. Assoc.* 96: 183–188.

Itoigawa, J. and S. Tomida. 1982. *Miohaliotis amabilis*, a new haliotid fossil from the Miocene Mizunami Group, with special reference to fossil haliotid fauna in Neogene and Quaternary of Japan. Mizunami Fossil Museum Bulletin 9: 1–14.

Jackson, J. B. C., P. Jung, A. G. Coates and L. S. Collins. 1993. Diversity and extinction of tropical American mollusks and emergence of the Isthmus of Panama. *Science* 260: 1624–1626.

Jackson, J. B. C., A. F. Budd and A. G. Coates (eds.). 1996. *Evolution and Environment in Tropical America*. University of Chicago Press, Chicago.

Johnson, K. G., A. F. Budd and T. A. Stemann. 1995. Extinction selectivity and ecology of Neogene Caribbean reef corals. *Paleobiology* 21: 52–73.

Johnson, M. E. 1988. Why are ancient rocky shores so uncommon? *J. Geol.* 96: 469–480.

Jung, P. 1969. Miocene and Pliocene mollusks from Trinidad. *Bull. Am. Paleontol.* 55: 293–657.

Kadolsky, D. 1988. Stratigraphie und Molluskenfaunen von "Landschnecken-kalk" und "Cerithienschichten" im Mainzer Becken (Oberoligozän bis Untermiozän?). *Geol. Jahrb.* A 110: 69–133.

Kafanov, A. I. 1978. Center of origin and some features of ecological evolution of cold-water malacofauna of the northern hemisphere. *Sov. J. Mar. Biol.* 4: 485–489.

Kafanov, A. I. 1980. Systematics of the subfamily Clinocardiinae Kafanov, 1975 (Bivalvia, Cardiidae). *Malacologia* 19: 297–328.

Kafanov, A. I. 1984. The Cenozoic history of the molluscan fauna of the North Pacific shelf. Canadian Translations in Fisheries and Aquatic Sciences 5052: 1–77.

Kafanov, A. I. 1986. Comparison of the geographical and stratigraphical ranges of For-

tipectininae and Patinopectininae (Bivalvia: Pectinidae). *Monogr. Mizunami Fossil Mus.* 6: 23–40.

Kafanov, A. I. 1987. Podsemeistvo Mytilinae Rafinesque 1815 (Bivalvia, Mytilidae) v Kainozoe severnoi patsifiki. In *Fauna i raspledelenie mollyuskov: Severnaya patsifika i polyarnui bassein*, pp. 65–103. Akademiya Nauk SSSR, Vladivostok.

Kafanov, A. I. and V. O. Savizky. 1982. A survey of the Paleogene–Neogene representatives of *Ciliatocardium* (Bivalvia, Cardiidae) from Sakhalin. *Paleontol. J.* 16: 51–59.

Kafanov, A. I. and V. O. Savizky. 1995. Paleogene Nuculanidae (Bivalvia) of South Sakhalin: Composition and distribution. *Bull. Mizunami Fossil Mus.* 22: 73–102.

Kafanov, A. I. and I. V. Volvenko. 1997. Bivalve molluscs and Cenozoic climatic events in the northwestern Pacific Ocean. *Palaeogeogr. Palaeoclimatol. Palaeoecol.* 129: 119–153.

Kanno, S. 1973. Japanese Tertiary cassidids (Gastropoda) and their related mollusks from the west coast of North America. Science Reports of Tohoku University (Ser. 2, Geology), Special Volume 6: 217–233.

Kantor, Yu. I. 1990. *Gastropods of the Subfamily Volutopsiinae of the World Ocean*. "Nauka", Moscow.

Kantor, Yu. I. and A. V. Sysoev. 1991. Mollusks of the genus *Antiplanes* (Gastropoda: Turridae) of the northwestern Pacific Ocean. *Nautilus* 105: 119–146.

Keen, A. M. 1941. Molluscan species common to western North America and Japan. Sixth Pacific Science Congress, Oceanography and Marine Biology, 3: 479–483.

Keller, G., C. E. Zenker and S. M. Stone. 1989. Late Neogene history of the Pacific-Caribbean gateway. *S. Am. J. Earth Sci.* 2: 73–108.

Kelley, P. H. 1989. Evolutionary trends within bivalve prey of Chesapeake Group naticid gastropods. *Histor. Biol.* 2: 139–156.

Kelley, P. H. 1991a. Apparent cannibalism by Chesapeake Group naticid gastropods: A predictable result of selective predation. *J. Paleontol.* 65: 75–79.

Kelley, P. H. 1991b. The effect of predation intensity on rate of evolution of five Miocene bivalves. *Histor. Biol.* 5: 65–78.

Kelley, P. H. 1992. Coevolutionary patterns of naticid gastropods of the Chesapeake Group: An example of coevolution? *J. Paleontol.* 66: 794–800.

Kennett, J. P., G. Keller and M. S. Srinivasan. 1985. Miocene planktonic foraminiferal biogeography and paleoceanographic development of the Indo-Pacific region. *Geol. Soc. Am. Mem.* 163: 197–236.

Kidwell, S. M. 1984. Outcrop features and origin of basin margin unconformities in the Lower Chesapeake Group (Miocene), Atlantic Coastal Plain. *AAPG Mem.* 36: 37–58.

Knowlton, N., L. A. Weigt, L. A. Solorzano, D. K. Mills and E. Bermingham. 1993. Divergence in proteins, mitochondrial DNA, and reproductive compatibility across the Isthmus of Panama. *Science* 260: 1629–1632.

Kollmann, H. A. 1979. Distribution patterns and evolution of gastropods around the

Cretaceous–Tertiary boundary. In W. Kegel Christensen and T. Birkelund (eds.), *Cretaceous–Tertiary Boundary Events*. II. *Proceedings*, pp. 83–87. University of Copenhagen, Copenhagen.

Kollmann, H. A. and J. S. Peel. 1983. Paleocene gastropods from Nügssuaq, West Greenland. *Grönlands Geologiske Undersögelse Bull.* 146: 1–115.

Krantz, D. E. 1991. A chronology of Pliocene sea-level fluctuations: The U.S. middle Atlantic Coastal Plain record. *Quat. Sci. Rev.* 10: 163–174.

Kussakin, O. G. 1990. Biogeography of the isopod crustaceans in the boreal Pacific. *Bull. Mar. Sci.* 46: 620–639.

Lee, D. E., R. M. Carter, R. P. King and A. F. Cooper. 1983. An Oligocene rocky shore community from Mount Luxmore, Fiordland. *NZ J. Geol. Geophys.* 26: 123–126.

Leigh, E. G., Jr., R. T. Paine, J. F. Quinn and T. H. Suchanek. 1987. Wave energy and intertidal productivity. *Proc. Natl. Acad. Sci. USA* 84: 1314–1318.

Lessios, H. A., B. D. Kessing, G. M. Wellington and A. Graybeal. 1996. Indo-Pacific echinoids in the tropical eastern Pacific. *Coral Reefs* 15: 133–142.

Lindberg, D. R. 1988a. The Patellogastropoda. *Malacol. Rev.* (Suppl.) 4: 35–63.

Lindberg, D. R. 1988b. Recent and fossil species of the genus *Erginus* from the North Pacific Ocean (Patellogastropoda: Mollusca). *Paleobios* 12: 1–7.

Lindberg, D. R. 1991. Marine biotic interchange between the northern and southern hemispheres. *Paleobiology* 17: 308–324.

Lindberg, D. R. 1992. Evolution, distribution and systematics of Haliotidae. In S. A. Shepherd, M. J. Tegner and S. A. Guzmän del Proo (eds.), *Abalone of the World: Biology, Fisheries and Culture: Proceedings of the First International Symposium on Abalone*, pp. 3–18. Oxford; Cambridge, MA, Fishing News Books.

Lindberg, D. R. and J. H. Lipps. 1996. Reading the chronicle of temperate rocky shore faunas. In D. Jablonski, D. H. Erwin and J. H. Lipps (eds.), *Evolutionary Paleobiology: In honor of James W. Valentine*, pp. 161–182. University of Chicago Press, Chicago.

Lindberg, D. R., J. A. Estes and K. I. Warheit. 1998. Human influences on trophic cascades along rocky shores. *Ecol. Appl.* 8: 880–890.

Lozouet, P. and P. Le Renard. 1998. Les Coralliophilidae, Gastropoda de l'Oligocène et du Miocène inferieur d'Aquitaine (sud-ouest de la France): Systématique et coraux hotes. *Géobios* 31: 171–184.

Lüning, K., M. D. Guiry and M. Masuda. 1987. Upper temperature tolerance of North Atlantic and North Pacific geographical isolates of *Chondrus* species (Rhodophyta). *Helgoländer Meeresuntersuchungen* 41: 297–307.

MacNeil, F. S. 1965. Evolution and distribution of the genus *Mya*, and Tertiary migrations of Mollusca. U.S. Geological Survey Professional Paper 483-G: G1-G51.

Maestrati, P. and P. Lozouet. 1996. Les Glycymerididae (Mollusca, Bivalvia) de l'Oligocène superieur (Chattien) du Bassin de l'Adour, France. *Ann. Paléont. (Vert-Invert.)* 82: 3–25.

Majima, R. 1989. Cenozoic fossil Naticidae (Mollusca: Gastropoda) in Japan. *Bull. Am. Paleontol.* 96: 1–159.

Mallinson, D. J. and J. S. Compton. 1997. Linking phosphogenic episodes on the southeast U.S. margin to marine δ^{13}C and δ^{18}O records. *Geology* 25: 103–106.

Marincovich, L.,, Jr. 1977. Cenozoic Naticidae (Mollusca: Gastropoda) of the northeastern Pacific. *Bull. Am. Paleontol.* 70: 169–494.

Marincovich, L., Jr. 1984. Eastern Pacific molluscan bio-events and their relation to Neogene planktonic datum planes. In N. Ikebe and R. Tsuchi (eds.), *Pacific Neogene Datum Planes: Contributions to Biostratigraphy and Chronology*, pp. 69–73. University of Tokyo Press, Tokyo.

Marincovich, L., Jr. 1988. The recognition of an earliest middle Miocene warm-water event in the southwestern Alaskan molluscan fauna. Saito Ho-On Kai Special Publication 2: 1–24.

Marincovich, L., Jr. 1990. Molluscan evidence for early middle Miocene marine glaciation in southern Alaska. *Geol. Soc. Am. Bull.* 102: 1591–1599.

Marincovich, L., Jr. 1993. Danian mollusks from the Prince Creek Formation, northern Alaska, and implications for Arctic Ocean paleogeography. *Paleontol. Soc. Mem.* 35: 1–35.

Marincovich, L., Jr. and A. Yu. Gladenkov. 1999. Evidence for an early opening of the Bering Strait. *Nature* 397: 149–151.

Marincovich, L., Jr. and S. Moriya. 1992. Early middle Miocene mollusks and benthic foraminifers from Kodiak Island, Alaska. U.S. Geological Survey Bulletin 1999: 163–169.

Marincovich, L., Jr. and V. D. Wiggins. 1991. Oligocene age of strata on Unga Island, Shumagin Islands, southwestern Alaska. U.S. Geological Survey Bulletin 1946: 39–43.

Marincovich, L., Jr. and W. J. Zinsmeister. 1991. The first Tertiary (Paleocene) marine mollusks from the Eureka Sound Group, Ellesmere Island, Canada. *J. Paleontol.* 65: 242–248.

Marincovich, L., Jr., E. M. Brouwers, D. M. Hopkins and M. C. McKenna. 1990. Late Mesozoic and Cenozoic paleogeographic and paleoclimatic history of the Arctic Ocean basin: Based on shallow-water marine faunas and terrestrial vertebrates. In A. Grantz, L. Johnson and J. F. Sweeney (eds.), *The Arctic Ocean Region*, pp. 403–426. Geological Society of America, Boulder, CO.

Marko, P. B. and G. J. Vermeij. 1999. Molecular phylogenetics and the evolution of labral spines among Eastern Pacific ocenebrine gastropods. *Mol. Phylogenet. Evol.* 13: 275–288.

Marquet, R. 1993. The molluscan fauna of the Kruisschans Member (Lillo Formation, Late Pliocene) in the Antwerp area, Belgium. *Contrib. Tert. Quat. Geol.* 30: 83–103.

Marquet, R. 1995. Pliocene gastropod faunas from Kallo (Oost-Vlaanderen, Belgium). Part 1, Introduction and Archaeogastropoda. *Contrib. Tert. Quat. Geol.* 32: 53–85.

Marquet, R. 1997a. Pliocene gastropod faunas from Kallo (Oost-Vlaanderen, Belgium). Part 2, Caenogastropoda: Potamididae to Tornidae. *Contrib. Tert. Quat. Geol.* 34: 9–29.

Marquet, R. 1997b. Pliocene gastropod faunas from Kallo (Oost-Vlaanderen, Belgium). Part 3, Caenogastropoda: Aporrhaidae to Muricidae, and Part 4, Buccinidae to Helicidae. *Contrib. Tert. Quat. Geol.* 34: 69–149.

Marquet, R. 1997c. The Pliocene turrid gastropods of Belgium. Part 1, Drilliidae, Turridae, Conidae (genus *Bela*). Bulletin de l'Institut Royal des Sciences Naturelles de Belgique, Sciences de la Terre 67: 119–151.

Masuda, K. 1972. *Swiftopecten* of the northern Pacific. *Trans. Proc. Palaeontol. Soc. Japan*, New Series 87: 395–408.

Masuda, K. 1978. Neogene Pectinidae of the northern Pacific. *Veliger* 21: 197–202.

Masuda, K. 1986. Notes on origin and migration of Cenozoic pectinids in the northern Pacific. Paleontological Society of Japan Special Paper 29: 95–110.

Matsubara, T. 1994. A new Miocene *Rexithaerus* (Bivalvia) from the Kadonosawa Formation of Iwate Prefecture, northeast Japan. Saito Ho-On Kai Museum of Natural History Research Bulletin 62: 23–34.

Matsukuma, A., S. Goshima and Y. Kuwahara. 1988. Taxonomy and geographical distribution of *Megangulus* (Mollusca) from the northern Pacific. *Mem. Nat. Sci. Mus.* 23: 113–122.

McLean, J. H. 1995. Three additional new genera and two replacement names for northeastern Pacific prosobranch gastropods. *Nautilus* 108: 80–82.

McMillan, W. O. and S. R. Palumbi. 1995. Concordant evolutionary pattern among Indo-West Pacific butterflyfishes. *Proc. R. Soc. Lond.* B 260: 229–236.

Mead, J. G. and E. D. Mitchell. 1984. Atlantic gray whales. In M. L. Jones, S. L. Schwartz and S. Leatherwood (eds.), *The Gray Whale Eschrichtius robustus*, pp. 33–53. Academic Press, Orlando, FL.

Menge, B. A. 1992. Community regulation: Under what conditions are bottom-up factors important on rocky shores? *Ecology* 73: 755–765.

Menge, B. A. 1995. Indirect effects in marine rocky intertidal interaction webs: Patterns and importance. *Ecol. Monogr.* 65: 21–74.

Menge, B. A. and T. M. Farrell. 1989. Structure and interaction webs in shallow marine hard-bottom communities: Tests of an environmental stress model. *Adv. Ecol. Res.* 19: 189–262.

Miller, K. G., G. S. Mountain, the Leg 150 Shipboard Party, and Members of the New Jersey Coastal Plain Drilling Project. 1996. Drilling and dating New Jersey Oligocene-Miocene sequences: Ice volume, global sea level, and Exxon records. *Science* 271: 1092–1095.

Moore, E. J. 1984. Middle Tertiary molluscan zones of the Pacific Northwest. *J. Paleontol.* 58: 718–737.

Moore, E. J. and W. O. Addicott. 1987. Miocene Pillarian and Newportian (Molluscan) stages of Washington and Oregon and their usefullness in correlations from Alaska to California. U.S. Geological Survey Bulletin 1664: A1-A13.

Nations, J. D. 1975. The genus *Cancer* (Crustacea: Brachyura): Systematics, biogeography and fossil record. Natural History Museum of Los Angeles County Science Bulletin 23: 1–104.

Nations, J. D. 1979. The genus *Cancer* and its distribution in time and space. *Bull. Biol. Soc. Wash.* 3: 153–187.

Newman, W. A. and A. Ross. 1976. Revision of the balanomorph barnacles; including a catalog of the species. Memoirs of the San Diego Society of Natural History 9: 1–108.

Nisiyama, S. 1966. The echinoid fauna in Japan and adjacent regions. Part I. Palaeontological Society of Japan Special Paper 11: 1–277.

Nisiyama, S. 1968. The echinoid fauna of Japan and adjacent regions. Part II. Palaeontological Society of Japan Special Paper 13: 1–491.

Noda, H. 1988. Molluscan fossils from the Ryukyu Islands, Southwest Japan. Part 2, Gastropoda and Pelecypoda from the Shinzato Formation in the middle part of Okinawa-Jima. Science Reports of the Institute of Geoscience, University of Tsukuba, Section B (Geological Sciences) 9: 29–85.

Noda, Y. 1992. Neogene molluscan faunas from the Haboro Coalfield, Hokkaido, Japan. Science Reports of the Tohoku University (Ser. 2, Geology) 62: 1–140.

Ogasawara, K. 1981. Paleogeographic significance of the Omma-Manganjian fauna of Japan Sea borderland. Saito Ho-On Kai Museum Research Bulletin 49: 1–17.

Ogasawara, K. 1986. Notes on origin and migration of the Omma-Manganzian fauna, Japan. Palaeontological Society of Japan Special Paper 29: 227–244.

Oleinik, A. E. 1993. The genus *Fulgoraria* (Gastropoda: Volutidae) of the northeastern Kamchatka Peninsula and Sakhalin Island, with notes on the paleoecology and distribution of the subfamily Fulgorariinae in the Oligocene of the northern Pacific. *Nautilus* 106: 137–146.

Oleinik, A. E. 1996. Genus *Arctomelon* (Gastropoda, Volutidae) in the Tertiary of the northwestern Pacific: Evolution and adaptations. *J. Paleontol.* 70: 236–246.

Olson, S. L. 1985. The fossil record of birds. In D. S. Farmer, J. R. King and K. C. Parkes (eds.), *Avian Biology*, Vol. 8, pp. 79–252. Academic Press, New York.

Olsson, A. A. 1964. *Neogene Mollusks from Northwestern Ecuador.* Paleontological Research Institute, Ithaca, NY.

Ostfeld, R. S. 1982. Foraging strategies and prey switching in the California sea otter. *Oecologia* 53: 170–178.

Paine, R. T. 1966. Food web complexity and species diversity. *Am. Nat.* 100: 65–75.

Paine, R. T. 1969. A note on trophic complexity and community stability. *Am. Nat.* 103: 91–93.

Paine, R. T. 1974. Intertidal community structure: Experimental studies on the relationship between a dominant competitor and its principal predator. *Oecologia* 15: 93–120.

Paine, R. T. 1980. Food webs: Linkage, interaction strength and community infrastructure. *J. Anim. Ecol.* 49: 667–685.

Palumbi, S. R. and B. D. Kessing. 1991. Population biology of the trans-Arctic exchange: MtDNA sequence similarity between Pacific and Atlantic sea urchins. *Evolution* 45: 1790–1805.

Palumbi, S. R. and A. C. Wilson. 1990. Mitochondrial DNA diversity in the sea urchins *Strongylocentrotus purpuratus* and *S. droebachiensis*. *Evolution* 44: 403–415.

Pandolfi, J. M. 1992. Successive isolation rather than evolutionary centres for the origination of Indo-Pacific reef corals. *J. Biogeogr.* 19: 593–609.

Paulay, G. 1996. Dynamic clams: Changes in the bivalve fauna of Pacific islands as a result of sea-level fluctuations. *Am. Malacol. Bull.* 12: 45–57.

Petersen, S. K., K. L. Rasmussen, J. Heinemeier and N. Rud. 1992. Clams before Columbus. *Nature* 359: 679.

Petuch, E. J. 1988. *Neogene History of Tropical American Mollusks: Biogeography and Evolutionary Patterns of Tropical Western Atlantic Mollusca.* Coastal Education and Research Foundation, Charlottesville. 217 pp.

Petuch, E. J. 1993. Patterns of diversity and extinction in Transmarian muricacean, buccinacean, and conacean gastropods. *Nautilus* 106: 155–173.

Petuch, E. J. 1995. Molluscan diversity in the Late Neogene of Florida: Evidence for a two-stage mass extinction. *Science* 270: 275–277.

Petuch, E. J. 1997. *Coastal Paleoceanography of Eastern North America (Miocene-Pleistocene).* Kendall/Hunt, Dubuque, IA. 373 pp.

Petuch, E. J. and D. M. Sargent. 1986. *Atlas of the Living Olive Shells of the World.* Coastal Education and Research Foundation, Fort Lauderdale, FL.

Pitt, W. D. and L. J. Pitt. 1992. Naticidae (Mollusca, Mesogastropoda) from the Neogene of northwestern Ecuador. Tulane Studies in Geology and Paleontology 25: 109–138.

Pomerol, C. (ed.). 1981. Stratotypes of Paleogene stages. Bulletin d'Information des Géologues du Bassin de Paris (Ser. 2), Mémoire.

Popov, S. V. 1983. Pozdne Kainozoiskie i sovremennye dvustvorchatye mollyuski semeistva Carditidae SSSR. Akademiya Nauk SSSR Paleontologicheskii Institut Trudy 203: 1–118.

Por, F. D. 1989. *The Legacy of Tethys: An Aquatic Biogeography of the Levant.* Kluwer, Dordrecht.

Raffi, S., S. M. Stanley and R. Marasti. 1985. Biogeographic patterns and Plio-Pleistocene extinction of Bivalvia in the Mediterranean and southern North Sea. *Paleobiology* 11: 368–388.

Ray, C. E. 1976. Geography of phocid evolution. *Syst. Zool.* 25: 391–406.

Reid, D. G. 1989. The comparative morphology, phylogeny and evolution of the gastropod family Littorinidae. *Phil. Trans. R. Soc. Lond.* B 324: 1–110.

Reid, D. G. 1990. Trans-Arctic migration and speciation induced by climatic change: The biogeography of Littorina (Mollusca: Gastropoda). *Bull. Mar. Sci.* 47: 35–49.

Reid, D. G. 1996. *Systematics and Evolution of Littorina.* The Ray Society, London.

Repenning, C. A. 1976a. Adaptive evolution of sea lions and walruses. *Syst. Zool.* 25: 375–390.

Repenning, C. A. 1976b. *Enhydra* and *Enhydriodon* from the Pacific coast of North America. *J. Res. US Geol. Surv.* 4: 305–315.

Repenning, C. A., C. E. Ray and D. Grigorescu. 1979. Pinniped biogeography. In J. Gray and A. J. Boucot (eds.), *Historical Biogeography, Plate Tectonics, and the Changing Environment*, pp. 357–369. Oregon State University Press, Corvallis.

Richmond, R. H. 1990. The effects of the El Niño/Southern Oscillation on the dispersal of corals and other marine organisms. In P. W. Glynn (ed.), *Global Ecological Consequences of the 1982–83 El Niño-Southern Oscillation*, pp. 127–140. Elsevier, Amsterdam.

Ricklefs, R. E. and R. E. Latham. 1993. Global patterns of diversity in mangrove floras. In R. E. Ricklefs and D. Schluter (eds.), *Species Diversity in Ecological Communities: Historical and Geographical Perspectives*, pp. 215–229. University of Chicago Press, Chicago.

Ridgway, S. A., D. G. Reid, J. D. Taylor, G. M. Branch and A. N. Hodgson. 1998. A cladistic phylogeny of the family Patellidae (Mollusca: Gastropoda). *Phil. Trans. R. Soc. Lond.* B 353: 1645–1671.

Riedman, M. L. and J. A. Estes. 1988. A review of the history, distribution and foraging ecology of sea otters. In G. R. VanBlaricom and J. A. Estes (eds.), *The Community Ecology of Sea Otters*, pp. 4–21. Springer, Berlin.

Riggs, S. R. 1984. Paleoceanographic model of Neogene phosphorite deposition, U.S. Atlantic continental margin. *Science* 223: 123–131.

Rögl, F. and F. F. Steininger. 1984. Neogene Paratethys, Mediterranean and Indo-Pacific seaways: Implications for the paleobiogeography of marine and terrestrial biotas. In P. J. Brenchley (ed.), *Fossils and Climate*, pp. 171–200. Wiley, Winchester.

Roopnarine, P. D. 1996. Systematics, biogeography and extinction of chionine bivalves (Bivalvia: Veneridae). *Malacologia* 38: 103–142.

Roughgarden, J., S. Gaines and H. Possingham. 1988. Recruitment dynamics in complex life cycles. *Science* 241: 1460–1466.

Roy, K. 1994. Effects of the Mesozoic marine revolution on the taxonomic, morphologic, and biogeographic evolution of a group: Apporhaid gastropods during the Mesozoic. *Paleobiology* 20: 274–296.

Saul, L. R. 1989. California Late Cretaceous donaciform bivalves. *Veliger* 32: 188–208.

Savin, S. M., L. Abel, E. Barrera, D. Hodell, J. P. Kennett, M. Murphy, G. Keller, J. Lillingley and E. Vincent. 1985. The evolution of Miocene surface and near-surface marine temperatures: Oxygen isotope evidence. *Geol. Soc. Am. Mem.* 163: 49–82.

Scheltema, R. S. 1971. Larval dispersal as a means of genetic exchange between geographically separated populations of shallow-water benthic marine gastropods. *Biol. Bull.* 140: 284–322.

Schenck, H. G. 1936. Nuculid bivalves of the genus *Acila*. Geological Society of America Special Paper 4: 1–149.

Schneider, J. A. 1998. Phylogeny of the Cardiidae (Bivalvia): Phylogenetic relationships and morphological evolution within the subfamilies Clinocardiinae, Limnocardiinae, Fraginae and Tridacninae. *Malacologia* 40: 321–373.

Seed, R. 1992. Systematics, evolution and distribution of mussels belonging to the genus *Mytilus*: An overview. *Am. Malacol. Bull.* 9: 123–137.

Sher, A. 1999. Traffic lights and the Beringian crossroads. *Nature* 397: 103–104.

Simenstad, C. A., J. A. Estes and K. W. Kenyon. 1978. Aleuts, sea otters, and alternate stable state communities. *Science* 200: 403–411.

Smith, J. T. 1970. Taxonomy, distribution, and phylogeny of the cymatiid gastropods *Argobuccinum, Fusitriton, Mediargo*, and *Priene*. *Bull. Am. Paleontol.* 56: 441–573.

Smith, J. T. 1991. Cenozoic giant pectinids from California and the Tertiary Caribbean Province: *Lyropecten*, "*Macrochlamis*," *Vertipecten*, and *Nodipecten* species. U.S. Geological Survey Professional Paper 1391: 1–155.

Squires, R. L. and J. L. Goedert. 1991. New Late Eocene mollusks from localized limestone deposits formed by subduction-related methane seeps, southwestern Washington. *J. Paleontol.* 65: 412–416.

Stanley, S. M. 1986a. Anatomy of a regional mass extinction: Plio-Pleistocene decimation of the western Atlantic bivalve fauna. *Palaios* 1: 17–36.

Stanley, S. M. 1986b. Population size, extinction, and speciation: The fission effect in Neogene Bivalvia. *Paleobiology* 12: 89–110.

Steurbaut, E. 1998. High-resolution holostratigraphy of Middle Paleocene to Early Eocene strata in Belgium and adjacent areas. *Palaeontographica* A 247: 91–156.

Strauch, F. 1972. Phylogenese, Adaptation und Migration einiger nordischer mariner Molluskengenera (*Neptunea, Panomya, Cyrtodaria* und *Mya*). Abhandlungen der Senckenbergischen Naturforschenden Gesellschaft 531: 1–211.

Sysoev, A. V. and Yu. I. Kantor. 1987. Deep-sea gastropods of the genus *Aforia* (Turridae) of the Pacific: Species composition, systematics, and functional morphology of the digestive system. *Veliger* 30: 105–126.

Takahashi, S., D. P. Domning and T. Saito. 1986. *Dusisiren dewana*, n. sp. (Mammalia: Sirenia), a new ancestor of Steller's sea cow from the Upper Miocene of Yamagata Prefecture, northeastern Japan. *Trans. Proc. Palaeontol. Soc. Japan*, New Series 141: 296–321.

Tembrock, M. L. 1968. Taxonomisch-stratigraphische Studie über *Scalaspira*-Gruppe (Gastropoda, Tertiär). *Paläontol. Abhandl.* (A, Paläontologie) 3: 195–322.

Titova, L. V. 1993. The early history of the North Pacific Ancistrolepidinae (Gastropoda: Buccinidae). *Ruthenica* 3: 1–16.

Titova, L. V. 1994a. Cenozoic history of Turritelloidea and Buccinoidea (Mollusca: Gastropoda) in the North Pacific. *Palaeogeogr. Palaeoclimatol. Palaeoecol.* 108: 319–334.

Titova, L. V. 1994b. A revision of Paleogene turritellids (Mollusca: Gastropoda) from Kamchatka. *Paleontol. J.* 28: 48–66.

Titova, L. V. 1994c. Revision of the Neogene Turritellidae (Mollusca: Gastropoda) from Kamchatka. *Ruthenica* 4: 1–20.

Tsuchi, R. 1990a. Accelerated evolutionary events in Japanese endemic Mollusca during the latest Neogene. In R. Tsuchi (ed.), *Pacific Neogene Events: Their Timing, Nature and Interrelationship*, pp. 85–97. University of Tokyo Press, Tokyo.

Tsuchi, R. 1990b. Neogene events in Japan and the Pacific. *Palaeogeogr. Palaeoclimatol. Palaeoecol.* 77: 355–365.

Tsuchi, R. and M. Ibaraki. 1988. Notes on the Omma-Manganji molluscan fauna: Its geologic age and paleoceanographic implications. Saito Ho-On Kai Special Publication 2: 557–565.

Tsuchi, R. and T. Shuto. 1984. Western Pacific molluscan bioevents and their relation to Neogene planktonic datum planes. In N. Ikebe and R. Tsuchi (eds.), *Pacific Neogene Datum Planes: Contributions to Biostratigraphy and Chronology*, pp. 75–81. University of Tokyo Press, Tokyo.

Uozumi, S., M. Akamatsu and T. Takagi. 1986. Takikawa-Honbetsu and Tatsunokuchi faunas (*Fortipecten takahashii*-bearing Pliocene faunas). Palaeontological Society of Japan Special Paper 29: 211–226.

Urk, R. M. van. 1971. Fossil *Ensis* species in the Netherlands. *Basteria* 35: 1–37.

Urk, R. M. van. 1972. Notes on American fossil *Ensis* species. *Basteria* 36: 131–142.

Urk, R. M. van. 1980. Fossil and Recent *Lutraria* (Mollusca: Bivalvia) in Europe, with descriptions of four new species. *Mededelingen van de Werkgroep voor Tertiaire en Kwartaire Geologie* 17: 235–266.

van Oppen, M. J. H., S. G. A. Draisma, J. L. Olsen and W. T. Stam. 1995. Multiple trans-Arctic passages in the red alga *Phycodrys rubens*: Evidence from nuclear rDNA ITS sequences. *Mar. Biol.* 123: 179–188.

Vermeij, G. J. 1974. Marine faunal dominance and molluscan shell form. *Evolution* 28: 656–664.

Vermeij, G. J. 1978. *Biogeography and Adaptation: Patterns of Marine Life*. Harvard University Press, Cambridge, MA.

Vermeij, G. J. 1986. Survival during biotic crises: The properties and evolutionary significance of refuges. In D. K. Elliott (ed.), *Dynamics of Extinction*, pp. 231–246. Wiley, New York.

Vermeij, G. J. 1987. The dispersal barrier in the tropical Pacific: Implications for molluscs speciation and extinction. *Evolution* 41: 1046–1058.

Vermeij, G. J. 1989a. Geographical restriction as a guide to the causes of extinction: The case

of the cold northern oceans during the Neogene. *Paleobiology* 15: 335–356.

Vermeij, G. J. 1989b. Interoceanic differences in adaptation: Effects of history and productivity. *Mar. Ecol. Prog. Ser.* 57: 293–305.

Vermeij, G. J. 1991a. Anatomy of an invasion: The trans-Arctic interchange. *Paleobiology* 17: 281–307.

Vermeij, G. J. 1991b. Generic identity and relationships of the northeastern Pacific buccinid *Searlesia dira* (Reeve, 1846). *Veliger* 34: 264–271.

Vermeij, G. J. 1991c. When biotas meet: Understanding biotic interchange. *Science* 253: 1099–1104.

Vermeij, G. J. 1992. Time of origin and biogeographical history of specialized relationships between northern marine plants and herbivorous molluscs. *Evolution* 46: 657–664.

Vermeij, G. J. 1993. The biological history of a seaway. *Science* 260: 1602–1604.

Vermeij, G. J. 1994. The evolutionary interaction among species: Selection, escalation, and coevolution. *Annu. Rev. Ecol. Syst.* 25: 219–36.

Vermeij, G. J. 1995. Morphology and possible relationships of *Ecphora* (Cenozoic Gastropoda: Muricidae). *Nautilus* 109: 120–126.

Vermeij, G. J. 1997. Strait answers from a twisted isthmus. *Paleobiology* 23: 263–269.

Vermeij, G. J. 1998. *Sabia* on shells: A specialized Pacific-type commensalism in the Caribbean Neogene. *J. Paleontol.* 72: 465–472.

Vermeij, G. J. and R. Dudley. 2000. Why are there so few evolutionary transitions between aquatic and terrestrial ecosystems? *Biol. J. Linn. Soc.* 70: 541–554.

Vermeij, G. J. and E. J. Petuch. 1986. Differential extinction in tropical American molluscs: Endemism, architecture, and the Panama land bridge. *Malacologia* 27: 29–41.

Vermeij, G. J. and G. Rosenberg. 1993. Giving and receiving: The tropical Atlantic as donor and recipient region for invading species. *Am. Malacol. Bull.* 10: 181–194.

Vokes, E. H. 1964. The genus *Turbinella* (Mollusca, Gastropoda) in the New World. Tulane Studies in Geology 2: 39–68.

Vokes, E. H. 1966. The genus *Vasum* (Mollusca: Gastropoda) in the New World. Tulane Studies in Geology 5: 1–36.

Vokes, E. H. 1972. *Pterynopsis*, new genus of Trophoninae (Gastropoda). Bulletin de l'Institut Royale des Sciences Naturelles de Belgique (Sciences de la Terre) 48: 1–7.

Vokes, E. H. 1988. Muricidae (Mollusca: Gastropoda) of the Esmeraldas beds, northwestern Ecuador. Tulane Studies in Geology and Paleontology 21: 1–50.

Vokes, E. H. 1990. Cenozoic Muricidae of the western Atlantic region. Part VIII, *Murex* s.s., *Haustellum, Chicoreus*, and *Hexaplex*: Additions and corrections. Tulane Studies in Geology and Paleontology 23: 1–96.

Wagner, C. D. 1974. Fossil and Recent sand dollar echinoids of Alaska. *J. Paleontol.* 48: 105–123.

Waller, T. M. 1991. Evolutionary relationships among commercial scallops (Mollusca: Bivalvia: Pectinidae). In S. E. Shumway (ed.),

Scallops: Biology, Ecology and Aquaculture, pp. 1–73. , Elsevier, Amsterdam.

Waller, T. R. 1993. The evolution of *"Chlamys"* (Mollusca: Bivalvia: Pectinidae). *Am. Malacol. Bull.* 10: 195–249.

Ward, L. W. 1992. Molluscan biostratigraphy of the Miocene, Middle Atlantic Coastal Plain of North America. Virginia Museum of Natural History Memoir 2: 1–159.

Ward, L. W. and B. W. Blackwelder. 1980. Stratigraphic revision of Upper Miocene and Lower Pliocene beds of the Chesapeake Group, middle Atlantic Coastal Plain. U.S. Geological Survey Bulletin 1482-D: D1-D61.

Warheit, K. I. 1992. A review of the fossil seabirds from the Tertiary of the North Pacific: Plate tectonics, paleoceanography, and faunal change. *Paleobiology* 18: 401–424.

Weaver, C. E. 1945. Stratigraphy and paleontology of the Tertiary formations at Coos Bay, Oregon. University of Washington Publications in Geology 6: 31–62.

Williams, S. T. and J. A. H. Benzie. 1998. Evidence of a biogeographic break between populations of a high dispersal starfish: Congruent regions within the Indo-West Pacific defined by color morphs, mtDNA, and allozyme data. *Evolution* 52: 87–99.

Wilson, M. E. J. and B. R. Rosen. 1998. Implications of paucity of corals in the Paleogene of Southeast Asia: Plate tectonics or centre of origin? In R. Hall and J. D. Holloway (eds.), *Biogeography and Geological Evolution of SE Asia,* pp. 165–195. Backhuys, Leiden.

Woodring, W. P. 1966. The Panama land bridge as a sea barrier. *American Philosophical Society Proceedings* 110: 425–433.

Wyss, A. R. 1987. The walrus auditory region and the monophyly of pinnipeds. *Am. Mus. Novitates* 2871: 1–31.

Wyss, A. R. 1988. Evidence from flipper structure for a single origin of pinnipeds. *Nature* 334: 427–428.

Zinsmeister, W. J. 1982. Late Cretaceous-Early Tertiary molluscan biogeography of the southern circum-Pacific. *J. Paleontol.* 56: 84–102.

Zinsmeister, W. J. and H. H. Camacho. 1980. Late Eocene Struthiolariidae (Mollusca: Gastropoda) from Seymour Island, Antarctic Peninsula, and their significance to the biogeography of Early Tertiary shallow-water faunas of the southern hemisphere. *J. Paleontol.* 54: 1–14.

Zullo, V. A. 1979. Thoracican Cirripedia of the Lower Pliocene Pancho Rico Formation, Salinas Valley, Monterey County, California. Contributions in Science, Natural History Museum of Los Angeles County 303: 1–13.

Zullo, V. A. 1992. Revision of the balanid barnacle genus *Concavus* Newman, 1982, with the description of a new subfamily, two new genera, and eight new species. Paleontological Society Memoir 27: 1–46.

Zullo, V. A. and R. B. Guruswami-Naidu. 1982. Late Miocene balanid Cirripedia from the basal Wilson Ranch beds ("Merced" Formation), Sonoma County, northern California. *Proc. Calif. Acad. Sci.* 42: 525–535.

Zullo, V. A. and L. Marincovich, Jr. 1990. Balanoid barnacles from the Miocene of the Alaska Peninsula, and their relevance to the extant boreal barnacle fauna. *J. Paleontol.* 64: 128–135.

chapter 3

Genetic Structure in the Sea
From Populations to Communities

Rick Grosberg and C. W. Cunningham

Virtually all species of marine organisms, whether pelagic, planktonic, or benthic, are patchily distributed, consisting of local populations linked to a greater or lesser extent by dispersal. Ecologists are primarily concerned with characterizing this geographic structure in terms of the distributions and movements of individual organisms within and among local populations. Evolutionary biologists, on the other hand, often think in terms of the spatial distribution of genetic variation within and among local populations. Ecological and evolutionary approaches thus differ in their emphasis on the spatial distribution of individuals versus genes; where they converge is in their attempts to understand the processes that cause geographic variation in a species. In other words, ecology shapes the distribution of genetic variation in a species (Endler 1992), whereas genetic structure provides the evolutionary context in which to interpret a species' ecological interactions with its environment.

Genetic structure in marine populations reflects the historical and contemporary interplay among a complex set of ecological, demographic, behavioral, genetic, oceanographic, climatic and tectonic processes (reviewed in Hedgecock 1986; Palumbi 1995; Benzie 1999; Bohonak 1999). The combined effects of these mechanisms, acting across a range of spatial and temporal scales, determine rates and patterns of dispersal of gametes, zygotes, larvae, and adults. It is these movements, along with the survival and successful reproduction of immigrants, that, in turn, control the scale and rate at which random (i.e., genetic drift) and deterministic (i.e., natural selection) processes build or erode structure within and among groups of individuals.

A number of recent papers have explored the population-level ramifications of genetic structure in marine systems, highlighting the relationships among developmental mode, dispersal, gene flow (i.e., migration of gametes or individuals that leads to the incorporation of their genes into a recipient population), and speciation (e.g., Burton 1983, 1996; Hedgecock 1986; Palumbi 1994, 1995; Benzie 1999; Bohonak 1999). In keeping with the theme of this book, we expand this population-level perspective to the community, and explore four facets of the following basic question: What can information about the spatial distribution of genetic variation within a species, and the processes that generate these patterns, tell ecologists about the nature and outcomes of species' interactions with their biotic and physical environment?

The first aspect of the question relates to the scale at which a species' predators, competitors, parasites, pathogens, and symbionts regulate its population dynamics (Roughgarden and Iwasa 1986; Roughgarden et al. 1988; Possingham and Roughgarden 1990; Gaines and Lafferty 1995). The spatial scales over which marine populations exhibit "open" versus "closed" dynamics are generally not obvious, and they vary according to the magnitude of migration among subpopulations. Genetic structure can be used to place bounds on the spatial scales over which species are likely to be demographically closed.

The second facet concerns the scales over which species exhibit genetic structure, and how these patterns influence responses to spatially varying selection (see papers in Mopper and Strauss 1998 for a terrestrial perspective; for a marine perspective, see Warner 1997). The spatial distribution of neutral genetic variation determines the degree and scale over which subpopulations have been (or are) evolutionarily independent, and consequently free to evolve in response to local variation in selection. With high levels of gene flow among selective regimes, the selective costs of local adaptation increase, perhaps prohibitively. For example, if a polymorphic predator (or parasite or herbivore) population genetically varies over a finer spatial scale than its prey (or host), it is unlikely that the prey population will evolve local adaptations in response to geographic variation in its predator (e.g., Menge 1976; Vermeij 1978, 1987; Palmer 1984).

Third, a number of recent genetic studies have revealed the existence of sibling species complexes in what were once thought to be a single polymorphic species (Knowlton 1993). Such discoveries suggest that many marine species may have more limited distributions than previously thought and may be far more ecologically specialized as well.

Finally, when set into a phylogenetic context, genetic structure can reveal a great deal about a population's history of subdivision and gene flow, in particular the history of its interactions with other species (Avise et al. 1987; Brooks and McLennan 1993; Avise 1994). Are strong interactions between competitors, predators and prey, or parasites and their hosts the result of a long, shared selective history (Brooks and McLennan 1993), or are these associations the result of recent introductions (e.g., Vermeij 1991)? Do traits that appear to be adaptive in their current selective contexts reflect a genetically based response to selection in a particular place, or were these traits shared by sister taxa prior to the evolutionary and geographic divergence of these taxa? For example, if we can determine that taxa on both sides of the North Atlantic lack geographic subdivision as a result of ongoing gene flow, then we might predict that differences in their morphology, physiology, behavior, or ecology result from environmentally mediated phenotypic, rather than cumulative genetic, responses to different environments. Conversely, if the lack of genetic structure is due to recent colonization with low levels of ongoing gene flow, then cumulative genetic change becomes a more plausible explanation for phenotypic divergence.

The process of characterizing genetic structure, and using this information to estimate gene flow, effective population size, and other ecologically relevant parameters has a long and complex history. Different methods make different assumptions about the equilibrium status of populations, migration patterns, population structure, and the attributes of genetic markers (Gillespie 1998). Not surprisingly, the different approaches can lead to very different conclusions about the distribution of genetic variation, and the historic and contemporary processes that underlie these distributions (Slatkin 1994; Neigel 1997). For this reason, we begin by summarizing the basic methods used to detect genetic structure and estimate gene flow. Because genetically based inferences of population subdivision and gene flow depend on a host of assumptions about migration patterns, mutation rates, selective neutrality, and equilibrium status (Gillespie 1998), we next consider problems associated with developing a mechanistic interpretation of patterns of genetic structure in natural populations. With this foundation in place, we finally return to the basic ecological questions and use a series of case studies to explore how genetic structure can provide crucial insights into the nature and outcomes of species' interactions with their biotic and physical environments.

CHARACTERIZING GENETIC STRUCTURE AND ESTIMATING GENE FLOW

The first quantitative attempts to depict genetic structure originated with Wahlund's (1928) observation that there should be heterozygote deficiencies in structured populations and Wright's (1951) analyses of the expected distribution of neutral genetic variation in spatially subdivided populations. Wright's approach built on the premise that species can be reduced to a set of freely interbreeding (panmictic) units, and that these units will resemble each other depending on the degree of gene flow between them (Slatkin 1994). Wright developed statistics that summarize the distribution of genetic variation within and among sampling units based on the spatial (and sometimes temporal) distribution of gene and genotypic frequencies. However, it was not until the advent of allozyme electrophoresis in the 1960s that population geneticists could build an extensive multilocus database from which to characterize the spatial distribution of gene frequencies in natural populations.

There is no reliable way to infer the genealogical relationships among allozyme variants, because there is no obvious connection between the migration patterns of proteins on an electrophoretic gel and the degree of divergence of the underlying DNA sequences. The development in the 1980s of indirect and direct methods for detecting nucleotide sequence variation made it possible for the first time to reconstruct the ancestral–descendant relationships among genes, populations, and species. With this information, it became possible for the first time to interpret the geographic distribution of alleles, haplotypes, or sequences in terms of their phylogenetic relationships (phylogeography, sensu Avise et al. 1987).

Both the gene frequency and genealogical approaches can be used to estimate the degree of geographic subdivision, the amount of gene flow between populations, and effective population size, all critical elements in forging a synthesis between population genetics and community ecology. Gene-frequency approaches have the advantage of using data that are relatively easy to generate, often for multiple loci; but they lack an explicit historical component. In contrast, the main advantage of genealogical methods is their ability to reconstruct the spatial histories of populations. This includes distinguishing between populations whose size has remained constant and populations that have experienced a recent population expansion. In a geographic context, genealogical data can be used to detect introgression between species, and to identify previously unrecognized cryptic species. Finally, when extended to the members of a community, a genealogical approach makes it possible to test hypotheses about the common processes that generate genetic structure, and the geographic histories of interactions among species.

F_{ST}-Based Approaches

CHARACTERIZING GENETIC STRUCTURE USING F_{ST}. Wright (1931, 1951, 1965) developed the classic theory for portraying genetic structure by partitioning the population-wide inbreeding coefficient into contributions from population substructure (F_{ST}, the fixation index) and nonrandoming mating within subpopulations (F_{IS}). The basic idea is simple: In a subdivided population, individuals are more likely to mate with members of their own subpopulation than with members of other subpopulations. Thus, at the level of the entire population, a subdivided population will have a higher than expected (under completely random mating) frequency of homozygotes.

Wright initially limited his analysis to two levels of structure: subpopulations and the total population, where subpopulations represent panmictic units within the total population. He further assumed that observed genetic structure was a stable feature of a population. However, populations often exhibit structure at a variety of spatial scales (reviewed in Neigel 1997), and genetic structure may only be evident during specific periods of the life cycle (McCauley and Goff 1998). For this reason, more complex hierarchical models of genetic structure have been developed (Nei 1973; Weir and Cockerham 1984).

F_{ST} measures the magnitude of population subdivision in terms of deviations from heterozygosities expected under Hardy-Weinberg equilibrium:

$$F_{ST} = \frac{H_T - \overline{H}_S}{H_T}$$

where H_T is the probability that two alleles drawn at random (with replacement) from the entire population differ in state (i.e., the probability with no population structure), and $\overline{H}_S$ is the probability that two alleles drawn at random from a subpopulation differ in state (which, for a two-allele system, will always be $2p_iq_i$, where p_i is the observed allelic frequency in subpopulation i), averaged over subpopulations. In a completely randomly mating population, $H_T = \overline{H}_S$, and $F_{ST} = 0$. If that population were to become subdivided, with limited migration among subpopulations, then genetic drift would eventually lead to differences in allelic frequencies among subpopulations, and $H_T > \overline{H}_S$. As the magnitude of this difference increases, F_{ST} will approach its maximum value of 1.

It is also possible to define F_{ST} as the standardized variance in allelic frequencies among subpopulations (or any sampling unit). From this perspective, F_{ST} reflects the amount of genetic variance among subpopulations (usually the smallest sampling units) relative to the total variance expected if all subpopulations actually represented a single panmictic unit (Wright 1943, 1951). It is then a small step to think of F-statistics in terms of a nested analysis of variance, in which the distribution of variance of allelic and genotypic frequencies is partitioned within and among sampling units (Weir 1990; Neigel 1997).

With the rapid growth of a database on DNA sequences, techniques have been developed to use this information to characterize genetic structure. For example, the ratio of sequence divergences within and among subpopulations can be used to estimate F_{ST} (reviewed in Hudson et al. 1992).

Other methods explicitly incorporate the nested ANOVA approach by partitioning sequence divergence between alleles into the relative contributions of population subsets from spatially nested samples (AMOVA, Excoffier et al. 1992). It is important to remember that all methods for calculating F_{ST} assume that subpopulations are the same sizes and have equal variances in allelic frequencies (discussed in Whitlock and McCauley 1999). When these assumptions are violated, highly biased inferences about genetic structure and, consequently, gene flow can result (e.g., Palumbi et al. 1997).

INFERRING LEVELS OF GENE FLOW. There are two basic ways that population geneticists estimate gene flow. Direct measurements (sensu Slatkin 1985a) involve the tracking of individual or group movements (e.g., Gerrodette 1981; Burton and Swisher 1984; Olson 1985; Grosberg 1987, 1991; Stoner 1990; Willis and Oliver 1990; Jones et al. 1999; Swearer et al. 1999). In principle, these migration or dispersal patterns could then be translated into estimates of gene flow by determining whether the movements lead to successful breeding within the recipient population. In practice, the difficulties of (1) detecting rare, long-distance movements that can disproportionately contribute to gene flow, (2) tracking small, rare propagules across the expanses of the oceans, and (3) determining whether immigrants successfully reproduce generally doom this direct approach for the vast majority of marine organisms (Hedgecock 1986; Grosberg 1987; Grosberg and Levitan 1992; Johnson and Black 1995; Palumbi 1999).

Indirect methods use the spatial distribution of genetic variation to estimate gene flow, under the assumption that different patterns of dispersal and levels of gene flow will generate distinctive genetic structures at evolutionary equilibrium (Slatkin 1985a). Indirect approaches circumvent some of the logistical problems of direct estimates of gene flow, in part because indirect methods do not require the monitoring of individuals through time. Furthermore, indirect methods only incorporate movements that lead to successful establishment of the genes carried by immigrants, and thus reflect the cumulative effects of gene flow (and perhaps selection), averaged over space and time (Slatkin 1985a). In one sense, this is a virtue of indirect methods; however, indirect methods generally estimate gene flow averaged across subpopulations in an idealized model of migration (Whitlock and McCauley 1999). As such, these estimates almost certainly do not represent actual rates of gene flow everywhere within the total population at a given time and potentially sacrifice crucial details of the processes that produce genetic structure.

Indirect measures of gene flow are expressed in terms of two parameters that are extremely difficult to measure independently: (1) the genetically effective migration rate, m (or the fraction of individuals, on average, that migrate between subpopulations each generation) and (2) the genetically effective population size, N_e (Slatkin 1993; see the section in this chapter entitled Gene Flow, Selection, and Local Adaptation). Roughly speaking, N_e is the size of an idealized population (i.e., stationary dynamics, equal sex ratios, binomial variance in reproductive success) that loses neutral genetic variation due to drift at the same rate as the "real" population (reviewed in Crow and Kimura 1970; Ewens 1982; Whitlock and Barton 1997). The product of N_e and m yields M, the average number of migrants exchanged between subpopulations per generation. As a general rule of thumb, when M exceeds approximately one individual per generation, gene flow—given sufficient time—will eventually offset the diversifying effects of genetic drift (Slatkin 1994). As we discuss in the section Scale of Population Regulation, the trivial levels of genetically effective migration necessary to homogenize allelic frequencies at neutral loci limit the power of gene flow estimates for reckoning demographically significant migration or dispersal.

The literature devoted to inferring levels of gene flow from allelic frequencies is massive, complex, and often arcane (reviewed by Slatkin 1985a; Slatkin and Barton 1989; Cockerham and Weir 1993; Slatkin 1994; Neigel 1997; Bossart and Prowell 1998; Waples 1998; Hutchison and Templeton 1999; Whitlock and McCauley 1999). By far the most popular methods are based on F_{ST}. With the appropriate spatial model of migration (a term we use interchangeably from here on with gene flow), plus a variety of other assumptions we discuss below, F-statistics can be used to estimate M (reviewed in Neigel 1997). The basic and most widely used formula is based on Wright's (1931) island model of migration, and assumes equal likelihood of migration throughout a species range. The relationship between F_{ST} and gene flow ($N_e m$ or M) is

$$F_{ST} \approx \frac{1}{1+4N_e m} \text{ or } N_e m \approx \frac{1}{4}\left(\frac{1}{F_{ST}}-1\right)$$

As values of F_{ST} increase from their theoretical minimum of 0 (which implies that there is no detectable genetic structure and high levels of gene flow) to their maximum of 1 (which implies that subpopulations are fixed for different alleles and there is no gene flow), M declines to 0.

Slatkin (1985b) developed an alternative method for estimating $N_e m$, based on the distribution of alleles uniquely occurring in single subpopulations. The approach builds on the idea that the "lifespan" of such private alleles will depend on the rate at which they arise by mutation (and are lost due to drift) and the rate at which gene flow erases their uniqueness. Thus, at an equilibrium between drift and migration, the distribution of private alleles can be related to migration rate.

ASSUMPTIONS UNDERLYING ESTIMATES OF GENE FLOW. The mathematically simple inverse relationship between F_{ST} and $N_e m$ (= M) makes it easy to forget that this equation rests on many unstated and often difficult to verify assumptions (reviewed in Slatkin and Barton 1989; Neigel 1997; Bossart and Prowell 1998; Waples 1998; Whitlock and McCauley 1999). Populations of many marine species likely violate at least some of these assumptions. Therefore, we explore briefly the nature of these assumptions, and some of the effects of their violation on estimates of gene flow.

The first assumption is that sampling, in terms of (1) number of individuals, (2) number of loci, and (3) spatial scale, can accurately reveal underlying genetic structure. Insufficient sampling of individuals, subpopulations, and loci can introduce substantial error into estimates of F_{ST} (and analogous estimators such as G_{ST} and θ), and consequently M (Weir and Cockerham 1984; Weir 1990; Neigel 1997; Waples 1998; Holsinger 1999; Whitlock and McCauley 1999). Moreover, most F_{ST}-based analyses require a priori specification of hierarchical structure (but see Holsinger and Mason-Gramer 1996). When the scale of sampling (or data partitioning) does not match the scale at which a population exhibits genetic structure, structure may be exaggerated or obscured (Husband and Barrett 1996; Rousset and Raymond 1997; Bohonak 1999). This potentially confounds comparisons between taxa or studies that use different sample sizes, sampling regimes, and loci. Additionally, because the relationship between F_{ST} and M is nonlinear, large values of M are nearly impossible to estimate within several orders of magnitude (Templeton 1998). For these reasons alone, estimates of gene flow based on F_{ST} may have large associated errors.

The second assumption is that migration rates (m) must greatly exceed mutation rates (μ). This is because mutation reduces estimates of F_{ST} (Crow and Aoki 1984), and consequently upwardly biases inferred levels of gene flow (Neigel 1997). For most allozyme markers with low mutation rates, this effect will be minimal with respect to other sources of error. However, this assumption will almost certainly be violated for more rapidly evolving markers such as microsatellites. This prompted Slatkin (1995) to develop a statistic, R_{ST}, analogous to F_{ST}, that incorporates a stepwise mutation process potentially applicable to microsatellite loci. Neigel (1997) critically analyzed alternatives that putatively control for the effects of mutation on F_{ST}-based estimates of gene flow inferred from DNA sequence data. He concluded that when significant mutation affects a marker, genealogy-based methods, based on the ancestral-descendant relationships of alleles, may have considerable advantages over gene-frequency approaches (see the section entitled Genealogical Approaches).

Third, the model assumes that there is no selection on the marker alleles (i.e., they are neutral). In theory, weak selection should not greatly bias estimates of gene flow, as long as selection on the marker alleles does not vary spatially (Slatkin and Barton 1989). However, several empirical studies on marine systems suggest that selection on allozymes (and perhaps other markers) may strongly influence the spatial distribution of allelic variation (Koehn et al. 1980; Burton 1986; Karl and Avise 1992; Johannesson et al. 1995; reviewed in Avise 1994; Hilbish 1996; Bohonak 1999). Selection can either increase or decrease estimates of F_{ST} (and consequently inferred levels of gene flow). For example, undetected spatially varying selection on marker loci can enhance differences among subpopulations over that expected for neutral markers. On the other hand, balancing selection on genetic markers may spatially homogenize allelic frequencies, reducing structure at the loci under selection and creating the illusion of high inferred levels of gene flow (Slatkin and Barton 1989; Karl and Avise 1992).

Fourth, the simple formula that relates F_{ST} to $N_e m$ builds on a classic island model of dispersal in which a species consists of a large number of equally sized subpopulations, all of which have an equal probability of exchanging migrants. As we discuss in the section Genetic Homogeneity, this may be a realistic approximation of dispersal in those species for which the scale of larval dispersal substantially exceeds the scale over which there are suitable patches of habitat. However, migration patterns for those species that live along coastlines or hydrothermal vent systems, especially those whose propagules have limited dispersal potential, may better fit a one-dimensional stepping-stone model of dispersal, in which migrants only move between adjacent linearly arrayed patches of habitat (Slatkin 1993; Vrijenhoek 1997). Similarly, for species with limited dispersal that live in island groups, a two-dimensional stepping-stone model may be a better approximation of actual migration patterns. In both classes of stepping-stone migration model, genetic differentiation should increase with the distance separating subpopulations and inferred gene flow should attenuate (Kimura and Weiss 1964). In theory, the exact migration model should minimally bias estimates of gene flow based on F_{ST} (Slatkin and Barton 1989); however, with more complex patterns of gene flow among subpopulations, the failure to sample on a scale or pattern corresponding to the existing genetic structure can substantially bias F_{ST}-based estimates of gene flow (Husband and Barrett 1996).

Finally, estimates of gene flow based on F_{ST}-like statistics (and even coalescent methods, as described in the next section) assume that populations are at a genetic equilibrium between the homogenizing effects of gene flow and the diversifying effects of genetic drift (Felsenstein 1982). In other words, historical effects no longer leave a signature on genetic structure. As we discuss in some detail in later sections, when populations have not reached an equilibrium between gene flow and drift, inferred gene flow may be highly biased (Whitlock and McCauley 1999), and non-F_{ST}-based methods may be more suitable (Slatkin and Barton 1989; Neigel 1997; Hutchison and Templeton 1999). For example, a large difference in allele frequencies between subpopulations can reflect either restricted gene flow (the equilibrium inference, as assumed by most F_{ST}-based methods), or a recent founding event or bottleneck (McCauley 1993; Hutchison and Templeton 1999). Conversely, subpopulations could be genetically similar either because they are linked by high levels of contemporary gene flow (the equilibrium inference), or because they were relatively recently isolated from each other (Felsenstein 1982).

THE APPROACH TO EQUILIBRIUM AND WHY IT MATTERS. Under an island model of migration, the time, t (in generations), it takes for F_{ST} to approach the equilibrium between the homogenizing effects of gene flow and the diversifying effects of genetic drift is related to N_e and m by the following expression (Crow and Aoki 1984):

$$\frac{1}{2m + \dfrac{1}{2N_e}}$$

For high migration rates and small effective population sizes, this equilibrium may be approached quite rapidly. However, for the large populations that may typify many species of marine invertebrates, or for the low migration rates characteristic of many clonal forms (Jackson 1986), this time may be on the order of thousands, or even millions, of generations. In addition, a stepping-stone, as opposed to island, pattern of migration can considerably lengthen the time it takes to reach this equilibrium (Slatkin 1993).

This raises the important question of whether many marine invertebrate populations ever reach genetic equilibrium throughout their ranges. Imagine under an island-migration model a population with $N_e = 10^5$, $m = 0.0001$ (i.e., $N_e m = 10$ migrants exchanged between subpopulations), and with a generation time of one year. Following a perturbation to migration patterns, it would take F_{ST} roughly 5000 years to reach its eventual genetic equilibrium (Whitlock and McCauley 1999). As we discuss later, many populations of marine organisms—particularly those more complex patterns of gene flow, larger populations, or lower levels of gene flow—may never have time to attain fully this equilibrium between gene flow and drift before being perturbed again. To the extent this is true, patterns of genetic structure in many species of marine invertebrate may not reflect contemporary levels of gene flow. For example, the last glacial period, approximately 10,000–12, 000 years ago, made many intertidal and nearshore temperate and polar habitats unsuitable for numerous species, and drove their distributions equatorially. It also lowered sea level in the tropics, potentially strengthening the isolation between tropical island systems and basins (Paulay 1990; Benzie 1999). Depending upon the period of isolation of these populations, the magnitude of isolation, and their prior histories of isolation, the effect of these glacial periods may be either to inflate or reduce observed F_{ST}'s over that expected at equilibrium between contemporary gene flow and drift.

The fact that allelic frequencies and, consequently, genetic parameters such as F_{ST} may vary even over ecological time scales further cautions against taking estimates of gene flow at face value. For example, a growing number of studies show that allelic frequencies vary from generation-to-generation at a particular site, even in species with extensive dispersal potential (e.g., Johnson and Black 1982, 1984a,b; Watts et al. 1990; Kordos and Burton 1993; Lessios et al. 1994; Edmands et al. 1996; Li and Hedgecock 1998; Ruckelshaus 1998). Thus, historical (e.g., vicariance, founder events/range expansions, rare bouts of dispersal) and demographic (e.g., asexual propagation, low recruitment rates or long generation times, overlapping generations, and temporal variance in reproductive or recruitment rates) processes may be as important as levels of contemporary gene flow in determining the current genetic structure of some marine species (Felsenstein 1982; Hedgecock 1986; Ayre 1990; Cunningham and

Collins 1994, 1998; Palumbi 1995; Hilbish 1996; Benzie 1999; Hutchison and Templeton 1999).

EFFECTIVE POPULATION SIZE. N_e, or effective population size, is a crucial element of any analysis of the relationship between genetic structure and ecology. N_e is one of the two parameters (the other being m, the per generation migration rate) that together determine gene flow. Moreover, the value of N_e determines the relative importance of selection, drift, and mutation, and especially a population's potential for long-term adaptive genetic response to changing selective regimes (Hill 1985; also discussed here in the next section). Selection and mutation generally play a relatively less important role than drift and gene flow in determining gene frequencies in populations with a small effective population size. In addition, populations with a small N_e typically reach an equilibrium between gene flow and genetic drift relatively quickly. Such populations may be far more prone to extinction due to demographic stochasticity, reduction in gene diversity, or accumulation of deleterious mutations (Lynch and Gabriel 1990; Lande 1993, 1994; Hastings and Harrison 1994; Lynch et al. 1995).

In species that exhibit some combination of high individual variance in reproductive success, large changes in population size, or local extinctions and recolonizations, N_e can be much smaller than the censused number of individuals in a population (Nei and Tajima 1981; Waples 1989; Gilpin 1991; Nunney 1996, 1999; reviewed in Luikart and England 1999; also see the later section Range Expansion and Population Growth). It is notoriously difficult to obtain the demographic data necessary to estimate effective population size. However, temporal and spatial variation in allelic frequencies (Nei and Tajima 1981; Pollack 1983; Waples 1989; Li and Hedgecock 1998), as well as linkage disequilibrium (Hill 1981) and heterozygote excess (Pudovkin et al. 1996) can also be used to estimate N_e (given many of the assumptions cited above).

The few genetically based estimates of N_e for marine populations have so far yielded some unexpected results. Analysis of temporal variation in allelic frequencies in oysters indicates that the effective numbers of breeders in a population may be only a few percent, or less, of the censused population (Hedgecock et al. 1992; Li and Hedgecock 1998). Other high fecundity free-spawners, such as sea urchins, may also have surprisingly small effective population sizes (e.g., Edmands et al. 1996). Nunney (1996) contended that there is no theoretical reason to expect that high fecundity predisposes a population to low N_e relative to its census population size, and that reported differences may be largely methodological. However, Li and Hedgecock (1998) countered that the discrepancy between N_e and census population size in free-spawning marine invertebrates is not necessarily an artifact of the way N_e is inferred, but instead results from enormous among-individual variation in their genetic contributions to the next generation. It remains to be seen how general this pattern is. If small N_e is widespread in numerically large marine populations, then it has profound implications for how they will respond to selection.

GENE FLOW, SELECTION, AND LOCAL ADAPTATION. Gene flow hastens the spread of alleles across a species' range. In so doing, gene flow can either augment or counteract the effects of selection, depending on the spatial scale over which selection varies (Slatkin 1985a; 1994). What follows is a tremendous oversimplification of how gene flow and selection interact; the aim is to give a basic picture. For neutral alleles, in an island model of population structure, if $N_e m$ substantially exceeds one migrant per generation, then gene flow will ultimately prevent local genetic differentiation at neutral loci. Adding the effects of selection to those of gene flow gets complicated fast, especially when populations exhibit complex genetic structure and extinction–recolonization dynamics (Nunney 1999). In the simplest form, if different alleles are favored in different subpopulations, then the equilibrium frequency (p) of an allele favored in a subpopulation will be $1 - {}^s/_m$, where s is the selection coefficient in favor of that allele and m is the immigration rate of the alternative, unfavored allele, when $s > m$ (Haldane 1930; Nagylaki 1975). (When $s < m$, $p = 0$.) The time it takes to reach this equilibrium is approximately.

So, the details aside, gene flow can offset some or all of the differentiating effects of drift and spatially variable selection. When gene flow among subpopulations inhabiting distinct selective regimes is high, local adaptation is less likely to occur (Endler 1977; Hedgecock 1986; Johnson and Black 1995). Selection should favor either a reduction in dispersal potential or the evolution of phenotypic plasticity. Conversely, when gene flow among subpopulations is low, small and persistent differences in selective regimes among subpopulations can eventually lead to their adaptive genetic divergence (but see Holt and Gomulkiewicz 1997).

Genealogical Approaches

F_{ST}, GENE GENEALOGIES, AND COALESCENCE. Many evolutionary biologists are familiar with using DNA sequence information to reconstruct species-level phylogenetic relationships. Our concern in this chapter is with depicting patterns of genetic structure (and gene flow) *within* species. F-statistics and their analogues use the spatial distribution of allelic frequencies, usually at multiple loci, to portray genetic structure and to estimate rates of migration. F_{ST}-based approaches explicitly assume that the primary determinant of genetic structure is a balance between gene flow and drift, and do not consider that every pair of alleles in a species has descended from a common ancestor sometime in the past. Ignoring the relationships between alleles is a necessary evil for some kinds of data, such as studies based on allozyme variation. However, for the last two decades, restriction enzyme analysis and direct sequencing have made it possible to use DNA sequences to characterize genetic structure. Sequence information has two major advantages over allozymes. First, allozyme studies reveal differences only at the amino acid level, whereas DNA studies can detect substitutions that do not affect the amino acid sequence. Second, allozyme studies do not identify which amino acid has changed in a protein, making it impossible to infer relationships between alleles. Sequence information, on the other hand, can be used to deduce genealogical relationships between alleles by any of a number of standard phylogenetic approaches (Hudson 1990; Avise 1994).

The development of coalescence theory has provided a powerful framework for interpreting these gene genealogies in a population genetic framework. This framework has generated novel insights into patterns of genetic structure and the historical mechanisms that can generate genetic structure (e.g., Hudson 1990; Barton and Wilson 1995; Templeton 1998). Coalescent theory analyzes the structure of the tree moving backward in time (i.e., from the top of the tree to its base), with time usually measured in number of generations. Each of the nodes represents the point in time at which two allelic lineages "coalesce" or merge in their most recent common ancestor.

In this section, we first introduce a coalescent approach for estimating gene flow from gene genealogies. We then consider how genealogical approaches are useful for diagnosing especially deep divergences (reciprocal monophyly) between geographically separated populations, and the importance of reciprocal monophyly for reconstructing the history of genetic subdivision. We conclude this section by analyzing some of the crucial differences between intraspecific versus interspecific phylogenies, and between gene genealogies and population phylogenies.

CHARACTERIZING GEOGRAPHIC STRUCTURE AND GENE FLOW USING GENE GENEALOGIES. In DNA-based studies, alleles are defined as sets of homologous sequences that differ by at least one substitution. If the sequences are from mitochondrial genes, alleles are referred to as haplotypes. The first step in a phylogenetically based analysis of intraspecific genetic structure is to reconstruct the genealogical relationships among alleles using parsimony or some alternative method (reviewed in Swofford et al. 1996). These gene genealogies can also be referred to as gene trees. The geographic distribution of the sampled alleles can then be mapped onto a genealogy, and the pattern and degree of association between genealogical and geographic structure assessed (see the section Genetic Homogeneity later in this chapter). For example, if groups of closely related alleles are consistently found in the same geographically restricted areas, then limited gene flow over long periods of time is the simplest explanation.

Slatkin and Maddison (1989, 1990) were the first to develop a coalescent approach to estimating migration rates from gene genealogies. Their method considers the collection locality of an allele as a character state. If closely related alleles are collected in different locations, then parsimony will infer a migration event between the locations. Slatkin and Maddison's method uses parsimony to calculate the minimum number of migration events across the entire gene genealogy. This method is easiest to employ if phylogenetic methods find a single gene genealogy; however, it is possible to calculate the mean number of migration events across alternative

trees using MacClade 3.0 (Maddison and Maddison 1992). Slatkin and Maddison (1989, 1990) used a simulation approach that assumes both evolutionary equilibrium and constant population size to relate the minimum number of inferred migration events on a gene genealogy to M (defined above). The method is easy to apply, and recombination has surprisingly little effect on estimates of M (Hudson et al. 1992).

Slatkin and Maddison's parsimony approach has one conspicuous limitation: it does not consider variation in branch lengths when reconstructing migration events. In other words, the method implicitly assumes that the probability of a migration event is independent of branch length. This is unrealistic because longer branch lengths indicate that more time has passed between nodes. Recently developed maximum likelihood methods are more realistic because they assume that migration events are more likely on long branches than on short ones (Nath and Griffiths 1996; Beerli and Felsenstein 1999). However, it remains to be seen how well these methods perform when applied to real data.

As with F_{ST}-based measures, coalescent approaches can use randomization methods to test whether a reduced level of gene flow between populations represents significant geographical subdivision. For example, if the minimum number of migration events between two populations is significantly lower than expected from a distribution of random trees, then the degree of population subdivision is considered significant (Maddison and Slatkin 1991).

THE HISTORY OF POPULATION SUBDIVISION AND THE IMPORTANCE OF RECIPROCAL MONOPHYLY. Significant geographic subdivision can occur between populations that still occasionally exchange individuals, but are at an equilibrium between gene flow and drift. However, significant genetic structure can also result when an historical event has permanently interrupted gene flow between the populations being considered. These historical interruptions of gene flow violate the assumption of equilibrium that are at the heart of traditional population genetic theory. Although allele-frequency approaches can be used to detect nonequilibrium situations (e.g., Slatkin 1993), these approaches offer few insights into the historical processes that produce genetic structure.

Genealogical methods, are particularly well-suited to detecting ancient interruption of gene flow. Whenever gene flow between populations ceases, a combination of mutation and random extinction of lineages (lineage sorting) will eventually generate reciprocal monophyly, where alleles from each location form a monophyletic group relative to the alleles collected from the other location (Figure 3.1; Neigel and Avise 1986; Avise 1994; see the section Range Expansion and Population Growth, later in this chapter). In terms of coalescence theory, reciprocal monophyly occurs when the alleles from each locality each have a unique common ancestor, meaning that they coalesce with each other before they coalesce with alleles in the other subpopulation. This process takes on the order of $4N_e$ generations (Neigel and Avise 1986).

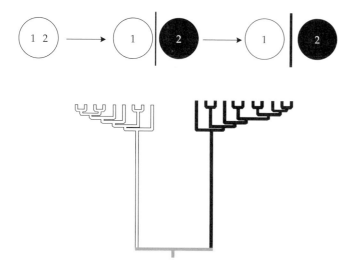

Figure 3.1 The establishment of reciprocal monophyly in subdivided populations. Reciprocal monophyly takes on the order of $4N_e$ generations, and results when a combination of mutation and lineage sorting in a pair of isolated subpopulations eventually causes all of the alleles in each subpopulation to be more closely related to each other than they are to any alleles in the other subpopulation.

The establishment of reciprocal monophyly has several important implications for population and community ecologists. First, reciprocal monophyly between spatially disjunct subpopulations demonstrates a lack of genetically effective migration between the subpopulations. Second, because reciprocal monophyly takes a considerable time to evolve, its existence indicates that both subpopulations have resisted local extinction for at least that much time (Cunningham and Collins 1998; discussed further in the section entitled Community Assembly and the History of Species Interactions).

Finally, when populations isolated for a long period of time come into secondary contact, F_{ST}-based approaches should generally reveal significant subdivision if the secondary contact is recent, or along a sharply defined hybrid zone. One of the best-known marine examples is the zone of contact between Gulf and Atlantic populations of numerous distantly related marine species at Cape Canaveral in Eastern Florida (reviewed in Avise 1992). In this case , F_{ST}-based approaches reveal significant geographic subdivision, but cannot distinguish whether the genetic subdivision is due to an extended historical interruption of gene flow, or an ongoing but significant reduction of gene flow. Gene genealogies, however, reveal that the contacting populations are reciprocally monophyletic, and clarify the status of the populations as evolutionarily independent units (Cunningham and Collins 1994).

GENE GENEALOGIES VERSUS SPECIES-LEVEL PHYLOGENIES. Like species-level phylogenies, *intra*specific gene genealogies can be inferred from DNA sequences or restriction fragment profiles using conventional search methods implemented in such widely used software packages as PAUP* 4.0 (Swofford 1999) or PHYLIP (Felsenstein 1999). There are, however, two

important differences between species-level phylogenies and *intra*specific gene genealogies that are crucial to constructing and interpreting gene genealogies (reviewed by Crandall and Templeton 1996).

First and most importantly, the nodes in *inter*-specific phylogenetic trees represent ancestral populations that have gone extinct. In contrast, truly ancestral alleles are almost always found in *intra*specific gene genealogies. Although counterintuitive, this situation is expected because not every actual bifurcation in an *intra*specific gene genealogy is reflected by a mutation. Consider a mother who passes on her mitochondria to two daughters. Only the first daughter's mtDNA experiences a mutation, whereas the other daughter's does not. The first daughter's offspring will inherit a derived allele, while the second daughter's offspring will inherit the ancestral allele. In this way, alleles that are identical to the true ancestor remain in the population. These ancestral alleles are easily identified in parsimony analyses because they (1) have no unique substitutions (i.e., autapomorphies), (2) are deeply nested, and (3) are often quite common in the population (Figure 3.2). When one searches for gene genealogies using parsimony or other method, zero-length branches should be collapsed to reflect the existence of actual ancestors in the population (Figure 3.2B).

Second, the traditional outgroup method for rooting interspecific phylogenies is not reliable for intraspecific gene genealogies. This is because the distance to the outgroup for an intraspecific gene genealogy is vastly greater than the distance between individuals in the population (Castelloe and

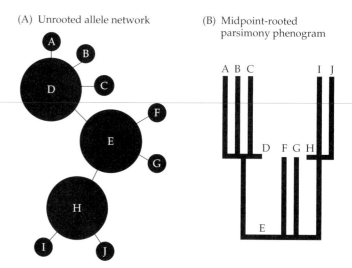

Figure 3.2 (A) An unrooted allele (or haplotype) genealogy. The letters denote a unqiue haplotype, the size of the circles corresponds to the relative frequency of that haplotype, and the lines connecting the circles represent a single base pair substitution. (B) Midpoint-rooted parsimony phenogram of the same genealogy shown in (A) from PAUP* (Swofford 1999), with zero-length branches collapsed. As expected from the retention of ancestral haplotypes in population-level genealogies, haplotypes D, E, and H have no branch length of their own.

Templeton 1994; Crandall and Templeton 1996). This means that any site along the outgroup branch may have experienced multiple substitutions, thereby erasing the historical signal [similar to "long branch attraction" in interspecific phylogenies (Felsenstein 1978)]. One option is to present a gene genealogy as an unrooted allele network (Avise 1994; Crandall 1994; Smouse 1998). Alternatively, there are several methods that use coalescent theory to root the network (Castelloe and Templeton 1994; Griffiths and Tavaré 1994). These methods build on the premise that the oldest alleles should be the most deeply nested in the network, because they will have had more time to generate descendants.

GENE GENEALOGIES VERSUS POPULATION PHYLOGENIES AND F_{ST}-BASED APPROACHES. The preceding discussion focused on gene genealogies based on alleles sampled from *individuals*. There are, however, many cases in which populations, not individuals, represent the taxonomic units in a phylogeny. For allozyme data, the genealogical relationships between individual alleles are unknown. Instead, allele frequencies are used to generate distances between populations (e.g., Cavalli-Sforza and Edwards 1967; Nei 1972), and population phylogenies are inferred from these distances. Population phylogenies can be built from almost any kind of frequency data, such as DNA allele frequencies, microsatellite allelic frequencies, or—of course—allozymes.

Unlike gene genealogies, population phylogenies have the benefit of being estimated from multiple loci, and usually from relatively large samples. In contrast, most gene genealogies are inferred from relatively small samples of individuals at a single locus. It is important, however, to keep in mind that a population phylogeny does not necessarily predict the relationship of any two individuals from distinct populations. If there has been recent migration between long-isolated subpopulations, the populations will exhibit sharp differences in allele frequencies, even though some individuals in the two populations share closely related alleles due to the recent migration (e.g., Van Syoc 1994). Moroever, because population phylogenies are based on distances inferred from allele frequencies, they are subject to many of the same pitfalls as pairwise F_{ST}'s calculated from gene frequencies (see F_{ST}-Based Approaches).

On the other hand, gene genealogies represent the history of only a single locus, and are not necessarily equivalent to organismal or population-level phylogenies. For several reasons, the genealogy inferred from one gene may be contradicted by other loci collected from the same individual. For example, interspecific hybridization can lead to mitochondrial introgression from one species into another, leading nuclear and mitochondrial genes from the same individual to have very different histories (e.g., Lamb and Avise 1986; Quesada et al. 1995). Similarly, in recombining loci, different parts of the same gene may have distinct histories (Slatkin 1994). This difficulty can be overcome by generating gene genealogies from multiple loci. When multiple loci yield congruent patterns, then confidence in the inferred history is greatly increased.

Conclusions

With the appropriate significance tests (reviewed in Weir 1996; Neigel 1997), F_{ST} and analogues [e.g., G_{ST} (Nei 1973), θ_{ST} (Weir and Cockerham 1984), N_{ST} (Lynch and Crease 1990), and R_{ST} (Slatkin 1993)] provide simple indices of the magnitude and scale over which populations exhibit significant genetic structure, based on readily obtainable data. F_{ST}-based approaches are best-suited to large samples, with data from multiple, independent loci (Slatkin and Barton 1989; Neigel 1997). F_{ST}-based approaches have the virtue (and evil) of reducing potentially very complex genetic structures into simple metrics, facilitating comparisons on the one hand, and obscuring differences on the other (Gillespie 1998). The fact that F-statistics and inferences of gene flow may be time-, locus-, and scale-dependent is also both a blessing and a curse. This sort of variation can provide critical insights into the ways that mating patterns, dispersal, and selection influence genetic structure. However, this variation cautions against taking estimates of gene flow at face value, especially when they involve different spatial and temporal scales, different loci, and different species.

Perhaps the most important limitation of approaches based on the spatial distribution of allelic and haplotypic frequencies is that estimates of gene flow assume that a population is in evolutionary equilibrium with respect to gene flow and genetic drift, and that historical effects no longer persist. Some genealogical methods for estimating migration rates and the magnitude of genetic subdivision make similar equilibrium assumptions, and the number of loci and individuals that are usually sampled limits their power. However, to the extent that populations of marine organisms deviate from migration-drift equilibria, genealogical approaches at the level of the individual and populations may be essential for deciphering the imprint of history on genetic structure and the nature and outcomes of species interactions.

INTERPRETING PATTERNS OF GENETIC STRUCTURE IN MARINE POPULATIONS

The main problem with interpreting genetic patterns in natural populations arises because a particular pattern may be generated by both historical and contemporary processes, acting singly or combined, at different spatial and temporal scales. Many of the methods for detecting patterns of genetic structure and inferring gene flow assume that the genetic signature of past historical events has been erased by a combination of migration and drift. The assumption of an equilibrium between migration and genetic drift also underlies the most important generalization in the evolutionary genetics of benthic marine organisms. Larval dispersal ability should be the primary determinant of genetic structure (Palumbi 1995; Bohonak 1999), and ultimately rates and patterns of speciation and extinction (Jablonski and Lutz 1983; Palumbi 1994; cf. Hedgecock 1986).

Of course, the pattern of genetic structure at equilibrium depends on many factors, including developmental mode, larval behavior, circulation patterns, distribution of suitable habitats, and geographical scale of sampling (reviewed in Lessios et al. 1998; Benzie 1999; Bohonak 1999). At one extreme, a species with exceptionally broadly dispersing larvae should be panmictic over all but perhaps the largest spatial scales. Species with somewhat more limited dispersal potential may show panmixia over fine and moderate spatial scales, and isolation by distance (sensu Wright 1943; Malécot 1968) at much larger scales. At the other extreme, species with effectively nondispersing larvae should show a pattern of isolation by distance at all but the very finest spatial scales.

In the most recent review of the subject, Bohonak (1999) found a statistically significant relationship between larval dispersal ability and degree of geographic subdivision (measured by F_{ST}). However, like his predecessors (e.g., Burton 1983; Hedgecock 1986; Ayre 1990; Palumbi 1994, 1995; Hilbish 1996; Cunningham and Collins 1998; Ruckelshaus 1998), Bohonak (1999) identified numerous cases in which dispersal potential only weakly predicted genetic structure (also see Cunningham and Collins 1994, 1998; Hellberg 1994; Marko 1998; Benzie 1999). These exceptions emphasize that our understanding of how contemporary processes generate genetic structure in the sea is, not surprisingly, incomplete. Moreover, several lines of evidence suggest that the imprint of historical processes on contemporary genetic structure may be both pervasive and persistent. For example, genetic breaks may not correspond to known barriers to dispersal (reviewed in Cunningham and Collins 1994, 1998; Shulman and Bermingham 1995; Palumbi 1997; Benzie 1999), genetic continuity may occur where there are no obvious contemporary dispersal pathways (e.g., Palumbi et al. 1997), and phylogeographic analysis may reveal that sister taxa are nonadjacent (e.g., Marko 1998).

One of the best-studied marine examples of this kind concerns the distribution of genetic variation among benthic invertebrates along the coast of the southeastern United States (also see examples from the Indo-Pacific in Benzie 1999). Here, many species, regardless of their dispersal potential, are subdivided into two reciprocally monophyletic populations in the Atlantic and the Gulf of Mexico, with a narrow hybrid zone at Cape Canaveral (reviewed in Avise 1992, 1994). It is not certain whether local adaptation or oceanographic barriers maintain the genetic distinctions between these populations (see Hare and Avise 1996). What is certain is that a massive vicariant event interrupted gene flow for many co-occurring taxa, regardless of their dispersal ability, and that larval dispersal has yet to restore genetic homogeneity between the Gulf and Atlantic populations, even in those species with broadly dispersing larvae.

In this section, we analyze some of the problems of distinguishing the contributions that historical and contemporary processes make to genetic structure. We first evaluate from equilibrium and nonequilibrium perspectives the two simplest and most extreme patterns expected at genetic equilibrium: genetic homogeneity and isolation by distance. We note that true uniformity may be difficult to detect, and that apparent examples of both homogeneity and isolation by distance may reflect the operation of a mixture of historical, as well as contemporary, processes. We then review some statistical methods that can be used to identify historical contributions to genetic structure, especially the effects of range expansions (and contractions) and population growth.

Genetic Homogeneity

The lack of obvious physical barriers to dispersal in many of the world's oceans led early marine population geneticists to predict that species with broadly dispersing larvae should exhibit little genetic structure across their ranges (reviewed in Burton 1983; Hedgecock 1986; Benzie 1999). The presence of larvae from near-shore species in the middle of the Atlantic and Pacific Oceans reinforced this expectation (Scheltema 1986), and several recent genetic studies on fish (reviewed in Graves 1998; Waples 1998) and invertebrates suggest that broadly dispersing larvae (and adults) can maintain genetic cohesiveness over large distances. For example, in an allozyme study of a solitary coral (*Paracyathus stearnsii*) with planktonic larvae, Hellberg (1996) found no significant geographic subdivision over thousands of kilometers along the West Coast of the United States. Similarly, both solitary and clonal forms of the freely spawning sea anemone *Anthopleura elegantissima* lack significant genetic structure over the same geographic range (McFadden et al. 1997). Perhaps the most spectacular and best-documented example of genetic homogeneity concerns the sea urchin *Echinothrix diadema* (Lessios et al. 1998). *E. diadema* is one of the few species whose distribution spans the Eastern Pacific Barrier (EPB), 5400 km of abyssal water without any shallow habitats that could serve as stepping stones for dispersal. Neither nuclear (allozymes) nor mitochondrial markers reveal any geographic structure reflecting restricted gene flow across the Eastern Pacific Barrier, leading Lessios et al. (1998) to propose that El Niño events propel larvae across the EPB sufficiently often to homogenize genetic structure at this vast scale.

Equilibrium explanations invoking panmixia over broad geographic expanses should, however, be interpreted cautiously for several reasons. First, in several cases, extension of a sampling regime to include the entire range of a species changed the initial inference of panmixia and extensive gene flow. For instance, allozyme studies of genetic structure in the free-spawning giant clam *Tridacna gigas* (Benzie and Williams 1992) and the starfish *Linckia laevigata* (Williams and Benzie 1996) revealed little genetic differentiation over thousands of kilometers in Australia. In both cases, expanded sampling revealed significant geographic subdivision (Benzie and Williams 1995; Williams and Benzie 1998). Similarly, Palumbi and Wilson (1990) reported that mitochondrial DNA diversity was homogeneous over a range of 1,500 km in the sea urchin *Strongylocentrotus purpuratus*. Wider sampling, however, revealed subtle but significant genetic differentiation between two California locations south of Point Conception (Edmands et al. 1996).

Second, some early reports of broad genetic uniformity based on allozymes have been contradicted by subsequent analysis using DNA markers (reviewed in Hilbish 1996). Buroker's (1983) allozyme study of the American oyster *Crassostrea virginica* is a classic example. Buroker (1983) reported panmixia from Georgia to Texas; however, subsequent analysis using mitochondrial (Reeb and Avise 1990) and nuclear DNA markers (Karl and Avise 1992) showed reciprocal monophyly between the Atlantic and the Gulf of Mexico. Whether there is geographic structure in the allozyme dataset is debatable (Cunningham and Collins 1994); however, there is no doubt that in the absence of migration allozyme frequencies can fail to reach genetic equilibrium even after millions of years of isolation. For example, geminate pairs of the sea urchin genus *Diadema* (Bermingham and Lessios 1993) and the snapping shrimp *Alpheus* (Knowlton et al. 1993) show no significant allozyme divergence on either side of the Isthmus of Panama. In both cases, mitochondrial DNA showed deep divergences whereas allozymes did not (reviewed in Cunningham and Collins 1994). Similarly, allozymes failed to reveal any genetic structure across the Indo-Pacific in the sea star *Linckia laevigata* (Williams and Benzie 1996), whereas a subsequent analysis using mtDNA revealed significant differentiation among some populations (Williams and Benzie 1997).

Finally, there are several surprising examples of genetic uniformity that challenge equilibrium explanations, because they occur in species with demersal larvae and limited dispersal potential. These include an allozyme study of North Sea and Irish Sea populations of the sea anemone *Urticina equs* (Solé-Cava et al. 1994), and mitochondrial DNA analyses of genetic structure in three benthic invertebrates found on both sides of the North Atlantic: the gastropods *Nucella lapillus* and *Littorina obtusata,* and the isopod *Idotea baltica* (Wares et al., in press). These populations may currently be panmictic over these regional scales; however, their dispersal potential suggests that they should exhibit isolation by distance (see the next section). Consequently, nonequilibrium alternatives should be seriously considered (Slatkin 1993). For example, if a vicariant event recently subdivided the formerly panmictic North and Irish Sea populations of *U. equs*, divergence in allozymes due to drift may not have had time to accumulate to detectable levels (Solé-Cava et al. 1994).

Isolation by Distance

If the geographic range of a species is large relative to the dispersal potential of its propagules, then genetic drift will lead to divergence between subpopulations, even at equilibrium (isolation by distance, sensu Wright 1943; Malécot 1968). Under this isolation-by-distance scenario, the relationship between genetic differentiation and spatial separation of subpopulations can be described in terms the $\log_{10}$ of $\hat{M}$ (the amount of inferred gene flow between pairs of populations as defined above) versus the $\log_{10}$ of geographic distance. At equilibrium, this relationship should have a characteristic slope, the value of which depends upon (1) whether gene flow follows a one- or two-dimensional stepping-stone model (Kimura and Weiss 1964) and (2) the spatial distribution and

separation of suitable habitats (Slatkin 1993; Hellberg 1996; Hutchison and Templeton 1999). Values of $\hat{M}$ can be estimated by any of the methods described earlier (in the sections Inferring Levels of Gene Flow and The History of Population Subdivision and the Importance of Reciprocal Monophyly; Slatkin 1993). Isolation by distance can also be detected using spatial autocorrelation (e.g., McFadden 1996), which circumvents some of the scale-dependent biases of *F*-statistics, or by nested clade analysis (Templeton 1994, 1998). A full discussion of these methods is beyond the scope of this paper.

The pattern of isolation by distance should be most apparent in species that live in continuously distributed habitats and whose propagules have limited dispersal potential (e.g., Ayre and Dufty 1994; reviewed in Knowlton and Jackson 1993). For instance, the cup coral *Balanophyllia elegans* internally broods large, sexually produced, demersal larvae, and lives in the shallow subtidal and low intertidal along the West Coast of North America (Gerrodette 1981; Fadlallah 1983). Hellberg (1994, 1995, 1996) found a highly significant negative relationship between genetic ($\hat{M}$, inferred from allozymes) and geographic distance in *B. elegans*. Over scales less than 50 km, the 95% confidence intervals of this slope include the predicted value of 1.0 for a one-dimensional stepping-stone model at equilibrium between limited larval dispersal and genetic drift (Hellberg 1995). However, beyond approximately 50 km the magnitude of genetic differentiation no longer increased (Hellberg 1994, 1995). Similar observations in marine systems of the genetic signal of isolation by distance fading at larger regional scales occur in the intertidal gastropod *Nucella emarginata* (Marko 1998), the splash-zone harpacticoid copepod *Tigriopus californicus* (reviewed in Burton 1998), and the mangrove littorine *Littoraria cingulata* (Johnson and Black 1998).

The failure to find a pattern consistent with isolation by distance at larger scales may be due to an historical disruption of genetic structure, caused by events such as the Pleistocene glaciations in the Northern Hemisphere. Following such a disruption, neighboring populations should achieve equilibrium before more distant ones. The resulting pattern of genetic structure could be quite complex, especially when the historical events produce multiple barriers to dispersal, across which reequilibration occurs at different rates. In fact, Hellberg (1995) estimated that the time to reach an equilibrium between migration and gene flow in *B. elegans* is on the order of 40,000 years. Because this exceeds the amount of time between major climatically induced fluctuations in sea level, temperate species such as *B. elegans* and *N. emaginata*, whose larvae have a very limited capacity for dispersal, may only rarely reach an equilibrium between migration and gene flow throughout their ranges.

Taken together, these examples imply that even when there is a significant relationship between the magnitude of genetic subdivision and geographic distance at some spatial scales, historical processes may contribute to the pattern at other spatial scales. Furthermore, apparent isolation by distance can be generated by distinctly nonequilibrium process-

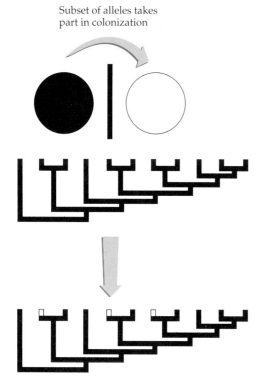

Subset of alleles takes
part in colonization

Figure 3.3 The effects of range expansions or long-distance dispersal on gene genealogies. When a source population (in black) colonizes a new area (in white), the newly founded population will likely contain a subset of the haplotypic diversity in the source population. Thus, the newly founded population will be less diverse than the source population, and the haplotypes in the newly founded population will be phylogenetically nested within haplotypes of the source population (bottom panel).

es (Slatkin 1993; Barton and Wilson 1995). For example, in a widely ranging species that consists of several reciprocally monophyletic populations inhabiting geographically restricted areas, genetic distances between areas will tend to be large, whereas distances within areas will tend to be small. This can produce a regional pattern that resembles isolation by distance at equilibrium, despite the absence of any ongoing migration among areas.

Range Expansion and Population Growth

We have argued that, at least in temperate regions, the ranges of many nearshore species of marine organisms are unlikely to be static over the periods necessary to establish a range-wide equilibrium between gene flow and drift. It is possible to use information about genetic structure to reconstruct the history of range expansions (and contractions). This is because, after a species expands its range—whether by way of gradual expansion or long-distance colonization—the newly colonized area will generally carry only a subset of the alleles in the source population (Figure 3.3; Hewitt 1996; Templeton 1994, 1998). This leads to three straightforward predictions about genetic structure following recent range expansions. First, newly colonized areas should have significantly lower

genetic diversity than the parent population (Hewitt 1996; Grant and Bowen 1998; Marko 1998). For DNA sequence data, the significance of a difference in genetic diversity can be assessed by simple permutation. Second, alleles in the colonized area should be phylogenetically nested within the diversity of alleles from the source area (Templeton 1994, 1998). Third, rapid population growth is more likely in newly colonized areas compared to source areas, and this should leave a characteristic signature on a gene genealogy (see below).

Figure 3.4 illustrates the rationale for the first two predictions. The figure shows an invasion of North America from Europe in terms of geographical maps of allele genealogies. Because we are considering mitochondrial data, alleles that differ by at least one substitution will be referred to as haplotypes. The invading species initially exists only in Europe, with at least six unique haplotypes (Figure 3.4A). The species subsequently colonizes North America (Figure 3.4B). At this point, all haplotypes sampled from North America will be identical to one another and to one of the European haplotypes from which they descended. If there is no further migration from the European source, new haplotypes (from mutation)—descended from the invading haplotype—will appear in North America (Figure 3.4C).

Because the expected shape of the gene genealogy at equilibrium is well known, coalescent theory can be used to distinguish between populations that have undergone recent growth from those that have remained at a constant size. This makes it possible to explore the third prediction of rapid population growth in the newly founded populations. The genetic signatures of rapid population growth were originally explored using the simple distributions of pairwise distances (Slatkin and Hudson 1991; Rogers and Harpending 1992). Two recent advances now make it possible to use patterns of genealogical relationships to characterize population dyanmics. The first approach predicts the number of lineages through time under models assuming either constant population size or exponential growth (e.g., Nee et al. 1995; Rambaut et al. 1997), and then tests the fit of linear transformed empirical data to the models (software End-Epi, http://evolve.zps.ox.ac.uk; Rambaut et al., 1997). These transformations can be interpreted graphically so as to distinguish between exponential and linear growth, and whether a population has been growing exponentially at a changing rate.

Kuhner et al. (1998) recently developed a maximum likelihood method that simultaneously estimates θ (effective population size X mutation rate), as well as a growth parameter. A sampling procedure is used to estimate these parameters across many alternative trees (software Fluctuate, http://www.evolution.genetics.washington.edu/lamarc/fluctuate.html). Given an independent estimate of mutation rate, a trajectory of effective population size through time can be estimated from this approach. An old population that has had no recent bottleneck should have a shallow growth trajectory, whereas a recently founded population should have experienced explosive growth from a few founding individuals. Although this approach makes unrealistic assumptions, such as assum-

(A)

(B)

(C)

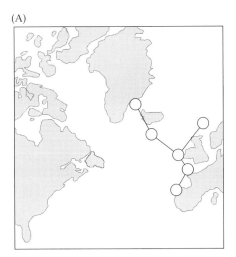
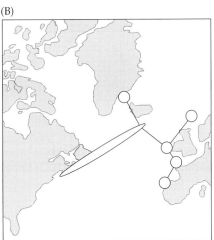
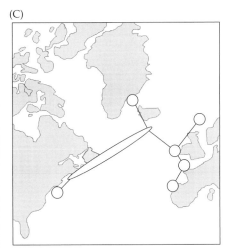

Figure 3.4 An unrooted gene genealogy illustrating the process of colonization of North America from Europe by a single mitochondrial haplotype. Each circle (or oval) represents a single haplotype, and approximates the geographical range of that haplotype. (A) Prior to the colonization event, the species is endemic to Europe. (B) A propagule (or propagules) carrying a single European haplotype colonizes North America. (C) Mutation and drift will eventually cause the North American haplotypes to diverge from their European progenitors. In the absence of subsequent colonization from European sources, all new haplotypes in North America will be descended from from the founding haplotype.

ing that the shape of the curve will always be exponential (Kuhner et al., 1998), it may be useful to distinguish between very different classes of histories.

Range expansions often occur naturally, especially following climatic or tectonic changes. However, human-mediated introductions are becoming distressingly common in the sea (Carlton and Geller 1993). With adequate genetic sampling, it should be possible to rule out human-mediated transport if there are at least a few unique alleles in the newly colonized area (Ó Foighil and Jozefowicz 1999). The evidence against human-mediated colonization is especially strong if most or all of these unique alleles are descended from one of the common, or "founding" alleles (as in Figure 3.4B). If, however, all alleles in the colonized area are shared with the hypothetical source population, other information, including historical records, must be incorporated into the reconstruction of colonization.

Summary and Conclusions

As others have argued (e.g., Palumbi 1994; Hilbish 1996; Benzie 1999), the evidence summarized in this section suggests that there are relatively few marine species that fully satisfy the expectations of equilibrium between genetic drift and migration across their entire ranges. At one extreme, the absence of significant genetic structure cannot always be equated with true equilibrial panmixia. It may take millions of years following subdivision for allozyme markers to reveal genetic structure. Although mtDNA-based markers may be more sensitive to vicariance, migration models that assume equilibrium will yield low but detectable levels of migration between populations that have long since stopped exchanging migrants. Similarly, recently founded populations and their putative sources may not show significant genetic dif-

ferences; however, their levels of genetic diversity should significantly differ. In all of these cases, the absence of detectable genetic structure cannot necessarily be equated with significant present-day gene flow.

At the other extreme, a simple correspondence between geographical distance and genetic distance (or inferred migration rate) does not necessarily mean that populations are at equilibrium. The details of scale, once again, count: If the correspondence occurs only across small spatial scales, then it suggests that subpopulations have yet to equilibrate at regional scales (Hutchison and Templeton 1999). When a population consists of an aggregate of more-or-less contiguous local populations that are internally panmictic, but that do not exchange migrants with the other subpopulations, an analysis of genetic structure that includes both within- and among-subpopulation comparisons can yield a significant relationship between genetic and geographic distances, despite the absence of gene flow among subpopulations.

We conclude that the present-day genetic structure of many species of marine invertebrates often reflects the operation of *both* contemporary gene flow and historical factors, and that populations are often not in equilibrium throughout their ranges. More specifically, in species with extensive dispersal potential, and at local scales, the effects of gene flow and drift may predominate; in species with less extensive dispersal potential, or at relatively larger spatial scales, nonequilibrial processes may prevail. With allele frequency approaches to the analysis of genetic structure, the relative contributions of historic and contemporary are often impossible to distinguish. Phylogeographic approaches, on the other hand, now make it possible to begin to assess the relative contributions that historical factors and contemporary gene flow make to current genetic structure. The few studies of marine organisms that employ such methodologies suggest that many species of marine invertebrates consist of genetically differentiated subpopulations whose evolutionary histories geographically vary. To the extent that this is generally true, it raises a critical series of questions for the community ecologist concerning the spatial and temporal scales over which populations of marine organisms interact with their competitors, predators, and pathogens.

FROM POPULATIONS TO COMMUNITIES

In this section, we return at last to the question posed at the beginning of this chapter: What can information about patterns of genetic variation within a species, and the historical and recent processes that generate these patterns, tell us about the ecological and evolutionary outcomes of species interactions? We first consider the strengths and weaknesses of using genetic structure to address questions concerning open and closed ecological systems, and the scales over which interacting species can influence each other's population dynamics. We then extend this analysis into predicting the nature of genetic and phenotypic responses to spatially varying selection. Third, we consider how genetic information can be used to distinguish sibling species, and the importance of these distinctions for understanding the evolution of ecological specialization. Finally, we explore how genetic structure can be used to reconstruct the history of species interactions, specifically to distinguish long-term, locally adapted residents from recent arrivals with less potential for local adaptation.

Scale of Population Regulation

The spatial scale and magnitude of demographic connection among subpopulations of the species that compose a local community depend on species-specific modes of development, larval behavior, and local and regional patterns of water movement (Gaines and Roughgarden 1985; Possingham and Roughgarden 1990; Gaines and Bertness 1993; Todd 1998; reviewed in Booth and Brosnan 1995; Caley et al. 1996; Cowen et al. 2000). The debate over whether populations of marine organisms exhibit open or closed dynamics was ignited in the early 1980s when marine ecologists rediscovered the importance of recruitment limitation to the demography of benthic invertebrates and reef fish populations (Doherty 1981; Underwood and Denley 1984; Gaines and Roughgarden 1985; Roughgarden et al. 1985; Young 1987; Hughes 1990; Grosberg and Levitan 1992; Booth and Brosnan 1995; Caley et al. 1996; Waples 1998). Recruitment levels can affect population dynamics and species interactions by regulating the intensity of competition (both intra- and interspecific) and predation (Menge and Sutherland 1987; Connolly and Roughgarden 1999). To the extent that the adults of many marine organisms are relatively sedentary and their propagules are relatively motile, the supply of recruits to a local population of adults could be governed by processes occurring outside the local population, instead of by local reproductive output (Menge and Olson 1990). This is what is conventionally meant by "open" population dynamics.

In most benthic marine communities, occupants of different trophic levels, and competitors at the same trophic level, often have different developmental modes. For example, two of the keystone predator genera of the Northern Hemisphere rocky intertidal have dramatically different dispersal potential. The major gastropod predator *Nucella* has direct development, whereas the predatory seastars *Asterias* and *Pisaster* have planktotrophic larvae. Since the major prey of all of these predators are mussels and barnacles, both of which have planktotrophic larvae with extensive dispersal potential, the scales over which prey abundance regulates predator population dynamics (or vice versa) should differ for interactions with *Nucella* compared to those involving *Asterias* and *Pisaster*. Gaines and Lafferty (1995) developed a series of models exploring the dynamics of predators and prey, competitors, and hosts and pathogens, when interacting species exhibited different combinations of locally closed versus open populations. These models nearly uniformly yield dramatically different dynamics than conventional models in which interacting species are closed or open at matching spatial scales.

From the perspective of community ecology, the critical problem is therefore to determine not only the magnitude and scale of demographic exchange among subpopulations (i.e., how open or closed are they?) of each interacting species, but also the degree to which the population dynamics of interacting species spatially correspond (McLaughlin and Roughgarden 1993; Holt 1993; Underwood and Petraitis 1993; Booth and Brosnan 1995; Gaines and Lafferty 1995; Connolly and Roughgarden 1999). This problem has remained an unanswered challenge in most marine systems because of the difficulties of directly tracking migration of motile propagules. One approach, widely used in agricultural systems, is to breed "genetically engineered" stocks that carry rare markers, introduce them into natural or experimental arrays, and sample offspring for the marker gene. Such genetic tags have also been used in marine invertebrates (e.g., Grosberg and Quinn 1986; Grosberg 1991) and fish (Wilson et al. 1997; Wilson and Donaldson 1998; Perez-Enrique and Tanigushi 1999). It is now also possible to track fish larvae using natural or artificial chemical tags (Campana et al. 1995; Jones et al. 1999; Swearer et al. 1999).

The value of naturally occurring genetic markers for characterizing demographic units (and identify larval sources) relies on the presence of detectable genetic differences among subpopulations (Utter and Ryman 1993; Hedgecock 1994; Burton 1994, 1996; Palumbi 1995; Waples 1998). In turn, the existence of such differences depends upon the relationship between the genetically effective migration rate, m, and the mutation rate, μ. In general, if m is greater than μ for a marker, then at equilibrium, the marker will not reveal differences among subpopulations. If, however, m is less than μ, new alleles will arise within subpopulations more frequently than they are exchanged with adjacent subpopulations, and unique alleles characteristic of that specific subpopulation should be detectable in at least some individuals.

If selectively neutral markers reveal genetic structure at a particular spatial scale, and this structure is temporally stable, then the genetically distinct subpopulations cannot be experiencing much present-day gene flow (e.g., Bulnheim and Scholl 1981; Burton et al. 1979; Todd et al. 1988; Burton and Lee 1994; Lessios et al. 1994; Lewis and Thorpe 1994; Burton 1997; Edmands et al. 1996; see Waples (1998) for caveats when F_{ST} is small (< 0.05), but nonetheless, significant). Such subpopulations ought to be independently regulated by their parasites, pathogens, predators, and competitors, with substantially different population dynamics than would be the case in demes connected by extensive migration (Antonovics 1994; Gaines and Lafferty 1995).

Unfortunately, the absence of genetic structure may say relatively little about *demographic* interconnectedness, because a demographically insignificant amount of gene flow among subpopulations—on the order of one migrant per generation—will eventually homogenize allelic frequencies at neutral loci. As we discussed earlier (in the section entitled The Approach to Equilibrium and Why It Matters), the time it takes to reach this equilibrium depends on the migration rate, effective population size, and mutation rate (Takahata 1983). With low mutation rates, and demographically plausible migration rates, this equilibrium will be reached quickly, even in relatively large populations, leaving no detectable genetic signature. However, as the mutation rate, μ, of a marker increases with respect to the migration rate, m, the rate of approach to equilibrium will be slowed.

In this respect, the development of hypervariable markers such as microsatellites has dramatically improved the power to distinguish previously undetectable levels of genetically effective migration among subpopulations. Coupled with a variety of recent statistical innovations, hypervariable markers potentially allow more detailed inferences about the pattern, scale, and history of gene flow than has been possible with less variable markers (e.g., Bertorelle and Excoffier 1999; Waser and Strobeck 1998; reviewed in Luikart and England 1999). For example, hypervariable markers such as some microsatellite loci can be used [with some caveats about mutational models, estimating allelic frequencies, and so forth; see papers in Goldstein and Schlötterer (1999)] to estimate gene flow using the procedures described earlier for F_{ST}-like statistics (e.g., R_{ST}). Such indirect estimates of gene flow can then be compared to direct estimates based on genetic identification of the sources of individual immigrants. One way to do this is to "engineer" genetically or chemically migrants so that they can be distinguished from residents upon resampling. Alternatively, if populations are even slightly genetically differentiated, hypervariable markers dramatically improve the prospects for using likelihood methods to assign individual genotypes in a sample to their correct source population (reviewed in Waser and Strobeck 1998; also see http://www.biology.ualberta.ca/jbrzusto/Doh.html). Similarly, maximum-likelihood methods can be sometimes be used to distinguish between sets of subpopulations with the same F_{ST}'s that are linked by gene flow (i.e., in equilibrium)

from those that are partially or fully independent (Beaumont and Bruford 1999).

To some, these advances promise to bridge the gap between the shortcomings of direct and indirect measures of gene flow. A more precise understanding of the short- and long-term outcomes of the interaction between spatially varying selection and gene flow should follow (see the next section). Nonetheless, for all but the lowest rates of exchange among subpopulations, it is unlikely that naturally occurring genetic markers alone will ever be able to reveal fully the geographic sources of immigrants to a population and the magnitude of demographic connections.

Responses to Spatially Varying Selection

When populations are at equilibrium, the scale and magnitude of genetic subdivision strongly reflects the extent to which (1) individuals experience different selective regimes over their lifetimes and (2) subpopulations can independently evolve in response to spatially varying selection. Thus, the correspondence between the scale and magnitude of genetic structure and the scale over which diversifying selection operates determines the likelihood of cumulative genetic change and local adaptation (Endler 1992). In general, species with limited gene flow should be more likely than species with extensive gene flow to exhibit local adaptation to spatially varying selection (Holt and Gaines 1992). They should also do so on finer spatial scales than species with more widespread gene flow. Genetically differentiated subpopulations may ultimately diverge to such an extent that they become reproductively isolated.

At the other extreme, when the spatial scale of gene flow exceeds the scale over which selection varies, cumulative adaptive genetic changes are unlikely to occur. In other words, spatially varying selection favoring a specific genotype in a particular location can overcome the homogenizing effects of gene flow within generations; however, a continuing flow of recruits from neighboring populations limits the opportunity for the accumulation of genetically based local specialization to spatially varying selection (Ament 1979; Strathmann and Branscomb 1979; Strathmann et al. 1981; Warner 1997). Selection should instead favor the evolution of generalist phenotypes or reduced dispersal (Slatkin 1973; Gooch 1975; Endler 1979; Hedgecock 1986; Warner 1997). When the appropriate environmental cues exist, phenotypic plasticity or habitat selection may also evolve (Adler and Harvell 1990). Thus, there should be a tradeoff between the expected degree of local genetic adaptation and the magnitude of dispersal.

Does empirical reality in marine species match these predictions? Many of the classic marine studies of the scale of genetic differentiation concern spatially varying selection imposed by the physical environment (reviewed in Janson and Ward 1984; Hedgecock 1986; Behrens Yamada 1989; Ayre 1995; Warner 1997). Behrens Yamada (1989) contrasted geographic variation in life-history traits in two species of *Littorina*, an intertidal, herbivorous snail common in temperate waters of the eastern Pacific. *L. sitkana* embryos directly develop into crawl-away juveniles, whereas *L. scutulata* larvae develop in the plankton. Both species exhibit significant geographic variation in the expression of growth rates and reproductive timing, attributed to selection imposed by variation in desiccation stress (Behrens Yamada 1989). These life-history differences persisted in common garden experiments as well as reciprocal transplants, suggesting that at least some of the demographic variation is heritable. Consistent with the predicted tradeoff between scale of local adaptation and dispersal potential, the scale of geographic differentiation for these traits is on the order of tens of kilometers in the directly developing *L. sitkana* versus hundreds of kilometers in *L. scutulata*. Unfortunately, the study lacked a genetic assessment using neutral markers of geographic structure, making it impossible to reject the scenario that the regional pool of recruits is genetically homogeneous, with post-recruitment selection within generations producing the observed local pattern.

Other studies of the response to spatial variation in the physical environment that explicitly consider genetic structure also support some of the basic predictions of the tradeoff model. *Tigriopus californicus* is an intertidal and supralittoral harpacticoid copepod common in tidepools along the West Coast of North America. The life history of *T. californicus* implies that it should have very limited dispersal potential, a prediction verified by high levels of temporally stable genetic differentiation at very fine spatial scales (reviewed in Burton 1998). Patterns of micro-geographic and regional variation at several allozyme loci associated with osmoregulation strongly correspond to spatial variation in salinity and temperature along both intertidal and latitudinal gradients. Physiological studies and transplant experiments confirm that these loci are under selection by the thermal and salinity regime. Whether selection favored the evolution of reduced dispersal in *T. californicus* remains to be seen; nevertheless, it appears that limited gene flow in this species permits selection to cause cumulative adaptive change at very fine spatial scales.

In species with extensive dispersal potential, such as barnacles (Hedgecock 1986; Schmidt and Rand 1999) and mussels (e.g., Hilbish and Koehn 1985), genetic data, either in the form of allozymes or mtDNA data, show that cohorts of new recruits appear to be genetically well-mixed over local and sometimes regional scales. However, at some loci (associated with thermal, salinity, or desiccation tolerance), the genetic composition of cohorts recurrently diverges following recruitment, presumably due to diversifying selection imposed by local variation in temperature or salinity. In these examples, the perhaps unexpected product of the interaction between high gene flow and fine-scale post-recruitment selection appears to be the short-term maintenance of a balanced genetic polymorphism within populations for variation in the physiological traits under selection, rather than phenotypic plasticity or reduced dispersal.

The effects of spatial variation in predation intensity on phenotypic variation in prey populations are far better studied than the effects of other species interactions such as competition or parasitism. What are the effects of genetic structure on the evolution of this phenotypic variation, and to what extent does this variation represent local adaptation versus predator-induced phenotypic plasticity? Conspecific populations of many marine gastropods, including members of the genera *Nucella* and *Littorina*, often exhibit site-specific variation in shell thickness that corresponds to the intensity of predation by crabs (Janson 1982, 1987; Palmer 1985, 1990; Trussell 1996). Thin-shelled morphs are more resistant to dislodgement by waves, and predominate on exposed shores where crab predators are relatively rare; in adjacent protected waters, where crab predation intensifies, thick-shelled morphs predominate (reviewed in Trussell 1996).

The whelk genus *Nucella* consists entirely of directly developing species with demersal, crawl-away juveniles. Studies of genetic structure based on both allozymes (e.g., Day 1990; Day et al. 1993) and mtDNA sequences (Marko 1998) show that populations exhibit extensive genetic structure at spatial scales corresponding to phenotypic variation in shell thickness and the abundance of predators. Unlike the previously cited barnacle and mussel examples, where it appears that recruits are well mixed (at least at local scales), the existence of substantial genetic structure at a scale roughly corresponding to that over which selection varies suggests that phenotypic variation in shell thickness signifies true local adaptation. However, several experimental studies indicate that much of the phenotypic variation in shell thickness can be induced by crab predators (Appleton and Palmer 1988; Palmer 1990), and thus may not entirely represent local genetic adaptation.

In the North Atlantic, two species of *Littorina* have been especially well characterized in terms of genetic structure and geographic variation in shell structure. Like the North Pacific species pair studied by Behrens Yamada (1989), *L. saxatalis* is a direct developer, with crawl-away juveniles; *L. littorea* is sympatric with *L. saxatalis*, but its larvae remain in the plankton for 4–6 weeks (Janson 1987). Allozyme studies show the expected genetic patterns, with *L. saxatalis* exhibiting fine-scale genetic structure on the order of meters (Janson 1987) and *L. littorea* lacking detectable genetic structure over hundreds of kilometers (Berger 1973; Janson 1987). In both species, the degree of variation in shell morphology corresponds to the pattern of genetic structure. *L. saxatalis* displays variation in shell-thickness according to local variation in wave exposure, and *L. littorea* lacks such phenotypic variation (Currey and Hughes 1982; but see Dudley 1980).

Once again, the question is, does the variation in the shell morphology of the direct-developing *L. saxatalis* represent genetic differentiation or phenotypic plasticity? As with *Nucella*, the answer remains equivocal. Newkirk and Doyle (1975) showed that variation in shell morphology is partially under genetic control in *L. saxatalis*, a result consistent with the expectation of local adaptation. However, a recent study on *L. obtusata* (also a direct developer) demonstrated that crab-predation can directly induce a substantial increase in shell thickness (Trussell 1996), suggesting a role for phenotypic plasticity.

To what extent can information about the genetic structure of marine populations be used to predict a species response to spatially varying selection? The answer at this point remains equivocal. Species with minimal structure and extensive gene flow that we might expect to exhibit phenotypic plasticity often do not. Species with substantial structure and minimal gene flow often exhibit phenotypic plasticity. Studies conducted at different scales and on different populations can produce conflicting results.

Part of the failure to match expectations is almost certainly due to our extremely limited knowledge of the nature of spatial and temporal variation in selection. In addition, our understanding of the genetics of adaptation remains in its infancy (Orr 1998). But just as importantly, we still know remarkably little about genetic structure and the history of gene flow in natural populations of marine organisms. In terms of the response to selection, the details of genetic structure and the equilibrium status of populations are critical: Populations with identical inferred levels of gene flow may differ in their actual degree of isolation from one another. For instance, populations may lack significant genetic structure for neutral markers either because they are currently exchanging migrants, or because they have been recently subdivided and not yet reached evolutionary equilibrium (e.g., Benzie 1999). Conversely, populations that appear to be equally differentiated may actually represent a mosaic of formerly isolated subpopulations, some of which are now interconnected (but have yet to reach equilibrium), and others of which remain unconnected. In both situations, subpopulations with the same apparent genetic structure may differ in their responses to spatially varying selection because some subpopulations may be partially or fully evolutionarily independent, whereas others may only appear to be.

For this reason alone, future studies at the interface between ecology and genetics should incorporate an explicit historical component that utilizes some combination of genealogical methods and high-resolution genetic markers capable of distinguishing low levels of ongoing gene flow from the recent cessation of genetic exchange. In this respect, intrapecific genealogical information can be used in some situations to identify those species in an assemblage with the greatest potential for local adaptation. If a species can be recognized as a recent colonist (see the section entitled Range Expansion and Population Growth), then it may have had little opportunity to respond to local selection. If populations in one area are reciprocally monophyletic with respect to populations in other areas, then it is most parsimonious to infer that the species has survived in both areas with little gene flow between them (see Genealogical Approaches). The length of time populations have persisted in both areas corresponds roughly to the number of substitutions along the internal branch dividing the populations (Figure 3.5). Reciprocally monophyletic populations therefore satisfy two requirements for local adaptation: long-term residence, and little or no genetic exchange with other populations.

Figure 3.5 Establishment of reciprocal monophyly following the colonization process shown in Figure 3.4. If there is no further migration across the Atlantic, then mutations (represented by hatch marks) will accumulate between European and North American populations, producing a long internal branch in the genealogy (see Templeton 1994). Such a pattern would indicate the independence of resident populations on opposite coasts.

Cryptic Species: Intraspecific Polymorphism versus Interspecific Diversification

In the previous section we concluded that recent and historic patterns of gene flow are key determinants of the evolutionary response of populations to spatially varying selection. Given sufficient time and limited gene flow, diversifying selection and drift can eventually lead to the acquisition of genetically based post- and pre-reproductive isolation between populations (reviewed in Coyne and Orr 1998). In many cases, there are few reliable morphological clues to this transition from a polymorphic species to interspecific diversification, and lab tests of reproductive compatibility are notoriously difficult to implement and interpret. Yet this transition from a state of intraspecific polymorphism to two or more cryptic ("sibling") species is critical to identify, because in many organisms (plants and corals may be exceptions) it signifies the irreversible evolutionary independence of lineages.

The existence of numerous complexes of sibling marine species is now well established (see review in Knowlton 1993). Although an unambiguous definition of cryptic or sibling species is controversial (for a good discussion see Knowlton and Weigt 1997), cryptic species can often be identified by genetic data, especially when populations show fixed allelic differences or reciprocal monophyly (see the section entitled The History of Population Subdivision and the Importance of

Reciprocal Monophyly). For this reason, Avise and Ball (1990) used gene genealogies as the basis for their concordance species concept. They argued that if multiple unlinked loci show congruent patterns of reciprocal monophyly, the individuals so defined should be considered distinct species.

When they are not diagnosed, cryptic species that have fully or partially sympatric distributions can be confused with stable intraspecific polymorphisms. Such confusion can, in turn, dramatically alter interpretations of outcomes of ecological interactions. For example, the snail *Acanthina angelica* preys on the barnacle *Chthamalus anisopoma*, and induces the production of a hooded morph that is more resistant to predation than the normal conical morph (Lively 1986; reviewed in Lively et al. 2000). The conical morph of *C. anisopoma* occurs throughout the Gulf of California, whereas the hooded morph occurs primarily in the northern Gulf. The predator, *A. angelica*, lives only in the northern Gulf of California, suggesting that geographic variation in the prey's phenotypic polymorphism is the result of environmental induction by the predator. However, Lively et al. (2000) recently showed that barnacles collected from the northern Gulf differed in their inducibility by *Acanthina*, raising the possibility that there is also an underlying genetic polymorphism controlling the amount of phenotypic plasticity in the northern Gulf population.

Why are there noninducible morphs in the northern Gulf? One option is that some sort of balancing selection maintains an equilibrial genetic polymorphism within the northern Gulf (Lively et al. 2000), as appears to be the case in the barnacles and mussels discussed above. An unexplored nonequilibrial alternative is that the inducible and uninducible forms represent genetically differentiated populations, or even cryptic species. Uninducible southern Gulf populations or species may be continually swept into the northern Gulf in such large numbers that they persist in the northern Gulf, maintaining apparent polymorphism for inducibility despite their selective disadvantage in the face of *Acanthina* predation. If this scenario were correct, then our ecological and historical interpretation of the distribution of hooded morphs of *C. anisopoma* would substantially differ from that based on a genetic or environmentally induced intraspecific polymorphism.

One of the most ecologically dramatic examples in marine systems of the importance of distinguishing interspecific differentiation among cryptic species from intraspecific phenotypic polymorphisms concerns the symbiosis between hermatypic corals and their zooxanthellae. Until recently, this symbiosis was thought to represent an association between a diversity of host coral species and a single species of dinoflagellate in the genus *Symbiodinium*. However, Rowan and Powers (1991, 1992), following previous speculation (e.g., Kinzie and Chee 1979; Jokiel and York 1982), challenged the longstanding hypothesis that the *Symbiodinium* that inhabited all hermatypic corals belonged to the same ecologically generalized "cultivar." Using RFLPs of genes encoding small ribosomal RNAs, they showed that there are three very distinct taxa of symbionts, designated *A*, *B*, and *C*. Later work revealed that each of these three cultivars of *Symbiodinium* had different irradiance optima. At least in the corals *Montastrea annularis* and *M. faveolata*, symbionts *A* and *B* are common in shallow, high irradiance habitats; *C* predominates in deeper, low irradiance habitats (Rowan and Knowlton 1995; Rowan et al. 1997).

The mere discovery that *Symbiodinium* was not a monotypic species, but instead a species complex, consisting of at least three very distinct members with different physiologies, was in and of itself a major revolution in our understanding of the natural history of coral symbioses. It also helped to clarify why there is so much variation within and among coral heads in intensity of bleaching. Rowan et al. (1997) sampled tissue from low and high irradiance parts of individual coral heads, and from corals living at different depths. Samples from a single coral head contained different relative amounts of each symbiont, and the relative abundance of each type of symbiont corresponded to predictions based on irradiance optima (i.e., symbiont *C* was most common in low irradiance positions on individual coral heads, and increased in relative abundance in corals sampled from increasing depth). In other words, there is zonation within and among coral heads, and subsequent experimental manipulations showed that irradiance plays a major role in controlling community composition of the symbionts (Rowan et al. 1997).

These findings do not exclude other important intrinsically driven effects on coral bleaching such as physiological acclimitization of hosts and symbionts, and genetically based physiological differences among host corals. But the data do highlight the existence of previously unknown genetically based differences among the symbionts, and the role that such variation may have in producing the distinct patterns of bleaching so commonly observed throughout the Caribbean. Without this genetic information about the taxonomy of *Symbiodinium*, and the fine-scale distribution of the symbiotic taxa within and among coral heads, the evolutionary and ecological relationships between corals and their algal symbionts, not to mention the ecological interactions and maintenance of diversity among symbionts, would at best be half told stories (Rowan and Knowlton 1995).

Community Assembly and the History of Species Interactions

Do the recurrent similarities and differences that characterize modern species assemblages of marine organisms principally reflect the outcomes of contemporary ecological interactions, repeated in time or space, or do the members of similar assemblages also share a genealogical connection? The great promise of "historical ecology" was that phylogenetic analysis would bring two new perspectives to our understanding of the historical and contemporary contributions to community assembly (Brooks 1985; Brooks and McLennan 1991). First, a phylogeny should allow identification of a species' closest relatives, and thus allow one to reconstruct ancestral and derived character states. With this knowledge, it would be possible to infer which features evolved *in situ*, and which were inherited from its ancestor. For example, ecological character displacement can lead to differences in size between competing species (e.g., Schluter et al. 1985). If, however, the closest relatives of one or both species were the same size as the competing species, then the size difference between the interacting species more likely represents a retained ancestral difference, rather than the outcome of the ongoing competitive interaction.

Second, phylogeographic analysis should make it possible to identify species that have had a long shared history with one another. If two interacting species collected from the same area have congruent phylogenies, then these species probably shared a long history (reviewed in Cunningham and Collins 1994; Page and Hafner 1996). Conversely, if one of the members of the interaction has been a long-term resident, and the other arrived recently from elsewhere, then the species have had relatively little time to evolve in response to one another.

Shared history can also be inferred if a number of species share congruent patterns of reciprocal monophyly on either side of a genetic break (reviewed in Avise 1994). In the case of the North Atlantic fauna, the set of species that show reciprocal monophyly between Europe and North America must have persisted on both coasts with little appreciable gene flow, despite glacial fluctuations (Cunningham and Collins 1998). If, on the other hand, there is consistent genetic evidence for recent colonization of a particular area by members of an assemblage, then the newly colonizing species may have had a long history in the source—but not the recipient—area (e.g., Europe in Figure 3.5).

SUMMARY

Ecology has two fundamental goals. The first is to identify the processes that regulate species distribution and abundance, and the temporal and spatial scales over which these processes operate. The second is to understand the nature and outcomes of species' interactions with their biotic and physical environments and how these interactions regulate community structure. It remains difficult to identify many of these processes (and their scale of operation) and to predict these outcomes, in part because there has been little concerted effort by systematists and population geneticists to provide marine ecologists with the information necessary to decipher the history of species distributions and the spatial scales over which populations are genetically connected.

Promising beginnings have been made in the southeastern United States (reviewed in Avise 1994; Cunningham and Collins 1998), the Isthmus of Panama (Knowlton et al. 1993; Collins 1996; Lessios 1998), the Indo-Pacific (reviewed in Benzie 1999), the West Coast of the United States (e.g., Burton 1998), and hydrothermal vent systems (reviewed in Vrijenhoek 1997). These studies, along with the analyses of genetic structure presented in this chapter, suggest that few, if any, marine species are in equilibrium with respect to gene flow, drift, and selection throughout their ranges. To the extent that this proves to be correct, we should expect substantial geographic variation in the nature and outcomes of these interactions, both as a result of ongoing spatial variation in selection, as well as the different histories of selection, colonization, and extinction experienced by different populations.

Understanding the history of species distributions in terms of contemporary and historic patterns of selection, extinction, and colonization also underlies the development of a tradition of "comparative marine ecology." How do we interpret ecological similarities and differences among communities? To what extent are these similarities the result of shared histories or shared selective regimes? To what extent are differences possible despite shared histories? Do the biogeographic boundaries that define major breaks in community composition correspond to genetic discontinuities in their constituent taxa (Burton 1998; *cf.* Avise 1994)? Are the species that occupy adjacent biogeographic provinces closely related? For example, the rocky intertidal community of New England differs dramatically from that of the temperate Pacific, yet the New England assemblage consists largely of species that arrived from the Pacific in the past few million years (Vermeij 1991). Answers to these ecological questions fundamentally depend on growing collaboration among ecologists, population geneticists, and systematists. This collaboration remains to be fully implemented, but with it will come a much deeper understanding of the principles that govern community structure and dynamics.

ACKNOWLEDGMENTS

We were both supported by grants from the National Science Foundation while we wrote this chapter. R.K.G. was also supported by a California Sea Grant.

LITERATURE CITED

Adler, F. R. and C. D. Harvell. 1990. Inducible defenses, phenotypic variability, and biotic environments. *Trends Ecol. Evol.* 5: 407–410.

Ament, A. 1979. Geographic variation in relation to life history in three species of the marine gastropod genus *Crepidula*: Growth rates of newly hatched larvae and juveniles. In S. E. Stancyk (ed.), *Reproductive Ecology of Marine Invertebrates*, pp. 61–76. University of South Carolina Press, Columbia.

Antonovics, J. 1994. Ecological genetics of metapopulations: The *Silene–Ustilago* plant–pathogen system. In L. A. Real (ed.),

Ecological Genetics, pp. 146–170. Princeton University Press, Princeton, NJ.

Appleton, R. D. and A. R. Palmer. 1988. Water-borne stimuli released by predatory crabs and damaged prey induce more predator-resistant shells in a marine gastropod. *Proc. Natl. Acad. Sci. USA* 85: 4387–4391

Avise, J. C. 1992. Molecular population structure and the biogeographic history of a regional fauna: A case history with lessons for conservation biology. *Oikos* 63: 62–76.

Avise, J. C. 1994. *Molecular Markers, Natural History, and Evolution*. Chapman and Hall, New York.

Avise, J. C. and R. M. Ball. 1990. Principles of genealogical concordance in species concepts and biological taxonomy. *Oxford Surveys in Evolutionary Biology* 7: 45–67.

Avise, J. C., J. Arnold, R. M. Ball, E. Bermingham, T. Lamb, J. E. Neigel, C. A. Reeb and N. C. Saunders. 1987. Intraspecific phylogeography: The mitochondrial bridge between population genetics and systematics. *Annu. Rev. Ecol. Syst.* 18: 489–522.

Ayre, D. J. 1990. Population subdivisions in Australian temperate marine invertebrates: Larval connections versus historical factors. *Aust. J. Ecol.* 15: 403–411.

Ayre, D. J. 1995. Localized adaptation of sea anemone clones: Evidence from transplantation over two spatial scales. *J. Anim. Ecol.* 64: 186–196.

Ayre, D. J. and S. Duffy. 1994. Evidence for restricted gene flow in the viviparous coral *Seriatopra hystrix* on Australia's Great Barrier Reef. *Evolution* 48: 1183–1201.

Barton, N. H. and I. Wilson. 1995. Genealogies and geography. *Philos. Trans. R. Soc. London B* 349: 49–59.

Beaumont, M. A. and M. W. Bruford. 1999. Microsatellites in conservation genetics. In D. B. Goldstein and C. Schlötterer (eds.), *Microsatellites: Evolution and Applications*, pp. 165–182. Oxford University Press, Oxford.

Beerli, P. and J. Felsenstein. 1999. Maximum-likelihood estimation of migration rates and effective population numbers in two populations using a coalescent approach. *Genetics* 152: 763–773.

Behrens Yamada, S. 1989. Are direct developers more locally adapted than planktonic developers? *Mar. Biol.* 103: 403–412.

Benzie, J. A. H. 1999. Genetic structure of coral reef organisms: Ghosts of dispersal past. *Amer. Zool.* 39: 131–145.

Benzie, J. A. H. and S. T. Williams. 1992. No genetic differentiation of giant clam (*Tridacna gigas*) populations in the Great Barrier Reef, Australia. *Mar. Biol.* 113: 373–37.7

Benzie, J. A. H. and S. T. Williams. 1995. Gene flow among giant clam (*Tridacna gigas*) populations in the Pacific does not parallel ocean circulation. *Mar. Biol.* 123: 781–787.

Berger, E. 1973. Gene-enzyme variation in three sympatric species of *Littorina. Biol. Bull.* 145: 83–90.

Bermingham, E. and H. A. Lessios. 1993. Rate variation of protein and mitochondrial DNA evolution as revealed by sea urchins separated by the Isthmus of Panama. *Proc. Natl. Acad. Sci. USA* 90: 2734–2738.

Bertorelle, G. and L. Excoffier. 1999. Inferring admixture proportions from molecular data. *Mol. Biol. Evol.* 15:1298–1311.

Bohonak, A. J. 1999. Dispersal, gene flow, and population structure. *Q. Rev. Biol.* 74: 21–45.

Booth, D. J. and D. M. Brosnan. 1995. The role of recruitment dynamics in rocky shore and coral reef fish communities. *Adv. Ecol. Res.* 26: 309–385.

Bossart, J. L. and D. P. Prowell. 1998. Genetic estimates of population structure and gene flow: Limitations, lessons and new directions. *Trends Ecol. Evol.* 13: 202–206.

Brooks, D. R. 1985. Historical ecology: A new approach to studying the evolution of ecological associations. *Ann. Mo. Bot. Gard.* 72: 660–680.

Brooks, D. R. and D. A. McLennan. 1991. *Phylogeny, Ecology, and Behavior: A Research Program in Comparative Biology.* University of Chicago Press, Chicago.

Brooks, D. R. and D. A. McLennan. 1993. Historical ecology: Examining phylogenetic components of community ecology. In R. E.

Ricklefs and D. Schluter (eds.), *Species Diversity in Ecological Communities*, pp. 267–280. University of Chicago Press, Chicago.

Bulnheim, H. P. and A. Scholl. 1981. Genetic variation between geographic populations of the amphipods *Gammarus zaddachi* and *G. salinus. Mar. Biol.* 64: 105–115.

Buroker, N. E. 1983. Population genetics of the American oyster *Crassostrea viginica* along the Atlantic coast and the Gulf of Mexico. *Mar. Biol.* 75: 99–112.

Burton, R. S. 1983. Protein polymorphisms and genetic differentiation of marine invertebrate populations. *Mar. Biol. Let.* 4: 193–206.

Burton, R. S. 1986. Evolutionary consequences of restricted gene flow in the intertidal copepod *Tigriopus californicus. Bull. Mar. Sci.* 39: 526–535.

Burton, R. S. 1994. Inferring the genetic structure of marine populations: A case study comparing allozyme and DNA sequence data. *CalCOFI Rep.* 35: 52–60.

Burton, R. S. 1996. Molecular tools in marine ecology. *J. Exp. Mar. Biol. Ecol.* 200: 85–101.

Burton, R. S. 1997. Genetic evidence for persistence of marine invertebrate populations in an ephemeral environment. *Evolution* 51: 993–998.

Burton, R. S. 1998. Intraspecific phylogeography across the Point Conception biogeographic boundary. *Evolution* 52: 734–745.

Burton, R. S. and B.-N. Lee. 1994. Nuclear and mitochondrial gene genealogies and allozyme polymorphism across a major phylogeographic break in the copepod *Tigriopus californicus. Proc. Natl. Acad. Sci. USA* 91: 5197–5201.

Burton, R. S. and S. G. Swisher. 1984. Population structure of the intertidal copepod *Tigriopus californicus* as revealed by field manipulation of allele frequencies. *Oecologia* 65: 108–111.

Burton, R. S., M. W. Feldman and J. W. Curtsinger. 1979. Population genetics of *Tigriopus californicus* (Copepoda: Harpacticoida). I. Population structure along the central California coast. *Mar. Ecol. Prog. Ser.* 1: 29–39.

Caley, M. J., M. H. Carr, M. A. Hixon, T. P. Hughes, G. P. Jones and B. A. Menge. 1996. Recruitment and the local dynamics of open marine populations. *Annu. Rev. Ecol. Syst.* 27: 477–500.

Campana, S. E., J. A. Gagne and J. W. McLaren. 1995. Elemental fingerprinting of fish otoliths using ID-ICPMS. *Mar. Ecol. Prog. Ser.* 122: 115–120.

Carlton, J. T. and J. B. Geller. 1993. Ecological roulette: The global transport of nonindigenous marine organisms. *Science* 261: 78–82.

Castelloe, J. and A. R. Templeton. 1994. Root probabilities for intraspecific gene trees under neutral coalescent theory. *Mol. Phylog. Evol.* 3: 102–113.

Cavalli-Sforza, L. L. and A. W. F. Edwards. 1967. Phylogenetic analysis: Models and estimation procedures. *Evolution* 21: 550–570.

Cockerham, C. C. and B. S. Weir. 1993. Estimation of gene flow from *F*-statistics. *Evolution* 47: 855–863.

Collins, T. 1996. Molecular comparisons of transisthmian species pairs: Rates and patterns of evolution. In *Evolution and Environment in Tropical America*, J. B. C. Jackson, A. F. Budd and A. G. Coates (eds.), pp. 303–334. University of Chicago Press, Chicago.

Connolly, S. R. and J. Roughgarden. 1999. Theory of marine communities: Competition, predation, and recruitment-dependent interaction strength. *Ecol. Monogr.* 69: 277–296.

Cowen, R. K., K. M. Luiza, S. Sponaugle, C. B. Paris and D. B. Olson. 2000. Connectivity of marine populations: Open or closed? *Science* 287: 857–859.

Coyne, J. A. and H. A. Orr. 1998. The evolutionary genetics of speciation. *Philos. Trans. R. Soc. Lond. B* 353: 287–305.

Crandall, K. A. 1994. Intraspecific cladogram estimation: Accuracy at higher levels of divergence. *Syst. Biol.* 43: 222–235.

Crandall, K. A. and A. Templeton. 1996. Applications of intraspecific phylogenetics. In P. H. Harvey, A. J. Leigh Brown, J. Maynard Smith and S. Nee (eds.), *New Uses for New Phylogenies*, pp. 81–99. Oxford University Press, Oxford.

Crow, J. F. and K. Aoki. 1984. Group selection for a polygenic behavioral trait: Estimating the degree of population subdivision. *Proc. Natl. Acad. Sci. USA* 81: 6073–6077.

Crow, J. F. and M. Kimura. 1970. *An Introduction to Population Genetics Theory.* Harper & Row, New York.

Cunningham, C. W. and T. M. Collins. 1994. Developing model systems for molecular biogeography: Vicariance and interchange in marine invertebrates. In *Molecular Ecology and Evolution: Approaches and Applications*, B. Schierwater, B. Streit, G. P. Wagner and R. DeSalle (eds.), pp. 405–433. Birkhauser Verlag, Basel, Switzerland.

Cunningham, C. W. and T. M. Collins. 1998. Beyond area relationships: Extinction and recolonization in molecular marine biogeography. In *Molecular Approaches to Ecology and Evolution*, R. DeSalle and B. Schierwater, (eds.). Birkhauser Verlag, Basel, Switzerland, pp. 297–321.

Currey, J. D. and R. N. Hughes. 1982. Strength of the dog-whelk *Nucella lapillus* and the winkle *Littorina littorea* from different habitats. *J. Anim. Ecol.* 51: 47–56.

Day, A. J. 1990. Microgeographic variation in allozyme frequencies in relation to the degree of wave action in the dogwhelk *Nucella lapillus* (L.) (Prosobranchia: Muricacea). *Biol. J. Linn. Soc.* 40: 245–261.

Day, A. J., H. P. Leinaas and M. Anstensrud. 1993. Allozyme differentiation of populations of the dogwhelk *Nucella lapillus* (L.): The relative effects of geographic distance and variation in chromosome number. *Biol. J. Linn. Soc.* 51: 257–277.

Doherty, P. J. 1981. Coral reef fishes: Recruitment-limited assemblages? *Proc. 4th Coral Reef Symp.* 2: 465–470.

Dudley, R. 1980. Crab-crushing of periwinkle shells, *Littorina littorea*, from two adjacent geographical provinces. *Nautilus* 94: 108–112.

Edmands, S., P. E. Moberg and R. S. Burton. 1996. Allozyme and mitochondrial DNA evidence of population subdivision in the purple sea urchin, *Strongylocentrotus purpuratus*. *Mar. Biol.* 126: 443–450.

Endler, J. A. 1977. *Geographic Variation, Speciation, and Clines*. Monographs in Population Biology Vol. 10. Princeton University Press, Princeton, NJ.

Endler, J. A. 1979. Gene flow and life history patterns. *Genetics* 93: 263–284.

Endler, J. A. 1992. Genetic heterogeneity and ecology. In *Genes in Ecology*, R. J. Berry, T. J. Crawford and G. M. Hewitt (eds.), pp. 315–334. Blackwell Scientific, Oxford.

Ewens, W. J. 1982. On the concept of effective population size. *Theor. Pop. Biol.* 21: 373–378.

Excoffier, L., P. E. Smouse and J. M. Quattro. 1992. Analysis of molecular variance inferred from metric distances among DNA haplotypes: Application to human mitochondrial DNA restriction sites. *Genetics* 131: 479–491.

Eyre-Walker, A., N. H. Smith and J. M. Smith. 1999. How clonal are human mitochondria? *Proc. R. Soc. Lond. B* 266: 477–483.

Fadlallah, Y. H. 1983. Population dynamics and life history of a solitary coral, *Balanophyllia elegans*, from Central California. *Oecologia* 58: 200–207.

Felsenstein, J. 1978. Cases in which parsimony or compatibility methods will be positively misleading. *Syst. Zool.* 27: 401–410.

Felsenstein, J. 1982. How can we infer geography and history from gene frequencies? *J. Theor. Biol.* 96: 9–20.

Felsenstein, J. 1999. PHYLIP (Phylogeny Inference Package) Version 3.5c. Distributed by the author, University of Washington, Seattle.

Gaines, S. D. and M. D. Bertness. 1993. The dynamics of juvenile dispersal: Why field ecologists must integrate. *Ecology* 74: 2430–2435.

Gaines, S. D. and K. D. Lafferty. 1995. Modeling the dynamics of marine species: The importance of incorporating larval dispersal. In L. McEdward (ed.), *Ecology of Marine Invertebrate Larvae*, pp. 389–412. CRC Press, Boca Raton, FL.

Gaines, S. D. and J. Roughgarden. 1985. Larval settlement rate: A leading determinant of structure in an ecological community of the marine intertidal zone. *Proc. Natl. Acad. Sci. USA* 82: 3707–3711.

Gerrodette, T. 1981. Dispersal of the solitary coral Balanophyllia elegans by demersal planular larvae. *Ecology* 62: 611–619.

Gillespie, J. H. 1998. *Population Genetics : A Concise Guide*. The Johns Hopkins University Press, Baltimore, MD.

Gilpin, M. 1991. The genetic effective size of a metapopulation. *Biol. J. Linn. Soc.* 42: 165–175.

Goldstein, D. B. and C. Schlötterer. 1999. *Microsatellites: Evolution and Applications*. Oxford University Press, Oxford.

Gooch, J. L. 1975. Mechanisms of evolution and population genetics. In *Marine Ecology: A Comprehensive Treatise on Life in Oceans and Coastal Waters*, Volume 2, Part 1, O. Kinne (ed.), pp. 351–409. John Wiley and Sons, New York.

Grant, W. S. and B. W. Bowen. 1998. Shallow population histories in deep evolutionary lineages of marine fishes: Insights from sardines and anchovies and lessons for conservation. *J. Hered.* 89: 415–426.

Graves, J. E. 1998. Molecular insights into the population structures of cosmopolitan marine fishes. *J. Hered.* 89: 427–437.

Griffiths, R. C. and S. Tavaré. 1994. Sampling theory for neutral alleles in a varying environment. *Philos. Trans. R. Soc. Lond. B* 344: 403–410.

Grosberg, R. K. 1987. Limited dispersal and proximity-dependent mating success in the sessile colonial ascidian *Botryllus schlosseri*. *Evolution* 41: 372–384.

Grosberg, R. K. 1991. Sperm-mediated gene flow and the genetic structure of a population of the colonial sea squirt *Botryllus schlosseri*. *Evolution* 45: 130–142.

Grosberg, R. K. and D. R. Levitan. 1992. For adults only? Supply-side ecology and the history of larval biology. *Trends. Ecol. Evol.* 7: 130–133.

Grosberg, R. K. and J. F. Quinn. 1986. The genetic control and consequences of kin recognition by the larvae of a colonial marine invertebrate. *Nature* 322: 456–459.

Haldane, J. B. S. 1930. A mathematical theory of natural and artificial selection. IV. Isolation. *Proc. Cambridge Philos. Soc.* 26: 220–230.

Hare, M. P. and J. C. Avise. 1996 Molecular genetic analysis of a stepped multilocus cline in the American oyster (*Crassostrea virginica*). *Evolution* 50: 2305–2315.

Hastings, A. and S. Harrison. 1994. Metapopulation dynamics and genetics. *Annu. Rev. Ecol. Syst.* 25: 167–188.

Hedgecock, D. 1986. Is gene flow from pelagic larval dispersal important in the adaptation and evolution of marine invertebrates? *Bull. Mar. Sci.* 39: 550–564.

Hedgecock, D. 1994. Does variance in reproductive success limit effective population size of marine organisms? In *Genetics and Evolution of Aquatic Organisms*, A. Beaumont (ed.), pp. 122–134. Chapman and Hall, London.

Hedgecock, D., V. Chow and R. S. Waples. 1992. Effective population numbers of shellfish broodstocks estimated from temporal variance in allelic frequencies. *Aquaculture* 108: 215–232.

Hellberg, M. E. 1994. Relationships between inferred levels of gene flow and geographic distance in a philopatric coral, *Balonophyllia elegans*. *Evolution* 48: 1829–1854.

Hellberg, M. E. 1995. Stepping-stone gene flow in the solitary coral *Balanophyllia elegans*: Equilibrium and nonequilibrium at different spatial scales. *Mar. Biol.* 123: 573–581.

Hellberg, M. E. 1996. Dependence of gene flow on geographic distance in two solitary corals with different larval dispersal capabilities. *Evolution* 50: 1167–1175.

Hewitt, G. M. 1996. Some genetic consequences of ice ages and their role in divergence and speciation. *Biol. J. Linn. Soc.* 58: 247–276.

Hilbish, T. J. 1996. Population genetics of marine species: The interaction of natural selection and historically differentiated populations. *J. Exp. Mar. Biol. Ecol.* 200: 67–83.

Hilbish, T. J. and R. K. Koehn. 1985. The physiological basis of natural selection at the *Lap* locus. *Evolution* 39: 1302–1317.

Hill, W. G. 1981. Estimation of effective population size from data on linkage disequilibrium. *Genet. Res.* 38: 209–216.

Hill, W. G. 1985. Effects of population size on response to short and long-term selection. *Sonderdruck aus Zetschrift für Tierzüchtung und Züchtungbiologie* 102(3): 161–173.

Holsinger, D. E. 1999. Analysis of genetic diversity in geographically structured populations: A Bayesian perspective. *Hereditas* 130: 245–255.

Holsinger, D. E. and R. J. Mason-Gamer. 1996. Hierarchical analysis of nucleotide diversity in geographically structured populations. *Genetics* 142: 629–639.

Holt, R. D. 1993. Ecology at the mesoscale: The influence of regional processes on local communities. In *Species Diversity in Ecological Communities: Historical and Geographic Perspectives*, R. Ricklefs and D. Schluter (eds.), pp. 77–88. University of Chicago Press, Chicago.

Holt, R. D. and M. S. Gaines. 1992. Analysis of adaptation in heterogeneous niches—implications for the evolution of fundamental niches. *Evol. Ecol.* 6: 433–447.

Holt, R. D. and R. Gomulkiewicz. 1997. How does immigration influence local adaptation? A reexamination of a familiar paradigm. *Amer. Nat.* 149: 563–572.

Hudson, R. R. 1990. Gene genealogies and the coalescent process. *Oxford Surveys in Evolutionary Biology* 7: 1–44.

Hudson, R. R., M. Slatkin and W. P. Maddison. 1992. Estimation of levels of gene flow from DNA sequence data. *Genetics* 132: 583–589.

Hughes, T. P. 1990. Recruitment limitation, mortality, and population regulation in open systems: A case study. *Ecology* 71: 12–20.

Husband, B. C. and S. C. H. Barrett. 1996. A metapopulation perspective in plant population biology. *J. Ecol.* 84: 461–469.

Hutchison, D. W. and A. R. Templeton. 1999. Correlation of pairwise genetic and geographic distance measures: Inferring the relative influences of gene flow and drift on the distribution of genetic variability. *Evolution* 53: 1898–1914.

Jablonski, D. and R. A. Lutz. 1983. Larval ecology of marine benthic invertebrates: Paleobiological implications. *Biol. Rev.* 58: 21–89.

Jackson, J. B. C. 1986. Modes of dispersal of clonal benthic invertebrates: Consequences for species' distribution and genetic structure of local populations. *Bull. Mar. Sci.* 39: 588–606.

Janson, K. 1982. Phenotypic differentiation in *Littorina saxatilis* Olivi (Mollusca, Prosobranchia) in a small area on the Swedish west coast. *J. Moll. Stud.* 48: 167–173.

Janson, K. 1987. Allozyme and shell variation in two marine snails (*Littorina*, Prosobranchia) with different dispersal abilities. *Biol. J. Linn. Soc.* 30: 245–256.

Janson, K. and R. D. Ward, 1984. Microgeographic variation in allozyme and shell characters in *Littorina sazatilis* Olivi (Prosobranchia: Littorinidae). *Biol. J. Linn. Soc.* 22: 289–307.

Johannesson, K., B. Johannesson and U. Lundgren. 1995. Strong natural selection causes microscale allozyme variation in a marine snail. *Proc. Natl. Acad. Sci. USA* 92: 2602–2606.

Johnson, M. S. and R. Black. 1982. Chaotic genetic patchiness in an intertidal limpet, *Siphonaria* sp. *Mar. Biol.* 79: 295–302.

Johnson, M. S. and R. Black. 1984a. Pattern beneath the chaos: The effect of recruitment on genetic patchiness in an intertidal limpet. *Evolution* 38: 1371–1383.

Johnson, M. S. and R. Black. 1984b. The Wahlund effect and the geographical scale of variation in the intertidal limpet *Siphonaria* sp. *Mar. Biol.* 79: 295–302.

Johnson, M. S. and R. Black. 1995. Neighbourhood size and the importance of barriers to gene flow in an intertidal snail. *Heredity* 75: 142–154.

Johnson, M. S. and R. Black. 1998. Effects of isolation by distance and geographical discontinuity on genetic subdivision of *Littoraria cingulata*. *Mar. Biol.* 132: 295–303.

Jokiel, P. L. and R. H. York, Jr. 1982. Solar ultraviolet photobiology of the reef coral, *Pocillopora damicornis* and symbiotic zooxanthellae. *Bull. Mar. Sci.* 32: 301–315.

Jones, G. P., M. J. Milicich, M. J. Emslie and C. Lunow. 1999. Self-recruitment in a coral reef population. *Nature* 402: 802–804.

Karl, S. A. and J. C. Avise. 1992. Balancing selection at allozyme loci in oysters: Implications from nuclear RFLPs. *Science* 256: 100–102.

Kimura, M. and G. H. Weiss. 1964. The stepping stone model of population structure and the decrease of genetic correlation with distance. *Genetics* 49: 561–576.

Kinzie, R. A. and G. S. Chee. 1979. The effect of different zooxanthellae on the growth of experimentally reinfected hosts. *Biol. Bull.* 156: 315–327.

Knowlton, N. 1993. Sibling species in the sea. *Annu. Rev. Ecol. Syst.* 24: 189–216.

Knowlton, N. and J. B. C. Jackson. 1993. Inbreeding and outbreeding in marine invertebrates. In *The Natural History of Inbreeding and Outbreeding: Theoretical and Empirical Perspectives*, N. W. Thornhill (ed.), pp. 200–249. University of Chicago Press, Chicago.

Knowlton, N. and L. A. Weigt. 1997. Species of marine invertebrates: A comparison of the biological and phylogenetic species concepts. In *Species: The Units of Biodiversity*, M. F. Claridge, H. A. Dawah and M. R. Wilson (eds.), pp. 199–219. Systematics Association Special Volume Series 54.

Knowlton, N., L. A. Weigt, L. A. Solorzano, D. K. Mills and E. Bermingham. 1993. Divergence in proteins, mitochondrial DNA, and reproductive compatibility across the Isthmus of Panama. *Science* 260: 1629–1632.

Koehn, R. K., R. I. E. Newell and F. Immerman. 1980. Maintenance of an aminopeptidase allele frequency cline by natural selection. *Proc. Natl. Acad. Sci. USA* 77: 5385–5389.

Kordos, L. M. and R. S. Burton. 1993. Genetic differentiation of Texas Gulf coast populations of the blue crab *Callinectes sapidus*. *Mar. Biol.* 117: 227–233.

Kuhner, M. K. J. Yamato and J. Felsenstein. 1998. Maximum likelihood estimation of population growth rates based on the coalescent. *Genetics* 149: 429–434.

Lamb, T and J. C. Avise. 1986. Directional introgression of mitochondrial DNA in a hybrid population of tree frogs: The influence of mating behavior. *Proc. Natl. Acad. Sci. USA* 83: 2526–2530.

Lande, R. 1993. Risks of population extinction from demographic and environmental stochasticity and random catastrophes. *Amer. Nat.* 142: 911–927.

Lande, R. 1994. Risk of population extinction from new deleterious mutations. *Evolution* 48: 1460–1469.

Lessios, H. A. 1998. The first stage of speciation as seen in organisms separated by the Isthmus of Panama. In *Endless Forms: Species and Speciation*, D. J. Howard and S. H. Berlocher (eds.), pp. 186–201. Oxford University Press, Oxford.

Lessios, H. A., J. R. Weinberg and V. R. Starczak. 1994. Temporal variation in populations of the marine isopod *Excirolana*: How stable are gene frequencies and morphology? *Evolution* 48: 549–563.

Lessios, H. A., B. D. Kessing and D. R. Robertson. 1998. Massive gene flow across the world's most potent marine biogeographic barrier. *Proc. R. Soc. Lond. B* 265: 583–588.

Lewis, R. I. and J. P. Thorpe. 1994. Temporal stability of gene frequencies within genetically heterogeneous populations of the queen scallop *Aequipecten* (*Chlamys*) *opercularis*. *Mar. Biol.* 121: 117–126.

Li, G. and D. Hedgecock. 1998. Genetic heterogeneity, detected by PCR-SSCP, among samples of larval Pacific oysters (*Crassostrea gigas*) supports the hypothesis of large variance in reproductive success. *Can. J. Fish. Aqaut. Sci.* 55: 1025–1033.

Lively, C. M. 1986. Predator-induced shell dimorphism in the acorn barnacle *Chthamalus anisopoma*. *Evolution* 40: 232–242.

Lively, C. M., W. N. Hazel, M. J. Schellenberger and K. S. Michelson. 2000. Predator-induced plasticity: Variation for inducibility in an intertidal barnacle. *Ecology* 81: 1240–1247.

Luikart, G. and P. R. England. 1999. Statistical analysis of microsatellite data. *Trends Ecol. Evol.* 14: 253–256.

Lynch, M. and T. J. Crease. 1990. The analysis of population survey data on DNA sequence variation. *Mol. Biol. Evol.* 7: 377–394.

Lynch, M. and W. Gabriel. 1990. Mutation load and the survival of small populations. *Evolution* 44: 1725–1737.

Lynch, M., J. Conery and R. Bürger. 1995. Mutation accumulation and the extinction of small populations. *Amer. Nat.* 146: 489–518.

Maddison, W. P. and D. R. Maddison. 1992. *MacClade: Analysis of Phylogeny and Character Evolution*, version 3.0. Sinauer Associates, Sunderland, MA.

Maddison, W. P. and M. Slatkin. 1991. Null models for the number of evolutionary steps in a character on a phylogenetic tree. 45: 1184–1197.

Malécot, G. 1968. *The Mathematics of Heredity.* W. H. Freeman, San Francisco.

Marko, P. 1998. Historical allopatry and the biogeography of speciation in the prosobranch snail genus *Nucella*. *Evolution* 52: 757–774.

McCauley, D. E. 1993. Evolution in metapopulations with frequent local extinction and recolonization. *Oxford Surveys in Evolutionary Biology* 9: 109–134.

McCauley, D. E. and P. W. Goff. 1998. Intrademic genetic structure and natural selection in insects. In *Genetic Structure and Local Adaptation in Natural Insect Populations: Effects of Ecology, Life History, and Behavior*, S. Mopper and S. Y. Strauss (eds.), pp. 181–204. Chapman and Hall, New York.

McFadden, C. S. and K. Y. Aydin. 1996. Spatial autocorrelation analysis of small-scale genetic structure in a clonal soft coral with limited larval dispersal. *Mar. Biol.* 126: 215–224.

McFadden, C. S., R. K. Grosberg, B. B. Cameron, D. P. Karlton and D. Secord. 1997. Genetic relationships within and between clonal and solitary forms of the sea anemone *Anthopleura elegantissima* revisited: Evidence for the existence of two species. *Mar. Biol.* 128: 127–139.

McLaughlin J. F. and J. Roughgarden. 1993. Species interactions in Space. In *Species Diversity in Ecological Communities: Historical and Geographical Perspectives*. R. E. Ricklefs and D. Schluter (eds.), pp. 89–98. University of Chicago Press, Chicago.

Menge, B. A. 1976. Organization of the New England rocky intertidal community: Role of predation, competition, and environmental heterogeneity. *Ecol. Monogr.* 46: 355–393.

Menge, B. A. and A. M. Olson. 1990. Role of scale and environmental factors in regulation of community structure. *Trends Ecol. Evol.* 5: 52–57.

Menge, B. A. and J. P. Sutherland. 1987. Community regulation: Variation in disturbance, competition, and predation in relation to environmental stress and recruitment. *Amer. Nat.* 130: 730–57.

Mopper, S. and S. Y. Strauss (eds.). 1998. *Genetic Structure and Local Adaptation in Natural Insect Populations: Effects of Ecology, Life History, and Behavior*. Chapman and Hall, New York.

Nagylaki, T. 1975. Conditions for the existence of clines. *Genetics* 80: 595–615.

Nath, H. and R. Griffiths. 1996. Estimation in an island model using simulation. *Theor. Popul. Biol.* 50: 227–253.

Nee, S., E. C. Holmes, A. Rambaut and P. H. Harvey. 1995. Inferring population history from molecular phylogenies. *Philos. Trans. R. Soc. Lond. B* 349: 25–31.

Nei, M. 1972. Genetic distance between populations. *Amer. Nat.* 105: 385–398.

Nei, M. 1973. Analysis of gene diversity in subdivided populations. *Proc. Natl. Acad. Sci USA* 70: 3321–3323.

Nei, M. and F. Tajima. 1981. Genetic drift and estimation of effective population size. *Genetics* 98: 625–640.

Neigel, J. E. 1997. A comparison of alternative strategies for estimating gene flow from genetic markers. *Annu. Rev. Ecol. Syst.* 28: 105–128.

Neigel, J. E. and J. C. Avise. 1986. Phylogenetic relationships of mitochondrial DNA under various demographic models of speciation. In *Evolutionary Processes and Theory*, E. Nevo and S. Karlin (eds.), pp. 515–534. Academic Press, New York.

Newkirk, G. F. and R. W. Doyle. 1975. Genetic analysis of shell shape variation in *Littorina saxatilis* on an environmental cline. *Mar. Biol.* 30: 227–237.

Nunney, L. 1996. The influence of variation in female fecundity on effective population size. *Biol. J. Linn. Soc.* 59: 411–425.

Nunney, L. 1999. The effective size of a hierarchically structured population. *Evolution* 53: 1–10.

Ó Foighil, D. and C. J. Jozefowicz. 1999. Amphi-Atlantic phylogeography of the marine clam *Lasaea*. *Mar. Biol.* 135: 115–122.

Olson, R. R. 1985. The consequences of short distance larval dispersal in a sessile marine invertebrate. *Ecology* 66: 30–39.

Orr, H. A. 1998. The population genetics of adaptation: The distribution of factors fixed during adaptive evolution. *Evolution* 52: 935–949

Page, R. D. M. and M. S. Hafner. 1996. Molecular phylogenies and host–parasite cospeciation: Gophers and lice as a model system. In *New Uses for New Phylogenies*, P. H. Harvey, A. J. Leigh Brown, J. Maynard Smith and S. Nee (eds.), pp. 255–270. Oxford University Press, Oxford.

Palmer, A. R. 1984. Species cohesiveness and genetic control of shell color and form in *Thais emarginata* (Prosobranchia, Muricacea): Preliminary results. *Malacologia* 25(2): 477–491.

Palmer, A. R. 1985. Quantum changes in gastropod shell morphology need not reflect speciation. *Evolution* 39: 699–705.

Palmer, A. R. 1990. Effect of crab effluent and scent of damaged conspecifics on feeding growth and shell morphology of the Atlantic dog whelk *Nucella lapillus* L. *Hydrobiologia* 193: 155–182

Palumbi, S. R. 1994. Genetic divergence, reproductive isolation, and marine speciation. *Annu. Rev. Ecol. Syst.* 25: 547–572.

Palumbi, S. R. 1995. Using genetics as an indirect estimator of larval dispersal. In *Ecology of Marine Invertebrate Larvae*, L. McEdward (ed.), pp. 369–387. CRC Press, New York

Palumbi, S. R. 1997. Molecular biogeography of the Pacific. *Coral Reefs* 16 (Suppl): S47–S52.

Palumbi, S. R. 1999. The prodigal fish. *Nature* 402: 733–734.

Palumbi, S. R. and A. C. Wilson. 1990. Mitochondrial DNA diversity in the sea urchins *Strongylocentrotus purpuratus* and *S. droebachiensis*. *Evolution* 44: 403–415

Palumbi, S. R., G. Grabosky, T. Duda, L. Geyer and N. Tachino. 1997. Speciation and population genetic structure in tropical Pacific sea urchins. *Evolution* 51: 1506–1517.

Paulay, G. 1990. Effects of late Cenozoic sea-level fluctuations on the bivalve faunas of tropical oceanic islands. *Paleobiology* 16: 415–434.

Perez-Enrique, R. and N. Tanigushi. 1999. Use of microsatellite DNA as genetic tags for the assessment of a stock enhancement program of Red Sea bream. *Fish. Sci.* 65: 374–379.

Pollack, E. 1983. A new method for estimating the effective population size from allele frequency changes. *Genetics* 104: 531–548.

Possingham, H. P. and J. Roughgarden. 1990. Spatial population dynamics of a marine organism with a complex life cycle. *Ecology* 71: 973–985.

Pudovkin, A. I., D.V. Zaykin and D. Hedgecock. 1996. On the potential for estimating the effective number of breeders from heterozygote-excess in progeny. *Genetics* 144: 383–387.

lQuesada, H., R. Wenne and D. O. F. Skibinski. 1995. Differential introgression of mitochondrial DNA across species boundaries within the marine mussel genus *Mytilus*. *Proc. R. Soc. Lond. B* 262: 51–56.

Rambaut, A., P. Harvey and S. Nee. 1997. End-Epi: An application for inferring phylogenetic and population dynamical processes from molecular sequences. *Comp. Appl. Biosci.* 13: 303–306.

Reeb, C. A. and J. C. Avise. 1990. A genetic discontinuity in a continuously distributed species: Mitochondrial DNA in the American oyster, *Crassostrea virginica*. *Genetics* 124: 397–406.

Rogers, A. R. and H. Harpending. 1992. Population growth makes waves in the distribution of pairwise genetic differences. *Mol. Biol. Evol.* 9: 552–569.

Roughgarden, J. and Y. Iwasa. 1986. Dynamics of a metapopulation with space-limited subpopulations. *Theor. Pop. Biol.* 29: 235–261.

Roughgarden, J., Y. Iwasa and C. Baxter. 1985. Demographic theory for an open marine population with space-limited recruitment. *Ecology* 66: 54–67.

Roughgarden, J., S. D. Gaines and H. Possingham. 1988. Recruitment dynamics in complex life cycles. *Science* 241: 1460–1466.

Rousset, F. and M. Raymond. 1997. Statistical analyses of population genetic data: New tools, old concepts. *Trends Ecol. Evol.* 12: 313–317.

Rowan, R. and N. Knowlton. 1995. Intraspecific diversity and ecological zonation in coral-algal symbiosis. *Proc. Natl. Acad. Sci.* 92: 2850–2853.

Rowan, R. and D. A. Powers. 1991. Molecular genetic classification of zooxanthellae and the evolution of animal–algal symbioses. *Science* 251: 1348–1351.

Rowan, R. and D. A. Powers. 1992. Ribosomal RNA sequences and the diversity of symbiotic dinoflagellates (Zooxanthellae). *Proc. Natl. Acad. Sci. USA* 89: 3639–3643.

Rowan, R., N. Knowlton, A. Baker and J. Jara. 1997. Landscape ecology of algal symbionts creates variation in episodes of coral bleaching. *Nature* 388: 265–269.

Ruckelshaus, M. 1998. Spatial scale of genetic structure and an indirect estimate of gene flow in eelgrass, *Zostera marina*. *Evolution* 52: 330–343.

Scheltema, R. S. 1986. On dispersal and planktonic larvae of benthic invertebrates: An eclectic overview and summary of problems. *Bull. Mar. Sci.* 39: 290–322.

Schluter, D., T. D. Price and P. R. Grant. 1985. Ecological character displacement in Darwin's finches. *Science* 227: 1056–1059.

Schmidt, P. S. and D. M. Rand. 1999. Intertidal microhabitat and selection at *MPI*: Interlocus contrasts in the northern acorn barnacle, *Semibalanus balanoides*. *Evolution* 53: 135–146.

Shulman, M. J. and E. Bermingham. 1995. Early life histories, ocean currents, and the population genetics of Caribbean reef fishes. *Evolution* 49: 897–910.

Slatkin, M. 1973. Gene flow and selection in a cline. *Genetics* 75: 735–756.

Slatkin, M. 1985a. Gene flow in natural populations. *Annu. Rev. Ecol. Syst.* 16: 393–430.

Slatkin, M. 1985b. Rare alleles as indicators of gene flow. *Evolution* 39: 53–65.

Slatkin, M. 1987. The average number of sites separating DNA sequences drawn from a subdivided population. *Theoret. Pop. Biol.* 32: 42–49.

Slatkin, M. 1993. Isolation by distance in equilibrium and nonequilibrium populations. *Evolution* 47: 264–279.

Slatkin, M. 1994. Gene flow and population structure. In *Ecological Genetics*, L. Real (ed.), pp. 3–17. Princeton University Press, Princeton, NJ.

Slatkin, M. 1995. A measure of population subdivision based on microsatellite allele frequencies. *Genetics* 139: 457–462.

Slatkin, M. and N. H. Barton. 1989. A comparison of three indirect methods for estimating average levels of gene flow. *Evolution* 43: 1349–1368.

Slatkin, M. and R. R. Hudson. 1991. Pairwise comparisons of mitochondrial DNA sequences in stable and exponentially growing populations. *Genetics* 129: 555–562.

Slatkin, M. and W. P. Maddison. 1989. A cladistic measure of gene flow inferred from the phylogenies of alleles. *Genetics* 123: 603–613.

Slatkin, M. and W. P. Maddison. 1990. Detecting isolation by distance using phylogenies of genes. *Genetics* 126: 249–260.

Smouse, P. E. 1998. To tree or not to tree. *Mol. Ecol.* 7: 399–412.

Solé-Cava, A. M., J. P. Thorpe and C. D. Todd. 1994. High genetic similarity between geographically distant populations in a sea anemone with low dispersal capabilities. *J. Mar. Biol. Assoc. U.K.* 74: 895–902.

Stoner, D. S. 1990. Recruitment of a tropical ascidian: Relative importance of pre-settlement vs. post-settlement processes. *Ecology* 71: 1682–1690.

Strathmann, R. R. and E. S. Branscomb. 1979. Adequacy of cues to favorable sites used by settling larvae of two intertidal barnacles. In *Reproductive Ecology of Marine Invertebrates*, S. E. Stancyk (ed.), pp. 77–89. University of South Carolina Press, Columbia.

Strathmann, R. R., E. S. Branscomb and K. Vedder. 1981. Fatal errors in set as a cost of dispersal and the influence of intertidal flora on set of barnacles. *Oecologia* 48: 13–18.

Swearer, S. E., J. E. Caselle, D. W. Lea and R. R. Warner. 1999. Larval retention and recruitment in an island population of a coral-reef fish. *Nature* 402: 799–802.

Swofford, D. L. 1999. *PAUP*: Phylogenetic Analysis Using Parsimony* (*and other methods), version 4.0. Sinauer Associates, Sunderland, MA.

Swofford, D. L., G. J. Olsen, P. J. Waddell and D. M. Hillis. 1996. Phylogenetic inference. In *Molecular Systematics*, 2nd ed., D. M. Hillis, C. Moritz and B. K. Mable (eds.), pp. 407–514. Sinauer Associates, Sunderland, MA.

Takahata, N. 1983. Gene identity and genetic differentiation of populations in the finite island model. *Genetics* 104: 497–512.

Templeton, A. R. 1994. The role of molecular genetics in speciation studies. In *Molecular Ecology and Evolution: Approaches and Applications*, B. Schierwater, B. Streit, G. P. Wagner and R. DeSalle (eds.), pp. 455–478. Birkhauser Verlag, Berlin.

Templeton, A. R. 1998. Nested clade analyses of phylogeographic data: Testing hypotheses about gene flow and population history. *Mol. Ecol.* 7: 381–397.

Todd, C. D. 1998. Larval supply and recruitment of benthic invertebrates: Do larvae always disperse as much as we believe? *Hydrobiologia* 375/376: 1–21.

Todd, C. D., J. N. Havenhand and J. P. Thorpe. 1988. Genetic differentiation, pelagic larval transport and gene flow between local populations of the intertidal marine mollusc *Adalaria proxima* (Alder & Hancock). *Func. Ecol.* 2: 441–451.

Trussell, G. C. 1996. Phenotypic plasticity in an intertidal snail: The role of a common crab predator. *Evolution* 50: 448–454.

Underwood, A. J. and E. J. Denley. 1984. Paradigms, explanations and generalizations in models for the structure of intertidal communities on rocky shores. In *Ecological Communities: Conceptual Issues and the Evidence*, D. R. Strong, D. Simberloff, L. G. Abele and A. B. Thistle (eds.), pp. 151–180. Princeton University Press, Princeton, NJ.

Underwood, A. J. and P. S. Petraitis. 1993. Structure of intertidal assemblages in different locations: How can local processes be compared? In *Species Diversity in Ecological Communities: Historical and Geographic Perspectives*, R. E. Ricklefs and D. Schluter (eds.), pp. 39–51. University of Chicago Press, Chicago.

Utter, F. and N. Ryman. 1993. Genetic markers and mixed stock fisheries. *Fisheries* 18: 11–21.

Van Syoc, R. J. 1994. Genetic divergence between subpopulations of the eastern Pacific goose barnacle *Pollicipes elegans:* Mitochondrial cytochrome C subunit I nucleotide sequences. *Mol. Mar. Biol. Tech.* 3: 338–346.

Vermeij, G. 1978. *Biogeography and Adaptation.* Harvard University Press, Cambridge, MA.

Vermeij, G. 1987. *Evolution and Escalation: An Ecological History of Life.* Princeton University Press, Princeton, NJ.

Vermeij, G. 1991. Anatomy of an invasion: The trans-Arctic interchange. *Paleobiology* 17: 281–307.

Vrijenhoek, R. C. 1997. Gene flow and genetic diversity in naturally fragmented metapopulations of deep-sea hydrothermal vent animals. *J. Heredity* 88: 285–293.

Wahlund, S. 1928. Zusammersetung von Populationen und Korrelation-serscheinungen von Standpunkt der Verebungslehre aus betratchet. *Hereditas* 11: 65–106.

Waples, R. S. 1989. A generalized approach for estimating effective population size from temporal changes in allele frequency. *Genetics* 121: 379–391.

Waples, R. S. 1998. Separating the wheat from the chaff: Patterns of genetic differentiation in high gene flow species. *J. Heredity* 89: 438–450.

Wares, J. P., S. D. Gaines and C. W. Cunningham. In press. A comparative study of the effects of ocean currents on gene flow across Point Conception. *Evolution* 55.

Warner, R. R. 1997. Evolutionary ecology: How to reconcile pelagic dispersal with local adaptation. *Coral Reefs* 16 (Suppl.): S115–S120.

Waser, P. M. and C. Strobeck. 1998. Genetic signatures of interpopulation dispersal. *Trends Ecol. Evol.* 13: 43–44.

Watts, R. J., M. S. Johnson and R. Black. 1990. Effects of recruitment on genetic patchiness in the urchin *Echinometra mathaei* in Western Australia. *Mar. Biol.* 105: 145–151.

Weir, B. S. 1990. *Genetic Data Analysis.* Sinauer Associates, Sunderland, MA.

Weir, B. S. 1996. *Genetic Data Analysis II.* Sinauer Associates, Sunderland, MA.

Weir, B. S. and C. C. Cockerham 1984. Estimating *F*-statistics for the analysis of population structure. *Evolution* 38: 1358–1370.

Whitlock, M. C. and N. H. Barton. 1997. The effective size of a subdivided population. *Genetics* 146: 427–441.

Whitlock, M. C. and D. E. McCauley. 1999. Indirect measures of gene flow. *Heredity* 82: 117–125.

Williams, S. T. and J. A. H. Benzie. 1996. Genetic uniformity of widely separated populations of the coral reef starfish *Linckia laevigata* from the West Pacific and East Indian Oceans, revealed by allozyme electrophoresis. *Mar. Biol.* 126: 99–108.

Williams, S. T. and J. A. H. Benzie. 1997. Indo-West Pacific patterns of genetic differentiation in the high-dispersal starfish *Linckia laevigata. Mol. Ecol.* 126: 99–108.

Williams, S. T. and J. A. H. Benzie. 1998. Evidence of a biogeographic break between populations of a high-dispersal starfish: Congruent regions within the Indo-West Pacific defined by colour morphs, mtDNA, and allozyme data. *Evolution* 52: 87–99.

Willis, B. I. And J. K. Oliver. 1990. Direct tracking of coral larvae: Implications for dispersal in topographically complex environments. *Ophelia* 32: 145–162.

Wilson, R. R. and K. A. Donaldson. 1998. Restriction digest of PCR-amplified mtDNA from fin clips is an assay for sequence genetic tags among hundreds of fish in wild populations. *Mol. Mar. Biol. Biotech.* 7: 39–47.

Wilson, R. R., K. A. Donaldson, M. E. Frischer and T. B. Young. 1997. Mitochondrial DNA control region of common snook and its prospect for use as a genetic tag. *Trans. Amer. Fish. Soc.* 126: 594–606.

Wright, S. 1931. Evolution in Mendelian populations. *Genetics* 16: 97–159.

Wright, S. 1943. Isolation by distance. *Genetics* 28: 114–138.

Wright, S. 1951. The genetical structure of populations. *Ann. Eugen.* 15: 323–353.

Wright, S. 1965. The interpretation of population structure by *F*-statistics with special regard to systems of mating. *Evolution* 19: 395–420.

Young, C. M. 1987. Novelty of "supply-side" ecology. *Science* 235: 415–416.

chapter 4

Natural Disturbance and the Dynamics of Marine Benthic Communities

Wayne P. Sousa

All marine communities, past and present, experience biological or physical disturbance. However, it was not until the publication of Dayton's (1971) classic monograph, "Competition, disturbance and community organization: The provision and subsequent utilization of space in a rocky intertidal community," that disturbance began to be appreciated as one of the key processes that structures marine communities. During the decade prior to Dayton's study, most experimental studies of marine communities focused on the roles of biological interactions such as competition, predation, and herbivory in determining species' distributions and abundances (see references in Connell 1972, 1974; Paine 1977). Although a number of these studies demonstrated that the strengths of such interactions were affected by variation in the physical environment, only near the extremes of environmental gradients were physical stresses considered to play a primary role in determining community structure. There was a clear tendency to emphasize the importance of biological interactions over physical processes, especially among intertidal studies of this period. This emphasis was a byproduct of a concerted effort by numerous investigators to test the long-standing dogma that the structure of intertidal communities was primarily the product of variation in the mechanical and physiological tolerances of the component species to gradients and thresholds in the physical environment (e.g., Colman 1933; Doty 1946). Sanders (1968, p. 267) took this early view to its extreme when he declared, "...all rocky intertidal assemblages, independent of latitude, especially at higher intertidal levels, must be considered predominantly physically regulated communities, and the adaptations are primarily to the physical environment and the biological interactions are poorly developed."

By the time of Dayton's study, the structure of intertidal communities was well known to vary predictably along gradients of wave exposure (Lewis 1964), and transplantation experiments (e.g., Hatton 1938; Harger 1970) had demonstrated the role of wave action as an environmental factor limiting the horizontal distributions of individual species. By highlighting the direct and indirect effects of disturbance in structuring the community as a whole, Dayton's investigation moved the field a giant step forward. In particular, he demonstrated the complementary roles of wave shock and battering by drift logs in renewing primary space. By provisioning open space, a key limiting resource for many species in the community, these disturbances initiated local recolonization and affected the strength and outcome of interspecific competition. The effects of these agents of physical disturbance were spatially and temporally variable, but nonetheless of primary importance across the intertidal zone, not just at the limits of species' distributions.

In the nearly 30 years since the publication of Dayton's monograph, we have learned a lot about natural disturbance in marine communities. This chapter will discuss the role of natural disturbance in structuring marine communities, including its interaction with other processes. For example, through its influence on the species composition and three-dimensional structure of an assemblage and on the physiological state of component individuals, competition can influence the assemblage's susceptibility to disturbance. Reciprocally, by freeing limiting resources from the control of residents, disturbance can alter the rate and outcome of competition and the likelihood that competitors will coexist locally or regionally. Further, characteristics of the disturbance and of the affected patches of habitat can influence the rate and trajectory of succession, in which competitive interactions often play a large role. The spatiotemporal relationships of a series of disturbances affect the structure of the resulting mosaic of successional stages as well as the persistence of competitively inferior "fugitive" species (Hutchinson 1951) within the landscape.

The vast majority of observational and experimental studies of disturbance in marine systems have examined its effects on assemblages of organisms that are sessile or sedentary as adults. This emphasis undoubtedly reflects the relative ease with which the impact of disturbance can be observed and studied in such assemblages, as compared to those comprised of mobile species. Studies of the effects of disturbance on assemblages that live on hard substrata have focused primarily on the larger sessile species that represent the bulk of the biomass, cover, and three-dimensional structure of the assemblage—organisms such as mussels, corals, kelps, and seagrasses. These "structural" species (*sensu* Huston 1994) provide food or habitat for "interstitial" species including mobile organisms (e.g., Orth 1977; Suchanek 1979, 1992; Orth et al. 1984; Summerson and Peterson 1984; Dean and Connell 1987a, b, c; Seed 1996; Connell et al. 1997; Jones and Syms 1998). Therefore, the effects of disturbance on "structural" species may percolate throughout the community. Although most of the examples and much of the conceptual framework presented here concerns the effects of disturbance on assemblages of sessile or sedentary organisms, I devote a separate section to the effects of disturbance on assemblages of mobile species. The chapter focuses on assemblages that live on or in natural substrates as opposed to artificial surfaces (e.g., fouling panels) or containers (e.g., trays or boxes of sediment).

I will examine (1) the features of individuals and assemblages that influence disturbance regimes, (2) the interacting effects of disturbance characteristics and biological processes on patterns of recolonization and subsequent changes in the assemblage, and (3) the effect of disturbance on the persistence and coexistence of species. The chapter ends with a discussion of promising directions for future research.

DEFINITIONS OF TERMS

Disturbance

At the outset, I need to be clear about what I mean by *disturbance* in this chapter. The term has been used rather loosely in the ecological literature (Rykiel 1985). Sometimes, it refers to the external agent or force that causes damage or mortality. In other cases, it refers to the damage or mortality itself, that is, the effect of some external agent or force. I prefer the latter interpretation, and that is the way I use the term here. Even when referring to disturbance as an effect on an ecological system, authors differ in how broadly they apply the term. In some papers, disturbance refers to damage (removal of biomass) or mortality caused by any physical or biological phe-

nomenon, and the adjectives *physical* and *biological* distinguish the nature of the causative agent.

Interpreted most broadly, biological disturbance includes partial or complete consumption of prey by predators or grazers, the deaths of parasitized hosts, harmful alterations of the environment caused by activities of animals (e.g., bioturbation: the reworking and resuspension of soft sediments by feeding and burrowing infauna, Figure 4.1) or movements of plants (e.g., algal whiplash), and the displacement of mobile, space-holding prey due to behavioral escape from predators. Dayton (1975) described a clear case of the latter phenomenon in tide pools on the outer coast of Washington State: large numbers of sea urchins "stampeded" away from a sea star predator, thereby creating open, ungrazed space for algal colonization within tide pools. Biological disturbance also includes inadvertent mortality, damage, or displacement suffered by nonprey species as an indirect result of foraging or other behaviors of consumers. For example, a variety of vertebrate and invertebrate predators in soft-sediment environments displace sediment and nonprey species as they excavate in search of prey (Table 4.1, Figure 4.2a). Likewise, seals inadvertently crush and abrade intertidal invertebrates and algae when they haul out of the water to rest onshore (Boal 1980; Figure 4.2b).

I agree with McGuinness (1987a, p. 417) that applying the term *disturbance* in an umbrella fashion to all sources of damage and mortality including predation, herbivory, and parasitism has little heuristic value and often muddles discus-

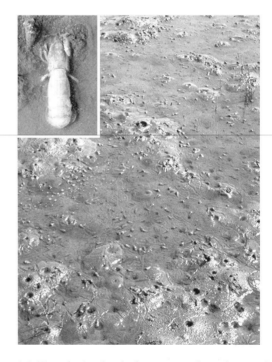

Figure 4.1 Bioturbation by the burrowing ghost shrimp, *Callianassa californiensis*, on a mudflat in Bolinas Lagoon, California. (Photos by the author.)

TABLE 4.1   Kinds of natural disturbance in marine benthic communities.

Agent of disturbance	Direct impacts on organisms or substrate	Habitat or assemblage	Examples
PHYSICAL DISTURBANCE			
Storm waves and currents	Sessile organisms detached or broken; mobile animals displaced, may be injured/ killed	Emergent rocky shore	Jones and Demetropoulos 1968, Seed 1969, Dayton 1971, 1973, 1975, Harger and Landenberger 1971, Paine 1974, Grant 1977, Lubchenco and Menge 1978, Suchanek 1978, Menge 1979, Underwood 1980, 1998, 1999, Paine and Levin 1981, Paine and Suchanek 1983, Sousa 1984, Denny et al 1985, Barry 1989, Vadas et al. 1990, 1992.
		Tide pool	Dethier 1984, Benedetti-Cecchi and Cinelli 1996
		Mangrove prop root epifauna	Bingham and Young 1995
		Coral reef	Stoddart 1963, 1969, 1974, Connell 1973,1978, 1979, Highsmith et al. 1980, Pearson 1981, Kaufman 1983, Walsh 1983, Porter et al. 1981, Woodley et al 1981, Knowlton et al 1981, Rogers et al. 1982, Dollar 1982, Hughes 1989, Bouchon et al. 1991, Dollar and Tribble 1993, Scoffin 1993, Liddell and Ohlhorst 1994,Wulff 1995, Connell et al. 1997
		Kelp forest	Rosenthal et al. 1974, Barrales and Lobban 1975, Dayton and Tegner 1984, Dayton 1985, Ebeling et al. 1985, Kennelly 1987a, b, Tegner and Dayton 1987, Witman 1987, Seymour et al 1989, Dayton et al. 1992,
	Substrate overturned (attached organisms abraded, crushed, smothered, or shaded)	Boulder field	Osman 1977, Lieberman et al. 1979, Sousa 1979a, b, Davis and Wilce 1987, McGuinness 1987a, b
	Sediment and resident organisms eroded and displaced; latter may be injured or killed	Soft sediment	Eagle 1975, Rees et al. 1977, Yeo and Risk 1979, Oliver et al. 1980, Hogue 1982, Moverley et al. 1986, Posey et al. 1996, Okey 1997
		Seagrass beds	Thomas et al. 1961, Patriquin 1975, Birch and Birch 1984, Kirkman 1985, Williams 1988, Kirkman and Kuo 1990, Bouchon et al. 1991, vanTussenbroek 1994, Preen et al. 1995, Reusch and Chapman 1995, Valiela et al. 1998, Bell et al. 1999, Ramage and Schiel 1999
		Salt marsh	Guntenspergen et al. 1995
Wave or current-borne marine or terrigenous sediment	Organisms abraded or buried and smothered	Emergent rocky shore	Markham 1973, Daly and Mathieson 1977, Robles 1982, Seapy and Littler 1982, Taylor and Littler 1982, Littler et al 1983, Turner 1983a, 1985, D'Antonio 1986, McGuinness 1987a, b, Underwood 1998
		Subtidal hard substrate	Airoldi et al. 1996, Airoldi and Cinelli 1997, Airoldi and Virgilio 1998, Airoldi 1998
		Kelp forest	Dayton et al. 1989, Seymour et al. 1989
		Seagrass bed	Onuf and Quammen 1983, Onuf 1987, Preen et al. 1995, Duarte et al. 1997, Bell et al. 1999
		Coral reefs	Hodgson 1990, Rogers 1990, Cortés 1993, Umar et al. 1998, Wesseling et al. 1999
		Soft sediment	Peterson 1985, Onuf and Quammen 1983

TABLE 4.1   *continued*

Agent of disturbance	Direct impacts on organisms or substrate	Habitat or assemblage	Examples
		Salt marsh	Onuf 1987, Rejmanek et al. 1988, Zedler et al. 1992, Guntenspergen et al. 1995, Nyman et al. 1995, Allison 1996
		Mangrove forest	Ellison 1998
Wave or current-borne cobbles	Organisms abraded, crushed, or detached	Emergent rocky shore	Lubchenco and Menge 1978, Sousa 1979b, Wethey 1979, Robles 1982, Underwood 1998
		Tide pool	Dethier 1984, Benedetti-Cecchi and Cinelli 1996, vanTamelen 1996
		Kelp forest	Dayton et al. 1989, Seymour et al. 1989
Drifting logs	Organisms abraded, crushed, or detached	Emergent rocky shore	Dayton 1971, Sousa 1984
		Tide pool	Dethier 1984
		Coral reef flat	J. Cubit, pers comm
		Salt marsh	Seliskar and Gallagher 1983
Ice	Organisms abraded, crushed, or detached; sediments and associated organisms excavated and displaced	Emergent rocky shore	Stephenson and Stephenson 1954, 1972, Schwenke 1971, Keats et al. 1985, Wethey 1985, Minchinton and Scheibling 1991, Åberg 1992 a, b, McCook and Chapman 1997, Minchinton et al. 1997, Pugh and Davenport 1997
		Subtidal hard substrate	Slattery and Bockus 1997, Barnes 1999
		Seagrass bed	Short 1983, Robertson and Mann 1984
		Soft sediment	Dayton et al. 1970, Gordon and Desplanque 1983, Wilson 1988, Lenihan and Oliver 1995, Gutt et al. 1996, Conlan et al. 1998, Sahade et al. 1998
		Salt marsh	Redfield 1972, Richard 1978, Bertness and Grosholz 1985, Roberts and Robertson 1986, Hardwick-Witman 1985
Exfoliation or fracture of rock surface and displacement by strong flow	Substrate removed along with attached organisms	Emergent rocky shore	Frank 1965, DeVogelaere 1991
		Kelp bed	Ebeling et al 1985, Dayton et al. 1989
Tectonic activity that uplifts substrate	Organisms experience increased or permanent aerial exposure with associated desiccation, heat, and UV stress	Emergent rocky shore	Haven 1971, Johansen 1971, Castilla 1988
		Seagrass bed	Johansen 1971
		Coral reef	Stoddart 1972, Cortés 1993
Landslide	Organisms abraded, crushed, or buried and smothered	Emergent rocky shore	Garwood et al 1979
		Subtidal hard substrate	Grange and Singleton 1988, Van Dissen et al 1994, Smith and Witman 1999
Sediment slumps on subtidal slopes	Organisms displaced or buried and smothered	Hard substrate	Slattery and Bockus 1997
		Soft sediment	VanBlaricom 1978, Oliver et al. 1980, Okey 1997
Lava flow or volcanic ash	Organisms injured/killed by hot lava or smothered under ash	Emergent rocky shore	Townsley et al. 1962
		Subtidal hard substrate	Gulliksen et al. 1980
		Seagrass bed	M. Fortes, pers. comm. in Short and Wyllie-Echeverria 1996
		Coral reef	Grigg and Maragos 1974

TABLE 4.1 *continued*

Agent of disturbance	Direct impacts on organisms or substrate	Habitat or assemblage	Examples
Extended aerial exposure	Organisms injured/killed by desiccation, heat, or UV radiation	Emergent rocky shore	Lewis 1954, Hodgkin 1960, Connell 1961, Frank 1965, Sutherland 1970, Ottaway 1973, 1979, Wolcott 1973, Branch 1975, Emerson and Zedler 1978, Menge 1978, Suchanek 1978, Sousa 1979a, Underwood 1980, Seapy and Littler 1982, Taylor and Littler 1982, Tsuchiya 1983, Turner 1983b, Pineda and Escofet 1989
		Coral reef flat	Glynn 1968, 1976, Fishelson 1973, Yamaguchi 1975, Loya 1976, Hay 1981, Fadlallah et al. 1995, Connell et al. 1997
		Seagrass bed	Bell et al. 1999
	Organisms injured/killed by cold or freezing	Emergent rocky shore	Crisp 1964, Connell 1970, Dayton 1971, Paine 1974, Brosnan 1994, Carroll and Highsmith 1996,
		Seagrass bed	R. Thom and C. Simenstad, pers. comm. in Short and Wyllie-Echeverria 1996
		Mangroves	Lugo and Patterson-Zucca 1977
High water temperature	Organisms injured/killed by heat	Tide pools	Hodgkin 1959, Dethier 1984
		Kelp forest	Tegner and Dayton 1987
	Organisms injured/killed by bleaching: loss of symbiotic zooxanthellae (others stressors may be involved)	Coral reef	Brown and Suharsono 1990, Glynn 1990, 1993, Williams and Bunkley-Williams 1990, Glynn and Colgan 1992, Gleason 1993, Jones et al. 1997, Wilkinson et al. 1999
Low water temperature	Organisms injured/killed by cold	Coral reef	Davis 1982, Porter et al. 1982, Bohnsack 1983, Lassig 1983
Freshwater flooding	Organisms injured/killed by osmotic stress or prolonged submergence with anoxia	Subtidal hard substrate	Andrews 1973
		Mangrove prop root epifauna	Goodbody 1961, Farnsworth and Ellison 1996
		Coral reef	Jokiel et al. 1993
		Soft sediment	Thomas and White 1969, Peterson 1975, Moverley et al. 1986, Onuf 1987, Nordby and Zedler 1991
		Salt marsh	Zedler 1983, Zedler et al. 1986, 1992, Guntenspergen et al. 1995
		Mangrove forest	Forbes and Cyrus 1992
High soil salinity	Organisms injured/killed by osmotic stress	Salt marsh	Zedler et al 1992
Anoxia	Organisms injured/killed by metabolic stress	Soft sediment	Boesch et al. 1976, Kitching et al. 1976, Santos and Simon 1980a, b, Boesch and Rabalais 1991, Pihl et al. 1991, 1992, Breitburg 1992, Breitburg et al. 1994, 1997, Diaz and Rosenberg 1995
		Mangrove fishes	Bouchon et al. 1994
Fire	Organisms injured/killed by heat	Salt marsh	Nyman and Chabreck 1995
Lightning strikes	Organisms injured/killed by heat and cavitation	Mangrove forest	Paijmans and Rollet 1977, Smith 1992, Smith et al. 1994, Sousa and Mitchell 1999, Sherman et al. 2000
Storm-related high winds and surge	Plants defoliated, uprooted, or trunks snapped	Mangrove forest	Craighead and Gilbert 1962, Jiménez et al 1985, Bouchon et al. 1991, McGuinness 1992, Roth 1992, Smith et al. 1994, Imbert et al. 1996
		Salt marsh	Chabreck and Palmisano 1973

TABLE 4.1   *continued*

Agent of disturbance	Direct impacts on organisms or substrate	Habitat or assemblage	Examples
Hail	Trees defoliated; branches and trunks injured/killed by impact	Mangrove forest	Houston 1999
BIOLOGICAL DISTURBANCE			
Accumulations of living or dead plant material (i.e., seasonal algal mats, deposits of drifting detached algae or seagrass, or stranded salt marsh wrack)	Organisms buried and smothered or shaded	Soft sediment	Thrush 1986a, Everett 1991, 1994, Gamenick et al. 1996, Thiel et al. 1998
		Seagrass bed	Holmquist 1997
		Salt marsh	Reidenbaugh and Banta 1980, Hartman et al. 1983, Bertness and Ellison 1987, Ellison 1987, Hartman 1988, Bertness 1991, Bertness et al. 1992a, Guntenspergen et al. 1995, Valiela and Rietsma 1995, Brewer and Bertness 1996, Brewer et al. 1998, Pennings and Richards 1998, see Pennings and Bertness, this volume.
Algal whiplash	Organisms abraded; newly settled/recruited especially vulnerable	Emergent rocky shore	Hawkins 1983, Dayton 1975, Benedetti-Cecchi and Cinelli 1992, Vadas et al. 1992
Bioturbation: sediment reworking and resuspension by infaunal burrowers	Organisms buried and suffocated, or sediment load interferes with feeding	Soft sediment	Rhoads and Young 1970, Aller and Dodge 1974, Gray 1974, Rhoads 1974, Myers 1977, Brenchley 1981, Wilson 1981, Rhoads and Boyer 1982, Thayer 1983, Posey 1986, Brey 1991, Everett 1991, Hall 1994, Dahlgren et al. 1999
		Seagrass bed	Philippart 1994, Grant 1983, Short and Wyllie-Echeverria 1996, Suchanek 1983, Harrison 1987
Sediment excavation and redistribution by foraging predators	Organisms displaced, uprooted, or buried and suffocated	Soft sediment	**rays:** Reidenauer and Thistle 1981, Sherman et al. 1983, VanBlaricom 1982, Everett 1991, Thrush et al. 1991; **crabs:** Woodin 1978, 1981, Thrush 1986b, Findlay et al. 1990, Warwick et al. 1990, Hall et al. 1991, 1993, Commito et al. 1995; **sea turtles:** Preen 1996; **whales:** Nerini and Oliver 1983, Johnson and Nelson 1984, Oliver and Kvitek 1984, Oliver and Slattery 1985; **walrus:** Oliver et al. 1985; **sea otters:** Hines and Loughlin 1980, Kvitek et al. 1988; **ducks and gulls:** Savidge and Taghon 1988, Cadée 1990; **bony fishes:** Summers 1980, Billheimer and Coull 1988, Raffaelli et al. 1990
		Seagrass bed, especially margins	**rays:** Orth 1975, Grant 1983, Valentine et al. 1994, Townsend and Fonseca 1998; **crabs:** Valentine et al. 1994, Townsend and Fonseca 1998
Red tide	Organisms suffocated	Soft sediment	Simon and Dauer 1977

sions and models of the phenomenon. In this chapter, I use the term *disturbance* in a more restricted way to mean damage, displacement, or mortality caused by physical agents or incidentally by biotic agents. Such incidental biological disturbance might be caused, for example, by actions of animals other than actual ingestion of prey, by wave-induced algal whiplashing of the substrate, or by burial under plant debris. I readily acknowledge, however, that in some cases, such as disturbance of soft-sediment assemblages by foraging predators, it will be difficult, if not impossible, to determine unambiguously whether an observed reduction in abundance of a resident population was due to predation as opposed to displacement, emigration, or smothering.

How much damage or mortality must these agents cause before we consider it a disturbance? My interest here is with the population and community-level effects of disturbance,

(A)

(B)

Figure 4.2 (A) Pits made by foraging rays on a mudflat on the Gulf coast of Florida; (B) Elephant seal hauled out onto mussel beds at Año Nuevo Island, California. (Photos by the author.)

so an event that does not alter population size or community structure, even though causing physiological or mechanical stress to individuals, would not constitute a disturbance. Only when an organism's tolerance is exceeded, resulting in its death or a sufficient loss of biomass that the recruitment or survival of other individuals is affected, has a disturbance occurred. My use of the terms *stress* and *disturbance* is consistent with Grime's (1977) definitions: A stress reduces an organism's potential for growth whereas a disturbance removes biomass. From a population dynamics perspective, the removal of even a single individual constitutes a disturbance, albeit small and probably inconsequential to overall dynamics. In other words, a disturbance has occurred when a force: (1) kills one or more resident organisms, or (2) damages them sufficiently to indirectly affect the abundance of other organisms, either positively by enhancing opportunities for recruitment, or negatively, by disrupting positive intra- or interspecific interactions.

Disturbance Regime

Individual disturbances vary in their size, severity (degree or amount of damage), and duration. The regime of disturbance at a site is characterized by particular distributions of each of these characteristics, as well as a spatiotemporal pattern of occurrence of each type of disturbance. The term *intensity* is sometimes used synonymously with *severity* (e.g., Sousa 1985; Huston 1994; Connell et al. 1997); that is, an intense disturbance is one that does a lot of damage. However, following Sousa (1984), I will use the term *intensity* to mean the strength of the disturbing force. This follows its definition in physics, as the magnitude of force or energy applied per unit area or volume (*Webster's New Universal Unabridged Dictionary* 1983).

Disturbances range in duration from discrete, short-term events that last for a small fraction of the average life span of the affected species to events that exert their impact over much longer periods, sometimes generations. Connell et al. (1997) referred to disturbances near the extremes of this continuum as "acute" and "chronic," respectively. At some point, as the frequency of acute disturbance increases, the interval between them becomes so short that little if any recovery can occur. At that point, their cumulative effect is identical to that of a single chronic disturbance of similar severity (Chapman and Johnson 1990, p. 113). Note that other authors have defined these terms differently. For example, Westman and O'Leary (1986) used them to denote different severities rather than durations of disturbance, that is, a chronic disturbance reduces biomass partially whereas an acute disturbance removes all biomass. I will use these terms according to Connell et al. (1997).

The frequency and predictability of disturbance are key temporal components of the disturbance regime. Frequency refers to the number of disturbances that occur over an interval of time and can be quantified for a particular point in space or across a larger region (see discussion of spatial scales that follows). The recurrence or return interval is the inverse of local disturbance frequency; it is the average time between disturbances at a particular point in space. The predictability of disturbance is inversely related to the variance in the time between disturbances at a particular location. See Sousa (1984) for details concerning these and other measures of temporal variation in the occurrence of disturbance.

Types of Disturbed Patches

When I refer to a disturbed "patch," I mean a contiguous area or volume in which resident organisms have been disturbed, as defined earlier. Sousa (1985) and Connell and Keough (1985) distinguished two types of habitat patches created by disturbance: (a) patches within continuous habitat, that are bounded by living organisms that were unaffected by the event that damaged or killed the original residents of the patch (Type 1), and (b) patches that are isolated from occupied sites (Type 2). Subsequently, Holt et al. (1995) referred to these two types of patches as "embedded" and "isolated," respectively. In this chapter, I have adopted Holt et al.'s more descriptive names for the two patch types. Patches of space cleared in continuous mussel or algal beds are examples of embedded patches, whereas disturbances that clear the surfaces of more insular substrates such as boulders or bivalve shells create isolated patches. An entirely new substrate that results from a lava flow or landslide could be viewed, at least initially, as a large isolated patch. As discussed in detail later, this distinction has important implications for the mode and rate of patch colonization and for regional population dynamics.

Spatial Scales

How disturbance affects marine communities depends on multiple processes operating across a range of spatial scales. As shorthand, I will often refer to "local" and "regional" scales. By "local" scale, I mean within a patch of disturbed habitat, whereas "regional" scale means an area that encompasses more than one patch of disturbed habitat.

EFFECTS OF DISTURBANCE ON RESOURCE AVAILABILITY AND ENVIRONMENTAL QUALITY

Disturbances often free up limiting resources for exploitation by regenerating survivors and individuals that newly recruit to the disturbed area or by organisms living in its immediate vicinity. In marine benthic assemblages, disturbances most often renew space (usually two-dimensional on hard substrata and three-dimensional in soft sediments) and those resources acquired by organisms while holding space (e.g., nutrients, light, benthic, or suspended food). In some instances, the production or passive accumulation of a limited resource is enhanced by the environmental conditions created by disturbance, increasing its local availability beyond what was present prior to the disturbance or in surrounding undisturbed areas. For example, colonizing infauna feed on organic detritus that differentially accumulates in ray and whale feeding pits (VanBlaricom 1982; Oliver and Slattery 1985). In mangrove forests, soil concentrations of plant-available N can be twice as high within lightning-created canopy gaps (Figure 4.3) where plant uptake is less and warm and sunlit conditions stimulate microbial decomposition, than in the undisturbed, shaded understory (W. Sousa, unpublished data for newly created gaps at Punta Galeta, Panama; N =6, paired t = 4.05, P = 0.01). Disturbances may also make available entirely new kinds of resources. For example, scavenging amphipods feed on wounded infauna left behind in whale or walrus feeding pits (Oliver et al 1985; Oliver and Slattery 1985). Regardless of the mechanism, this increase in resource availability following disturbance often enhances recruitment and growth. Disturbance may also enhance recruitment of particular species by reducing the density and local impact of their natural enemies.

On the other hand, disturbance can increase rates of subsequent mortality by reducing the ameliorating effect of residents on the physical environment or by eliminating refuges from consumers. Particularly severe disturbances can irreversibly change or destroy part or all of the habitat. In the ex-

Figure 4.3 Lightning-created canopy gap in mangrove forest on Punta Galeta, Panama. (Photo by the author.)

treme, a site may become uninhabitable to prior occupants and their offspring. Such disturbance-caused changes in environmental quality can occur either rapidly or gradually. For example, when storm waves broke away a short section of the exposed reef crest on Heron Island, Australia, drainage patterns of the ebbing tide were immediately altered, lethally exposing hundreds of meters of reef crest corals to the air during low tide (Figure 4.4; Connell et al. 1997). Similarly, sudden vertical displacement of substrata by tectonic activity (Haven 1971; Johansen 1971; Stoddart 1972; Castilla 1988; Cortés 1993) has irreversible effects on the local environment. Gradual unidirectional changes in the physical environment can have similar effects over longer time scales. At first, a change in environmental conditions may alter absolute and relative rates of growth, reproduction, and recruitment. In turn, these changes may affect population density and rates

Figure 4.4 Exposed reef crest on Heron Island, Great Barrier Reef, Australia, killed by aerial exposure following storm-caused alterations in drainage of ebbing tidal flow. (Photo by the author.)

and outcomes of biological interactions. As environment conditions continue to change, the levels of one or more physical factors may exceed the physiological tolerances of the affected organisms, directly causing mortality, that is, the stress produces a disturbance. Conditions may have changed to such a degree that juveniles of species that comprised the assemblage on the site prior to the environmental shift cannot reestablish populations. Instances of persistent, large-scale hypoxia, which are increasing in frequency in shallow coastal and estuarine areas due to human-caused eutrophication, fit this scenario (Diaz and Rosenberg 1995). Similarly, gradual warming of nearshore waters appears to have been responsible for marked latitudinal shifts in the species composition of intertidal assemblages in Britain (Southward et al. 1995) and California (Barry et al. 1995; Sagarin et al. 1999). The extent to which these water temperature-related shifts in distribution are driven by increased rates of mortality (i.e., disturbance) of those species that have declined in abundance versus changes in rates of reproduction and recruitment is not known.

Natural disturbances that fundamentally and irreversibly alter habitat quality are certainly important, but uncommon on an ecological time scale. This review focuses on the more typical situation in which the species that occupied the affected area prior to disturbance are potentially able to reestablish populations afterward. It is important to recognize, however, that many forms of human-caused disturbance and environmental change cause very long term, and often irreversible changes in environmental conditions—both abiotic and biotic—that dictate the rate and pattern of regeneration. See Steneck and Carleton (this volume) for a detailed discussion of such anthropogenic impacts on marine populations.

AGENTS AND REGIMES OF NATURAL DISTURBANCE IN MARINE COMMUNITIES

Numerous agents of physical and incidental biological disturbance have been documented from marine communities (Table 4.1). Previous reviews cover in detail the effects of disturbance on specific marine communities including rocky seashores (Sousa 1985), subtidal hard substrata (Connell and Keough 1985), coral reefs (Pearson 1981; Huston 1985; Connell 1997; Jones and Syms 1998), soft sediments (Thistle 1981; Probert 1984; Hall 1994; Hall et al. 1994), and seagrasses (Short and Wyllie-Echeverria 1996). The habitat-specific chapters in this volume update this information. A suite of different disturbance agents may affect any particular assemblage, each with its own spatial and temporal regime. Some are tightly linked in space and time. For example, forces associated with strong water currents apply potentially damaging mechanical stress to organisms, but also often carry sediments or projectiles that may abrade, crush, or break them.

Detailed, quantitative records of natural disturbance regimes in marine habitats are steadily accumulating. Such records are difficult to maintain for more than relatively short periods due to intermittent research funding, the labor-intensive nature of the work, and the limited opportunities for

publishing the results of monitoring programs. Most of those documented in studies listed in Table 4.1 were gathered over the course of a single experimental study, usually conducted at one location and lasting no more than a year or two. Thus, we know little about spatial and temporal variation in disturbance regimes within a given habitat. Such short-term records tend, on average, to miss rare, large, and severe disturbance events (Weatherhead 1986; see Connell and Sousa 1983 for a similar conclusion concerning the effect of census record length on estimates of population variability). Although long-term studies are less likely to miss these extreme events, they have tended to focus on the major interannual events (e.g., cyclone damage to reefs, Connell et al. 1997; effects of El Niño-Southern Oscillation (ENSO) associated storms on kelp forests, Dayton et al. 1992), with less attention to smaller-scale disturbances that occur on the time scale of days, weeks, or months.

Spatial Variation in Disturbance

Within a geographic region, the disturbance regime in a particular habitat varies from site to site. For example, Dayton (1971) showed that the risk of being battered by drift logs differed substantially among his rocky intertidal study sites in Puget Sound and on the outer coast of Washington State. The relative importance of different agents of disturbance may also vary among sites as Wethey (1979) found for ice scour and cobble impact, the primary agents of physical disturbance to intertidal barnacle populations in New England. Such spatial variation is the norm and has been well documented in rocky intertidal (e.g., in addition to the studies just cited, Sousa 1979b; Paine and Levin 1981; Dethier 1984; McGuinness 1987a; Farrell 1989), kelp forest (e.g., Foster and Schiel 1985; Seymour et al. 1989), coral reef (e.g., Connell 1978; Aronson and Precht 1995; Connell et al. 1997), salt marsh (e.g., Valiela and Rietsma 1995; Pennings and Bertness, this volume), seagrass (e.g., Kirkman and Kuo 1990; Townsend and Fonseca 1998), and soft-sediment (e.g., Oliver et al 1980) communities.

Variation in the frequency of particular kinds of disturbance occurs at larger spatial scales as well. For example, winter ice is a common source of disturbance to rocky seashores, salt marshes, and soft-sediment habitats at higher latitudes (see examples in Table 4.1), but with decreasing latitude, the climate warms, and the frequency of ice damage declines to zero. Hurricane winds frequently disturb the canopies of mangrove forests in the central and northern Caribbean region (Figure 4.5; Craighead and Gilbert 1962; Jiménez et al. 1985; Roth 1992; Smith et al. 1994; Imbert et al. 1996), but rarely affect the forests of Panama or South America. Other geographical gradients in the quantity and quality of disturbance can be subtler. For example, in northern marshes along the Atlantic coast of the U. S., wrack deposition that kills marsh plants is an important disturbance (Figure 4.6), although its effects are variable among marshes (e.g., Hartman et al. 1983; Hartman 1988; Bertness and Ellison 1987; Valiela and Rietsma 1995; Pennings and Bertness, this

Figure 4.5 Stands of mangroves killed and defoliated by high winds associated with Hurricane Andrew in 1992, on the shores of Biscayne Bay, Florida. (Photo by the author.)

volume). In southern marshes, however, wrack deposits are much lighter, and they may even benefit marsh plants by reducing evaporative water loss from soils and thereby limiting salt buildup in soils (Pennings and Richards 1998).

Temporal Variation in Disturbance

The intensities and frequencies of disturbing forces vary in time as well, often seasonally and among years. Numerous studies have documented the seasonal effects of wave action and storm surge. For example, on the outer coast of Washington State, the mean rate at which patches are cleared in beds of the mussel, *Mytilus californianus*, is more than an order of magnitude greater in winter when large storm waves strike

Figure 4.7 Patch recently cleared in mussel beds on Bodega Head in central California (quadrant is 0.25 m²). (Photo by the author.)

the shore than during summer when waves are much smaller (Figure 4.7; Paine and Levin 1981). Also, the rate of bed disturbance varies 4- to 5-fold among years, depending on the frequency and intensity of storm activity. Wethey (1979, 1985) documented strong seasonality and interannual variability in the physical disturbances that kill intertidal barnacles at Nahant, Massachusetts. Similarly, in southern California, intertidal boulders are much more likely to be moved and overturned in winter when waves are large than in summer when they are small (Figure 4.8; Sousa 1979b). Rates of

Figure 4.6 Accumulations of wrack in the Rumstick Cove salt marsh, Narragansett Bay, Rhode Island. (Photo by J. Levine.)

Figure 4.8 Overturned intertidal boulder covered with early successional green algae surrounded by undisturbed boulders dominated by late successional red algae at Ellwood Beach in southern California. (Photo by the author.)

movement are also higher in stormier years. There are, however, some notable exceptions to the seasonal pattern of disturbance in intertidal habitats. In some areas of the world, such as the coast of New South Wales, Australia, rough weather and large storm waves can occur at any time of year with no obvious seasonality in the disturbance they cause (Underwood 1981; McGuinness 1987a).

Disturbance in subtidal, hard substrate habitats is also usually seasonal and variable among years. Kelp forests in southern California are disturbed by strong surge generated by winter storms, which vary in frequency and intensity among years depending on the strength of ENSO conditions (Dayton et al. 1992). Wave action and strong currents associated with cyclones are important agents of disturbance to corals on Heron Island on Australia's Great Barrier Reef (Connell et al. 1997). Cyclonic storms are strongly seasonal in this area (early January to early April), but quite unpredictable in occurrence from year to year. Cyclones passed near the island in 11 out of the 30 study years, but caused significant damage in only 5 of them. Similarly, coral bleaching (Figure 4.9) has most often occurred during the summer or near the end of a protracted warming period associated with ENSO events, but the onset of these conditions is irregular at any one location (Glynn 1993; Jones et al. 1997; Wilkinson et al. 1999).

In soft-sediment environments, the primary agents of disturbance change seasonally. In many areas, lethal hypoxia is a natural phenomenon that regularly develops as the water column becomes sharply stratified during warm summer or autumnal months (e.g., Kitching et al. 1976; Santos and Simon 1980a, b; Diaz and Rosenberg 1995); in other areas, these conditions are aperiodic or persistent. Sediment disturbance by foraging predators (e.g., Woodin 1978, 1981; Reidenauer and Thistle 1981; VanBlaricom 1982; Oliver et al. 1984; Oliver and Slattery 1985; Thrush et al. 1991; Townsend and Fonseca 1998) and bioturbation by infauna (Rhoads 1974) also typically occur in summer or fall when these organisms are most active or abundant on the feeding grounds. In contrast, wave action and strong currents displace and kill infau-

nal populations primarily during the winter storm season (e.g., Eagle 1975; Rees et al. 1977; Yeo and Risk 1979), although cyclones and hurricanes can have important effects, albeit irregularly, at other times of year.

Spatiotemporal Variation in Disturbance

The season of occurrence of a particular kind of disturbance can vary among local sites or geographically. For example, mortality due to heat and desiccation stress at low tide occurs during periods of calm, clear weather when there is little wave splash to ameliorate these harsh conditions. Along the Pacific coast of North America, the seasonal timing of such events depends on local tidal and climatic regimes. In southern California, these stressful conditions occur in winter, when extreme low tides shift into daylight hours and frequently coincide with hot and dry Santa Ana wind conditions (Sousa 1979a; Seapy and Littler 1982). At more northern latitudes (northern California, Oregon, and Washington), daytime low tides and long, desiccating exposures occur in summer (Frank 1965; Sutherland 1970; Dayton 1971; Cubit 1984). Patterns of intertidal inundation by sand exhibits similar interactions between site and season. Most commonly, sand is deposited in summer, when wave energy and current velocities are low (Hedgepeth 1957; Markham 1973; Daly and Mathieson 1977; Robles 1982; D'Antonio 1986), but at certain sites, unique aspects of the local topography and current regime, or proximity to flooding streams and rivers, combine to cause higher deposition of sand or terrigenous sediments in winter (Seapy and Littler 1982; Taylor and Littler 1982; Littler et al. 1983; Turner 1985; D'Antonio 1986).

Variation in Disturbance Size

The sizes of disturbed areas often vary over several orders of magnitude within a given habitat. They range from as small as the space created by the death of a single organism, or part thereof, to in some cases, areas of many square kilometers (e.g., due to hypoxia: Santos and Simon 1980a, b; Boesch and Rabalais 1991; Diaz and Rosenberg 1995; or coral bleaching: Brown and Suharsono 1990; Glynn 1990, 1993; Wilkinson et al. 1999). The size distribution of the disturbed patches created by any particular agent will vary seasonally and among years and sites, reflecting temporal and spatial variation in the intensity of the disturbing force. Paine and Levin (1981) documented such variability in size for patches cleared by wave forces in beds of the mussel, *Mytilus californianus*, on the outer coast of Washington State. Patches created during relatively calm summer months or at protected mainland sites were an order of magnitude smaller than those generated in stormy winter months or at sites receiving heavy wave action. Similarly, I found that the percentage of large intertidal boulders moved by waves was greater in winter months and at the more exposed of my two study sites (Sousa 1979b).

Correlations among Disturbance Characteristics

Depending on the particular habitat, agent of disturbance, and affected organisms, two or more of the disturbance characteristics (size, severity, and frequency) may be correlated.

Figure 4.9 Bleached coral colonies on the shallow fore-reef of Moorea, French Polynesia. (Photo by M. Gleason.)

Generally, large severe disturbances occur less frequently and predictably than smaller, less severe ones (Connell and Keough 1985; Sousa 1985). Often, this simply reflects the frequency distribution of storm intensities and severity of damage they cause, but as discussed in the next section, there may be temporal changes in characteristics of individual organisms or assemblages of organisms that affect their vulnerability to disturbance. In such cases, the disturbance regime will be the product of the interaction between the rate and pattern of these "ontogenetic" changes in vulnerability and the timing and intensity of different agents of disturbance.

SUSCEPTIBILITY OF INDIVIDUALS AND ASSEMBLAGES TO DISTURBANCE

The severity of a disturbance depends on the intensity of the disturbing force, the vulnerability of the target organisms, and in some cases, qualities of the substratum to which the organisms are attached. Vulnerability to disturbance varies with the particular agent of disturbance and with characteristics of affected species, individuals, and assemblages.

Characteristics of Species Affect Disturbance Rates

Species-specific differences in vulnerability are often related to inherent morphological or physiological features, as demonstrated in the following studies from hard substrate and soft-sediment environments. Due to their less robust skeleton and upright growth form, erect branching corals suffer greater damage from wave forces associated with cyclones than massive or encrusting species (Connell 1976, 1978, 1979; Porter et al. 1981;Woodley et al. 1981; Liddell and Ohlhorst 1994; Hughes 1989; Connell et al. 1997). Similarly, vulnerability to damage from storm surge differs among species of erect coral reef sponges, apparently due to differences in the composition of their skeletal fibers (Wulff 1995). Variation in morphological characteristics and physiological tolerances explains interspecific differences in the loss of cover and mortality suffered by rocky intertidal algae and invertebrates due to desiccation, high or low air temperatures, exposure to wave action, or burial and scour by sand or terrigenous sediments (Schonbeck and Norton 1978, 1979; Sousa 1980; Seapy and Littler 1982; Taylor and Littler 1982; Littler et al. 1983; Lüning 1984; D'Antonio 1986; Lüning and Freshwater 1988; Chapman 1995). For similar reasons, salt marsh plant species differ in their response to burial under wrack and soil hypersalinity (Bertness and Ellison 1987; Bertness et al. 1992a; Valiela and Rietsma 1995). Anoxic or hypoxic conditions and associated high concentrations of hydrogen sulfide cause differential mortality among species living in soft-sediment environments (Diaz and Rosenberg 1995; Gamenick et al. 1996). Such conditions can develop beneath dense, seasonal algal mats on intertidal mud flats. Mobile taxa that feed at the sediment-water interface and deeply buried deposit feeders are little affected, but sedentary species that feed at the sediment-water interface, including bivalves and tubicolous suspension feeders, suffer high mortality (Everett 1991, 1994). Species of bivalves with long siphons that can be extended through the mat survive better than those with short, less-extensible siphons that are unable to penetrate it (Thiel et al. 1998). Peterson (1985) found that different species of bivalves differ in their ability to survive burial under sediments, with deposit feeders surviving better than suspension feeders, and smaller species of deposit feeders surviving better than larger ones.

Characteristics of Individual Organisms Affect Disturbance Rates

The size and shape of an individual organism, and ontogenetic changes in these features, affect its vulnerability to potentially disturbing forces, contributing to variation in disturbance rates within and among species. These effects are very evident when organisms are subjected to the forces associated with flowing water, an important agent of disturbance in marine intertidal and subtidal communities. Organisms living in flow experience drag, lift, and accelerational forces (Koehl 1982, 1984; Denny et al. 1985; Denny 1988, 1995, 1999; Gaylord et al. 1994; Gaylord 2000). As an organism grows, with associated changes in shape and volume, the relative magnitudes of these forces also change. Generally speaking, as an organism grows larger, the hydrodynamic forces impinging on it increase, making adhesive failure or breakage more likely. Ongoing studies are attempting to identify the specific forces that disturb intertidal organisms and determine the degree to which they are responsible for setting an upper limit to the size of organisms living on wave-swept shores. See Denny and Wethey (this volume) for a detailed treatment of the influence of hydrodynamic forces on marine organisms and communities.

Size and shape also affect an organism's vulnerability to agents of disturbance such as desiccation and extreme air temperatures. In this case, the influence of these morphological traits is often indirect, reflecting the physiological consequences of changing surface-to-volume ratios. Smaller individuals with their greater surface-to-volume ratio are more likely to be killed by environmental extremes because their internal condition is less buffered from rapid or large changes in the external environment. Among intertidal invertebrates, small individuals have been shown to suffer higher mortality than large ones under the same regime of desiccation. Examples include barnacles (Connell 1961), limpets (Wolcott 1973), and sea anemones (Ottaway 1973, 1979; Pineda and Escofet 1989). Similarly, differences in thallus size and shape, by their influence on surface-to-volume ratios, contribute to variation in desiccation resistance within and among species of intertidal algae (Schonbeck and Norton 1979; Dromgoole 1980; Bell 1995). On the other hand, as discussed later, the microclimate experienced by small individuals is often moderated by the presence of larger neighboring organisms that block the wind, cast shade, or retain moisture.

In some cases, smaller size is advantageous in stressful environments. For example, small individuals may be better able than larger ones to escape extremes of the physical environment by moving into cracks and crevices in the substratum (Figure 4.10). When suspension-feeding bivalve popula-

Figure 4.10 Littorine snails in a rock crevice on Bodega Head in central California—note the greater number of small individuals occupying the refuge. (Photo by the author.)

tions become buried beneath sediment, small individuals suffer less mortality than large ones, because small clams are better able to reestablish their normal vertical feeding positions in the unconsolidated new sediment (Peterson 1985).

Aggregation and Species Interactions Affect Disturbance Rates

Living in either conspecific or heterospecific groups can alter an individual's risk of being damaged or killed by an agent of disturbance. Whereas living at high density in physically benign habitats often increases the risk of mortality due to competition and, in some cases, disturbance by hydrodynamic forces (see later examples), living at high density often lowers the risk of mortality in physically harsh environments because the presence of neighbors directly or indirectly buffers environmental extremes. For example, at physically stressful higher tidal elevations, the barnacle, *Semibalanus balanoides*, suffers less mortality when living in medium- to high-density aggregations than at low density (Bertness 1989). A dense cover of barnacles shields the rock surface from the sun so that it remains cooler than areas where barnacles are sparser. Because rock temperature is the primary determinant of barnacle tissue temperature, barnacles in dense aggregations experience less thermal stress. Mussels (*Mytilus edulis* and *Guekensia demissa*) and fucoid algae (*Fucus distichus* and *Ascophyllum nodosum*) also suffer less mortality from heat and desiccation near the upper limit of their vertical distributions when living at high as compared to low density (Bertness and Leonard 1997). Similarly, rocky intertidal sea anemones (e.g., *Actinia tenebrosa*: Ottaway 1979; *Anthopleura elegantissima*: Pineda and Escofet 1989) and algae on coral reef flats (Hay 1981) survive desiccation better when living in clonal aggregations and turfs, respectively, than as solitary individuals. Heat and desiccation stress are not the only agents of disturbance that can be ameliorated by living in aggregations. In high-latitude salt marshes, mussels (*G. demissa*) living in beds suffer less mortality from winter ice scour that do isolated mussels (Bertness and Grosholz 1985).

Heterospecific associations can also reduce the rate of disturbance in physically stressful habitats. For example, mortality from thermal and desiccation stress is often reduced for intertidal algae that live beneath the canopy of other species (Dayton 1975). Beds of the mussel, *Mytilus californianus*, that become overgrown with algal turfs are less likely to be killed by freezing air temperatures, although algae-covered mussels have lower body weights and suffer modestly higher rates of dislodgment by intense wave action (Brosnan 1994). Reusch and Chapman (1995) demonstrated experimentally that mussels (*Mytilus edulis*) living within stands of eelgrass (*Zostera marina*) were less likely to be dislodged during storms of moderate intensity than mussels living without eelgrass neighbors. However, eelgrass afforded mussels no measurable protection from dislodgement during intense storms. There was no evidence of a reciprocal effect: the presence versus absence of mussels made no difference to the storm damage suffered by patches of eelgrass.

The presence of other species may also afford protection from agents of biological disturbance. For example, infaunal invertebrates that live amongst dense seagrass (e.g., Orth 1977; Orth et al. 1984; Summerson and Peterson 1984; Townsend and Fonseca 1998) or large worm tubes (Woodin 1978) suffer lower mortality from the activities of foraging crabs or rays than those that inhabit areas of the bottom where seagrasses or worm tubes are sparse or absent. High densities of seagrass stems and rhizomes or worm tubes interfere with the movement and foraging behaviors of these epifaunal predators, creating refugia not only from predation but also from the negative effects of being displaced or buried as crabs and rays excavate or otherwise disturb surface sediments while searching for food or simply moving about the bottom.

In other instances, an increase in the local density of organisms and associated effects of competition on the morphology or physiology of individuals, and, in some cases, on the three-dimensional structure of the assemblage increases the per capita risk of mortality due to disturbance. For example, when barnacles settle densely at lower tidal heights and experience little predation, they soon grow to fill the available space. The ensuing competition forces neighboring individuals to coalesce and form hummocks of weakly attached, elongate individuals (Figure 4.11; Barnes and Powell 1950; Connell 1961; Menge 1976; Grant 1977; Bertness 1989; Bertness et al. 1998). These hummocks of barnacles are more easily torn loose by wave action than are isolated individuals of the conical or columnar form that develops under less-crowded conditions. Similarly, although mussels living in beds may experience a lower per capita risk of dislodgement by wave forces as compared to isolated mussels (Bell and Gosline 1997), as mussel beds become older and multilayered, the risk of massive dislodgment and patch formation increases (Harger and Landenberger 1971; Paine 1974; Paine and Levin 1981). Multilayered beds of the mussel, *Mytilus californianus*, have a higher profile than single-layered beds, exhibit areas of hummocking where groups of densely packed individuals have been lifted away from the substratum, and a higher proportion of their members are attached by byssal threads to other mussels

Figure 4.11 Hummocked barnacles—unstable elongate individuals at center have been removed by wave action. (Photo by the author.)

Figure 4.12 Entangled, detached kelp plants washed onto a beach in California following a large winter storm. (Photo by M. Foster.)

rather than to the rock surface. Lift, generated by the pressure difference between the slow-moving water in the interstices within the bed and the fast-moving water within waves that break over it, detaches individual mussels (Denny 1987). Once a few mussels have been removed, the features of multilayered beds just described make it likely that sections of the "fabric" of the bed will begin flapping in flow and be peeled away from the substratum forming a bare patch. Thus, up to a point, mussels reduce their risk of being disturbed by wave forces by living in beds, but once the bed becomes deeply layered, the risk of massive dislodgment increases.

Similarly, algae that grow in aggregations may face a greater risk of disturbance than isolated individuals. For example, in dense kelp beds, broken, as well as intact, plants frequently become entangled with neighbors (e.g., *Macrocystis pyrifera*, Rosenthal et al. 1974; Dayton et al. 1984; Seymour et al. 1989; Dayton et al. 1992; *Nereocystis luetkeana*, Koehl and Wainwright 1977). When these clumps of tangled thalli are subjected to a current, the holdfasts and stipes of intact members of the tangle experience increased drag, compared to untangled individuals. As a result, holdfasts of entangled intact plants can be ripped from the substratum, or their stipes broken (Figure 4.12). By comparison, kelp plants growing in sparser beds are less likely to become entangled with their neighbors and experience a lower rate of this kind of disturbance.

Populations that have experienced a history of competition for food may suffer higher rates of mortality (i.e., disturbance) following severe environmental conditions than populations that have not. For example, when buried under sediment, suspension-feeding clams that had been maintained at high densities suffered nearly twice the mortality of clams that had been growing at low density over the same period of time (Peterson and Black 1988). The former showed clear symptoms of competitive stress prior to the addition of sediment, including lower shell growth and gonadal weight, and higher mortality than low-density controls. Apparently, competition among

clams for suspended food when growing at high density compromises their ability to survive the physiological stresses associated with burial under sediment. Peterson (1985) documented similar density-dependent mortality of suspension-feeding bivalve following a natural sedimentation event.

Heterospecific associations can increase the risk of disturbance. For example, heavily epiphytized macroalgae are more likely to be detached or broken by hydrodynamic forces than nonepiphytized individuals (Menge 1975; Sousa 1979a; D'Antonio 1985). Likewise, subtidal mussels that have been overgrown by kelp plants are much more susceptible to being torn loose by storm surge than mussels that are free of kelp; by reducing kelp cover, urchin grazing indirectly increases mussel survival (Witman 1987).

Partial predation, herbivory, and parasitism can also indirectly increase the mortality caused by a potentially disturbing force. For example, wounds from grazing or boring organisms increase the risk of breakage because the force is imposed on a smaller cross-sectional area, that is, the mechanical stress is increased (Black 1976; Koehl and Wainwright 1977; Santelices et al. 1980; Tegner et al. 1995). Likewise, animal parasites may reduce the physiological tolerance of their host to environmental extremes, and thereby increase the mortality they cause. For example, the salt marsh snail, *Cerithidea californica*, is much more likely to be killed by low oxygen conditions if it is infected with larval digenetic trematodes than if it is uninfected (Sousa and Gleason 1989).

Effects of Species Diversity and Composition on Disturbance Rates

So far, I have discussed how individual and population-level characteristics and pair-wise species interactions can affect the rate of disturbance. The frequency and severity of disturbance also varies among assemblages differing in species composition and diversity. In most cases, these assemblage-level differences seem to reflect characteristics of their dominant species, but there have been very few marine studies that have explicitly addressed the question of whether there are higher-order properties that cause multispecies assemblages to differ in their resistance to potentially disturbing forces. In other words, does the aggregate response of a multi-species assemblage to a disturbing force, in terms of lost cover or biomass, differ from what would be the sum of independent responses by the member species?

Two studies conducted with assemblages of intertidal macroalgae have tested for such higher-order effects. I experimentally disturbed intertidal boulders that supported different successional stages (see Figure 4.8) by overturning them for different lengths of time, effectively manipulating the intensity of disturbance (Sousa 1980). These successional stages differed in species composition and diversity. I measured both the severity of damage (i.e., loss of percent cover) and the pattern of regeneration after the boulders were righted. In terms of resistance to disturbance, our present focus, differences among the assemblages in the amount of cover lost at a given intensity of disturbance were entirely explained by physiological and life history characteristics of the component species. Early successional assemblages suffered the greatest loss of cover for a given length of overturning because they were dominated by the ephemeral, sheetlike, green alga *Ulva sp.*, which is particularly vulnerable to abrasion and shading. Late successional assemblages, dominated by the perennial red alga, *Gigartina canaliculata*, suffered the least damage, because this species has a tougher, more elastic thallus and is shade tolerant. Middle successional assemblages, being a diverse mixture of these two species plus several other perennial red algae, were intermediate in their resistance to damage. Diversity per se had no additional influence on the amount of cover lost to disturbance.

The second study, by Allison (1997), tested the effects of species diversity and composition on the resistance and resilience of a high intertidal, algal-dominated assemblage to an experimental heat treatment. He selectively weeded plots to create macroalgal assemblages that differed in diversity and species composition, then exposed them to a heat lamp for 90 minutes. Changes in algal cover over the first month following the heat treatment were considered a measure of the resistance of the experimental assemblages to change. Allison found that differences in pretreatment cover and biomass explained the greatest proportion of the variance among plots with respect to resistance; the greater the cover and biomass prior to heat treatment, the greater the loss of cover and biomass in response to the treatment. Similar to my result (Sousa 1980), most of the significant effects of the diversity manipulation on resistance to damage were parsimoniously explained by characteristics of the component populations, rather than by some higher-order effect of species diversity per se. For example, higher diversity treatments, especially those dominated by fucoids, suffered greater loss than lower diversity treatments because, on average, the diverse plots had greater cover and biomass than the low diversity plots, that is, they had more to lose.

Differences in the vulnerability of different successional stages to disturbance can dictate the temporal patterning of disturbance in a habitat. Fairly predictable cycles of disturbance may result if later stages are more vulnerable than earlier ones. For example, on the outer coast of Washington State, where patches are cleared in beds of the mussel, *Mytilus californianus*, by a combination of wave forces and the impact of drifting logs (see Figure 4.7; Dayton 1971; Paine 1974; Suchanek 1978, 1979, 1981; Paine and Levin 1981), succession proceeds through a series of stages dominated in turn by diatoms, macroalgae, barnacles, and finally, back to mussels. Mussel beds, particularly older multilayered ones, are more likely to be dislodged by wave action than are earlier successional stands of macroalgae or barnacles. Thus, the rate at which species are replaced during succession, in this case by hierarchical interspecific competition, will control, to some degree, the frequency of disturbance. The complete successional sequence from diatoms to mussels takes a minimum of 7–8 years, and this is approximately the interval between successive disturbances of the same patch of space at the most exposed sites (Paine and Levin 1981). The recurrence interval is longer at less-exposed sites.

The frequency of disturbance need not always be influenced by the successional state of the assemblage. In intertidal boulder fields, I studied (see Figure 4.8; Sousa 1979a, b, 1980) the sessile organisms that grew on the upper surfaces of the boulders consisted mostly of short, turflike macroalgae and barnacles. Successional variation in the composition of these assemblages probably has little, if any, influence on the probability that wave forces would overturn a boulder. Similarly, the occurrence of landslides and lava flows that kill benthic organisms are unaffected by the abundance, size or age of their victims.

Substrates Affect Disturbance Rates

Characteristics of the substrate itself can influence the disturbance regime. Barnes and Topinka (1969) showed that the force required to detach the alga *Fucus* from the test of a barnacle is less than that necessary to remove it from the rock surface itself. In some cases, the adhesive strength of an organism exceeds that of other organisms to which it is attached, or the breaking stress of the rock itself. When the rock or host organism breaks, the attached individual is carried away (Dayton 1973; Denny et al. 1985; Witman 1987; Bell and Gosline 1997).

REGENERATION OF SESSILE ASSEMBLAGES FOLLOWING DISTURBANCE

Environmental Alterations That Affect Regeneration

As discussed by Connell et al. (1997), disturbances not only kill or damage resident organisms, but also directly or indirectly alter the biological or physical environment of survivors and individuals that recruit to the affected area following the event. These alterations of the environment can strongly influence subsequent patterns of recolonization and succession. Direct changes to the physical environment include alterations of the substrate and local topography, which in turn affect currents, light levels, and sedimentation rates. Direct impacts on the biological environment include changes in the abundance and distribution of associated species that potentially interact with the residents. The biological environment will be indirectly modified by disturbances that alter the local abundance of spatial refuges, food, or nutrients available to resident species or others that interact with them, or the supply of propagules.

Life History and Mode of Reestablishment

There are four mechanisms by which populations become reestablished in a patch of disturbed substrate or sediment: (1) vegetative regrowth of survivors within the patch; (2) recruitment from propagules that survive the disturbance (e.g., seed banks in salt marshes: Hopkins and Parker 1984; Hutchings and Russell 1989; Ungar and Woodell 1993, 1996; Baldwin et al. 1996; Baldwin and Mendelssohn 1998; Staniforth et al. 1998; seagrass beds: Inglis 2000; banks of microscopic juvenile stages of algae on rocky seashores: Santelices et al. 1995; Blanchette 1996; Worm et al. 1999; Edwards 2000); (3) lateral inward encroachment by juveniles or adults from the surrounding undisturbed assemblage, by vegetative spreading, active movement, or passive transport in flow; and (4) recruitment from dispersing propagules including spores, larvae, or fragments capable of attaching to the substrate and growing vegetatively. Of the four, the role of seed and spore banks is the least well documented. The relative contributions of these different modes of recolonization depend in part on the severity of the initial disturbance, as does the rate of recovery. Following disturbances that cause low to moderate levels of damage, vegetative propagation is often the predominant mechanism of recovery for populations of species that are able to survive their injuries and regrow (e.g., red algal turfs, fucoid algae, crustose and rhizoidal species: Dayton 1975; Lubchenco and Menge 1978; Lubchenco 1980; Sousa 1980; Dethier 1984; Williams 1988; McCook and Chapman 1992; Airoldi 1998; Scrosati 1998; Underwood 1998; Umar et al. 1998; corals: Connell 1973; Highsmith et al 1980; Tunnicliffe 1981; Highsmith 1982; Fong and Lirman 1995; Smith and Hughes 1999; salt marsh plants: Allison 1995, 1996; Bertness and Ellison 1987; Baldwin and Mendelssohn 1998; seagrasses: Patriquin 1975; Short 1983; Turner 1983a, b; 1985; Kirkman 1985; Williams 1988, 1990; Kirkman and Kuo 1990; Rollon et al. 1998; Bell et al. 1999; Ramage and Schiel 1999; Rasheed 1999). If vegetative regrowth is sufficiently robust, it may even preempt the space and inhibit propagule settlement or juvenile recruitment (Denley and Underwood 1979; Sousa 1979a; Connell et al. 1997; Osman and Whitlatch 1995a, b). As the severity of disturbance increases, the fragments of clonal species that remain are so small or damaged that they cannot reestablish or survive, and their populations can only regenerate via colonists from outside the patch. For example, on coral reefs, the stronger the disturbance, the less vegetative

recovery, because surviving fragments are badly scoured and suffer delayed mortality (Knowlton et al 1981).

For nonclonal invertebrates (e.g., mussels, barnacles, some tunicates, and most infaunal species) and many kelps, disturbance is an all-or-none phenomenon. Lacking the ability for somatic regeneration, such solitary organisms (*sensu* Jackson 1977a) are either killed or displaced (i.e., disturbed), or left intact and in place (i.e., not disturbed). For example, patches newly cleared in continuous mussel beds or stands of barnacles are initially devoid of living macroorganisms (Paine and Levin 1981), leaving no opportunity for vegetative regeneration. When recolonization is completely dependent on propagules arriving from outside the patch, recovery will generally be slower than in situations where vegetative regeneration plays a substantive role in regeneration (Connell and Slatyer 1977, see later examples).

Severity of Initial Damage

Only the most severe disturbances remove all resident individuals from the affected area. Such events are relatively rare. More typically, some resident organisms are killed or displaced, but others either sustain injuries from which they recover or escape harm altogether (Foster and Sousa 1985; Malanson 1984). As discussed in the last section, the capacity for vegetative regrowth is a critical life history feature that often affects the rate and course of succession. Given how common this situation is, it is surprising how few experimental studies have explicitly compared the response of assemblages to different severities of disturbance. One would expect assemblages to recover more quickly and with greater fidelity from disturbances of low to moderate severity as compared to those that kill most or all of the residents.

This prediction held true for the boulder field algal assemblage that I experimentally disturbed in the manner described earlier (Sousa 1980). Regardless of successional stage, assemblages growing on the upper surface of boulders that were overturned for shorter periods recovered more rapidly and completely than those that suffered greater damage from longer periods of overturning. Other studies that have manipulated the severity of disturbance include De Vogelaere's (1991) of an intertidal algal-invertebrate assemblage, Underwood's (1998) of stands of the intertidal fucoid alga, *Hormosira banksii*, and Airoldi's (1998) of a red algal turf-dominated assemblage in the shallow subtidal. These studies experimentally mimicked partial disturbance to compare its effects on successional dynamics to those of complete clearing. Partial disturbance consisted of superficially removing macroalgal and/or invertebrate cover, leaving behind live algal holdfasts and crusts. All living cover, including holdfasts and crusts, was removed from the complete disturbance plots. All three studies found that the severity of experimental disturbance affected the rate and pattern of recolonization. Assemblages that developed in partially disturbed plots converged more rapidly with those in unmanipulated control plots, in terms of species composition and extent of algal and invertebrate cover, than did completely cleared plots. De Vogelaere and Airoldi observed that completely cleared plots underwent a longer succession, the stages of which were characterized by species that never became common in the partially cleared plots. Underwood found that grazers had a greater impact on *Hormosira* recolonization in the complete than partial removal plots.

Kennelly (1987b) examined, with a series of field manipulations, the effects on understory algae and invertebrates of different severities of disturbance to the canopy of an *Ecklonia*-dominated kelp forest. The extent to which the kelp canopy was thinned and the degree to which the kelp plants were removed (fronds only, fronds and stipes only, or entire plant including holdfast) had significant effects on the understory assemblage. Individual species differed in their responses to the treatments, and there was considerable heterogeneity among replicates due to variation either in propagule availability or postsettlement survival.

I know of only one study that has experimentally investigated the effect of disturbances of differing severity on marsh communities. Baldwin and Mendelssohn (1998) applied three severities of disturbance to replicate plots in two different kinds of oligohaline marsh, one dominated by *Spartina patens* and the other by *Sagittaria lancifolia*. The treatments were (1) no disturbance, (2) nonlethal clipping of aboveground vegetation, and (3) application of a lethal herbicide. In both vegetation types, plants in the nonlethal disturbance plots quickly resprouted vegetatively, reestablishing assemblages similar in composition to unmanipulated controls. The lethal disturbances, however, produced marked shifts in the composition of the vegetation that persisted throughout the two-year study. Plots that experienced lethal disturbance were recolonized entirely by recruitment of seedlings, in some cases from a buried seed bank. Individual species responded differently to the treatment, but the abundances of a number of annual and perennial species that are uncommon in the undisturbed marsh were clearly enhanced by the removal of the dominant, perennial clonal species, *Spartina* and *Sagittaria*.

Most experimental studies of disturbance in marine communities have applied a single level of disturbance—complete removal of resident organisms. The studies just discussed highlight the importance of examining the effects of a more realistic range of disturbance severities in future studies. Results from completely cleared plots may not represent conditions following a typical disturbance.

Patch Characteristics That Affect Recolonization and Succession

Characteristics of a disturbed patch and of the area surrounding it can have a variety of direct and indirect effects on the rate and pattern of recolonization. These characteristics include patch type, size, shape, surface characteristics, location, and time of creation.

PATCH TYPE. The relative contributions of the four modes of reestablishment (see "Life History and Mode of Reestablishment") differ with patch type. Embedded patches are bounded by a living assemblage, so all four means of colonization are possible, whereas lateral encroachment of individuals from surrounding areas cannot occur in isolated patches.

PATCH SIZE AND SHAPE. Recolonization of a disturbed patch can be affected directly or indirectly by its size and shape. The influence of these features often varies with patch type. Next, I discuss the most conspicuous and well studied of these effects. See Sousa (1984, 1985) for a more complete treatment.

A direct effect of patch size is its influence on the number and species composition of colonizing propagules. Larger clearings would be expected, all else being equal, to receive a greater total number of colonists per unit time that smaller ones. In the process, large clearings "sample" a greater proportion of the pool of available propagules than do small patches, affording species whose propagules are less well represented in the pool a greater opportunity to recruit. This effect is more likely to be observed in disturbed isolated than embedded patches because the former have no neighboring organisms to exert either positive or negative effects on recolonization, and colonization is primarily by dispersing propagules. In such systems, if the dominant competitors produce fewer propagules or disperse them less broadly than competitively inferior species, this direct effect of patch size on colonization rates and resulting differences in species interactions within patches can generate marked spatial variation in the composition of the assemblage among patches. Small patches, to which weakly dispersing, dominant competitors recruit less often, will serve as refuges for inferior competitors, which will often be competitively excluded from large patches.

To my knowledge, this "propagule sampling" effect has yet to be demonstrated in a real system of disturbed patches, but the scenario fits well with the dynamics of invertebrate assemblages that grow on the shells of the bivalve *Pinna*, which protrude from the soft sediments in which they live, forming small, discrete isolated patches. These assemblages are comprised of small, determinate sheetlike bryozoans and solitary organisms, including serpulids. In contrast, assemblages on nearby pier pilings (which could be considered large isolated patches) are dominated by indeterminate, sheetlike, colonial tunicates that are competitively dominant over the forms that characterize the *Pinna* assemblages (Kay and Keough 1981). Keough (1984) experimentally confirmed the mechanisms generating these patterns. He also presented evidence that competitively inferior species such as bryozoans and serpulids settle preferentially in small, isolated patches where they experience less competition, whereas larvae of competitively superior tunicates prefer larger substrates that allow greater colony size and higher reproductive output. Keough attributed the evolution of these differences in settlement preference to the distinct selection regimes experienced by individuals that recruit to the different types of patches. Other studies have documented very similar differential distributions of invertebrate life forms among insular patches of subtidal hard substrate that differ in size (Jackson

1977b; Karlson 1978). Rates of recruitment to isolated patches will also be affected by interactions between flow and various features of the insular substrate, especially the shape and thickness of its edges (Mullineaux and Garland 1993).

The processes that influence recolonization of embedded disturbed patches, which are immediately surrounded by living organisms, may be very different from those just discussed for isolated patches. Organisms that surround an embedded patch can have positive or negative effects on recruitment, and the direction and strength of these effects will vary not only with patch size and shape, but with characteristics of these neighbors (e.g., their size, morphology, or feeding biology) and the prevailing environmental conditions (e.g., during exposure to air at low tide versus submerged in flowing water). In these situations, indirect effects of patch size can overwhelm the direct effect previously described. For example, because small patches have a greater ratio of edge to internal area, the number of reproductive adults near the patch will often be greater per unit patch area than for large patches. For species whose propagules do not disperse far, settling in greatest numbers close to the adult, this may result in a denser settlement and more rapid recruitment to small patches than large ones, opposite to the prediction for isolated patches. Even animals whose larvae travel long distances, but are attracted to settle gregariously near conspecific adults, may do so more densely in small versus large embedded patches of the same shape. In this case, the stimulus for settlement is locally enhanced in smaller patches because of the greater numbers of nearby adults per unit area of patch. The latter result was obtained in two experimental field studies of intertidal invertebrates whose larvae are chemically stimulated to settle near adults, the barnacle, *Chthamalus anisopoma* (Raimondi 1990) and the tubeworm, *Galeolaria caespitosa* (Minchinton 1997). Similarly, Navarrete and Castilla (1990) found that the mussel, *Perumytilus purpuratus*, recruited only to the walls of adult barnacles, and never to bare rock. Consequently, smaller clearings in stands of barnacles, which have a higher ratio of perimeter recruitment sites to internal area, were more rapidly colonized and dominated by mussels than larger clearings.

Variation in the supply of propagules to embedded disturbances of different size may or may not result in correlated differences in settlement and recruitment, depending on the effects of neighboring organisms on these processes. For example, the very feature that could promote an enhanced supply of propagules to smaller embedded clearings, namely a high edge-to-area ratio, can indirectly make the internal environment of such clearings inimical to settlement or recruitment. The smaller the clearing, the more completely organisms living along its edge may shade or whiplash its surface, deplete the local supply of nutrients and suspended food, or ingest dispersing propagules (e.g., Young and Gotelli 1988). The strength of these effects will depend on numerous details of the particular situation, including mainstream flow dynamics, height and morphology of the surrounding organisms, and the topography of the surrounding substrate (Abel-

son and Denny 1997). On the other hand, especially at mid and upper levels of rocky intertidal shores, the presence of neighboring organisms often ameliorate the harsh physical conditions that usually develop during low tide following the removal of cover. In summer, the surface of the rock within clearings in intertidal assemblages receives higher levels of solar radiation and airflow, which cause higher air and substrate temperatures and lower humidity, compared to the surrounding undisturbed sites. However, in winter at high latitudes, the opposite may occur: Organisms that colonize clearings will be exposed to colder air temperatures and greater risk of freezing that those in the surrounding assemblage where the canopy provides insulation. The buffering effect of neighboring organisms on the internal environment of the patch will be greater in smaller patches because the neighboring canopy will cover or cast shade on a greater proportion of their internal area.

Another very important consequence of the greater edge-to-area ratio of smaller embedded patches is that they are more rapidly filled than larger patches by vegetative ingrowth of clonal organisms or immigration of mobile or attached, but semimobile, solitary organisms that live on the perimeter of the disturbed area or in the area surrounding it (e.g., mussels: Suchanek 1979; Paine and Levin 1981; Sousa 1984; De Vogelaere 1991; Littorin and Gilek 1999; colonial invertebrates: Kay and Keough 1981; Palumbi and Jackson 1982; Connell and Keough 1985; algae: Dye 1993; salt marsh plants: Bertness and Ellison 1987; Ellison 1987; Hartman 1988; infaunal invertebrates: Smith and Brumsickle 1989). Conversely, recruitment from dispersed larvae, spores, or seeds generally makes a greater contribution to recolonization of large patches. What constitutes a small versus large embedded patch in any particular system depends on the mobility of the species in the assemblage. The greater the mobility of potential postlarval and adult colonizers, the larger the disturbed patch must be before larval settlement makes a significant contribution.

Experimental studies examining the effect of patch size on recolonization following disturbance have been conducted in a variety of marine habitats. All have created embedded clearings of different sizes, in some cases crossed with manipulations of other variables. By far, the greatest number of such studies has been conducted in rocky intertidal or subtidal habitats. Many of these have demonstrated differential recruitment or growth of species among experimental clearings differing in area. As discussed earlier, differences in settlement rate as a function of patch size, explain some of these results (e.g., barnacles: Jernakoff 1983; Raimondi 1990; tubeworms: Minchinton 1997; mussels: Navarrete and Castilla 1990), but in other cases, it is uncertain which of the previously discussed mechanisms or others were responsible for the observed patterns. Variation in desiccation stress or intensity of algal whiplash, the former more important in large clearings and the latter in small, has been suggested as the cause of differential success of various algal species and barnacles among experimental clearings of different size (Sousa 1984;

Kim and DeWreede 1996). By comparison, Airoldi (1998) found that clearing size had little effect on the recovery of a subtidal turf-dominated algal assemblage, where neither desiccation stress nor algal whiplash occurs. On the other hand, in a taller stature, fucoid-dominated algal assemblage, also in the subtidal, shading or some form of adult interference caused the density of recruits to be lower in smaller clearings and on the edges, as compared to centers, of larger ones (Emmerson and Collings 1998).

Another indirect mechanism by which the size of a disturbed patch has been demonstrated to affect recolonization and subsequent succession on rocky seashores is through its interaction with herbivory. This interaction has been most convincingly documented for disturbance-generated clearings in beds of the mussel, *Mytilus californianus*, on Pacific Northwest shores. Small clearings often support higher densities of limpets than large ones (Suchanek 1978, 1979; Paine and Levin 1981). Furthermore, during the early stages of succession in larger patches, limpet grazing is restricted to a 10 to 20 cm-wide browse zone on the perimeter of the patch, resulting in a nearly algal-free halo around the edge of the clearing (Figure 4.13; also see photos in Dayton 1973; Suchanek 1978, 1979; Sousa 1984). It had been hypothesized that this pattern occurs because beds of mussels surrounding a cleared patch afford limpets and other small grazers a refuge from wave shock, desiccation stress, and possibly predation. Because small clearings have a greater ratio of edge-to-area, they are accessible to a greater number of these grazers per unit area. The consequence of this spatially restricted foraging is that the total area of small patches is subject to relatively intense grazing, whereas the centers of large patches experience little grazing and therefore develop a more extensive cover of algae. By simultaneously manipulating clearing size and access to herbivores, I confirmed that this interaction between patch size and herbivory produced marked differences in succession between experimental clearings of two different sizes at a mussel-dominated site in northern California (Sousa 1984). Several other studies that have monitored recolonization in experimental clearings of different size, but did not manipulate herbivores, nonetheless observed patterns that were entirely consistent with an interaction between patch size and herbivory. The studies were conducted in a high-intertidal algal-barnacle assemblage in Oregon (Farrell 1989), a midintertidal assemblage dominated by mussels, barnacles, and coralline algae in central California (De Vogelaere 1991), and a low-intertidal coralline-dominated assemblage in southern Africa (Dye 1993). In each case, one or more species of molluscan herbivore developed higher densities in small than large clearings and near the edges as compared to the centers of the larger clearings. The species composition and successional dynamics of the sessile assemblage that developed in the clearings of different size varied in a predictable fashion with their respective herbivore densities. In contrast, Benedetti-Cecchi and Cinelli (1993, 1994, 1996) found little consistency in the effect of clearing size on patterns of colonization and succession in three intertidal habitats on the west coast of Italy: low intertidal sandstone platforms dominated by coralline algae, midintertidal mixed-species algal assemblages, and algal-dominated tide pools. In the midintertidal and tide pool habitats, where an herbivore exclusion treatment was crossed with the clearing size manipulation, limpets recruited in higher densities to the smaller control clearings, and their grazing may have contributed to the lower algal cover that developed in those plots, but the interaction between clearing size and herbivore exclusion was not statistically significant. Nor did they detect a difference in species composition or abundance in the center versus edges of clearings that might be attributable to limpets foraging inward from the periphery. Benedetti-Cecchi and Cinelli suggested the alternative explanation that some factor other than limpet grazing was responsible for the lower algal cover in small plots and that limpets were simply responding to the availability of space free of fast-growing algae that might otherwise exclude them from the substratum. Similarly, Worm and Chapman (1998) found no evidence that a grazing-patch size interaction affected recruitment of *Fucus evanescens* to clearings in a dense turf of the red alga, *Chondrus crispus*.

Few experimental manipulations of disturbed patch size have been conducted in other marine habitats. Shumway and Bertness (1994) found that mechanisms of succession differed markedly between experimental clearings of different size in a New England salt marsh that were intended to mimic bare patches created by wrack deposition. The soil in the large clearings became highly saline due to evaporation, whereas

Figure 4.13 Patch cleared in intertidal mussel beds showing central stand of early successional algae surrounded by peripheral grazed halo on Tatoosh Island, Washington. (Photo by the author.)

soil salinity in small clearings differed little from that under undisturbed vegetation. As a result, large patches were colonized almost exclusively by seedlings of a highly salt-tolerant species, *Salicornia europaea*. Once established, this species ameliorated the extreme salt levels by shading the soil, thereby reducing evaporation, and allowing less salt tolerant, but competitively superior species, to establish. In other words, facilitation was initially the primary mode of succession in large patches. In small patches, the dominant perennial species could invade from the outset and competitive interactions dictated patterns of succession. Working in the same study site, Ellison (1987) found that seedlings of *Salicornia europaea* that recruited to areas from which competitors had been removed suffered much higher levels of herbivory by a chrysomelid beetle than seedlings that recruited beneath an intact canopy. Ellison suggested that the beetles might more easily locate the seedlings in open disturbed sites. If this were the case, one would predict that rates of herbivory might differ among patches of different size, possibly in the opposite fashion to the common pattern on intertidal shores. That is, *Salicornia* plants might suffer greater damage in large than small clearings.

It has proved very challenging to conduct similar experiments examining the recolonization of disturbed patches in soft-sediment environments because of the technical difficulties of defaunating the sediment without completely altering its structure. Early studies of recolonization patterns in soft sediments attempted to circumvent this problem by deploying trays or cups of defaunated sediments (e.g., McCall 1977) as a mimic of the intact seafloor. Smith and Brumsickle (1989) demonstrated that this technique introduces a serious bias, selectively excluding postlarval immigrants from the surrounding undisturbed sediment. As discussed later, Smith and Brumsickle's experiments and other studies (VanBlaricom 1982; Bell and Devlin 1983; Levin 1984; Oliver and Slattery 1985; Savidge and Taghon 1988; Frid 1989; Emerson and Grant 1991; Thrush et al. 1991, 1992; Günther 1992; Hall et al. 1994; Shull 1997) have shown that postlarval immigration by juveniles and adults plays a large role in the colonization process and affects subsequent patterns of community development. To study the effect of disturbed patch size on recolonization, Smith and Brumsickle (1989) collected replicates of two different sizes of cores of intact sediment, defaunated them by freezing, and returned them to their original positions, flush with the undisturbed sediment surface. The small cores were colonized more rapidly that the large cores, with higher accumulation rates of total fauna, species, and individuals in the five dominant taxa. The relative contributions of different modes of colonization also differed with core size. The proportion of colonists that were postlarval immigrants was nearly twice as high in the small cores as the large ones. Conversely, larval recruits constituted a greater proportion of the individuals colonizing large cores. Further, successional patterns differed markedly between core sizes, probably as a consequence of the differences in mode of colonization. The authors attributed these differences to the same indirect ef-

fects of patch geometry that can affect recolonization of disturbed patches in the rocky intertidal. The greater edge-to-area ratio of smaller patches affords relatively greater access to postlarval immigrants. Conversely, as disturbance size increases, so does the contribution of larval recruitment (e.g., Santos and Simon 1980a; Levin 1984; Butman 1987; Günther 1992), although recruitment by postlarvae and adults may continue to contribute significantly to recolonization of large disturbances in high-energy environments (i.e., intertidal sand flats) where waves or strong currents erode sediments and disperse the resident infauna widely (e.g., Emerson and Grant 1991; Commito et al. 1995; Thrush et al. 1996).

Thrush et al. (1996) created disturbance patches of three sizes in an intertidal sand flat habitat by "smothering" the sediment in place. They found that small patches recovered more rapidly from disturbance than large ones and attributed the difference to the greater instability of sediment in the large patches where tube-building polychaetes that stabilize sediments were slower to colonize. These tube builders dominated the assemblage that surrounded the experimentally defaunated patches.

Scale-dependency in the patterns and processes of infaunal response to disturbance is receiving increased theoretical attention (Zajac and Whitlatch 1985, 1991; Whitlatch et al. 1998; Zajac et al. 1998). A major goal of this work is to generate specific predictions about the relative contributions of larval recruitment versus postlarval juvenile and adult immigration (by crawling, burrowing, or passive transport by currents) to the recolonization of disturbed patches (Günther 1992). Specifically, how do these relative contributions change as a function of size and other characteristics of a disturbed area, and what consequences do these differences have for rates, patterns, and variability of succession? Most of our current understanding of this phenomenon is based on experimental studies conducted at spatial scales of generally less than 1 m² (Hall et al. 1994). Our knowledge of infaunal responses to larger-scale disturbances comes largely from fortuitous observations.

The effects of patch shape on recolonization and succession following a disturbance have rarely been studied in marine benthic communities. In fact, very few studies have quantified this feature of disturbed patches (e.g., Paine and Levin 1981). One might predict that the effect of shape would often be a simple extension of the size-related, edge-to-area ratio effects described earlier. These would be enhanced in more irregularly shaped patches where this ratio is greater. Indeed, Raimondi (1990) observed denser barnacle recruitment in rectangular than square clearings of the same size, consistent with the hypothesis that a higher ratio of patch edge to area enhances recruitment of gregariously settling organisms. Generalizations concerning the effect of disturbance shape on recovery from disturbance await additional observational and experimental studies of its influence, independent of disturbance size and severity. In some instances, patch size and shape may be correlated, as Paine and Levin (1981) found for clearings in intertidal mussel beds: the length/width ratio increased with clearing size. Clearly, however, the perimeter to area ratio of disturbed patches strongly influences, both directly and indirectly, patterns and processes of recolonization in a wide variety of benthic marine habitats.

PATCH SURFACE CHARACTERISTICS.   The composition, rugosity, topography, and orientation of the substratum can strongly influence patterns of recolonization and succession, either directly or indirectly. Although these effects have been little studied in the context of natural disturbance events, experimental investigations suggest that variation in such characteristics among disturbed patches could account for a substantial amount of spatial heterogeneity in assemblage structure. Field (e.g., Connell 1961; Foster 1975; Harlin and Lindbergh 1977; Wethey 1986; Chabot and Bourget 1988; Morse et al. 1988; Raimondi 1990; Vadas et al. 1990) and laboratory studies (e.g., Crisp 1974, 1976; Norton and Fetter 1981; Norton 1983; Morse et al. 1988) have demonstrated the influence of small-scale surface heterogeneity, and its interaction with flow, on the settlement and/or recruitment of algae and invertebrates to hard substrata. The composition of the rock itself, and its influence on environmental conditions at the rock surface, can also affect these processes (e.g., McGuinness and Underwood 1986; Raimondi 1988a; Bavestrello et al. 2000; see Caffey 1982 for an exception).

Similarly, the course of succession in soft sediments can vary with sediment type (Zajac and Whitlatch (1982a, b), the properties of which are often further modified by the activities of colonizing infauna (e.g., Rhoads and Young 1970; Gray 1974; Rhoads 1974; Rhoads and Boyer 1982; Thayer 1983; Probert 1984; Hall 1994). The settlement of larvae onto soft sediments and the passive transport of larvae, postlarvae, and adults across them, are also strongly affected by surface topography including the presence of biogenic structures, such as worm tubes, and their interaction with flow (Eckman 1983; Eckman et al 1981; Butman 1987; Snelgrove and Butman 1994). This and other effects of tube builders, including their influence on sediment stability, can exert a strong influence on successional dynamics following disturbance in soft-sediment habitats (Gallagher et al. 1983; Whitlatch and Zajac 1985; Noji and Noji 1991; Thrush et al. 1996).

Invertebrate larvae are often attracted to, or repelled from, potential settlement sites by chemical cues released by conspecifics, other species, or the substrate itself (Crisp 1974, 1976; Meadows and Campbell 1972; Butman 1987; Chabot and Bourget 1988; Raimondi 1988b; Morse et al. 1988; Chia 1989; Woodin 1986, 1991; Pawlik 1992). Disturbed patches on hard substrates or in soft sediments may differ in the kinds and strengths of positive or negative cues they provide to dispersing larvae (see examples in "Patch size and shape").

Recolonization of disturbed sites may also be affected by larger-scale variation in surface topography, such as cracks and crevices in rocks, which may provide protection from physical hazards such as desiccation and hydrodynamic forces. Such heterogeneity in the rock surface may also afford prey species a refuge from grazers or predators (e.g., Brock

1979; Menge and Lubchenco 1981; Lubchenco 1983; Hixon and Brostoff 1985). In some cases, however, consumers themselves escape stressful physical conditions or their own predators by living in crevices, concentrating their foraging in the immediate vicinity. In this case, colonists might be at greater risk in patches with a greater degree of substrate heterogeneity (Menge 1976, 1978; Levings and Garrity 1983; Fairweather et al. 1984; McGuinness and Underwood 1986). Variation in surface characteristics is likely to be greater among small patches than large ones because the former "sample" a smaller portion of the underlying substratum. For just the opposite reason, within-patch variation in such characteristics should be greater for large than small patches.

PATCH LOCATION.   The location of a disturbed patch can markedly affect the rate and pattern of its recolonization. It does so in two fundamental ways, by determining (1) the availability of propagules and (2) the physical and biological characteristics of the environment in which recolonization and succession will take place. For species whose propagules are not dispersed far from the parent, proximity of the patch to a source of propagules can strongly affect patterns of recolonization and succession. Experiments and observations suggest that short-distance dispersal is an important source of small-scale, spatial variation in recruitment of some species of intertidal and subtidal algae (Dayton 1973; Paine 1979; Sousa 1984; Reed et al. 1988; Farrell 1989; Kendrick and Walker 1991, 1995; Kim and DeWreede 1996; Allison 1997; Johnson and Brawley 1998; Stiger and Payri 1999; but see Menge et al. 1993), seagrasses (Orth et al. 1994), subtidal epifauna (Grosberg 1987; Keough and Chernoff 1987; Davis and Butler 1989; Stoner 1990; Hurlbut 1992; Osman and Whitlatch 1998; Uriz et al. 1998; Smith and Witman 1999), and soft-sediment bivalves that brood (Commito et al. 1995). Other taxa for which larval dispersal is quite limited or nonexistent include corals with brooded planula larvae (Harrison and Wallace 1990), crustaceans that brood, and gastropods with direct development. Distance from source should affect the contribution of such organisms to the recolonization of disturbed patches.

Even though distance from source may be unimportant to the colonization of species whose propagules disperse long distances, the availability of their propagules will often vary among patches created in different locations. The supply of such propagules to a particular location will be affected by flow patterns, physical and biological barriers, the timing of release, and larval behavior and can strongly affect rates of settlement and recruitment (e.g., Hruby and Norton 1979; Caffey 1985; Gaines and Roughgarden 1985, 1987; Gaines et al 1985; Butman 1987; Young and Chia 1987; Raimondi 1990; Gaines and Bertness 1991, 1992; Minchinton and Scheibling 1991; Bertness et al. 1992b; Hurlbut 1992; Sanford et al 1994; Hills and Thomason 1996; Harris et al. 1998; Leonard et al. 1998; Todd 1998; Underwood and Keough, this volume; Morgan, this volume).

Patches created in different locations will also differ in the composition of the assemblages that surround them. This will obviously affect the rate and pattern of colonization by vegetative ingrowth or lateral movement of neighboring adults. As discussed earlier, if filter- feeders are a major component of the organisms that surround a patch, they may intercept and consume larvae or spores before they ever reach the patch.

The physical and biological environment of the patch's location affects all aspects of its repopulation, including the survival and growth of settling propagules, recruits, and adults. The degrees to which species differ in their tolerances of these conditions will determine their success at colonizing and growing to maturity within the disturbed patch.

TIME OF PATCH CREATION. The timing of disturbance can affect both the rate and course of recolonization and succession. Timing is important for at least two reasons. First, the availability of propagules is temporally variable, often having a strong seasonal component. All else being equal, recruitment of a species will be most enhanced by disturbances that create space during periods when its propagules are available in greatest numbers. Second, characteristics of the physical and biological environment that affect the recruitment, survival, and growth of colonists and survivors also vary in time. Temporal variation in these conditions affects the performance of individuals that recruit from settled propagules, as well as those that spread into the disturbed patch from its edges, or vegetatively regenerate from surviving fragments. Variation in rates and patterns of recolonization and succession related to the timing of disturbance has been clearly demonstrated by experiments in rocky intertidal communities (e.g., Paine 1977; Emerson and Zedler 1978; Sousa 1979a; Hawkins 1981; Benedetti-Cecchi and Cinelli 1993, 1994, 1996; Blanchette 1996; Kim and DeWreede 1996; Airoldi 1998; Chapman and Underwood 1998). In a number of these studies, however, differences in the early stages of succession among plots cleared at different times disappeared over time as the later successional stages converged to the composition and structure of the undisturbed assemblage of long-lived animals and plants that surrounded the plots. Thus, in these intertidal assemblages, differences in the timing of disturbance affected the rate and trajectory of succession, but not its endpoint.

Studies of the effects of time of disturbance on recolonization and succession in subtidal habitats are rare. Kennelly (1987a) studied the effect of temporal variation in disturbance on successional patterns in an *Ecklonia radiata* kelp forest. The season in which he experimentally removed stipes and fronds from the study plots had a large effect on the rate and pattern of algal recruitment and succession. If the clearings were made in winter, when the kelp recruits, *Ecklonia* reestablished a canopy relatively quickly. In contrast, summer, autumn, and spring clearings developed an extensive cover of turf algae, which subsequently inhibited kelp recruitment. This turf persisted over the next year, but was gradually being invaded and shaded out by kelp that recruited on the edges of the plots. Therefore, as is typical of intertidal systems, differences in the time of disturbance in subtidal kelp

forests have a sizeable effect on the structure and species composition of early and middle successional stages as a result of temporal differences in propagule availability. Over time, however, these differences disappear as the assemblages converge toward their predisturbance state. The timing of disturbance also affects the demography of giant kelp (*Macrocystis pyrifera*) populations along the southern coast of California. Tegner et al. (1997) followed the fates of two cohorts of this species that had established in the same kelp bed after two severe storms that occurred in different years. The environmental conditions that followed these disturbances were dramatically different, which in turn led to very different fates for the two kelp cohorts

As for subtidal hard substrate habitats, the effects of disturbance timing have seldom been examined for soft-sediment infaunal assemblages. Nevertheless, the few studies that have documented recolonization patterns in plots of defaunated sediment deployed at different times of year have seen large effects of the timing of simulated disturbance on infaunal succession (e.g., Zajac and Whitlatch 1982a, b; Ford et al. 1999).

Mechanisms of Succession Following a Disturbance

Succession, the sequence of species replacements that follow the initial recolonization of a disturbed patch, can proceed by a variety of mechanisms. Succession is driven by differences in species' reproductive biology, growth rates, competitive abilities, vulnerabilities to natural enemies and extremes of the physical environment (i.e., longevity), and their direct and indirect interaction with patch characteristics discussed earlier (Sousa 1985). Connell and Slatyer (1977) summarized the evidence for three alternative models of successional species replacement: facilitation, tolerance, and inhibition. Under the facilitation model, early successional species modify the environment so that it is more suitable for later successional species to establish and grow, while making the site less suitable for the local recruitment of conspecifics. According to the tolerance model, the presence of early successional species has little influence, positive or negative, on the recruitment and growth of later successional species. However, late species are more efficient at exploiting limited resources and competitively exclude the early species. The inhibition model predicts that early successional species can preempt resources and resist the establishment of late successional species as long as they remain healthy and undamaged. In most cases, this inhibition is transient. Successional replacement occurs because late species replace early species by outliving them, gradually accumulating as early species succumb to physical stress or attacks of natural enemies.

Although a number of authors have criticized the Connell-Slatyer models for oversimplifying successional processes in a variety of ways and for being phenomenological rather than mechanistic (Dean and Hurd 1980; Day and Osman 1981; Turner 1983a; Quinn and Dunham 1983; Breitburg 1985; Pickett et al. 1987; Walker and Chapin 1987; McCook 1994), there is no question that by clearly differentiating the alternative mechanisms in a testable form, Connell and Slatyer reinvigorated experimental research on successional patterns and processes. A comprehensive review of these studies is beyond the scope of this chapter, but they clearly demonstrate the diversity of mechanisms that drive successional sequences in marine communities (e.g., Sousa 1979a; Dean and Hurd 1980; Day and Osman 1981; Zajac and Whitlatch 1982b; Gallagher et al. 1983; Lubchenco 1983; Turner 1983a, b; Breitburg 1985; Foster and Sousa 1985; Whitlatch and Zajac 1985; vanTamelen 1987; Johnson and Mann 1988; Williams 1990; Bertness 1991; Farrell 1991; McCook and Chapman 1991,1997; Bertness and Shumway 1993; Wootton 1993; Shumway and Bertness 1994; Benedetti-Cecchi and Cinelli 1996; Hixon and Brostoff 1996; Berlow 1997; Kim 1997). There is good evidence for all three models, operating either alone or in concert within a given successional sequence. Facilitation tends to occur most frequently in physically stressful environments where stress-tolerant, early colonists may ameliorate the extreme conditions, or in areas of high consumer pressure where positive associations with other species may provide defense against natural enemies (Bertness and Callaway 1994; Bertness and Leonard 1997). In areas with more moderate physical conditions or consumer densities, the tolerance and inhibition mechanisms of succession predominate. Many, if not most, interspecific interactions involve simultaneous and directly opposing positive and negative effects (Callaway 1995; Holmgren et al. 1997), the relative importance and net outcome of which vary with environmental conditions.

Farrell (1991) extended the Connell-Slatyer models with a set of predictions of how different patterns of damage or mortality by consumers would affect the rate of species replacement under the three Connell-Slatyer models of succession. Sousa and Connell (1992) found generally good agreement between Farrell's predictions and the results of experimental studies of the influence of marine grazers on algal succession.

Effects of Species Diversity and Composition on Recovery from Disturbance

The experimental perturbation studies of Sousa (1980) and Allison (1997) not only examined how the species diversity and composition of an intertidal algal assemblage affected its resistance to a potentially disturbing force, as described earlier, but also how these features influenced its rate of recovery (i.e., resilience). In my study, the rate and pattern of recovery varied with the intensity and severity of damage and among assemblages of differing succession age. The latter effect was entirely attributable to differences in the life history characteristics of the component species, including their capacity for vegetative regeneration and rates of recruitment and growth from propagules. The diversity of the assemblage did not explain any additional variation in the response of the assemblage to disturbance. Allison (1997) found that rate of recovery to the reference state was affected by both the initial diversity of the assemblage and the intensity of the heat treat-

ment. However, as in my study, the effect of diversity on the assemblage's response to disturbance appeared to be "strongly contingent on the characteristics of the stress and the characteristics of the removed species" (Allison 1997, p. 136), and not a simple function of the number of species in the assemblage. Thus, as with resistance to disturbance, there is no evidence from these studies that higher-order effects of the diversity of species within a trophic level influence the process of recovery from disturbance.

Complex and Historically Contingent Interactions Precipitated by Disturbance

Many of the examples I have discussed thus far concern the effects of disturbance on particular species or pair-wise species interactions. There are a number of examples of disturbances that catalyze a series of cascading interactions that can dramatically affect community structure. Here, I describe some striking examples.

Disturbances can initiate trophic cascades. During a five-year monitoring study of a *Macrocystis pyrifera* forest off the coast of southern California, Ebeling et al. (1985) documented the effects of two unusually severe winter storms on kelp forest structure and dynamics. The study forest grew on an isolated shale outcrop, and in the summer of 1979 a large surface canopy of *Macrocystis* covered the reef. The first storm hit in February of 1980; the powerful surge stripped the entire *Macrocystis* canopy from the reef. Most understory kelp survived to regrow new blades the following spring, and *Macrocystis* sporophytes recruited to open space. This regeneration was cut short, as large numbers of adult sea urchins emerged from refuges in cracks and crevices to forage for food. Elimination of the *Macrocystis* canopy had cut off the supply of drift kelp, the urchins' preferred food. By the fall of 1980, urchins had removed all the newly recruited kelp plants and much of the understory kelp that had regrown vegetatively after the storm. Similar dynamics have since been observed in other southern California kelp forests following large ENSO associated storms (Tegner and Dayton 1987; Dayton et al 1992). The reef remained in this barren state until the spring of 1983, when strong surge from another intense storm swept sea urchins off the exposed part of the reef. By June of 1983, sporophytes of *Macrocystis* and understory kelps had recruited densely on the reef, and within a few months formed an extensive canopy. The insular nature of the reef, which was bounded by area of sand bottom, precluded its recolonization by adult urchins from other areas. Larval sea urchins did settle onto the reef in large numbers after the second storm, but these small urchins were unable to control the expanding kelp population (Breitburg 1996). Once a canopy of large invulnerable plants was reestablished, urchins returned to feeding on drift kelp, coexisting with the mature plants.

In addition to their direct effects on kelp populations, urchins apparently had an indirect negative effect on the abundance of surfperch on the reef. Prior to the first storm, these fish fed on small crustaceans that live within the algal

turf that seasonally covered more that 15% of the rock surface. Stands of understory kelps provided an essential refuge
for young-of-the-year of five species of surfperch from predation by adult surfperch and kelp bass. Following the storm,
as urchins grazed away the turf and understory kelp, surfperch densities declined sharply and young-of-the-year
perch disappeared entirely from the reef (Ebeling and Laur
1985; Ebeling et al. 1985). In addition, adult surfperch altered
their foraging patterns in response to the loss of kelp canopy
(Stouder 1987). Surfperch populations were recovering in
spring/summer of 1983 as the algal turf and kelps redevel-
oped on the reef following removal of urchins by the second
storm.

This example not only demonstrates how the strength and
effects of trophic interactions can be modified by disturbance,
but also that the same agent and intensity of disturbance can
have dramatically different effects depending on the state of
the community. That state is determined, in part, by the community's history of disturbance. The coral reefs of Jamaica
provide another case of a system's prior history of disturbance dictating its response to subsequent perturbations.
Hughes (1989) documented how selective mortality of corals
caused by a previous storm indirectly determined the outcome of competition between algae and corals following the
mass mortality of sea urchins by disease. Hughes and Connell (1999) discuss the interactive effects of recurrent disturbances on Australian and Jamaican reefs.

Another example comes from coral reefs in the eastern Pacific that were strongly impacted by the intense 1982–83
ENSO (Glynn and Colgan 1992). Sea surface warming associated with this event caused extensive reef coral bleaching and
up to 70–95% mortality of corals on reefs in Costa Rica, Panama, Colombia, and Ecuador. In addition to the direct mortality due to bleaching, this disturbance indirectly altered trophic interactions on the reefs in a way that magnified coral
mortality. Glynn (1990) quantified the latter effect on Uva Island in the Gulf of Chiriqui, on the Pacific coast of Panama,
where bleaching killed 96% of the corals. As *Pocillopora*
colonies died, the small crustacean "guards" that normally
shelter in living colonies of this species disappeared. These
crustaceans defend their host colonies from attack by the sea
star corallivore, *Acanthaster planchi*, and generally reduce the
impact of this predator on the reef. With the loss of the
guards, predation rates on surviving corals increased, adding
to the disturbance's already strong direct negative effects.

RESPONSES OF MOBILE ANIMALS TO DISTURBANCE

Compared to sessile organisms, the responses of mobile marine animals to disturbance have been little studied, except in
soft-sediment assemblages where the dispersal of postlarval
stages and adults plays such an integral role in the recolonization of disturbed sediments (see earlier discussion). I believe
there are two major reasons for the comparative inattention to
the responses of mobile animals to disturbance (Sousa 1984).

First, their responses are often less-easily observed and quantified than those of sessile species, and certainly more difficult
to study experimentally. Second, for much of the past three
decades, mobile animals, especially vertebrates, have been the
"poster children" for competition-based, equilibrium theories
of community organization (Wiens 1977; Karr and Freemark
1985). If mobile animal populations are considered fundamentally equilibrial in nature, then disturbances are relegated
to the category of exceptional events that temporarily obscure
our view of the "true" regulatory processes. As such, there is
little reason to study their effects in detail. In recent years, a far
more balanced vision of the myriad processes that affect populations of mobile animals has taken root, with increasing
numbers of studies of the direct and indirect effects of disturbance on assemblages of mobile animals.

Extreme environmental conditions and physical forces
can directly kill appreciable numbers of mobile marine animals. For example, cold temperatures and large storm waves
have been observed to kill coral reef fishes (Bohnsack 1983;
Lassig 1983); juveniles appear to be especially vulnerable to
wave surge (Bouchon et al. 1994). Anoxic conditions that developed after a hurricane killed large numbers of mangrove
fishes (Bouchon et al. 1994). As described earlier, strong, bottom surge from large storm waves and associated scour by
sand and rocks decimated sea urchin populations on a subtidal reef in southern California (Ebeling et al. 1985; see also
Dayton et al. 1989). Heavy sedimentation and low salinity
conditions following winter storms extirpated a large sand
dollar population from a California coastal lagoon (Onuf
1987). Hypoxic water kills benthic fishes, especially newly recruited individuals, which are less able to avoid these conditions by moving to better oxygenated shallow sites, as Breitburg (1992) showed for the naked goby, *Gobiosoma bosc*, in
Chesapeake Bay. Even nonlethal hypoxic conditions can affect the survival of larval fish by increasing or decreasing
their risk of being consumed by predators (Breitburg et al.
1994, 1997). Predation by sea nettles, which are less sensitive
to the debilitating effects of low oxygen concentration than
larval gobies, increased, whereas predation by juvenile
striped bass, which are more sensitive to hypoxia than goby
larvae, decreased. Pihl et al. (1992), also working in Chesapeake Bay, observed similar increases in predation by mobile
fish and crustaceans on benthic invertebrate prey that became incapacitated during periods of hypoxia.

Mobile animals can behaviorally avoid potentially lethal
environmental stresses, an option not available to sessile
species. Whether they are successful or not depends on the
rapidity with which harsh conditions develop and their intensity, as well as the mobility of the organisms in question.
Sea anemones (*Anthopleura elegantissima*) avoid lethal levels
of heat and desiccation by moving to more shaded and wet
microhabitats (Pineda and Escofet 1989). Juvenile and adult
fishes and crustaceans escape potentially lethal hypoxic conditions in deeper water by migrating inshore where dissolved oxygen concentrations are higher, then they recolonize
deeper sites after hypoxic conditions have dissipated (Loesch

1960; Kramer 1987; Pihl et al. 1991; Breitburg 1992; Diaz and Rosenberg 1995).

Physical disturbances also cause short- and long-term changes in the habitat that can have major indirect effects on populations of mobile animals. Changes in the physical and biogenic structure of the habitat often lead to reductions in the abundance of particular mobile animals or changes in species composition. One example is the indirect effect of storms on kelp bed surfperch populations described earlier (Ebeling and Laur 1985; Ebeling et al. 1985; Stouder 1987). In a comparable *Ecklonia radiata* kelp forest, Syms and Jones (1999) studied the response of a guild of demersal blennies to experimental removal of the kelp plants from plots of three different sizes. They observed significant effects of canopy removal and plot size on the persistence and resilience of resident populations, with the assemblages in small plots showing greater variability in both characteristics. Some of this variability was attributed to greater edge effects in the small plots, particularly with respect to the movement of fish in and out of the plots.

Similarly, disturbance-induced changes in the three-dimensional structure of coral reefs can affect the structure of associated fish assemblages (e.g., Kaufman 1983; Walsh 1983; reviewed by Jones and Syms 1998). A wide range of species-specific responses has been documented to such changes in habitat structure, many negative, but some positive. However, there have been few well-designed tests of alternative explanations for these responses, so the mechanisms underlying them are poorly understood. Syms (1998) attempted such a test by applying three levels of physical disturbance to 10 x 10 m plots on the fringing reef at Lizard Island on Australia's Great Barrier Reef. However, none of the fish groups he monitored responded very strongly to disturbance at that spatial scale; most of the variation among experimental plots was explained by larger scale spatial heterogeneity across the study reef. Syms highlighted the need for future studies to examine the responses of reef fish to habitat disturbance over a range of spatial scales.

Changes in habitat structure due to disturbance within coastal lagoons can also exert negative indirect effects on mobile species. As a result of unusually heavy rains associated with large storms in 1978 and 1980, large quantities of fine sediment were deposited in Mugu Lagoon in southern California. These deposits reduced the low-tide volume of the lagoon and eliminated most of the previously extensive cover of eel grass, *Zostera marina*. Probably for lack of sufficient habitat, rather then direct mortality from sedimentation or lowered salinity, the total density of water column fishes declined by almost 50% and species richness by more than 30% between 1977 and 1981 (Onuf and Quammen 1983). There were also marked shifts in spatial distributions of species as they aggregated in surviving areas of preferred habitat.

Disturbance to structural species can also indirectly affect interactions involving mobile predators and their sessile prey. For example, on a rocky shore in New South Wales, Australia, where intense storm waves removed large portions of a previously extensive canopy of the fucoid alga *Hormosira banksii*, the barnacle *Chamaesipho tasmanica* recruited heavily to the cleared patches. The barnacle had been absent beneath the intact canopy prior to the disturbance and remained so beneath undisturbed fucoid canopies. Experiments demonstrated that this spatial variation in barnacle abundance resulted from a reduction in the foraging efficiency (but not numbers) of predatory whelks (*Morula marginalba*) in areas where shelter afforded by the algal canopy had been eliminated.

As described in "Patch Characteristics That Affect Recolonization and Succession," the responses of mobile consumers to various characteristics of disturbed patches can strongly affect the rate and pattern of recolonization and succession. Interactions between patch size and grazing intensity are especially notable (e.g., Sousa 1984). More generally, mobile consumers can strongly affect the recovery of sessile populations from disturbance, and spatial and temporal variation in their influence can generate substantial and sometimes persistent heterogeneity in the abundance and age structure of populations of sessile prey species (e.g., Knowlton et al. 1990; Carroll and Highsmith 1996). The rate at which consumers recolonize disturbed areas and the life stage with which they do so (e.g., as larvae versus juveniles or adults) affect the degree to which they can limit the recruitment and growth of prey populations and thus the relative importance of predation versus competition during colonization (Breitburg 1996). The strength of these effects depends on the functional response of the consumer and the absolute and relative sizes and growth rates of consumers and prey.

The impact of consumers on prey populations within a disturbed patch will also vary with the location of the patch because the density and foraging efficiency of consumers varies spatially with environmental conditions. For example, on rocky shores, some predators forage less efficiently in wave-swept environments (Menge 1978; Lubchenco and Menge 1978), and grazers are generally less abundant at sites where sediment scour is common (Robles 1982; D'Antonio 1986). Consequently, the influence of these consumers on patch colonization by sessile species is likely to be less in such areas. In Caribbean mangrove forests, species of large, herbivorous crabs that feed on mangrove propagules are abundant in the low intertidal, but rare at higher tidal levels where detritivorous species predominate. Consequently, rates of crab predation on mangrove propagules that disperse into lightning-created canopy gaps decrease with increasing tidal elevation (Sousa and Mitchell 1999).

In some instances, disturbance of sessile assemblages improves conditions for mobile species and results in a net increase in their abundance. For example, in the intertidal boulder fields where I worked, limpet density was inversely related to boulder size; that is, the highest densities were found on small boulders (Sousa 1985). This pattern is probably explained by the fact that small boulders are more frequently disturbed by wave action and therefore have more open space for limpet attachment and grazing than large boulders (Sousa 1979a). In addition, limpets prefer to graze on microscopic algae or immature thalli of macroalgae (Nicotri 1977) that are more abundant on frequently disturbed substrata. In contrast, the upper surfaces of rarely disturbed large boulders are covered with larger, turflike perennial algae that are not consumed by limpets. These turfs occupy space and trap sediment, making the substratum uninhabitable to limpets. Dense stands of macroalgae, particularly at mid- and low intertidal, commonly outcompete limpets for space (e.g., Dixon 1978; Sousa 1979a, 1984; Underwood and Jernakoff 1981; Benedetti-Cecchi and Cinelli 1993). The consequence of this interaction is that the surfaces of small boulders are more intensively grazed by limpets than the surfaces of large boulders.

Finally, the sessile organisms that comprise each stage of succession following a disturbance differ in many characteristics critical to the survival, growth, and reproduction of mobile animals that live amongst them. These features include species composition, structural complexity, secondary chemistry, microclimate, and the quantity and quality of the food and shelter they provide. Consequently, the composition of mobile animal assemblages often changes with the successional stage of the sessile assemblage. In the most thorough study of its kind in marine environments, Dean and Connell (1987a, b, c) documented these changes for the early, middle, and late seral stages of the boulder field algal assemblage that I studied (Sousa 1979a, b, 1980) in southern California. Altogether, they collected 214 animal species belonging to 12 phyla from these algal assemblages, the majority of them mobile. Species richness, diversity, composition, and trophic structure varied among the stages, as well as seasonally within each stage. Using lab and field experiments, Dean and Connell demonstrated that a variety of processes contributed to the patterns and that different mechanisms were important for different species. The primary mechanisms determining associations of animal species with seral stages appeared to be active habitat selection and differential predation by fishes.

EFFECTS OF DISTURBANCE ON LOCAL AND REGIONAL POPULATION PERSISTENCE AND SPECIES DIVERSITY

Persistence of Populations

The immediate effect of disturbance is to reduce biomass and abundance, but its net effect in many benthic assemblages is to increase the local abundances of numerous species that would be less abundant or absent altogether in the absence of disturbance. It does so by freeing up resources held by prior occupants of the disturbed area or by generating new resources. Some of these species are strict fugitives, meaning that in the absence of disturbance they would be driven regionally extinct by competitive exclusion or some other mechanism of successional replacement (Hutchinson 1951). They persist by colonizing newly disturbed sites via dispersal of progagules from older ones. For other species, disturbance leads to increases in local abundance, but their persistence does not depend on it. A portion of the population of such a species permanently occupies a part of the habitat that provides refuge from their competitors, while taking advantage of habitatwide opportunities for recruitment afforded by disturbance. In areas outside of this refuge, where the species faces competition, it may persist as a true fugitive or in a source-sink relationship with the portion of the population that lives in the refuge (Shmida and Ellner 1984; Holt 1985; Pulliam 1988).

The local and regional dynamics of fugitive species populations reflect the interplay of life history traits, species interactions, and the regime of disturbance. For a fugitive species to persist, disturbances must generate colonizable space within the dispersal distance of extant local populations and before those populations go extinct. Paine's (1979, 1988) long-term study of populations of the sea palm, *Postelsia palmaeformis* (Figure 4.14), on Tatoosh Island off the coast of Washington State, provides one of the clearest examples of a fugitive species that requires a specific frequency and quantity (percent of space cleared) of disturbance to persist. At this and other sites, sea palm sporophytes recruit primarily to wave-generated clearings in beds of the mussel, *Mytilus californianus* (Dayton 1973; Blanchette 1996). During a 10-year period, Paine monitored the abundance of this annual plant at 26 sites, with varying regimes of mussel bed disturbance. Sea palm populations persisted for all 10 years at the 7 sites that regularly experienced high levels of disturbance. Sea palms were absent from the other 19 sites where either the frequency of disturbance or the quantity of open space it generated was lower. Paine was able to establish populations of sea palms at the latter sites, and these persisted for at least two generations. This ruled out the possibility that sites lacking sea palm populations were simply unsuitable for their establishment. At sites where *Postelsia* naturally persisted, the subpopulations of sea palms within any particular clearing eventually go extinct due primarily to competition for space with mussels and turflike algae. In fact, local populations go extinct rather precipitously as their density falls below about

Figure 4.14 Stands of the sea palm, *Postelsia palmaeformis*, surrounded by mussel beds on Bodega Head in central California. (Larger photo by author; inset photo by A. De Vogelaere.)

30 plants per m². Apparently, this density of plants produces insufficient spores to compensate for losses to grazers and competition. The dispersal distance of sea palm spores is very limited, only about 1–3 m from a stand of adult plants (Dayton 1973; Paine 1979, 1988). Therefore, the persistence of sea palm populations at a particular site requires that, within the time it takes for local subpopulations to go extinct, there be adequate dispersal of spores to open space created within 1–3 m of an extant stand. Regional extinction will occur if the average disturbance rate is too low or the interval between disturbances too long to ensure this. Establishment of new populations beyond the short range of spores dispersed from intact stands may occur when detached, but buoyant and fertile sporophytes are transported by currents to remote sites where they strand and deposit spores (Paine 1988).

Other species clearly benefit from disturbance, although their persistence does not depend on it. For example, recruitment of the sabellid polychaete, *Phragmatopoma californica*, which forms aggregations in intertidal and shallow subtidal habitats from central California to Panama, is greatly enhanced by wave disturbance (Barry 1989). Individual worms live in tubes constructed of cemented sand grains; larvae settle gregariously and their tubes become fused together into dense honeycomblike aggregations that grow to be as much as 50 cm thick and may cover many square meters of hard substratum. These aggregations persist for several months to years, but are eventually broken apart by wave forces or water-borne projectiles. When the tubes break open, large numbers of eggs are spawned, which are then fertilized in the water column. Larvae are competent to settle and metamorphose into the adult stage 2–8 weeks later, but can delay settlement and remain in the plankton for several months. The aggregations are most commonly disturbed during winter storms. As a result, *Phragmatopoma* larvae are most abundant in the plankton during winter and spring, which is also the period of heaviest settlement. Barry (1989) found that the level of *Phragmatopoma* recruitment on an intertidal reef in southern California was highly correlated with estimated wave power 2.5 to 5 months earlier, with the highest correlation at a 5-month lag interval. There was large interannual variability in *Phragmatopoma* recruitment over the nearly four years that Barry monitored it; years with the most recruitment were those with the greatest storm activity.

Several studies have demonstrated the strong effects of different disturbance regimes on the demography of affected populations. These include Åberg's (1992a, b) elegant analysis of the demographics of populations of the fucoid alga, *Ascophyllum nodosum*, under different regimes of ice scouring, and Wethey's (1985) innovative use of historical weather records to build a population projection model for populations of the intertidal barnacle, *Semibalanus balanoides*, at Nahant, Massachusetts. One of the predictions from Wethey's model was that species that lived exclusively in the zone affected by sea ice scouring would have gone extinct under the regime of sea ice occurrence that has existed in New England during the past 300 years. This result may explain the absence from New England shores of large, long-lived species with delayed reproduction that are common at mid- to low intertidal zones elsewhere in the world where sea ice does not form.

My previous discussion of the role of disturbance in promoting the persistence of fugitive species leads directly to a major question in community ecology: how does disturbance affect species diversity in natural communities? This question has been tackled in a variety of ways: with correlation analyses, experimental field studies, and theoretical models. The effect of disturbance on species diversity, that is, the coexistence of species, is intimately tied to changes in diversity over the course of succession. Species diversity within a disturbed patch is low immediately after a moderate to severe disturbance that has killed many or all of the residents. As species reestablish populations within the patch, diversity rises, in terms of both species richness and evenness. In many, if not most, benthic marine assemblages (exceptions discussed later), diversity is maximal at some intermediate stage of succession, declining thereafter as one or a few species come to dominate the assemblage and effectively block the recruitment of other species (see references on succession cited earlier). At that point, generally referred to as the climax stage, successional replacement of species ceases, and the dominants maintain their populations by recruitment from propagules or vegetative propagation.

Hierarchical interspecific competition is one process that commonly causes the decline in species diversity late in succession. In these cases, later successional species are better competitors for the increasingly limited resources available as populations build up within the patch (i.e., the tolerance succession model of Connell and Slatyer 1977). Competition is not, however, the only mechanism that can produce this decline. The late successional dominants may be species that have simply outlived others that recruited earlier to the patch by being better defended against natural enemies or environmental stresses (i.e., the inhibition succession model of Connell and Slatyer 1977; Sousa 1979a). As vulnerable species succumb to these sources of mortality, the defended species secure the space or other resources they held. By virtue of their longevity, defended species will retain these resources for long periods, and thereby prevent other species from invading.

Given this form of successional trajectory in species diversity, under what conditions will disturbance maintain high diversity? The answer to this question depends on the spatial scale of interest (Collins and Glenn 1997): local (within a patch) or regional (among patches). Under certain conditions, disturbance can maintain a persistently diverse assemblage within an area equivalent to the size of a single disturbed patch of space. However, even when disturbance cannot prevent a small number of species from monopolizing individual patches of space, asynchronous disturbances can maintain regional diversity by transforming the landscape into a mosaic of different successional stages that vary in species composition. I will now discuss, in turn, the potentially diversifying effects of disturbance at these two spatial scales.

Maintenance of Local Species Diversity

Disturbance can maintain local diversity in at least two ways. Connell (1978) coined the terms *compensatory mortality* and *intermediate disturbance* for these hypothesized mechanisms. According to the compensatory mortality hypothesis (CMH), local diversity will be maintained if the potential late successional dominant suffers a disproportionately higher rate of damage or mortality from disturbance than the species that it would otherwise exclude from the patch. If such disturbance is chronic, this diverse condition may be a fairly stable condition, but in many cases, disturbance rates vary in time, so the assemblage will likely seesaw back and forth over a range of diversity. As long as the rate of disturbance is moderately greater than the rate of exclusion and recruitment of the inferior competitor is sufficient, diversity within a patch will be maintained at a higher level than if the patch were never disturbed.

The intermediate disturbance hypothesis (IDH) embodies a second mechanism by which disturbance can maintain local diversity. In this case, the effects of disturbance are nonselective, but nonetheless promote local diversity by renewing resources, such as space, at a rate sufficient to allow continued recruitment and persistence of species that would otherwise be driven locally extinct by interactions with late successional dominants. On the other hand, disturbance must not occur so often, or with such severity, that many species are eliminated. As the name of the hypothesis implies, disturbance must occur at some intermediate frequency or severity that allows species to accumulate within the patch, but prevents one or a few of them from monopolizing its resources. In other words, as in the case of intermittent compensatory mortality, the assemblage within the patch is maintained in a nonequilibrium state, and assuming sufficient dispersal, local coexistence of species is insured.

These thumbnail sketches of the two mechanisms oversimplify the conditions under which each of them will maintain local diversity. These conditions have been explored with a number of graphical and mathematical models that differ in their basic structures and assumptions. Before I discuss their general conclusions, I will briefly describe the different ways in which these models have explored the effects of disturbance on local diversity and the roles of various processes in mediating these effects. Huston (1979, 1994) presented graphical predictions of how the growth rates of competitors influence the rate of competitive exclusion, and therefore the level of disturbance necessary to maintain diversity. Graphical models by Petraitis et al. (1989) and Collins and Glenn (1997) examined how the interplay of life history traits, competitive ability, and disturbance determines local species richness through their influence on species' immigration and extinction rates. Caswell and Cohen (1991) developed a Markov chain model to study the effects of disturbance on the dynamics of 2–3 interacting species in a spatially subdivided habitat, in which the patches are linked by random dispersal (i.e., no neighborhood effects). By numerical simulation, they investigated the interacting effects of different rates of disturbance and competitive exclusion, mechanisms of succession, and transitive vs. intransitive competitive interactions on local and regional diversity within the metapopulation. Disturbance was indiscriminate in this model: A disturbance eliminates all species and returns the patch to an empty state. More recently, Dial and Roughgarden (1998) explored the conditions for disturbance-enhanced diversity with a two-species extension of an earlier one-species model by Roughgarden and Iwasa (1986). These models explicitly incorporate the dynamics of two demographic stages that are common to the life histories of many species of marine organisms—space-limited adults and pelagic propagules. The Dial and Roughgarden model examines the effects on species coexistence of varying relative rates of adult survival, reproduction, propagule survival, and settlement. It assumes that higher rates of disturbance produce higher levels of adult mortality, and that higher rates of propagule settlement lead to greater numbers of adults. Dial and Roughgarden investigated a number of different scenarios including cases in which: (1) the subordinate competitor is neither more resistant to disturbance, nor a better colonizer than the dominant competitor; (2) the subordinate is superior to the dominant in both respects; (3) the subordinate is a better colonizer, but more susceptible to disturbance; and (4) the subordinate is more resistant to disturbance, but a poor colonizer.

The general conclusion of all five of these models is the same: Intermediate rates of disturbance will maintain local diversity under certain conditions. In specifying these conditions, recent theory has added critical details and therefore predictive power to the original, simple graphical presentation of the IDH (Connell 1978). One feature that clearly enhances the diversifying effects of disturbance is the existence of particular trade-offs in the life histories of the interacting species. Disturbance is more likely to maintain diversity if subordinate competitors are better than dominant competitors at colonizing the open space created by disturbance. Disturbance-mediated coexistence is also more easily realized when dominant competitors are less resistant to disturbance, as in the CMH. Only when subordinate competitors are both more susceptible to disturbance and weaker colonizers than the dominant competitor is it impossible for disturbance to maintain diversity. For all other combinations of traits (Cases 2–4), some intermediate level of disturbance, contingent on the rate of propagule settlement, will act to maintain diversity. Dial and Roughgarden's (1998) model also predicts an "intermediate recruitment effect" in these situations. That is, at a given level of disturbance, coexistence will only occur at intermediate rates of recruitment. Only the subordinate competitor persists when the overall recruitment rate is low, the species coexist when recruitment rates are intermediate, and the superior competitor dominates when recruitment rates are high. Their model also predicts that positive covariation between disturbance and overall rates of recruitment reduces the diversifying influence of disturbance because open space is more rapidly filled, reducing the opportunity for the subordinate species to recruit. On the other hand, negative covariance between disturbance and recruitment rates is predicted to intensify the diversifying effect of disturbance. The Dial and Roughgarden model (1998) makes the explicit assumption that benthic populations are recruitment-limited: Higher settlement rates result in higher adult densities. If instead, the density of adults of some or all of the interacting species were limited by post-recruitment biotic interactions, the predictions might be different. This question seems ripe for theoretical exploration.

The level of disturbance necessary to maintain local diversity, and the degree to which diversity will be enhanced, are also predicted to vary with the rate of competitive exclusion, transitivity of species interactions, frequency of positive interspecific interactions, and model of succession (Karlson and Buss 1984; Huston 1979, 1994; Sebens 1987; Caswell and Cohen 1991; Hacker and Gaines 1997). Higher levels of disturbance are required to ensure local species coexistence with more asymmetrical competitive interactions and higher rates of competitive displacement. The rate of competitive exclusion tends to be slower when competitive interactions are nontransitive (e.g., in the three-species case: A > B > C, but C > A) as compared to transitive or hierarchical (A > B > C, and A > C) so that less disturbance is necessary to maintain diversity when nontransitive interactions predominate. Similarly, positive interactions, particularly those that ameliorate harsh physical conditions, are predicted to increase the range of disturbance rates over which species can coexist, and increase the peak levels of diversity maintained by intermediate levels of disturbance. Predictions from the Caswell and Cohen model (1991) concerning the effects of different successional mechanisms on disturbance-mediated coexistence depend on the colonization rates of earlier versus later successional species. Under the tolerance model, hierarchical competition drives successional replacements, and intermediate levels of indiscriminate disturbance will enhance diversity as long as the early successional species is the better colonizer. Intermediate levels of indiscriminate disturbance also enhance diversity when succession is driven by facilitation, but neither the degree of enhancement nor the frequency of disturbance that maximizes diversity are greatly affected by absolute or relative rates of dispersal. The prediction for a strict inhibition model, in which the first species to colonize an open patch excludes all others until removed by disturbance, is that diversity will only be maximized at intermediate rates of indiscriminate disturbance when the dispersal rates of early and late species are equal. Regardless of the successional model, the higher the rate of competitive exclusion, the greater the rate of disturbance must be to maintain diversity.

In many respects, existing models have explored only the tip of a very large iceberg of factors that dictate the effects of disturbance on natural populations and communities. These include many of the features I have discussed here, including the spatially and temporally explicit nature of recruitment, variation in the severity of damage and opportunity for vegetative recovery, and the myriad consequences of variation in patch size. In addition, Petraitis et al. (1989) identify some po-

tentially important effects of correlations among disturbance characteristics such as size, severity, and frequency that merit more theoretical attention. The effects of some of these interactions among disturbance characteristics have been explored in verbal and graphical models of the effects of disturbance on regional species diversity described in the next section.

Empirical studies that unambiguously demonstrate the diversifying influence of disturbance on local diversity are not as numerous as one might expect, given the attention that this phenomenon receives. Correlational studies relating coral species richness to surrogate measures of disturbance frequency, such as percent living cover or topographic complexity, suggest that intermediate frequencies of storm-induced disturbance are responsible for high diversity in some areas on coral reefs (e.g., the hump-shaped relationships reported by Connell 1978 and Aronson and Precht 1995). However, projected dynamics from a matrix model of the probabilities of species replacements estimated from Connell's long-term permanent plots (Tanner et al. 1994) indicated that the IDH did not fully predict successional changes in species diversity following disturbance by cyclones. Patterns at a wave-protected, shallow subtidal site were generally in accord with the hypothesis; diversity peaked some time after cyclone disturbance, then declined, as a few species competitively dominated the assemblage during the subsequent storm-free interval. In some areas, however, such as the reef flat, diversity remained high long after a cyclone because other sources of mortality ensured that some space was always available for colonization by competitively inferior species. These additional agents of mortality included exposure to air at low tide, which damages erect fast-growing corals disproportionately. Storm damage can also be compensatory, as it often falls most heavily on faster-growing branching corals that are competitively dominant in subtidal areas of the reef in the absence of wave damage (Connell 1976, 1978, 1979; Porter et al. 1981; Woodley et al. 1981; Hughes 1989). Rogers (1993) critically evaluated observational evidence for the IDH in the literature on the effects of hurricanes on coral reefs. Patterns of species diversity and evenness in shallow-water coral assemblages are generally consistent with the predictions of the IDH, but deeper water assemblages tend to be diverse despite a generally lower disturbance rate.

My study of the effects of disturbance in algal-dominated intertidal boulder fields in southern California (Sousa 1979a, b) remains one of the only studies that has experimentally tested the IDH in a marine habitat. At the site where I worked, wave action that overturns boulders is the predominant agent of disturbance. As I described earlier, when a boulder is overturned, the organisms on what was formerly its top surface are damaged or killed. The longer it remains overturned, the greater the mortality, and therefore the greater the amount of open space that becomes available when the boulder is righted. Boulders of intermediate size (or mass) are overturned by wave action more frequently than large boulders and less frequently than small boulders. As a result, boulders of intermediate size support, on average, the most diverse assemblage of organisms (Sousa 1979b). The interval between disturbances of small boulders is short, so relatively few species have time to establish populations on their surfaces. On large boulders, which are rarely disturbed, succession proceeds without interruption, resulting in domination of the cover by a single species of long-lived, turflike algae. I was able to confirm that the rate of disturbance rather than substratum size was responsible for these patterns by experimentally stabilizing small boulders and monitoring succession on their surfaces as compared to nonstabilized boulders of the same size. The trajectory of succession on the stabilized small boulders was identical to that on larger, more stable boulders. Observations of diversity patterns in subtidal boulder or cobble fields (Osman 1977; Davis and Wilce 1987) suggest that the same process maintains diversity there. However, McGuinness (1984, 1987a, b) found little support for the mechanism in intertidal boulder fields on the coast of New South Wales, Australia. At his sites, wave disturbance as well as sand burial were important, but only the assemblages on the undersides of low intertidal boulders exhibited patterns of diversity with respect to boulder size that were consistent with the IDH. Other intertidal habitats in which disturbance has been shown to enhance or maintain diversity of sessile species include tide pools (Dethier 1984) and salt marshes (Bertness and Ellison 1987; Ellison 1987; Bertness et al. 1992a; Brewer et al. 1997, 1998; but see Valiela and Reitsma 1995).

The foregoing discussion of the diversifying influence of disturbance on local diversity presumes that the diversity of an assemblage of species that colonizes a disturbed patch of habitat rises, then falls over the course of an uninterrupted succession. This is not a universal pattern. For example, in some seagrass beds, diversity seems to monotonically increase over time to some maximum set by the regional species pool (Williams 1990). In these cases, the climax state is a mixture of coexisting species that live interspersed throughout the bed. Williams (1990) hypothesized that these species coexist at equilibrium by partitioning nutrients and light within a three-dimensional habitat in the manner of Tilman's (1982, 1985) resource ratio hypothesis. Similarly, experimental exclusion of predators (and by inference, elimination of disturbance in general) from assemblages of soft-sediment infauna, often does not result in a decline in diversity, a common outcome of similar experiments in rocky intertidal habitats where one or a few competitively superior species usually exclude the others (Peterson 1979). Instead, both the total density of organisms and species richness increases when predators are excluded. Peterson (1979) suggested that competitive exclusion is rare in soft-sediment environments because interference competition by crushing or overgrowth, both common mechanisms on hard substrates, is uncommon among inhabitants of soft sediments. In addition, the low metabolic rates of infaunal organisms make exclusion by exploitation competition ineffective or extremely slow. Further, the three-dimensional nature of soft-sediment habitats allows resource partitioning, and negative adult-larval interactions may keep densities below carry-ing capacity. Furthermore, as Frid and Townsend (1989) have argued, rapid recolonization of disturbed sites by highly mobile juvenile and adult life stages from surrounding areas, which is typical of many soft-sediment assemblages (see earlier references) will often preclude an increase in local diversity by larval recruitment (e.g., Thrush et al. 1991).

A hump-shaped relationship between diversity and time since the last disturbance also may not obtain in physiologically stressful habitats. For example, Brewer et al. (1997, 1998) did not observe a decline in species richness in the late stages of patch succession in the more stressful low intertidal areas of a New England salt marsh, where soil salinity is high and redox potential low. Instead, species richness increased monotonically in these areas following experimental removal of the vegetation. Edaphic conditions in newly cleared patches in the low marsh are particularly severe, and they can only be colonized by vegetatively spreading, salt-tolerant species. However, as the cover of these species increases, the harsh conditions are ameliorated, facilitating the recruitment of less tolerant species; hence, the increase in species richness. Thus, in the low marsh, positive interactions were more important than competition in determining species richness, which never overshot predisturbance levels. In contrast, the trajectory of species richness during succession in areas cleared of vegetation in the less stressful high marsh did exhibit an intermediate peak. Late in succession, competitively dominant clonal perennial excluded annual fugitive species.

In such cases where diversity increases monotonically during succession, disturbance will not enhance or maintain local (i.e., within-patch) species diversity. It can only reduce diversity. Nevertheless, disturbance will generate spatial heterogeneity in assemblage structure among patches disturbed at different times in the past (Thrush 1991; Hall et al. 1994). Furthermore, even if there is an overall decline in diversity in response to disturbance, it may still mediate interactions within certain suites or guilds of species, and for these the intermediate disturbance hypothesis could apply. For example, recent soft-sediment mesocosm experiments have shown that intermediate levels of biological disturbance by heart urchins (*Bryopsis lyrifera*) and bivalves (*Abra alba* and *Nuculoma tenuis*) result in more diverse assemblages (both locally and regionally) of meiobenthic nematodes and macrofauna (Widdicombe and Austen 1998, 1999; Austen et al. 1998). The precise mechanisms producing this response were not identified, but both bioturbation and predation were probably involved.

Maintenance of Regional Species Diversity

Certain regimes of disturbance can maintain regional diversity among a collection of disturbed patches, even when they do not maintain it locally within the patches. In essence, this is the fugitive species case extended to multiple species. For example, at Paine and Levin's (1981) midintertidal, mussel-dominated sites on Tatoosh Island, the organisms occupying any particular area of substratum are disturbed, at most, every 7–8 years. As discussed earlier, this interval is to a large extent determined by changes in the intrinsic vulnerability of the assemblage to disturbance over the course of succession. A 7–8 year interval between disturbances is sufficiently long that a large number of species is able to establish in a newly cleared patch of open substratum. For a time, within-patch diversity increases as species accumulate. However, this frequency of disturbance is too low to maintain high diversity within the patch. Over 7–8 years, lateral encroachment of adult mussels or recruitment of larval mussels will close all but the largest patches. In the process, the diversity of the assemblage within the patch declines as species are competitively excluded. Eventually, all species other than mussels that occupy primary space will be driven locally extinct. Nevertheless, localized disturbances to the mussel beds can enhance regional diversity by creating opportunities for colonization in areas that mussels will inevitably come to dominate. Asynchronous, localized disturbances transform the assemblage into a mosaic of different successional stages. Theory (e.g., Hastings 1980; Abugov 1982; Caswell and Cohen 1991) indicates that regional diversity is generally enhanced by intermediate rates of disturbance (i.e., area or number of patches cleared per unit of time). When the average rate at which individual patches are disturbed is either high or low, regional diversity will be less than when patches are disturbed at some intermediate rate. This is because at high average disturbance rates, early successional species dominate most patches, whereas at low average rates, late successional species do. The position along an axis of disturbance rate at which regional diversity will be maximal varies with all the same features that affect disturbance-mediated patterns of local diversity (see earlier discussion).

In addition, regional diversity will be affected by the average size and severity of disturbances and how synchronously they occur. Assuming that large disturbed patches favor colonizing or early successional species, and small patches favor competitive or late successional species, Miller (1982) made the following predictions about the effects of average patch size on regional diversity. At a low average disturbance rate, competitive exclusion within patches is likely, so regional diversity will be higher if the mean size of cleared patches is large, thus favoring the continued persistence of colonizing species. Conversely, when the average rate of disturbance is high, regional diversity will be greater when the areas disturbed are small, as this will insure the continued persistence of competitive species. Malanson (1984) has taken this model one step further, by incorporating the effects of disturbance severity (he uses the term *intensity*). He noted that for many disturbances, size and severity are indirectly correlated with frequency, so that severity of disturbance can be substituted for disturbance size in Miller's model. In other words, when the average rate of disturbance is high, regional diversity will be maximized when the average severity of damage is low, favoring competitive species, which should be better able to survive the disturbance or reestablish populations at lower levels of resource availability. When the average rate of disturbance is low, regional diversity will be enhanced by severe disturbances that free up more resources for colonizing

species. Malanson makes a number of other predictions from his graphical model, including the prediction that regional diversity will be maximal under disturbance regimes characterized by either (1) infrequent, large, and severe disturbances, or (2) frequent, small, and low-severity disturbances.

Abugov (1982) has examined how the phasing of disturbance might affect regional diversity. Disturbances are in phase when they occur synchronously and are unphased if the probability of each occurrence is independent of any other. In the simplest case, as phasing increases, so does the proportion of colonizing species in the assemblage. So, one would predict that an increase in the phasing of disturbances will decrease regional diversity when colonizing species predominate, but increase it when competitively dominant species occupy most of the space. More complicated patterns are also possible if one allows for changes in the relative competitive and dispersal abilities of the species. To my knowledge, none of the predictions from these models have been formally tested in marine communities.

CONCLUSIONS

Dayton (1971) concluded that the intertidal community he studied was "characterized by continuous physical and biological disturbance, an abundance of free space, and a large number of species which utilize this same potentially limiting resource." He wondered whether his system was a special case because its features differed so strikingly from those predicted by the paradigm that dominated community ecology at the time—that natural assemblages are primarily structured by interspecific competition. We now know that his observations were not unusual. Disturbance is an integral part of the environmental template (Southwood 1977) of every marine habitat. In the nearly 30 years since Dayton's paper, regimes of disturbance and its effects on community structure and dynamics have been studied in most marine benthic environments, and we have a much better understanding of the ways in which its effects interact with numerous biological and physical processes. Debates over whether marine communities are biologically accommodated or physically controlled have been replaced by a more balanced appreciation of the critical roles played by both kinds of processes. Disturbances, particularly multiple events that occur in rapid succession (Paine et al. 1998), are now recognized as prime initiators of shifts in community structure between alternate compositional states (e.g., Knowlton et al. 1990; Knowlton 1992; Hughes 1994; Petraitis and Latham 1999), which may or may not be persistent (Connell and Sousa 1983). Such shifts are increasingly likely as the rate and severity of anthropogenic disturbance increase worldwide.

So many factors affect the impact of disturbance agents on natural communities and subsequent patterns of succession, that sweeping generalizations are difficult (and probably unwise) to make. Nonetheless, several common patterns emerge from the body of benthic disturbance literature I have reviewed here:

1. The frequency, areal extent, and severity of a particular kind of disturbance vary spatially and usually have a strong seasonal component. Disturbance characteristics are often correlated: Large, severe disturbances occur less frequently and predictably than small, less-severe ones.

2. The impact of a disturbance agent depends on its dynamic properties as well as those of the affected organisms. Ontogenetic changes in organisms and successional changes in the three-dimensional structure and species composition of their assemblages alter their susceptibility to disturbance and thus its temporal and spatial patterning and severity. Substantial progress is being made in developing biomechanics-based models of these phenomena.

3. The influence of intra- and interspecific aggregation on vulnerability to disturbance appears to vary in a predictable manner along gradient of environment harshness. In physically harsh areas, aggregation often lowers the risk of disturbance (i.e., death due to physiological stress) by ameliorating potentially lethal environmental conditions. In contrast, high-density populations living in physiologically more benign conditions may suffer higher rates of disturbance because morphological or physiological changes caused by competition make them more vulnerable to other agents of disturbance (e.g., wave impact, sedimentation). On the other hand, members of dense aggregations living in benign environments may be at lower risk of disturbance from biological agents.

   The effects of intimate interspecific associations such as epiphytism and parasitism on disturbance rates have been less studied. The effects of epiphytes appear to parallel those of aggregation in general: Epiphytes reduce their host's risk of mortality in harsh environments, but can increase the risk under physiologically benign conditions. Parasitism often tends to act synergistically with other agents of physiological stress to increase rates of mortality under physically harsh conditions, causing less mortality when environmental conditions are favorable.

4. Whether diversity begets stability is an old, but still vital question in ecology. To date, there have been only two studies that have directly addressed this question in marine benthic environments, and both were conducted on rocky seashores. Neither lends strong support to the hypothesis that the diversity of an assemblage affects its resistance or recovery from disturbance in a manner that differs from the aggregate responses of its component populations. With so few studies, and these conducted in but a single habitat, it is impossible to generalize about higher-order effects of benthic diversity on disturbance regimes or recovery from disturbance.

5. The severity of a disturbance, and therefore the extent to which survivors contribute to recolonization, strongly affects both the rates and patterns of succession. Yet, most experimental studies of succession have imposed a single level of unnaturally severe disturbance: complete removal of residents.

6. The size and shape of disturbed patches seem to be broadly important to patterns and rates of recolonization in marine benthic assemblages. The effects of patch size and shape are often related to the corresponding change in perimeter to area ratio, which mediates the influence of neighboring sessile and mobile species, both competitors and consumers, and the flux of resources and propagules.

7. We tend to focus on the effects of individual disturbances, but each assemblage has a history of disturbance, and we know from a handful of studies that history can dictate the present state of the system and how it will respond to a new event.

8. The interplay between life history and disturbance characteristics accounts for a substantial amount of spatiotemporal variation in population demography and community structure. It transforms many marine landscapes into mosaics comprised of habitat patches that differ in the time since they were last disturbed, and hence the structure and species composition of the assemblages that occupy them. As in terrestrial systems, the persistence of some species within such landscapes depends on a particular frequency and quantity of disturbance. If either the amount of resource renewed by disturbance is too low, or the interval between disturbances is too long, such populations will go extinct. Other species that exploit disturbances, but do not necessarily depend on them for persistence, will decline in numbers.

9. Considerable observational and some experimental evidence indicates that intermediate levels of indiscriminate disturbance and disturbance that causes differential (i.e., compensatory) mortality of, or damage to, dominant competitors enhances or maintains local and regional species diversity in a variety of assemblages of sessile marine organisms. These assemblages include those of rocky seashores, subtidal hard substrates, coral reefs, and less-physiologically stressful areas within salt marshes. These are systems in which diversity peaks at a middle stage of succession, declining later in succession as one or a few species come to dominate the assemblage. Intermediate frequencies of disturbance maintain the assemblage in an earlier, more diverse stage of succession, whereas compensatory mortality or damage prevents competitive exclusion from occurring. In contrast, such a diversifying effect of disturbance has rarely been observed or experimentally demonstrated in seagrass beds or assemblages of soft-sediment infauna. These are systems in which diversity often rises monotonically following disturbance, peaking late in succession. It has been suggested in the case of seagrasses that the three-dimensional distribution of light and nutrient resources affords greater opportunity for coexis-

tence by resource partitioning, although the same should be true for salt marsh plants. Infauna coexistence may similarly be enhanced by the three-dimensional distribution of living space. In addition, the unstable nature of the sediment substrate precludes certain forms of interference competition that are common mechanisms of competitive exclusion on hard substrates. Further, disturbances in soft sediments are often so rapidly colonized by postlarvae and adults transported by currents from surrounding areas that there is little opportunity for new, nonresident species to establish. In physically harsh portions of salt marshes, the stressful conditions prevent the establishment of species other than those that occupied the site prior to disturbance.

Frankly, however, such generalizations are premature, as very few studies have directly manipulated disturbance rates in any benthic community. In fact, recent manipulative studies using mesocosms show that intermediate rates of bioturbation can enhance the diversity of certain assemblages of soft-sediment infauna.

FUTURE RESEARCH DIRECTIONS

I have already mentioned a number of patterns and questions that beg additional investigation. Without being exclusive, I see several additional directions for novel and useful future research on the role of disturbance in marine benthic communities.

Spatially Explicit Studies of Disturbance in Benthic Landscapes

Most of the empirical work on disturbance in marine communities has focused on the local or within-patch scale, asking questions about the effects of disturbance and disturbed patch characteristics, life history features, and species interactions on recolonization, succession, and local diversity. As a result, we know a lot about the responses of species to different kinds of disturbance, and the postdisturbance dynamics of populations and assemblages within individual patches of disturbed habitat. But as I discussed earlier, populations occupy landscapes comprised of mosaics of patches, so their dynamics are the product of processes operating within collections of patches connected by varying amounts of migration. How does the regime of disturbance, species life history characteristics, dispersal, and interspecific interactions affect the aggregate dynamics of the subpopulations living in different patches? In other words, how are metapopulation and metacommunity dynamics linked to the spatiotemporal regime of disturbance? Answering this question requires a spatially explicit approach that integrates the demography of patches and their internal dynamics with their arrangement in space. For some species with long-distance dispersal of propagules, the arrangement of patches within a particular landscape may matter little to their dynamics, but for many species with more limited dispersal, the spatial relationships

of newly disturbed sites and older "source" patches will matter. Paine's (1979, 1988) studies of subdivided populations of the sea palm, *Postelsia palmaeformis*, provide a clear example of a system where a spatially explicit metapopulation model would be necessary for predicting dynamics. Paine and Levin's (1981; see also Levin and Paine 1974) model of disturbance-generated patches in mussel beds describes the dynamics of patch age and size distributions, but takes no account of the spatial relationships of patches because colonists are assumed to come from a large bath of broadly dispersing propagules, the composition of which is unrelated to the local abundance of adults. For situations in which patch colonization is a local phenomenon, the descendants of their model, in particular, recent spatially explicit simulation models of the patch dynamics of grassland disturbance (Wu and Levin 1994; Moloney and Levin 1996) could be adapted to marine systems. The latter models clearly demonstrate that spatial and temporal autocorrelation of disturbances play as great a role in determining landscape-scale dynamics as the rate and intensity of disturbance.

Disturbance and Biological Invasions

There is substantial evidence that disturbance, both natural and anthropogenic, can promote the invasion of nonindigenous species into terrestrial and freshwater habitats (e.g., Hobbs and Huenneke 1992; Moyle and Light 1996; D'Antonio et al. 1999). In turn, these terrestrial invaders often differ qualitatively from native species in traits that affect their susceptibility to disturbance. Their presence can thus alter the natural regime of disturbance or introduce entirely new forms of disturbance (Mack and D'Antonio 1998). On the other hand, there are also clear examples of terrestrial, nonindigenous invasions that were facilitated by anthropogenic suppression of natural disturbance.

Such phenomena are very poorly documented in marine communities, despite a general impression in the literature that disturbance promotes invasion into marine habitats as well (Cohen and Carlton 1998). Most introductions of nonindigenous marine species are effected by accidental or intentional introductions of immature stages (e.g., larvae in ballast water) or adults (e.g., salt marsh plants used in restoration efforts) by humans (Carlton and Geller 1993; Ruiz et al. 1997). These invaders often establish in portions of habitats that are relatively underutilized by native species and not especially disturbed. Examples include invasion by cordgrass, *Spartina* spp, onto mudflats along the Pacific coast of the United States where there are no native marsh plant competitors and few herbivores (Daehler and Strong 1996), and the establishment of the desiccation-tolerant, introduced snail, *Ovatella myosotis*, in the semiterrestrial zone of Pacific Northwest marshes from which the two common native species of marsh snails are excluded by the dry conditions (Berman and Carlton 1991).

Clear-cut cases of disturbance promoting the establishment of nonindigenous species are few. Nichols et al. (1999) observed that populations of the introduced clam, *Potamocor-*

bula amurensis, rapidly increased to dominate the benthos in northern San Francisco Bay following the near extirpation of native assemblages by a major flood. Reusch and Williams (1999) found that an introduced mussel, *Musculista senhousia*, grew best and most densely in native eelgrass (*Zostera marina*) beds that had been fragmented by disturbance, as compared to continuous undisturbed beds in which suspended food was less available due to slower flow rates. Meng et al. (1994) observed an increased rate of invasion by nonindigenous fish species into the Sacramento-San Joaquin estuary in California following the reduction by a major flood of already drought-stressed populations of native fishes.

Obviously, there is insufficient information to make any generalizations concerning the relationship between nonindigenous invasions and disturbance in marine benthic habitats. Given the remarkable rate at which nonindigenous species are being dispersed around the world by humans, it is imperative that we move from anecdotal impression to rigorous investigation of this relationship.

Effects of Patch Size and Shape

Our ability to predict the effects of disturbance on community composition and dynamics would greatly benefit from more experimental work on the direct and indirect effects of patch size and shape and the mechanisms that generate them. These characteristics, particularly as they affect the perimeter to area ratio of disturbed patches, appear to be generally important to successional dynamics in marine habitats. Patch shape is rarely measured in studies of disturbance, and its effects have been much less thoroughly investigated than patch size. Most studies of the effects of patch size and shape have been conducted on very small scales, usually less than a square meter. Where logistics and ethics allow, comparable studies at larger scales could provide valuable information on the scaling of such edge effects that might aid predictions concerning the effects of large-scale anthropogenic disturbance and habitat fragmentation.

Effects of Disturbance Severity

Much of our understanding of the processes of recolonization and succession following disturbance comes from experimental studies of the most severe level of disturbance: complete removal of the resident organisms and sterilization of the substrate. A more general picture of these processes will come from future studies that examine patterns and mechanisms of recovery from a range of severities of damage.

Effects of Correlations among Disturbance Characteristics

We know that the size, severity, and frequency of disturbance covary, but such correlations are seldom quantified, and their effects on population and assemblage dynamics are rarely studied. Theory predicts that patterns of regional species diversity will be strongly influenced by the pattern of covariation among disturbance characteristics. Studies of these relationships, especially when coupled with the development of spatially explicit patch models, described earlier, should be very fruitful.

Effects of Species Diversity on Susceptibility to, and Recovery from, Disturbance

As discussed earlier, we know very little about the independent influence of species diversity on rates of disturbance and recovery. Existing studies suggest subtle effects, if any. However, ongoing declines in the biodiversity of numerous marine habitats in response to human activities make rigorous experimental investigations of these relationships all the more urgent.

Long-Term Records of Disturbance Regimes

There is a pressing need for the collection of long-term records of natural disturbance regimes. Such records can provide a baseline against which we can objectively measure the effects of global climate change. As the frequency and intensity of storms or the density and distribution of agents of biological disturbance change in response to a changing climate, so too will the regimes of disturbance in many marine benthic habitats. It is critical to document not only changes in mean values of disturbance characteristics (e.g., frequency, size, and severity), but also in their variances. As discussed earlier, variation in the time interval between disturbances, for example, can greatly affect the abundance and persistence of species. Ideally, such studies should pay equal attention to small, "everyday" disturbances and larger "unusual" ones, and document the regime of disturbance at multiple sites to quantify the full range of natural variation in disturbance regimes.

Such long-term records will also provide detailed histories of the disturbances experienced by particular assemblages and a better understanding of the nature and mechanisms by which the response of a system to disturbance is contingent on how it was affected by, and responded to, past disturbances.

Interactions among Disturbances Occurring on Different Spatial and Temporal Scales

Every marine habitat is affected by multiple agents of disturbance. These agents exert their effects at different spatial and temporal scales. Do these effects interact and how? An example from Florida mangrove forests suggests that there can be important interactions between disturbances that occur at different spatial scales. In 1992, Hurricane Andrew caused extensive damage and mortality of mangroves in south Florida; particularly hard hit were stands of *Rhizophora mangle*, a species that lacks the capacity to resprout from adventitious meristems. However, in the midst of these swaths of dead or dying adult trees were small, dense patches of surviving juvenile trees, which were flexible enough to escape wind damage. These patches of young trees had established within canopy gaps, up to 1000 m^2 in area, caused by lightning strikes that had formed months or years prior the hurricane. In this case, the prior occurrence of small-scale disturbance in the form of lightning gaps provided opportunities for recruitment of young trees whose offspring will eventually internally repopulate the much larger areas damaged or destroyed by the hurricane (Smith et al. 1994). Undoubtedly similar phenomena await discovery in other marine habitats.

Direct and Indirect Effects of Disturbance on "Interstitial" Species

Disturbance to "structural" species has been well studied, but the secondary effects on so-called "interstitial" species that live amongst them, including mobile species, are less well documented, including the patterns and processes by which their populations recover following a disturbance. Anthropogenic disturbances such as blast fishing on reefs and bottom trawling drastically reduce structural complexity of the affected assemblage. The reestablishment of habitat complexity during succession and the associated recovery of populations of organisms that require it beg additional study.

Can the Findings of Relatively Small-Scale Studies of Natural Disturbance Meaningfully Inform Investigations of Anthropogenic Disturbance?

Anthropogenic disturbances often occur over larger spatial scales than natural disturbances and are usually more severe (e.g., fishing with bottom trawls and dredges), frequent (e.g., damage from anchors, and dynamite and poison fishing on coral reefs, bait and clam diggers on mud and sand flats, foot traffic on rocky seashores), and chronic in their impact. They may also differ qualitatively from natural forms of disturbance (e.g., chemical pollution), and as noted previously, some forms of anthropogenic disturbance dramatically reduce the structural complexity of the habitat. Predicting the response of marine communities to anthropogenic damage from information on their responses to natural disturbance is complicated by these multivariate differences. It is often not just a simple matter of scaling up from small to larger disturbed areas. Nevertheless, if we know enough about the natural history of the affected systems, we should be able to make sound and testable predictions about the consequences of a particular change in a disturbance regime. As yet, concepts emerging from basic studies of disturbance ecology have had little influence on investigations of anthropogenic disturbances such as bottom trawling or blast fishing on reefs (but see Watling and Norse 1998). Such studies are still in an early descriptive phase; concepts and predictions should develop in time. With the rate of anthropogenic disturbance ever increasing, there is, unfortunately, no shortage of work to be done in this area.

ACKNOWLEDGMENTS

I thank M. Bertness for the invitation to write this chapter and for his immeasurable patience and sage editorial advice. I am grateful to S. Brewer, N. Hausmann, J. Levine, P. Kennedy, T. Minchinton, B. Mitchell, and an anonymous reviewer for insightful criticisms of my drafts; J. Connell, M. Fonseca, M. Koehl, and J. Levine for recommending references from their areas of expertise; and G. Mendoza, C. Nerney, and A. Cundiff for assisting with library searches. I also thank N. Hausmann for his expert assistance with production of the images in the figures throughout this chapter. Special thanks to B. Mitchell for giving me the time to work on this arduous project. Several NSF grants have supported my own research and that of my graduate students on the effects of disturbance on the communities of rocky seashores (OCE 75-23635, OCE 80-08530), coral reefs (BSR 91-00975), and mangrove forests (DEB92-21074, DEB-9615887). I am also grateful for support from the Committee for Research and the MPF, University of California at Berkeley.

LITERATURE CITED

Abelson, A. and M. Denny. 1997. Settlement of marine organisms in flow. *Annu. Rev. Ecol. Syst.* 28: 317–339.

Åberg, P. 1992a. A demographic study of two populations of the seaweed *Ascophyllum nodosum. Ecology* 73: 1473–1487.

Åberg, P. 1992b. Size-based demography of the seaweed *Ascophyllum nodosum* in stochastic environments. *Ecology* 73: 1488–1501.

Abugov, R. 1982. Species diversity and phasing of disturbance. *Ecology* 63: 289–293.

Airoldi, L. 1998. Roles of disturbance, sediment stress, and substratum retention on spatial dominance in algal turf. *Ecology* 79: 2759–2770.

Airoldi, L. and F. Cinelli. 1997. Effects of sedimentation on subtidal macroalgal assemblages: An experimental study from a Mediterranean rocky shore. *J. Exp. Mar. Biol. Ecol.* 215: 269–288.

Airoldi, L. and M. Virgilio. 1998. Responses of turf-forming algae to spatial variations in the deposition of sediments. *Mar. Ecol. Prog. Ser.* 165: 271–282.

Airoldi, L., M. Fabiano and F. Cinelli. 1996. Sediment deposition and movement over a turf assemblage in a shallow rocky coastal area of the Ligurian Sea. *Mar. Ecol. Prog. Ser.* 133: 241–251.

Aller, R. C. and R. E. Dodge. 1974. Animal sediment relations in a tropical lagoon Discovery Bay, Jamaica. *J. Mar. Res.* 32: 209–232.

Allison, G. W. 1997. Ecological consequences of the reduction of species diversity: Experimental approaches. PhD Dissertation, Oregon State University, Corvallis, OR.

Allison, S. K. 1995. Recovery from small-scale anthropogenic disturbances by northern California salt marsh plant assemblages. *Ecol. Appl.* 5: 693–702.

Allison, S. K. 1996. Recruitment and establishment of salt marsh plants following disturbance by flooding. *Amer. Midl. Natur.* 136: 232–247.

Andrews, J. D. 1973. Effects of Tropical Storm Agnes on epifaunal invertebrates in Virginia estuaries. *Chesapeake Science* 14: 223–234.

Aronson, R. B. and W. F. Precht. 1995. Landscape patterns of reef coral diversity: A test of the intermediate disturbance hypothesis. *J. Exp. Mar. Biol. Ecol.* 192: 1–14.

Austen, M. C., S. Widdicombe and N. Villano-Pitacco. 1998. Effects of biological disturbance on diversity and structure of meiobenthic nematode communities. *Mar. Ecol. Prog. Ser.* 174: 233–246.

Baldwin, A. H. and I. A. Mendelssohn. 1998. Response of two oligohaline marsh communities to lethal and nonlethal disturbance. *Oecologia* 116: 543–555.

Baldwin, A. H., K. L. McKee and I. A. Mendelssohn. 1996. The influence of vegetation, salinity, and inundation on seed banks of oligohaline coastal marshes. *Amer. J. Bot.* 83: 470–479.

Barnes, D. K. A. 1999. The influence of ice on polar nearshore benthos. *J. Mar. Biol. Assoc. U.K.* 79: 401–407.

Barnes, H. and H. T. Powell. 1950. The development, general morphology and subsequent elimination of barnacle populations,

Balanus crenatus and *B. balanoides*, after a heavy initial settlement. *J. Anim. Ecol.* 19: 175–179.

Barnes, H. and J. A. Topinka. 1969. Effect of the nature of the substratum on the force required to detach a common littoral alga. *Amer. Zool.* 9: 753–758.

Barrales, H. L. and C. S. Lobban. 1975. The comparative ecology of *Macrocystis pyrifera*, with emphasis on the forests of Chubut, Argentina. *J. Ecol.* 63: 657–677.

Barry, J. P. 1989. Reproductive response of a marine annelid to winter storms: An analog to fire adaptation in plants? *Mar. Ecol. Prog. Ser.* 54: 99–107.

Barry, J. P., C. H. Baxter, R. D. Sagarin and S. E. Gilman. 1995. Climate-related, long-term faunal changes in a California rocky intertidal community. *Science* 267: 672–675.

Bavestrello, G., C. N. Bianchi, B. Calcinai, R. Cattaneo-Vietti, C. Cerrano, C. Morri, S. Puce and M. Sara. Bio-mineralogy as a structuring factor for marine epibenthic communities. *Mar. Ecol. Prog. Ser.* 193: 241–249.

Bell, E. C. 1995. Environmental and morphological influences on thallus temperature and desiccation of the intertidal alga *Mastocarpus papillatus* Kützing. *J. Exp. Mar. Biol. Ecol.* 191: 29–55.

Bell, E. C. and J. M. Gosline. 1997. Strategies for life in flow: Tenacity, morphology, and the probability of dislodgment of two *Mytilus* species. *Mar. Ecol. Prog. Ser.* 159: 197–208.

Bell, S. S. and D. J. Devlin. 1983. Short-term macrofaunal recolonization of sediment and epibenthic habitats in Tampa Bay, Florida. *Bull. Mar. Sci.* 33: 102–108.

Bell, S. S., B. D. Robbins and S. L. Jensen. 1999. Gap dynamics in a seagrass landscape. *Ecosystems* 2: 493–504.

Benedetti-Cecchi, L. and F. Cinelli. 1992. Effects of canopy cover, herbivores, and substratum type on patterns of *Cystoseira* sp. settlement and recruitment in littoral rock pools. *Mar. Ecol. Prog. Ser.* 90: 183–191.

Benedetti-Cecchi, L. and F. Cinelli. 1993. Early patterns of algal succession in a midlittoral community of the Mediterranean sea: A multifactorial experiment. *J. Exp. Mar. Biol. Ecol.* 169: 15–31.

Benedetti-Cecchi, L. and F. Cinelli. 1994. Recovery of patches in an assemblage of geniculate coralline algae: Variability of different successional stages. *Mar. Ecol. Prog. Ser.* 110: 9–18

Benedetti-Cecchi, L. and F. Cinelli. 1996. Patterns of disturbance and recovery in littoral rock pools: Non-hierarchical competition and spatial variability in secondary succession. *Mar. Ecol. Prog. Ser.* 135: 145–161.

Berlow, E. L. 1997. From canalization to contingency: Historical effects in a successional rocky intertidal community. *Ecol. Monogr.* 67: 435–460.

Berman, J. and J. T. Carlton. 1991. Marine invasion processes: Interactions between native and introduced marsh snails. *J. Exp. Mar. Biol. Ecol.* 150: 267–281.

Bertness, M. D. 1989. Intraspecific competition and facilitation in a northern acorn barnacle population. *Ecology* 70: 257–268.

Bertness, M. D. 1991. Interspecific interactions among high marsh perennials in a New England salt marsh. *Ecology* 72: 125–137.

Bertness, M. D. and R. M. Callaway. 1994. Positive interactions in communities. *Trends Ecol. Evol.* 9: 191–193.

Bertness, M. D. and A. M. Ellison. 1987. Determinants of pattern in a New England salt marsh plant community. *Ecol. Monogr.* 57: 129–147.

Bertness, M. D. and E. Grosholz. 1985. Population dynamics of the ribbed mussel, *Geukensia demissa*: The costs and benefits of an aggregated distribution. *Oecologia* 67: 192–204.

Bertness, M. D. and G. H. Leonard. 1997. The role of positive interactions in communities: Lessons from intertidal habitats. *Ecology* 78: 1976–1989.

Bertness, M. D. and S. W. Shumway. 1993. Competition and facilitation in marine plants. *Amer. Nat.* 142: 718–724.

Bertness, M. D., L. Gough and S. W. Shumway. 1992a. Salt tolerances and the distribution of fugitive salt-marsh plants. *Ecology* 73: 1842–1851.

Bertness, M. D., S. D. Gaines, E. G. Stephens and P. O. Yund. 1992b. Components of recruitment in populations of the acorn barnacle *Semibalanus balanoides* (Linnaeus). *J. Exp. Mar. Biol. Ecol.* 156: 199–215.

Bertness, M. D., S. D. Gaines and S. Yeh. 1998. Making mountains out of barnacles: The dynamics of acorn barnacle hummocking. *Ecology* 79: 1382–1394.

Billheimer, L. E. and B. C. Coull. 1988. Bioturbation and recolonization in juvenile spot (Pisces) feeding pits. *Estuarine, Coastal and Shelf Sci.* 27: 335–340.

Bingham, B. L. and C. M. Young. 1995. Stochastic events and dynamics of a mangrove root epifaunal community. *Pubblicazioni Della Stazione Zoologica Di Napoli* 16: 145–163.

Birch, W. R. and M. Birch. 1984. Succession and patterns of tropical intertidal seagrasses in Cockle Bay, Queensland, Australia: A decade of observations. *Aquatic Bot.* 19: 343–367.

Black, R. 1976. The effects of grazing by the limpet, *Acmaea insessa*, on the kelp, *Egregia laevigata*, in the intertidal zone. *Ecology* 57: 265–277.

Blanchette, C. A. 1996. Seasonal patterns of disturbance influence recruitment of the sea palm, *Postelsia palmaeformis*. *J. Exp. Mar. Biol. Ecol.* 197: 1–14.

Boal, J. 1980. Pacific harbor seal (*Phoca vitulina richardii*). Haul out impact on the rocky midtidal zone. *Mar. Ecol. Prog. Ser.* 2: 265–269.

Boesch, D. F., R. J. Diaz and R. W. Virnstein. 1976. Effects of the tropical storm Agnes on soft-bottom macrobenthic communities of the James and York Estuaries and the Lower Chesapeake Bay. *Chesapeake Science* 17: 246–259.

Boesch, D. F. and N. N. Rabalais. 1991. Effects of hypoxia on continental shelf benthos: Comparisons between the New York Bight and the Northern Gulf of Mexico. In R. V. Tyson and T. H. Pearson (eds.), *Modern and Ancient Continental Shelf Anoxia*, pp. 27–34. Geological Society Special Publication No. 58.

Bohnsack, J. A. 1983. Resiliency of reef fish communities in the Florida Keys following a January 1977 hypothermal fish kill. *Env. Biol. Fishes* 9: 41–53.

Bouchon, C., Y. Bouchon-Navaro, D. Imbert and M. Louis. 1991. Effets de l'ouragan Hugo sur la communauté côtières de Guadeloupe (Antilles françaises). *Annales de l'Institut Océanographique Paris* 67: 5–33.

Bouchon, C., Y. Bouchon-Navaro and M. Louis. 1994. Changes in the coastal fish communities following Hurricane Hugo in Guadeloupe Island (French West Indies). *Atoll Research Bulletin* 422. National Museum of Natural History, Smithsonian Institution, Washington, DC.

Branch, G. M. 1975. The ecology of *Patella* species from the Cape Peninsula, South Africa. 4. Desiccation. *Mar. Biol.* 32: 179–188.

Breitburg, D. L. 1985. Development of a subtidal epibenthic community: Factors affecting species composition and the mechanisms of succession. *Oecologia* 65: 173–184.

Breitburg, D. L. 1992. Episodic hypoxia in Chesapeake Bay: Interacting effects of recruitment, behavior, and physical disturbance. *Ecol. Monogr.* 62: 525–546.

Breitburg, D. L. 1996. Consumer mobility and the relative importance of consumption and competition following physical disturbance. *Mar. Ecol. Prog. Ser.* 138: 83–92.

Breitburg, D. L., N. Steinberg, S. DuBeau, C. Cooksey and E. D. Houde. 1994. Effects of low dissolved oxygen on predation on estuarine fish larvae. *Mar. Ecol. Prog. Ser.* 104: 235–246.

Breitburg, D. L., T. Loher, C. A. Pacey and A. Gerstein. 1997. Varying effects of low dissolved oxygen on trophic interactions in an estuarine food web. *Ecol. Monogr.* 67: 489–507.

Brenchley, G. A. 1981. Disturbance and community structure: An experimental study of Bioturbation in marine soft-bottom environments. *J. Mar. Res.* 39: 767–790.

Brewer, J. S. and M. D. Bertness. 1996. Disturbance and intraspecific variation in the clonal morphology of salt marsh perennials. *Oikos* 77: 107–116.

Brewer, J. S., J. M. Levine and M. D. Bertness. 1997. Effects of biomass removal and elevation on species richness in a New England salt marsh. *Oikos* 80: 333–341.

Brewer, J. S., J. M. Levine and M. D. Bertness. 1998. Interactive effects of elevation and burial with wrack on plant community structure in some Rhode Island salt marshes. *J. Ecol.* 86: 125–136.

Brey, T. 1991. The relative significance of biological and physical disturbance: An example from intertidal and subtidal sandy bottom communities. *Estuarine, Coastal and Shelf Sci.* 33: 339–360.

Brock, R. E. 1979. An experimental study on the effects of grazing by parrotfishes and role of refuges in benthic community structure. *Mar. Biol.* 51: 381–388.

Brosnan, D. M. 1994. Environmental factors and plant-animal interactions on rocky shores along the Oregon coast. PhD Dissertation, Oregon State University, Corvallis.

Brown, B. E. and Suharsono. 1990. Damage and recovery of coral reefs affected by El Niño related warming in the Thousand Islands, Indonesia. *Coral Reefs* 8: 163–170.

Butman, C. A. 1987. Larval settlement of soft-sediment invertebrates: The spatial scales of pattern explained by active habitat selection and the emerging role of hydrodynamic processes. *Oceanog. Mar. Biol. Annu. Rev.* 25: 113–165.

Cadée, G. C. 1990. Feeding traces and bioturbation by birds on a tidal flat, Dutch Wadden Sea. *Int. J. Plant Animal Traces* 1: 23–30.

Caffey, H. M. 1982. No effect of naturally-occurring rock types on settlement or survival in the intertidal barnacle, *Tesseropora rosea* (Krauss). *J. Exp. Mar. Biol. Ecol.* 63: 119–132.

Caffey, H. M. 1985. Spatial and temporal variation in settlement and recruitment of intertidal barnacles. *Ecol. Monogr.* 55: 313–332.

Callaway, R. M. 1995. Positive interactions among plants. Botanical Review 61: 306–349.

Carlton, J. T. and J. B. Geller. 1993. Ecological roulette: The global transport of nonindigenous marine organisms. *Science* 261: 78–82.

Carroll, M. L. and R. C. Highsmith. 1996. Role of catastrophic disturbance in mediating *Nucella-Mytilus* interactions in the Alaskan rocky intertidal. *Mar. Ecol. Prog. Ser.* 138: 125–133.

Castilla, J. A. 1988. Earthquake-caused coastal uplift and its effects on rocky intertidal kelp communities. *Science* 242: 440–443.

Caswell, H. and J. E. Cohen. 1991. Disturbance, interspecific interaction and diversity in metapopulations. *Biol. J. Linnean Soc.* 42: 193–218.

Chabot, R. and E. Bourget. 1988. Influence of substratum heterogeneity and settled barnacle density on the settlement of cypris larvae. *Mar. Biol.* 97: 45–56.

Chabreck, R. H. and A. W. Palmisano. 1973. The effects of Hurricane Camille on the marshes of the Mississippi River delta. *Ecology* 54: 1118–1123.

Chapman, A. R. O. 1995. Functional ecology of fucoid algae: 23 years of progress. *Phycologia* 34: 1–32.

Chapman, A. R. O. and C. R. Johnson. 1990. Disturbance and organization of macroalgal assemblages in the Northwest Atlantic. *Hydrobiologia* 192: 77–121.

Chapman, M. G. and A. J. Underwood. 1998. Inconsistency and variation in the development of rocky intertidal assemblages. *J. Exp. Mar. Biol. Ecol.* 224: 265–289.

Chia, F.-S. 1989. Differential larval settlement of benthic marine invertebrates. In J. S. Ryland and P. A. Tyler (eds.), *Reproduction, Genetics and Distribution of Marine Organisms*, pp. 3–12. 23rd European Maine Biology Symposium, Fredensborg, Denmark.

Cohen, A. N. and J. T. Carlton. 1998. Accelerating invasion rate in a disturbed highly invaded estuary. *Science* 279: 555–558.

Collins, S. L. and S. M. Glenn. 1997. Intermediate disturbance and its relationship to within- and between-patch dynamics. *New Zealand J. Ecol.* 21: 103–110.

Colman, J. 1933. The nature of intertidal zonation of plants and animals. *J. Mar. Biol. Assoc. U.K.* 18: 325–476.

Commito, J. A., C. A. Currier, L. R. Kane, K. A. Reinsel and I. M. Ulm. 1995. Dispersal dynamics of the bivalve *Gemma gemma* in a patchy environment. *Ecol. Monogr.* 65: 1–20.

Conlan, K. E., H. S. Lenihan, R. G. Kvitek and J. S. Oliver. 1998. Ice scour disturbance to benthic communities. *Mar. Ecol. Prog. Ser.* 166: 1–16.

Connell, J. H. 1961. Effects of competition, predation by *Thais lapillus*, and other factors on natural populations of the barnacle *Balanus balanoides*. *Ecol. Monogr.* 31: 61–104.

Connell, J. H. 1970. A predator-prey system in the marine intertidal region. 1. *Balanus glandula* and several predatory species of *Thais*. *Ecol. Monogr.* 40: 49–78.

Connell, J. H. 1972. Community interactions on rocky intertidal shores. *Annu. Rev. Ecol. Syst.* 3: 169–192.

Connell, J. H. 1973. Population ecology of reef-building corals. In O. A. Jones and R. Endean (eds.), *Biology and Geology of Coral Reefs*, Vol. 2: *Biology 1*, pp. 205–245. Academic Press, New York.

Connell, J. H. 1974. Ecology: Field experiments in marine ecology. In R. Mariscal (ed.), *Experimental Marine Ecology*, pp. 21–54. Academic Press, New York.

Connell, J. H. 1976. Competitive interactions and the species diversity of corals. In G. O. Mackie (ed.), *Coelenterate Ecology and Behavior*, pp. 51–58. Plenum Press, New York.

Connell, J. H. 1978. Diversity in tropical rain forests and coral reefs. *Science* 199: 1302–1310.

Connell, J. H. 1979. Tropical rain forests and coral reefs as open non-equilibrium systems. In R. M. Anderson, B. D. Turner and L. R. Taylor (eds.), *Population Dynamics*, pp. 141–163. Blackwell Scientific Publications, Oxford.

Connell, J. H. 1997. Disturbance and recovery of coral assemblages. *Coral Reefs* 16 (Suppl.): S101–S113.

Connell, J. H., T. P. Hughes and C. C. Wallace. 1997. A 30-year study of coral abundance, recruitment, and disturbance at several scales in space and time. *Ecol. Monogr.* 67: 461–488.

Connell, J. H. and M. J. Keough. 1985. Disturbance and patch dynamics of subtidal marine animals on hard substrata. In S. T. A. Pickett and P. S. White (eds.), *The Ecology of Natural Disturbance and Patch Dynamics*, pp. 125–151. Academic Press, Orlando, FL.

Connell, J. H. and R. O. Slatyer. 1977. Mechanisms of succession in natural communities and their role in community stability and organization. *Amer. Nat.* 111: 1119–1144.

Connell, J. H. and W. P. Sousa. 1983. On the evidence needed to judge ecological stability or persistence. *Amer. Nat.* 121: 789–824.

Cortés, J. 1993. A reef under siltation stress: A decade of degradation. In R. N. Ginsburg (ed.), *Proceedings of the Colloquium on Global*

Aspects of Coral Reefs: Health, Hazards, and History, pp. 240–246. Rosenthiel School of Marine and Atmospheric Science, University of Miami, FL.

Craighead, F. C. and V. Gilbert. 1962. The effects of Hurricane Donna on the vegetation of southern Florida. *Q. J. Florida Acad. Sci.* 25: 1–28.

Crisp, D. J. 1964. The effects of the severe winter of 1962–63 on marine life in Britain. *J. Anim. Ecol.* 33: 165–210.

Crisp, D. J. 1974. Factors influencing the settlement of marine invertebrate larvae. In P. T. Grant and A. M. Mackie (eds.), *Chemoreception in Marine Organisms*, pp. 177–265. Academic Press, London.

Crisp, D. J. 1976. Settlement responses in marine organisms. In R. C. Newell (ed.), *Adaptations to Environment: Essays on the Physiology of Marine Animals*, pp. 83–124. Butterworth, London.

Cubit, J. D. 1984. Herbivory and the seasonal abundance of algae on a high intertidal rocky shore. *Ecology* 65: 1904–1917.

Daehler, C. C. and D. R. Strong. 1996. Status, prediction and prevention of introduced cordgrass *Spartina* spp. invasions in Pacific estuaries, U.S.A. *Biol. Cons.* 78: 51–58.

Dahlgren, C. P. M. H. Posey and A. W. Hulbert. 1999. The effects of bioturbation on the infaunal community adjacent to an offshore hardbottom reef. *Bull. Mar. Sci.* 64: 21–34.

Daly, M. A. and A. C. Mathieson. 1977. The effects of sand movement on intertidal seaweeds and selected invertebrates at Bound Rock, New Hampshire, USA. *Mar. Biol.* 43: 45–55.

D'Antonio, C. 1985. Epiphytes on the rocky intertidal red alga *Rhodomela larix* (Turner) C. Agardh: Negative effects on the host and food for herbivores? *J. Exp. Mar. Biol. Ecol.* 86: 197–218.

D'Antonio, C. 1986. Role of sand in the domination of hard substrata by the intertidal alga Rhodomela larix. *Mar. Ecol. Prog. Ser.* 27: 263–275.

D'Antonio, C. M., T. L. Dudley and M. Mack. 1999. Disturbances and biological invasions: Direct effects and feedbacks. In L. R. Walker (ed.), *Ecosystems of Disturbed Ground*, pp. 429–468. Elsevier, Amsterdam.

Davis, A. N. and R. T. Wilce. 1987. Algal diversity in relation to physical disturbance–a mosaic of successional stages in a subtidal cobble habitat. *Mar. Ecol. Prog. Ser.* 37: 229–237.

Davis, A. R. and A. J. Butler. 1989. Direct observations of larval dispersal in the colonial ascidian *Podoclavella moluccensis* Sluiter: Evidence for closed populations. *J. Exp. Mar. Biol. Ecol.* 127: 189–203.

Davis, G. E. 1982. A century of natural change in coral distribution at the Dry Tortugas: A comparison of reef maps from 1881 and 1976. *Bull. Mar. Sci.* 32: 608–623.

Day, R. W. and R. W. Osman. 1981. Predation by *Patiria miniata* (Asteroidea) on bryozoans: Prey diversity may depend on the mechanism of succession. *Oecologia* 51: 300–309.

Dayton, P. K. 1971. Competition, disturbance, and community organization: The provision and subsequent utilization of space in a rocky intertidal community. *Ecol. Monogr.* 41: 351–389.

Dayton, P. K. 1973. Dispersion, dispersal, and persistence of the annual intertidal alga, *Postelsia palmaeformis* Ruprecht. *Ecology* 54: 433–438.

Dayton, P. K. 1975. Experimental evaluation of ecological dominance in a rocky intertidal algal community. *Ecol. Monogr.* 45: 137–159.

Dayton, P. K. 1985. Ecology of kelp communities. *Annu. Rev. Ecol. Syst.* 16: 215–245.

Dayton, P. K., V. Currie, T. Gerrodette, B. Keller, R. Rosenthal and D. Ven Tresca. 1984. Patch dynamics and stability of some California kelp communties. *Ecol. Monogr.* 54: 253–289.

Dayton, P. K., G. A. Robilliard and R. T. Paine. 1970. Benthic faunal zonation as a result of anchor ice at McMurdo Sound, Antarctica. In M. W. Holdgate (ed.), *Antarctic Ecology*, Vol. 1, pp. 244–258. Academic Press, New York.

Dayton, P. K., R. J. Seymour, P. E. Parnell and M. J. Tegner. 1989. Unusual marine erosion in San Diego County from a single storm. *Estuarine, Coastal and Shelf Sci.* 29: 151–160.

Dayton, P. K. and M. J. Tegner. 1984. Catastrophic storms, El Niño, and patch stability in a California kelp community. *Science* 224: 283–285.

Dayton, P. K., M. J. Tegner, P. E. Parnell and P. B. Edwards. 1992. Temporal and spatial patterns of disturbance and recovery in a kelp forest community. *Ecol. Monogr.* 62: 421–445.

Dean, R. L. and J. H. Connell. 1987a. Marine invertebrates in an algal succession: I. Variations in abundance and diversity with succession. *J. Exp. Mar. Biol. Ecol.* 109: 195–216.

Dean, R. L. and J. H. Connell. 1987b. Marine invertebrates in an algal succession: II. Tests of hypotheses to explain changes in diversity with succession. *J. Exp. Mar. Biol. Ecol.* 109: 217–248.

Dean, R. L. and J. H. Connell. 1987c. Marine invertebrates in an algal succession: III. Mechanisms linking habitat complexity with diversity. *J. Exp. Mar. Biol. Ecol.* 109: 249–274.

Dean, T. A. and L. E. Hurd. 1980. Development in an estuarine fouling community: The influence of early colonizers on later arrivals. *Oecologia* 46: 295–301.

Denley, E. J. and A. J. Underwood. 1979. Experiments on factors influencing settlement, survival, and growth of two species of barnacles in New South Wales. *J. Exp. Mar. Biol. Ecol.* 36: 269–293.

Denny, M. W. 1987. Lift as a mechanism of patch initiation in mussel beds. *J. Exp. Mar. Biol. Ecol.* 113: 231–245.

Denny, M. W. 1988. *Biology and Mechanics of the Wave-Swept Environment.* Princeton University Press, Princeton, NJ.

Denny, M. W. 1995. Predicting physical disturbance: Mechanistic approaches to the study of survivorship on wave-swept shores. *Ecol. Monogr.* 65: 371–418.

Denny, M. W. 1999. Are there mechanical limits to size in wave-swept organisms? *J. Exp. Biol.* 202: 3463–3467.

Denny, M. W., Daniel, T. L. and M. A. R. Koehl. 1985. Mechanical limits to size in wave-swept organisms. *Ecol. Monogr.* 55: 69–102.

Dethier, M. N. 1984. Disturbance and recovery in intertidal pools: Maintenance of mosaic patterns. *Ecol. Monogr.* 54: 99–118.

De Vogelaere, A. P. 1991. Disturbance, succession and distribution patterns in rocky intertidal communities of central California. PhD Dissertation, University of California, Santa Cruz.

Dial, R. and J. Roughgarden. 1998. Theory of marine communities: The intermediate disturbance hypothesis. *Ecology* 79: 1412–1424.

Diaz, R. J. and R. Rosenberg. 1995. Marine benthic hypoxia: A review of its ecological effects and the behavioural responses of benthic macrofauna. *Oceanog. Mar. Biol. Ann. Rev.* 33: 245–303.

Dixon, J. D. 1978. Determinants of the local distribution of four closely-related species of herbivorous marine snails. PhD Thesis, University of California, Santa Barbara.

Dollar, S. J. 1982. Wave stress and coral community structure in Hawaii. *Coral Reefs* 1: 71–81.

Dollar, S. J. and G. W. Tribble. 1993. Recurrent storm disturbance and recover: A long-term study of coral communities in Hawaii. *Coral Reefs* 12: 223–233.

Doty, M. S. Critical tide factors that are correlated with the vertical distribution of marine algae and other organisms along the Pacific coast. *Ecology* 27: 315–328.

Dromgoole, F. I. 1980. Desiccation resistance of intertidal and subtidal algae. *Botanica Marina* 23: 149–159.

Duarte, C. M., J. Terrados, N. S. R. Agawin, M. D. Fortes, S. Bach and W. Judson Kenworthy. 1997. Response of a mixes Philippine seagrass meadow to experimental burial. *Mar. Ecol. Prog. Ser.* 147: 285–294.

Dye, A. H. 1993. Recolonization of intertidal macroalgae in relation to gap size and molluscan herbivory on a rocky shore on the east coast of southern Africa. *Mar. Ecol. Prog. Ser.* 95: 263–271.

Eagle, R. A. 1975. Natural fluctuations in a soft bottom benthic community. *J. Mar. Biol. Assoc. U.K.* 55: 865–878.

Ebeling, A. W. and D. R. Laur. 1985. The influence of plant cover on surfperch abundance at an offshore temperate reef. *Env. Biol. Fishes* 12: 169–180.

Ebeling, A. W., D. R. Laur and R. J. Rowley. 1985. Severe storm disturbances and reversal of community structure in a southern California kelp forest. *Mar. Biol.* 84: 287–294.

Eckman, J. E. 1983. Hydrodynamic processes affecting benthic recruitment. *Limnol. Oceanog.* 28: 241–257.

Eckman, J. E., A. R. Nowell and P. A. Jumars. 1981. Sediment destabilization by animal tubes. *J. Mar. Res.* 39: 361–374.

Edwards, M. S. 2000. The role of alternate life-history stages of a marine macroalga: A seed bank alternative? *Ecology* 81: 2404–2415.

Ellison, A. M. 1987. Effects of competition, disturbance, and herbivory on *Salicornia europaea*. *Ecology* 68: 576–586.

Ellison, J. C. 1998. Impacts of sediment burial on mangroves. *Mar. Pollut. Bull.* 37: 420–426.

Emerson, C. W. and J. Grant. 1991. The control of soft-shell clam (*Mya arenaria*) recruitment on intertidal sandflats by bedload sediment transport. *Limnol. Oceanog.* 36: 1288–1300.

Emerson, S. E. and J. B. Zedler. 1978. Recolonization of intertidal algae: An experimental study. *Mar. Biol.* 44: 315–324.

Emmerson, L. M. and G. J. Collings. 1998. Macroalgal recruitment in artificially disturbed areas: Interactive effects of temporal and spatial scale. *Marine and Freshwater Research* 49: 541–546.

Everett, R. A. 1991. Intertidal distribution of infauna in a central California lagoon: The role of seasonal blooms of macroalgae. *J. Exp. Mar. Biol. Ecol.* 150: 223–247.

Everett, R. A. 1994. Macroalgae in marine soft-sediment communities–effects on benthic faunal assemblages. *J. Exp. Mar. Biol. Ecol.* 175: 253–274.

Fadlallah, Y. H., K. W. Allen and R. A. Estudillo. 1995. Mortality of shallow reef corals in the western Arabian Gulf following aerial exposure in winter. *Coral Reefs* 14: 99–107.

Fairweather, P. G., A. J. Underwood and M. J. Moran. 1984. Preliminary investigations of predation by the whelk *Morula marginalba*. *Mar. Ecol. Prog. Ser.* 17: 143–156.

Farnsworth, E. J. and A. M. Ellison. 1996. Scale-dependent spatial and temporal variability in biogeography of mangrove root epibiont communities. *Ecol. Monogr.* 66: 45–66.

Farrell, T. M. 1989. Succession in a rocky intertidal community: The importance of disturbance size and position within a disturbed patch. *J. Exp. Mar. Biol. Ecol.* 128: 57–73.

Farrell, T. M. 1991. Models and mechanisms of succession: An example from a rocky intertidal community. *Ecol. Monogr.* 61: 95–113.

Findlay, R. H., M. B. Trexler and D. C. White. 1990. Response of a benthic microbial community to biotic disturbance. *Mar. Ecol. Prog. Ser.* 62: 135–148.

Fishelson, L. 1973. Ecological and biological phenomena influencing coral-species ccomposition on the reef tables of Eilat (Gulf of Aquaba, Red Sea). *Mar. Biol.* 19: 183–196.

Fong, P. and D. Lirman. 1995. Hurricanes cause population expansion of the branching coral *Acropora palmata* (Scleractinia): Wound healing and growth patterns of asexual recruits. *Mar. Ecol.* 16: 317–335.

Forbes, A. T. and D. P. Cyrus. 1992. Impact of a major cyclone on a southeast African estuarine lake system. *Nether. J. Sea Res.* 30: 265–272.

Ford, R. B., S. F. Thrush and P. K. Probert. 1999. Macrobenthic colonisation of disturbances on an intertidal sandflat: The influence of season and buried algae. *Mar. Ecol. Prog. Ser.* 191: 163–174.

Foster, M. S. 1975. Regulation of algal community development in a *Macrocytis pyrifera* forest. *Mar. Biol.* 32: 331–342.

Foster, M. S. and D. R. Schiel. 1985. The ecology of giant kelp forests in California: A community profile. U. S. Fish and Wildlife Service Biological Report 85(7.2).

Foster, M. S. and W. P. Sousa. 1985. Succession. In M. M. Littler and D. S. Littler (eds.), *Eco-*

logical Field Methods: Macroalgae, pp. 269–290. Cambridge University Press, Cambridge.

Frank, P. W. 1965. The biodemography of an intertidal snail population. *Ecology* 46: 831–834.

Frid, C. L. J. 1989. The role of recolonization processes in benthic communities, with special reference to the interpretation of predator-induced effects. *J. Exp. Mar. Biol. Ecol.* 126: 163–172.

Frid, C. L. J. and C. R. Townsend. 1989. An appraisal of the patch dynamics concept in stream and marine benthic communities whose members are highly mobile. *Oikos* 56: 137–141.

Gaines, S. D. and M. Bertness. 1991. The dynamics of juvenile dispersal: Why field biologists must integrate. *Ecology* 74: 2430–2435.

Gaines, S. D. and M. Bertness. 1992. Dispersal of juveniles and variable recruitment in sessile marine species. *Nature* 360: 579–580.

Gaines, S. and J. Roughgarden. 1985. Larval settlement rate: A leading determinant of structure in an ecological community of the marine intertidal zone. *Proc. Natl. Acad. Sci. USA* 82: 3707–3711.

Gaines, S. D. and J. Roughgarden. 1987. Fish in offshore kelp forests affect recruitment to intertidal barnacle populations. *Science* 235: 479–481.

Gaines, S., S. Brown and J. Roughgarden. 1985. Spatial variation in larval concentrations as a cause of spatial variation in settlement for the barnacle, *Balanus glandula*. *Oecologia* 67: 267–272.

Gallagher, E. D., P. A. Jumars and D. D. Trueblood. 1983. Facilitation of soft-bottom benthic succession by tube builders. *Ecology* 64: 1200–1216.

Gamenick, I., A. Jahn, K. Vopel and O. Giere. 1996. Hypoxia and sulphide as structuring factors in a macrozoobenthic community on the Baltic Sea shore: Colonization studies and tolerance experiments. *Mar. Ecol. Prog. Ser.* 144: 73–85.

Garwood, N. C., D. P. Janos and N. Brokaw. 1979. Earthquake caused landslides: A major disturbance to tropical forests. *Science* 205: 997–999.

Gaylord, B. 2000. Biological implications of surf-zone flow complexity. *Limnol. Oceanog.* 45: 174–188.

Gaylord, B., C. A. Blanchette and M. W. Denny. 1994. Mechanical consequences of size in wave-swept algae. *Ecol. Monogr.* 64: 287–313.

Gleason, M. G. 1993. Effects of disturbance on coral communities: Bleaching in Moorea, French Polynesia. *Coral Reefs* 12: 193–201.

Glynn, P. W. 1968. Mass mortalities of echinoids and other reef flat organisms coincident with midday, low water exposures in Puerto Rico. *Mar. Biol.* 1: 226–243.

Glynn, P. W. 1976. Some physical and biological determinants of coral community structure in the eastern Pacific. *Ecol. Monogr.* 46: 451–456.

Glynn, P. W. 1990. Coral mortality and disturbances to coral reefs in the tropical eastern Pacific. In P. W. Glynn (ed.), *Global Ecological Consequences of the 1982–83 El Niño-Southern Oscillations*, pp. 55–126. Elsevier, Amsterdam.

Glynn, P. W. 1993. Coral reef bleaching: Ecological perspectives. *Coral Reefs* 12: 1–17.

Glynn, P. W. and M. W. Colgan. 1992. Sporadic disturbances in fluctuating coral reef environments: El Niño and coral reef development in the eastern Pacific. *Amer. Zool.* 32: 707–718.

Goodbody, I. 1961. Mass mortality of a marine fauna following tropical rains. *Ecology* 42: 150–155.

Gordon, D. C., Jr. and C. Desplanque. 1983. Dynamics and environmental effects of ice in the Cumberland Basin of the Bay of Fundy. *Canad. J. Fish. Aquatic Sci.* 40: 1331–1342.

Grange, K. R. and R. J. Singleton. 1988. Population structure of black coral, *Antipathes aperta*, in the southern fiords of New Zealand. *New Zealand J. Zool.* 15: 481–489.

Grant, J. 1983. The relative magnitude of biological and sediment reworking in an intertidal community. *J. Mar. Res.* 41: 673–689.

Grant, W. S. 1977. High intertidal community organization on a rocky headland in Maine, USA. *Mar. Biol.* 44: 15–25.

Gray, J. S. 1974. Animal-sediment relationships. *Oceanog. Mar. Biol. Annu. Rev.* 12: 223–261.

Grigg, R. W. and J. E. Maragos. 1974. Recolonization of hermatypic corals on submerged lava flows in Hawaii. *Ecology* 55: 387–395.

Grime, J. P. 1977. Evidence for the existence of three primary strategies in the plants and its relevance to ecological and evolutionary theory. *Amer. Nat.* 111: 1169–1194.

Grosberg, R. K. 1987. Limited dispersal and proximity-dependent mating success in the colonial ascidian *Botryllus schlosseri*. *Evolution* 41: 372–384.

Gulliksen, B., T. Haug and O. K. Sandnes. 1980. Benthic macrofauna on new and old lava grounds at Jan Mayen. *Sarsia* 65: 136–148.

Guntenspergen, G. R., D. R. Cahoon, J. Grace, G. D. Steyer, S. Fournet, M. A. Townson and A. L. Foote. 1995. Disturbance and recovery of the Louisiana coastal marsh landscape from the impacts of Hurricane Andrew. *J. Coast. Res.* 21 (Special Issue): 324–339.

Günther, C. 1992. Dispersal of intertidal invertebrates: A strategy to react to disturbances of different scales? *Nether. J. Sea Res.* 30: 45–56.

Gutt, J., A. Starmans and G. Dieckman. 1996. Impact of iceberg scouring on polar benthic habitats. *Mar. Ecol. Prog. Ser.* 137: 311–316.

Hacker, S. D. and S. D. Gaines. 1997. Some implications of direct positive interactions for community species diversity. *Ecology* 78: 1990–2003.

Hall, S. J. 1994. Physical disturbance and marine benthic communities: Life in unconsolidated sediments. *Oceanog. Mar. Biol. Ann. Rev.* 32: 179–239.

Hall, S. J., D. J. Basford, M. R. Robertson, D. G. Rafaelli and I. Tuck. 1991. Patterns of recolonisation and the importance of pit-digging by the crab *Cancer pagurus* in a subtidal sand habitat. *Mar. Ecol. Prog. Ser.* 72: 93–102.

Hall, S. J., D. Raffaelli and S. F. Thrush. 1994. Patchiness and disturbance in shallow water benthic assemblages. In P. S. Giller,

A. G. Hildrew and D. G. Raffaelli (eds.), *Aquatic Ecology: Scale, Pattern and Process*, pp. 333–375. Blackwell Scientific Publications, London.

Hall, S. J., M. R. Robertson, D. J. Basford and R. Fryer. 1993. Pit-digging by the crab *Cancer pagurus*: A test for long-term, large-scale effects on infaunal community structure. *J. Anim. Ecol.* 62: 59–66.

Hardwick-Witman, M. N. 1985. Biological consequences of ice rafting in a New England salt marsh community. *J. Exp. Mar. Biol. Ecol.* 87: 283–298.

Harger, J. R. E. 1970. The effect of wave impact on some aspects of the biology of sea mussels. *Veliger* 12: 401–414.

Harger, J. R. E. and D. E. Landenberger. 1971. The effect of storms as a density dependent mortality factor on populations of sea mussels. *Veliger* 14: 195–201.

Harlin, M. M. and J. M. Lindbergh. 1977. Selection of substrata by seaweeds: Optimal surface relief. *Mar. Biol.* 40: 33–40.

Harris, J. M., G. M. Branch, B. L. Elliott, B. Currie, A. H. Dye, C. D. McQuaid, B. J. Tomalin and C. Velasquez. 1998. Spatial and temporal variability in recruitment of intertidal mussels around the coast of southern Africa. *S. African J. Zool.* 33: 1–11.

Harrison, P. and C. C. Wallace. 1990. Reproduction, dispersal, and recruitment of scleractinian corals. In Z. Dubinsky (ed.), *Ecosystems of the World: Coral Reefs*, pp. 133–207. Elsevier, Amsterdam.

Harrison, P. G. 1987. Natural expansion and experimental manipulation of seagrass (*Zostera* spp.) abundance and the response of infaunal invertebrates. *Estuarine, Coastal and Shelf Sci.* 24: 799–812.

Hartman, J. M. 1988. Recolonization of small disturbance patches in a New England salt marsh. *Amer. J. Bot.* 75: 1625–1631.

Hartman, J. M., H. Caswell and I. Valiela. 1983. Effects of wrack accumulation on salt marsh vegetation. In Proceedings of the 7th European Marine Biology Symposium. *Oceanologica Acta*, Special Issue, pp. 99–102.

Hastings, A. 1980. Disturbance, coexistence, history and competition for space. *Theoret. Pop. Biol.* 18: 363–373.

Hatton, H. 1938. Essais de bionomie explicative sur quelques especes intercotidales d'algues et d'animaux. *Annales de l'Institute Océanographique Monaco* 17: 241–348.

Haven, S. B. 1971. Effects of land-level changes on intertidal invertebrates, with discussion of earthquake ecological succession. In *The Great Alaskan Earthquake of 1964: Biology*, pp. 82–126. Publ. No. 1604, Committee on the Great Alaskan Earthquake of 1964, National Research Council–National Academy of Sciences, Washington, DC.

Hawkins, S. J. 1981. The influence of season and barnacles on the algal colonization of *Patella vulgata* exclusion areas. *J. Mar. Biol. Assoc. U.K.* 61: 1–15.

Hawkins, S. J. 1983. Interactions of *Patella* and macroalgae with settling *Semibalanus balanoides* (L.). *J. Exp. Mar. Biol. Ecol.* 71: 55–72.

Hay, M. E. 1981. The functional morphology of turf-forming seaweeds: Persistence in stressful marine habitats. *Ecology* 62: 739–750.

Hedgpeth, J. W. 1957. Sandy beaches. In J. W. Hedgpeth (ed.), *Treatise on Marine Ecology and Paleontology*, Vol. 1, Ecology, pp. 587–608. Mem. No. 76. Geological Society of America, Boulder, CO.

Highsmith, R. C. 1982. Reproduction by fragmentation in corals. *Mar. Ecol. Prog. Ser.* 7: 207–226.

Highsmith, R. C., A.C. Riggs and C. M. D'Antonio. 1980. Survival of hurricane-generated coral fragments and a disturbance model of reef calcification/growth rates. *Oecologia* 46: 322–329.

Hills, J. M. and J. C. Thomason. 1996. A multi-scale analysis of settlement density and pattern dynamics of the barnacle *Semibalanus balanoides*. *Mar. Ecol. Prog. Ser.* 138: 103–115.

Hines, A. H. and T. R. Loughlin. 1980. Observations of sea otters digging for clams in Monterey Harbor, California. *Fishery Bull.* 78: 159–163.

Hixon, M. A. and W. N. Brostoff. 1985. Substrate characteristics, fish grazing, and epibenthic reef assemblages off Hawaii. *Bull. Mar. Sci.* 37: 200–213.

Hixon, M. A. and W. N. Brostoff. 1996. Succession and herbivory: Effects of differential fish grazing on Hawaiian coral-reef algae. *Ecol. Monogr.* 66: 67–90.

Hobbs, R. J. and L. F. Huenneke. 1992. Disturbance, diversity, and invasion: Implications for conservation. *Conserv. Biol.* 6: 324–337.

Hodgkin, E. P. 1959. Catastrophic destruction of littoral fauna and flora near Fremantle January 1959. *J. R. Soc. W. Aust.* 42: 6–11.

Hodgkin, E. P. 1960. Patterns of life on rocky shores. *J. R. Soc. W. Aust.* 43: 35–45.

Hodgson, G. 1990. Sediment and the settlement of larvae of the reef coral *Pocillopora damicornis*. *Coral Reefs* 9: 41–43.

Hogue, E. W. 1982. Sediment disturbance and the spatial distribution of shallow-water meiobenthic nematodes on the open Oregon coast. *J. Mar. Res.* 40: 551–573.

Holmgren, M., M. Scheffer and M. A. Huston. 1997. The interplay of facilitation and competition in plant communities. *Ecology* 78: 1966–1975.

Holmquist, J. G. 1997. Disturbance and gap formation in a marine benthic mosaic: Influence of shifting macroalgal patches on seagrass structure and mobile invertebrates. *Mar. Ecol. Prog. Ser.* 158: 121–130.

Holt, R. D. 1985. Population dynamics in two-patch environments: Some anomalous consequences of an optimal habitat distribution. *Theoret. Pop. Biol.* 28: 181–208.

Holt, R. D., G. R. Robinson and M. S. Gaines. 1995. Vegetation dynamics in an experimentally fragmented landscape. *Ecology* 76: 1610–1624.

Hopkins, D. R. and V. T. Parker. 1984. A study of the seed bank of a salt marsh in northern San Francisco Bay. *Am. J. Bot.* 71: 348–355.

Houston, W. A. 1999. Severe hail damage to mangroves at Port Curtis, Australia. *Mangroves and Salt Marshes* 3: 29–40.

Hruby, T. and T. A. Norton. 1979. Algal colonization on rocky shores in the Firth of Clyde. *J. Ecol.* 67: 65–77.

Hughes, T. P. 1989. Community structure and diversity of coral reefs: The role of history. *Ecology* 70: 275–279.

Hughes, T. P. 1994. Catastrophes, phase shifts, and large-scale degradation of a Caribbean coral reef. *Science* 265: 1547–1551.

Hughes, T. P. and J. H. Connell. 1999. Multiple stressors on coral reefs: A long-term perspective. *Limnol. Oceanog.* 44: 932–940.

Hurlbut, C. J. 1992. Larval release and supply predict temporal variation in settlement of a colonial ascidian. *Mar. Ecol. Prog. Ser.* 80: 215–219.

Huston, M. A. 1979. A general hypothesis of species diversity. *Amer. Nat.* 113: 81–101.

Huston, M. A. 1985. Patterns of species diversity on coral reefs. *Annu. Rev. Ecol. Syst.* 16: 149–177.

Huston, M. A. 1994. Biological diversity. Cambridge University Press, Cambridge.

Hutchings, M. J. and P. J. Russell. 1989. The seed regeneration dynamics of an emergent salt marsh. *J. Ecol.* 77: 615–637.

Hutchinson, G. E. 1951. Copepodology for the ornithologist. *Ecology* 32: 571–577.

Imbert, D., P. Labbé and A. Rousteau. 1996. Hurricane damage and forest structure in Guadeloupe, French West Indies. *J. Trop. Ecol.* 12: 663–680.

Inglis, G. J. 2000. Disturbance-related heterogeneity in the seed banks of a marine angiosperm. *J. Ecol.* 88: 88–99.

Jackson, J. B. C. 1977a. Competition on marine hard substrata: The adaptive significance of solitary and colonial strategies. *Amer. Nat.* 111: 743–767.

Jackson, J. B. C. 1977b. Habitat area, colonization and development of epibenthic community structure. In B. F. Keegan, P. O. Ceidigh and P. J. S. Boaden (eds.), *Biology of Benthic Organisms*, pp. 349–358. Pergamon Press, Oxford.

Jernakoff, P. 1983. Interactions among animals and algae in an intertidal zone dominated by barnacles. PhD Dissertation, University of Sydney, Australia.

Jiménez, J. A., A. E. Lugo and G. Cintrón. 1985. Tree mortality in mangrove forests. *Biotropica* 17: 177–185.

Johansen, H. W. 1971. Effects of elevational changes on benthic algae in Prince William Sound. In *The Great Alaskan Earthquake of 1964: Biology*, pp. 35–68. Publ. No. 1604, Committee on the Great Alaskan Earthquake of 1964, National Research Council–National Academy of Sciences, Washington, DC.

Johnson, C. R. and K. H. Mann. 1988. Diversity, patterns of adaptation, and stability of Nova Scotian kelp beds. *Ecol. Monogr.* 58: 129–154.

Johnson, K. R. and C. H. Nelson. 1984. Side-scan sonar assessment of gray whale feeding in the Bering Sea. *Science* 225: 1150–1152.

Johnson, L. E. and S. H. Brawley. 1998. Dispersal and recruitment of a canopy-forming intertidal alga: The relative roles of propagule availability and post-settlement processes. *Oecologia* 117: 517–526.

Jokiel, P. L., C. L. Hunter, S. Taguchi and L. Watarai. 1993. Ecological impact of a fresh-water "reef kill" in Kaneohe Bay, Oahu, Hawaii. *Coral Reefs* 12: 177–184.

Jones, G. P. and C. Syms. 1998. Disturbance, habitat structure and the ecology of fishes on coral reefs. *Austral. J. Ecol.* 23: 287–297.

Jones, R. J., R. Berkelmans and J. K. Oliver. 1997. Recurrent bleaching of corals at Magnetic Island (Australia) relative to air and seawater temperatures. *Mar. Ecol. Prog. Ser.* 158: 289–292.

Jones, W. E. and A. Demetropoulos. 1968. Exposure to wave action: Measurements of an important ecological parameter on rocky shores in Anglesey. *J. Exp. Mar. Biol. Ecol.* 2: 46–63.

Karlson, R. 1978. Predation and space utilization patterns in a marine epifaunal community. *J. Exp. Mar. Biol. Ecol.* 31: 225–239.

Karlson, R. and L. Buss. 1984. Competition, disturbance, and local diversity patterns of substratum-bound clonal organisms: A simulation. *Ecol. Model.* 23: 243–255.

Karr, J. R. and K. E. Freemark. 1985. Disturbance and vertebrates: An integrative perspective. In S. T. A. Pickett and P. S. White (eds.), *The Ecology of Natural Disturbance and Patch Dynamics*, pp. 153–168. Academic Press, Orlando, FL.

Kaufman, L. S. 1983. Effects of Hurricane Allen on reef fish assemblages near Discovery Bay, Jamaica. *Coral Reefs* 2: 43–47.

Kay, A. M. and M. J. Keough. 1981. Occupation of patches in the epifaunal communities on pier pilings and the bivalve *Pinna bicolor* at Edithburgh, South Australia. *Oecologia* 48: 123–130.

Keats, D. W., G. R. South and D. H. Steele. 1985. Algal biomass and diversity in the upper subtidal at a pack-ice disturbed site in eastern Newfoundland. *Mar. Ecol. Prog. Ser.* 25: 125–134.

Kendrick, G. A. and D. I. Walker. 1991. Dispersal distances for propagules of *Sargassum spinuligerum* (Sargassaceae, Phaeophyta) measured directly by vital staining and Venturi suction sampling. *Mar. Ecol. Prog. Ser.* 79: 133–138.

Kendrick, G. A. and D. I. Walker. 1995. Dispersal of propagules of *Sargassum* spp. (Sargassaceae, Phaeophyta)–observations of local patterns of dispersal and consequences for recruitment and population structure. *J. Exp. Mar. Biol. Ecol.* 192: 273–288.

Kennelly, S. J. 1987a. Physical disturbances in an Australian kelp community. I. Temporal effects. *Mar. Ecol. Prog. Ser.* 40: 145–153.

Kennelly, S. J. 1987b. Physical disturbances in an Australian kelp community. II. Effects on understorey species due to differences in kelp cover. *Mar. Ecol. Prog. Ser.* 40: 155–165.

Keough, M. J. 1984. Effects of patch size on the abundance of sessile marine invertebrates. *Ecology* 65: 423–437.

Keough, M. J. and H. Chernoff. 1987. Dispersal and population variation in the bryozoan *Bugula neritina*. *Ecology* 68: 199–210.

Kim, J. H. 1997. The role of herbivory, and direct and indirect interactions, in algal succession. *J. Exp. Mar. Biol. Ecol.* 217: 119–135.

Kim, J. H. and R. E. DeWreede. 1996. Effects of size and season of disturbance on algal patch recovery in a rocky intertidal community. *Mar. Ecol. Prog. Ser.* 133: 217–228.

Kirkman, H. 1985. Community structure in seagrasses in southern western Australia. *Aquatic Bot.* 21: 363–375.

Kirkman, H. and J. Kuo. 1990. Pattern and process in southern western Australian seagrasses. *Aquatic Bot.* 37: 367–382.

Kitching, J. A., F. J. Ebling, J. C. Gamble, R. Hoare, A. A. Q. R. McLeod and T. A. Norton. 1976. The ecology of Loch Ine. XIX. Seasonal changes in the western trough. *J. Anim. Ecol.* 45: 731–758.

Knowlton, N. 1992. Thresholds and multiple stable states in coral reef community dynamics. *Amer. Zool.* 32: 674–682.

Knowlton, N., J. C. Lang and B. D. Keller. 1981. Evidence for delayed mortality in hurricane-damaged Jamaican staghorn corals. *Nature* 294: 251–252.

Knowlton, N., J. C. Lang and B. D. Keller. 1990. Case study of natural population collapse: Post-hurricane predation on Jamaican staghorn corals. *Smithsonian Contributions to the Marine Sciences* 31: I–III, 1–25.

Koehl, M. A. R. 1982. The interaction of moving water and sessile organisms. *Scientific American* 247: 124–134.

Koehl, M. A. R. 1984. How do benthic organisms withstand moving water. *Amer. Zool.* 24: 57–70.

Koehl, M. A. R. and S. A. Wainwright. 1977. Mechanical adaptations of a giant kelp. *Limnol. Oceanog.* 22: 1067–1071.

Kramer, D. L. 1987. Dissolved oxygen and fish behavior. *Env. Biol. Fishes* 18: 81–92.

Kvitek, R. G., A. K. Fukayama, B. S. Anderson and B. K. Grimm. 1988. Sea otter foraging on deep-burrowing bivalves in a California coastal lagoon. *Mar. Biol.* 98: 157–167.

Lassig, B. R. 1983. The effects of a cyclonic storm on coral reef fish assemblages. *Env. Biol. Fishes* 9: 55–63.

Lenihan, H. S. and J. S. Oliver. 1995. Anthropogenic and natural disturbances to marine benthic communities in Antarctica. *Ecol. Appl.* 5: 311–326.

Leonard, G. H., J. M. Levine, P. R. Schmidt and M. D. Bertness. 1998. Flow-driven variation in intertidal community structure in a Maine estuary. *Ecology* 79: 1395–1411.

Levin, L. A. 1984. Life history and dispersal patterns in a dense infaunal polychaete assemblage: Community structure and response to disturbance. *Ecology* 65: 1185–1200.

Levin, S. A. and R. T. Paine. 1974. Disturbance, patch formation, and community structure. *Proc. Natl. Acad. Sci. USA* 71: 2744–2747.

Levings, S. C. and S. D. Garrity. 1983. Diel and tidal movement of two co-occuring neritid snails; differences in grazing patterns on a tropical rocky shore. *J. Exp. Mar. Biol. Ecol.* 67: 261–278.

Lewis, J. R. 1954. Observations on a high-level population of limpets. *J. Anim. Ecol.* 23: 85–100.

Lewis, J. R. 1964. *The Ecology of Rocky Shores.* English Universities Press, London.

Liddell, W. D. and S. L. Ohlhorst. 1994. Ten years of disturbance and change on a Jamaican fringing reef. Proceedings of the 7th International Coral Reef Symposium, Guam 1: 144–150.

Lieberman, M., D. M. John and D. Lieberman. 1979. Ecology of subtidal algae on seasonally devastated cobble substrates off Ghana. *Ecology* 60: 1151–1161.

Littler, M. M., Martz, D. R. and D. S. Littler. 1983. Effects of recurrent sand deposition on rocky intertidal organisms: Importance of substrate heterogeneity in a fluctuating environment. *Mar. Ecol. Prog. Ser.* 11: 129–139.

Littorin, B. and M. Gilek. 1999. A photographic study of the recolonization of cleared patches in a dense population of *Mytilus edulis* in the northern Baltic proper. *Hydrobiologia* 393: 211–219.

Loesch, H. 1960. Sporadic mass shoreward migrations of demersal fish and crustaceans in Mobile Bay, Alabama. *Ecology* 41: 292–298.

Loya, Y. 1976. Recolonization of Red Sea corals affected by natural catastrophes and man-made perturbations. *Ecology* 57: 278–289.

Lubchenco, J. 1980. Algal zonation in the New England rocky intertidal community: An experimental analysis. *Ecology* 61: 333–344.

Lubchenco, J. 1983. *Littorina* and *Fucus*: Effects of herbivores, substratum heterogeneity, and plant escapes during succession. *Ecology* 64: 1116–1123.

Lubchenco, J. and B. A. Menge. 1978. Community development and persistence in a low rocky intertidal zone. *Ecol. Monogr.* 48: 67–94.

Lugo, A. E. and C. Patterson-Zucca. 1977. The impact of low temperature stress on mangrove structure and growth. *Trop. Ecol.* 18: 149–161.

Lüning, K. 1984. Temperature tolerance and biogeography of seaweeds: The marine algal flora of Helgoland (North Sea) as an example. *Helgoländer Meeresuntersuchungen* 38: 305–317.

Lüning, K. and W. Freshwater. 1988. Temperature tolerance of northeast Pacific marine algae. *J. Phycol.* 24: 310–315.

Mack, M. C. and C. M. D'Antonio. 1998. Impacts of biological invasions on disturbance regimes. *Trends Ecol. Evol.* 13: 195–198.

Malanson, G. P. 1984. Intensity as a third factor of disturbance regime and its effects on species diversity. *Oikos* 43: 411–413.

Markham, J. W. 1973. Observations on the ecology of *Laminaria sinclairii* on three northern Oregon beaches. *J. Phycol.* 9: 336–341.

McCall, P. L. 1977. Community patterns and adaptive strategies of the infaunal benthos of Long Island Sound. *J. Mar. Res.* 35: 221–266.

McCook, L. J. 1994. Understanding ecological community succession: Causal models and theory, a review. *Vegetatio* 110: 115–147.

McCook, L. J. and A. R. O. Chapman. 1991. Community succession following massive ice-scour on an exposed rocky shore: Effects of *Fucus* canopy algae and of mussels during late succession. *J. Exp. Mar. Biol. Ecol.* 154: 137–169.

McCook, L. J. and A. R. O. Chapman. 1992. Vegetative regeneration of *Fucus* rockweed canopy as a mechanism of secondary succession on an exposed rocky shore. *Botanica Marina* 35: 35–46.

McCook, L. J. and A. R. O. Chapman. 1997. Patterns and variations in natural succession following massive ice-scour of a rocky intertidal seashore. *J. Exp. Mar. Biol. Ecol.* 214: 121–147.

McGuinness, K. A. 1984. Species-area relations of communities on intertidal boulders: Testing the null hypothesis. *J. Biogeog.* 11: 439–456.

McGuinness, K. A. 1987a. Disturbance and organisms on boulders. I. Patterns in the environment and the community. *Oecologia* 71: 409–419.

McGuinness, K. A. 1987b. Disturbance and organisms on boulders. II. Causes of patterns in diversity and abundance. *Oecologia* 71: 420–430.

McGuinness, K. A. 1992. Disturbance and the mangrove forests of Darwin Harbour. In I. Moffatt A. Webb (eds.), *Conservation and Development Issues in North Australia*, pp. 55–62. ANU Press, Canberra.

McGuinness, K. A. and A. J. Underwood. 1986. Habitat structure and the nature of communities on intertidal boulders. *J. Exp. Mar. Biol. Ecol.* 104: 97–123.

Meadows, P. S. and J. I. Campbell 1972. Habitat selection by marine invertebrates. *Adv. Mar. Biol.* 10: 271–382.

Meng, L., P. B. Moyle and B. Herbold. 1994. Changes in abundance and distribution of native and introduced fishes of Suisun marsh. *Trans. Amer. Fish. Soc.* 123: 498–507.

Menge, B. A. 1976. Organization of the New England rocky intertidal community: Role of predation, competition, and environmental heterogeneity. *Ecol. Monogr.* 46: 355–393.

Menge, B. A. 1978. Predation intensity in a rocky intertidal community. Relation between predator foraging activity and environmental harshness. *Oecologia* 34: 1–16.

Menge, B. A. 1979. Coexistence between seastars *Asterias vulgaris* and *A. fobesi* in a heterogeneous environment: A non-equilibrium explanation. *Oecologia* 41: 245–272.

Menge, B. A. and J. Lubchenco. 1981. Community organization in temperate and tropical rocky intertidal habitats: Prey refuges in relation to consumer pressure gradients. *Ecol. Monogr.* 51: 429–450.

Menge, B. A., T. M. Farrell, A. M. Olson, P. van Tamelen and T. Turner. 1993. Algal recruitment and the maintenance of a plant mosaic in the low intertidal region on the Oregon coast. *J. Exp. Mar. Biol. Ecol.* 170: 91–116.

Menge, J. L. 1975. Effect of herbivores on community structure of the New England rocky intertidal region: Distribution, abundance and diversity of algae. PhD Dissertation, Harvard University, Cambridge, MA.

Miller, T. E. 1982. Community diversity and interactions between the size and frequency of disturbance. *Amer. Nat.* 120: 533–536.

Minchinton, T. E. 1997. Life on the edge: Conspecific attraction and recruitment of populations to disturbed habitats. *Oecologia* 111: 45–52.

Minchinton, T. E. and R. E. Scheibling. 1991. The influence of larval supply and settlement on the population-structure of barnacles. *Ecology* 72: 1867–1879.

Minchinton, T. E., R. E. Scheibling and H. L. Hunt. 1997. Recovery of an intertidal assemblage following a rare occurrence of scouring by sea ice in Nova Scotia, Canada. *Botanica Marina* 40: 139–148.

Moloney, K. A. and S. A. Levin. 1996. The effects of disturbance architecture on landscape-level population dynamics. *Ecology* 77: 375–394.

Morse, D. E., N. Hooker, A. N. C. Morse and B. A. Jensen. 1988. Control of larval metamorphosis and recruitment in sympatric agaricid corals. *J. Exp. Mar. Biol. Ecol.* 116: 193–217.

Moverley, J. H., P. Saenger and M. A. Curtis. 1986. Patterns of polychaete recolonization in Queensland subtropical estuaries following severe flooding. *Hydrobiologia* 134: 227–235.

Moyle, P. B. and T. Light. 1996. Fish invasions in California: Do abiotic factors determine success? *Ecology* 77: 1666–1670.

Mullineaux, L. S. and E. D. Garland. 1993. Larval recruitment in response to manipulated flows. *Mar. Biol.* 116: 667–683.

Myers, A. C. 1977. Sediment processing in a marine subtidal sandy bottom community. II. Biological consequences. *J. Mar. Res.* 35: 633–647.

Navarrete, S. A. and J. C. Castilla. 1990. Barnacle walls as mediators of intertidal mussel recruitment: Effects of patch size on the utilization of space. *Mar. Ecol. Prog. Ser.* 68: 113–119.

Nerini, M. K. and J. S. Oliver. 1983. Gray whales and the structure of the Bering Sea benthos. *Oecologia* 39: 224–225

Nichols, F. H., J. K. Thompson and L. Schemel. 1990. Remarkable invasion of San Francisco Bay (California, U.S.A.) by the Asian clam *Potamocorbula amurensis*. II. Displacement of a former community. *Mar. Ecol. Prog. Ser.* 66: 95–101.

Nicotri, M. E. 1977. Grazing effects of four marine intertidal herbivores on the microflora. *Ecology* 58: 1020–1032.

Noji, C. I.-M. and T. T. Noji. 1991. Tube lawns of spionid polychaetes and their significance for recolonization of disturbed benthic substrates. *Meeresforschung* 33: 235–246.

Nordby, C. S. and J. B. Zedler. 1991. Responses of fishes and benthos to hydrologic disturbances in Tijuana Estuary and Los Peñasquitos Lagoon, California. *Estuaries* 14: 80–93.

Norton, T. A. 1983. The resistance to dislodgment of *Sargassum muticum* germlings under defined hydrodynamic conditions. *J. Mar. Biol. Assoc. U.K.* 63: 181–193.

Norton, T. A. and R. Fetter. 1981. The settlement of *Sargassum muticum* propagules in stationary and flowing water. *J. Mar. Biol. Assoc. U.K.* 61: 929–940.

Nyman, J. A. and R. H. Chabreck. 1995. Fire in coastal marshes: History and recent concerns. In S. I. Cerulean and R. T. Engstrom (eds.), *Fire in Wetlands: A Management Perspective*, pp. 134–141. Proceedings of the Tall Timbers Fire Ecology Conference, No. 19. Tall Timbers Research Station, Tallahassee, FL.

Nyman, J. A., C. R. Crozier and R. D. Delaune. 1995. Roles and patterns of hurricane sedimentation in an estuarine marsh landscape. *Estuarine, Coastal and Shelf Sci.* 40: 665–679.

Okey, T. A. 1997. Sediment flushing observations, earthquake slumping, and benthic community changes in Monterey Canyon head. *Continental Shelf Research* 17: 877–897.

Oliver, J. S. and R. G. Kvitek. 1984. Side-scan sonar records and diver observations of the gray whale (*Eschrictius robustus*) feeding grounds. *Biol. Bull.* 167: 264–269.

Oliver, J. S. and P. N. Slattery. 1985. Destruction and opportunity on the sea floor: Effects of gray whale feeding. *Ecology* 66: 1965–1975.

Oliver, J. S., P. N. Slattery, L. W. Hulberg and J. W. Nybakken. 1980. Relationships between wave disturbance and zonation of benthic invertebrate communities along a subtidal high-energy beach in Monterey Bay. *Calif. Fish. Bull.* 78: 437–454.

Oliver, J. S., P. N. Slattery, M. A. Silberstein and E. F. O'Connor. 1984. Gray whale feeding on dense ampeliscid amphipod communities near Bamfield, British Columbia. *Canad. J. Zool.* 62: 41–49.

Oliver, J. S., R. G. Kvitek and P. N. Slattery. 1985. Walrus feeding disturbance: Scavenging habits and recolonization of the Bering sea benthos. *J. Exp. Mar. Biol. Ecol.* 91: 233–246.

Onuf, C. P. 1987. The ecology of Mugu Lagoon, California: An estuarine profile. U.S. Fish and Wildlife Service Biological Report 85(7.15), National Wetlands Research Center, U.S. Department of the Interior, Washington, DC.

Onuf, C. P. and M. L. Quammen. 1983. Fishes in a California coastal lagoon: Effects of major storms on distribution and abundance. *Mar. Ecol. Prog. Ser.* 12: 1–14.

Orth, R. J. 1975. Destruction of eelgrass *Zostera marina* by the cownose ray *Rhinoptera bonasus* in the Chesapeake Bay. *Chesapeake Science* 16: 205–208.

Orth, R. J. 1977. The importance of sediment stability in seagrass communities. In B. C. Coull (ed.), *Ecology of Marine Benthos*, pp. 281–300. Belle W. Baruch Library in Marine Science, University of South Carolina Press, Columbia.

Orth, R. J., K. L. Heck, Jr. and J. van Montfrans. 1984. Faunal communities in seagrass beds: A review of the influence of plant structure and prey characteristics on predator-prey relationships. *Estuaries* 7: 329–350.

Orth, R. J., M. Luckenbach and K. A. Moore. 1994. Seed dispersal in a marine macrophyte–Implications for colonization and restoration. *Ecology* 75: 1927–1939.

Osman, R. W. 1977. The establishment and development of a marine epifaunal community. *Ecol. Monogr.* 47: 37–63.

Osman, R. W. and R. B. Whitlatch. 1995a. The influence of resident adults on recruitment: A comparison to settlement. *J. Exp. Mar. Biol. Ecol.* 190: 169–198.

Osman, R. W. and R. B. Whitlatch. 1995b. The influence of resident adults on larval settlement–experiments with four species of ascidians. *J. Exp. Mar. Biol. Ecol.* 190: 199–220.

Osman, R. W. and R. B. Whitlatch. 1998. Local control of recruitment in an epifaunal community and the consequences to colonization processes. *Hydrobiologica* 376: 113–123.

Ottaway, J. R. 1973. Some effects of temperature, desiccation, and light on the intertidal anemone *Actinia tenebrosa* Farquhar (Cnidaria: Anthozoa). *Aust. J. Mar. Freshwater Res.* 24: 103–126.

Ottaway, J. R. 1979. Population ecology of the intertidal anemone *Actinia tenebrosa*. III. Dynamics and environmental factors. Australian *J. Marine and Freshwater Research* 30: 41–62.

Paijmans, K. and B. Rollet. 1977. The mangroves of Galley Reach, Papua New Guinea. *Forest Ecol. Manag.* 1: 119–140.

Paine, R. T. 1974. Intertidal community structure: Experimental. studies on the relationship between a dominant competitor and its principle predator. *Oecologia* 15: 93–120.

Paine, R. T. 1977. Controlled manipulations in the marine intertidal zone and their contributions to ecological theory. Academy of Natural Sciences, Philadelphia, Special Publication 12: 245–270.

Paine, R. T. 1979. Disaster, catastrophe, and local persistence of the sea palm *Postelsia palmaeformis*. *Science* 205: 685–687.

Paine, R. T. 1988. Habitat suitability and local population persistence of the sea palm *Postelsia palmaeformis*. *Ecology* 69: 1787–1794.

Paine, R. T. and S. A. Levin. 1981. Intertidal landscapes: Disturbance and the dynamics of pattern. *Ecol. Monogr.* 51: 145–178.

Paine, R. T. and T. H. Suchanek. 1983. Convergence of ecological processes between indepedently evolved competitive dominants: A tunicate-mussel comparison. *Evolution* 37: 821–831.

Paine, R. T., M. J. Tegner and E. A. Johnson. 1998. Compounded perturbations yield ecological surprises. *Ecosystems* 1: 535–545.

Palumbi, S. R. and J. B. C. Jackson. 1982. Ecology of cryptic coral reef communities. II. Recovery from small disturbances by encrusting bryozoa: The influence of "host" species and lesion size. *J. Exp. Mar. Biol. Ecol.* 64: 103–115.

Patriquin, D. G. 1975. "Migration" of blowouts in seagrass beds at Barbados and Carriacou, West Indies, and its ecological and geological implications. *Aquatic Bot.* 1: 163–189.

Pawlik, J. R. 1992. Chemical ecology of the settlement of benthic marine invertebrates. *Oceanogr. Mar. Biol.* 30: 273–335.

Pearson, R. G. 1981. Recovery and recolonization of coral reefs. *Mar. Ecol. Prog. Ser.* 4: 105–122.

Pennings, S. C. and C. L. Richards. 1998. Effects of wrack burial in salt-stressed habitats: *Batis maritima* in a southwest Atlantic salt marsh. *Ecography* 21: 630–638.

Peterson, C. H. 1975. Stability of species and of community for the benthos of two lagoons. *Ecology* 56: 958–965.

Peterson, C. H. 1979. Predation, competitive exclusion, and diversity in the soft-sediment benthic communities of estuaries and lagoons. In R. J. Livingston (ed.), *Ecological Processes in Coastal and Marine Systems*, pp. 233–264. Plenum Press, New York.

Peterson, C. H. 1985. Patterns of lagoonal bivalve mortality after heavy sedimentation and their paleoecological significance. *Paleobiology* 11: 139–153.

Peterson, C. H. and R. Black. 1988. Density-dependent mortality caused by physical stress interacting with biotic history. *Amer. Nat.* 131: 257–270.

Petraitis, P. S. and R. E. Latham. 1999. The importance of scale in testing the origins of alternative community states. *Ecology* 80: 429–442.

Petraitis, P. S., R. E. Latham and R. A. Niesenbaum. 1989. The maintenance of species diversity by disturbance. *Q. Rev. Biol.* 64: 393–418.

Philippart, C. J. M. 1994. Interactions between *Arenicola marina* and *Zostera noltii* on a tidal flat in the Wadden Sea. *Mar. Ecol. Prog. Ser.* 111: 251–257.

Pickett, S. T. A., S. L. Collins and J. J. Armesto. 1987. Models, mechanisms and pathways of succession. *Bot. Rev.* 53: 335–371.

Pihl, L., S. P. Baden and R. J. Diaz. 1991. Effects of periodic hypoxia on distribution of demersal fish and crustaceans. *Mar. Biol.* 108: 349–360.

Pihl, L., S. P. Baden, R. J. Diaz and L. C. Schaffner. 1992. Hypoxia-induced structural changes in the diet of bottom-feeding fish and crustacea. *Mar. Biol.* 112: 349–361.

Pineda, J. and A. Escofet. 1989. Selective effects of disturbance on populations of sea anemones from northern Baja California, Mexico. *Mar. Ecol. Prog. Ser.* 55: 55–62.

Porter, J. W., J. D. Woodley, G. J. Smith, J. E. Neigel, J. F. Battey and D. G. Dallmeyer. 1981. Population trends among Jamaican reef corals. *Nature* 294: 249–250.

Porter, J. W., J. F. Batty and G. J. Smith. 1982. Perturbation and change in coral communities. *Proc. Natl. Acad. Sci. USA* 79: 1678–1681.

Posey, M. H. 1986. Changes in a benthic community associated with dense beds of a burrowing deposit feeder, *Callianassa californiensis*. *Mar. Ecol. Prog. Ser.* 31: 15–22.

Posey, M., W. Lindberg, T. Alphin and F. Vose. 1996. Influence of storm disturbance on an offshore benthic community. *Bull. Mar. Sci.* 59: 523–529.

Preen, A. R. 1996. Infaunal mining: A novel foraging method of loggerhead turtles. *J. Herpetol.* 30: 96–97.

Preen, A. R., W. J. Lee Long and R. G. Coles. 1995. Flood and cyclone related loss, and partial recovery, of more than 1000 km² of seagrass in Hervey Bay, Queensland, Australia. *Aquatic Bot.* 52: 3–17.

Probert, P. K. 1984. Disturbance, sediment stability, and trophic structure of soft-bottom communities. *J. Mar. Res.* 42: 893–921.

Pugh, P. J. A. and J. Davenport. 1997. Colonisation vs. disturbance: The effects of sustained ice scouring on intertidal communities. *J. Exp. Mar. Biol. Ecol.* 210: 1–21.

Pulliam, H. R. 1988. Sources, sinks, and population regulation. *Amer. Nat.* 132: 652–661.

Quinn, J. F. and A. E. Dunham. 1983. On hypothesis testing in ecology and evolution. *Amer. Nat.* 122: 602–617.

Raffaelli, D., H. Richter, R. Summers and S. Northcott. 1990. Tidal migrations in the flounder (*Platichthys flesus*). *Mar. Behav. Physiol.* 16: 249–260.

Raimondi, P. T. 1988a. Rock type affects settlement, recruitment, and zonation of the barnacle *Chthamalus anisopoma* Pilsbury. *J. Exp. Mar. Biol. Ecol.* 123: 253–267.

Raimondi, P. T. 1988b. Settlement cues and determination of the vertical limit of an intertidal barnacle. *Ecology* 69: 400–407.

Raimondi, P. T. 1990. Patterns, mechanisms, consequences of variability in settlement and recruitment of an intertidal barnacle. *Ecol. Monogr.* 60: 283–309.

Ramage, D. L. and D. R. Schiel. 1999. Patch dynamics and response to disturbance of the seagrass *Zostera novazelandica* on intertidal platforms in southern New Zealand. *Mar. Ecol. Prog. Ser.* 189: 275–288.

Rasheed, M. A. 1999. Recovery from experimentally created gaps within a tropical *Zostera capricorni* (Aschers.) seagrass meadow, Queensland Australia. *J. Exp. Mar. Biol. Ecol.* 235: 183–200.

Redfield, A. C. 1972. Development of a New England salt marsh. *Ecol. Monogr.* 42: 201–237.

Reed, D. C., D. R. Laur and A. W. Ebling. 1988. Variation in algal dispersal and recruitment: The importance of episodic events. *Ecol. Monogr.* 58: 321–335.

Rees, E. I. S., A. Nicholaidou and P. Laskaridou. 1977. The effects of storms on the dynamics of shallow water benthic associations. In B. F. Keegan, P. O. Ceidigh and P. J. S. Boaden (eds.), *Biology of Benthic Organisms*, 11th European Symposium on Marine Biology, pp. 465–474. Pergamon Press, Oxford.

Reidenauer, J. A. and D. Thistle. 1981. Response of a soft-bottom harpacticoid community to stingray (*Dasyatis sabina*) disturbance. *Mar. Biol.* 65: 261–167.

Reidenbaugh, T. G. and W. C. Banta. 1980. Origin and effects of tidal wrack in Virginia salt marsh. *Gulf Research Reports* 6: 393–401.

Rejmanek, M., C. Sasser and G. W. Peterson. 1988. Hurricane-induced sediment deposition in a Gulf coast marsh. *Estuarine, Coastal, and Shelf Sci.* 27: 217–222.

Reusch, T. B. H. and A. R. O. Chapman. 1995. Storm effects on eelgrass (*Zostera marina* L.) and blue mussel (*Mytilus edulis* L.) beds. *J. Exp. Mar. Biol. Ecol.* 192: 257–271.

Reusch, T. B. H. and S. L. Williams. 1999. Macrophyte canopy structure and the success of an invasive marine bivalve. *Oikos* 84: 398–416.

Rhoads, D. C. 1974. Organism–sediment relations on the muddy sea floor. *Oceanog. Mar. Biol. Annu. Rev.* 12: 263–300.

Rhoads, D. C. and L. F. Boyer. 1982. The effects of marine benthos on physical properties of sediments: A successional perspective. In P. L. McCall and M. J. S. Tevesz (eds.), *Animal–Sediment Relations*, pp. 3–52. Plenum Press, New York.

Rhoads, D. C. and D. K. Young. 1970. The influence of deposit-feeding organisms on sediment stability and community trophic structure. *J. Mar. Res.* 28: 150–178.

Richard, G. A. 1978. Seasonal and environmental variations in sediment accretion in a Long Island salt marsh. *Estuaries* 1: 29–35.

Roberts, B. A. and A. Robertson. 1986. Salt marshes of Atlantic Canada: Their ecology and distribution. *Canad. J. Bot.* 64: 455–467.

Robertson, A. I. and K. H. Mann. 1984. Disturbance by ice and life-history adaptations of the seagrass *Zostera marina*. *Mar. Biol.* 80: 131–141.

Robles, C. D. 1982. Disturbance and predation in an assemblage of herbivorous diptera and algae on rocky shores. *Oecologia* 54: 23–31.

Rogers, C. S. 1990. Responses of coral reefs and reef organisms to sedimentation. *Mar. Ecol. Prog. Ser.* 62: 185–202.

Rogers, C. S. 1993. Hurricanes and coral reefs: The intermediate disturbance hypothesis revisted. *Coral Reefs* 12: 127–137.

Rogers, C. S., T. H. Suchanek and F. A. Pecora. 1982. Effects of hurricanes David and Frederic (1979) on shallow *Acropora palmata* reef communities: St. Croix, U. S. Virgin Islands. *Bull. Mar. Sci.* 32: 532–548.

Rollon, R. N., E. D. D. Van Steveninck, W. Van Vierssen and M. D. Fortes. 1998. Contrasting recolonization strategies in multispecies seagrass meadows. *Mar. Pollut. Bull.* 37: 450–459.

Rosenthal, R. J., W. D. Clarke and P. K. Dayton. 1974. *Ecology* and natural history of a stand of giant kelp, *Macrocystis pyrifera*, off Del Mar, California. *Fish. Bull.* 72: 670–684.

Roth, L. C. 1992. Hurricanes and mangrove regeneration: Effects of Hurricane Joan, October 1988, on the vegetation of Isla del Venado, Bluefields, Nicaragua. *Biotropica* 24: 375–384.

Roughgarden, J. and Y. Iwasa. 1986. Dynamics of a metapopulation with space-limited subpopulations. *Theoret. Pop. Biol.* 29: 235–261.

Ruiz, G. M., J. T. Carlton, E. D. Grosholz and A. H. Hines. 1997. Global invasions of marine and estuarine habitats by non-indigenous species: Mechanisms, extent, and consequences. *Amer. Zool.* 37: 621–632.

Rykiel, E. J., Jr. 1985. Towards a definition of ecological disturbance. *Austral. J. Ecol.* 10: 361–365.

Sagarin, R. D., J. P. Barry, S. E. Gilman and C. H. Baxter. 1999. Climate-related change in an intertidal community over short and long time scales. *Ecol. Monogr.* 69: 465–490.

Sahade, R., M. Tatian, J. Kowalke, S. Kuhne, G. B. Esnal. 1998. Benthic faunal associations on soft substrates at Potter Cove, King George Island, Antarctica. *Polar Biology* 19: 85–91.

Sanders, H. L. 1968. Marine benthic diversity: A comparative study. *Amer. Nat.* 102: 243–282.

Sanford, E., D. Bermudez, M. D. Bertness and S. D. Gaines. 1994. Flow, food supply and acorn barnacle population dynamics. *Mar. Ecol. Prog. Ser.* 104: 49–62.

Santelices, B., Castilla, J. C., Cancino, J. and P. Schmiede. 1980. Comparative ecology of *Lessonia nigrescens* and *Durvillaea antarctica* (Phaeophyta) in central Chile. *Mar. Biol.* 59: 119–132.

Santelices, B., A. J. Hoffman, D. Aedo, M. Bobadilla and R. Otaiza. 1995. A bank of microscopic forms on disturbed boulders and stones in tide pools. *Mar. Ecol. Prog. Ser.* 129: 215–228.

Santos, S. L. and J. L. Simon. 1980a. Marine soft-bottom community establishment following annual defaunation: Larval or adult recruitment? *Mar. Ecol. Prog. Ser.* 2: 235–241.

Santos, S. L. and J. L. Simon. 1980b. Response of soft-bottom benthos to annual catastrophic disturbance in a south Florida estuary. *Mar. Ecol. Prog. Ser.* 3: 347–355.

Savidge, W. B. and G. L. Taghon. 1988. Passive and active components of colonization following two types of disturbance on intertidal sandflat. *J. Exp. Mar. Biol. Ecol.* 115: 137–155.

Schonbeck, M. and T. A. Norton. 1978. Factors controlling the upper limits of fucoid algae on the shore. *J. Exp. Mar. Biol. Ecol.* 31: 303–313.

Schonbeck, M. and T. A. Norton. 1979. An investigation of drought avoidance in intertidal fucoid algae. *Botanica Marina* 22: 133–144.

Schwenke, H. 1971. Water movement: Plants. In O. Kinne (ed.), *Marine Ecology*, Vol. I, *Environmental Factors*, Part 2, pp. 1091–1121. Wiley Interscience, New York.

Scoffin, T. P. 1993. The geological effects of hurricanes on coral reefs and the interpretation of storm deposits. *Coral Reefs* 12: 203–221.

Scrosati, R. 1998. Mechanisms of recolonization of the clonal intertidal alga *Mazzaella cornucopiae* (Rhodophyta, Gigartinaceae) after disturbances. *Canad. J. Bot.* 76: 1717–1724.

Seapy, R. R. and M. M. Littler. 1982. Population and species diversity fluctuations in a rocky intertidal community relative to severe aerial exposure and sediment burial. *Mar. Biol.* 71: 87–96.

Sebens. K. P. 1987. Competition for space: Effects of disturbance and indeterminate competitive success. *Theoret. Pop. Biol.* 32: 430–441.

Seed, R. 1969. The ecology of *Mytilus edulis* L. (Lamellibranchiata) on exposed rocky shores. 2. Growth and mortality. *Oecologia* 3: 317–350.

Seed, R. 1996. Patterns of biodiversity in the macro-invertebrate fauna associated with mussel patches on rocky shores. *J. Mar. Biol. Assoc. U.K.* 76: 203–210.

Seliskar, D. M. and J. L. Gallagher. 1983. The ecology of tidal marshes of the Pacific Northwest coast: A community profile. FWS/OBS-82/32, U. S. Fish and Wildlife Service, Division of Biological Sciences, Washington, DC.

Seymour, R. J., M. J. Tegner, P. K. Dayton and P. E. Parnell. 1989. Storm wave induced mortality of giant kelp, *Macrocystis pyrifera* in Southern California. *Estuarine, Coastal and Shelf Sci.* 28: 277–292.

Sherman, K. M., J. A. Reidenauer, D. Thistle and D. Meeter. 1983. Role of a natural disturbance in an assemblage of marine free-living nematodes. *Mar. Ecol. Prog. Ser.* 11: 23–30.

Sherman, R. E., T. J. Fahey and J. J. Battles. 2000. Small-scale disturbance and regeneration dynamics in a neotropical mangrove forest. *J. Ecol.* 88: 165–178.

Shmida, A. and S. Ellner. 1984. Coexistence of plants species with similar niches. *Vegetatio* 58: 20–55.

Short, F. T. 1983. The response of interstitial ammonium in eelgrass (*Zostera marina* L.) beds to environmental perturbations. *J. Exp. Mar. Biol. Ecol.* 68: 195–208.

Short, F. T. and S. Wyllie-Echeverria. 1996. Natural and human-induced disturbance of seagrasses. *Env. Conserv.* 23: 17–27.

Shull, D. H. 1997. Mechanisms of infaunal polychaete dispersal and colonization in an intertidal sandflat. *J. Mar. Res.* 55: 153–179.

Shumway, S. W. and M. D. Bertness. 1994. Patch size effects on marsh plant secondary succession mechanisms. *Ecology* 75: 564–568.

Simon. J. L. and D. M. Dauer. 1977. Restablishment of a benthic community following natural defaunation. In B. C. Coull (ed.), *Ecology of Marine Benthos*, pp. 139–154. Belle W. Baruch Library in Marine Science, University of South Carolina Press, Columbia.

Slattery, M. and D. Bockus. 1997. Sedimentation in McMurdo Sound, Antarctica: A disturbance mechanism for benthic invertebrates. *Polar Biology* 18: 172–179.

Smith, C. R. and S. J. Brumsickle. 1989. The effects of patch size and substrate isolation on colonization modes and rates in an intertidal sediment. *Limnol. Oceanog.* 34: 1263–1277.

Smith, F. and J. D. Witman. 1999. Species diversity in subtidal landscapes: Maintenance by physical processes and larval recruitment. *Ecology* 80: 51–69.

Smith, L. D. and T. P. Hughes. 1999. An experimental assessment of survival, re-attachment and fecundity of coral fragments. *J. Exp. Mar. Biol. Ecol.* 235: 147–164.

Smith, T. J., III. 1992. Forest structure. In A. I. Robertson and D. M. Alongi (eds.), *Tropical Mangrove Ecosystems*, pp. 101–136. American Geophysical Union, Washington, DC.

Smith, T. J., III, M. B. Robblee, H. R. Wanless and T. W. Doyle. 1994. Mangroves, hurricanes, and lightning strikes. *BioScience* 44: 256–262.

Snelgrove, P. V. R. and C. A. Butman. 1994. Animal–sediment relationships revisited: Cause versus effect. *Oceanog. Mar. Biol. Annu. Rev.* 32: 111–177.

Sousa, W. P. 1979a. Experimental investigations of disturbance and ecological succession in a rocky intertidal algal community. *Ecol. Monogr.* 49: 227–254.

Sousa, W. P. 1979b. Disturbance in marine intertidal boulder fields: The nonequilibrium maintenance of species diversity. *Ecology* 60: 1225–1239.

Sousa, W. P. 1980. The responses of a community to disturbance: The importance of successional age and species' life histories. *Oecologia* 45: 72–81.

Sousa, W. P. 1984. Intertidal mosaics: Patch size, propagule availability, and spatial variable patterns of succession. *Ecology* 65: 1918–1935.

Sousa, W. P. 1985. Disturbance and patch dynamics on rocky intertidal shores. In S. T. A. Pickett and P. S. White (eds.), *The Ecology of Natural Disturbance and Patch Dynamics*, pp. 101–124. Academic Press, Orlando, FL.

Sousa, W. P. and J. H. Connell. 1992. Grazing and succession in marine algae. In D. M. John, S. J. Hawkins and J. H. Price (eds.), *Plant–Animal Interactions in the Marine Benthos*, pp. 425–441. Systematics Association Special Volume No. 46, Clarendon Press, Oxford.

Sousa, W. P. and M. Gleason. 1989. Does parasitic infection compromise host survival under extreme environmental conditions? The case for *Cerithidea californica* (Gastropoda: Prosobranchia). *Oecologia* 80: 456–464.

Sousa, W. P. and B. J. Mitchell. 1999. The effect of seed predators on plant distributions: Is there a general pattern in mangroves? *Oikos* 86: 55–66.

Southward, A. J., S. J. Hawkins and M. T. Burrows. 1995. Seventy years' observations of changes in distribution and abundance of zooplankton and intertidal organisms in the western English Channel in relation to rising sea temperature. *J. Thermal Biol.* 20: 127–155.

Southwood, T. R. E. 1977. Habitat, the template for ecological strategies? *J. Anim. Ecol.* 46: 337–365.

Staniforth, R. J., N. Griller and C. Lajzerowicz. 1998. Soil seed banks from coastal subarctic ecosystems of Bird Cove, Hudson Bay. *Ecoscience* 5: 241–249.

Stephenson, T. A. and A. Stephenson. 1954. Life between tide-marks in North America. IIIB. Nova Scotia and Prince Edward Island: The geographical features of the region. *J. Ecol.* 12: 46–70.

Stephenson, T. A. and A. Stephenson. 1972. *Life between Tidemarks on Rocky Shores*. W.H. Freeman, San Francisco.

Stiger, V. and C. E. Payri. 1999. Spatial and temporal patterns of settlement of the brown macroalgae *Turbinaria ornata* and *Sargassum mangarevense* in a coral reef on Tahiti. *Mar. Ecol. Prog. Ser.* 191: 91–100

Stoddart, D. R. 1963. Effects of Hurricane Hattie on the British Honduras reefs and cays, October 30–31, 1961. *Atoll Res. Bull.* 95: 1–142.

Stoddart, D. R. 1969. Post-hurricane changes on the British Honduras reefs and cays: Resurvey of 1965. *Atoll Res. Bull.* 131: 1–25.

Stoddart, D. R. 1972. Catastrophic damage to coral reef communities by earthquake. *Nature* 239: 51–52.

Stoddart, D. R. 1974. Post-hurricane changes on the British Honduras reefs: Re-survey of 1972. In *Proceedings of the Second International Coral Reef Symposium*, Vol. 2, pp. 473–483. Great Barrier Reef Committee, Brisbane, Australia.

Stoner, D. S. 1990. Recruitment of a tropical colonial ascidian: Relative importance of pre-settlement versus post-settlement processes. *Ecology* 71: 1682–1690.

Stouder, D. J. 1987. Effects of a severe weather disturbance on foraging patterns within a

California surfperch guild. *J. Exp. Mar. Biol. Ecol.* 114: 73–84.

Suchanek, T. H. 1978. The ecology of *Mytilus edulis* L. in exposed rocky intertidal communities. *J. Exp. Mar. Biol. Ecol.* 31: 105–120.

Suchanek, T. H. 1979. The *Mytilus californianus* community: Studies on the composition, structure, organization, and dynamics of a mussel bed. PhD Dissertation, University of Washington, Seattle.

Suchanek, T. H. 1981. The role of disturbance in the evolution of life history strategies in the intertidal mussels *Mytilus edulis* and *Mytilus californianus*. *Oecologia* 50: 143–152.

Suchanek, T. H. 1983. Control of seagrass communities and sediment distribution by *Callianassa* (Crustacea, Thalassinidea) bioturbation. *J. Mar. Res.* 41: 281–298.

Suchanek, T. H. 1992. Extreme biodiversity in the marine environment: Mussel bed communities of *Mytilus californianus*. *NW Env. J.* 8: 150–152.

Summers, R. W. 1980. The diet and feeding behaviour of the flounder *Platichthys flesus* (L.) in the Ythan estuary, Aberdeenshire, Scotland. *Estuarine, Coastal and Shelf Sci.* 11: 217–232.

Summerson, H. C. and C. H. Peterson. 1984. Role of predation in organizing benthic communities of a temperate-zone seagrass bed. *Mar. Ecol. Prog. Ser.* 15: 63–77.

Sutherland, J. P. 1970. Dynamics of high and low populations of the limpet, *Acmaea scabra* (Gould). *Ecol. Monogr.* 40: 169–188.

Syms, C. 1998. Disturbance and the structure of coral reef communities on the reef slope. *J. Exp. Mar. Biol. Ecol.* 230: 151–167.

Syms, C. and G. P. Jones. 1999. Scale of disturbance and the structure of a temperate fish guild. *Ecology* 80: 921–940.

Tanner, J. E., T. P. Hughes and J. H. Connell. 1994. Species coexistence, keystone species, and succession: A sensitivity analysis. *Ecology* 75: 2204–2219.

Taylor, P. R. and M. M. Littler. 1982. The roles of compensatory mortality, physical disturbance, and substrate retention in the development and organization of a sand-influenced, rocky-intertidal community. *Ecology* 63: 135–146.

Tegner, M. J. and P. K. Dayton. 1987. El Niño effects on Southern California kelp forest communities. *Adv. Ecol. Res.* 17: 243–279.

Tegner, M. J., P. K. Dayton, P. B. Edwards and K. L. Riser. 1995. Sea-urchin cavitation of giant-kelp (*Macrocystis pyrifera* Agardh, C.) holdfasts and its effects on kelp mortality across a large California forest. *J. Exp. Mar. Biol. Ecol.* 191: 83–99.

Tegner, M. J., P. K. Dayton, P. B. Edwards and K. L. Riser. 1997. Large-scale, low-frequency oceanographic effects on kelp forest succession: A tale of two cohorts. *Mar. Ecol. Prog. Ser.* 146: 117–134.

Thayer, C. D. 1983. Sediment-mediated biological disturbance and the evolution of marine benthos. In M. J. S. Tevesz and P. L. McCall (eds.), *Biotic Interactions in Recent and Fossil Benthic Communities*, pp. 479–625. Plenum Press, New York.

Thiel, M., L. M. Stearns and L. Watling. 1998. Effects of green algal mats on bivalves in a New England mud flat. *Helgolander Meeresuntersuchungen* 52: 15–28.

Thistle, D. 1981. Natural physical disturbances and communities of marine soft bottoms. *Mar. Ecol. Prog. Ser.* 6: 223–228.

Thomas, L. P., D. R. Moore and R. C. Work. 1961. Effects of Hurricane Donna on the turtle grass beds of Biscayne Bay, Florida. *Bull. Mar. Sci. Gulf Caribb.* 11: 191–197.

Thomas, M. L. and G. N. White. 1969. Mass mortality of estuarine fauna at Bideford P. E. I. associated with abnormally low salinities. *J. Fish. Res. Board Can.* 26: 701–704.

Thrush, S. F. 1986a. The sublittoral macrobenthic community structure of an Irish sealough: Effect of decomposing accumulations of seaweed. *J. Exp. Mar. Biol. Ecol.* 96: 199–212.

Thrush, S. F. 1986b. Spatial heterogeneity in subtidal gravel generated by the pit-digging activities of *Cancer pagurus*. *Mar. Ecol. Prog. Ser.* 30: 221–227.

Thrush, S. F. 1991. Spatial patterns in soft-bottom communities. *Trends Ecol. Evol.* 6: 75–79.

Thrush, S. F., R. D. Pridmore, J. E. Hewitt and V. J. Cumings. 1991. Impact of ray feeding disturbances on sandflat macrobenthos: Do communities dominated by polychaetes or shellfish respond differently? *Mar. Ecol. Prog. Ser.* 69: 245–252.

Thrush, S. F., R. D. Pridmore, J. E. Hewitt and V. J. Cumings. 1992. Adult infauna as facilitators of colonization on intertidal sandflats. *J. Exp. Mar. Biol. Ecol.* 159: 253–265.

Thrush, S. F., R. B. Whitlatch, R. D. Pridmore, J. E. Hewitt, V. J. Cummings and M. R. Wilkinson. 1996. Scale-dependent recolonization: The role of sediment stability in a dynamic sandflat habitat. *Ecology* 77: 2472–2487.

Tilman, D. 1982. Resource competition and community structure. Princeton University Press, Princeton, NJ.

Tilman, D. 1985. The resource ratio hypothesis of succession. *Amer. Nat.* 125: 827–852.

Todd, C. D. 1998. Larval supply and recruitment of benthic invertebrates: Do larvae always disperse as much as we believe? *Hydrobiologia* 375/376: 1–21.

Townsend, E. C. and M. S. Fonseca. 1998. Bioturbation as a potential mechanism influencing spatial heterogeneity of North Carolina seagrass beds. *Mar. Ecol. Prog. Ser.* 169: 123–132.

Townsley, S. J., L. Trott and E. Trott. 1962. A preliminary report on the rehabilitation of the littoral marine community on a new lava flow at Kapoho, Hawaii. *Ecology* 43: 728–730.

Tsuchiya, M. 1983. Mass mortality in a population of mussel *Mytilus edulis* L. caused by high temperature on rocky shores. *J. Exp. Mar. Biol. Ecol.* 66: 101–111.

Tunnicliffe, V. 1981. Breakage and propagation of the stony coral Acropora cervicornis. *Proc. Natl. Acad. Sci. USA* 78: 2427–2431.

Turner, T. 1983a. Complexity of early and middle successional stages in a rocky intertidal surfgrass community. *Oecologia* 60: 56–65.

Turner, T. 1983b. Facilitation as a successional mechanism in a rocky intertidal community. *Amer. Nat.* 121: 729–738.

Turner, T. 1985. Stability of rocky intertidal surfgrass beds: Persistence, preemption, and recovery. *Ecology* 66: 83–92.

Umar, M. J., L. J. McCook and I. R. Price. 1998. Effects of sediment deposition on the seaweed *Sargassum* on a fringing coral reef. *Coral Reefs* 17: 169–177.

Underwood, A. J. 1980. The effects of grazing by gastropods and physical factors on the upper limits of distribution of intertidal macroalgae. *Oecologia* 46: 210–213.

Underwood, A. J. 1981. Structure of a rocky intertidal community in New South Wales: Patterns of vertical distrbution and seasonal changes. *J. Exp. Mar. Biol. Ecol.* 51: 57–85.

Underwood, A. J. 1998. Grazing and disturbance: An experimental analysis of patchiness in recovery from a severe storm by the intertidal algal *Hormosira banksii* on rocky shores in New South Wales. *J. Exp. Mar. Biol. Ecol.* 231: 291–306.

Underwood, A. J. 1999. Physical disturbances and their direct effect on an indirect effect: Responses of an intertidal assemblage to a severe storm. *J. Exp. Mar. Biol. Ecol.* 232: 125–140.

Underwood, A. J. and P. Jernakoff. 1981. Effects of interactions between algae and grazing gastropods on the structure of a low-shore intertidal algal community. *Oecologia* 48: 221–233.

Ungar, I. A. and S. R. J. Woodell. 1993. The relationship between the seed bank and species composition of plant communities in two British salt marshes. *J. Veget. Sci.* 4: 531–536.

Ungar, I. A. and S. R. J. Woodell. 1996. Similarity of seed banks to aboveground vegetation in grazed and ungrazed salt marsh communities on the Gower Peninsula, South Wales. *Int. J. Plant Sci.* 157: 746–749.

Uriz, M. J., M. Maldonado, X. Turon and R. Marti. 1998. How do reproductive output, larval behaviour, and recruitment contribute to adult spatial patterns in Mediterranean encrusting sponges? *Mar. Ecol. Prog. Ser.* 167: 137–148.

Vadas, R. L., W. A. Wright and S. L. Miller. 1990. Recruitment of *Ascophyllum nodosum*: Wave action as a source of mortality. *Mar. Ecol. Prog. Ser.* 61: 263–272.

Vadas, R. L., S. Johnson and T. A. Norton. 1992. Recruitment and mortality of early post-settlement stages of benthic algae. *Brit. Phycol. J.* 27: 331–351.

Valentine, J. F., K. L. Heck, P. Harper and M. Beck. 1994. Effects of bioturbation in controlling turtlegrass (*Thalassia testudinum* Banks ex Konig) abundance: Evidence from field enclosures and observations in the northern Gulf of Mexico. *J. Exp. Mar. Biol. Ecol.* 178: 181–192.

Valiela, I. and C. S. Rietsma. 1995. Disturbance of salt marsh vegetation by wrack mats in Great Sippewissett Marsh. *Oecologia* 102: 106–112.

Valiela, I., P. Peckol, C. D'Avanzo, J. Kremer, D. Hersh, K. Foreman, K. Lajtha, B. Seely, W. R. Geyer, T. Isaji and R. Crawford. 1998. Ecological effects of major storms on coastal watersheds and coastal waters: Hurricane Bob on Cape Cod. *J. Coast. Res.* 14: 218–238.

VanBlaricom, G. R. 1978. Disturbance, predation, and resource allocation in a high-energy sub-littoral sand bottom ecosystem: Experimental analyses of critical structuring processes for the infaunal community. Ph. D. Dissertation, University of California, San Diego.

VanBlaricom, G. R. 1982. Experimental analyses of structural regulation in a marine sand community exposed to oceanic swell. *Ecol. Monogr.* 52: 283–305.

Van Dissen, R., J. Cousisns, R. Robinson and M. Reyners. 1994. The Fiordland earthquake of 10 August 1993: A reconnaissance report covering tectonic settling, peak ground acceleration and landslide damage. *Bulletin of the New Zealand National Society for Earthquake Engineering* 27: 147–154.

vanTamelen, P. G. 1987. Early successional mechanisms in the rocky intertidal–the role of direct and indirect interactions. *J. Exp. Mar. Biol. Ecol.* 112: 39–48.

vanTamelen, P. G. 1996. Algal zonation in tidepools: Experimental evaluation of the roles of physical disturbance, herbivory and competition. *J. Exp. Mar. Biol. Ecol.* 201: 197–231.

vanTussenbroek, B. I. 1994. The impact of Hurricane Gilbert on the vegetative development of *Thalassia testudinum* in Puerto Morelos coral reef lagoon, Mexico: A retrospective study. *Botanica Marina* 37: 421–428.

Walker, L. R. and F. S. Chapin III. 1987. Interactions among processes controlling successional change. *Oikos* 50: 131–135.

Walsh, W. J. 1983. Stability of a coral reef fish community following a catastrophic storm. *Coral Reefs* 2: 49–63.

Warwick, R. M., K. R. Clarke and J. M. Gee. 1990. The effect of disturbance by soldier crabs *Mictyris platycheles* H. Milne Edwards on meiobenthic community structure. *J. Exp. Mar. Biol. Ecol.* 135: 19–33.

Watling, L. and E. A. Norse. 1998. Disturbance of the seabed by mobile fishing gear: A comparison to forest clearcutting. *Conserv. Biol.* 12: 1180–1197.

Weatherhead, P. J. 1986. How unusual are unusual events? *Amer. Nat.* 128: 150–154.

Webster's New Universal Unabridged Dictionary, 2nd ed. 1983. Simon and Schuster, New York.

Wesseling, I., A. J. Uychiacco, P. M. Aurin and J. E. Vermaat. 1999. Damage and recovery of four Philippine corals from short-term sediment burial. *Mar. Ecol. Prog. Ser.* 176: 11–15.

Westman, W. E. and J. F. O'Leary. 1986. Measures of resilience: The response of coastal sage to fire. *Vegetatio* 65: 179–189.

Wethey, D. S. 1979. Demographic variation in intertidal barnacles. PhD Dissertation. University of Michigan, Ann Arbor.

Wethey, D. S. 1985. Catastrophe, extinction andspecies diversity: A rocky intertidal example. *Ecology* 66: 445–456.

Wethey, D. S. 1986. Ranking of settlement cues by barnacle larvae: Influence of surface contour. *Bull. Mar. Sci.* 39: 393–400.

Whitlatch, R. B. and R. N. Zajac. 1985. Biotic interactions among estuarine infaunal opportunistic species. *Mar. Ecol. Prog. Ser.* 21: 299–311.

Whitlatch, R. B., A. M. Lohrer, S. F. Thrush, R. D. Pridmore, J. E. Hewitt, V. J. Cummings

and R. N. Zajac. 1998. Scale-dependent benthic recolonization dynamics: Life stage-based dispersal and demographic consequences. *Hydrobiologia* 375/376: 217–226.

Widdicombe, S. and M. C. Austen. 1998. Experimental evidence for the role of *Brissopsis lyrifera* (Forbes, 1841) as a critical species in the maintenance of benthic diversity and the modification of sediment chemistry. *J. Exp. Mar. Biol. Ecol.* 228: 241–255.

Widdicombe, S. and M. C. Austen. 1999. Mesocosm investigation into the effects of bioturbation on the diversity and structure of a subtidal macrobenthic community. *Mar. Ecol. Prog. Ser.* 189: 181–193.

Wiens, J. A. 1977. On competition and variable environments. *Amer. Sci.* 65: 590–597.

Wilkinson, C., O. Lindén, H. Cesar, G. Hodgson, J. Rubens and A. E. Strong. 1999. Ecological and socioeconomic impacts of 1998 coral mortality in the Indian Ocean: An ENSO impact and a warning of future change? *Ambio* 28: 188–196.

Williams, E. H. and L. Bunkley-Williams. 1990. The worldwide coral reef bleaching cycle and related sources of coral mortality. *Atoll Res. Bull.* 335: 1–71.

Williams, S. L. 1988. Disturbance and recovery of a deep-water Caribbean seagrass bed. *Mar. Ecol. Prog. Ser.* 42: 63–71.

Williams, S. L. 1990. Experimental studies of Caribbean seagrass bed development. *Ecol. Monogr.* 60: 449–469.

Wilson, W. H. 1981. Sediment-mediated interactions in a densely populated infaunal assemblage: The effects of the polychaete *Abarenicola pacifica. J. Mar. Res.* 39: 735–748.

Wilson, W. H. 1988. Shifting zones in a Bay of Fundy soft-sediment community: Patterns and processes. *Ophelia* 29: 227–245.

Witman, J. D. 1987. Subtidal coexistence: Storms, grazing, mutualism, and zonation of kelps and mussels. *Ecol. Monogr.* 57: 167–187.

Wolcott, T. G. 1973. Physiological ecology and intertidal zonation in limpets (*Acmaea*): A critical look at "limiting factors." *Biol. Bull.* 145: 389–422.

Woodin, S. A. 1978. Refuges, disturbance and community structure: A marine soft-bottom example. *Ecology* 59: 274–284.

Woodin, S. A. 1981. Disturbance and community structure in a shallow water sandflat. *Ecology* 62: 1052–1066.

Woodin, S. A. 1986. Settlement of infauna: Larval choice? *Bull. Mar. Sci.* 39: 401–407.

Woodin, S. A. 1991. Recruitment of infauna: Positive or negative cues? *Amer. Zool.* 31: 797–807.

Woodley, J. D., E. A. Chornesky, P. A. Clifford, J. B. C. Jackson, L. S. Kaufman, N. Knowlton, J. C. Lang, M. P. Pearson, J. W. Porter, M. C. Rooney, K. W. Rylaarsdam, V. J. Tunnicliffe, C. M. Wahle, J. L. Wulff, A. W. G. Curtis, M. D. Dallmeyer, B.P. Jupp, M. A. R. Koehl, J. Neigel and E. M. Sides. 1981. Hurricane Allen's impact on Jamaican reefs. *Science* 214: 749–755.

Wootton, J. T. 1993. Size-dependent competition: Effects on the dynamics and the end-point of mussel bed succession. *Ecology* 74: 195–206.

Worm, B. and A. R. O. Chapman. 1998. Relative effects of elevated grazing pressure and competition from a red algal turf on two post-settlement stages of *Fucus evanescens* C. Ag. *J. Exp. Mar. Biol. Ecol.* 220: 247–268.

Worm, R., H. K. Lotze, C. Bostrom, R. Engkvist, V. Labanauskas and U. Sommer. 1999. Marine diversity shift linked to interactions among grazers, nutrients and propagule banks. *Mar. Ecol. Prog. Ser.* 185: 309–314.

Wu, J. G. and S. A. Levin. 1994. A spatial patch dynamics modeling approach to pattern and process in an annual grassland. *Ecol. Monogr.* 64: 447–464.

Wulff, J. L. 1995. Effects of a hurricane on survival and orientation of large erect coral-reef sponges. *Coral Reefs* 14: 55–61.

Yamaguchi, M. 1975. Sea level fluctuations and mass mortalities of reef animals in Guam, Mariana Islands. *Micronesica* 11: 277–243.

Yeo, R. K. and M. J. Risk. 1979. Intertidal catastrophes: Effect of storms and hurricanes on intertidal benthos of the Minas Basin, Bay of Fundy. *J. Fish. Res. Board Can.* 36: 667–669.

Young, C. M. and F.-S. Chia. 1987. Abundance and distribution of pelagic larvae as influenced by predation, behavior, and hydrographic factors. In A. C. Giese, J. S. Pearse and V. B. Pearse (eds.), *Reproduction of Marine Invertebrates,* Vol. 9, *General Aspects: Seeking Unity in Diversity.* Blackwell Scientific Publications and Boxwood Press, Palo Alto and Pacific Grove, CA.

Young, C. M. and N. J. Gotelli. 1988. Larval predation by barnacles: Effects on patch colonization in a shallow subtidal community. *Ecology* 69: 624–634.

Zajac, R. N. and R. B. Whitlatch. 1982a. Responses of estuarine infauna to disturbance. I. Spatial and temporal variation of initial recolonization. *Mar. Ecol. Prog. Ser.* 10: 1–14.

Zajac, R. N. and R. B. Whitlatch. 1982b. Responses of estuarine infauna to disturbance. II. Spatial and temporal variation of succession. *Mar. Ecol. Prog. Ser.* 10: 15–27.

Zajac, R. N. and R. B. Whitlatch. 1985. A hierarchical approach to modeling soft-sediment successional dynamics. In P. Gibbs (ed.), Proceedings of the 19th European Marine Biological Symposium, pp. 265–276. Cambridge University Press, Cambridge.

Zajac, R. N. and R. B. Whitlatch. 1991. Demographic aspects of marine, soft sediment patch dynamics. *Amer. Zool.* 31: 808–820.

Zajac, R. N., R.B. Whitlatch and S. F. Thrush. 1998. Recolonization and succession in soft-sediment infaunal communities: The spatial scale of controlling factors. *Hydobiologia* 375/376: 227–240.

Zedler, J. B. 1983. Freshwater impacts on normally hypersaline marshes. *Estuaries* 6: 346–355.

Zedler, J. B. J. Covin, C. S. Nordby, P. Williams and J. Boland. 1986. Catastrophic events reveal the dynamic nature of salt marsh vegetation. *Estuaries* 9: 75–80.

Zedler, J. B., C. S. Nordby and B. E. Kus. 1992. The ecology of Tijuana Estuary, California: A National Estuarine Research Reserve. NOAA Office of Coastal Resource Management, Sanctuaries and Reserves Division, Washington, DC.

chapter 5

The Ecology and Evolution of Marine Consumer–Prey Interactions

J. Emmett Duffy and Mark E. Hay

*P*redation is a nearly universal pressure affecting the phenotypes of organisms as well as the organization and functioning of communities and ecosystems. The impacts of consumers (herbivores and predators) on population and community structure are often determined by, or interact with, processes covered in other chapters of this volume (e.g., physical processes, competition, recruitment). To prevent excessive overlap, we minimize focus on these interactions and review selected examples of direct effects of consumers on prey, and of the indirect consequences of these effects for communities and ecosystems. We focus primarily on organism-level interactions between consumers and prey, and on their adaptive responses to one another.

Consumer pressure is intense in many marine ecosystems. In subtidal marine communities such as coral reefs or kelp beds, for example, herbivory is commonly one of the primary forces determining the distribution and abundance of plants, and often the species composition and diversity of the entire community. Indeed, in numerous marine systems, the activity of consumers so dramatically alters local communities that these systems change fundamentally when consumers are removed. For example, herbivorous fishes or sea urchins can remove approximately 100% of daily algal production on shallow coral reefs (Carpenter 1986), with herbivorous fishes sometimes taking more than 150,000 bites/m²/day (Figure 5.1). These fishes and urchins keep reefs largely devoid of macroalgae and allow corals to flourish by reducing competition from the more rapidly growing seaweeds (Lewis 1986; Miller 1998). As these herbivores severely declined around the Caribbean island of Jamaica due to a combination of overfishing and urchin disease, coral reefs suffered severe overgrowth by seaweeds, and live coral cover declined from more than 50% to less than 5% throughout this entire island nation

(Hughes 1994; Figure 5.2). Removing herbivores from these habitats converted species-rich, structurally complex coral reefs into a completely different community dominated by a limited number of seaweeds.

Herbivores have equally dramatic impacts in temperate systems. Numerous ecological and paleontological studies show that subtidal benthic communities in the temperate northeastern Pacific shift from sea urchin–grazed barrens to lush kelp beds depending on the presence or absence of sea otters, which selectively forage on sea urchins and molluscan herbivores, reducing grazer biomass, and allowing kelps to flourish (Estes and Palmisano 1974; Simenstad et al. 1978; Duggins et al. 1989; Estes and Duggins 1995; Estes et al. 1998). Where otters have been removed from kelp communities by hunting or predation, urchin densities increased, urchins drove kelps to local extinction (Figure 5.3), and fishes, kelp-associated invertebrates, and seals or sea lions that feed on kelp-bed fishes also declined dramatically. Because kelp beds normally export organic matter to other nearby communities (Duggins et al. 1989), these adjacent systems and their species (e.g., bivalves to bald eagles) are impacted as well. Thus, in the reef example, grazers increased diversity by removing seaweeds and allowing corals to produce the biogenic structure that enhances reef biodiversity, while in the kelp-bed system grazers directly removed the major biogenic structure (kelps) and caused a decline in biodiversity, productivity, and transport of kelp-derived resources to associated near-shore communities.

Similarly pervasive system-level impacts of consumers have been documented in pelagic communities. A spectacular example is the unwitting manipulation of the subarctic Pacific pelagic zone by release of pink salmon from hatcheries. In (alternating) years when pink salmon are abundant in this region, zooplankton are rarer and phytoplankton more

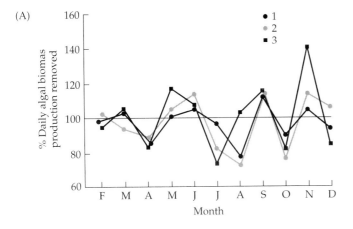

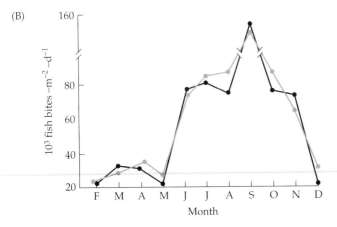

Figure 5.1 (A) Herbivorous fishes and sea urchins consume ~100% of daily algal production on a coral reef. The different curves represent experimental treatments with (1) all herbivores, (2) fishes and mesograzers only, and (3) urchins and mesograzers only. (B) Bite rates by herbivorous fishes throughout the year on a shallow fore-reef in St. Croix, U.S. Virgin Islands. (After Carpenter 1986.)

abundant (Shiomoto et al. 1997). These observations of strong top-down control in a pelagic ecosystem lend credence to suggestions that whaling could have allowed large population increases in their prey, krill, with concomitant changes elsewhere in the food web, pushing back to the last century the time when human impacts on consumers began to change the oceans on a very large scale. Indeed, Jackson (1997) has marshaled evidence that human hunting of green turtles, manatees, and other formerly abundant megafauna began to change Caribbean marine ecosystems shortly after Europeans arrived in the region in the sixteenth century. It is clear that current fishing has global-scale impacts because the mean trophic level of animals harvested from the sea is decreasing (Pauly et al. 1998).

HOW DO PREY DEAL WITH CONSUMER PRESSURE?

Escapes in Space, Time, or Size

The intensity of consumer pressure common in marine systems should exert strong selection on prey to avoid being eaten. Escape from consumers often entails avoidance in time, in space, or in both time and space. An especially impressive example involves the daily vertical migrations of zooplankton. The pelagic zone offers little structure to shield prey from visually orienting predators so that many zooplankters undertake vertical (in the open ocean) and horizontal (in estuaries) migrations to avoid predators. Indeed, the daily vertical migration of zooplankton and small nekton (e.g., fishes, squids, and shrimps) is one of the most conspicuous biological phenomena of the open oceans. Many such animals forage in food-rich surface waters at night and migrate

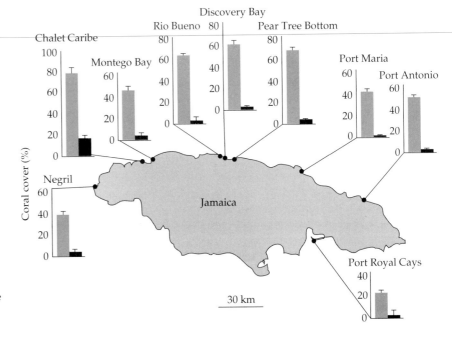

Figure 5.2 Large-scale changes in the cover of live coral at fore-reef sites along >300 km of the Jamaican coastline surveyed in the late 1970s (hatched bars) and the early 1990s (filled bars). (After Hughes 1994.)

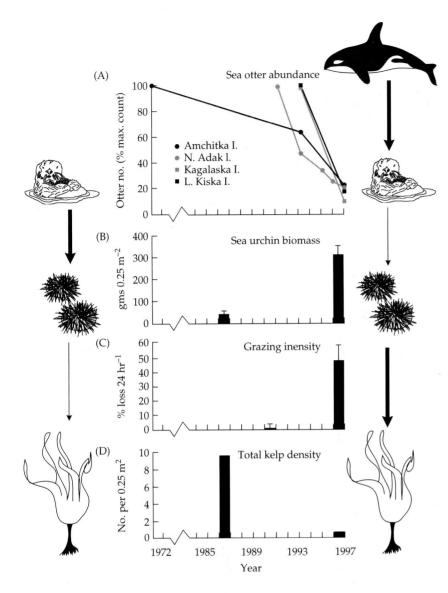

Figure 5.3 A marine trophic cascade extending through four trophic levels. Declines in sea otter abundance at several islands in the Aleutian archipelago (A) were correlated with increased sea urchin abundance (B), and grazing intensity (C), and greatly reduced kelp abundance (D) at Adak island. Sea otters declined concurrently with a sudden increase in killer whale predation on them. The cartoons show the proposed mechanisms controlling the food chain before (left) and after (right) the sea otter decline. Thick and thin arrows represent strong and weak interactions respectively. (After Estes et al. 1998.)

tens to hundreds of meters downward (>800 m in the salp *Salpa aspersa*, Wiebe et al. 1979) into dimmer waters each day during those periods when the visually hunting predators of surface waters are most active. Several observations suggest that this behavior functions primarily to avoid predation. Vertical migrations are more pronounced in large and strongly pigmented species, which are more conspicuous to visual predators (Hays et al. 1994). Vertical migration of copepods can be induced by exposure to predatory fishes in enclosures (Bollens and Frost 1989a). And finally, there are seasonal and interannual correlations between predatory fish abundance and the strength of vertical migration (Bollens and Frost 1989b; Hays 1995). These consumer-induced migrations have important consequences for global ocean biogeochemistry, as the migrants transport materials from the euphotic zone to the deep ocean (Longhurst et al. 1989; Hays et al. 1997).

Planktonic larvae of many estuarine crabs similarly reduce their risk of predation by undertaking large-scale horizontal, rather than vertical, migrations. Field surveys of predator abundance and gut contents showed that fishes that eat crab larvae are predictably more abundant in estuaries than in coastal waters during summer when crab zoeae are released (Morgan 1990). Most estuarine crab species efficiently move their vulnerable larvae out of dangerous estuarine waters by releasing larvae during spring high tides at night; this serves to transport them rapidly to deeper, safer waters without detection by visual predators (Morgan and Christy 1997). As is true of vertically migrating copepods in the open ocean (Hays et al. 1994), species of crab larvae that are more heavily pigmented enter predator-rich waters primarily during darkness, whereas those that are exposed during daylight are more transparent (Morgan and Christy 1997).

Sessile prey that cannot migrate between habitats can still exploit predictable temporal variance in consumer activity to escape in time. Several seaweeds seasonally shift morphologies in ways that minimize losses to herbivores (Lubchenco and Cubit 1980). For example, temperate herbivores are often active primarily during the summer, and several genera of algae have life histories that capitalize on these seasonal changes in grazing pressure. Complex life histories, involving alternation of morphologically distinct generations that differ in growth potential and resistance to herbivores, are common among seaweeds (*Ulothrix, Urospora, Petalonia, Scytosiphon, Bangia,* and *Porphyra* are examples). Upright forms of these species are good competitors but are more susceptible to herbivores and occur primarily during seasons when herbivore activity is low. The less competitive, but more herbivore-resistant, crustose forms dominate during seasons when herbivores are active. Though upright forms normally occur in the field only during winter when herbivore activity is suppressed, these forms persist during the summer if grazers are experimentally excluded (Lubchenco and Cubit 1980).

Some species can also shift morphology very rapidly (within a few days), without the shift being tied to life-cycle stages, and can do so in direct response to the recent history of herbivore activity. Working on a Caribbean reef, Lewis et al. (1987) demonstrated such a dramatic shift in the brown seaweed *Padina jamaicensis*. In areas heavily impacted by grazing fishes, *Padina* grew as an uncalcified turf of small, irregularly branched creeping axes that had a single apical cell and that were closely adherent to the substratum. On areas of the reef where herbivory was slight, *Padina* grew as a calcified, upright, and foliose blade that was generated by meristematic cells along the entire leading edge of the fan-shaped blade. Because of their morphological dissimilarity, these two forms had at times been assigned to separate genera. When herbivorous fishes were excluded from portions of the reef for as little as 96 h, the uncalcified turf form shifted to the calcified upright form. Transplant and caging experiments showed that the upright form grew rapidly, reproduced, and was a superior competitor, but it was highly susceptible to removal by herbivorous fishes. In contrast, the turf form could persist in areas of high herbivore impact, but it did not competitively exclude other reef species, and it was never observed to reproduce sexually.

Seaweeds may also minimize herbivore damage by flushing their new, most palatable growth during periods of predictably low herbivory. An extreme example is the tropical algal genus *Halimeda*, which synchronously produces its youngest, and most nutritious, portions only at night while herbivorous reef fishes are not feeding (Hay et al. 1988, Paul and Van Alstyne 1988). New segments are uncalcified and more nutritious than the rest of the plant, but these young segments are defended with more potent chemical defenses than are present in older segments. During the following day, as the new segments calcify, become more heavily invested with structural defenses, and less valuable nutritionally, concentrations of chemical defenses decrease. Thus, these seaweeds minimize exposure of their newly produced tissues by producing them very rapidly during the night while herbivorous fishes are inactive.

Nonmobile prey also escape consumers by growing in habitats or microhabitats in which consumers are not active. On a microhabitat scale, prey may escape by living in cracks and holes that are inaccessible to consumers. For example, on intertidal rock surfaces of Pacific Panama where consumer pressure is particularly intense, herbivore-resistant algal crusts dominate exposed surfaces while less resistant foliose algae occur primarily, or exclusively, in holes and cracks (Menge et al. 1985). On a larger, between-habitat scale, many seaweeds, corals, and sponges that are physiologically capable of growing on topographically complex, but consumer-rich, reef slopes occur only, or primarily, on topographically simple sand plains or reef flats, or in mangrove or seagrass areas where consumer densities are lower (Randall 1965; Ogden et al. 1973; Hay 1981a, 1984, 1985; Lewis 1986; Littler et al. 1989; Dunlap and Pawlik 1996). Similar escapes also occur on larger spatial scales. Along the Great Barrier Reef of Australia, algal mass is much greater on inshore reefs than on offshore reefs. Although this difference in abundance has commonly been assumed to result from greater availability of nutrients inshore, it now appears to be due primarily to higher grazing on offshore reefs (McCook 1996, 1997; McCook et al. 1997). Finally, on a geographic scale, Bolser and Hay (1996) recently demonstrated that seaweeds from the tropical Caribbean were considerably less palatable to both temperate and tropical herbivores than were seaweeds from the warm temperate western Atlantic. This palatability difference was due primarily to greater chemical defenses among the tropical seaweeds. Thus, it is possible that temperate areas serve as large-scale spatial escapes from tropical consumers. Consistent with this idea, many of the tropical seaweeds that are restricted to unstructured, consumer-poor reef flats or sand plains in the tropics extend into temperate areas and grow well on reefs there; conversely, the herbivore resistant seaweeds that co-occur with consumers on tropical reefs rarely extend very far into temperate areas (Hay 1981a; M. E. Hay pers. obs.).

In contrast to their usually negative impacts on prey, consumers sometimes create spatial refuges for certain types of prey. Reef damselfishes are small aggressive herbivores that establish and vigorously defend gardens of palatable algae upon which they feed. These gardens experience reduced herbivory compared to areas not defended by damselfishes. Some seaweeds depend on these herbivore-created escapes, and algal diversity may be higher in territories than in either caged or uncaged areas outside territories (Hixon and Brostoff 1983, 1996). The algal-dominated territories also serve as refuges for a wide variety of small invertebrates that shelter there (Klumpp et al. 1988).

Finally, prey may also escape in size if they become too large for consumers to handle effectively. Such size-related escapes presumably result from larger individuals being tougher, harder, less nutritious, or more easily recognized as unpalatable. Strictly speaking, this phenomenon is not an escape since consumers detect, but do not significantly damage, the prey. Size-related differences in susceptibility are important, however, since most prey must pass through a juvenile stage that often is more vulnerable to consumers. Even for chemically defended prey that are avoided as adults, newly settled juveniles may be eaten by unselective consumers because they are not recognized, and thus not avoided, at this small size, or because smaller prey are easier to handle or more nutritious. The challenge for many sessile prey, then, is to survive until they reach a size at which they are less vulnerable. For example, kelp sporelings are more vulnerable to herbivores than are larger plants, and the kelp sporelings escape herbivores more often when hidden among filamentous brown algae than when growing on bare rock (Harris et al. 1984). Similarly, small (< 3 cm) *Fucus vesiculosus* plants are more susceptible to grazing snails than are larger plants, and survival of small plants is enhanced by settlement in small cracks or among barnacles where herbivores cannot graze effectively (Lubchenco 1983). In contrast, recruitment and growth of algae can be so great that they swamp the ability of molluscan herbivores to eat the young plants; under these conditions, the plants may quickly reach a refuge in size beyond which they no longer suffer mortality at the normal herbivore densities (Dayton 1975). In extreme cases, algal growth may be heavy enough to alter the habitat in such a way that the area becomes unsuitable for some herbivores (Underwood and Jernakoff 1981). These prey might thus be producing their own spatial escapes, via habitat modification.

Associational Escapes

Communities strongly affected by consumers are often dominated by unpalatable prey. These unpalatable species can create spatial escapes for more palatable species (Hay 1986; Littler et al. 1986; Pfister and Hay 1988). For example, field experiments demonstrated that the palatable red alga *Hypnea musciformis* was quickly eaten by fishes when growing alone, but grew more rapidly than it was consumed when placed in contact with its herbivore-resistant competitor, the brown alga *Sargassum filipendula* (Hay 1986). During the yearly peak in herbivore abundance, *Hypnea* and other palatable seaweeds were found exclusively in association with unpalatable plants, whereas during seasons when herbivores were less active, palatable plants were not strongly associated with unpalatable species. In communities where associational refuges are important, dominance of the community by a few unpalatable species can increase species richness rather than decreasing it, as would be expected if competition were of primary importance (Hay 1986). This occurs because palatable species that would have been eliminated by consumers can persist only in association with their unpalatable competitors. Similarly, on coral reefs, nearly twice as many taxa occurred within 10 cm of the chemically defended brown alga *Stypopodium zonale* than in similar-sized areas away from *Stypopodium* (Littler et al. 1986). As a final example, temperate seaweeds in the genus *Desmarestia* contain sulfuric acid at up to 18% of plant dry mass (Anderson and Velimirov 1982). In South American kelp beds heavily grazed by sea urchins, the palatable kelp *Macrocystis* often cannot colonize unless it invades an area encircled by *Desmarestia* plants; these plants act as "acid brooms," prohibiting urchins from entering the area (Dayton 1985). Associational escapes can thus be effective in a variety of habitats and against very different kinds of consumers.

There are numerous other associations among marine animals that similarly appear to offer protection to one, or both, of the partners. Examples include pomacentrid fishes that live exclusively in association with sea anemones, whose stinging nematocysts protect both species from enemies; hermit crabs that place stinging anemones on their claws and use these as defenses (Vermeij 1983); and shrimps and other animals that live in obligate association with often chemically rich coral-reef sponges (Pawlik 1983; Duffy 1992, 1996) or stony corals (Patton 1976). Interestingly, some such guests return the favor to their host by defending it against its own predators or competitors. For example, several species of crustaceans and polychaetes that associate with the East Pacific coral *Pocillopora damicornis* attack and even kill crown-of-thorns starfish that molest their host coral (Glynn 1980, 1981), increasing survival of the coral host (Glynn 1983). Similarly, some crustaceans form nonobligate associations with various branching corals or coralline algae (Coen 1988; Stachowicz and Hay 1996; Stachowicz and Hay 1999). The crabs receive a topographically complex refuge from fish predators but also protect their host by removing fouling seaweeds and invertebrates. For a few species, these refuges can be made more mobile and carried with them. As an example, in geographic areas where consumers are most active, the juvenile decorator crab *Libinia dubia* selectively decorates with a chemically noxious seaweed that lowers its susceptibility to consumers (Stachowicz and Hay 1999, 2000).

Tolerating Consumers

Some prey can coexist with attacking consumers if being attacked has minimal effects on prey fitness. Such prey can be considered to be tolerant of consumer activity. In a rather extreme example, when the freshwater phytoplankter *Sphaerocystis schroeteri* is consumed by the zooplankter *Daphnia magna*, more than 90% of the *Sphaerocystis* cells are undamaged, and the nutrient enrichment that occurs during gut passage enhances the growth of gut-passed cells by more than 60%, thus more than compensating for the slight damage the grazers do to the algal population (Porter 1976). In situ grazing experiments indicated that densities of this alga increased with increases in grazer density. The alga appeared to rely on grazers as a rich localized source of nutrients.

Some coralline algae show a similar pattern of tolerance to, or even reliance on, their associated herbivores. A recent study by Littler et al. (1995) provides an excellent example. On reef fronts in the Caribbean, the coralline crust *Porolithon pachydermum* is heavily grazed by the chiton *Choneplax lata*, with approximately 50% of the chiton's gut contents being composed of this alga. However, the alga is predictably associated with the chiton, and it grows well and produces reef structure best when the chiton is present. If the herbivorous chiton is removed, the coralline is overgrown by fleshy algae. These fleshy algae attract grazing fishes, and the fishes bite deeply into the substrate, removing not only fleshy algae but the coralline as well. Thus, removal of *Porolithon*'s major herbivore causes bioerosion in excess of production. The coralline is tolerant of chiton grazing, in part because its meristematic region is protected below the depth to which the chiton's radula scrapes algal cells. A somewhat similar example of gastropod and coralline algal interactions in subarctic systems is provided by Steneck (1982).

Consistent with the above studies, the dominant plants in areas most affected by herbivory represent the extreme ends of the spectrum of susceptibility to herbivores—small filamentous forms that are very susceptible (Carpenter 1986; Lewis 1986) and heavily calcified, crustose corallines that are very resistant (Steneck 1986) to herbivores. Both of these forms may depend on herbivores to prevent their exclusion by larger macroalgae (Lewis 1986), even though such reliance may entail loss of the plant's own tissues. Small filamentous algae persist on reefs despite large losses to grazers by growing very rapidly, and by having basal portions that escape herbivores due to the topographic complexity of the substrate (Carpenter 1986; Lewis 1986; Steneck 1988). This strategy of "tolerating" rather than deterring herbivory allows inconspicuous filamentous algae to make up much of the plant biomass on grazed areas of coral reefs. These plants are in fact more productive on a mass-specific basis when they are grazed because cropping prevents self-shading, and herbivore excretion may increase available nutrients (Carpenter 1986, 1988).

In some cases, fitness losses to herbivores may be minimized if ingested propagules remain viable and are dispersed via defecation by the herbivore, a situation reminiscent of seed dispersal by birds and mammals on land (Figure 5.4). For several opportunistic algae exposed to grazing by gastropods, gut passage significantly increases the production of motile spores and the growth rate of sporelings relative to uningested controls (Santelices and Ugarte 1987). In contrast, spores and vegetative portions of late successional plants are rarely resistant to digestion. However, grazing may provide some benefits even for late successional plants. For example, amphipods graze on cystocarps (reproductive structures) of the red alga *Iridaea laminarioides*, releasing spores into the water column when the cystocarps are opened (Buschmann and Santelices 1987). Spores released by amphipods were as viable as naturally released spores, and surprisingly, ungrazed fronds often had cystocarps that remained closed and did not naturally release their spores. The percentage of such unopened cystocarps was significantly greater at sites without amphipods than at sites with high amphipod densities. Although a lower proportion of spores ingested by amphipods germinated compared with uningested spores, those that did germinate had higher growth rates, presumably due to nutrients absorbed by the algal cells during passage through the herbivore gut (Buschmann and Santelices 1987). Gut passage of viable algal propagules has now been documented in a variety of herbivores including fishes, sea urchins, amphipods, and gastropods (Santelices and Ugarte 1987; Paya and Santelices 1989).

A final example of a prey adaptation that may involve elements of both escape and tolerance is the mass spawning of

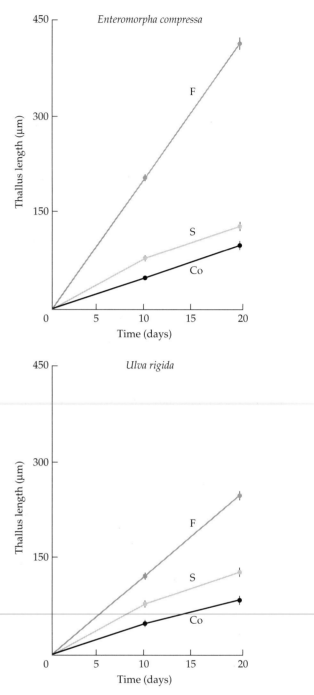

Figure 5.4 In some cases, consumers may benefit their prey. Reproductive propagules of several algal taxa, such as these two green seaweeds, passed intact through the guts of grazing molluscs (F = *Fissurella*, S = *Siphonaria*). Sporelings derived from the gut-passed propagules grew significantly faster than those that had not been passed through a grazer's gut (Co = Control). (After Santelices and Ugarte 1987.)

reef corals. On the Great Barrier Reef, corals of at least 32 species release gametes synchronously during a brief but predictable period of four to five nights after full moons in late spring, resulting in huge densities of gametes and larvae in the water (Harrison et al. 1984). These authors suggested that one function of this synchronous, rare spawning may be to overwhelm the capacity of potential predators, such that a relatively small proportion of larvae from any individual colony are eaten. An intriguingly similar multispecies mass spawning occurs in some tropical green algae (Clifton 1997).

Deterring Consumers

If prey do not escape or tolerate consumers, they must deter them so that rates of consumption do not exceed rates of production. This deterrence commonly occurs through chemical, structural, or behavioral defenses. In some cases, prey use mixed strategies of defense in which chemical and structural deterrents are combined to form additive or synergistic defenses, with these sometimes varying spatially, seasonally, or even hourly to maximize effectiveness (Hay et al. 1988; Hay et al. 1994; Schupp and Paul 1994; Hay 1996).

MORPHOLOGICAL AND STRUCTURAL DETERRENTS. Armor, spines, and other such morphological elaborations are obvious features of many organisms living in environments where consumer pressure is substantial. Studies of gastropod prey have demonstrated that narrow apertures and various sculptural features such as spines and thickened shells all reduce gastropod vulnerability to predation by crabs and fishes, and that predation-deterrent morphologies, moreover, are much more frequent in habitats and geographic regions where predation is more intense (Vermeij 1976; Zipser and Vermeij 1978; Palmer 1979; Bertness 1981; Bertness and Cunningham 1981; Bertness et al. 1981). Although not confirmed by experiments, similar patterns of covariance between predator activity and frequency of body sculpture are found in marine isopods (Wallerstein and Brusca 1982).

For seaweeds, general models have been proposed that predict how morphology should affect susceptibility to herbivores (Littler and Littler 1980; Steneck and Watling 1982; Littler et al. 1983a,b; Steneck 1983; Steneck and Dethier 1994). In general, microalgae are predicted to be most susceptible to herbivores, with resistance of other algal forms increasing in the following order: filamentous algae, sheetlike algae, coarsely branched algae, leathery or rubbery algae, jointed calcareous algae, and crustose corallines. This prediction is based in part on the decreasing food value expected as seaweeds allocate more production to less digestible structural materials that make them tougher and more difficult to bite. Feeding choices of some molluscs and sea urchins are broadly supportive of the predicted relationship (Steneck and Watling 1982; Littler et al. 1983a,b), but other molluscs diverge from predicted patterns (Padilla 1985), as does feeding by reef fishes (Hay 1984; Lewis 1985). Predictions based on morphology alone are also difficult to evaluate because morphological trends can be confounded by chemical defenses. For example, many calcified tropical seaweeds also produce chemical defenses (Hay 1984; Paul and Hay 1986); thus the low palatability of calcified species could be due to either trait, or to both (Hay et al. 1994; Schupp and Paul 1994).

A few investigations have directly addressed how algal morphology affects susceptibility to herbivores. Steneck and Adey (1976) demonstrated that the encrusting coralline *Lithophyllum congestum* grew as a smooth crust on reef slopes where feeding by herbivorous fishes was intense but produced upright branches when it occurred on the edges of reef flats where fish feeding was reduced. When compared with the crustose form, the form with upright branches had higher growth and reproduction, but it was also much more susceptible to parrotfishes, which excluded the upright form from the reef slope. Similarly, various clonal seaweeds can occur in low-herbivory habitats as loose aggregations that grow rapidly but lose more tissues to herbivorous fishes and sea urchins, whereas in habitats most affected by herbivores, they occur as densely packed colonies of uprights that grow slowly but have lower losses to herbivores (Hay 1981b). The study of *Padina jamaicensis* by Lewis et al. (1987) discussed earlier documented one of the most dramatic cases of altered morphology in response to herbivory. All of these examples indicate that morphological plasticity helps seaweeds persist in areas that are heavily grazed, but that the morphologies that resist herbivory entail a significant cost in terms of growth and reproduction.

CHEMICAL DETERRENTS. Recent reviews of chemical defenses against marine consumers are numerous (e.g., Hay and Fenical 1988, 1996; Hay 1992, 1996; Hay and Steinberg 1992; Steinberg 1992; Paul 1992; Pawlik 1993), so our coverage here will be brief. Sessile marine organisms that do not have physical defenses against consumers (e.g., spines, hard shells) commonly produce unusual chemical compounds (Faulkner 1999 and references therein), termed secondary metabolites because they are not necessary for primary metabolic processes. Several thousand novel secondary metabolites, including terpenes, acetogenins, alkaloids, and polyphenolics, have been described from sponges, ascidians, soft corals, bryozoans, polychaetes, seaweeds, marine microbes, and other benthic and pelagic organisms (Fenical 1993; Faulkner 1999 and his previous reviews cited therein). These diverse metabolites appear to be most common and ecologically important among tropical benthic organisms that are subject to high rates of attack by consumers (Hay and Steinberg 1992; Paul 1992; Pawlik 1993; Faulkner 1994; Bolser and Hay 1996). However, secondary metabolites also play important roles in temperate communities (King 1986; Hay and Steinberg 1992; Steinberg 1992; Woodin et al. 1993; Duffy and Hay 1994; Cronin and Hay 1996a, b; Stachowicz and Hay 1999) and Antarctic benthic communities (McClintock 1994), and potentially in pelagic (Huntley et al. 1986; Shaw et al. 1995; McClintock et al. 1996; Wolfe et al. 1997) communities worldwide.

Experimental investigations in both the field and laboratory have confirmed that many secondary metabolites from seaweeds and benthic invertebrates serve as defenses against consumers (reviewed by Hay and Fenical 1988, 1996; Hay 1991a, 1996, 1997; Hay and Steinberg 1992; Paul 1992; Pawlik 1993; Pawlik et al. 1995). Because consumer pressure in marine systems is often high and because these systems are often more experimentally tractable than terrestrial systems, it has been possible to identify clearly the ecologically important consumers against which compounds should be tested, and often to test compounds in the field against the diverse assemblage of natural consumers that occur there (reviewed by Hay and Steinberg 1992; Hay et al. 1998). Thus, marine investigators can apply purified metabolites at natural concentrations to otherwise palatable foods in the field and determine in a short period of time whether or not the compounds decrease predation under natural field conditions (Hay et al. 1987a; Paul 1987; Hay 1991a; Hay and Steinberg 1992; Pawlik et al. 1995). These types of assays have shown that many marine secondary metabolites function as defenses against consumers, and that potential prey without these defenses are often excluded from habitats where large, generalist consumers such as fishes and sea urchins are common (Hay 1985, 1991a, 1997; Littler et al. 1989; Dunlap and Pawlik 1996).

Spatial patterns in the distribution of marine secondary metabolites over a range of scales also support the general hypothesis that these compounds serve as defenses against consumers. At the geographic scale, for example, there is much evidence that intensity of consumer activity generally increases toward the equator (Jeanne 1979; Bertness at al. 1981; Menge and Lubchenco 1981; Heck and Wilson 1987; Coley and Aide 1990), which should select for better prey defenses at low latitudes. The geographic distribution of morphological defenses in marine invertebrates strongly supports this hypothesis (Palmer 1979; Vermeij and Currey 1980; Bertness et al. 1981). Thus, it has generally been assumed that chemical defenses are also best elaborated and most important in tropical systems (Bakus and Green 1974; Levin and York 1978; Vermeij 1978; Fenical 1980; Gaines and Lubchenco 1982; Faulkner 1984; Hay and Fenical 1988; Coley and Aide 1990; Hay 1991a). Yet there are few critical tests of this assumption. Consistent with this hypothesis, Bolser and Hay (1996) found that tropical seaweeds from reefs in the Bahamas were, on average, about half as palatable to both temperate and tropical sea urchins as were related seaweeds from temperate reefs in North Carolina. Direct assays of chemical extracts from these seaweeds demonstrated that most of the difference was attributable to more deterrent chemical extracts from the tropical plants. Thus, seaweeds from tropical habitats with higher rates of herbivory were less palatable and better defended chemically than were similar seaweeds from temperate locations where herbivory rates are lower. Similarly, salt-marsh plants from southern marshes (Georgia) where herbivore diversity and abundance are greater, were less palatable to both southern and northern herbivores than were plants of the same species from northern (Rhode Island) marshes with lower herbivore diversity and abundance and presumably lower grazing intensity (Pennings et al., in press). Although these latitudinal patterns support the conventional wisdom, it should be emphasized that selection for defenses is imposed by consumers, not geography, as evidenced by the finding that Antarctic inverte-

brates are often chemically defended from local consumers (McClintock 1994). At smaller spatial scales, between-habitat differences in algal palatability reflect similar patterns of spatial variation in consumer activity (Hay 1984).

Once prey have become chemically defended from most larger consumers, they appear to become targets of evolutionary opportunity for smaller specialist consumers that selectively live on and consume chemically noxious prey (Hay 1992; Hay and Fenical 1996). By associating with or consuming these well-defended prey, the specialist consumers often escape or deter their own predators. For example, the Spanish dancer nudibranch, *Hexabranchus sanguineus*, feeds on sponges that contain oxazole macrolides that deter feeding by reef fishes (Pawlik 1993). The nudibranch slightly alters these compounds and concentrates them in its dorsal mantle and egg masses, where they serve as highly effective defenses against consumers. Small consumers can also lower their susceptibility to their own consumers through simple physical association with noxious prey—they need not sequester defensive metabolites. For example, the tube-building amphipod *Ampithoe longimana* consumes a wide variety of seaweeds, but in coastal North Carolina, it prefers to live on and feed from chemically defended brown algae in the genus *Dicytota* (Hay et al. 1987b; Duffy and Hay 1991b, 1994). The amphipod is relatively resistant to the alga's chemical defenses, while local fishes and sea urchins are strongly deterred (Cronin and Hay 1996a,b). Because local fishes feed on both undefended seaweeds and on amphipods, the amphipods are relatively safe from predation when on *Dicytota* (which the fishes rarely visit) but are much more susceptible when on an alga that is palatable to fishes. During seasons when fishes are feeding most actively, these *Dicytota*-tolerant amphipods increase in abundance, whereas co-occurring amphipod species that do not associate with *Dicytota* and that are not resistant to its chemical defenses are driven to local extinction (Duffy and Hay 1994). Other small herbivores similarly reduce predation by associating with chemically defended algae (Hay et al. 1989, 1990a,b). The role of predator avoidance in the evolution of such associations is especially compelling in associations where the smaller organism specializes on a defended host but does not feed from that host (Sotka et al. 1999; Stachowicz and Hay 1999).

Although chemical defenses against consumers have been studied most extensively in benthic systems, chemical defenses also occur in variety of planktonic organisms, including invertebrate meroplanktonic larvae (Lindquist et al. 1992; Lindquist and Hay 1996), invertebrate holoplankton (Shanks and Graham 1988; McClintock and Janssen 1990), and phytoplankton (Wolfe et al. 1997), suggesting that chemical defenses are pervasive components of marine systems.

CALCIFICATION AS A DETERRENT. Many seaweeds incorporate $CaCO_3$ into their tissues. This calcification could deter herbivores by making seaweeds harder and more difficult to bite or by diminishing their nutritional value due to the addition of indigestible structuring materials (Littler and Littler 1980;

Steneck 1983, 1986; Hay 1984; Duffy and Hay 1990; Targett and Targett 1990; Duffy and Paul 1992; Pennings and Paul 1992; Pitlik and Paul 1997). These suggestions are consistent with findings that CaCO₃-producing seaweeds are commonly low-preference foods for reef herbivores (Littler et al. 1983a,b; Hay 1984; Paul and Hay 1986; Steneck 1988). Although calcification undoubtedly prevents some herbivores from feeding on these harder seaweeds (Steneck and Watling 1982), many reef herbivores (e.g., parrotfishes, sea urchins) can easily bite into calcified seaweeds, and several recent investigations (Hay et al. 1994; Schupp and Paul 1994; Meyer and Paul 1995; Pennings et al. 1996) suggest that the CaCO₃ in seaweed thalli may actually serve as a chemical, as well as a structural, deterrent.

Pennings and Paul (1992) and Hay et al. (1994) added CaCO₃ to artificial foods so as to mimic the presence of CaCO₃ in the food without increasing food hardness. Assays with gastropods, fishes, sea urchins, and amphipods indicated that CaCO₃ could significantly affect the feeding of some herbivores, even when the CaCO₃ had no effect on the nutritional value or toughness of the food (Pennings and Paul 1992; Hay et al. 1994; Schupp and Paul 1994). The study by Schupp and Paul (1994) gave the clearest indication of what mechanisms might produce this effect. Adding CaCO₃ to foods significantly decreased the feeding rates of fishes with acid-mediated digestion, but stimulated, or did not affect, feeding by fishes with neutral or more basic guts (also see Hay et al. 1994; Meyer and Paul 1995; Pennings et al. 1996). This suggests that CaCO₃ may deter some species through the neutralizing effect that it has in a low-pH gut and possibly because of the large amount of CO₂ that would be released. Thus, CaCO₃ may deter some herbivores by increasing plant toughness (Pitlik and Paul 1997), but CaCO₃ can also deter consumers in other ways, possibly by functioning as a chemical defense. Schupp and Paul (1994) suggested using the term mineral defense to distinguish this chemical effect from that of CaCO₃ serving as a hardening agent or from the chemical effects of bioactive secondary metabolites.

Similar assumptions of defensive function have often been made for the mineral spicules common among sessile invertebrates such as sponges and corals. Experimental studies support this hypothesis for some soft corals and gorgonians (Harvell et al. 1988; Gerhart et al. 1988; Van Alstyne and Paul 1992; Van Alstyne et al. 1992, 1994), whereas predatory fishes are indifferent to sponge spicules when incorporated into realistic artificial foods (Chanas and Pawlik 1995, 1996), and spicules of a soft coral even stimulated feeding by a specialist predator (Wylie and Paul 1989).

THE INTEGRATION OF MULTIPLE DEFENSES. The effectiveness of many structural and chemical defenses is influenced by other prey traits or the environmental and recent historical context in which prey–consumer interactions occur (Duffy and Paul 1992; Cronin and Hay 1996b; Hay 1996). For example, estuarine crab zoeae bear spines that reduce their vulnerability to planktivorous fishes, but the crabs also time larval release

and dispersal to minimize encounter with fishes (Morgan 1987, 1989, 1990). Such context-dependency of defenses is likely to be widespread and important but has received little attention.

Many marine prey produce multiple defenses, yet interactions among defensive traits have rarely been assessed. Chemical and mineral defenses (i.e., CaCO₃) commonly co-occur in marine algae, for example, and have been demonstrated to function either additively or synergistically to reduce susceptibility to consumers (Hay et al. 1994; Schupp and Paul 1994; Meyer and Paul 1995). As an example, the green alga *Halimeda goreauii* contains both an unusual secondary metabolite and a heavily calcified thallus. When sea urchins were offered a nutritionally valuable food containing the metabolite alone or CaCO₃ alone, neither trait had any deterrent effect; when these traits were combined, however, they interacted synergistically to suppress feeding strongly (Hay et al. 1994). This interaction changed when the experiment was repeated using a food of lower quality, indicating that food value, CaCO₃, and secondary metabolites interacted to affect sea urchin food choice. Chemical defenses of other reef seaweeds and sponges also can be more effective in foods of lower nutritional quality (Duffy and Paul 1992). Because benthic invertebrates such as sponges, gorgonians, and ascidians commonly produce both defensive secondary metabolites and siliceous or calcified spicules, such interactions could be common in invertebrates as well as seaweeds.

Moreover, the co-occurrence of multiple defenses often appears to be important in defending prey against the broad range of consumers that occur in marine systems. Working with seaweeds, Paul and coworkers have demonstrated numerous instances in which a combination of chemical and CaCO₃-based defenses provides protection against a broader range of herbivores than would either trait acting in isolation from the other. In general, feeding by parrotfishes was commonly deterred by chemical, but not CaCO₃, defenses, whereas feeding by surgeonfishes was commonly deterred by CaCO₃, but not by chemicals (Schupp and Paul 1994; Meyer and Paul 1995; Pennings et al. 1996; Paul 1997).

WHY ISN'T EVERYONE WELL DEFENDED?

Given the effectiveness of defenses such as those discussed above, why are defenses not universal among organisms? The most likely answer is that defenses are generally costly in terms of growth, reproduction, or competitive ability. This conclusion is supported on a broad scale by the generally positive spatial correlation between intensity of predation and frequency of defenses or of low susceptibility to consumers (Hay 1984, 1985, 1991a; Lewis 1986; Bolser and Hay 1996), suggesting that where predation intensity is low, less-defended forms have a competitive advantage over better-defended forms.

The most direct evidence that defenses are costly comes from organisms with phenotypically plastic defensive traits, in which fitness can be compared in better-defended and less-defended morphs of the same genotype, or within the same population. The evolutionary interplay between costs and benefits of defense is illustrated most clearly by inducible defenses, a form of phenotypic plasticity in which a given genotype produces defenses in response to specific cues from a consumer. Induced defenses should be favored when predation is partial, is a reliable predictor of further damage, and when there is sufficient time after an attack (or after detection of the predator) to mount an effective defense (Harvell 1990). Conversely, constitutive (permanent) defenses should be favored where the probability of attack is unpredictable in time and space but high on average, and the prey is unable to mount an effective defense after attack or detection. Since defenses and costs can be measured within individual genotypes in inducible taxa, they provide promising opportunities for examining the tradeoffs involved.

One of the most thoroughly documented marine example of induced defenses involves induction of defensive spines in the bryozoan *Membranipora membranacea* in response to the specialist nudibranch predator *Doridella steinbergae* (Harvell 1984). Focusing on the cues involved in spine induction and how these benefitted the bryozoan, Harvell (1986) found that curved spines were produced only in the presence of the specialist predator, and that spines could be induced by waterborne cues from the predator even without contact. Spines effectively reduced predation; nudibranchs were less than half as successful when spines were present. Lab experiments supported the hypothesis that spine induction entailed a cost: Spined colonies grew significantly less than unspined colonies. When similar assays of cost were conduced in the field, costs for spined colonies were small relative to those predicted from laboratory assays (Harvell 1992), suggesting that the occurrence or magnitude of costs may be context dependent. Other examples of induced defenses, discussed above, include several marine algae that show marked morphological plasticity in the face of consumer pressure, changing their growth form when subjected to grazing (Lubchenco and Cubit 1980; Lewis et al. 1987).

Predator-induced phenotypic plasticity has long been known in a variety of clonally propagating animals and plants. But it has also been demonstrated with increasing frequency in unitary animals. A good example comes from the intertidal acorn barnacle *Chthamalus anisopoma*, which exhibits two co-occurring morphs in the Gulf of California (Figure 5.5); the conic form typical of acorn barnacles and an asymmetric "bent" morph in which the aperture is perpendicular to the base (Lively 1986a,b). Lively's field experiments demonstrated clearly that the bent morph functioned as a defense against predatory gastropods. The bent form survived better than the conic form in the presence of a predatory snail, and field quadrats stocked with predatory snails recruited barnacle populations with substantial proportions of bents, whereas no bents developed in predator-free control quadrats. But the defense was costly; bents grew more slowly and averaged 27% lower fecundity than conics, apparently because the bent morphology constrains available

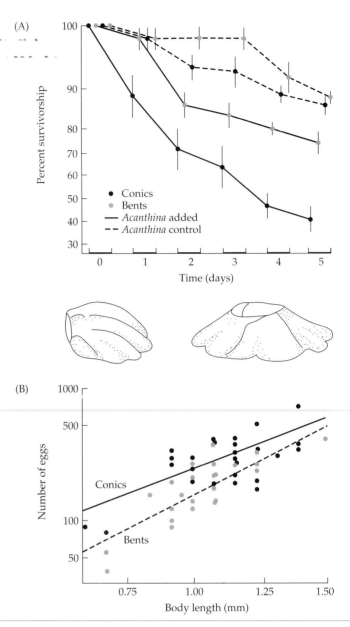

Figure 5.5 The fitness cost of defense in a polymorphic barnacle. (A) Field experiments showed that the bent morph (left) survived better than the conic morph (right) in the presence of the predatory gastropod *Acanthina*. (B) The bent morph, however, pays for this advantage in lower fecundity, and the conic morph predominates in the absence of predators. (After Lively 1986a,b.)

brood volume. Thus bents should be outcompeted by conics in the absence of predation. Other examples of induced defenses in nonclonal organisms include bivalves (Reimer and Tedengren 1996; Leonard et al. 1999), gastropods (Appleton and Palmer 1988; Trussell 1998), and even fishes (Brönmark and Miner 1992). In all of these cases, the predator—or a chemical effluent thereof—induces a switch in the prey individual's developmental pathway, producing a stronger or better-defended adult.

There are also examples of induced chemical defenses in marine algae, but the costs associated with chemical induction are less clear than for those of morphological defenses. Van Alstyne (1988) demonstrated that *Fucus* plants attacked by gastropods increased their levels of phenolics and became less palatable. Similarly, amphipod grazing on the brown alga *Dicytota menstrualis* induced production of defensive diterpenes and reduced susceptibility to future attack (Cronin and Hay 1996b). For some seaweeds, the spatial variation in secondary metabolites among habitats experiencing different levels of herbivory is also suggestive of induction. For example, seaweeds from areas of coral reefs where herbivory is intense often produce more potent and higher concentrations of chemical defenses than plants of the same species from habitats where herbivory is less intense (Paul and Fenical 1986; Paul and Van Alstyne 1988). However, in the green seaweeds *Halimeda*, *Udotea*, and *Caulerpa* that show this pattern, clipping experiments failed to induce increased terpenoid chemical defenses (Paul and Van Alstyne 1992). Clipping or urchin grazing of temperate seaweeds also failed to induce higher levels of phlorotannins in the kelps *Ecklonia* and *Alaria* or in the rockweed *Sargassum* (Pfister 1992; Steinberg 1994, 1995). Thus, the higher levels of constitutive chemical defenses from sites with many herbivores may have been generated by preferential grazing that removed the more susceptible individuals, by local genetic adaptation to strong consumer pressure, or by among-habitat differences in other variables. The frequency of induced defenses in marine algae, and its implications for costs of defense, remain uncertain.

Although induced defenses have received considerable attention in terrestrial systems, their frequency, importance, and consequences are still debated (Baldwin 1990; Tallamy and Raupp 1991; Alder and Karban 1994; Karban and Baldwin 1997). Most terrestrial investigations of induction have focused on insect grazing, whereas most marine investigations have focused on larger herbivores such as fishes and urchins rather than on mesograzers, such as amphipods, that may be more ecologically similar to insects (Hay et al. 1987b). Mesograzers have been considered less important than larger herbivores because of the perception that they remove little seaweed biomass relative to the larger herbivores (see the debate among Bell 1991; Duffy and Hay 1991a; Brawley 1992). Grazing by mesograzers has been inadequately investigated, however, and there are convincing cases of mesograzers having large impacts on seaweed populations (Kangas et al. 1982; Haahtela 1984; Brawley 1992) or even on total community structure (Brawley and Adey 1981; Tegner and Dayton 1987; Duffy and Hay 2000) under certain circumstances, particularly when activity of their predators is low.

Several lines of evidence suggest that mesograzers are the grazers most likely to induce seaweed chemical defenses. First, these consumers feed over temporal and spatial scales that would allow induced responses to benefit the individual prey organism. Second, because mesograzers often are not deterred by constitutive levels of defenses, induction to higher levels may be needed to deter them. The two clear examples of induced chemical defenses in seaweeds (Van Alstyne 1988; Cronin and Hay 1996b) both involve mesograzers (a snail and an amphipod), each of which could graze for long periods on a plant without killing it and could thus be affected by a defense that took days, or weeks, to induce. The nudibranch predator that caused defensive spine induction in bryozoan prey (Harvell 1984, 1986) is also, in essence, a mesograzer. In contrast, fishes and urchins are generally large relative to their prey and are often capable of rapidly killing prey that they find palatable. Thus, to avoid being killed by these larger more mobile consumers, prey organisms may need to be constantly defended rather than inducing defenses following attack. For many chemically defended seaweeds and invertebrates, low concentrations of chemical defenses are generally effective deterrents against fishes and urchins, but are less effective or may even stimulate feeding by mesograzers (Hay et al. 1987b; Hay 1991b, 1992; Van Alstyne and Paul 1992; Pawlik 1993; Duffy and Hay 1994; Hay and Fenical 1996). Thus, constitutive levels of chemical defenses appear to be effective against the larger consumers. It is therefore possible that induction in seaweeds has appeared deceptively uncommon because it rarely occurs in response to clipping or grazing by larger herbivores, whereas it may occur more often in response to mesograzer feeding.

Mechanistic understanding is critical to evaluating induced (and other) defenses, as induction of chemical changes does not always translate to reduced palatability. For example, when the brown alga *Fucus vesiculosus* was grazed by amphipods, the alga's phenolic levels increased by a statistically significant 100% (M. Deal and M. Hay, pers. comm.); however, this had no effect on feeding by the amphipods and did not lead to amphipods choosing ungrazed over grazed plants. Increases of specific chemicals following grazing may occur to minimize microbial invasion of wounds, or for other reasons unrelated to the initial grazer. Some terrestrial studies show that microbes entering plants via insect bites have a much greater effect on chemical induction than does the direct damage done by the insect (Raffa and Smalley 1995); the above example of *Fucus* might involve a similar explanation. Because resistance to consumers can change for reasons other than secondary metabolites, and because concentrations of secondary metabolites can change in response to many factors other than herbivory, studies of induction should assess induction using consumer feeding (e.g., Renaud et al. 1990; Cetrulo and Hay 2000), rather than chemical analyses alone. If feeding is significantly affected, bioassay-guided investigations can then be conducted to determine directly the mechanisms altering resistance.

EVOLUTION OF PREY DEFENSES

The cases discussed above offer compelling evidence that particular phenotypic characters reduce the prey's vulnerability to predation and thus that those features currently serve a defensive function. In many cases it also seems likely that those features evolved for the purpose of reducing predation. The abundance of marine consumers (many of which have recently been depleted from natural systems;

Hughes 1994; Jackson 1997; Dayton et al. 1998) and their intense feeding rates in many ecosystems (e.g., see Figure 5.1) clearly suggest that consumers have exerted strong selection on prey populations and communities. But plausibility and apparent ecological "fit" are not proof that a given defensive trait arose by selection from consumers rather than through fortuitous preadaptation (see Steneck 1992 and Vermeij 1992 as examples). Questions about such historical processes are by their nature more difficult to answer confidently than questions about current ecological processes, and one must generally rely on indirect evidence. A growing body of data supports the conclusion that consumer pressure has commonly driven the evolution of a wide range of prey traits that allows escape, tolerance, or deterrence of consumers. Sources of evidence include direct experimental demonstration of prey evolution, historical or fossil evidence, and comparative data. Nevertheless, several well-known cases of apparent coevolution between marine consumers and prey appear on closer examination to be more complicated, and less convincing, than originally thought. Thus, reconstructing the evolutionary history of consumer–prey interactions must be approached rigorously.

Evolution of Escape Mechanisms

Many prey reduce predation through life history patterns that minimize overlap with predators in time and space, that is, by escaping predators. Life history patterns are molded by a plethora of selection pressures (Stearns 1992), and it is likely that many life history characters evolved in part as responses to selection pressures other than predation. Thus, prey that coexist with consumers may simply be those prey whose existing life histories allowed them to persist in the presence of active consumers. Nonetheless, there are convincing cases of consumers selecting for life history characters that allow prey escape. The strongest evidence for evolution of prey traits in response to predation comes from experimental demonstration that predators cause heritable changes in phenotype that reduce the prey's vulnerability to predation. We know of no marine examples, but such historical time series have been documented experimentally in a small number of other cases, notably the rapid (6–18 generations) adaptive changes in several life history characters of freshwater guppies after their transplantation from predator-rich streams to streams where predators are rare (Reznick et al. 1997). Transplanted guppies showed heritable increases in generation time and body size at maturity, and reduction in fecundity and allocation to reproduction, as predicted by life history theory (Stearns 1992). These changes parallel differences between populations occurring naturally in low- versus high-predation streams (Reznick et al. 1996; Reznick and Bryga 1996), and are expected to influence the prey's odds of escaping from larger generalist predators.

Comparative data suggest that the life histories and behaviors of many pelagic organisms are adapted to escape predation. In the upper oceans, for example, most zooplankton are very small and transparent, presumably as an adaptation to escape detection by visually hunting predators (Hobson and Chess 1976; Hamner 1995). The dispersal patterns of estuarine crab larvae also appear adapted to escape predators (Morgan 1989, 1990; Morgan and Christy 1997). A combination of experiments, field surveys, and comparative data show that interspecific variation in larval morphology (spination), pigmentation, body size, and behavior are all consistent with predation as an important selective pressure molding these phenotypic traits. Crab species whose larvae remain in predator-rich estuarine habitats during development tend to be larger, more heavily spined, and less pigmented than species whose larvae are exported to the coastal ocean. Species who release larvae during daytime also have less pigmented larvae than those with the typical patterns of nighttime release. Similarly, among sessile benthic invertebrates such as sponges, gorgonians, and ascidians, larvae that are chemically defended from fishes tend to be more brightly colored, to stay close above the reef where predators are common, and to be released during the day when they can use photic cues to help choose appropriate microsites for settlement (Lindquist and Hay 1996). In contrast, larvae without chemical defenses tend to be less visually obvious, released at night, and to stay in the plankton for long enough to disperse into offshore waters, rather than staying on consumer-rich reefs. Among coastal plankton, Hobson and Chess (1976) found that large and pigmented taxa entered the water column primarily at night when least visible to fish predators. Similarly, Hays et al. (1994) found that large and pigmented species of oceanic zooplankton showed more pronounced vertical migration than small, less pigmented species, as expected if these migrations function primarily to avoid predation. Thus, it appears that predation has been a primary selective force driving one of the most conspicuous biological processes in the world ocean.

Evolution of Grazing Tolerance: A Cautionary Tale

There are few rigorous data bearing on the evolution of grazing tolerance in marine organisms. One of the initially most convincing examples of apparent coevolution between marine consumers and prey involved such a case—the interaction between the encrusting coralline alga *Clathromorphum circumscriptum* and its relatively specialized limpet grazer *Tectura testudinalis* (previously *Acmaea testudinalis*). Initial studies found a number of apparently coevolved adaptations that were of mutual benefit to both organisms (Steneck 1982). Evidence of this coevolved relationship included: (a) positive correlation between abundances of the alga and limpet, (b) production of a unique protective covering of tissue over the alga's regions of active growth, (c) apparent adaptation of the limpet's radula to eat this thickened tissue in a way that minimally damages the host alga or its sunken reproductive structures, (d) prevention by limpet grazing of the algal host's being overgrown by potentially lethal epiphytic algae, (e) reduced susceptibility of the limpet to its predators when clamped down on the hard smooth surface of the alga (Steneck 1990), and (f) a balance, over a wide range of depths, between the rate of cell removal by limpets and algal production.

Fortunately, in addition to this very suggestive ecological information, Steneck (1992) was also able to evaluate the paleontological record involving coralline algae and herbivores. Because coralline algae are calcified, they have left an excellent fossil record that includes a history of their anatomical characteristics, which have been interpreted as evolutionary responses to herbivores, as well as grazing scars on their surfaces that can be identified as being produced by limpets, urchins, fishes, and so on (Steneck 1983, 1986). Thus, the fossil record for coralline algae and their associated herbivores is apparently the most complete record for any plant–herbivore association, either terrestrial or marine (Steneck 1992). This record shows that virtually all of the coralline's major morphological characteristics that had been interpreted as adaptations to herbivores were present at least 100 million years before the evolution of marine herbivores that could feed on corallines (Steneck 1992). Recent analysis of 12 specialist molluscs and their temperate seaweed hosts similarly suggests that these associations are more opportunistic than coevolved (Vermeij 1992). In 50% of the cases studied, Vermeij found that the associations were geologically recent (no earlier than the Pliocene) and resulted following invasion of the plant or the herbivore from geographical regions other than the one in which the association was forged. In contrast to the commonly held view that associations between specialized herbivores and host plants evolve by reciprocal adaptation over a long period of time, Vermeij's study suggests that many such relationships originate opportunistically and rapidly with little, if any, reciprocal evolution. Of course it is quite possible that, once the plant and grazer have come into contact, their physiology, behavior, and/or life history, which are not generally detectable in the fossil record, are molded by reciprocal adaptation. Nevertheless, these examples emphasize the difficulty of extrapolating evolutionary from ecological interactions.

Evolution of Consumer Deterrence

MORPHOLOGICAL DEFENSES. There is abundant evidence that consumer pressure selects for the evolution of deterrent traits in prey. The next best thing to an experimental demonstration of evolution would be convincing historical evidence of a change in phenotype coincident with increases in predation pressure. Several such cases have been described. Perhaps the best documented involves the rapid change in shell thickness and strength of the intertidal snail *Littorina obtusata* following introduction of the predatory European green crab (*Carcinus maenas*) into northern New England around 1900. This example is important both because of the fine time resolution of the process and as an additional cautionary tale for interpreting historical evidence. Seeley (1986) showed that shells collected from northern New England prior to 1900 were relatively thin and had high spires, whereas shells collected in the 1980s (and in 1915 at one site), after crabs were established in the region, were significantly thicker and lower-spired. Laboratory and field experiments confirmed that the thicker, lower-spired morphs were substantially less vulnerable to crab predation than thinner, high-spired morphs (Seeley 1986). Although these data strongly indicate that crab predation caused phenotypic change in the snail populations, it is less clear whether or how much of this change was genetically based, and thus whether natural selection or only phenotypic plasticity was involved. Trussell and Smith (2000) have shown experimentally that shell thickness and shape in *L. obtusata* are phenotypically plastic, with exposure to crabs inducing changes similar to those seen after the invasion of green crabs in the field (Seeley 1986; see also the section above on inducible defenses). Such experiments are of course not possible with fossils and suggest caution in interpretation of similar patterns in the fossil record, at least on relatively short time scales.

Large-scale trends in the fossil record provide numerous similar examples of the strengthening and diversification of morphological defenses and the adoption of cryptic and burrowing habits, coincident with evolution of increasingly effective consumers (Vermeij 1977, 1987). As one of several possible examples, Palmer (1982) described parallel trends in morphological evolution within several barnacle lineages coincident with radiation of muricacean gastropods, which appear to be the primary predators of barnacles in most temperate areas. Observations of predation on extant barnacles in the field and lab showed that drilling predation by gastropods (*Thais* spp.) is 2 to 3 times more successful at sutures between the barnacle's skeletal plates than is drilling through the plate. Remarkably, the fossil data indicate ~18 independent reductions in plate number (and thus number of sutures) during the evolution of balanomorph barnacles, and they indicate a major increase in proportion of genera with reduced plate number, during or shortly after the period when muricacean predators radiated. Interestingly, the exception to this trend also supports the rule: The barnacle genus *Chelonibia* lives on the carapace of sea turtles where it rarely if ever encounters drilling gastropods; consistent with the predation hypothesis, this barnacle retains evidence of the ancestral condition of eight parietal plates. Similar trends toward stronger, more heavily sculptured exoskeletons occurred in many benthic invertebrate taxa during the late Mesozoic, coincident with the radiation of more powerful predators (the "Mesozoic marine revolution"; Vermeij 1977), and in benthic algae and their grazers during the same period (Steneck 1983). These trends suggest that consumers have had a profound and pervasive influence both on evolution of organismal phenotypes and on the organization of communities (Vermeij 1987; Vermeij, this volume).

In the absence of historical data, evidence for the evolution of defenses against consumers comes from arguments from design and from comparative data. In the first category, Morgan (1989) conducted critical tests of alternative hypotheses for the adaptive significance of the long spines common in zoea larvae of crabs. Experiments with larvae of the mud crab *Rhithropanopeus harrisii* rejected the hypothesis that spines functioned to retard sinking; settling velocity, swimming and sinking behavior of spined and unspined larvae were similar. Nor did spines deter invertebrate predators: only one of ten invertebrate predators ate more unspined than spined larvae. Instead, the primary function of spines appears to be reduction of predation by planktivorous fishes, whose feeding was deterred by spines. Moreover, spines enhanced survival of attacked larvae, regenerated quickly, and were effective when partially regenerated. Individual fish quickly learned to avoid spined prey. These results suggest that individual-level natural selection could have favored the evolution of spines, as has also been argued for the evolution of chemical defense in larvae (Lindquist and Hay 1996). Finally, comparative experiments with larvae of six decapod species (Morgan 1987) showed that small planktivorous fish preferred the two zoea species that are exported from the estuary over four species that are retained in the estuary. The exported species are smaller and have shorter spines than retained species. Two of the retained species combined morphological defenses (spines) with postcontact evasive and escape behavior that helped them escape predation. Taken together, the various lines of evidence are most consistently explained as reflecting adaptation to minimize predation by fishes.

CHEMICAL DEFENSES.   Comparative approaches have been applied to explore the evolution of chemical defenses. For example, Estes and Steinberg (1988) noted that rocky shores in temperate Australasia support broadly similar communities as those of the northeast Pacific, dominated by large brown seaweeds and grazing gastropods and sea urchins. Australasian shores, however, have apparently never supported top predators ecologically equivalent to the sea otter that occupies a keystone predator role in the northeast Pacific (see above). These authors (see also Steinberg et al. 1995) reasoned that the historical absence of such top predators in Australasia (probably since at least the late Tertiary) should have resulted in higher densities and feeding intensity of grazers, and consequently in stronger selection pressure for defenses in seaweeds in that region compared with the northeast Pacific. These predictions were consistent with results of experiments (Steinberg et al. 1995); rates of algal tissue loss to herbivory were significantly greater in Australasia than in otter-dominated locations in the northeast Pacific, and concentrations of hypothesized chemical defenses (phlorotannins) in Australasian brown seaweeds were five to six times greater than in related algae from the northeast Pacific. Moreover, there is also evidence of escalation (sensu Vermeij 1987) between Australasian seaweeds and grazers; grazers in this region were generally tolerant of seaweed phlorotannins, whether derived from co-occurring seaweeds or from northeast Pacific algae. In contrast, grazers from the northeast Pacific were consistently deterred from feeding by phlorotannins from either region. It is unsettling, however, that the high levels of phenolics in Australasian algae are not deterrent to local herbivores (Steinberg and Van Altena 1992). It is thus unclear why these seaweeds would continue to allocate high levels of resources to the production of these compounds when they appear to have no current function against local consumers.

We discussed above the evidence that selection for prey defenses is strongest at low latitudes. If tropical seaweeds more commonly produce chemical defenses, then tropical herbivores should also be under greater selection than temperate herbivores to tolerate or circumvent these defenses. This notion has rarely been tested, but the one such study we know of does support the hypothesis that tropical herbivores are more tolerant of chemical defenses than are temperate herbivores. Cronin et al. (1997) tested a series of secondary metabolites from the brown alga *Dictyota acutiloba* against both temperate and tropical fishes and sea urchins. In general, feeding by the temperate herbivores was suppressed by lower concentrations of metabolites than were necessary to suppress feeding by the tropical herbivores. Although many more such studies are needed before one could confidently draw rigorous conclusions, the available data suggest that herbivore activity in the tropics has selected for greater levels of chemical defenses in seaweeds and that tropical herbivores have, in turn, been under greater selection to tolerate or circumvent these defenses.

Evolution of Associational Defenses

In the absence of historical data, perhaps the most compelling evidence for antipredator adaptation comes from demonstration that intraspecific variation in defensive traits is correlated with consumer pressure. Stachowicz and Hay (1999, 2000) used such a comparative approach to explore variance in camouflaging behavior of the decorator crab *Libinia dubia* along the Gulf and East Coasts of the United States. Juvenile *L. dubia* camouflage themselves from predators by attaching bits of algae and sessile invertebrates to their carapace. In North Carolina, the crabs decorate almost exclusively with the brown macroalga *Dictyota menstrualis*, despite its low relative abundance in the habitat. This alga is chemically defended from the omnivorous fishes that are the dominant predators of decorator crabs in this area, and field experiments showed that crabs decorated with *D. menstrualis* were only ~20% as likely to be consumed by fishes as crabs decorated with an alga palatable to the fishes. That the specialized decorating behavior is an evolved response to predation pressure is supported by geographic variation in the crab's decorating preferences (Figure 5.6). Whereas *D. menstrualis* extends northward only as far as southern Virginia, the crab ranges into New England. Field surveys showed that crabs in the northern range decorated with a variety of algae and sessile invertebrates in approximate proportion to their availability, whereas crabs from North Carolina specialized on *D. menstrualis*. Lab assays corroborated these patterns, showing that northern crabs decorated with a variety of algae and did not specialize on *Dictyota*, even when it was made available to them, whereas southern crabs from North Carolina and Alabama used *D. menstrualis* almost exclusively. These patterns are consistent with the hypothesis that southern crabs

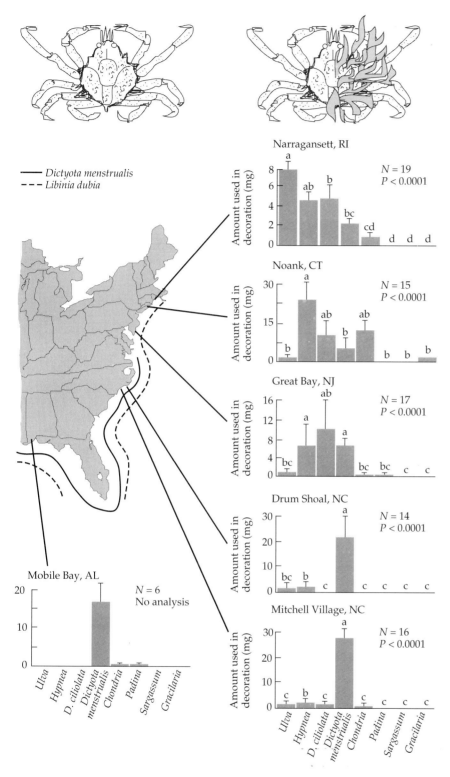

Figure 5.6 Apparently adaptive geographic variation in use of the chemically noxious seaweed *Dictyota menstrualis* by the decorator crab *Libinia dubia*. In laboratory choice assays, crabs collected within the range of this alga select it almost exclusively for decoration, thereby protecting themselves from omnivorous fish predators (Stachowicz and Hay 1999), whereas crabs collected from northern areas rely on camouflage, decorating themselves with various algae in proportion to their abundance in the environment. (From Stachowicz and Hay 2000.)

have been selected to recognize and preferentially decorate with a chemically defended seaweed that provides especially effective protection from omnivorous fish predators. Interestingly, although this alga produces multiple diterpene metabolites, the single compound that the crabs use as a cue for decorating is the compound that most strongly deters fish

feeding. Northern crabs that do not normally have access to *Dictyota* decorate nonselectively and simply match their background. Given that these crabs will most commonly be attacked by carnivorous rather than omnivorous fishes, this behavior may be sufficient to avoid predation. Thus, *L. dubia* appears to have adapted to geographic variance in the protective value of potential algal associates as well as to varying consumer pressure.

Who Selects for Prey Defenses?

There are numerous patterns in prey defensive traits, suggesting that large mobile generalists like fishes and sea urchins have been the major consumers selecting for defense and that smaller mesograzers such as amphipods and polychaetes have played a secondary, but maybe not insignificant, role. A few examples that illustrate this include: (1) seaweeds on tropical reefs have more potent chemical defenses than seaweeds from temperate reefs. This increase in defense correlates with increased herbivory by fishes and urchins on tropical reefs, not with greater herbivory by mesograzers (Carpenter 1986; Hay 1991a); (2) in both the Caribbean and Pacific, seaweeds in the genus *Halimeda* produce their new and potentially more vulnerable growth at night during a short window of time when herbivorous fishes are inactive (Hay et al. 1988; Paul and Van Alstyne 1988); mesograzers are generally more, rather than less, active at night (Brawley 1992); and (3) experimental field studies have demonstrated that seaweeds that undergo large shifts in morphology in response to grazing pressure, generally do this in response to grazing by fishes and/or urchins rather than as a function of mesograzer densities (Steneck and Adey 1976; Hay 1981b; Lewis et al. 1987), although morphological responses of algae to mesograzers have not been explicitly tested. Finally, human harvesting has greatly reduced abundances of large marine consumers throughout the world, such that our perceptions of "pristine" environments probably greatly underestimate the former abundance of large animals (Safina 1995; Jackson 1997; Dayton et al. 1998), which must have had strong selective impacts on prey organisms.

General patterns in the effectiveness of prey chemical defenses also support the greater importance of larger generalist consumers in selecting for prey defenses. In both seaweeds and benthic invertebrates, many secondary metabolites strongly deter feeding by fishes and urchins, but often are relatively ineffective against a variety of mesograzers such as amphipods, small crabs, polychaetes, ascoglossan gastropods, nudibranchs, and flatworms (Hay and Fenical 1988, 1996; Hay 1991b, 1996; Paul 1992; Pawlik 1993). In many instances, the mesograzers are, in fact, stimulated to feed or choose hosts by the metabolites that most strongly deter the larger consumers. As discussed above, it appears that prey evolved defenses against the larger, generalist consumers, that these chemically defended prey then become microhabitats where small mesograzers can predictably escape their predators, and that the mesograzers then evolve a tolerance for these chemical defenses as a means of acquiring a safe microhabitat for both living and feeding (see reviews in Hay and Fenical 1988, 1996; Hay 1992, 1996).

PREY EFFECTS ON PREDATORS

A central point in understanding the evolutionary interaction between consumer and prey is that it is inherently asymmet-

rical. Whether or not a consumer is successful in a particular encounter with the victim is potentially a matter of life and death for the victim, but only one in a lifetime of meals for the consumer (the "life-dinner principle"; Dawkins and Krebs 1979). That is, a successful predator immediately reduces the prey's future fitness to zero, so we expect selection to be stronger for prey defenses than for consumer adaptations to catching particular prey, and we might guess that in an "arms race" between them, the prey will generally stay slightly ahead of the consumer (or it will go extinct). Nevertheless, prey defenses can have significant effects on consumer fitness and in some cases can select for evolutionary change in the consumer as well.

In marine systems, we know too little about the effects that prey defenses have on consumer fitness. That is, why do consumers evolve the ability to detect and avoid prey with certain traits? For morphological defenses, such as those common in shelled gastropods, the costs to a consumer of dealing with defended prey are often relatively straightforward to estimate in terms of increased handling time per unit food consumed (Palmer 1979; Bertness 1981) and potentially increased exposure of the consumer to its own predators. For example, Palmer (1979) showed experimentally that filing off the stout spines from the shells of tropical muricid gastropods decreased their effective diameter by 10–20%, rendering previously invulnerable shells crushable by pufferfish.

For chemical defenses, in contrast, there are many documented cases of prey defenses changing consumer feeding behavior, but very few where we can say what effect the avoided metabolite would have on the consumer if it ingested the compound. Such direct tests of the effects of defensive metabolites on consumer physiology or fitness are rare, in part because it is very difficult to get consumers to eat defended prey so that the effects of the compounds can be assessed. Hay et al. (1987b) demonstrated that a diterpene alcohol that deters fish from consuming the brown alga *Dictyota menstrualis* significantly slowed growth of the fish when the compound was consumed as 1% of the diet for a period of several days. Although this concentration can occur in some tropical species of the Dictyotales, the ecological relevance of this assay can be questioned because it is extremely unlikely that any fish would consume only this one genus of seaweed for an extended period. A different approach was taken by Targett and Targett (1990), who assayed the effect of crude extracts from a chemically deterrent green seaweed by coating this on a palatable seagrass and evaluating its effects on parrotfish assimilation efficiency. Although the extract had no effect on assimilation efficiency, this does not exclude the possibility of negative effects on growth, development, or fecundity. Irelan and Horn (1991) tested the physiological effects of *Fucus* extract (which the fish would not eat) by anesthetizing fish and force feeding them control diets versus diets treated with the *Fucus* extracts and then determining their digestive efficiency over the next several days. These treatments did not affect digestion of carbon, but *Fucus* polar extract did lower assimilation efficiency of nitrogen (often a limiting resource for herbivores) relative to the control. Boettcher and Targett (1993) used a similar approach to test the effects of different-sized algal phlorotannins on fish digestive efficiency and found that larger phlorotannins commonly suppressed digestive efficiency, whereas smaller ones did not. Such interference with consumer nutrition could translate to reduced fitness, a necessary requisite for natural selection to mold consumer-feeding biology.

If a newly arisen defensive trait is to increase to fixation in a prey population, it must confer a selective advantage when rare, as it will necessarily be immediately after its origin. Some experimental evidence points to significant negative consequences for the consumer's fitness because of limited feeding on chemically defended prey, such as might occur when a generalist consumer samples rare, defended prey in a diverse natural community (Figure 5.7). Lindquist and Hay (1995) fed anemones large meals of nutritious food followed several hours later by small meals of larval mimics containing either defensive compounds (treatment) or no defensive compounds (controls). This was meant to mimic anemones getting the majority of their food from appropriate sources but feeding at low levels (1.8% of the total daily diet) on defended foods (e.g., consuming a few chemically rich invertebrate larvae). Even this low-level consumption of defended prey strongly suppressed both growth and vegetative reproduction of treatment anemones. This demonstrates that, even at low frequency, chemical defenses can have negative effects on consumer fitness and thus select for recognition and avoidance of foods containing these compounds.

On a grander time scale, the number of families of marine animals specialized for shell-breaking predation increased dramatically in the late Cretaceous through early Tertiary, as did the frequency of fossils with drilling damage (Vermeij 1987) and the depth of penetration into the substratum of excavating herbivores (Steneck 1983). The timing and magnitude of these trends relative to the evolution of prey defenses argue that increasing effectiveness of consumers evolved at least partially in response to the increasing difficulty of obtaining their quarry (Vermeij 1987).

INDIRECT IMPACTS OF CONSUMERS ON COMMUNITIES AND ECOSYSTEMS

Trophic Cascades

In addition to their strong direct effects on prey documented above, consumers can have pervasive indirect impacts on community organization when the prey are themselves strong interactors with other species in the community. These indirect effects can extend well beyond the particular prey taxa consumed. The classic demonstration of this phenomenon was the fundamental change in community structure following removal of the predatory seastar *Pisaster ochraceous* from a northeast Pacific rocky intertidal habitat (Paine 1966, 1974). Despite its relatively low abundance at Paine's study site, removal of *Pisaster* resulted in a dramatic reduction in species diversity of primary space occupiers because its principal prey, the mussel *Mytilus edulis*, was competitively dominant and excluded other species when released from predation. Paine (1969) coined the term keystone for species that have strong community impacts that are disproportionate to their abundance.

Such indirect interaction chains reach their most extreme development in "trophic cascades" (Carpenter et al. 1985), in which an apex predator's impact penetrates through the intervening trophic levels to influence plant abundance. A few experimental studies have shown that predation by marine birds and fish can cascade down to influence the standing stock and species composition of benthic algae (Wootton 1995; Duffy and Hay 2000). The most spectacular example of such far-reaching impacts is the case of the sea otter in the northeast Pacific (see Figure 5.3). Sea otters are voracious predators on herbivorous sea urchins and molluscs. Comparisons among islands with and without sea otter populations suggested that otter feeding drastically reduces herbivore abundance and grazing pressure on seaweeds to depths of tens of meters and that this grazing in turn releases the giant kelp *Macrocystis* and other seaweeds from grazer control (Estes and Palmisano 1974; Estes and Duggins 1995). Islands

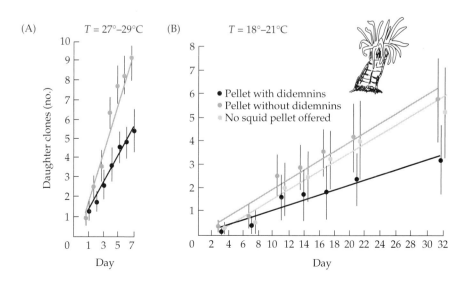

(A) *T* = 27°–29°C   (B) *T* = 18°–21°C

• Pellet with didemnins
• Pellet without didemnins
○ No squid pellet offered

Daughter clones (no.)

Day

Figure 5.7 Consumption of even small quantities of chemically defended prey can significantly reduce predator fitness. In this case, food pellets laced with noxious compounds (didemnins) from the sea squirt *Trididemnum solidum* made up <2% of the daily food ration of the anemone *Aiptasia pallida*, yet the compounds reduced the rate of asexual reproduction (production of daughter clones) by ~40% relative to that of anemones fed with the same quantity of didemnin-free pellets. Such effectiveness enhances the probability that an initially rare defense mutation would confer sufficient advantage to spread through the population. (After Lindquist and Hay 1995.)

with otters thus have lush kelp forests, whereas islands without otters support mainly "urchin barrens," areas dominated by crustose coralline algae and sea urchins, but nearly devoid of fleshy algae. Since kelps dominate their physical and biological environment, their removal by grazers in otter-free areas has pervasive consequences not only for the benthos, but also for fishes and nearshore terrestrial wildlife that depend on the structure and production of kelp beds (Estes and Palmisano 1974; Duggins et al. 1989). Recently, Estes et al. (1998) demonstrated that the strong consumer–prey interactions driving this trophic cascade extend through four trophic levels: A sudden increase in killer whale predation on otters was correlated with dramatic decreases in otter densities, increases in urchin biomass and grazing intensity, and a drastic reduction in kelp abundance. This type of shifting trophic cascade may have been going on for thousands of years, with human hunters in the role played by killer whales in the above study. Analyses of Indian middens suggests that nearshore marine communities in Alaska shifted between urchin barrens and kelp communities as otters were overharvested by humans and then allowed to recover (Simenstad et al. 1978). Indeed, humans as apex predators increasingly provide the most dramatic and alarming examples of trophic cascades (Steneck 1998).

In the pelagic zone, there are several suggestive cases of trophic cascades, most involving zooplanktivorous ctenophores or medusae as top predators (Verity and Smetacek 1996). Among the more compelling cases is that involving the estuarine ctenophore *Mnemiopsis leidyi* in New England (Deason and Smayda 1982). Like many gelatinous zooplankters, this ctenophore periodically blooms to high densities and feeds heavily on crustacean zooplankton, most of which are herbivorous. A 6-year time series of plankton dynamics in Narragansett Bay revealed that the summer pulse in ctenophore abundance coincided with a rapid decline in zooplankton biomass and a concomitant phytoplankton bloom in four of the six years. When abundances of the ctenophore and the dominant phytoplankter (the diatom *Skeletonema costatum*) were integrated over the summer season for each year, there was a strong positive correlation across years between the predator and the phytoplankter ($r^2 = 0.77$). Anecdotal observations suggested that this trophic cascade could extend through a fourth level as well: In 1974 a large population of the predatory ctenophore *Beröe ovata* rapidly reduced *M. leidyi* populations. This was followed by a sharp increase in zooplankton and a crash of the diatom bloom (Deason and Smayda 1982).

Whereas the ctenophore example comes from a restricted estuary, recent data suggest that anthropogenic perturbations of upper trophic levels can cascade down to affect phytoplankton dynamics even in the open ocean. Shiomoto et al. (1997) presented time-series measurements of surface phytoplankton and zooplankton abundance in the subarctic Pacific from 1985 to 1994, along with abundance of juvenile pink salmon, which feed on zooplankton. Between 1990 and 1994, surface chlorophyll and salmon abundance alternated synchronously between high values in odd years and low val-

ues in even years, whereas zooplankton biomass was exactly opposite in phase, low in odd and high in even years. As temperature and nutrients (nitrate plus nitrite) were roughly constant throughout the time series, the variation in phytoplankton biomass is unlikely to be explained by bottom-up forcing. The most likely explanation for this curious interannual pattern involves the influence of hatchery-stocked salmon released in the northwestern United States. The importance of top-down control in these patterns is also supported by the finding that carnivorous zooplankton cycled with the same pattern as total zooplankton, suggesting that all zooplankton were similarly controlled by a higher trophic level (salmon). These examples support a growing recognition of the importance of top-down control of food-web structure in pelagic systems (Verity and Smetacek 1996).

Such examples of strong interactions cascading through the food web are spectacular, but how common are they? Micheli (1999) addressed this question for marine pelagic ecosystems by conducting a meta-analysis of published studies, including both mesocosm experiments and time series of trophic-level covariance in unmanipulated systems (Figure 5.8). The results suggest that trophic cascades are uncommon in marine pelagic ecosystems. In enclosed pelagic mesocosms, experimental additions of zooplanktivorous fishes or invertebrates consistently depressed zooplankton abundance, but their effects cascaded down to enhance phytoplankton abundance only in nitrogen (N)-enriched (eutrophic) conditions. Conversely, experimental enrichment with nitrogen (a limiting resource for plant production in many shallow marine systems) consistently increased phytoplankton abundance but had no significant effect on zooplankton abundance. Thus, bottom-up processes also do not penetrate far through the food chain. The latter result was corroborated by time-series analysis of unmanipulated pelagic ecosystems—estimates of nitrogen availability and plant production were consistently correlated with phytoplankton abundance but not with abundances at higher trophic levels (Figure 5.8). Micheli's (1999) meta-analysis of the results from marine pelagic systems differs from a similar meta-analysis of experiments in fresh water, which showed that cascading effects of predators are common therein (Brett and Goldman 1996). More such experimental tests of the influence of abiotic forcing and food-web structure (including diversity) on interaction strength will be necessary before we can make informed predictions about how global environmental perturbations will change ecosystems.

Patterns in Interaction Strengths within Communities

Examples of trophic cascades illustrate that individual consumers can have strong and far-reaching impacts throughout an entire ecosystem. In the few cases where interaction strength has been estimated for a large number of species in a benthic food web, it has generally been found that most interactions are weak, having negligible impacts on populations of the participants, whereas a few have strong impacts on other taxa (Paine 1992; Raffaelli and Hall 1995; Wootton

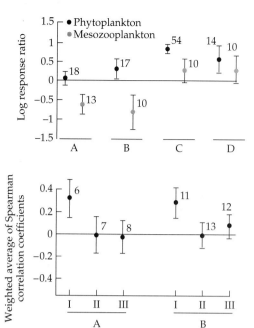

Figure 5.8 Trophic cascades are uncommon in marine pelagic ecosystems. *Top:* Log response (treatment biomass/control biomass) to addition of zooplanktivores (A and B) or inorganic nitrogen (C and D) in pelagic mesocosm experiments. In (A) both zooplanktivore and control treatments were conducted with unenriched water, whereas in (B) both treatments received nitrogen (N) enrichment. In (C) both unenriched (treatment) and N-enriched (control) treatments contained only phytoplankton and zooplankton, whereas in (D) both treatments also contained zooplanktivores. Plotted are the means + 95% CI from a meta-analysis (number of studies is shown above each mean). Note that zooplanktivore addition consistently depresses zooplankton biomass (A and B) but cascades down to increase phytoplankton only under N-enriched conditions (B). N addition consistently enhances phytoplankton, but not zooplankton, biomass 8, and D. *Bottom:* Correlations of winter nitrogen availability (left) and mean annual primary productivity (right) with biomass of (i) phytoplankton, (ii) mesozooplankton, and (iii) zooplanktivorous fishes in time series of unmanipulated pelagic systems. Consistent with the mesocosm results, N correlates only with phytoplankton and not with biomass of higher trophic levels. (After Micheli 1999.)

1997; Duffy and Hay 2000; Figure 5.9). Several plankton biologists also have recently emphasized that unique characteristics of particular species often have an overriding influence on energy and material fluxes in pelagic ecosystems; these investigators have called for a new focus on the biology of individual species in pelagic ecology (Lehman 1988, 1991; Banse 1994; Verity and Smetacek 1996). Thus, the degree of skew in interaction strengths within a community is of central importance to understanding the regulation of community structure and how structure will respond to perturbation.

Can we generalize about what characteristics of organism and environment result in keystone status, that is, which have disproportionately strong interaction strength? And how frequent is strong skew in interaction strength? Strong (1992) suggested that control by a few strong interactors, such as seen in the celebrated trophic cascades, is most likely in low-diversity systems where there is little functional re-

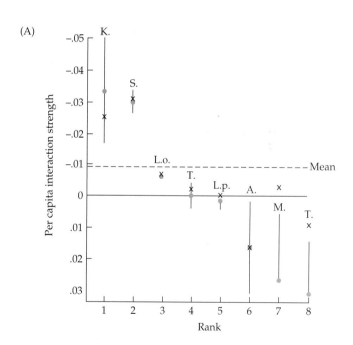

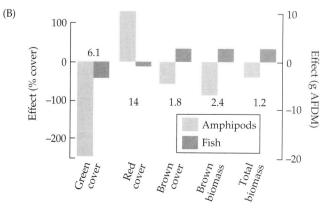

Figure 5.9 Two examples of variation in interaction strength among co-occurring consumers. (A) Variation in per capita interaction strength (impact on brown algae, the dominant space-occupiers in this system) among eight common invertebrate herbivores in a rocky intertidal community of Washington State. Per capita interaction strength = $(E - C)/Cd$, where E and C are brown algal sporeling densities in the herbivore removal and control treatments, respectively, and d is the number of individual herbivores in the C treatment. The chiton *Katharina tunicata* (K.) and the sea urchin *Strongylocentrotus purpuratus* (S.) strongly influence brown algal abundance, whereas effects of the other six species (all gastropods) are negligible. (After Paine 1992.) (B) Relative interaction strengths of omnivorous fish (*Diplodus holbrooki*) and herbivorous amphipods (mostly *Ampithoe longimana*) on major taxa of benthic space-occupiers, expressed per unit of herbivore biomass. Numbers show the ratio of amphipod to fish impacts for each algal taxon. Per-biomass impacts of the inconspicuous amphipods are up to an order of magnitude greater than those of the fish. AFDM = ash-free dry mass. (After Duffy and Hay 2000.)

dundancy among species and one or a few species dominate processes within each level. In more diverse systems, strong consumer impacts on one species are likely to be compensated by increased abundance in another species such that, for instance, aggregate biomass of that trophic level is little affected by the consumer. A key issue in evaluating this suggestion is the degree of functional redundancy among co-occurring species. Ecologists often have tended to approach functional diversity by lumping species with similar morphology and biology into guilds or functional groups (Littler and Littler 1980; Steneck and Watling 1982; Peters 1991) and such grouping has proven useful in many cases (e.g., Steneck and Dethier 1994). Yet even superficially similar consumer taxa can have substantially different impacts on community structure and function (Paine 1992; Wootton 1997; Duffy et al. 2001). For example, experimental comparisons of three similar-sized species of small crustacean grazers in an eelgrass bed showed that both grazer secondary production and per capita impacts on algal biomass varied by an order of magnitude among species and that their impacts on eelgrass differed in sign as well as magnitude (Duffy et al. 2001). Thus, effective generalization about how diversity and functional redundancy affect ecosystem structure and function will require more systematic empirical studies of how individual species traits translate to functional processes (see Lawton 1994).

Some Methodological Issues

Ecological research is necessarily constrained in spatial and temporal scale by a variety of social, economic, and other human factors. It is a well-known cliche, for example, that the duration of the average ecological study conforms closely to the duration of a dissertation project or funding cycle. What are we missing as a result?

The heightened awareness among both ecologists and the public of the importance of biodiversity has done little to change the fact that most ecologists focus on very small subsets of the communities they study. Kareiva (1994) observed that over 60% of the papers published in *Ecology* from 1981 to 1990 dealt with at most two species, and he emphasized the irony in our habit of using special jargon ("higher-order interactions," "indirect effects," and so on) to describe processes within more complete systems. This situation is worrisome: "[It is] clear that higher-order interactions and interaction modifications should be widespread in communities; but their presence is not what is at issue . . . . The question is whether a neglect of these higher-order effects causes us to get substantially wrong answers." In an exhaustive review of experimental studies in rocky intertidal habitats, Menge (1995) concluded that ~40% of the changes in community structure resulting from manipulation were indirect effects, and that each species was involved in more strong interactions and more indirect interactions as food-web diversity increased. The celebrated examples of trophic cascades, such as the sea otter–grazer–kelp interaction discussed above, surely have received widespread attention in part because they conform to simple, straightforward models of how we expect the world to function (e.g., Hairston et al. 1960). But the very fact that each new example of a trophic cascade generates attention suggests that such simple interaction chains are the exception in nature. Even these relatively simple examples illustrate dramatically a phenomenon with sobering implications for both basic and applied ecology, namely that perturbing an ecosystem may produce strong and unexpected effects on organisms that do not interact directly with the perturbed species. The apparent shift in feeding behavior of killer whales, and its pervasive consequences for coastal ecosystems in the northeast Pacific (see Figure 5.3), likely resulted from changes in abundance of the pinnipeds that formerly comprised the primary prey of killer whales; these changes in turn are probably related to human fishing pressure (Estes et al. 1998). Fishing pressure on top predators also appears to explain major shifts in marine community composition in several other putative cases of marine trophic cascades (Steneck 1998). And the changes in the north Pacific pelagic food web appear related to human stocking of predatory fish (Shiomoto et al. 1997). We need to know more about how such interactions ripple out across ecosystems if ecology is to be an effective tool for confronting environmental problems.

A related issue involves the extent to which we can extrapolate usually short-term manipulative experiments to longer-term field consequences. Most ecological manipulations are relatively short-term "press" experiments, adding or removing a component of the community and following the consequences. Such studies have shown repeatedly that consumers have major impacts on community composition, biomass, and so forth, in a variety of habitats and systems. Commonly, these results are extrapolated, usually implicitly, to conclusions about the likely states of the community in the presence and absence of the consumer. Leibold et al. (1997) noted that results of such manipulations are often at odds with correlational studies of unmanipulated ecosystems. They emphasized the potentially confounding, and underappreciated, role in such scenarios of species turnover—the change in prey-species composition that frequently accompanies large changes in consumer pressure in open systems over extended time periods. Changes in species composition—as from undefended to strongly defended prey in the presence of heavy consumer pressure—can largely compensate for the strong impacts of predators on, for example, prey trophic-level biomass, seen in short-term press experiments. Strong (1992) developed a similar argument to explain the relative rarity of well-defined trophic cascades in food webs with high species diversity. Understanding the role of species turnover will be important to predicting how open ecosystems will respond to accelerating global change.

ABIOTIC FORCING OF COMMUNITY STRUCTURE AND FUNCTION

The different traditions of benthic and pelagic marine ecology have resulted in distinctly different visions of what forces regulate biological structure and functional processes in the two realms (Lehman 1988; Verity and Smetacek 1996). Benthic ecologists have traditionally ascribed a primary role to the top-down processes of predation and grazing in regulating community structure, due in large part to the success and influence of the classic experimental studies of community structure on rocky intertidal shores, nearshore kelp beds, and coral reefs, where direct experimental manipulation of consumers produced dramatic changes in species distributions and community structure (Connell 1961; Randall 1961; Paine 1966, 1974; Dayton 1971; Ogden et al. 1973; Menge 1976; Lubchenco 1978; Carpenter 1986; Lewis 1986; Hay 1991a). In contrast, oceanographers working in the pelagic realm have emphasized bottom-up control of ecology through abiotic forcing of primary production and its transfer up the food chain (e.g., Parsons et al. 1984; Mann and Lazier 1991). This perspective is undoubtedly due in part to the microscopic sizes of the dominant pelagic organisms and the numerous difficulties of conducting controlled field experiments in the open ocean. Despite the history of different practical approaches in benthic and pelagic ecology, however, we see no clear a priori reason to believe that ecological processes governing community structure in the two realms are fundamentally different.

In recent years, these contrasting perspectives have begun to converge. Oceanographers increasingly emphasize the importance of top-down processes in the structure and function of pelagic communities (Hamner 1995; Verity and Smetacek 1996). And benthic ecologists increasingly recognize the pervasive influence on ecological structure and function of abiotic forcing, in the form of physical energy (Nixon 1988; Leigh et al. 1987), water flow (Leichter and Witman 1997; Leonard et al. 1998), factors affecting water-column productivity (Witman et al. 1993; Bustamante et al. 1995; Menge et al. 1997), and most particularly larval supply (Underwood and Denley 1984; Roughgarden et al. 1988; Grosberg and Levitan 1992). As is often the case with artificial dichotomies, it is increasingly clear that abiotic (bottom-up) forcing and consumer (top-down) regulation interact to mold ecological patterns and processes, rather than being alternative explanations (McQueen et al. 1986; Power 1992). A few examples from marine systems illustrate this interaction.

Menge et al. (1997) documented pervasive differences between two Oregon rocky intertidal communities that apparently reflect between-site differences in nearshore phytoplankton concentration, productivity, and suspended particulates. The site with higher phytoplankton production and biomass showed concomitantly higher recruitment, growth, and adult density of sessile (suspension-feeding) invertebrates, as well as higher density and feeding rates of both herbivores and predators. Ultimately the higher water-column productivity at this site appeared attributable to differences between the sites in the intensity of upwelling and circulation patterns that deliver phytoplankton and larvae to intertidal habitats.

Strikingly similar patterns were demonstrated in the intertidal community of a New England estuary as a function of water flow (Leonard et al. 1998). Comparison of three high-flow and three low-flow sites showed that flow resulted in a threefold higher flux of chlorophyll to the benthos at high-flow sites, with pervasive consequences for the intertidal community (Figure 5.10). As in the Oregon study, sites with higher phytoplankton flux supported higher cover of sessile organisms (mostly barnacles and mussels) and higher growth of passive suspension feeders, but also higher recruitment and adult abundances of both herbivores and predators. Growth of a carnivorous snail was also greater at high-flow sites. Thus, as in the Oregon study, enhanced recruitment and phytoplankton flux resulted in higher prey densities and growth rates, which "cascaded" up the food chain to predators. Flow simultaneously affected both production (larval supply) and predator effectiveness, so the strengths of bottom-up and top-down effects were correlated.

The patterns documented in these studies of intertidal communities thus suggest that bottom-up forcing resulted in higher abundances at all trophic levels, despite increasing the feeding rates of consumers. Although such "upward cascading" effects of resource supply have been shown or suggested in pelagic systems (e.g., Aebischer et al. 1990), they appear rare (see Figure 5.8; see discussion above). The marine data thus contrast with the simple model of Hairston et al. (1960; see also Oksanen et al. 1981), which predicts that resource subsidy affects alternate trophic levels most strongly, and with results of resource manipulation in some simple fresh-

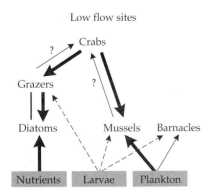
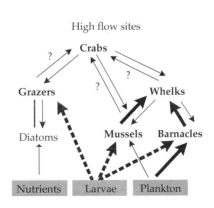

Figure 5.10 An example of abiotic forcing of community structure and function. The two food webs are schematic summaries derived from experimental studies of rocky intertidal communities at adjacent sites of low- and high-water flow in Rhode Island. Ascending and descending arrows indicate energy transfer and interaction effects, respectively. Biomass (font size) at all trophic levels, the relative strength of specific links in the food web (arrow width), and the presence of whelks differ among sites, responding to differences in the flux of planktonic larvae and resources (shown in boxes). (After Leonard et al. 1998.)

water food webs that support the model of Hairston et al. (Wootton and Power 1993). Meta-analyses of marine (Micheli 1999) and freshwater (Brett and Goldman 1997) results were in agreement, however, that resource subsidy generally has greatest impacts low in the food chain and diminishes upwards, rather than affecting alternate trophic levels.

These case studies indicate that, at least in some cases, productivity and the abiotic forces that regulate it can have pervasive effects on the organization of communities and the strength of consumer–prey interactions. Scaling up such processes to the broad sweep of evolutionary time, Vermeij (1987) has argued that consistently high energy availability (primary production and temperature) is the ultimate environmental factor limiting the "scope of adaptation," that is, the diversity and degree of expression of potential adaptations. The rationale is that where energy availability allows high metabolic rates, fitness differences among alternative phenotypes—whether genetic variants within a population, or co-occurring species—are greatest, and selection or interaction among them will be most intense. Moreover, high energy availability fosters larger population sizes, which are more likely to produce mutants, the raw material of adaptation. Although energy availability ultimately dictates the rate and scope of adaptation, Vermeij argues that competition and predation are the most important selective agents. As evidence, he offers the familiar patterns of increasing incidence of consumer pressure and defensive phenotypes with latitude, depth, and other ecological gradients that are correlated with energy availability.

SUMMARY

Consumer pressure is a pervasive influence on the evolution of populations and on the structure and function of nearly all marine communities and ecosystems. Studies conducted throughout temperate and tropical seas have shown that removal of herbivores or predators often produces profound changes in community organization, habitat structure, and ecosystem processes. The rise of humans as apex predators in an expanding range of marine (and terrestrial) habitats is similarly producing cascading impacts in both benthic and pelagic systems worldwide. Prey organisms may persist in the face of consumer pressure by escaping their consumers in time or space, by tolerating limited tissue loss to consumers, and/or by deterring consumers. Escape may be achieved through migration, rapid growth, other life history adaptations, or associations with defended neighbors. Tolerance often involves rapid growth or protection of reproductive structures in tissues inaccessible to consumers. Deterrence takes a wide array of forms, from deployment of diverse chemical compounds through various forms of structural armor. The generally positive association in time and space between intense consumer pressure and well-developed defenses implies that such defenses are costly to the prey and are selected against where consumer pressure is low. This cost hypothesis is supported by several experimental studies of phenotypically plastic or polymorphic species. In evolutionary time, consumers are important selective agents, molding the behavior, morphology, chemistry, and life history of prey organisms, particularly in the tropics where consumer pressure is especially intense. Many specific, and even obligate, associations between defended marine host species and undefended guest species appear to have evolved in response to intense predation pressure on the guest. Several unresolved issues deserve more attention in marine consumer–prey studies: What characteristics of organism and environment predispose a consumer to have strong (keystone) impacts on a community? Does the strength of consumer impacts in a system vary predictably as a function of community structure (species diversity, food chain length, and so on) or abiotic variables (physical energy, nutrient flux)? How do the results of typical experimental manipulations of marine communities scale up to broader scales in time and space, and how will evolutionary change and species turnover affect patterns seen in small-scale experiments? Answering such questions will be critical if we hope to predict, plan for, and mitigate the accelerating effects of global change on marine ecosystems.

ACKNOWLEDGMENTS

Our research during the preparation of this review has been supported by the National Science Foundation (OCE 95-21184 to JED and OCE-95-29784 to MEH), the Harry and Linda Teasley endowment to Georgia Tech, and the Virginia Institute of Marine Science. Discussions with Mark Bertness improved the manuscript. We are grateful to all. This is contribution # 2342 from the Virginia Institute of Marine Science.

LITERATURE CITED

Aebischer, N. J., J. C. Coulson and J. M. Colebrook. 1990. Parallel long-term trends across four marine trophic levels and weather. *Nature* 347: 753–755.

Alder, R. A. and R. Karban. 1994. Defended fortresses or moving targets? Another model of inducible defenses inspired by military metaphors. *Amer. Nat.* 144: 813–832.

Anderson, R. J. and B. Velimirov. 1982. An experimental investigation of the palatability of kelp bed algae to the sea urchin *Parechinus angulosus* Leske. *P.S.Z.N.I: Mar. Ecol.* 3: 357–73.

Appleton, R. D. and A. R. Palmer. 1988. Waterborne stimuli released by predatory crabs and damaged prey induce more predator-resistant shells in a marine gastropod. *Proc. Natl. Acad. Sci. USA* 85: 4387–4391.

Bakus, G. J. and G. Green. 1974. Toxicity in sponges and holothurians: A geographic pattern. *Science* 185: 951–953.

Baldwin, I. T. 1990. Herbivory simulation in ecological research. *Trends Ecol. Evol.* 5: 91–93.

Banse, K. 1994. Grazing and zooplankton production as key controls of phytoplankton production in the open ocean. *Oceanography* 7: 13–20.

Bell, S. S. 1991. Amphipods as insect equivalents? An alternative view. *Ecology* 72: 350–354.

Bertness, M. D. 1981. Crab shell-crushing predation and gastropod architectural defense. *J. Exp. Mar. Biol. Ecol.* 50: 213–230.

Bertness, M. D. and C. W. Cunningham. 1981. Crab shell-crushing predation and gastropod architectural defense. *J. Exp. Mar. Biol. Ecol.* 50: 213–230.

Bertness, M. D., S. D. Garrity and S. C. Levings. 1981. Predation pressure and gastropod foraging: A tropical–temperate comparison. *Evolution* 35: 995–1007.

Boettcher, A. A. and N. M. Targett. 1993. Role of polyphenolic molecular size in reduction of assimilation efficiency in *Xiphister mucosus*. *Ecology* 74: 891–903.

Bollens, S. M. and B. W. Frost. 1989a. Predator-induced diel vertical migration in a planktonic copepod. *J. Plankton Res.* 11: 1047–1065.

Bollens, S. M. and B. W. Frost. 1989b. Zooplanktivorous fish and variable diel vertical migration in the marine planktonic copepod *Calanus pacificus*. *Limnol. Oceanogr.* 34: 1072–1083.

Bolser, R. C. and M. E. Hay. 1996. Are tropical plants better defended? Palatability and defenses of temperate versus tropical seaweeds. *Ecology* 77: 2269–2286.

Brawley, S. H. 1992. Mesoherbivores. In D. M. John, S. J. Hawkins and J. H. Price (eds.), *Plant–Animal Interactions in the Marine Benthos*, pp. 235–263. Systematics Association Special Volume 46. Clarendon Press, Oxford.

Brawley, S. H. and W. H. Adey. 1981. The effect of micrograzers on algal community structure in a coral reef microcosm. *Mar. Biol.* 61: 167–177.

Brett, M. T. and C. R. Goldman. 1996. A meta-analysis of the freshwater trophic cascade. *Proc. Nat. Acad. Sci. USA* 93: 7723–7726.

Brett, M. T. and C. R. Goldman. 1997. Consumer versus resource control in freshwater pelagic food webs. *Science* 275: 384–386.

Brönmark, C. and J. G. Miner. 1992. Predator-induced phenotypical change in body morphology in crucian carp. *Science* 25: 1348–1350.

Buschmann, A. and B. Santelices. 1987. Micrograzers and spore release in *Iridaea laminarioides* (Rhodophyta: Gigartinales). *J. Exp. Biol. Ecol.* 108: 171–179.

Bustamante, R. H., G. M. Branch, S. Eekhout, B. Robertson, P. Zoutendyk, M. Schleyer, A. Dye, N. Hanekom, D. Keats, M. Jurd and C. McQuaid. 1995. Gradients of intertidal productivity around the coast of South Africa and their relationships with consumer biomass. *Oecologia* 102: 189–201.

Carpenter, R. C. 1986. Partitioning herbivory and its effects on coral reef algal communities. *Ecol. Monogr.* 56: 345–363.

Carpenter, R. C. 1988. Mass mortality of a Caribbean sea urchin: Immediate effects on community metabolism and other herbivores. *Proc. Natl. Acad. Sci. USA* 85: 511–514.

Carpenter, S. R., J. F. Kitchell and J. R. Hodgson. 1985. Cascading trophic interactions and lake productivity. *BioScience* 35: 634–639.

Cetrulo, G. L. and M. E. Hay. 2000. Activated chemical defenses in tropical versus temperate seaweeds. *Mar. Ecol. Prog. Ser.* In press.

Chanas, B. and J. R. Pawlik. 1995. Defenses of Caribbean sponges against predatory reef fish. II. Spicules, tissue toughness, and nutritional quality. *Mar. Ecol. Prog. Ser.* 127: 195–211.

Chanas, B. and J. R. Pawlik. 1996. Does the skeleton of a sponge provide a defense against predatory reef fish? *Oecologia* 107: 225–231.

Clifton, K. E. 1997. Mass spawning by green algae on coral reefs. *Science* 275: 1116–1118.

Coen, L. D. 1988. Herbivory by crabs and the control of algal epibionts on Caribbean host corals. *Oecologia* 75: 198–203.

Coley, P. D. and T. M. Aide. 1990. Comparison of herbivory and plant defenses in temperate and tropical broad-leaved forests. In P. W. Price, T. M. Lewinsotin, G. W. Fernandes and W. W. Besnon (eds.), *Plant–Animal Interactions: Evolutionary Ecology in Tropical and Temperate Regions*, pp. 25–49. Wiley, New York.

Connell, J. H. 1961. Effects of competition, predation by *Thais lapillus*, and other factors on natural populations of the barnacles *Balanus balanoides*. *Ecol. Monogr.* 31: 61–104.

Cronin, G. and M. E. Hay. 1996a. Within-plant variance in seaweed chemical defenses: Optimal defense theory versus the growth-differentiation balance hypothesis. *Oecologia* 105: 361–368.

Cronin, G. and M. E. Hay. 1996b. Susceptibility to herbivores depends on recent history of both the plant and animal. *Ecology* 77: 1531–1543

Cronin, G., V. J. Paul, M. E. Hay and W. Fenical. 1997. Are tropical herbivores more resistant than temperate herbivores to seaweed chemical defenses? Diterpenoid metabolites from *Dictyota acutiloba* as feeding deterrents for tropical versus temperate fishes and urchins. *J. Chem. Ecol.* 23: 289–302.

Dawkins, R. and J. R. Krebs. 1979. Arms races between and within species. *Proc. Royal Soc. London, Series B* 205: 489–511.

Dayton, P. K. 1971. Competition, disturbance, and community organization: The provision and subsequent utilization of space in a rocky intertidal community. *Ecol. Monogr.* 41, 351–389.

Dayton, P. K. 1975. Experimental evaluation of ecological dominance in a rocky intertidal algal community. *Ecol. Monogr.* 45: 137–159.

Dayton, P. K. 1985. The structure and regulation of some South American kelp communities. *Ecol. Monogr.* 55: 447–68.

Dayton, P. K., M. J. Tegner, P. B. Edwards and K. L. Riser. 1998. Sliding baselines, ghosts, and reduced expectations in kelp forest communities. *Ecol. Appl.* 8: 309–322.

Deason, E. E. and T. J. Smayda. 1982. Ctenophore–zooplankton–phytoplankton interactions in Narragansett Bay, Rhode Island, USA, during 1972–1977. *J. Plankton Res.* 4: 203–217.

Duffy, J. E. 1992. Host use patterns and demography in a guild of tropical sponge-dwelling shrimps. *Mar. Ecol. Prog. Ser.* 90: 127–138.

Duffy, J. E. 1996. Resource partitioning, sibling species and the radiation of sponge-dwelling alpheid shrimp. *Biol. J. Linnean Soc.* 58: 307–324.

Duffy, J. E. and M. E. Hay. 1990. Seaweed adaptations to herbivory. *BioScience* 40: 368–376.

Duffy, J. E. and M. E. Hay. 1991a. Amphipods are not all created equal: A reply to Bell. *Ecology* 72: 354–358.

Duffy, J. E. and M. E. Hay. 1991b. Food and shelter as determinants of food choice by an herbivorous marine amphipod. *Ecology* 72: 1286–1298.

Duffy, J. E. and M. E. Hay 1994. Herbivore resistance to seaweed chemical defense: The roles of mobility and predation risk. *Ecology* 75: 1304–1319.

Duffy, J. E. and M. E. Hay. 2000. Strong impacts of grazing amphipods on the organization of a benthic community. *Ecol. Monogr.* 70: 237–263.

Duffy, J. E. and V. J. Paul. 1992. Prey nutritional quality and the effectiveness of chemical defenses against tropical reef fishes. *Oecologia* 90: 333–339.

Duffy, J. E., K. S. Macdonald, J. M. Rhode and J. D. Parker. 2001. Grazer diversity, functional redundancy, and productivity in seagrass beds: An experimental test. *Ecology.* In press.

Duggins, D. O., S. A. Simenstad and J. A. Estes. 1989. Magnification of secondary production by kelp detritus in coastal marine ecosystems. *Science* 245: 170–173.

Dunlap, M. and J. R. Pawlik. 1996. Video-monitored predation by Caribbean reef fishes on an array of reef and mangrove sponges. *Mar. Biol.* 126: 117–123.

Estes, J. A. and D. O. Duggins. 1995. Sea otters and kelp forests in Alaska: Generality and variation in a community ecological paradigm. *Ecol. Monogr.* 65:75–100.

Estes, J. A. and J. F. Palmisano. 1974. Sea otters: Their role in structuring nearshore communities. *Science* 185: 1058–1060.

Estes, J. A. and P. D. Steinberg. 1988. Predation, herbivory, and kelp evolution. *Paleobiology* 14: 19–36.

Estes, J. A., M. T. Tinker, T. M. Williams and D. F. Doak. 1998. Killer whale predation on sea otters linking oceanic and nearshore ecosystems. *Science* 282: 473–476.

Faulkner, D. J. 1984. Marine natural products: Metabolites of marine algae and herbivorous marine molluscs. *Natural Prod. Rep.* 1: 251–280.

Faulkner, D. J. 1994. Marine natural products. *Natural Prod. Rep.* 11: 355–394.

Faulkner, D. J. 1999. Marine natural products. *Natural Prod. Rep.* 16: 155–198.

Fenical, W. 1980. Distributional and taxonomic features of toxin-producing marine algae. In I. A. Abbott, M. S. Foster and L. F. Eklund (eds.), *Pacific Seaweed Aquaculture*, pp. 144–151. California Sea Grant College Program, Institute of Marine Resources, University of California, La Jolla.

Fenical, W. 1993. Chemical studies of marine bacteria: Developing a new resource. *Chem. Rev.* 93: 1673–1683.

Gaines, S. D. and J. Lubchenco. 1982. A unified approach to marine plant–herbivore interactions. II. Biogeography. *Annu. Rev. Ecol. Syst.* 13: 111–138.

Gerhart, D. J., D. Rittschof and S. W. Mayo. 1988. Chemical ecology and the search for marine antifoulants. *J. Chem. Ecol.* 14: 1905–1917.

Glynn, P. W. 1980. Defense by symbiotic Crustacea of host corals elicited by chemical cues from predator. *Oecologia* 47: 287–290.

Glynn, P. W. 1981. Acanthaster population regulation by a shrimp and a worm. *Proc. Fourth Int. Coral Reef Symp.* 2: 607–612.

Glynn, P. W. 1983. Increased survivorship in corals harboring crustacean symbionts. *Mar. Biol. Lett.* 4: 105–111.

Grosberg, R. K. and D. R. Levitan. 1992. For adults only? Supply-side ecology and the history of larval biology. *Trends Ecol. Evol.* 7: 130–133.

Haahtela, I. 1984. A hypothesis of the decline of the bladder wrack (*Fucus vesiculosus* L.) in SW Finland in 1975–1981. *Limnologica* 15: 345–350.

Hairston, N. G., F. E. Smith and L. B. Slobodkin. 1960. Community structure, population control and competition. *Amer. Nat.* 94: 421–425.

Hamner, W. M. 1995. Predation, cover, and convergent evolution in epipelagic oceans. *Mar. Freshwat. Behav. Physiol.* 26: 71–89.

Harris, L. G., A. W. Ebeling, D. R. Laur and R. J. Rowley. 1984. Community recovery after storm damage: A case of facilitation in primary succession. *Science* 224: 1336–1338.

Harrison, P. L., R. C. Babcock, G. D. Bull, J. K. Oliver, C. C. Wallace and B. L. Willis. 1984. Mass spawning in tropical reef corals. *Science* 223: 1186–1189.

Harvell, C. D. 1984. Predator-induced defense in a marine bryozoan. *Science* 224: 1357–1359.

Harvell, C. D. 1986. The ecology and evolution of inducible defenses in a marine bryozoan: Cues, costs, and consequences. *Amer. Nat.* 128: 810–823.

Harvell, C. D. 1990. The ecology and evolution of inducible defenses. *Q. Rev. Biol.* 65: 323–340.

Harvell, C. D. 1992. Inducible defenses and allocation shifts in a marine bryozoan. *Ecology* 73: 1567–1576.

Harvell, C. D., W. Fenical and C. H. Greene. 1988. Chemical and structural defenses of Caribbean gorgonians (*Pseudopterogorgia* spp.). I. Development of an in situ feeding assay. *Mar. Ecol. Prog. Ser.* 49: 287–294.

Hay, M. E. 1981a. Herbivory, algal distribution, and the maintenance of between-habitat diversity on a tropical fringing reef. *Amer. Nat.* 118: 520–540.

Hay, M. E. 1981b. The functional morphology of turf-forming seaweeds: Persistence in stressful marine habitats. *Ecology* 62: 739–750.

Hay, M. E. 1984. Predictable spatial escapes from herbivory: how do these affect the evolution of herbivore resistance in tropical marine communities? *Oecologia* 64: 396–407.

Hay, M. E. 1985. Spatial patterns of herbivore impact and their importance in maintaining algal species richness. *Proc. Fifth Int. Coral Reef Congr.* 4: 29–34.

Hay, M. E. 1986. Associational plant defenses and the maintenance of species diversity: Turning competitors into accomplices. *Amer. Nat.* 128: 617–641.

Hay, M. E. 1991a. Fish-seaweed interactions on coral reefs: effects of herbivorous fishes and adaptations of their prey. In P. F. Sale (ed.), *The Ecology of Fishes on Coral Reefs*, pp. 96–119. Academic Press, San Diego, CA.

Hay, M. E. 1991b. Marine-terrestrial contrasts in the ecology of plant chemical defenses against herbivores. *Trends Ecol. Evol.* 6: 362–365.

Hay, M. E. 1992. The role of seaweed chemical defenses in the evolution of feeding specialization and in the mediation of complex interactions. In V. J. Paul (ed.), *Ecological Roles for Marine Natural Products*, pp. 93–118. Comstock Press, Ithaca, NY.

Hay, M. E. 1996. Marine chemical ecology: What is known and what is next? *J. Exp. Mar. Biol. Ecol.* 200: 103–134.

Hay, M. E. 1997. The ecology and evolution of seaweed-herbivore interactions on coral reefs. *Coral Reefs* 16 (Suppl): S67–S76.

Hay, M. E. and W. Fenical. 1988. Marine plant-herbivore interactions: the ecology of chemical defense. *Annu. Rev. Ecol. Syst.* 19: 111–145.

Hay, M. E. and W. Fenical. 1996. Chemical ecology and marine biodiversity: Insights and products from the sea. *Oceanography* 9: 10–20.

Hay, M. E. and P. D. Steinberg. 1992. The chemical ecology of plant-herbivore interactions in marine versus terrestrial communities. In J. Rosenthal and M. Berenbaum (eds.), *Herbivores: Their Interaction with Secondary Metabolites, Evolutionary and Ecological Processes*, pp. 371–413. Academic Press, San Diego.

Hay, M. E., W. Fenical and K. Gustafson. 1987a. Chemical defense against diverse coral reef herbivores. *Ecology* 68: 1581–1591

Hay, M. E., J. E. Duffy, C. A. Pfister and W. Fenical. 1987b. Chemical defense against different marine herbivores: Are amphipods insect equivalents? *Ecology* 68: 1567–1580.

Hay, M. E., V. J. Paul, S. M. Lewis, K. Gustafson, J. Tucker and R. Trindell. 1988. Can tropical seaweeds reduce herbivory by growing at night? Diel patterns of growth, nitrogen content, herbivory, and chemical versus morphological defenses. *Oecologia* 75: 233–245.

Hay, M. E., J. R. Pawlik, J. E. Duffy and W. Fenical. 1989. Seaweed–herbivore–predator interactions: Host-plant specialization reduces predation on small herbivores. *Oecologia* 81: 418–427.

Hay, M. E., J. E. Duffy, V. J. Paul, P. E. Renaud and W. Fenical. 1990a. Specialist herbivores reduce their susceptibility to predation by feeding on the chemically-defended seaweed *Avrainvillea longicaulis*. *Limnol. Oceanogr.* 35: 1734–1743.

Hay, M. E., J. E. Duffy and W. Fenical. 1990b. Host-plant specialization decreases predation on a marine amphipod: an herbivore in plant's clothing. *Ecology* 71: 733–743.

Hay, M. E., Q. E. Kappel and W. Fenical. 1994. Synergisms in plant defenses against herbivores: Interactions of chemistry, calcification, and plant quality. *Ecology* 75: 1714–1726.

Hay, M. E., J. J. Stachowicz, E. Cruz-Rivera, S. Bullard, M. S. Deal and N. Lindquist. 1998. Bioassays with marine and freshwater macroorganisms. In K. F. Haynes and J. G. Millar (eds.), *Methods in Chemical Ecology*, Volume 2, *Bioassay Methods*, pp. 39–141. Chapman and Hall, New York.

Hays, G. C. 1995. Zooplankton avoidance activity. *Nature* 376: 650.

Hays, G. C., C. A. Proctor, A. W. G. John and A. J. Warner. 1994. Interspecific differences in the diel vertical migration of marine copepods: The implications of size, color, and morphology. *Limnol. Oceanogr.* 39: 1621–1629.

Hays, G. C., R. P. Harris and R. N. Head. 1997. The vertical nitrogen flux caused by zooplankton diel vertical migration. *Mar. Ecol. Prog. Ser.* 160: 57–62.

Heck, K. L., Jr. and K. A. Wilson. 1987. Predation rates on decapod crustaceans in latitudinally separated seagrass communities: A study of spatial and temporal variation using tethering techniques. *J. Exp. Mar. Biol. Ecol.* 107: 87–100.

Hixon, M. A. and W. N. Brostoff. 1983. Damselfish as keystone species in reverse: Intermediate disturbance and diversity of reef algae. *Science* 220: 511–513.

Hixon, M. A. and W. N. Brostoff. 1996. Succession and herbivory: Effects of differential fish grazing on Hawaiian coral reef algae. *Ecol. Monogr.* 66: 67–90.

Hobson, E. S. and J. R. Chess. 1976. Trophic interactions among fish and zooplankters near shore at Santa Catalina Island, California. *Fish. Bull.* 74: 567–598.

Hughes, T. P. 1994. Catastrophes, phase shifts, and large-scale degradation of a coral reef. *Science* 256: 1547–1551.

Huntley, M., P. Sykes, S. Rohan and V. Martin. 1986. Chemically-mediated rejection of dinoflagellate prey by the copepods *Calanus pacificus* and *Paracalanus parvus*: Mechanism, occurrence and significance. *Mar. Ecol. Prog. Ser.* 28: 105–120.

Irelan, C. D. and M. H. Horn. 1991. Effects of macrophyte secondary chemicals on food choice and digestive efficiency of *Cebidichthys violaceus* (Girard), an herbivorous fish of temperate marine waters. *J. Exp. Mar. Biol. Ecol.* 153: 179–194.

Jackson, J. B. C. 1997. Reefs before Columbus. *Coral Reefs* 16 (Suppl): S23–S32.

Jeanne, R. L. 1979. A latitudinal gradient in rates of ant predation. *Ecology* 60: 1211–1224.

Kangas, P., H. Autio, G. Hällfors, H. Luther, Å. Niemi and H. Salemaa. 1982. A general model of the decline of *Fucus vesiculosus* at Tvärminne, south coast of Finland in 1977–1981. *Acta Botanica Fennica* 118: 1–27.

Karban, R. and L. T. Baldwin. 1997. Induced responses to herbivory. University of Chicago Press, Chicago.

Kareiva, P. 1994. Higher order interactions as a foil to reductionist ecology. *Ecology* 75: 1527–1528.

King, G. M. 1986. Inhibition of microbial activity in marine sediments by a bromophenol from a hemichordate. *Nature* 323: 257–259.

Klumpp, D. W., A. D. McKinnon and C. N. Mundy. 1988. Motile cryptofauna of a coral reef: Abundance, distribution and trophic potential. *Mar. Ecol. Prog. Ser.* 45: 95–108.

Lawton, J. H. 1994. What do species do in ecosystems? *Oikos* 71: 367–374.

Lehman, J. T. 1988. Ecological principles affecting community structure and secondary production by zooplankton in marine and freshwater environments. *Limnol. Oceanogr.* 33 (part 2): 931–945.

Lehman, J. T. 1991. Interacting growth and loss rates: The balance of top-down and bottom-up controls in plankton communities. *Limnol. Oceanogr.* 36: 1546–1554.

Leibold, M. A., J. M. Chase, J. B. Shurin and A. L. Downing. 1997. Species turnover and the regulation of trophic structure. *Annu. Rev. Ecol. Syst.* 28: 467–494.

Leichter, J. J. and J. D. Witman. 1997. Water flow over subtidal rock walls: Relation to distributions and growth rates of sessile suspension feeders in the Gulf of Maine. *J. Exp. Mar. Biol. Ecol.* 209: 293–307.

Leigh, E. G., Jr., R. T. Paine, J. F. Quinn and T. H. Suchanek. 1987. Wave energy and intertidal productivity. *Proc. Natl. Acad. Sci. USA* 84: 1314–1318.

Leonard, G. H., J. M. Levine, P. R. Schmidt and M. D. Bertness. 1998. Flow-driven variation in intertidal community structure in a Maine estuary. *Ecology* 79: 1395–1411.

Leonard, G. H., M. D. Bertness and P. O. Yund. 1999. Crab predation, waterborne cues, and inducible defenses in the blue mussel, *Mytilus edulis. Ecology* 80: 1–14.

Levin, D. A. and B. M. York. 1978. The toxicity of plant alkaloids: An ecogeographic perspective. *Biochem. Syst. Ecol.* 6: 61–76.

Lewis, S. M. 1985. Herbivory on coral reefs: Algal susceptibility to herbivorous fishes. *Oecologia* 65: 370–375.

Lewis, S. M. 1986. The role of herbivorous fishes in the organization of a Caribbean reef community. *Ecol. Monogr.* 56: 183–200.

Lewis, S. M., J. N. Norris and R. B. Searles. 1987. The regulation of morphological plasticity in tropical reef algae by herbivory. *Ecology* 68: 636–641.

Lindquist, N. and M. E. Hay. 1995. Can small rare prey be chemically defended? the case for marine larvae. *Ecology* 76: 1347–1358.

Lindquist, N. and M. E. Hay. 1996. Palatability and chemical defenses of marine invertebrate larvae. *Ecol. Monogr.* 66: 431–450.

Lindquist, N., M. E. Hay and W. Fenical. 1992. Chemical defense of ascidians and their conspicuous larvae. *Ecol. Monogr.* 62: 547–568.

Littler, M. M. and D. S. Littler. 1980. The evolution of thallus form and survival strategies in benthic marine macroalgae: Field and laboratory tests of a functional form model. *Amer. Nat.* 116: 25–44.

Littler, M. M., D. S. Littler and P. R. Taylor. 1983a. Evolutionary strategies in a tropical barrier reef system: Functional-form groups of marine macroalgae. *J. Phycol.* 19: 229–237.

Littler, M. M., P. R. Taylor and D. S. Littler. 1983b. Algal resistance to herbivory on a Caribbean barrier reef. *Coral Reefs* 2: 111–118.

Littler, M. M., P. R. Taylor and D. S. Littler. 1986. Plant defense associations in the marine environment. *Coral Reefs* 5: 63–71.

Littler, M. M., P. R. Taylor and D. S. Littler. 1989. Complex interactions in the control of coral zonation on a Caribbean reef flat. *Oecologia* 80: 331–340.

Littler, M. M., D. S. Littler and P. R. Taylor. 1995. Selective herbivore increases biomass of its prey: A chiton–coralline reef-building association. *Ecology* 76: 1666–1681.

Lively, C. M. 1986a. Competition, comparative life histories and the maintenance of shell dimorphism in the acorn barnacle *Chthamalus anisopoma. Ecology* 67: 858–864.

Lively, C. M. 1986b. Predator-induced shell dimorphism in the acorn barnacle *Chthamalus anisopoma. Evolution* 40: 232–242.

Longhurst, A. R., A. Bedo, W. G. Harrison, E. J. H. Head, E. P. Horne, B. Irwin and C. Morales. 1989. NFLUX: A test of vertical nitrogen flux by diel migrant biota. *Deep-Sea Res.* 36: 1705–1719.

Lubchenco, J. 1978. Plant species diversity in a marine intertidal community: Importance of herbivore food preference and algal competitive abilities. *Amer. Nat.* 112: 23–29.

Lubchenco, J. 1983. *Littorina* and *Fucus:* Effects of herbivores, substratum heterogeneity, and plant escapes during succession. *Ecology* 64: 1116–1123.

Lubchenco, J. and J. Cubit. 1980. Heteromorphic life histories of certain marine algae as adaptations to variations in herbivory. *Ecology* 61: 676–687.

Mann, K. H. and J. R. N. Lazier. 1991. *Dynamics of Marine Ecosystems: Biological–Physical Interactions in the Oceans.* Blackwell Scientific, Oxford.

McClintock, J. B. 1994. An overview of the chemical ecology of Antarctic marine invertebrates. The Ireland Lecture 1993, University of Alabama at Birmingham.

McClintock, J. B. and Janssen. 1990. Pteropod abduction as a chemical defence in a pelagic Antarctic amphipod. *Nature* 346: 462–464.

McClintock, J. B., D. P. Swenson, D. K. Steinberg and A. A. Michaels. 1996. Feeding-deterrent properties of common oceanic holoplankton from Bermudian waters. *Limnol. Oceanogr.* 41: 798–801.

McCook, L. J. 1996. Effects of herbivores and water quality on *Sargassum* distribution on the Great Barrier Reef: Cross-shelf transplants. *Mar. Ecol. Prog. Ser.* 139: 179–192.

McCook, L. J. 1997. Effects of herbivory on zonation of *Sargassum* spp. within fringing reefs of the central Great Barrier Reef. *Mar. Biol.* 129: 713–722.

McCook, L. J., I. R. Price and D. W. Klumpp. 1997. Macroalgae on the Great Barrier Reef: Causes or consequences, indicators or models of reef degradation? *Proc. 8th Int. Coral Reef Symp.* 2: 1851–1856.

McQueen, D. J., J. R. Post and E. L. Mills. 1986. Trophic relationships in freshwater pelagic ecosystems. *Canad. J. Fish. Aquat. Sci.* 43: 1571–1581.

Menge, B. A. 1976. Organization of the New England rocky intertidal community: Role of predation, competition and environmental heterogeneity. *Ecol. Monogr.* 46: 355–393.

Menge, B. A. 1995. Indirect effects in marine rocky intertidal interaction webs: Patterns and importance. *Ecol. Monogr.* 65: 21–74.

Menge, B. A. and J. Lubchenco. 1981. Community organization in temperate and tropical rocky intertidal habitats: Prey refuges in relation to consumer pressure gradients. *Ecol. Monogr.* 51: 429–450.

Menge, B. A., J. Lubchenco and J. R. Ashkenas. 1985. Diversity, heterogeneity and consumer pressure in a tropical rocky intertidal community. *Oecologia* 65: 394–405.

Menge, B. A., B. A. Daley, P. A. Wheeler, E. Dahlhoff, E. Sanford and P. T. Strub. 1997. Benthic-pelagic links and rocky intertidal communities: Bottom-up effects on top-down controls? *Proc. Natl. Acad. Sci. USA* 94: 14530–14535.

Meyer, K. D. and V. J. Paul. 1995. Variation in secondary metabolite and aragonite concentrations in the tropical green seaweed *Neomeris annulata:* Effects on herbivory by fishes. *Mar. Biol.* 122:. 537–545.

Micheli, F. 1999. Eutrophication, fisheries, and consumer-resource dynamics in marine pelagic ecosystems. *Science* 285: 1396–1398.

Miller, M. W. 1998. Coral/seaweed competition and the control of reef community structure within and between latitudes. *Oceanogr. Mar. Biol. Annu. Rev.* 36: 65–96.

Morgan, S. G. 1987. Morphological and behavioral antipredatory adaptations of decapod zoeae. *Oecologia* 73: 393–400.

Morgan, S. G. 1989. Adaptive significance of spination in estuarine crab zoeae. *Ecology* 70: 464–482.

Morgan, S. G. 1990. Impact of planktivorous fishes on dispersal, hatching, and morphology of estuarine crab larvae. *Ecology* 71:1639–1652.

Morgan, S. G. and J. H. Christy. 1997. Planktivorous fishes as selective agents for reproductive synchrony. *J. Exp. Mar. Biol. Ecol.* 209: 89–101.

Nixon, S. W. 1988. Physical energy inputs and the comparative ecology of lake and marine ecosystems. *Limnol. Oceanogr.* 33:1005–1025.

Ogden, J. C., R. A. Brown and N. Salesky. 1973. Grazing by the echinoid *Diadema antillarum:* Formation of halos around West Indian patch reefs. *Science* 182:715–717.

Oksanen, L., S. D. Fretwell, J. Arruda and P. Niemelä. 1981. Exploitation ecosystems in gradients of primary productivity. *Amer. Nat.* 118: 240–261.

Padilla, D. K. 1985. Structural resistance of algae to herbivores: A biomechanical approach. *Mar. Biol.* 90: 103–109.

Paine, R. T. 1966. Food web complexity and species diversity. *Amer. Nat.* 100: 65–75.

Paine, R. T. 1969. A note on trophic complexity and community stability. *Amer. Nat.* 103: 91–93.

Paine, R. T. 1974. Intertidal community structure: Experimental studies on the relationship between a dominant competitor and its principal predator. *Oecologia* 15: 93–120.

Paine, R. T. 1992. Food-web analysis through field measurements of per capita interaction strength. *Nature* 355: 73–75.

Palmer, A. R. 1979. Fish predation and the evolution of gastropod shell sculpture: Experimental and geographic evidence. *Evolution* 33: 697–713.

Palmer, A. R. 1982. Predation and parallel evolution: Recurrent parietal plate reduction in balanomorph barnacles. *Paleobiology* 8: 31–44.

Parsons, T. R., M. Takahashi and B. Hargrave. 1984. *Biological Oceanographic Processes*, 3rd ed. Pergamon Press, Oxford.

Patton, W. K. 1976. Animal associates of living reef corals. In O. A. Jones and R. Endean (eds.), *Biology and Geology of Coral Reefs*, Vol. III, *Biology 2*, pp. 1–43. Academic Press, New York.

Paul, V. J. 1987. Feeding deterrent effects of algal natural products. *Bull. Mar. Sci.* 41: 514–522.

Paul, V. J. 1992. *Ecological Roles of Marine Natural Products*. Comstock Press, Ithaca, NY.

Paul, V.J. 1997. Secondary metabolites and calcium carbonate as defenses of calcareous algae on coral reefs. *Proc. 8th Int. Coral Reef Symp.* 1: 707–711.

Paul, V. J. and W. Fenical. 1986. Chemical defense in tropical green algae, order Caulerpales. *Mar. Ecol. Prog. Ser.* 33: 255–264.

Paul, V. J. and M. E. Hay. 1986. Seaweed susceptibility to herbivory: Chemical and morphological correlates. *Mar. Ecol. Prog. Ser* 33: 255–264.

Paul, V. J. and K. L. Van Alstyne. 1988. Chemical defense and chemical variation in some tropical Pacific species of *Halimeda* (Halimedaceae; Chlorophyta). *Coral Reefs* 6: 263–269.

Paul, J. and K. L. Van Alstyne. 1992. Activation of chemical defenses in the tropical green algae *Halimeda* spp. *J. Exp. Mar. Biol. Ecol.* 160: 191–203.

Pauly, D., V. Christensen, J. Dalsgaard, R. Froese and F. Torres, Jr. 1998. Fishing down marine food webs. *Science* 279: 860–863.

Pawlik, J. R. 1983. A sponge-eating worm from Bermuda: *Branchiosyllis oculata* (Polychaeta, Syllidae). *P. S. Z. N. I. Mar. Ecol.* 4: 65–79.

Pawlik, J. R. 1993. Marine invertebrate chemical defenses. *Chem. Rev.* 93: 1911–1922.

Pawlik, J. R., B. Chanas, R. J. Toonen and W. Fenical. 1995. Defenses of Caribbean sponges against predatory reef fish. I. Chemical deterrency. *Mar. Ecol. Prog. Ser.* 127: 183–194.

Paya, I. and B. Santelices. 1989. Macroalgae survive digestion by fishes. *J. Phycol.* 25: 186–188.

Pennings, S. C. and V. J. Paul. 1992. Effect of plant toughness, calcification andchemistry on herbivory by *Dolabella auricularia*. *Ecology* 73: 1606–1619.

Pennings, S. C., M. P. Puglisi, T. J. Pitlik, A. C. Himaya and V. J. Paul. 1996. Effects of secondary metabolites and CaCO$_3$ on feeding by surgeonfishes and parrotfishes: Within-plant comparisons. *Mar. Ecol. Prog. Ser.* 134: 49–58.

Pennings, S. C., E. L. Siska and M. D. Bertness. In press. Latitudinal differences in plant palatability in Atlantic coast salt marshes. *Ecology*.

Peters, R. H. 1991. *A Critique for Ecology*. Cambridge University Press, Cambridge.

Pfister, C. A. 1992. Costs of reproduction in an intertidal kelp: Patterns of allocation and life history consequences. *Ecology* 73: 1586–1596.

Pfister, C. A. and M. E. Hay. 1988. Associational plant refuges: convergent patterns in marine and terrestrial communities result from differing mechanisms. *Oecologia* 77: 118–129.

Pitlik, T. J. and V. J. Paul 1997. Effects of toughness, calcite level, and chemistry of crustose coralline algae (Rhodophyta: Corallinales) on grazing by the parrotfish *Chlorurus sordidus*. *Proc. 8th Int. Coral Reef Symp.* 2: 701–706.

Porter, K. G. 1976. Enhancement of algal growth and productivity by grazing zooplankton. *Science* 192: 1332–1334.

Power, M. E. 1992. Top-down and bottom-up forces in food webs: Do plants have primacy? *Ecology* 73: 733–746.

Raffa, K. F. and E. B. Smalley. 1995. Interaction of pre-attack and induced monoterpene concentrations in host conifer defense against bark beetle-fungal complexes. *Oecologia* 102: 285–295.

Raffaelli, D. G. and S. J. Hall. 1995. Assessing the relative importance of trophic links in food webs. In G. Polis and K. Winemiller (eds.), *Foodwebs: Integration of Patterns and Dynamics*, pp. 185–191. Chapman and Hall, New York.

Randall, J. E. 1961. Overgrazing of algae by herbivorous marine fishes. *Ecology* 42: 812.

Randall, J. E. 1965. Grazing effects on seagrasses by herbivorous reef fishes in the West Indies. *Ecology* 46: 255–260.

Reimer, O. and M. Tedengren. 1996. Phenotypical improvement of morphological defences in the mussel *Mytilus edulis* induced by exposure to the predator *Asterias rubens*. *Oikos* 75: 383–390.

Renaud, P. E., M. E. Hay and T. M. Schmitt. 1990. Interactions of plant stress and herbivory: Interspecific variation in the susceptibility of a palatable versus an unpalatable seaweed to sea urchin grazing. *Oecologia* 82: 217–226.

Reznick, D. N. and H. A. Bryga. 1996. Life-history evolution in guppies (*Poecilia reticulata*: Poeciliidae). V. Genetic basis of parallelism in life histories. *Amer. Nat.* 147: 339–359.

Reznick, D. N., F. H. Rodd and M. Cardenas. 1996. Life-history evolution in guppies (*Poecilia reticulata*: Poeciliidae). IV. Parallelism in life-history phenotypes. *Amer. Nat.* 147: 319–338.

Reznick, D. N., F. H. Shaw, F. H. Rodd and R. G. Shaw. 1997. Evaluation of the rate of evolution in natural populations of guppies (*Poecilia reticulata*). *Science* 275: 1934–1937.

Roughgarden, J., S. Gaines and H. Possingham. 1988. Recruitment dynamics in complex life cycles. *Science* 241: 1460–1466.

Safina, C. 1995. The world's imperiled fish. *Sci. Amer.* 273: 46–53.

Santelices, B. and R. Ugarte. 1987. Algal life-history strategies and resistance to digestion. *Mar. Ecol. Prog. Ser* 35: 267–275.

Schupp, P. J. and V. J. Paul. 1994. Calcification and secondary metabolites in tropical seaweeds: Variable effects on herbivorous fishes. *Ecology* 75: 1172–1185.

Seeley, R. H. 1986. Intense natural selection caused a rapid morphological transition in a living marine snail. *Proc. Natl. Acad. Sci. USA* 83: 6897–6901.

Shanks, A. L. and W. M. Graham. 1988. Chemical defense in a scyphomedusa. *Mar. Ecol. Prog. Ser* 45: 81–86.

Shaw, B. A., P. J. Harrison and R. J. Anderson. 1995. Feeding deterrent properties of apo-fucoxanthinoids from marine diatoms. II. Physiology of production of apo-fucoxanthinoids by the marine diatoms *Phaeodactylum tricornutum* and *Thalassiosira pseudonana*, and their feeding deterrent effects on the copepod *Tigriopus californicus*. *Mar. Biol.* 124: 473–481.

Shiomoto, A., K. Tadakoro, K. Nagasawa and Y. Ishida. 1997. Trophic relations in the subarctic North Pacific ecosystem: Possible feeding effect from pink salmon. *Mar. Ecol. Prog. Ser* 150: 75–85.

Simenstad, C. A., J. A. Estes and K. W. Kenyon. 1978. Aleuts, sea otters, and alternate stable state communities. *Science* 200: 403–411.

Sotka, E. E., M. E. Hay and J. D. Thomas. 1999. Host-plant specialization by a non-herbivorous amphipod: Advantages for the amphipod and costs for the seaweed. *Oecologia* 118: 471–482.

Stachowicz, J. J. and M. E. Hay. 1996. Facultative mutualism between an herbivorous crab and its coralline algal host: Advantages of eating noxious seaweeds. *Oecologia* 105: 377–387.

Stachowicz, J. J. and M. E. Hay. 1999. Reducing predation through chemically-mediated camouflage: Indirect effects of plant defenses on herbivores. *Ecology* 80: 495–509.

Stachowicz, J. J. and M. E. Hay. 2000. Geographic variation in camouflaging behavior by a decorator crab: Southern populations specialize on chemically noxious decorations. *Amer. Nat.* 156. In press.

Stearns, S. C. 1992. *The Evolution of Life Histories*. Oxford University Press, Oxford.

Steinberg, P. D. 1992. Geographical variation in the interaction between marine herbivores and brown algal secondary metabolites. In V. J. Paul (ed.), *Ecological Roles for Marine Secondary Metabolites*, pp. 51–92. Comstock Press, Ithaca, NY.

Steinberg, P. D. 1994. Lack of short-term induction of phlorotannins in the Australasian brown algae *Ecklonia radiata* and *Sargassum vestitum*. *Mar. Ecol. Prog. Ser* 112: 129–133.

Steinberg, P. D. 1995. Interaction between the canopy dwelling echinoid *Holopneustes purpurescens* and its host kelp *Ecklonia radiata*. *Mar. Ecol. Prog. Ser* 127: 169–181.

Steinberg, P. D. and I. A. Van Altena. 1992. Tolerance of marine invertebrate herbivores to brown algal phlorotannins in temperate Australasia. *Ecol. Monogr.* 62: 189–222.

Steinberg, P. D., J. A. Estes and F. C. Winter. 1995. Evolutionary consequences of food chain length in kelp forest communities. *Proc. Natl. Acad. Sci. USA* 92: 8145–8148.

Steneck, R. S. 1982. A limpet–coralline alga association: Adaptations and defenses between a selective herbivore and its prey. *Ecology* 63: 507–522.

Steneck, R. S. 1983. Escalating herbivory and resulting adaptive trends in calcareous algal crusts. *Paleobiology* 9: 44–61.

Steneck, R. S. 1986. The ecology of coralline algal crusts: Convergent patterns and adaptive strategies. *Annu. Rev. Ecol. Syst.* 17: 273–303.

Steneck, R. S. 1988. Herbivory on coral reefs: A synthesis. *Proc. 6th Int. Coral Reef Symp.* 1: 37–49.

Steneck, R. S. 1990. Herbivory and the evolution of nongeniculate coralline algae (Rhodophyta, Corallinales) in the North Atlantic and North Pacific. Evolutionary biogeography of the marine algae of the North Atlantic. *NATO Advanced Science Institutes Series* G22: 107–129.

Steneck, R. S. 1992. Plant–herbivore coevolution: A reappraisal from the marine realm and its fossil record. In D. J. John, S. J. Hawkins and J. H. Price (eds.), *Plant–Animal Interactions in the Marine Benthos*, pp. 477–491. Systematics Association Special Volume 46. Clarendon Press, Oxford.

Steneck, R. S. 1998. Human influences on coastal ecosystems: Does overfishing create trophic cascades? *Trends Ecol. Evol.* 13: 429–430.

Steneck, R. S. and W. H. Adey. 1976. The role of environment in control of morphology in *Lithophyllum congestum*, a Caribbean algal ridge builder. *Botanica Marina* 19: 197–215.

Steneck, R. S. and M. N. Dethier. 1994. A functional group approach to the structure of algal-dominated communities. *Oikos* 69: 476–498.

Steneck, R. S. and L. Watling. 1982. Feeding capabilities and limitations of herbivorous molluscs: A functional group approach. *Mar. Biol.* 68: 299–319.

Strong, D. R. 1992. Are trophic cascades all wet? Differentiation and donor control in speciose ecosystems. *Ecology* 73: 747–754.

Tallamy, D. W. and M. J. Raupp. 1991. *Phytochemical Induction by Herbivores*. John Wiley and Sons, New York.

Targett, T. E. and N. M. Targett. 1990. Energetics of food selection by the herbivorous parrotfish *Sparisoma radians*: Roles of assimilation efficiency, gut evacuation rate, and algal secondary metabolites. *Mar. Ecol. Prog. Ser.* 66: 13–21.

Tegner, M. J. and P. K. Dayton. 1987. El Niño effects on southern California kelp forest communities. *Adv. Ecol. Res.* 17: 243–279.

Trussell, G. C. and L. D. Smith. 2000. Induced defenses in response to an invading crab predator: An explanation of historical and geographic phenotypic change. *Proc. Natl. Acad. Sci. USA* 97: 2123–2127.

Underwood, A. J. and E. J. Denley. 1984. Paradigms, explanations, and generalizations in models for the structure of intertidal communities on rocky shores. In D. R. Strong, Jr., D. Simberloff, L. G. Abele and A. B. Thistle (eds.), *Ecological Communities: Conceptual Issues and the Evidence*, pp. 151–180. Princeton University Press, Princeton, NJ.

Underwood, A. J. and P. Jernakoff. 1981. Interactions between algae and grazing gastropods in the structure of a low-shore intertidal algal community. *Oecologia* 4: 221–233.

Van Alstyne, K. L. 1988. Herbivore grazing increases polyphenolic defenses in the intertidal brown alga *Fucus distichus*. *Ecology* 69: 655–663.

Van Alstyne, K. L. and V. J. Paul. 1992. Chemical and structural defenses in the sea fan *Gorgonia ventalina*: Effects against generalist and specialist predators. *Coral Reefs* 11: 155–159.

Van Alstyne, K. L., C. R. Wylie, V. J. Paul and K. Meyer. 1992. Antipredator defenses in tropical Pacific soft corals (Coelenterata, Alcyonacea). *Biol. Bull.* 182: 231–240.

Van Alstyne, K. L., C. R. Wylie and V. J. Paul. 1994. Antipredator defenses in tropical Pacific soft corals (Coelenterata, Alcyonacea). II. The relative importance of chemical and structural defenses in three species of *Sinularia*. *J. Exp. Mar. Biol. Ecol.* 178: 17–34.

Verity, P. G. and V. Smetacek. 1996. Organism life cycles, predation, and the structure of marine pelagic ecosystems. *Mar. Ecol. Prog. Ser.* 130: 277–293.

Vermeij, G. J. 1976. Interoceanic differences in vulnerability of shelled prey to crab predation. *Nature* 260: 135–136.

Vermeij, G. J. 1977. The Mesozoic marine revolution: Evidence from snails, predators and grazers. *Paleobiology* 3: 245–258.

Vermeij, G. J. 1978. *Biogeography and Adaptation: Patterns of Marine Life*. Harvard University Press, Cambridge, MA.

Vermeij, G. J. 1983. Intimate associations and coevolution in the sea. In D. J. Futuyma and M. Slatkin (eds.), *Coevolution*, pp. 311–327. Sinauer Associates, Sunderland, MA.

Vermeij, G. J. 1987. *Evolution and Escalation: An Ecological History of Life*. Princeton University Press, Princeton, NJ.

Vermeij, G. J. 1992. Time of origin and biogeographical history of specialized relationships between northern marine plants and herbivorous molluscs. *Evolution* 46: 657–664.

Vermeij, G. J. and J. D. Currey. 1980. Geographical variation in the strength of thaidid snail shells. *Biol. Bull.* 158: 383–389.

Wallerstein, B. R. and R. C. Brusca. 1982. Fish predation: A preliminary study of its role in the zoogeography and evolution of shallow water idoteid isopods (Crustacea: Isopoda: Idoteidae). *J. Biogeogr.* 9: 135–150.

Wiebe, P. H., L. P. Madin, L. R. Haury, G. R. Harbison and L. M. Philbin. 1979. Diel vertical migration by *Salpa aspersa* and its potential for large-scale particulate organic matter transport to the deep-sea. *Mar. Biol.* 53: 249–255.

Witman, J. D., J. J. Leichter, S. J. Genovese and D. A. Brooks. 1993. Pulsed phytoplankton supply to the rocky subtidal zone: Influence of internal waves. *Proc. Natl. Acad. Sci. USA* 90: 1686–1690.

Wolfe, G. V., M. Steinke and G. O. Kirst. 1997. Grazing activated chemical defense in a unicellular marine alga. *Nature* 387: 894–897.

Woodin, S. A., R. L. Marinelli and D. E. Lincoln. 1993. Allelochemical inhibition of recruitment in a sedimentary assemblage. *J. Chem. Ecol.* 19: 517–530.

Wootton, J. T. 1995. Effects of birds on sea urchins and algae: A lower-intertidal trophic cascade. *Ecoscience* 2: 321–328.

Wootton, J. T. 1997. Estimates and tests of per capita interactions strength: Diet, abundance, and impact of intertidally foraging birds. *Ecol. Monogr.* 67: 45–64.

Wootton, J. T. and M. E. Power. 1993. Productivity, consumers, and the structure of a river food chain. *Proc. Natl. Acad. Sci. USA* 90: 1384–1387.

Wylie, C. R. and V. J. Paul. 1989. Chemical defenses in three species of *Sinularia* (Coelenterata, Alcyonacea): Effects against generalist predators and the butterflyfish *Chaetodon unimaculatus* Bloch. *J. Exp. Mar. Biol. Ecol.* 129: 141–160.

Zipser, E. and G. J. Vermeij. 1978. Crushing behavior of tropical and temperate crabs. *J. Exp. Mar. Biol. Ecol.* 31: 155–172.

chapter 6

The Larval Ecology of Marine Communities

Steven G. Morgan

There has been a resurgence of interest in marine larvae since the recent rediscovery of their role in determining the structure of benthic communities. I have been asked to discuss community ecology from a larval perspective without dwelling on larval recruitment, which is being covered by Underwood (this volume). This is a difficult assignment, because community ecologists have emphasized larval recruitment and postsettlement processes—that is, how larvae modify patterns of community structure that are widely believed to be established during the benthic phase of the life cycle. Larval recruitment occurs during the last moments of larval life, leaving us to ponder the relevance of events occurring earlier in the life cycle to community ecology. Ultimately, the "black box" of marine early life histories must be cracked to address this question. The intrinsically difficult study of microscopic, widely dispersing larvae in the ocean has historically yielded few compelling data, and dubious conventional wisdom has taken the place of scientific evidence. The prevailing view was, and to a large extent still is, that larvae are hapless victims of their environment, being overwhelmed by "stochastic planktonic processes" that result in erratic recruitment to adult populations. Because the safe return of larvae to adult habitats was perceived as random and unpredictable, many investigators were convinced that benthic processes regulated marine populations and communities, and that dispersal was the driving force behind the evolution of larvae. However, this line of thinking does not fully explain the observed dynamics and structures of marine populations and communities.

The goals of this chapter are to (1) draw attention to the need for a much better understanding of how events occurring throughout the planktonic phase of the life cycle affect benthic communities, (2) marshal the available evidence to address this issue, and (3) suggest avenues for future research. I will start by placing community ecology in the context of the history of larval ecology to show that ecologists have been wrestling with the same difficult problems throughout the twentieth century.

TEMPESTS IN A TEAPOT

> The polemic aspects of ecology and evolution are perhaps to be expected as consequences of a loss of patience with complexity.
>
> L. B. Slobodkin 1986

The lessons of the past often are overlooked in the rush to make our way in the challenging field of ecology. Fortunately, Young (1990a) provided an invaluable historical perspective on larval ecology that placed today's research in the context of past discoveries. I have summarized key developments in marine community ecology from the larval perspective in Table 6.1.

During the nineteenth century, larval mortality, behavior, and postsettlement mortality were suggested as potential mechanisms in regulating marine populations, and recruitment studies were undertaken. These studies became a mainstay of fisheries biology at the turn of the century in order to elucidate the variation in stock–recruitment relationships of commercially important species (reviewed by Frank and Leggett 1994). Investigators also began to show that larval forms were subject to natural selection and were adapted to the planktonic environment.

A strong relationship between community ecology and larval ecology did not blossom until the 1930s and 1940s. Manipulative field and laboratory experiments were conducted

TABLE 6.1   Key developments in marine community ecology from the larval perspective. The inclusion of the larval phase of the life cycle into community theory is shown relative to the history of larval ecology.

1800s	Importance of larval mortality, larval behavior, and postsettlement mortality in regulating benthic populations all proposed
1900s–1920s	Early studies on larval adaptations including vertical migration, retention, defense, feeding, delayed metamorphosis, and settlement behavior
1930s–1940s	European investigators show that larval supply, settlement behavior, and postsettlement mortality all can be important in regulating populations and communities
1950s–1970s	British investigators emphasize larval behavior in regulating populations and communities
	Thorson emphasizes the importance of larval mortality and adult–larval interactions in regulating populations and communities
	Passive versus active larval retention debated
1960s–1970s	American investigators emphasize benthic processes in regulating populations and communities
1980s–1990s	Larval supply reemerges as a strong structuring force
	Passive versus active settlement debated
	Pluralism emerges: multiple processes are increasingly viewed as important in regulating populations and communities, except for perhaps in soft-sediment communities, where benthic processes are still paramount
2000–	Determine the roles of larval (output, transport, mortality, supply, settlement) and benthic (top-down and bottom-up effects, including positive interactions, indirect effects, and vagile species) processes in regulating community dynamics and structure over large spatial and long temporal scales

in Europe that documented the effects of recruitment on the structure of intertidal communities. Investigators discovered consistent vertical and horizontal patterns in these communities that were variously thought to be maintained by reliable differences in larval availability, larval settlement behavior, or postsettlement mortality due to physiological stress, competition, or predation. Furthermore, they realized the necessity of monitoring survival right after settlement to determine whether larval settlement behavior or early postsettlement behavior established recruitment patterns.

The importance of larval settlement behavior in maintaining community structure was emphasized from the 1950s through the 1970s under the leadership of British researchers. Chemically and physically mediated settlement behaviors were documented experimentally in the laboratory, including (1) preferences for conspecifics, substrates (e.g., microbial films, algae, sediments, rough surfaces) and darkness; (2) delayed metamorphosis in the absence of suitable settlement sites; and (3) decreased discrimination among settlement sites by older larvae (see early reviews by Thorson 1950; Meadows and Campbell 1972; Scheltema 1974; Crisp 1976). These behaviors were believed to be critical in enhancing the survival and reproduction of the many sessile and sedentary organisms that have little or no capability of adjusting their position after metamorphosing into juveniles. Proposed benefits of settlement site selection included reduced physiological stress, dislodgment, competition, and predation and increased fertilization and feeding success. Moreover, larval

behavior was shown to play a key role in establishing the initial distributions and abundances of benthic invertebrates inhabiting subtidal and intertidal communities. Meanwhile, Thorson (1950, 1966) emphasized the importance of larval mortality and adult–larval interactions in regulating benthic populations and communities. Many studies also were conducted on larval retention in estuaries, and a debate grew over whether larvae regulated their horizontal transport by vertically migrating in response to tidal currents (e.g., Carriker 1951; Bousfield 1955; Haskin 1964; Wood and Hargis 1971; Sandifer 1975) or were transported passively (e.g., Manning and Whaley 1954; Banse 1955; DeWolf 1973).

The importance of larvae in maintaining community structure was not lost on Connell (1961), who imported the European field approach to America. The approach flourished and spread quickly from rocky intertidal communities to other marine communities throughout the world. During the last 40 years, the evolution of community ecology has been punctuated by controversies surrounding the role of larvae in structuring marine communities. Some of this contentiousness was avoidable, as I will argue by briefly reviewing the ecology of rocky intertidal, soft-sediment, hard-substrate, and coral reef communities from a larval perspective.

The role of larvae in regulating rocky intertidal communities is reviewed first, because the paradigm of marine community regulation was developed largely for these communities. Soft-sediment communities are then reviewed, because there is no reason to expect that these communities are organized in the same way as rocky intertidal communities, or that larval settlement is as important in regulating them, given the fundamental differences in the physical nature of the substrate (reviewed by Peterson 1979, 1991; Wilson 1991). Rocky shore and soft-sediment communities appear to differ in several fundamental ways. In contrast to rocky shore communities, competition in soft-sediment communities does not appear to be a dominant process. Rather than competing for limited surface space, most soft-sediment residents escape encounters in the third dimension by living in the substrate. As a result, overgrowth, undercutting, crushing, and ultimately competitive exclusion are not evident. Reduced competition also results in less distinct zonation patterns across the intertidal zone. Assortative deposition of sediments may be more important in structuring these communities. The intertidal gradient in shear stress from waves results in the deposition of coarse sediments high on the shore and fine sediments low on the shore. Consequently, deposit feeders are common in rich organic sediments low on the shore, whereas suspension feeders are common high on the shore, where faster currents deliver more food. Upper limits of species' distributions also may be less distinct because the sediment buffers residents from desiccation, thermal stress, and ultraviolet radiation damage during low tide, although animals still must cope with reduced aerobic respiration and feeding time. This reduction in physiological stress coupled with the mobility of the animals also suggests that positive interactions will be less important than on rocky shores (see Bertness and Leonard 1991), although added structure from burrows creates habitat for other species just as mussel beds do. Lower limits of species distributions also may be less distinct on mudflats and sandflats, where marine predators may forage effectively in quiet waters, although this may not be the case on wave-exposed beaches. Monopolization of space by several dominant species is unusual in soft-sediment communities for two more reasons: first, residents alter the substrate, and second, open patches are rapidly colonized by neighboring adults and juveniles rather than by larvae. This results in highly patchy distributions of burrowing deposit feeders, burrowing suspension feeders, and tube builders of various trophic types. I also highlight recent progress in understanding the effects of events occurring during each phase of the early life history of these species on the population dynamics of their communities.

Research on other types of marine communities has followed a trajectory similar to that of work on rocky intertidal and soft-sediment communities, and little would be gained by providing thorough reviews of each of them. Instead, I emphasize new lessons that have been learned by researchers working on hard-substrate and coral reef communities. Research on both of these community types has been distinguished by controversial discussions of the role of nonequilibrium processes in regulating them, and I review the evidence that chance recruitment structures them. My goal is to show how events occurring during the larval and adult phases of the life cycle are linked, and how this linkage may affect the dynamics and structure of marine communities.

PAROCHIALISM AND RELIGION AMID ROCKY INTERTIDAL COMMUNITIES?

Connell's (1961) experiments on British shores showed that larval settlement was not as important as postsettlement mortality in establishing interspecific differences in vertical distributions of barnacles. These results opened the way for researchers to concentrate on compelling adult interactions while minimizing the role of messy larval recruitment in regulating rocky intertidal and other benthic communities. In so doing, they tacitly assumed that any variation in settlement would be damped by postsettlement mortality. However, larvae were still seen as important in maintaining species diversity. The eventual monopolization of space by dominant competitors was prevented by disturbance that opened space for rapid colonization by inferior competitors (Dayton 1971; Sousa 1979, 1984). Competitive inferiors persisted by growing rapidly and reproducing before they were outcompeted for space by slowly growing, slowly colonizing dominant species.

Dayton (1979, 1984) questioned the easy transference of this paradigm to other communities that may function quite differently from rocky intertidal communities. He also perceived a tendency to overlook considerable unexplained variation in rocky intertidal communities and a failure to search for new, rigorous tests of the paradigm to account for this variation. It was becoming increasingly clear that competition and predation were much stronger structuring forces in some regions of the world than in others, and that differences occurred even among sites within regions (Menge and Lubchenco 1981; Underwood and Denley 1984; Foster 1990; Menge 1992; Menge et al. 1994).

Much of the unexplained variation in rocky intertidal communities and in the strengths of structuring forces appeared to arise from differences in larval settlement patterns. Based on their work with barnacles in Australia, Underwood and Denley (1984) suggested that variations in settlement were important in regulating communities in which settlement was light, in contrast to previously studied regions of the world where settlement was heavy. Fewer settlers resulted in lower densities, fewer competitive interactions, and more open space; consequently, pulses of larvae settling on the substrate were more likely to survive and contribute to the structure of the community. Caffey (1985) also found that settlement variation was important in structuring barnacle populations in Australia, and recommended that it be incorporated into theory. Connell (1985) was prompted to reexamine previously published data to determine whether settlement or postsettlement mortality was more important in regulating rocky intertidal communities. The data set was limited because most investigators measured recruitment, which already reflects early postsettlement mortality, rather than settlement, which does not. Conclusions may be biased if survival is not measured soon after settlement because substantial mortality occurs shortly thereafter. Nevertheless, Connell was able to tentatively conclude that both larval availability and postsettlement mortality were important in regulating rocky intertidal communities. As Underwood and Denley (1984) suggested, survival of juveniles was independent of adult density when settlement was light, but it was density dependent when settlement was heavy. A modified version of the paradigm was emerging.

A series of studies from the coast of central California produced results consistent with these insights (Gaines and Roughgarden 1985, 1987; Roughgarden et al. 1988). These timely, high-profile studies revived interest in larval recruitment to benthic communities that is still unflagging today. Menge (1991) was prompted to reanalyze his 15-year-old data set after incorporating settlement densities, and he developed a revised model of community regulation that took settlement intensity into account. New studies by Sutherland (1990a) and Minchinton and Scheibling (1991, 1993) also determined that larval settlement was more important at low larval densities and that postsettlement density-dependent processes were more important at high densities. Raimondi (1990) took the emerging paradigm a step further by suggesting that variation in settlement of barnacles has pronounced effects on adult populations even at the highest densities, and since then, many other investigators have shown the importance of larval settlement in regulating rocky intertidal populations (reviewed by Booth and Brosnan 1995). Thus, after more than half a century, we have come full circle and established with greater certainty the importance of larval availability, settlement behavior, and postsettlement mortality in structuring rocky intertidal communities (see also perspectives by Young 1987, 1990a; Underwood and Fairweather 1989; Grosberg and Levitan 1992).

Further improvement in our understanding of population dynamics in rocky intertidal communities will be achieved largely by understanding events that occur earlier in the life cycle. We still know very little about the critical events that occur in the water column, and we cannot fully understand the population dynamics of marine species by studying only the benthic phase of the life cycle. Reproductive output, fertilization success, larval survival, and larval transport all determine the strength of recruitment into adult populations, and therefore we cannot understand larval supply merely by measuring the effect of settlement on adult distributions and abundances (reviewed by Morgan 1995a). The remainder of this section is dedicated to highlighting recent progress made in each of these areas, working backward through the life cycle from larval supply to reproductive output (Figure 6.1).

The relationship between larval supply and settlement in rocky intertidal communities is best known for barnacles. As expected, the inshore availability of cyprids during their last moments of postlarval life usually is highly correlated with the distribution and abundance of settlers (Grosberg 1982; Gaines and Roughgarden 1985, 1987; Minchinton and Scheibling 1991; Bertness et al. 1992; Miron et al. 1995; Noda et al. 1998). However, there may be times when larval settlement is limited by availability of suitable settlement sites even when competent larvae are abundant nearby. Suitable settlement sites may be limited due to preemption (Crisp 1976; Bertness 1989), recent disturbance (McCook and Chapman 1993), or the abundance of competitors (Johnson 1989; Young 1989) or predators (Garbarini 1936; Grosberg 1981; Young and Chia 1981).

Just as the availability of competent larvae is usually related to the number of settlers, spatial and temporal patterns of larval availability inshore may be largely determined by reliable physical transport processes that return larvae from offshore waters to the shoreline (reviewed by Shanks 1995a). The reliability of these physical processes enables organisms to adapt to them, enhancing the return of larvae to shore (reviewed by Morgan 1995a). Larval transport behavior is not yet well known for rocky shore species, except for estuarine barnacles, which usually are retained in estuaries despite net

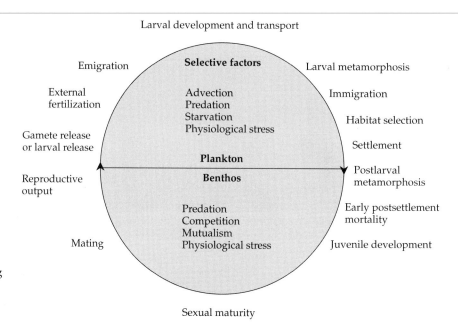

Figure 6.1 Critical junctures in the life cycles of marine animals with planktonic development. Key selective factors operating in the plankton and benthos that can determine reproductive output and recruitment success also are shown.

seaward flow (Bousfield 1955; Kunze 1995). One example of a reliable physical process that returns larvae to rocky shore communities is internal wave propagation. These waves occur regularly in some areas and may be absent in others, which may partially explain settlement patterns along the shoreline (Pineda 1994). Similarly, internal waves may typically propagate during one phase of the tidal amplitude cycle, which partially explains variation in temporal patterns of settlement along the shoreline (Pineda 1995). Even if physical processes are not predictable, their effects on larval transport can account for spatial and temporal variation in settlement. For example, prevailing winds usually drove barnacle larvae toward the downwind side of a bay, resulting in greater settlement there, and larvae settled only episodically on the lee shore when winds reversed direction (Bertness et al. 1996). As a second example, a 9-year record of settlement variation by barnacles in a bay and on the adjacent open coast was explained by variation in river runoff, which affected the number of larvae that were retained within the bay or exported into coastal waters; retention of barnacle larvae was ineffective when flushing rates were high (Gaines and Bertness 1992). As our understanding of coastal physical processes improves, it will be easier to identify areas where larvae are retained or exported to other areas, and the connection between larval transport, larval supply, settlement, and recruitment into adult populations will become clearer.

Recent progress has been made in relating broadscale variation in larval transport patterns to densities of juveniles and adults along the shoreline of the west coast of the United States. Differences in upwelling intensity between central California and the Pacific Northwest (Figure 6.2) apparently affect larval transport and settlement intensity in the two regions (Parrish et al. 1981; Roughgarden et al. 1988). In turn, regional differences in settlement intensity may affect the availability of free space and the intensity of interactions in rocky intertidal communities (Connolly and Roughgarden 1998). During spring and summer, when larvae of many rocky intertidal species develop, wind-driven upwelling may transport larvae released along the shoreline offshore in seaward-flowing surface waters. Larvae may accumulate at a front where the upwelled water meets the equatorward-flowing California Current. Upwelling periodically relaxes when prevailing equatorward winds diminish, and barnacle larvae at the front may then be transported shoreward (Farrell et al. 1991). Upwelling fronts move faster across a narrower continental shelf (~20 km) and remain there over more of the upwelling season along the coast of California, whereas they are confined to the inner portion of a broader shelf (~40 km) and may move onshore more often in the Pacific Northwest. Stronger, more persistent upwelling occurs during more months in central and northern California than in the Pacific Northwest (Parrish et al. 1981; Huyer 1983), resulting in regional differences in settlement and in the intensity of benthic interactions.

Upwelling intensity also varies within regions and partially explains mesoscale variation in larval density patterns along the shoreline. Upwelling is strongest at headlands,

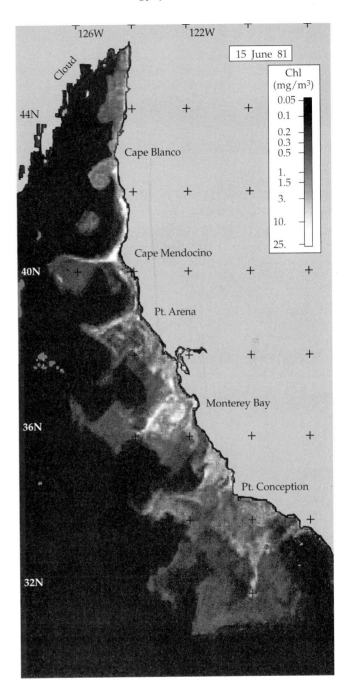

Figure 6.2 Differences in upwelling intensity between California and the Pacific Northwest as reflected by satellite images of sea surface chlorophyll on 15 June 1981. Upwelling is stronger, more persistent, and occurs during more months in central and northern California than in the Pacific Northwest. Consequently, larvae released in rocky shore communities may be carried farther offshore and settle less densely in California than in the Pacific Northwest. Upwelling is strongest at headlands, which are more common along the coastline of California than in the Pacific Northwest, and should generate more spatial variation in transport and settlement patterns. (From Strub et al. 1991.)

where the equatorward current is deflected offshore (Huyer 1983; Strub et al. 1991), and larvae may be exported offshore throughout much of the upwelling season (Ebert and Russell 1988; Ebert et al. 1994; Wing et al. 1995a,b, 1998). Gyres form in the lee of headlands, and larvae may be retained there during upwelling (Graham et al. 1992; Graham and Largier 1997; Wing et al. 1998). During relaxation events, larvae are transported poleward from these retention areas by longshore currents (Wing et al. 1995a,b). Headlands are more common along the coastline of California than in the Pacific Northwest, which should generate more spatial variation in transport and settlement patterns.

Although recent progress has been made in relating larval transport to adult population dynamics, we still know very little about the relative contribution of larval survival (reviewed by Morgan 1995a). Quantifying larval survival and the factors that contribute to it is particularly problematic, and will remain so until we track cohorts of microscopic larvae from hatching to settlement while monitoring environmental conditions. I previously suggested a variety of approaches to address this problem (Morgan 1995a), and more approaches can be obtained from the fisheries literature. We lag well behind fisheries biologists, who have emphasized the effect of larval mortality on population dynamics throughout the twentieth century, and considerable progress could be made by adapting their approaches to rocky shore species. Those interested in mining the fisheries literature may begin with several recent reviews on larval mortality (Bailey and Houde 1989; Heath 1992; Frank and Leggett 1994).

We also should have a much better understanding of the effect of variation in habitat quality on reproductive output than we do. Habitats across a species' range differ in quality, generating spatial variation in abundance, reproduction, growth, and mortality. Reproduction exceeds mortality in high-quality "source" habitats, and mortality exceeds reproduction in low-quality "sink" habitats (reviewed by Hastings and Harrison 1994; Gaines and Lafferty 1995; Dias 1996; Palmer et al. 1996). To understand the root cause of mosaic communities across rocky shore landscapes, we need to determine how variation in productivity generates differences in the basic demographics of the member species. Abundance, growth, and mortality of juveniles and adults often are measured, but productivity and reproduction usually are not documented. Reproductive output can be monitored easily, but investigators may have been discouraged by the long history of poor stock–recruitment relationships for commercial species. Presumably the consequences of variation in production for rocky shore communities have received little rigorous attention due to the difficulty of experimentally manipulating primary production (Bertness et al. 1991). Nevertheless, spatial and temporal differences in the productivity of phytoplankton, zooplankton, and macroalgae along shorelines mean that food availability for filter-feeding members of the benthic community varies in space and time (Meidel and Scheibling 1998; see Figure 6.2). In turn, differences in food availability affect growth and mortality due to physiological stress, competition, and predation, which are all size-dependent processes. Moreover, large animals generally are more fecund, perhaps contributing to spatial variation in larval supply. If larvae typically settle near their parents, then repro-

ductive output and settlement will tend to be coupled regardless of the productivity of the area. Alternatively, if most larvae settle far from parental populations, then productive areas yielding many larvae will contribute a disproportionate number of settlers within the region. In either case, predictable variation in productivity may have cascading effects on populations and generate diverse community patterns (Bertness et al. 1991; Menge 1992). For example, regional differences in reproductive output might explain the greater settlement densities of barnacles in the Pacific Northwest than in California just as well as would differential larval transport processes in the two regions (Roughgarden et al. 1988). If productivity along shorelines is greater in California than in the Pacific Northwest, then higher reproductive output should increase the potential number of settlers, reduce free space, and increase the intensity of benthic interactions in that region (Connolly and Roughgarden 1998).

Several recent studies have indicated that variation in productivity along the shoreline may have a dramatic influence on reproductive output, population dynamics, and community structure. Bertness et al. (1991) determined that food supply was predictably greater in a bay than along the adjacent open coast and resulted in greater growth and reproduction there, which may have strongly influenced larval supply and benthic interactions. Along the Oregon coast, greater phytoplankton abundance at a site resulted in higher food supplies for filter-feeding mussels and barnacles, which in turn generated greater recruitment, abundance, and growth (Menge 1992; Menge et al. 1994). This increase in secondary production fostered greater abundances of predatory sea stars and higher predation rates. Thus, community structure may depend on productivity and its influence on the abundances of organisms at lower trophic levels as well as predation by higher trophic levels (Figure 6.3). Like nutrients and suspended food, larvae are an external input that subsidizes benthic populations and can be considered to be a "bottom-up" influence (Leonard et al. 1998). Leonard et al. also found that that "top-down" and "bottom-up" forces were coupled and varied with flow rate in an estuary. High consumer pressure best explained patterns at low-flow sites, and nutrients, food, growth, and recruitment dominated at high-flow sites, where predators were inhibited from feeding by currents. They further suggested that hydrodynamics may commonly decouple predation and resources wherever physical processes responsible for variation in top-down forces also act as a strong bottom-up force. Thus, both bottom-up and top-down processes appear to regulate rocky shore communities, as they do freshwater and terrestrial habitats (Carpenter 1988; Hunter and Price 1992; Power 1992). It is time to begin fully exploring the effect of bottom-up influences on variation in rocky intertidal communities and to set aside disputes over the importance of these two sets of processes.

The long history of rocky intertidal ecology reveals the cyclical nature of ecological research, as interest in one piece of the puzzle or another waxed and waned. Again, we will not fully understand this complex community solely by ex-

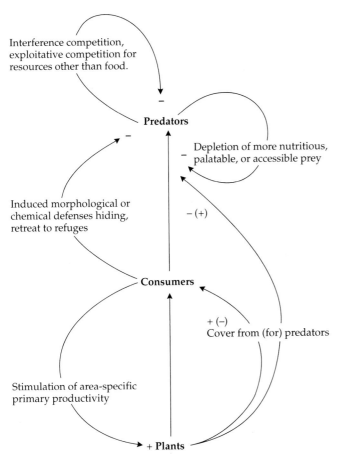

Interference competition, exploitative competition for resources other than food.

Predators

Depletion of more nutritious, palatable, or accessible prey

Induced morphological or chemical defenses hiding, retreat to refuges

– (+)

Consumers

+ (–)
Cover from (for) predators

Stimulation of area-specific primary productivity

+ Plants

Figure 6.3 Mechanisms (curved arrows) modulating bottom-up (straight arrows) and top-down processes in food chains. (From Power 1992.)

amining the effect of larval settlement on interspecific competition and predation among adults. Concurrent investigations of reproductive output, larval survival, and larval transport also must be included. The few empirical studies of the effects of events occurring during the early life histories of community members that have been conducted have all addressed the population dynamics of single species rather than interactions among key species.

INHIBITED SOFT-SEDIMENT COMMUNITIES?

Thorson's (1950, 1966) view that variation in larval settlement regulated soft-sediment communities was particularly influential to other investigators working in this habitat. However, a marked departure in thinking about how soft-sediment communities are regulated was ushered in by Sanders (1958), who proposed that benthic rather than planktonic processes were most important in structuring these communities. Soft-sediment communities are made up of highly patchy distributions of burrowing deposit feeders, burrowing suspension feeders, and tube builders of various trophic types. Sanders argued that the maintenance of these distinct assemblages

was explained by the relationship between sediment grain size and feeding mode (see Snelgrove and Butman 1994 for a discussion of the many factors that may account for this apparent relationship). Rhoads and Young (1970) elaborated on Sanders's study by discussing the role of succession in maintaining these distinct assemblages. They emphasized the role of inhibition, rather than facilitation or tolerance, in determining recruitment (see Connell and Slatyer 1977). According to their model, burrowing deposit feeders inhibited other groups from becoming established by continually reworking sediments, and open space was quickly colonized by juveniles and adults from surrounding sediments rather than by settling larvae. Suspension-feeding bivalves buried settlers of other infauna by their feeding activities and defecation. Although their model did not explain how distinct patches originated, it did influence the direction of research in this field for decades.

Both benthic and planktonic process were incorporated into a single model of community structure by Woodin (1976). She melded Rhoads and Young's (1970) benthic model with Thorson's (1966) adult–larval interactions hypothesis to develop a new, highly influential model. Woodin argued that tube builders inhibited burrowers from becoming established by stabilizing the sediment and making it difficult for burrowers to move among their tubes. Moreover, she argued that mortality of settling larvae by adults of both groups inhibited other infauna from becoming established. Bioturbators would bury and suffocate settlers, suspension feeders would filter larvae from the plankton, and tube builders would prevent larvae from settling by occupying space and defecating on the sediment surface. Peterson (1979) argued that adult–larval interactions hold densities of infauna below the carrying capacity of the environment, thereby alleviating competition. Meiofauna later were shown to also take a toll on settlers (Watzin 1986). Thus, inhibition was predicted to be the most important factor in structuring soft-sediment communities when densities of adults were high, much as eventually was demonstrated for rocky intertidal communities.

The adult–larval interactions hypothesis was tested 54 times, and 61% of the experiments supported it (reviewed by Olafsson et al. 1994). Recruitment of deposit–feeding and predatory infauna usually was found to be inhibited by interactions with recent settlers, but results for suspension feeding on larvae were mixed (see also Thrush et al. 1997). Most experiments were conducted in the laboratory, often at elevated densities, which may have biased results. On the other hand, inadequate experimental design in some of these studies may have contributed to the lack of support for the hypothesis, and various improvements have been recommended. The sizes of experimental patches or arenas may have been too small in some cases. Increasing patch size would increase the probability that larvae would encounter adults and be ingested (Peterson 1982; Ertman and Jumars 1988). Furthermore, predation may have been overshadowed by patchiness in larval supply in the field, or experiments may have lacked sufficient sample size and power to detect predation effects at the spatial scale being studied (Young 1990b). Studies should be conducted at very small spatial scales because suspension feeders have a minuscule radius of influence. In addition, high predation rates on settling larvae would have been easier to demonstrate by calculating feeding selectivities rather than inferring them from spatial distributions of recent settlers (Young 1990b).

Woodin (1978) and Gallagher et al. (1983) proposed that facilitation, rather than inhibition, may sometimes structure soft-bottom communities. The arrival of tube builders was shown to modify and stabilize sediments for later arrivals, thereby facilitating recruitment of other species. Wilson (1991) suggested that Gallagher et al.'s data better fit the tolerance than the facilitation model of succession. Support for the facilitation and tolerance models later was obtained by Thrush et al. (1992) and Zajac and Whitlach (1982a,b), who showed that recruitment did not depend on the density of resident adults (Wilson 1991). Whether inhibition, facilitation, or tolerance structures soft-sediment communities may depend on the composition of the assemblage and the relative abundances of the residents. Both facilitation and inhibition of recruitment may occur in the same community depending on the density of residents; facilitation of recruitment was found at low adult densities and inhibition occurred at high adult densities (Thrush et al. 1992, 1996). Although the body of evidence presently indicates that inhibition structures soft-sediment communities, facilitation and tolerance also play a role and warrant further investigation.

Absent from this discussion has been the role of larval settlement preferences, which were documented both for soft-sediment and hard-substrate species before any of these models of community structure were developed. Highsmith (1982) clearly demonstrated that settlement behavior, facilitation, and postsettlement mortality were all prominent in regulating soft-sediment communities. Pheromones from sand dollars cued larvae to settle, sediment reworking by adults facilitated survival of recruits and tanaids, and predation by tanaids inhibited other infauna from becoming established. Woodin (1985) also recognized the importance of settlement behavior when she found that a tube builder avoided settling near a burrower that could bury it. A review of the literature further indicated that larval settlement was important in regulating these communities (Woodin 1986), as did subsequent studies (Woodin et al. 1993; Hardege et al. 1998). So far, negative settlement cues appear to be especially common among soft-sediment animals, which may lend further support to the inhibition model of community maintenance or may reflect the greater interest in this model in general.

As in rocky intertidal communities, research on soft-sediment communities has focused on the importance of settlement and benthic processes in maintaining mosaic communities. However, this process actually begins in the water column through a combination of physics and behavior. Thirty investigations have found that larvae segregated into sediment traps that were suspended over the appropriate substrate (reviewed by Butman 1987), demonstrating that presettlement processes are important in maintaining patchy assemblages. However, the relative importance of behavioral choice and passive assortative deposition in this process was controversial. Butman (1987) argued that all but one of these 30 studies were biased. The only unbiased study (Hannan 1984) suggested that larvae were deposited passively in sediment traps and did not choose among them. Butman then argued that large-scale settlement patterns initially are established by passive deposition of larvae according to their species-specific fall velocities, as originally proposed by Baggerman (1953; cited in Butman 1987). Hence, near-bottom hydrodynamics may sort sediments and larvae together, resulting in sediment-specific patterns of settlement. Small-scale patterns may result from the passive accumulation of larvae in depressions or from habitat selection. Habitat selection may occur after weakly swimming larvae sink into the low-flow environment of the benthic boundary layer, where they have more control over their movements. Alternatively, habitat selection may occur after larvae have settled on the substrate. Since this review, both passive deposition and habitat selection by larvae of soft-sediment species have been demonstrated in a flume (Butman et al. 1988; Butman and Grassle 1992; Grassle et al. 1992a,b; Snelgrove et al. 1993, 1998) and in the field (Armonies and Hellwig-Armonies 1992; Snelgrove et al. 1994; Walters et al. 1997; Renaud et al. 1999), as has also been shown for hard-substrate species (Wethey 1984, 1986; Chabot and Bourget 1988; LeTourneaux and Bourget 1988; Pawlik et al. 1991; Pawlik and Butman 1993; Walters and Wethey 1996; Abelson 1997). Thus, the usual debate over the relative importance of behavior and physics in determining settlement patterns is rather specious. Both processes are important, and the ultimate question often gets lost in the shuffle: how do passive deposition and habitat choice together explain initial distributions and abundances of the various species that constitute benthic communities?

Larval settlement may not be as critical in structuring soft-sediment communities as it is in rocky intertidal communities because soft-sediment animals generally are much more mobile. In contrast to those of most rocky shore residents, the initial distributions of soft-sediment settlers are modified by drifting postlarvae, resuspension of recent recruits by storms and spring tides, and emigration of juveniles and adults (Butman 1987; Savidge and Taghon 1988; Beukema 1989; Bhaud and Cazaux 1990; Emerson and Grant 1991; Armonies 1992, 1996; Armonies and Hellwig-Armonies 1992; Cummings et al. 1993, 1995; Kube et al. 1996; Shull 1997). Drifting by sedentary invertebrates is common in freshwater streams (Palmer et al. 1996), but is unusual in the marine environment except in soft-sediment communities. In these communities, postlarvae secrete a mucous structure that lifts them into the water column and transports them 1 m to 1 km away (Gunther 1992). Habitat selection by suspended postlarvae and juveniles has been demonstrated, and therefore drifting enables postlarvae to migrate to more favorable habitats after settlement (Olivier et al. 1996). Each species evidently displays a different drifting pattern relative to tidal phase, current velocity, and wave action, which depends on its size, shape, balloon-forming mucous secretions, physiology, and density (Olivier et al. 1996). Massive drifting during maximum flood tides has been observed to transport postlarvae shoreward from initial settlement sites to more favorable adult habitats at a rate of 1800 m/hour. Therefore, larvae that are transported into unfavorable habitats for juvenile development may relocate after they settle, and it should not be assumed that they have died. Postsettlement movements remain to be incorporated into models of soft-sediment community structure, even though the high mobility of recent recruits has been well documented during the last decade and is clearly important in determining the structure and dynamics of these communities.

It remains unclear how postsettlement mortality can be widely perceived as the dominant process regulating soft-sediment populations and communities when recent recruits have repeated opportunities to migrate to more favorable habitats. Nevertheless, since Thorson's influence subsided in the 1970s, investigators have focused on the role of postsettlement mortality. Nearly 100 experiments have documented predation by large, mobile epibenthic predators; 54 experiments have demonstrated mortality due to adult–larval interactions; and 40 experiments (plus correlative studies) have determined that food limitation can be important, particularly for recruits (reviewed by Olafsson et al. 1994). Many studies also have documented the erosion of recruits by storms, and it is assumed that these animals die, even though there is little direct evidence of mortality. This body of work clearly demonstrates that postsettlement mortality occurs in soft-sediment communities, but there is no compelling reason to believe that it is more important than larval settlement or postsettlement migration in structuring these communities. As Olafsson et al. (1994) acknowledged, not one study has definitively compared presettlement and postsettlement mortality, because postsettlement mortality is much more difficult to monitor than on rocky shores. New recruits must be sieved destructively from the substrate using large mesh screens. Consequently, recruits rather than settlers are collected, and collections are made infrequently. Finally, emigration is much more commonplace in soft-sediment communities than it is in rocky shore communities.

In the absence of definitive tests of the recruitment limitation hypothesis, Olafsson et al. (1994) compared adult distributions of planktotrophs with those of lecithotrophs and direct developers. The rationale for this test originated with Thorson (1950), who proposed that species producing long-lived planktotrophic larvae should experience greater variation in larval mortality, settlement, and adult distributions. Based on only six studies, the authors concluded that this was not the case, and tentatively deemed recruitment limitation to be less important than postsettlement mortality in regulating soft-sediment communities. Putting aside the limitations of this survey, the results of this test demonstrated only that settlement is similar among developmental modes. These results have no bearing on recruitment limitation; all species alike

may or may not have been recruitment limited. Moreover, low recruitment variation may be typical in soft-sediment communities due to the drifting of postlarvae and the passive resuspension and redistribution of recruits. Unfortunately there is no substitute for carefully designed empirical studies to evaluate the relative contributions of larval supply, postsettlement mortality, and migration in structuring soft-sediment communities. Although it is challenging to work on these communities, investigators must rededicate themselves to determining the importance of larval settlement and migration in regulating them.

Development of this field of study also has been hampered by an overemphasis on the role of physical processes in governing larval supply. Larvae of most soft-sediment species swim weakly and are thought of as drifting passively in the plankton. Passive dispersal is invoked even to explain larval retention in estuaries, and dye and drifter studies often are used to determine larval trajectories (Manning and Whaley 1954; Boicourt 1982; Levin 1983, 1986; Seliger et al. 1982; Banse 1986). For instance, Banse (1986) concluded that polychaete and echinoderm larvae were retained in a bight by physical processes alone, because they remained tied to water masses without undergoing diurnal or ontogenetic vertical migrations. However, the role of behavior in maintaining larvae within the water mass was overlooked, as shown by Kunze 1995. In this study, weakly swimming larvae of two estuarine gastropod species were intensively sampled throughout the water column, together with passively distributed gastropod and fish eggs. Larvae of both species maintained different distributions from the eggs, despite strong vertical mixing during flood and ebb tides. Hence, they overcame passive mixing and maintained depth by swimming; larvae of one of the species even undertook diel vertical migrations. Larvae tended to remain within a water mass and generally stayed in the middle of the water column near the level of no net motion (0 residual velocity). By maintaining this position, larvae would have been transported upstream by flood currents and returned downstream by ebb currents, resulting in little net transport and the retention of larvae in the estuary. Although passive mechanisms alone sometimes can be sufficient to retain weakly swimming larvae in estuaries (Wood and Hargis 1971), decades of laboratory and field studies have shown that behavior facilitates retention (Nelson 1912; Nelson 1931, 1954; Prytherch 1928; Carriker 1951; Kunkle 1957; Haskin 1964).

Two sets of exemplary studies have demonstrated the importance of reproductive timing and larval transport in maintaining adult populations. First, Thiebaut et al. (1992, 1994) demonstrated that larvae of the polychaete *Owenia fusiformis* were released on the eastern side of a bay, where most of the adults occurred. Most larvae were retained in the bay by undertaking ontogenetic vertical migrations, and residual circulation returned most larvae to the easternside, where they reseeded adult populations. This comprehensive view was accomplished by monitoring the vertical and horizontal distributions of a cohort of larvae relative to water column structure, residual circulation, tides, winds, and adult distributions following their release in the spring.

Using a different approach, Young et al. (1996, 1998) showed that recruitment of the cockle *Cerastoderma edule* depended on the timing of reproduction and wind-driven transport. By correlating records of spatfall and stock size with those of gametogenesis and weather patterns for the twentieth century, they showed that recruitment was high when easterly winds retained larvae near adult populations (Young et al. 1996). A subsequent modeling study showed that wind-driven transport coupled with spawning date predicted annual recruitment patterns over a 7-year period and could produce a 40-fold variation in the number of successful recruits (Young et al. 1998). Young et al. also determined that recruitment of the mussel *Mytilus edulis* was largely determined by temperature rather than by wind-driven transport. Cold winters increased recruitment, perhaps by reducing predation by crabs on recruits or enhancing larval production. Thus, different mechanisms determined recruitment patterns for two soft-bottom species from the same area, precluding facile generalizations about the relative importance of presettlement and postsettlement processes in structuring these communities.

Both sets of studies clearly show that larval availability is important in regulating the dynamics of soft-sediment populations. Routinely including larval supply in investigations of soft-sediment communities would advance our understanding of how these communities are structured, much as it did for rocky shore communities in the mid-1980s. Combining the approaches used by Thiebaut et al. (1992, 1994) and Young et al. (1996, 1998) with concurrent studies of larval settlement and postsettlement mortality for dominant members of soft-sediment communities would go a long way toward establishing the importance of early life histories to community structure.

ALTERNATIVE HARD-SUBSTRATE COMMUNITIES?

Research in subtidal hard-substrate communities has been distinguished by the controversial search for alternative stable communities since Sutherland (1974) first argued for their existence (Figure 6.4). Previous terrestrial (e.g., Clark 1962; Mount 1964) and theoretical (Lewontin 1969) work suggested that more than one type of community can persist in a single environmental regime—that is, that alternative stable communities can exist in the same place at different times or side by side at the same time. Whether one community or another exists may depend on the order in which different species arrive, or on their initial densities (Law and Morton 1993). One stable community may replace another one following a perturbation that changes the densities of member species or environmental conditions; such changes then initiate a feedback loop that results in a switch (Bender et al. 1984; Peterson 1984; Petraitis and Latham 1999).

In the fouling communities that Sutherland studied, the order of larval recruitment on bare settlement plates deter-

mined which species monopolized the available space during the initial development of the community. Sutherland considered the assemblages of organisms that settled on small, suspended settlement plates to be communities, and these isolated communities were considered to be stable if the animals held and occupied space until they died. He found that the ultimate composition of these assemblages depended on the types of larvae that happened to colonize the open space first, because recruits could hold space thereafter; later arrivals presumably were inhibited from settling due to the preemption of space or postsettlement mortality from competition or predation. The assemblages were made up of short-lived species, and when they died, the vacated space was then colonized by different species. These species then dominated the assemblages, giving rise to an alternative stable community. Thus, each assemblage was determined by the pool of larvae that happened to be in the water column at the time, and each was considered to be a stable community.

Although the history of larval availability was shown to affect the composition of assemblages on small, isolated settlement plates, these experiments did not show communities to be stable at appropriate spatial and temporal scales. Multiple assemblages later were shown to be much more likely to arise at such small spatial scales, where the probability that larvae of any given species will colonize the patch is low, than in a larger area (Jackson 1977; Keough 1984). Small assemblages also are highly unlikely to ever be stable or persistent, because even small disturbances can cause extinction. Moreover, multiple assemblages were shown to be more likely to arise when the patch was isolated from the surrounding community (Kay and Keough 1981; Vance 1988; Osman and Whitlach 1998; Smith and Witman 1999). Isolated settlement plates were colonized by larvae of fast-growing, poorly competing, short-lived species, whereas open space in an established community was colonized by buds and fragments of slow-growing, long-lived neighbors that eventually replaced initial colonizers. Therefore, Sutherland's settlement plates artificially selected for species having a certain type of life history, , larval colonization, and annual turnover pattern, whereas the other studies found evidence of a regular repeatable succession toward a climax community.

Connell and Sousa (1983) established strict criteria for determining whether multiple stable states exist: Alternative stable states can be demonstrated only by first determining (1) whether the same physical environment is present during the alternative states and (2) the minimum area wherein the community is stable or persistent. This area must be large enough to provide adequate conditions for the replacement of all existing adults, and therefore it depends on the dispersal capabilities of the member species. Communities containing species with long-distance dispersal would need a greater minimum area than those containing species that disperse short distances. However, any marine community contains species that may disperse widely, and therefore studies dealing with the stability of marine communities must be conducted on broad spatial scales. Moreover, such studies must

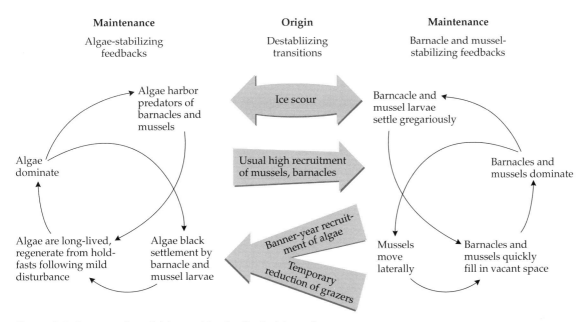

Figure 6.4 Conceptual model for positive feedback-driven alternative stable states in a New England rocky shore community. Ice scour removes large patches of algae, mussels, and barnacles, initiating a switch from a community dominated by algae to one dominated by mussels and barnacles, or vice versa. Several positive feedback mechanisms act collectively to return small clearances to their original state. Algae can prevent establishment of mussels and barnacles by creating a barrier to settlement and by providing a refuge for predators. Algae persists despite low recruitment levels because it is long-lived and regenerates from holdfasts. Barnacles and mussels can prevent establishment of algae by quickly settling into vacant space, which is facilitated by gregarious settlement by both animals and migration by mussels. A switch from barnacle and mussel beds to algal stands follows two rare concurrent events: extraordinary recruitment of algae and a temporary reduction of grazers. (From Petraitis and Lantham 1999.)

continue until all individuals within the area have turned over once to avoid a fundamental tautology that is present in this work: mature communities are stable because they are made up of long-lived organisms. Connell and Sousa reviewed putative examples of multiple stable states and concluded that there was little compelling evidence for this phenomenon.

Sutherland (1990b) agreed that it was necessary to observe at least one complete turnover of the community to detect a significant change in its structure, but he argued that it was unnecessary to observe a community for that long to evaluate its resistance to change. During his study, organisms presumably resisted invasions by other species before they turned over, and understanding how assemblages resist change is as important as understanding how they respond to perturbations.

Peterson (1984) also felt that Connell and Sousa's criteria were unnecessarily strict and disqualified good examples of persistent patches of self-replicating individuals. However, he also reminded them that they had overlooked many communities in which organisms typically modify their physical environment. Such organisms enhance their own replacement and inhibit invasions by their competitors, which could be the most likely mechanism for the maintenance of alternative communities. Sousa and Connell (1985) acknowledged the omission, but argued that none of Peterson's examples met the criteria for alternative stable states: either environmental differences did not result from the influence of the resident populations or they did not facilitate replacement of the resident populations while inhibiting invasion by alternative populations. For example, they disqualified Highsmith's (1982) and Woodin's (1976) soft-sediment communities (see above), in part because different patches were maintained primarily by direct interspecific interactions (predation on or burial of settlers) rather than by modification of the substrate.

The lack of convincing experimental evidence for alternative stable communities has prompted recent discussions on how best to remedy the situation. Knowlton (1992) noted that the most likely candidates for alternative stable states on coral reef communities follow large-scale natural disturbances, including widespread epidemics, hurricanes, and El Niño events. She argued that such natural experiments, when coupled with comparative, experimental, and theoretical approaches, offer the most likely path for documenting the existence of multiple stable states. Large-scale disturbances provide enough space and time for an alternative community to become established by increasing the size of the interior area that is beyond the reach of recruits from the original surrounding community (Jackson 1977; Kay and Keough 1981; Keough 1984; Vance 1988).

Petraitis and Latham (1999) agreed that Knowlton's approach may be necessary when the switch between alternative states depends on large or unusual disturbances to facilitate the establishment of individuals from the alternative community. However, they argued that powerful experiments can reveal the origins and maintenance of alternative communities on rocky shores. Disturbance typically occurs at small scales, and recruitment of dominant species commonly is heavy and predictable in these communities. Hence, small-scale disturbance can be readily simulated by clearing patches of various sizes, and the number and type of recruits can be controlled. Small clearings should return to the original state, whereas larger clearings should switch to the alternative community, depending on the relative abundance of recruits at the time. Although such experiments have been conducted many times on rocky shores, switches between alternative communities may not have been observed because clearings have been much too small.

Thus, the existence of multiple stable communities remains uncertain, and the role of larval recruitment in establishing and maintaining them awaits definitive field experiments. The exchange of ideas clarified the evidence needed to demonstrate their existence and has led us to the brink of resolving this central question in ecology.

CHANCE RECRUITMENT OF CORAL REEF FISHES?

Like Sutherland (1974), Sale (1977) suggested that chance recruitment regulated community structure and maintained species diversity. The prevailing view was that high species diversity in marine communities was maintained by an intermediate level of disturbance, which prevented exclusion of competitively inferior species (Dayton 1971; Figure 6.5). Sale (1977) proposed an alternative mechanism for maintaining high species diversity by suggesting that fishes underwent a lottery for living space on coral reefs. He proposed that space on the reef was limiting until it opened unpredictably, where-

upon larvae from an abundant, diverse larval pool would settle in the open patch strictly by chance. Hence, the habitat requirements of related species (damselfishes) were similar enough that any one of them could settle and survive well in a given patch within a "physiographic zone." According to this scenario, reproduction and settlement were decoupled; larvae dispersed widely and returned to reefs unpredictably, so that the number of larvae settling in a given area did not depend on the number of adults living there. Such randomness might prevent competitive exclusion and account for the patchiness and diversity of fishes on coral reefs. Structure would be more pronounced among zones due to stronger physical, chemical, and biotic differences of the habitat rather than to strong interspecific competition.

The lottery hypothesis was controversial, and it stimulated alternative hypotheses for the coexistence of similar species (Dale 1978; Smith 1978) as well as considerable research on the population dynamics and community structure of coral reef fishes. The hypothesis was challenged for the same reasons that the alternative stable states hypothesis was challenged: studies were conducted on small, isolated substrates (artificial and patch reefs) for too short a time. Reef fish surveys conducted over a wider area or for a longer time revealed niche segregation and persistent patterns of community structure, suggesting that deterministic rather than random processes were operating (Anderson et al. 1981; Ogden and Ebersole 1981). Moreover, larval availability, rather than available space on the reef, later was shown to be limiting for some coral reef fish populations (Victor 1983), prompting a spate of similar studies (reviewed by Doherty 1991). Eventually, it was shown that fishes on coral reefs, like those in temperate communities (Pfister 1996; Levin et al. 1997), sometimes were recruitment limited (Doherty and Fowler 1994) and sometimes were governed by density-dependent processes that were particularly strong soon after settlement, including competition (Forrester 1990, 1995; Jones 1990; Schmitt and Holbrook 1999), predation (Hixon and Carr 1997; Steele 1997; Steele et al. 1998), migration (Ault and Johnson 1998a), and facilitation (Booth 1995; Schmitt and Holbrook 1996). As a result, there has been greater acceptance of the importance of multiple processes in structuring reef fish assemblages, and calls for pluralism have been increasing (e.g., Sale 1990; Hixon 1991; Jones 1991; Steele 1997).

Much of the debate has been centered on the relative importance of presettlement and postsettlement processes on regulating the dynamics and structure of reef fish assemblages. One process that is becoming increasingly appreciated is habitat selection by settling fish larvae. As with invertebrates, recent evidence suggests that coral reef fish larvae settle into preferred habitats, producing much of the structure that is evident in reef fish assemblages (Sweatman 1985; Wellington 1992; Casselle and Warner 1996; Schmitt and Holbrook 1996; Risk 1997; Ault and Johnson 1998b; Booth and Wellington 1998; Gutierrez 1998; Tolimieri 1998).

Despite these recent advances, there is great deal more to be learned about the relative importance of presettlement,

	Postsettlement competition	
	Intense	Weak
Recruitment modified by postsettlement processes	1. Competition model (Smith and Tyler, 1972)	3. Predation disturbance models (e.g., Talbot et al. 1978)
Recruitment *not* modified by postsettlement processes	2. Lottery model (Sale 1977)	4. Recruitment limitation model (e.g., Victor 1983)

Figure 6.5 Classification of simple community models according to the relationship between settlement density and postsettlement competition, with the investigators who first applied the models to coral reef fish assemblages. The models are distinguished by the intensity of postsettlement competition and by the ability of competition, predation, and other postsettlement processes to modify the initial densities of settlers. (After Jones 1991.)

settlement, and postsettlement processes in regulating the dynamics and structure of reef fish assemblages. The vast majority of work has focused on similar, small, site-attached species living on patch reefs, which has severely limited our ability to generalize across species and reef types. It was a long time coming, but Ault and Johnson (1998a) filled this gap by contrasting larval recruitment of site-attached and vagile species to 36 sites on contiguous reefs and 39 patch reefs for one year. They found that species vagility and reef connectivity strongly influenced the relative importance of recruitment and postrecruitment processes in determining local population densities. As much of the earlier work had shown, larval recruitment appeared to explain most of the spatial and temporal variation in populations of site-attached fishes on small, isolated patch reefs. However, postrecruitment processes became much more important on contiguous reefs for both site-attached and moderately vagile species. These species apparently migrated to more favorable areas on contiguous reefs, where refuges from predators were available, but not on patch reefs, where they would have to cross open water (see also Robertson 1988a,b). Migration strengthens the relationship between population density and habitat structure, and consequently, the structure of reef fish assemblages on contiguous reefs varied predictably along habitat gradients, whereas it did not on patch reefs. Postrecruitment processes uniformly were most important for highly vagile species, which apparently moved among isolated patches in response to resource availability, competitors, and predators. These assemblages were not in a consistent state of succession, but they tended toward a stable state at some sites.

These results call into question not only the generality of the lottery hypothesis, but also sweeping generalizations about the relative importance of recruitment and postrecruitment processes. For instance, postrecruitment processes were found to be important for four site-attached species that were determined to be recruitment limited by Doherty and Fowler (1994) at the same locations. These differences probably arose because Doherty and Fowler selected habitats where recruitment rates typically were lower than in those selected by Ault and Johnson. Thus, these findings underscore the necessity of comparing the relative importance of recruitment and postrecruitment processes in structuring coral reef assemblages on reefs that vary in size, connectivity, and habitat, and for species that vary in vagility.

Still largely unexamined is the tacit assumption that reproduction and recruitment are decoupled, which is one of the central tenets of the lottery hypothesis. Although populations certainly are open, it does not necessarily follow that reproduction and recruitment are uncoupled; it depends on the degree of larval retention. Many larvae probably return to the vicinity of natal reefs on average, even though episodic oceanographic events may occasionally transport them farther away at some locales. Evidence for larval retention recently has begun to accumulate both for coral reef fishes (Jones et al. 1999; Swearer et al. 1999; Cowen et al. 2000) and for invertebrates (Chiswell and Roemmich 1998; Ayre and

Dufty 1994; Hughes et al. 1999). Because habitats are more likely to be favorable close to home than farther away, long-distance transport should be selected against (Strathmann 1974, 1980, 1985). Sale (1990, 1991) has begun to appreciate this in recent years, as indicated by the following passage from his 1991 chapter:

> While the present tendency is to emphasize the degree to which larval fish are advected away from their natal reefs, it is possible that we will discover that fish are capable of some considerable control of this process. Such control may be better expressed in oceanic regions, where advection may well be tantamount to death at sea.

Actually, the safe return of larvae to suitable settlement sites should be strongly favored in all species regardless of where they live. In addition to recent supporting evidence for coral reef fishes, it has become widely appreciated that even comparatively weakly swimming larvae of estuarine invertebrates are retained in estuaries throughout development despite net seaward flow (see above), whereas larvae of other estuarine species reliably migrate far onto the continental shelf and back (Morgan 1995a). Indeed, in contrast to expectations, it appears that larvae of retained species recruit to adult populations as reliably as do larvae that develop on the shelf (Hovel and Morgan 1997; Christy and Morgan 1998). These findings suggest that reliable cross-shelf transport mechanisms exist and that larval production and recruitment may be coupled, regardless of the extent of larval migration between adult and larval habitats.

It is becoming increasingly likely that directed swimming facilitates shoreward movements. Postlarvae of decapod crustaceans and fishes are relatively strong swimmers and may be capable of swimming at least part way across the shelf. Recent evidence from the field and laboratory suggests that competent reef fish larvae may quickly swim tens to hundreds of kilometers over periods of days to more than a week (Stobutzki and Bellwood 1997, 1998; Leis and Stobutzki 1997; Leis and Carson-Ewart 1998, 1999), and lobster and crab postlarvae have been observed to swim at similar speeds in the field (Phillips and McWilliam 1986; Rooney and Cobb 1991; Shanks 1995b). Recent evidence also suggests that competent larvae and postlarvae are able to detect and swim toward dissolved chemical cues and other cues that are associated with the shore (Phillips and McWilliam 1986; Wolcott and DeVries 1994; Forward et al. 1996; Leis et al. 1996; Leis and Carson-Ewart 1999). Strong directed swimming by late-stage larvae and postlarvae would reduce losses due to advection and enhance their return to natal populations.

Consistent patterns of temporal and spatial variation in larval recruitment of coral reef fishes are just beginning to be understood in light of physical and behavioral processes (Planes 1993; Hutchins and Pearce 1994; Milicich 1994; Casselle and Warner 1996; Kingsford and Finn 1997; Sponaugle and Cowen 1997; Ault and Johnson 1998a; Leichter et al. 1998; Stobutzki and Bellwood 1998; Cowen et al. 2000). However, in all likelihood, larval retention eventually will become increasingly apparent for reef fishes when our understanding of the interaction between physical transport mechanisms and larval behavior near coral reefs approaches that of estuarine systems (see Cowen et al. 2000) and when recent advances in larval tagging become more widely used (see Thorrold et al. 1998; Jones et al. 1999; Swearer et al. 1999). If so, coupling between reproduction and recruitment should be common in the vicinity of natal reefs, thereby strongly affecting the dynamics and structure of local communities. Even when most larvae settle farther away, they should be associated with the same pool of species and should initiate the same suite of cascading effects on communities throughout the region, much as high productivity in one area can affect population and community dynamics in another area (see above). For instance, a theoretical analysis of the relationship between recruitment limitation and density dependence by Chesson (1998) has predicted that the open nature of local marine systems simply makes density-dependent interactions more difficult to detect; local populations consisting of settled organisms may not experience density-dependent interactions under some circumstances, but the entire species population, consisting of the collection of local populations and their planktonic larvae, must have density-dependent dynamics. Although marine population dynamics are complex, there is no reason to assume that poorly understood planktonic processes are random, decoupling reproduction and recruitment (Morgan 1995a). Indeed, examples of coupled reproduction and recruitment have been documented by examining species with synchronous reproduction and invariant larval durations or by conducting investigations over broader temporal and spatial scales (Robertson et al. 1988; Doherty 1991; Meekan et al. 1993; Hughes et al. 2000). Thus, reef fish assemblages should reflect somewhat predictable processes occurring in the plankton as well as deterministic processes occurring on reefs. Indeed, Ault and Johnson (1998c) recently concluded that the patterns of species richness observed during their studies of reef fish assemblages could not be wholly attributed to stochastic planktonic processes and were at least in part determined by interspecific benthic interactions, based on a comparison with a null model.

Coupled reproduction and recruitment implies that fertilization success among free-spawning fishes is high. High fertilization rates of coral reef fishes have indeed been recorded for a limited number of field studies (Peterson et al. 1992; Warner et al. 1995). More fertilization studies have been conducted on marine invertebrates in the field than on reef fishes, and the results are more variable. Fertilization success rates for invertebrates range from high to poor, and depend on adult density, aggregative spawning behavior, spawning synchrony, sperm abundance, gamete quality and compatibility, turbulence, and water quality (Denny and Shibata 1989; Levitan 1995; Morgan 1995a; Wahle and Peckham 1999). Thus, failure at this crucial juncture of the life cycle could limit recruitment and affect the structure of marine populations and communities.

Until recently, most studies examining the importance of larval supply and postsettlement mortality have focused narrowly on the relationship between the total number of individuals on the reef and competition among them (Jones 1991). Postrecruitment events must be studied in the context of a complete demographic framework relative to multiple ecological processes to avoid overly simplistic conclusions. For example, competition for living space may not limit settlement, but it may affect subsequent growth, reproduction, and survival (Wellington and Victor 1988; Forrester 1990; Jones 1990; Robertson 1996; Schmitt and Holbrook 1999). Although it is more difficult, we also need to determine the demography of species during the planktonic phase of the life cycle, including reproductive output, fertilization success, larval migration, larval mortality, and larval duration, concurrently with investigations of the benthic phase. When the planktonic phase is no longer a black box, we will more thoroughly understand the dynamics and structure of reef fish assemblages. Eckman (1996) has made a good start by developing a population dynamics model that couples both phases of the life cycle.

Although much of the research on coral reef fish assemblages has been driven by community-level theory, addressing questions such as the mechanisms maintaining high diversity and community structure, the great majority of these studies have been concerned only with fishes (Booth and Brosnan 1994). It will be necessary to consider reef fishes in the context of the rest of the community to address these questions.

FUTURE DIRECTIONS

Since the heyday of marine community ecology studies in the two decades following Connell's (1961) seminal paper, most of the effort has been expended in evaluating the effects of larval availability and postsettlement mortality on population dynamics. One of the goals of my review has been to highlight several kinds of underrepresented studies that are just as critical to improving our understanding of how marine communities are regulated. Among these studies, the most effort has been devoted to documenting larval settlement patterns over wide spatial scales and long temporal scales and correlating them with physical processes, such as winds, tides, eddies, internal waves, upwelling-relaxation cycles, and the El Niño/Southern Oscillation. The goal of this type of study has been to determine larval availability and its predictability across the study area and to determine the physical processes responsible for it. Much less time has been spent in documenting the physical and behavioral processes underlying larval transport at sea and the return of larvae to adult habitats. Even fewer studies have determined the effects of temporal and spatial variation in larval production on larval availability, and consequently there has been little documentation of sources and sinks in marine populations. Nevertheless, all of these studies have improved our understanding of how the planktonic phase of the life cycle affects the dynamics of marine populations and have set the stage for fully integrating larval and community ecology. An integration of the two fields is imperative if we are to significantly advance our understanding of community ecology.

Additional information about all of the critical junctures in the complex life cycles of marine animals is needed. Failure at any one of these junctures will eliminate the supply of settlers and can affect the dynamics of marine communities. The types of early life studies that are needed are summarized below.

REPRODUCTIVE OUTPUT. Reproductive output by the various constituents of a community can be monitored readily to determine whether it is affected by observed patterns of productivity in the water column. The comparative approach then can be used to determine whether reproductive output is higher when animals are awash in nutrient-rich, productive waters than in less productive waters. More importantly, we also can determine whether or not density-dependent population and community dynamics within the region are affected by temporal and spatial variation in reproductive output. Although there have been at least two studies (Bertness et al. 1991; Leonard et al. 1998) that suggest that this is the case, this important avenue of research continues to remain unappreciated, perhaps because a regional, comprehensive, and interdisciplinary approach may be necessary to detect the link between reproductive output and community dynamics.

GAMETE RELEASE. Many factors determine the fertilization success of free-spawning invertebrates, and we still do not have a thorough understanding of how they operate for even one species. Field studies on the effects of adult density, aggregative spawning behavior, spawning synchrony, sperm abundance, gamete quality and compatibility, turbulence, and water quality on fertilization success are much needed. In addition to fertilization, other selective factors can determine reproductive success, but we know even less about them. Predation, food limitation, and dispersal have been suggested as causes for synchronous spawning by fishes (Johannes 1978; Barlow 1981), and factors that disrupt this timing could limit reproductive success.

LARVAL RELEASE. Although fertilization by most marine invertebrates occurs in the water column, many other marine animals fertilize eggs internally and release free-swimming larvae. Like free-spawned gametes, newly hatched larvae could be subject to considerable mortality if they were released at inappropriate times (reviewed by Morgan 1995b). Although we have a better understanding of how the timing of release promotes survival of larvae than of gametes (reviewed by Morgan 1995a), it remains to be demonstrated that mistiming results in recruitment failure.

LARVAL TRANSPORT AND MORTALITY. Shipboard work is needed to determine the fate of larvae at sea. Larval transport could be determined by coupling predictive models of larval trajectories with tagging techniques to follow cohorts. Prior knowledge of prevailing hydrodynamics and larval swimming patterns could be used to design sophisticated sampling strategies (Tremblay et al. 1994), and tagged larvae from a single cohort could be sampled frequently from spawning to settlement relative to current velocities and water column structure (Anastasia et al. 1998). Concurrent monitoring of other physical and biological variables (e.g., food, predators) could provide correlative insights into the main causes of larval mortality. However, experimental fieldwork and complementary laboratory studies are needed to determine the relative importance of selective factors that contribute to larval mortality. Working with larvae in natural habitats is difficult and often requires innovative approaches and technologies (reviewed by Heath 1992; Morgan 1995a), but our understanding of marine communities will be limited until we accurately estimate the contributions of various selective factors to larval mortality and transport in the plankton.

POSTLARVAL IMMIGRATION. Physical transport processes that return larvae from offshore waters to the coast should continue to be identified by monitoring larval supply along the shoreline. Our ability to determine the relative importance of multiple oceanographic processes in delivering larvae to adult communities would be enhanced by monitoring larval supply throughout the water column at high frequencies over long temporal and broad spatial scales while concurrently monitoring changing physical conditions, such as winds, currents, water masses, and internal waves. These shore-based settlement studies should be combined with complementary seagoing and laboratory studies of poorly known postlarval transport behavior. Specifically, vertical profiles of postlarvae relative to water column structure and current velocity should be coupled with field and laboratory observations of directed swimming. Swimming speed and direction should be measured relative to physical and chemical cues to determine the degree to which directed onshore swimming contributes to the settlement process.

HABITAT SELECTION. The physical and behavioral components governing larval settlement have been comparatively well studied. However, two areas need much more work. First, the choice of settlement sites can begin while larvae are in the water column, and we need to know how larvae settle in response to waterborne chemical cues, water velocity, depth, and other cues (Grosberg 1982; Pawlik et al. 1991; Tamburri et al. 1992). Second, knowing more about how larvae preferentially settle or avoid settling near conspecifics, hosts, prey, predators, and competitors is particularly important to our understanding of community dynamics and structure.

EARLY POSTSETTLEMENT GROWTH AND SURVIVAL. As more careful studies of early postsettlement mortality have been conducted, it has become increasingly apparent that many individuals die during this juncture of the life cycle. However, much less is known concerning the sublethal effects of the benthic environment on subsequent growth, age of first reproduction, reproductive output, and survival.

EMIGRATION AND IMMIGRATION. Larval tracking studies should be coupled with promising new techniques to determine the origins and destinations of larvae. Elemental fingerprinting (Secor et al. 1998; Thorrold et al. 1998) and genetic analysis of larvae, settlers, and adults may enable us to estimate immigration and emigration rates for demographic models and their effects on natal and adjacent communities.

Clearly, an enormous amount of work is required to understand the population dynamics of even a single species. As our understanding of how selective factors operate at each critical juncture of the life cycle improves, our chances of obtaining a predictive understanding of stock–recruitment relationships will increase concomitantly. The predictive value of stock–recruitment models is notoriously poor, largely because intervening steps in the life cycle are not examined. In an excellent study, Yoshioka (1986) demonstrated that documenting events that transpire during more steps in the life history improves the explanatory value of stock–recruitment relationships. He examined the size, fluctuations, and persistence of adult populations of bryozoans, while examining coupling between reproduction and larval abundance, larval abundance and recruitment, and recruitment and reproduction (Figure 6.6). This accomplishment by a single shore-based investigator suggests that conducting such thorough studies is not beyond our reach (see Bingham 1992 for another example). However, it should be noted that coupling between each of these phases in the life cycle was comparatively easy to demonstrate, because the study organism was sessile and annual with no overlapping generations. Otherwise, the species was typical of marine organisms in having a long planktonic duration (4–8 weeks). Other studies also have demonstrated the importance of understanding the effects of planktonic processes on adult populations by directly tracking the fate of individual ascidian larvae from their release through settlement (Olson and McPherson 1987; Davis 1988; Davis and Butler 1989; Stoner 1992). Although these animals are atypical in having very large larvae that spend only minutes in the water before settling, all of these studies suggest that the failure of stock–recruitment models is not because planktonic processes are chaotic. Rather, few investigators have designed studies so as to put sufficient effort into measuring the relative importance of events occurring during the entire recruitment process, from release through early postsettlement.

By extension, conducting more thorough studies on multiple species at the same time will improve our understanding of how temporal and spatial variation in larval abundances affect the dynamics and structure of communities. Investigating multiple species is not a great deal more work than researching a single species, as long as one is going to the effort of conducting the study in the first place, and this could be accomplished by a small team of investigators. Ultimately, however, we need a programmatic initiative to understand how abiotic and biotic factors affect reproductive output and timing, survival and development at sea, larval supply and settlement back into benthic communities, and postsettlement survival for the community as a whole. The thought of undertaking such a bold initiative may deter the faint-hearted, but the goal can be met through the concerted efforts of teams of larval ecologists, oceanographers, and community ecologists working together toward a common end. The aim would be to continuously monitor the effects of changing environmental conditions on the entire life cycle of community members over a large stretch of coastline for years. Studies must be conducted on broad spatial and temporal scales due to considerable spatial variation in community characteristics and recruitment variation in widely dispersing larvae. Only by studying repre-

Figure 6.6 Percentage of variability accounted for by regression analyses of intervening stages in the stock–recruitment relationships of the bryozoan *Membranipora membranacea*. Stock–recruitment relationships were highly variable ($r^2 = 16\%$), but recruitment-stock relationships were even more variable, suggesting that benthic processes are even more variable than are planktonic processes. Variability in these relationships was considerable when intervening life stages and environmental factors were considered. Stock–larval abundance and larval abundance–recruitment relationships explained 44% and 69% of the variability respectively. In the latter case, nudibranch predation, upwelling, and temperature together with stock size explained 64% of the variability in recruitment. Thus, recruitment is predictable in that variability can be explained by a few causal mechanisms operating by the process of natural selection. (From Yoshioka 1986.)

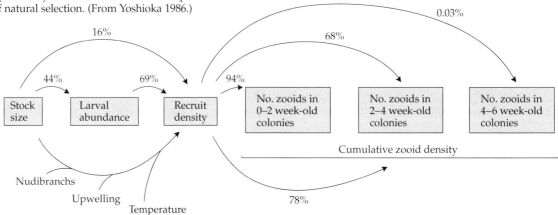

sentative habitats across a region over a long time will we achieve a general understanding of how these communities are regulated. Classic, labor-intensive, small-scale experiments involving the manipulation of these communities must be conducted at multiple sites and compared to determine which of the many potential factors underlie the observed variation in the dynamics and structure of these communities. Moreover, patterns and processes occurring in the water column must be linked to those occurring in intertidal communities. This means that multiple species must be monitored as larvae in coastal waters and as juveniles and adults on the shore. By determining the demography of their members, we can make major advances in understanding the dynamics and structure of marine communities.

The two goals of the oceanographic arm of this research program would be to determine (1) the coastal circulation patterns that deliver larvae to and from the shoreline and (2) larval mortality and behaviors that affect the number of larvae returning to settle into adult populations (Table 6.2). The two goals of the benthic arm would be to determine (1) reproductive output and (2) the relative influence of bottom-up and top-down processes in structuring rocky shore communities. Then, mathematical models of community processes on local scales must be coupled with models describing movement among populations. The relationship between lar-

val transport and population dynamics of member species can be examined using coupled benthic–oceanic models. For example, Alexander and Roughgarden (1996) have developed a two-dimensional model that could be used to explore the spatial pattern of abundance of settlers, juveniles, and adults as a function of the spatial pattern of oceanographic features along the west coast of North America. They suggest that changes in physical and biological parameters, such as spatial variation in the collision of upwelling fronts with the coastline, offshore and alongshore advection, diffusion, reproductive output, and mortality due to climate change can be explored using their model. Moreover, other physical transport processes such as eddies and meanders, which may provide a mechanism for larval retention near shore, and jets and squirts, which may carry larvae away from shore (Wing et al. 1995a,b; Graham and Largier 1997), can be included to develop a three-dimensional model by coupling the population dynamic model to an oceanographic circulation model. Alternatively, the two-dimensional model can be forced with real-time remote sensing data to move from investigating hypothetical scenarios to actual events, which would yield predictions about the recruitment and population dynamics of member species that could be tested directly against recruitment data. The proposed research initiative is challenging, but this comprehensive effort will enable us to unravel the

---

TABLE 6.2   Proposed research initiative to elucidate coupling between the larval and adult phases of marine life cycles on the dynamics and structure of benthic communities.

PELAGIC SAMPLING PROGAM
  Monitoring
    Circulation
      Shipboard surveys
      Moored arrays of instruments, zooplankton traps, and settlement collectors
      Satellite imagery
    Planktonic conditions
  Larval transport
    Larval tracking
    Elemental fingerprinting
    Genetic analysis
  Larval mortality experiments

BENTHIC SAMPLING PROGRAM
  Monitoring
    Microclimate
    Body temperatures
    Heat shock proteins
  Comparative studies of nutrient, food, larval supply, consumers and physical factors on:
    Reproductive output
    Community dynamics and structure, including vagile members of the community
  Experimental manipulations of these factors on:
    Reproductive output
    Community dynamics and structure

MATHEMATICAL MODELLING

great complexity of physical and biological factors regulating marine communities.

Conclusions

Controversy regarding the role of larvae in regulating marine communities occasionally has stimulated debate over both new and traditional views. Even though these controversies have advanced our understanding of larvae, they could have been quickly placed in proper perspective had benthic ecologists (1) had greater knowledge of existing information on larval ecology, (2) incorporated larval studies into their research programs from the outset, and (3) conducted studies on spatial and temporal scales appropriate for species with widely dispersing larvae. Although these controversial ideas concerned community-level processes, most of the research actually addressed population-level processes, which is not surprising, because we first need to know how marine populations are being regulated before we can understand how the community as a whole is being regulated. Nevertheless, these ideas challenged the scientific community to reconsider entrenched beliefs, and our understanding of population- and community-level processes advanced in fits and starts. The scientific community has tended to polarize over false dichotomies rather than accepting that multiple factors regulate complex life cycles and complex communities (see also Schoener 1987). The commonality among diverse marine communities also has tended to be overlooked, but an overarching perspective on diverse marine communities, and hopefully terrestrial and freshwater communities as well, will elucidate their dynamics and structure. After all, it is these shared secrets that ultimately will reveal how marine communities are assembled, maintained, and affected by environmental change. The search for these fundamental principles should be redoubled in an age of global environmental change when society will increasingly turn to us for answers about the prospects for marine communities.

The recent groundswell of studies on larval supply may have crested, and it is time to tackle the significance of earlier junctures in the life cycle. A concerted effort is needed to understand how multiple forces acting on reproductive output, survival, and transport affect the supply of larvae to marine communities. Ecological forces operating at each step of the life history of marine animals will determine whether individuals will live or die, populations will expand or contract, and communities will change or maintain their present composition and structure. After dwelling on the benthic phase of the life cycle, community ecologists largely appear to have accepted that the planktonic phase can be just as important in regulating marine communities. Larval availability, larval settlement behavior, and postsettlement mortality are all critical in regulating marine populations and communities. It is well past time to move beyond debates about whether one phase of the life cycle is more important than another in this process, and strive for a broader understanding of how multiple ecological forces operating at each juncture of the life cycle affect marine communities.

Acknowledgments

I thank Skyli McAfee for commenting on the manuscript. This manuscript was made possible by support from the National Science Foundation (OCE98–13983).

Literature Cited

Abelson, A. 1997. Settlement in flow: Upstream exploration of substrata by weakly swimming larvae. *Ecology* 78: 160–166.

Alexander, S. E. and J. Roughgarden. 1996. Larval transport and population dynamics of intertidal barnacles: A coupled benthic-oceanic model. *Ecol. Monogr.* 66: 259–275.

Anastasia, J. C., S. G. Morgan and N. S. Fisher. 1997. Tagging crustacean larvae: Assimilation and retention of trace elements. *Limnol. Oceanogr.* 43: 362–367.

Anderson, G. R. V., A. H. Ehrlich, P. R. Ehrlich, J. D. Roughgarden, B. C. Russell and F. H. Talbot. 1981. The community structure of coral reef fishes. *Amer. Nat.* 117: 476–495.

Armonies, W. 1992. Migratory rhythms of drifting juvenile molluscs in tidal waters of the Wadden Sea. *Mar. Ecol. Prog. Ser.* 83: 197–206.

Armonies, W. 1996. Changes in distribution patterns of 0-group bivalves in the Wadden Sea: Byssus-drifting releases juveniles from the constraints of hydrography. *Neth. J. Sea Res.* 35: 323–334.

Armonies, W. and M. Hellwig-Armonies. 1992. Passive settlement of *Macoma balthica* spat on tidal flats of the Wadden Sea and subsequent migration of juveniles. *Neth. J. Sea Res.* 29: 371–377.

Ault, T. R. and C. R. Johnson. 1998a. Relationships between habitat and recruitment of three species of damselfish (Pomacentridae) at Heron Reef, Great Barrier Reef. *J. Exp. Mar. Biol. Ecol.* 223: 145–166.

Ault, T. R. and C. R. Johnson. 1998b. Spatial variation in fish species richness on coral reefs: Habitat fragmentation and stochastic structuring processes. *Oikos* 82: 354–364.

Ault, T. R. and C. R. Johnson. 1998c. Spatially and temporally predictable fish communities on coral reefs. *Ecol. Monogr.* 68: 25–50.

Ayre, D. J. and S. L. Duffy. 1994. Evidence for restricted gene flow in the viviparous coral *Seriatopora hystrix* on Australia's Great Barrier Reef. *Evolution* 48: 1183–1201.

Baggerman, B. 1953. Spatfall and transport of *Cardium edule* L. *Arch. Neerl. Zool.* 10: 315–342.

Bailey, K. M. and E. D. Houde. 1989. Predation on eggs and larvae of marine fishes and the recruitment problem. *Adv. Mar. Biol.* 25: 1–83.

Banse, K. 1955. Uber das Verhalten von meroplanktischen Larven aus dem Kattegatt in die Kieler buch. *Ber. Dtsch. Wiss. Komm. Meeresforsch* 14: 147–164.

Banse, K. 1986. Vertical distribution and horizontal transport of planktonic larvae of echinoderms and benthic polychaetes in an open coastal sea. *Bull. Mar. Sci.* 39: 162–175.

Barlow, G. W. 1981. Patterns of parental investment, dispersal and size among coral-reef fishes. *Environ. Biol. Fishes* 6: 65–85.

Bender, E. A., T. J. Case and M. E. Gilpin. 1984. Perturbation experiments in community ecology: Theory and practice. *Ecology* 65: 1–13.

Bertness, M. D. 1989. Intraspecific competition and facilitation in a northern acorn barnacle population. *Ecology* 19: 175–179.

Bertness, M. D. and G. H. Leonard. 1997. The role of positive interactions in communities: Lessons from intertidal habitats. *Ecology* 78: 1976–1989.

Bertness, M. D., S. D. Gaines, D. Bermudez and E. Sanford. 1991. Extreme spatial variation in the growth and reproductive output of the acorn barnacle *Semibalanus balanoides*. *Mar. Ecol. Prog. Ser.* 75: 91–100.

Bertness, M. D., S. D. Gaines, E. G. Stephens and P. O. Yund. 1992. Components of recruitment in populations of the acorn barnacle *Semibalanus balanoides* (Linnaeus). *J. Exp. Mar. Biol. Ecol.* 156: 199–215.

Bertness, M. D., S. D. Gaines and R. A. Wahle. 1996. Wind-driven settlement patterns in the acorn barnacle *Semibalanus balanoides*. *Mar. Ecol. Prog. Ser.* 137: 103–110.

Beukema, J. J. 1989. Tidal-current transport of thread-drifting postlarval juveniles of the bivalve *Macoma balthica* from the Wadden Sea. *Neth. J. Sea Res.* 13: 331–353.

Bhaud, M. R. and C. P. Cazaux. 1990. Buoyancy characteristics of *Lanice conchilega* (Pallas) larvae (Terebellidae). Implications for settlement. *J. Exp. Mar. Biol. Ecol.* 141: 31–45.

Bingham, B. L. 1992. Life histories in an epifaunal community: Coupling of adult and larval processes. *Ecology* 73: 2244–2259.

Boicourt, W. C. 1982. Estuarine larval retention mechanisms on two scales. In V. Kennedy (ed.), *Estuarine Comparisons*, pp. 445–457. Academic Press, New York.

Booth, D. J. 1995. Juvenile groups in a coral-reef damselfish: Density-dependent effects on individual fitness and population demography. *Ecology* 76: 91–106.

Booth, D. J. and D. M. Brosnan. 1995. The role of recruitment dynamics in rocky shore and coral reef fish communities. *Adv. Ecol. Res.* 26: 309–386.

Booth, D. J. and G. Wellington. 1997. Settlement preferences in coral-reef fishes: Effects on patterns of adult and juvenile distributions, individual fitness and population structure. *Austral. J. Ecol.* 23: 274–279.

Bousfield, E. L. 1955. Ecological control of the occurrence of barnacles in the Miramichi estuary. *Natl. Mus. Can. Bull. Biol. Ser.* 137: 1–65.

Butman, C. A. 1987. Larval settlement of soft-sediment invertebrates: The spatial scales of pattern explained by active habitat selection and the emerging role of hydrodynamical processes. *Annu. Rev. Oceanogr. Mar. Biol.* 25: 113–165.

Butman, C. A. and J. P. Grassle. 1992. Active habitat selection by *Capitella* sp. I. Larvae. I. Two-choice experiments in still water and flume flows. *J. Mar. Res.* 50: 669–715.

Butman, C. A., J. P. Grassle and C. M. Webb. 1987. Substrate choices made by marine larvae settling in still water and in a flume flow. *Nature* 333: 771–773.

Caffey, J. M. 1985. Spatial and temporal variation in settlement and recruitment of intertidal barnacles. *Ecol. Monogr.* 55: 313–332.

Carpenter, S. C. 1987. *Complex Interactions in Lake Communities*. Springer-Verlag, New York.

Carriker, M. R. 1951. Ecological observations on the distribution of oyster larvae in New Jersey estuaries. *Ecol. Monogr.* 21: 19–37.

Caselle, J. E. and R. R. Warner. 1996. Variability in recruitment of coral reef fishes: The importance of habitat at two spatial scales. *Ecology* 77: 2488–2504.

Chabot, R. and E. Bourget. 1987. Influence of substratum heterogeneity and settled barnacle density on the settlement of cypris larvae. *Mar. Biol.* 97: 45–56.

Chesson, P. 1997. Recruitment limitation: A theoretical perspective. *Austral. J. Ecol.* 23: 234–240.

Chiswell, S. M. and D. Roemmich. 1997. The East Cape Current and two eddies: A mechanism for larval retention? *N. Z. J. Mar. Freshw. Res.* 32: 385–397.

Christy, J. H. and S. G. Morgan. 1997. Estuarine immigration by crab postlarvae: Mechanisms, reliability and adaptive significance. *Mar. Ecol. Prog. Ser.* 174: 51–65.

Clark, L. R. 1962. The general biology of *Cardiaspina albitextura* (Psyllidae) and its abundance in relation to weather and parasitism. *Austral. J. Zool.* 10: 537–586.

Connell, J. H. 1961. The influence of interspecific competition and other factors on the distribution of the barnacle *Chthamalus stellatus*. *Ecology* 42: 710–723.

Connell, J. H. 1985. The consequences of variation in initial settlement vs. post-settlement mortality in rocky intertidal communities. *J. Exp. Mar. Biol. Ecol.* 93: 11–45.

Connell, J. H. and R. O. Slatyer. 1977. Mechanisms of succession in natural communities and their role in community stability and organization. *Amer. Nat.* 111: 1119–1144.

Connell, J. H. and W. P. Sousa. 1983. On the evidence needed to judge ecological stability or persistence. *Amer. Nat.* 121: 789–824.

Connolly, S. R. and J. Roughgarden. 1997. A latitudinal gradient in northeast Pacific intertidal community structure: Evidence for an oceanographically based synthesis of marine community theory. *Amer. Nat.* 151: 311–326.

Cowen, R. K., K. M. M. Lwiza, S. Sponaugle, C. B. Limouzy Paris and D. B. Olson. 2000. Connectivity of marine populations: Open or closed? *Science* 287: 857–859.

Crisp, D. J. 1976. Settlement responses in marine organisms. In R. C. Newell (ed.), *Adaptation to Environment: Essays on the Physiology of Marine Animals*, pp. 83–124. Butterworths, London.

Cummings, V. J., R. D. Pridmore, S. F. Thrush and J. E. Hewitt. 1993. Emergence and floating behaviours of post-settlement juveniles of *Macomona liliana* (Bivalvia: Tellinacea). *Mar. Behav. Physiol.* 24: 25–32.

Cummings, V. J., R. D. Pridmore, S. F. Thrush and J. E. Hewitt. 1995. Post-settlement movement by intertidal benthic macroinvertebrates: Do common New Zealand species drift in the water column? *N. Z. J. Mar. Freshw. Res.* 29: 59–67.

Dale, G. 1977. Money-in-the-bank: A model for coral reef fish coexistence. *Environ. Biol. Fishes* 3: 103–107.

Davis, A. R. 1987. Effects of variation in initial settlement on distribution and abundance of *Podoclavella moluccensis* Sluiter. *J. Exp. Mar. Biol. Ecol.* 117: 157–167.

Davis, A. R. and A. J. Butler. 1989. Direct observations of larval dispersal in the colonial ascidian *Podoclavella moluccensis* Sluiter: Evidence for closed populations. *J. Exp. Mar. Biol. Ecol.* 127: 189–203.

Dayton, P. K. 1971. Competition, disturbance and community organization: The provision and subsequent utilization of space in a rocky intertidal community. *Ecol. Monogr.* 41: 351–389.

Dayton, P. K. 1979. Ecology: A science and a religion. In R. J. Livingston (ed.), *Ecological Processes in Coastal and Marine Systems*, pp. 3–17. Plenum Press, New York.

Dayton, P. K. 1984. Processes structuring some marine communities: Are they general? In D. R. Strong, Jr., D. Simberloff, L. G. Abele and A. B. Thistle (eds.), *Ecological Communities: Conceptual Issues and the Evidence*, pp. 181–197. Princeton University Press, Princeton, NJ.

Denny, M. W. and M. F. Shibata. 1989. Consequences of surf-zone turbulence for settlement and external fertilization. *Amer. Nat.* 134: 859–889.

DeWolf, P. 1973. Ecological observations on the mechanisms of dispersal of barnacle larvae during planktonic life and settling. *Neth. J. Sea Res.* 6: 1–129.

Dias, P. C. 1996. Sources and sinks in population biology. *Trends Ecol. Evol.* 11: 326–329.

Doherty, P. J. 1991. Spatial and temporal patterns in recruitment. In P. F. Sale (ed.), *The Ecology of Fishes on Coral Reefs*, pp. 261–293. Academic Press, New York.

Doherty, P. and T. Fowler. 1994. An empirical test of recruitment limitation in a coral reef fish. *Science* 263: 935–939.

Ebert, T. A. and M. P. Russell. 1987. Latitudinal variation in size structure of the west coast purple sea urchin: A correlation with headlands. *Limnol. Oceanogr.* 33: 286–294.

Ebert, T. A., S. C. Schroeter, J. D. Dixon and P. Kalvass. 1994. Settlement patterns of red and purple sea urchins (*Strongylocentrotus franciscanus* and *S. purpuratus*) in California, USA. *Mar. Ecol. Prog. Ser.* 111: 41–52.

Eckman, J. E. 1996. Closing the larval loop: Linking larval ecology to the population dynamics of marine benthic invertebrates. *J. Exp. Mar. Biol. Ecol.* 200: 207–237.

Emerson, C. W. and J. Grant. 1991. The control of soft-shell clam (*Mya arenaria*) recruitment on intertidal sandflats by bedload sediment transport. *Limnol. Oceanogr.* 36: 1288–1300.

Ertman, S. C. and P. A. Jumars. 1987. Effects of siphonal currents on settlement of inert particles on larvae. *J. Mar. Res.* 46: 797–813.

Farrell, T. M., D. Bracher and J. Roughgarden. 1991. Cross-shelf transport causes recruitment to intertidal populations in central California. *Limnol. Oceanogr.* 36: 279–287.

Forrester, G. E. 1990. Factors influencing the juvenile demography of a coral reef fish. *Ecology* 71: 1666–1681.

Forrester, G. E. 1995. Strong density-dependent survival and recruitment regulate the abundance of a coral reef fish. *Oecologia* 103: 275–282.

Forward, R. B., Jr., M. C. DeVries, D. Rittschof, D. A. Z. Frankel, J. P. Bischof, C. M. Fisher and J. M. Welch. 1996. Effects of environmental cues on metamorphosis of the blue crab *Callinectes sapidus. Mar. Ecol. Prog. Ser.* 1131: 165–177.

Foster, M. S. 1990. Organization of macroalgal assemblages in the Northeast Pacific: The assumption of homogeneity and the illusion of generality. *Hydrobiologia* 192: 21–33.

Frank, K. T. and W. C. Leggett. 1994. Fisheries ecology in the context of ecological and evolutionary theory. *Annu. Rev. Ecol. Syst.* 25: 401–422.

Gaines, S. D. and M. D. Bertness. 1992. Dispersal of juveniles and variable recruitment in sessile marine species. *Nature* 360: 579–580.

Gaines, S. D. and K. D. Lafferty. 1995. Modeling the dynamics of marine species: The importance of incorporating larval dispersal. In L. McEdward (ed.), *Ecology of Marine Invertebrate Larvae*, pp. 389–412. CRC Press, Boca Raton, FL.

Gaines, S. D. and J. Roughgarden. 1985. Larval settlement rate: A leading determinant of structure in an ecological community of the marine intertidal zone. *Proc. Natl. Acad. Sci. USA* 82: 3707–3711.

Gaines, S. D. and J. Roughgarden. 1987. Fish in offshore kelp forests affect recruitment to intertidal barnacle populations. *Science* 235: 479–481.

Gallagher, E. D., P. A. Jumars and D. D. Trueblood. 1983. Facilitation of soft-bottom benthic succession by tube builders. *Ecology* 64: 1200–1216.

Garbarini, P. 1936. Le choix du support pour les larves de *Spirorbis borealis* Daudin. *Compte Rendu Soc. Biol.* 122: 158–160.

Graham, W. M. and J. L. Largier. 1997. Upwelling shadows as nearshore retention sites: The example of northern Monterey Bay. *Continental Shelf Res.* 17: 509–532.

Graham, W. M., J. G. Field and D. C. Potts. 1992. Persistent "upwelling shadows" and their influence on zooplankton distributions. *Mar. Biol.* 114: 561–570.

Grassle, J. P., C. A. Butman and S. W. Mills. 1992a. Active habitat selection by *Capitella* sp. I larvae II. Multiple-choice experiments in still water and flume flows. *J. Mar. Res.* 50: 717–743.

Grassle, J. P., P. V. R. Snelgrove and C. A. Butman. 1992b. Larval habitat choice in still water and flume flows by the opportunistic bivalve *Mulinia lateralis. Neth. J. Sea Res.* 30: 33–44.

Grosberg, R. K. 1981. Competitive ability influences habitat choice in marine invertebrates. *Nature* 290: 700–702.

Grosberg, R. K. 1982. Intertidal zonation of barnacles: The influence of planktonic zonation of larvae on vertical zonation of adults. *Ecology* 63: 894–899.

Grosberg, R. K. and D. R. Levitan. 1992. For adults only? Supply-side ecology and the history of larval biology. *Trends Ecol. Evol.* 7: 130–133.

Gunther, C.-P. 1992. Settlement and recruitment of *Mya arenaria* L. in the Wadden Sea. *J. Exp. Mar. Biol. Ecol.* 159: 203–215.

Gutierrez, L. 1997. Habitat selection by recruits establishes local patterns of adult distribution in two species of damselfishes: *Stegastes*

dorsopunicans and *S. planifrons. Oecologia* 115: 268–277.

Hannan, C. A. 1984. Planktonic larvae may act like passive particles in turbulent near-bottom flows. *Limnol. Oceanogr.* 29: 1108–1116.

Hardege, J. D., M. G. Bentley and L. Snape. 1997. Sediment selection by juvenile *Arenicola marina. Mar. Ecol. Prog. Ser.* 166: 187–195.

Haskin, H. H. 1964. The distribution of oyster larvae. In N. Marshall, H. P. Jeffries, T. A. Napora and J. M. Sieburth (eds.). *Symposium on Experimental Marine Ecology.* Graduate School of Oceanography, Occ. Publ. Univ. Rhode Island 2: 76–80.

Hastings, A. and S. Harrison. 1994. Metapopulation dynamics and genetics. *Annu. Rev. Ecol. Syst.* 25: 167–187.

Heath, M. R. 1992. Field investigations of the early life stages of marine fish. *Adv. Mar. Biol.* 28: 1–174.

Highsmith, R. C. 1982. Induced settlement and metamorphosis of sand dollar (*Dendraster excentricus*) larvae in predator-free sites: Adult sand dollar beds. *Ecology* 63: 329–337.

Hixon, M. A. 1991. Predation as a process structuring coral reef fish communities. In P. F. Sale (ed.), *The Ecology of Fishes on Coral Reefs*, pp. 475–507. Academic Press, New York.

Hixon, M. A. and M. H. Carr. 1997. Synergistic predation, density dependence, and population regulation in marine fish. *Science* 277: 946–949.

Hovel, K. A. and S. G. Morgan. 1997. Planktivory as a selective force for reproductive synchrony and larval migration. *Mar. Ecol. Prog. Ser.* 157: 79–95.

Hughes, T. P., A. H. Baird, E. A. Dinsdale, N. A. Moltschaniwskyj, M. S. Pratchett, J. E. Tanner and B. L. Willis. 1999. Patterns of recruitment and abundance of corals along the Great Barrier Reef. *Science* 397: 59–63.

Hughes, T. P., A. H. Baird, E. A. Dinsdale, N. A. Moltschaniwskyj, M. S. Pratchett, J. E. Tanner and B. L. Willis. 2000. Supply-side ecology works both ways: The link between benthic adults, fecundity and larval recruits. *Ecology* 81: 2241–2249.

Hunter, M. D. and P. W. Price. 1992. Playing chutes and ladders: Heterogeneity and the relative roles of bottom-up and top-down forces in natural communities. *Ecology* 73: 724–732.

Hutchins, J. B. and A. F. Pearce. 1994. Influence of the Leeuwin Current on recruitment of tropical reef fishes at Rottnest Island, Western Australia. *Bull. Mar. Sci.* 54: 245–255.

Huyer, A., E. 1983. Coastal upwelling in the California Current System. *Prog. Oceanogr.* 12: 259–284.

Jackson, J. B. C. 1977. Habitat area, colonization and development of epibenthic community structure. In B. F. Keegan, P. O. Ceidigh and P. J. S. Boaden (eds.), *Biology of Benthic Organisms*, pp. 349–357. Pergamon Press, New York.

Johannes, R. E. 1977. Reproductive strategies of coastal marine fishes in the tropics. *Environ. Biol. Fishes* 3: 65–84.

Johnson, L. E. 1989. Settling barnacle larvae avoid substrata previously occupied by a mobile predator. *J. Exp. Mar. Biol. Ecol.* 128: 87–103.

Jones, G. P. 1990. The importance of recruitment to the dynamics of a coral reef fish population. *Ecology* 71: 1691–1697.

Jones, G. P. 1991. Postrecruitment processes in the ecology of coral reef fish populations: A multifactorial perspective. In P. F. Sale (ed.), *The Ecology of Fishes on Coral Reefs*, pp. 294–330. Academic Press, New York.

Jones, G. P., M. J. Milicich, M. J. Emslie and C. Lunow. 1999 Self-recruitment in a coral reef fish population. *Science* 402: 802–804.

Kay, A. M. and M. J. Keough. 1981. Occupation of patches in the epifaunal communities on pier pilings and the bivalve *Pinna bicolor* at Edithburgh, South Australia. *Oecologia* 48: 123–130.

Keough, M. J. 1984. Effects of patch size on the abundance of sessile marine invertebrates. *Ecology* 65: 423–437.

Kingsford, M. and M. Finn. 1997. The influence of phase of the moon and physical processes on the input of presettlement f ishes to coral reefs. *J. Fish. Biol.*, Suppl. A 51: 176–205.

Knowlton, N. 1992. Thresholds and multiple stable states in coral reef community dynamics. *Am. Zool.* 32: 674–682.

Kube, J., M. L. Zettler, F. Gosselck, S. Ossig and M. Powilleit. 1996. Distribution of *Marenzelleria viridis* (Polychaeta: Spionidae) in the southwestern Baltic Sea in 1993/94—ten years after introduction. *Sarsia* 81: 131–142.

Kunkle, D. E. 1957. The vertical distribution of larvae in Delaware Bay. *Proc. Natl. Shellfish Assoc.* 48: 90–91.

Kunze, H. 1995. Larval transport in the lower Hudson River estuary. Masters thesis, State University of New York, Sony Brook, NY.

Law, R. and R. D. Morton. 1993. Alternative permanent states of ecological communities. *Ecology* 74: 1347–1361.

Leichter, J. J., G. Shellenberger, S. J. Genovese and S. R. Wing. 1997. Breaking internal waves on a Florida (USA) coral reef: A plankton pump at work? *Mar. Ecol. Prog. Ser.* 166: 83–97.

Leis, J. M. and B. M. Carson-Ewart. 1997. Complex behaviour by coral-reef fish larvae in open-water and near-reef pelagic environments. *Environ. Biol. Fishes* 53: 259–266.

Leis, J. M. and B. M. Carson-Ewart. 1999. In situ swimming and settlement behaviour of larvae of an Indo-Pacific coral-reef fish, the coral trout *Plectropomus leopardus* (Pisces: Serranidae). *Mar. Biol.* 134: 51–64.

Leis, J. M. and I. C. Stobutzki. 1997. Swimming performance of late pelagic larvae of coral-reef fishes: In situ and laboratory-based measurements. *Soc. Fr. Ichthyol.* 1997: 1–9.

Leis, J. M., H. P. A. Sweatman and S. E. Reader. 1996. What the pelagic stages of coral reef fishes are doing out in blue water: Daytime field observations of larval behavioural capabilities. *Mar. Freshw. Res.* 47: 401–411.

Leonard, G. H., J. Levine, P. Schmidt and M. D. Bertness. 1997. Flow-driven variation in intertidal community structure in a Maine estuary. *Ecology* 79: 1395–1411.

LeTourneaux, F. E. and E. Bourget. 1987. Importance of physical and biological settlement cues used at different spatial scales. *Mar. Biol.* 97: 57–66.

Levin, L. A. 1983. Drift tube studies of bay-ocean water exchange and implications for larval dispersal. *Estuaries* 6: 364–371.

Levin, L. A. 1986. The influence of tides on larval availability in shallow waters overlying a mudflat. *Bull. Mar. Sci.* 39: 224–233.

Levin, P. S., W. Chiasson and J. M. Green. 1997. Geographic differences in recruitment and population structure of a temperate reef fish. *Mar. Ecol. Prog. Ser.* 161: 23–35.

Levitan, D. R. 1995. The ecology of fertilization in free-spawning invertebrates. In L. McEdward (ed.), *Ecology of Marine Invertebrate Larvae*, pp. 123–156. CRC Press, Boca Raton, FL.

Lewontin, R. C. 1969. The meaning of stability. In *Diversity and Stability in Ecological Systems*, pp. 13–24. Brookhaven Symposia in Biology, No. 22. Brookhaven National Laboratories, Brookhaven, NY.

Manning, J. H. and H. H. Whaley. 1954. Distribution of oyster larvae and spat in relation to some environmental factors in a tidal estuary. *Proc. Natl. Shellfish Assoc.* 45: 56–65.

McCook, L. J. and A. R. O. Chapman. 1993. Community succession following massive ice-scour on a rocky intertidal shore: Recruitment, competition and predation during early, primary succession. *Mar. Biol.* 115: 565–575.

Meadows, P. A. and J. J. Campbell. 1972. Habitat selection by aquatic invertebrates. *Adv. Mar. Biol.* 10: 271–382.

Meekan, M. G., M. J. Milicich and P. J. Doherty. 1993. Larval production drives temporal patterns of larval supply and recruitment of a coral reef damselfish. *Mar. Ecol. Prog. Ser.* 93: 217–225.

Meidel, S. K. and R. E. Scheibling. 1997. Annual reproductive cycle of the green sea urchin, *Strongylocentrotus droebachiensis*, in differing habitats in Nova Scotia, Canada. *Mar. Biol.* 131: 461–477.

Menge, B. A. 1991. Relative importance of recruitment and other causes of variation in rocky intertidal community structure. *J. Exp. Mar. Biol. Ecol.* 146: 69–100.

Menge, B. A. 1992. Community regulation: Under what conditions are bottom-up factors important on rocky shores? *Ecology* 73: 755–765.

Menge, B. A. and J. Lubchenco. 1981. Community organization in temperate and tropical rocky intertidal habitats: Prey refuges in relation to consumer pressure gradients. *Ecol. Monogr.* 51: 429–450.

Menge, B. A. and J. P. Sutherland. 1987. Community regulation: Variation in disturbance, competition and predation in relation to environmental stress and recruitment. *Amer. Nat.* 130: 730–757.

Menge, B. A., E. L. Berlow, C. A. Blanchette, S. A. Navarrete, and S. B. Yamada. 1994. The keystone species concept: Variation in interaction strength in a rocky intertidal habitat. *Ecol. Monogr.* 64: 249–286.

Milicich, M. J. 1994. Dynamic coupling of reef fish replenishment and oceanographic processes. *Mar. Ecol. Prog. Ser.* 110: 135–144.

Minchinton, E. and R. E. Scheibling. 1991. The influence of larval supply and settlement on the population structure of barnacles. *Ecology* 72: 1867–1879.

Minchinton, E. and R. E. Scheibling. 1993. Free space availability and larval substratum selection as determinants of barnacle population structure in a developing rocky intertidal community. *Mar. Ecol. Prog. Ser.* 95: 233–244.

Miron, G., B. Boudreau and E. Bourget. 1995. Use of larval supply in benthic ecology: Testing correlations between larval supply and larval settlement. *Mar. Ecol. Prog. Ser.* 124: 301–305.

Morgan, S. G. 1995a. Life and death in the plankton: Larval mortality and adaptation. In L. McEdward (ed.), *Ecology of Marine Invertebrate Larvae*, pp. 279–321. CRC Press, Boca Raton, FL.

Morgan, S. G. 1995b. The timing of larval release. In L. McEdward (ed.), *Ecology of Marine Invertebrate Larvae*, pp. 157–191. CRC Press, Boca Raton, FL.

Mount, A. B. 1964. The interdependence of the eucalypts and forest fires in southern Australia. *Austral. Forestry* 28: 166–172.

Nelson, J. 1912. Report of the Biological Department of the New Jersey Agricultural Experiment Station for the year 1911.

Nelson, T. C. 1931. Annual report of Department of Biology, 1 July 1929 to June 1930. New Jersey Agricultural Experiment Station.

Nelson, T. C. 1954. Observations of the behavior and distribution of oyster larvae. *Proc. Natl. Shellfish. Assoc.* 45: 23–27.

Noda, T., K. Fukushima and T. Mori. 1997. Daily settlement variability of the barnacle *Semibalanus cariosus*: Importance of physical factors and density-dependent processes. *Mar. Ecol. Prog. Ser.* 169: 289–293.

Ogden, J. C. and J. P. Ebersole. 1981. Scale and community structure of coral reef fishes: A long-term study of a large artificial reef. *Mar. Ecol. Prog. Ser.* 4: 97–103.

Olafsson, E. B., D. H. Peterson and W. G. Ambrose, Jr. 1994. Does recruitment limitation structure populations and communities of macro-invertebrates in marine soft sediments: The relative significance of pre- and post-settlement processes. *Annu. Rev. Oceanogr. Mar. Biol.* 32: 65–109.

Olivier, F., C. Vallet, J. C. Dauvin and C. Retiere. 1996. Drifting in post-larvae and juveniles in an *Abra alba* (Wood) community of the eastern part of the Bay of Seine (English Channel). *J. Exp. Mar. Biol. Ecol.* 199: 89–109.

Olson, R. R. and R. McPherson. 1987. Potential vs. realized larval dispersal: Fish predation on larvae of the ascidian *Lissoclinum patella* (Gottschaldt). *J. Exp. Mar. Biol. Ecol.* 110: 245–256.

Osman, R. W. and A. B. Whitlatch. 1997. Local control of recruitment in an epifaunal community and the consequences to colonization processes. *Hydrobiologia* 376: 113–123.

Palmer, M. A., J. D. Allan and C. A. Butman. 1996. Dispersal as a regional process affecting the local dynamics of marine and stream benthic invertebrates. *Trends Ecol. Evol.* 11: 322–326.

Parrish, R. H., C. S. Nelson and A. Bakun. 1981. Transport mechanisms and the reproductive success of fishes in the California Current. *Biol. Oceanogr.* 1: 175–203.

Pawlik, J. R. and C. A. Butman. 1993. Settlement of a marine tube worm as a function of current velocity: Interacting effects of hydrodynamics and behavior. *Limnol. Oceanogr.* 38: 1730–1740.

Pawlik, J. R., C. A. Butman and V. R. Starczak. 1991. Hydrodynamic facilitation of gregarious settlement of a reef-building tube worm. *Science* 251: 421–424.

Peterson, C. H. 1979. Predation, competitive exclusion, and diversity in the soft-sediment benthic communities of estuaries and lagoons. In R. J. Livingston (ed.), *Ecological Processes in Coastal and Marine Systems*, pp. 233–264. Plenum, New York.

Peterson, C. H. 1982. The importance of predation and intra- and interspecific competition in the suspension-feeding bivalves, *Prothothaca staminea* and *Chione undatella*. *Ecol. Monogr.* 52: 437–475.

Peterson, C. H. 1984. Does a rigorous criterion for environmental identity preclude the existence of multiple stable points? *Amer. Nat.* 124: 127–133.

Peterson, C. H. 1991. Intertidal zonation of marine invertebrates in sand and mud. *Am. Sci.* 79: 236–249.

Peterson, C. W., R. R. Warner, S. Cohen, H. C. Hess and A. T. Sewell. 1992. Variation in pelagic fertilization success: Implications for production estimates, mate choice, and the spatial and temporal distribution of spawning. *Ecology* 73: 391–401.

Petraitis, P. S. and R. E. Latham. 1999. The importance of scale in testing the origins of alternative community states. *Ecology* 80: 429–442.

Pfister, C. A. 1996. The role and importance of recruitment variability to a guild of tide pool fishes. *Ecology* 77: 1928–1941.

Phillips, B. F. and P. S. McWilliam. 1986. The pelagic phase of spiny lobster development. *Can. J. Fish. Aquat. Sci.* 43: 2153–2163.

Pineda, J. 1994. Spatial and temporal patterns in barnacle settlement rate along a southern California rocky shore. *Mar. Ecol. Prog. Ser.* 107: 125–137.

Pineda, J. 1995. An internal tidal bore regime at nearshore stations along western USA: Predictable upwelling within the lunar cycle. *Cont. Shelf Res.* 15: 1023–1041.

Planes, S. 1993. Genetic differentiation in relation to restricted larval dispersal of the convict surgeonfish *Acanthurus triostegus* in French Polynesia. *Mar. Ecol. Prog. Ser.* 98: 237–246.

Power, M. E. 1992. Top-down and bottom-up forces in food webs: Do plants have primacy? *Ecology* 73: 733–746.

Prytherch, H. F. 1927. Investigation of the physical conditions controlling spawning of oysters and the occurrence, distribution and setting of oyster larvae in Milford Harbor, Connecticut. *Bull. Bur. Fish., Wash.* 54: 429–503.

Raimondi, P. T. 1990. Patterns, mechanisms, consequences of variability in settlement and recruitment of an intertidal barnacle. *Ecol. Monogr.* 60: 283–309.

Renaud, P. E., D. A. Syster and W. G. Ambrose, Jr. 1999. Recruitment patterns of continental shelf benthos off North Carolina, USA: Effects of sediment enrichment and impact on community structure. *J. Exp. Mar. Biol. Ecol.* 237: 89–106.

Rhoades, D. C. and D. K. Young. 1970. The influence of deposit-feeding organisms on sediment stability and community trophic structure. *J. Mar. Res.* 28: 150–177.

Risk, A. 1997. Effects of habitat on the settlement and post-settlement success of the ocean surgeonfish *Acanthurus bahianus. Mar. Ecol. Prog. Ser.* 161: 51–59.

Robertson, D. R. 1988a. Abundances of surgeonfishes on patch-reefs in Caribbean Panama: Due to settlement or post-settlement events? *Mar. Biol.* 97: 495–501.

Robertson, D. R. 1988b. Settlement and population dynamics of *Abudefduf saxatilis* on patch reefs in Caribbean Panama. *Proc. Sixth Int. Coral Reef Symp.* 2: 839–844.

Robertson, D. R. 1996. Interspecific competition controls abundance and habitat use of territorial Caribbean damselfishes. *Ecology* 77: 885–899.

Robertson, D. R., D. G. Green and B. C. Victor. 1987. Temporal coupling of production and recruitment of larvae of a Caribbean reef fish. *Ecology* 69: 370–381.

Rooney, P. and J. S. Cobb. 1991. Effects of time of day, water temperature, and water velocity on swimming by postlarvae of the American lobster, *Homarus americanus. Can. J. Fish. Aquat. Sci.* 48: 1944–1950.

Roughgarden, J., S. Gaines and H. Possingham. 1987. Recruitment dynamics in complex life cycles. *Science* 241: 1460–1466.

Sale, P. F. 1977. Maintenance of high diversity in coral reef fish communities. *Amer. Nat.* 111: 253–344.

Sale, P. F. 1990. Recruitment of marine species: Is the bandwagon rolling in the right direction? *Trends Ecol. Evol.* 5: 25–27.

Sale, P. F. 1991. Reef fish communities: Open nonequilibrial systems. In P. F. Sale (ed.), *The Ecology of Fishes on Coral Reefs*, pp. 564–600. Academic Press, New York.

Sanders, H. L. 1957. Benthic studies in Buzzards Bay. I. Animal-sediment relationships. *Limnol. Oceanogr.* 3: 245–257.

Sandifer, P. A. 1975. The role of pelagic larvae in recruitment to populations of adult decapod crustaceans in the York River estuary and adjacent lower Chesapeake Bay, Virginia. *Estuarine, Coastal and Shelf Sci.* 3: 269–279.

Savidge, W. B. and G. L. Taghon. 1987. Passive and active components of colonization following two types of disturbance on intertidal sandflat. *J. Exp. Mar. Biol. Ecol.* 115: 137–155.

Scheltema, R. S. 1974. Biological interactions determining larval settlement of marine invertebrates. *Thal. Jugosl.* 10: 263–296.

Schmitt, R. J. and S. J. Holbrook. 1996. Local-scale patterns of larval settlement in a planktivorous damselfish—Do they predict recruitment? *Mar. Freshw. Res.* 47: 449–463.

Schmitt, R. J. and S. J. Holbrook. 1999. Mortality of juvenile damselfish: Implications for assessing processes that determine abundance. *Ecology* 80: 35–50.

Schoener, T. W. 1987. Axes of controversy in community ecology. In W. J. Matthews and D. C. Heins (eds.), *Community and Evolutionary Ecology of North American Stream Fishes*, pp. 8–16. University of Oklahoma Press, Norman.

Secor, D. H., T. Ohta, K. Nakayama and M. Tanaka. 1997. Use of otolith microanalysis to determine estuarine migrations of Japanese sea bass *Lateolabrax japonicus* distributed in Ariake Sea. *Fisheries Sci.* 64: 740–743.

Seliger, H. H., J. A. Boggs, R. B. Rivkin, W. H. Biggley and K. R. H. Aspden. 1982. The transport of oyster larvae in an estuary. *Mar. Biol.* 71: 57–72.

Shanks, A. L. 1995a. Mechanisms of cross-shelf dispersal of larval invertebrates and fishes. In L. McEdward (ed.), *Ecology of Marine Invertebrate Larvae*, pp. 323–367. CRC Press, Boca Raton, FL.

Shanks, A. L. 1995b. Orientated swimming by megalopae of several eastern north Pacific crab species and its potential role in their onshore migration. *J. Exp. Mar. Biol. Ecol.* 186: 1–16.

Shull, D. H. 1997. Mechanisms of infaunal polychaete dispersal and colonization in an intertidal sandflat. *J. Mar. Res.* 55: 153–179.

Slobodkin, L. B. 1986. The role of minimalism in art and science. *Amer. Nat.* 127: 257–265.

Smith, C. L. 1977. Coral reef fish communities: A compromise view. *Environ. Biol. Fishes* 3: 109–127.

Smith, F. and J. D. Witman. 1999. Species diversity in subtidal landscapes: Maintenance by physical processes and larval recruitment. *Ecology* 80: 51–69.

Snelgrove, P. V. R. 1994. Hydrodynamic enhancement of invertebrate larval settlement in microdepositional environments: Colonization tray experiment in a muddy habitat. *J. Exp. Mar. Biol. Ecol.* 176: 149–166.

Snelgrove, P. V. R. and C. A. Butman. 1994. Animal-sediment relationships revisited: Cause versus effect. *Annu. Rev. Oceanogr. Mar. Biol.* 32: 111–177.

Snelgrove, P. V. R., C. A. Butman and J. P. Grassle. 1993. Hydrodynamic enhancement of larval settlement in the bivalve *Mulinia lateralis* (Say) and the polychaete *Capitella* sp. I in microdepositional environments. *J. Exp. Mar. Biol. Ecol.* 168: 71–109.

Snelgrove, P. V. R., J. P. Grassle and C. A. Butman. 1997. Sediment choice by settling larvae of the bivalve, *Spisula solidissima* (Dillwyn), in flow and still water. *J. Exp. Mar. Biol. Ecol.* 231: 171–190.

Sousa, W. P. 1979. Experimental investigations of disturbance and ecological succession in a rocky intertidal algal community. *Ecol. Monogr.* 49: 227–254.

Sousa, W. P. 1984. The role of disturbance in natural communities. *Annu. Rev. Ecol. Syst.* 15: 353–391.

Sousa, W. P. and J. H. Connell. 1985. Further comments on the evidence for multiple stable points in natural communities. *Amer. Nat.* 125: 612–615.

Sponaugle, S. and R. K. Cowen. 1997. Early life history traits and recruitment patterns of Caribbean wrasses (Labridae) *Ecol. Monogr.* 67: 177–202.

Steele, M. A. 1997. The relative importance of processes affecting recruitment of two temperate reef fishes. *Ecology* 78: 129–145.

Steele, M. A., G. E. Forrester and G. R. Almany. 1997. Influences of predators and conspecifics on recruitment of a tropical and a temperate reef fish. *Mar. Ecol. Prog. Ser.* 172: 115–125.

Stobutzki, I. C. and D. R. Bellwood. 1997. Sustained swimming abilities of the late pelagic stages of coral reef fishes. *Mar. Ecol. Prog. Ser.* 149: 35–41.

Stobutzki, I. C. and D. R. Bellwood. 1998. Nocturnal orientation to reefs by late pelagic stage coral reef fishes. *Coral Reefs* 17: 103–110.

Stoner, D. S. 1992. Vertical distribution of a colonial ascidian on a coral reef: The roles of larval dispersal and life history variation. *Amer. Nat.* 139: 802–824.

Strathmann, R. R. 1974. The spread of sibling larvae of sedentary marine invertebrates. *Amer. Nat.* 108: 29–44.

Strathmann, R. R. 1980. Why does a larva swim so long? *Palaeobiology* 6: 373–376.

Strathmann, R. R. 1985. Feeding and nonfeeding larval development and life-history evolution in marine invertebrates. *Annu. Rev. Ecol. Syst.* 16: 339–361.

Strub, P. T., P. M. Kosro, A. Huyer, and CTZ collaborators. 1991. The nature of cold filaments in the California Current System. *J. Geophys. Res.* 96: 14743–14767.

Sutherland, J. P. 1974. Multiple stable points in natural communities. *Amer. Nat.* 108: 859–873.

Sutherland, J. P. 1990a. Perturbations, resistance, and alternative views of the existence of multiple stable points in nature. *Amer. Nat.* 136: 270–275.

Sutherland, J. P. 1990b. Recruitment regulates demographic variation in a tropical intertidal barnacle. *Ecology* 71: 955–972.

Swearer, S. E., J. E. Caselle, D. W. Lea and R. W. Warner. 1999. Larval retention and recruitment in an island population of a coral reef fish. *Science* 402: 799–802.

Sweatman, H. P. A. 1985. The influence of adults of some coral reef fishes on larval recruitment. *Ecol. Monogr.* 55: 469–485.

Talbot, F. H., B. C. Russell and G. R. V. Anderson. 1977. Coral reef fish communities: Unstable, high-diversity systems? *Ecol. Monogr.* 48: 425–440.

Tamburri, M. N., R. K. Zimmer-Faust and M. L. Tamplin. 1992. Natural sources and properties of chemical inducers mediating settlement of oyster larvae: A re-examination. *Biol. Bull.* 183: 327–337.

Thiebaut, E., J. C. Dauvin and Y. Lagadeuc. 1992. Transport of *Owenia fusiformis* larvae (Annelida: Polychaeta) in the Bay of Seine. I. Vertical distribution in relation to water column stratification and ontogenic vertical migration. *Mar. Ecol. Prog. Ser.* 80: 29–39.

Thiebaut, E., J. C. Dauvin and Y. Lagadeuc. 1994. Horizontal distribution and retention of *Owenia fusiformis* larvae (Annelida: Polychaeta) in the Bay of Seine. *J. Mar. Biol. Assoc. UK* 74: 129–142.

Thorrold, S. R., C. M. Jones, P. K. Swart and T. E. Targett. 1997. Accurate classification of juvenile weakfish *Cynoscion regalis* to estuarine nursery areas based on chemical signatures in otoliths. *Mar. Ecol. Prog. Ser.* 173: 253–265.

Thorson, G. 1950. Reproductive and larval ecology of marine bottom invertebrates. *Biol. Rev.* 25: 1–45.

Thorson, G. 1966. Some factors influencing the recruitment and establishment of marine benthic communities. *Neth. J. Sea Res.* 3: 267–293.

Thrush, S. F., R. D. Pridmore, J. E. Hewitt and V. J. Cummings. 1992. Adult infauna as facilitators of colonization on intertidal sandflats. *J. Exp. Mar. Biol. Ecol.* 159: 253–266.

Thrush, S. F., J. E. Hewitt, R. D. Pridmore and V. J. Cummings. 1996. Adult/juvenile interactions of infaunal bivalves: Contrasting outcomes in different habitats. *Mar. Ecol. Prog. Ser.* 132: 83–92.

Thrush, S. F., D. C. Schneider, P. Legendre, R. B. Whitlatch, P. K. Dayton, J. E. Hewitt, A. H. Hines, V. J. Cummings, S. M. Lawrie, J. Grant, R. D. Pridmore, S. J. Turner and B. H. McArdle. 1997. Scaling-up from experiments to complex ecological systems: Where to next? *J. Exp. Mar. Biol. Ecol.* 216: 243–254.

Tolimieri, N. 1997. Effects of substrata, resident conspecifics and damselfish on the settlement and recruitment of the stoplight parrotfish, *Sparisoma viride. Environ. Biol. Fishes* 53: 393–404.

Tremblay, M. J., J. W. Loder, F. E. Werner, C. E. Naimie, F. H. Page and M. M. Sinclair. 1994. Drift of sea scallop larvae *Placopecten magellanicus* on Georges Bank: A model study of the roles of mean advection, larval behavior and larval origin. *Deep-Sea Res.* Pt. II 41: 7–49.

Underwood, A. J. and E. J. Denley. 1984. Paradigms, explanations, and generalizations in models for the structure of ecological communities on rocky shores. In D. Strong, D. Simberloff, L. G. Abele and A. B. Thistle (eds.), *Ecological Communities: Conceptual Issues and the Evidence*, pp. 151–180. Princeton University Press, Princeton, NJ.

Underwood, A. J. and P. G. Fairweather. 1989. Supply-side ecology and benthic marine assemblages. *Trends Ecol. Evol.* 4: 16–20.

Vance, R. R. 1987. Ecological succession and the climax community on a marine subtidal rock wall. *Mar. Ecol. Prog. Ser.* 48: 125–136.

Victor, B. C. 1983. Recruitment and population dynamics of a coral reef fish. *Science* 219: 419–420.

Walters, L. J. and D. S. Wethey. 1996. Settlement, refuges, and adult body form in colonial marine invertebrates: A field experiment. *Biol. Bull.* 180: 112–117.

Walters, L. J., M. G. Hadfield and K. L. del Carmen. 1997. The importance of larval choice and hydrodynamics in creating aggregations of *Hydroides elegans* (Polychaeta: Serpulidae). *Invert. Biol.* 116: 102–114.

Warner, R. R., D. Y. Shapiro, A. Marcanato and C. W. Petersen. 1995. Sexual conflict: Males with highest mating success convey the lowest fertilization benefits to females. *Proc. R. Soc. Lond. B* 262: 135–139.

Watzin, M. C. 1986. Larval settlement into marine soft-sediment systems: Interactions with meiofauna. *J. Exp. Mar. Biol. Ecol.* 98: 65–113.

Wellington, G. M. 1992. Habitat selection and juvenile persistence control the distribution of two closely related Caribbean damselfishes. *Oecologia* 90: 500–507.

Wellington, G. M. and B. C. Victor. 1987. Variation in components of reproductive success in an undersaturated population of coral-reef damselfish: A field perspective. *Amer. Nat.* 131: 588–601.

Wethey, D. S. 1984. Spatial pattern in barnacle settlement: Day to day changes during the settlement season. *J. Mar. Biol. Assoc. UK* 64: 687–697.

Wethey, D. S. 1986. Ranking of settlement cues by barnacle larvae: Influence of surface contour. *Bull. Mar. Sci.* 39: 393–400.

Whale, R. A. and S. H. Peckham. 1999. Density-related reproductive tradeoffs in the green sea urchin, *Strongylocentrotus droebachiensis. Mar. Biol.* 134: 127–137.

Wilson, W. H. 1991. Competition and predation in marine soft-sediment communities. *Annu. Rev. Ecol. Syst.* 21: 221–241.

Wing, S. R., J. L. Largier, L. W. Botsford and J. F. Quinn. 1995a. Settlement and transport of benthic invertebrates in an intermittent upwelling region. *Limnol. Oceanogr.* 40: 316–329.

Wing, S. R., L. W. Botsford, J. L. Largier and L. E. Morgan. 1995b. Spatial variability in settlement of benthic invertebrates in a northern California upwelling system. *Mar. Ecol. Prog. Ser.* 128: 199–211.

Wing, S. R., L. W. Botsford, S. V. Ralson, and J. L. Largier. 1997. Meroplanktonic distribution and circulation in a coastal retention zone of the northern California upwelling system. *Limnol. Oceanogr.* 43: 1710–1721.

Wolcott, D. L. and M. C. DeVries. 1994. Offshore megalopae of *Callinectes sapidus*:

Depth of collection, molt stage and response to estuarine cues. *Mar. Ecol. Prog. Ser.* 109: 157–163.

Wood, L. and W. J. Hargis, Jr. 1971. Transport of bivalve larvae in a tidal estuary. In D. J. Crisp (ed.), *Fourth European Marine Biology Symposium*, pp. 29–44. Cambridge University Press, London.

Woodin, S. A. 1976. Adult–larval interactions in dense infaunal assemblages: Patterns of abundance. *J. Mar. Res.* 34: 25–41.

Woodin, S. A. 1977. Refuges, disturbance, and community structure: A marine soft-bottom example. *Ecology* 59: 274–284.

Woodin, S. A. 1985. Effects of defecation by arenicolid polychaete adults on spionid polychaete juveniles in field experiments: Selective settlement or differential mortality. *J. Exp. Mar. Biol. Ecol.* 87: 119–132.

Woodin, S. A. 1986. Settlement of infauna: Larval choice? *Bull. Mar. Sci.* 39: 401–407.

Woodin, S. A., R. L. Marinelli and D. E. Lincoln. 1993. Allelochemical inhibition of recruitment in a sedimentary assemblage. *J. Chem. Ecol.* 19: 517–530.

Yoshioka, P. M. 1986. Chaos and recruitment in the bryozoan, *Membranipora membranacea. Bull. Mar. Sci.* 39: 408–417.

Young, C. M. 1987. Novelty of "Supply-Side Ecology." *Science* 235: 415.

Young, C. M. 1989. Selection of predator-free settlement sites by larval ascidians. *Ophelia* 30: 131–140.

Young, C. M. 1990a. Larval ecology of marine invertebrates: A sesquicentennial history. *Ophelia* 32: 1–47.

Young, C. M. 1990b. Larval predation by epifauna on temperate reefs: Scale, power and the scarcity of measurable effects. *Austral. J. Ecol.* 15: 412–426.

Young, C. M. and F. S. Chia. 1981. Laboratory evidence for delay of metamorphosis of larval settlement in response to a dominant competitor. *Int. J. Invert. Reprod.* 3: 221–226.

Young, E. F., G. R. Bigg and A. Grant. 1996. A statistical study of environmental influences on bivalve recruitment in The Wash, England. *Mar. Ecol. Prog. Ser.* 143: 121–129.

Young, E. F., G. R. Bigg, A. Grant, P. Walker and J. Brown. 1997. A modelling study of environmental influences on bivalve settlement in The Wash, England. *Mar. Ecol. Prog. Ser.* 172: 197–214.

Zajac, R. N. and R. B. Whitlach. 1982a. Responses of estuarine infauna to disturbance. I. Spatial and temporal variation of initial recolonization. *Mar. Ecol. Prog. Ser.* 10: 1–14.

Zajac, R. N. and R. B. Whitlach. 1982b. Responses of estuarine infauna to disturbance. II. Spatial and temporal variation of succession. *Mar. Ecol. Prog. Ser.* 10: 15–27.

chapter 7

Supply-Side Ecology
The Nature and Consequences of Variations in Recruitment of Intertidal Organisms

A. J. Underwood and Michael J. Keough

Supply-side ecology was a pun invented by Lewin (1986) in *Science* in an essay on emerging conceptual difficulties with some of the general models being used to describe marine, coastal assemblages of species. The term covers (as also described by Morgan elsewhere in this volume) the consequences to structure and dynamics of assemblages due to variations in numbers and timing of offspring arriving into any area of habitat. Its importance, when coined by Lewin, was that models being discussed at that time were predominantly about the influences of competition (particularly due to the papers by Connell 1961a,b and influential reviews by Connell 1983 and Schoener 1983), predation (notably the influential papers by Paine 1966, 1974), and disturbance (for experimental analyses on rocky intertidal shores, see Sousa 1979, 1980, and McGuinness 1984, 1987). Several authors—among them Dayton (1971), Menge (1976), and Underwood et al. (1983)—had analyzed experimentally the interactions among these processes, and some consensus was emerging that much of the dynamics of organization of assemblages on rocky shores was accountable by combinations of these three processes.

A much earlier understanding had, however, also included recognition of important influences of variations in numbers of individuals arriving into habitats from planktonic dispersive phases of life history. This idea was reviewed by Young (1987) and Underwood and Fairweather (1989); see also Keough and Downes (1982).

It is a common-sense notion that an empty patch of habitat (resulting, for example, from a severe disturbance) will not be occupied by a given species if its propagules are unable to reach it. It is a small step from that simple concept to the realization that a dominant competitor can dominate only if it arrives in an area in sufficient numbers to exert its influences. However important a predator may be where and when it is in sufficient numbers to decimate its prey, it cannot be important where it is found only very sparsely. So, although processes acting after initial recruitment can be crucial in determining the actual or effective numbers of competitors or predators in any area, the supply of numbers of competitors or predators is still the first crucial step. To understand and to be able to make precise predictions about the outcomes of ecological processes depends on knowing whether or not the numbers of each interacting species are set or controlled by local processes. If local processes regulate the numbers of recruits into adult populations, reasonable predictions are possible. If, in contrast, the numbers of arrivals and the subsequent presence or intensity of processes are determined by the less well-understood processes of outcomes of reproduction going on elsewhere in the population and the extremely poorly understood processes of pelagic dispersal, predictions are going to be imprecise, if they are realistic at all.

The challenge is to attempt to integrate understanding of processes of reproduction, consequences of having dispersive stages in the life history, models of physical processes causing dispersal, and the behavioral repertoire of larvae as they disperse. By bringing together understanding of environmental and demographic influences on the supply of individuals, predictive capacity of ecological theory will increase.

In this chapter, we consider the roles of variations in numbers and timing of recruitment as they affect understanding of the ecology of assemblages. The emphasis is on demonstrating the need to consider roles of recruitment in development of conceptual models to explain patterns, processes, and interactions in marine assemblages. Unless alternative theories are developed early in a research program, quantitative and experimental analyses will be wrong, or, at best, incomplete. Experimental tests of hypotheses may not of great value because, although they may provide evidence to support whatever notion is being proposed, they fail to eliminate alternative theories (i.e., models about quite different processes and interactions) that lead to the same predictions. This point has been discussed in general by Chamberlin (1965) and specifically for rocky intertidal assemblages by Underwood and Denley (1984) and Underwood (1991). The examples described here identify the need for inclusion of predictions based on considerations of numbers of arrivals, rather than just assuming that arrivals are somehow invariant and are highly predictable. Thus, the intention is to reiterate the need to focus on arrivals, rather than just focusing on the processes that lead to removals and death (i.e., competition, predation, and disturbance). Supply-side concepts, at the very least, prevent ecology from being solely focused on the morbid side of the business!

Earlier Ventures into Supply-Side Issues

It is an extremely old concept that outcomes for populations are dependent on the numbers of recruits into those populations. This concept formed the basis for the biblical saga of the fates of seeds scattered by the sower who went forth to sow (King James Bible, *Matthew* 13:3).

For many marine populations, it has long been known that dynamics of adult populations can be determined largely by the vagaries of numbers of larvae or juveniles recruiting to them. One of the earliest modern examples was described for fish by Hjort (1914) and the idea has remained ever since a cornerstone of the study of dynamics of fisheries (Beverton and Holt, 1957; May et al., 1979; Hilborn and Walters, 1992). Despite an improved recognition that variations in recruitment of young fish have profound effects on numbers of future adults and therefore on the size of potential catches in a fishery, fisheries modeling still assumes reasonably tight correlations between numbers of breeding adults in a local area and the future supply of recruits to that area.

One early recognition of the importance of recruitment to populations of coastal animals was Orton's (1937) discovery that occasional large numbers of recruits would persist for long periods in a population. As a consequence, in long-lived species, the sizes and ages of individuals in a population could be dominated for long periods by one age-group that arrived in a single period of intense recruitment. So, clearly, differences from time to time in numbers of recruits would have large and lingering effects on structures of populations.

Long series of data have been used to demonstrate how numbers of adults fluctuate widely, largely in response to variations in recruitment (Coe 1956; Loosanoff 1964, 1966). In contrast to Orton's (1937) observations, Coe and Loosanoff found no correlation between the numbers of young bivalves settling in the areas studied and the numbers of adults pre-

sent. Even from the early attempts to understand process of variation in recruitment, there has been conflict in how to interpret the information and how to understand the physical and biological processes involved.

Processes Causing Variation in Arrival of Recruits

Variations in recruitment result from a combination of at least five processes: production of larvae, dispersal of those larvae in the plankton, the risk of mortality while dispersing, the settlement of the larvae, and, finally, growth and survival of young juveniles until they get counted as new recruits into populations.

Production of Larvae: Fertilization, a Neglected Component

Many animals, particularly those with planktonic development, release huge numbers of eggs, which, until fairly recently, was thought to result in the production of equally large numbers of larvae. Implicitly, most or all eggs were thought to be fertilized, but recent research has highlighted the potential for failure of fertilization, which greatly restricts numbers of larvae. Rates of fertilization of eggs produced during broadcast spawning events are less than 20% for a wide range of organisms, including sea stars, urchins, corals, and ascidians, across a wide range of habitats (Levitan 1995).

Rates of fertilization are small because of the following factors:

Sperm of most invertebrates are short-lived, surviving for only a few hours; even then, aging sperm may be less able to fertilize eggs.

In high-energy habitats, such as the intertidal zone of rocky shores, or in strong tidal flows, sperm may be dispersed rapidly from their point of release. Increased dispersal of sperm may allow sperm to encounter distant eggs, but will also result in reduced concentrations in the water column. The role of hydrodynamics in affecting fertilization in these environments is worth further investigation, because gametes are not necessarily dispersed rapidly in highly turbulent flows (Denny and Shibata 1989), but shear stresses can have deleterious effects (Mead and Denny 1995).

Donors are sparse. Because of limitations on sperm, individuals separated by only tens of meters may be unable to cross-fertilize. In some animals, this critical distance may be only a few meters or even centimeters for animals such as barnacles that depend on internal fertilization. In natural assemblages, many organisms do not have a conspecific neighbor that is so close; individuals may be sparsely distributed, or the assemblage may be a mosaic of many species, rather than dense populations of one or a few species. This problem may be particularly important for species that are uncommon, especially those reduced in number by harvesting or disturbances.

Small rates of fertilization have been reported mainly for invertebrates that release eggs and sperm into the water column, and many studies have involved artificially induced spawning, so there is some debate about how common it is for fertilization rates to be low (Yund 2000). In sharp contrast, most fish seem not to be limited by fertilization, with rates commonly greater than 95%, probably because many species have sophisticated spawning behavior (Levitan and Petersen 1995). Among invertebrates, fertilization is not likely to be limiting for species with appropriate behavior, such as mollusks that form spawning aggregations, and barnacles, which copulate directly. One explanation for the spectacular mass spawning of corals on a number of reefs around the world has been the increase in rate of fertilization that results from the large concentrations of gametes produced by the combination of simultaneous spawning and positively buoyant gametes.

Fertilization is an area of considerable research interest. Understanding its capacity to limit larval supply will become easier as we begin to understand the factors influencing fertilization rates. So far, we know that fertilization depends on time of year, age of eggs and sperm, size of egg, density of sperm (too few or too many), water movements (advection, shear, and so on), and temperature, via changes in viscosity of the water. The knowledge that fertilization may be problematical for many uncommon species in assemblages can provide a stimulus for research, to determine if, and how, such individuals can reproduce successfully. It also breaks the simplistic link between production of gametes and successful reproduction.

Current research seeks to understand the determinants of successful fertilization using field experimentation and, for the intertidal zone, modeling. Models of fertilization offer great promise by using laboratory estimates of parameters such as concentration and age of sperm and size of eggs. These are incorporated into physical models of dispersal of sperm and eggs in a range of hydrodynamic situations to predict how fertilization is likely to occur in the field (Levitan 1995,1996; Mead and Denny 1995; Denny 1988; Styan 1998; Denny and Shibata 1989). Determining how well these models fit field situations will be an exciting challenge for researchers.

Dispersal

The number of larvae arriving at a particular location will be the product of three processes—the transport of larvae by water currents, the period during which they disperse, and the mortality that they suffer during dispersal. When larval development is short, most larvae are likely to be retained in local populations, but, as the planktonic period increases, there can be extensive dispersal. It is also possible, however, that larvae may be retained in local areas as a result of either oceanographic features or the behavior of the larvae (Keough 1988; Gaines and Bertness 1992).

For many species, it is likely that there will be a wide range of dispersal distances, with some propagules retained and some exported from a local population on a shore. The potential for long-lived larvae to be retained in local populations has been suggested by oceanographic modeling (McShane et al. 1988), and it has recently been demonstrated to

be important in recruitment to populations of one species of reef fish (Swearer et al. 1999) and to occur in others (Jones et al. 1999). Recruits to the reef were often from larvae that had been retained nearby by local patterns of water flow, rather than being the result of widespread larval dispersal. It will be interesting to discover how often and for what sorts of species such retention in localized water masses may occur in intertidal organisms.

A full understanding of the dynamics of populations or assemblages requires us to understand how much exchange there is between local populations of adults (Downes and Keough 1998; their Fig. 1), that is, to develop true metapopulation models (e.g., Roughgarden and Iwasa 1986). Many metapopulations have the important ability that some local populations can act as sources for recruitment into other areas with other local populations producing few larvae to the pool but primarily acting as sinks. Identifying source and sink populations is an important step to understanding metapopulation dynamics. This identification in turn leads to an understanding of how competitive interactions and predation are structured spatially. Metapopulation models are a key part of establishing systems of refuges for marine conservation (Allison et al. 1998).

All invertebrate larvae and many dispersive stages of algae can swim actively using, for example, cilia, flagella, or setae. Only a few groups, primarily fish and late larval stages of some crustaceans (e.g., lobsters), however, have the capacity to swim fast. The vast majority of invertebrate larvae swim at speeds less than 1 mm s^{-1} (Chia et al. 1984). As a result, larvae are not likely to disperse far by their own swimming and must depend on ocean currents to transport them over considerable distances.

In general, larvae are too small to be seen with the naked eye, and, when planktotrophic development is involved, their time in the plankton is too great for them to be followed directly by observers. In a few cases, it has been possible to follow larvae from when they were released from a parent (or container!), to see how and where they disperse (Olson 1985; Davis and Butler 1989). These examples have almost all been from species of colonial ascidians with unusually large (2–4 mm long) larvae that spend only a very short time in the plankton. Information from these species is not particularly helpful in understanding events in most assemblages, because colonial ascidians are at one extreme of invertebrate larval size and duration of planktonic period. In addition, even for these species, it is uncommon for more than half of the all larvae to be followed successfully, so these estimates of dispersal are likely to be biased towards larvae dispersing very short distances. The only other technique that has proved useful is direct sampling of invertebrate larvae near known sources (Graham and Sebens 1996), which has been used to demonstrate very restricted dispersal, at a scale of meters, for some invertebrates on subtidal rock walls.

When there is no direct measure of dispersal, indirect methods must be used. Genetic approaches have been used to demonstrate that there is little gene flow between populations of some intertidal species (e.g., Ayre 1990; Burton 1983). Although these methods show clearly when there is almost no dispersal, they cannot measure even modest rates of transport between populations. A few immigrants per generation will usually be enough to prevent the accumulation of genetic differences, whereas much larger rates of exchange of individuals among populations are usually necessary for meaningful ecological interactions between populations. Some new approaches, such as the examination of otolith microchemistry in fish (e.g., Swearer et al. 1999), offer some hope of measuring rates and scales of dispersal.

The most productive approach has been to develop an understanding of the way in which a range of oceanographic and geomorphological features affect transport of larvae and then to use that information in models predicting dispersal. In making such models, it is necessary to decide how much biology to incorporate into the model. Are dispersing larvae like passive particles, or does their behavior influence their dispersal?

Oceanographic Influences

Long-lived larvae are quite likely to be transported far from shore. To settle into appropriate habitats, they must often be transported back to the coastline to settle. This is especially true of intertidal and estuarine organisms. Other species, including a range of fish, move offshore to spawn, but their larvae occur inshore in shallow bays and estuaries. Oceanographic features can act to move larvae offshore, along the shore, and also to return them to nearshore habitats. When larvae are moved offshore, there is a risk that they may not be returned to suitable habitat. Loss of larvae through this mechanism can be a substantial contributor to spatial and temporal variation in larval supply (Gaines and Bertness 1992). Its importance in particular species may well depend on the ability of larvae to enhance their transport shorewards (e.g., spiny lobsters; Phillips and Pearce 1997).

Along most major coastal margins are large-scale, relatively predictable currents—the Gulf Stream, the California Current, East Australian Current, and so on. These currents can be responsible for transport of larvae over long distances. They are relatively predictable, often resulting from the meeting of major ocean currents with continental margins, although their strength may vary from year to year, especially during El Niño Southern Oscillation (EÑSO) conditions. Part of their role in transporting larvae comes from observations made during EÑSO years, in which warm currents push farther up the Californian coastline than normal (Connolly and Roughgarden 1999). Changes in water currents between years can be important in changing the spatial patterns of recruitment.

Where different water bodies meet, fronts can be formed. These can entrain larvae and their food or predators (Zeldis and Jillet 1982; Kingsford 1990; Shanks 1995). Fronts can result from the interaction between various kinds of oceanic and tidal currents and by the meeting of water bodies differing in temperature or density, such as occur near the mouths of estuaries. In addition to entraining larvae, a moving front can transport larvae as a coherent group. It can move them, either to suitable areas for settlement (Shanks 1983), or in such a way as to counteract effects of cross-shelf transport (Eggleston et al. 1998). Estuarine fronts, in particular, are a common and important influence on larvae (Grimes and Kingsford 1996).

Coastal features modify currents and entrain water. Oceanography becomes much more complex in nearshore areas, particularly on highly reticulated coastlines. Coastal features can direct long-shore currents away from suitable habitats for intertidal animals, but they can also create features that promote retention of larvae (e.g., McShane et al. 1988).

Wing et al. (1995) elegantly demonstrated that variations in numbers of settling crabs (*Cancer* spp.) were well correlated with relaxations of upwelling along the Californian coast. North of Point Reyes, settlement of crabs varied from day to day as a thermal front moved northwards following relaxation of upwelling. Coastal morphology can dictate processes of transport and therefore numbers and timing of settlement of larvae.

Sometimes, nearshore features are biogenic structures formed by large organisms. Two of the best known are seagrass meadows and large brown algae, such as *Macrocystis* spp. Algal beds can act as baffles, reducing water flow and potentially impeding movement of larvae to and from a local shoreline. It is also possible that, as these beds often contain large densities of planktivorous fish, they can act as zones of very great larval mortality (Gaines and Roughgarden 1987). The roles of these offshore algal beds on whole assemblages have been studied most intensively for subtidal organisms (Eckman et al. 1989, 1990). Kelp beds may also act as filters for newly produced larvae from intertidal areas, either reducing the export from any local area, or providing an early opportunity for predators to consume the larvae.

The onshore transport of larvae can result from wind-driven currents, especially in embayments (e.g., Jenkins et al. 1999), but two of the most important transport mechanisms are internal waves and internal tidal bores. Internal waves are formed when tidal currents interact with seafloor features, as will occur around reefs and edges of continental shelves. They are common features of most coastlines, and their presence is often indicated by surface slicks. They can be very important for transporting larvae (Shanks 1983; Kingsford and Choat 1986), although biological features such as kelp beds can prevent transport of larvae because the kelp beds are large and dense enough to prevent physical processes, such as transport by internal waves (Eckman et al. 1989).

When internal waves are large, they can "break" to form an internal bore—see Shanks (1995) for a detailed description of this phenomenon. Such a bore is then capable of transporting larvae quite rapidly towards shore (Pineda 1991). Upwelling conditions can also move larvae towards shore (Shanks 1998), as can the cessation of upwelling, if it promotes exchange between offshore and nearshore water (Farrell et al.1991).

Larval Mortality

Mortality during the planktonic phase is generally presumed to be very great, but many estimates are based on rough calculations, linking individual fecundity to the number of recruits needed to maintain a stable population, supported by the presumed vulnerability of small, weakly swimming larvae (Thorson 1950). These calculations should be viewed with some caution because they combine failure of fertilization, actual planktonic mortality, and post-settlement and post-recruitment mortality. Nevertheless, for most species, there must be great mortality during planktonic phases of life history.

There have been some estimates of rates of mortality from tracking larval cohorts, in field sampling (Rumrill 1990) and, occasionally, by direct observation. The latter estimates, for very short-lived, large, ascidian tadpoles are reliable, but they are not representative of many other larvae.

Morgan (1995a), in his comprehensive review of larval mortality, identified physiological stress, food resources, predation, sinking, and advection as major potential sources of mortality. They are not considered in detail here because of Morgan's contribution to this volume.

Pelagic predators have long been thought to be the major source of larval mortality. A wide range of fish take invertebrate larvae. Morgan (1995a) regarded hydromedusae, scyphomedusae, and ctenophores to be the major predators among the invertebrates. Ctenophores and hydromedusae are the most important predators of invertebrate larvae, and scyphomedusae are most important as predators of larval fish. In contrast, benthic invertebrates, which can actively prey on larvae or accidentally ingest them as a part of suspension feeding, appear not to have major impacts on larval abundances (Young 1990), even when these potential predators occur in large densities. They may, however, have important influences on survival of late-stage larvae when they are beginning to settle into benthic habitats.

The final two sources of mortality, sinking and advection, are important for taking larvae away from areas of abundant food or potential sites for settlement. Losses from these two causes have not been described in detail.

Although the evidence for most of these causes of mortality is sparse and often equivocal, the planktonic period remains a period of great mortality for many species. Larvae do, however, have attributes that should reduce this mortality. The timing of release of larvae can greatly affect their survival. Over a day, larvae may be released to avoid times of peak UV radiation (Olson 1983), or they may follow tidal or lunar cycles (Morgan 1995b; especially his Table 4). Larvae may also be morphologically or chemically defended against predators (Lindquist and Hay 1996).

Note that there is also a feedback between the time taken to complete development and to find a suitable patch of habitat for later life and the probability of being consumed by predators (Vance 1973a, b; Christiansen and Fenchel 1979; Palmer and Strathmann 1981; Underwood and Fairweather

1989). Much of this material has been reviewed very well by others (Butman 1987; Eckman 1996). It is important, nevertheless, to realize that the variability associated with surviving numbers of dispersive larvae is not qualitatively different from that experienced by many animals that do not have a planktonic dispersive stage, but instead have direct development so that the young are hatched directly from the mother or from benthic egg capsules. Spight (1974, 1975) has demonstrated that the numbers of whelks (*Thais* spp.) hatching from egg capsules on the shore were variable because of chance disturbances and predators consuming the capsules. Variability in survival to the end of development is a widespread feature of the life history of the vast majority of marine animals. The interesting question is still whether longer planktonic periods result in more variability in recruitment, or comparable variability, due to different processes.

Larval Behavior

Because of the small size of larvae, their behavior during the dispersive phase is very poorly known (Young 1995). Swimming larvae do, however, respond to a wide range of cues that cause them to move through the water column. When water flow is not uniform, larvae that move between strata of water can change their final dispersal. The contribution of this behavior to dispersal has been studied in most detail for a range of estuarine crustaceans and fish along the East Coast of North America. The crustaceans generally spawn in estuaries. Their larvae must either be retained within the estuary or find their way back after being advected offshore. Usually, the fish spawn offshore and larvae must move inshore. For one fish, the Atlantic menhaden, larvae appear to use temperature as a cue to move between different strata of water (DeVries et al. 1995).

The potential importance of this sort of mechanism has been shown for barnacles. Recruitment varied with the patterns of flow of water in and out of an estuary (Gaines and Bertness 1992). It is, however, not yet clear how larvae behave in response to the various patterns of flow in different estuaries and at different times. The work so far indicates the potential influences on passive particles. What is needed, however, is an understanding of the ways active larvae respond to differences in water masses and whether or not the larvae can themselves behave to increase their likelihood of being retained in an estuary.

Larvae also respond to light and tidal cues. Their responses to some of these cues change with the age of the larvae, which suggests that they are swimming actively between water strata in such a way as to enhance their transport shorewards at appropriate times and to promote retention in the estuary at others (Forward et al. 1996). Other species move up and down in the water column in response to changes in tidal flow (DeVries et al. 1995)

Similarly, crustacean larvae respond to light, pressure, and salinity in ways that result in their being transported onshore at the surface of the water. Once they reach an estuary, they may be moved up it by being up in the water column on incoming tides and near the bottom on ebb tides (Tankersley et al. 1995; Tankersley and Forward 1994). At least one species, the blue crab *Callinectes sapidus*, shows a change in larval behavior between oceanic and estuarine water (Forward et al. 1997).

Settlement

Larvae of most marine organisms metamorphose when they encounter a suitable cue or when they run out of resources. The metamorphosis may be a complete transformation, such as undergone by most sessile organisms when the swimming appendages are lost and adult structures for feeding and attachment are formed. This transformation is usually irreversible and happens relatively quickly, being completed within a day or two. For many intertidal organisms, the morphological changes of metamorphosis begin almost immediately after settlement. For sessile organisms, settlement is particularly crucial because the site of attachment of the larva determines the fate of the adult and settlement determines the initial spatial distribution within populations. Eventual recruitment of individuals into a population of animals in a particular area or habitat will therefore depend not just on the arrival of larvae (i.e., their "supply"), but also on their rates of settlement in that particular place. It is therefore worth a brief review of the sorts of processes that influence the chances or choices of larvae settling.

"Distant" Cues: Identifying Appropriate Habitats

Larvae may identify appropriate habitats from a distance, or on contact with appropriate substrata. If they respond to cues strongly, then we may be able to explain variation in settlement by knowing the distribution of settlement cues, allowing (relatively) simple models of settlement. If, however, cues do not elicit strong responses, or if larval responses to cues are disrupted by the physical environment or weakened by depletion of energy reserves, knowing the distribution of cues will not be of much predictive value. In the simplest case, larvae might use light or gravity to identify benthic habitats, and many invertebrate larvae switch from positive to negative phototaxis towards the end of their dispersive period (e.g., Svane and Young 1989; Reed 1991). Detection of habitats from a distance may also involve water-borne cues. Such cues have been the subject of speculation, but there is some doubt about whether water-borne compounds could provide directional information in turbulent environments. The only convincing evidence that larvae use such cues is from the oyster *Crassostrea virginica* (Zimmer-Faust and Tamburri 1994), in soft-sediment habitats of the southeastern United States.

As larvae of benthic species encounter the substratum, they may show exploratory behavior, moving over the substratum surface (e.g., Reed 1991). They have a wide range of sensory structures and, under laboratory conditions, have been shown to respond to a wide range of stimuli (Crisp 1974, 1976; Meadows and Campbell 1972).

The substratum itself may provide a stimulus, with larvae capable of responding to its texture or its color. Many species respond to light at the time of settlement (Meadows and Campbell 1972).

A bewildering range of biogenic cues has been described; see Pawlik (1992) for a review of chemical cues. These cues may induce larvae to settle or act as deterrents (Pawlik 1992; Lindquist and Hay 1996). Cues may be derived from conspecific individuals, as in many barnacles, from food species, as in a number of predatory nudibranchs (Thompson 1958), or cues may be derived from species that are indicators of an appropriate habitat (e.g., algal cues from particular intertidal regions; Strathmann et al. 1981).

Benthic substrata present complex chemical cues derived from the substratum itself, from the matrix of micro-organisms and particulate organic matter (collectively, the biofilm), and from other macro-organisms. Many subtidal sessile animals respond to the presence of these biofilms, often in quite subtle ways (Todd and Keough 1994; Keough and Raimondi 1995).

There has obviously been very substantial work on the types of cues to which larvae respond when settling. Much of this has been in the laboratory, exploring the potential behavioral responses of larvae (Meadows and Campbell 1972). Much less has been in the field in attempts to understand actual responses and how the distribution and/or amount of various cues might actually influence the numbers of settling larvae, particularly under conditions causing different numbers to arrive at any site. A clear challenge for the future is the development of reliable techniques to monitor and manipulate biogenic cues and rates of larvae arrival in experiments under field conditions.

Hydrodynamics and Behavior: Can Larvae "Behave" in Physically Demanding Habitats?

For many years, there has been discussion about whether responses of settling larvae are real or are artifacts due to the ways they are investigated. This discussion has arisen because most studies of larval settlement have been done under controlled laboratory conditions. Even though these reveal very sophisticated behavior, the question is whether, in the field, larvae actually show the behavioral responses in the face of very complex cues, when there are possibly declining reserves of energy and, perhaps most importantly, when they are in a hydrodynamic environment in which they have little ability to navigate.

This question has been resolved with experimental demonstrations that larvae can and do respond to settlement cues in the most demanding hydrodynamic environment, the intertidal zone of rocky shores (e.g., Strathmann et al. 1981; Raimondi 1988). They can use complex cues, such as responding to the successional changes that occur during the development of biofilms (e.g., Keough and Raimondi 1995). Larvae are able to respond in two ways to cues for settlement. Perhaps most importantly, in most hydrodynamic environments, there are areas of low flow, such as boundary layers and areas in the lee of benthic objects. These areas may provide regions in which larvae are able to swim and explore the substratum and may be quite common in subtidal areas and in intertidal zones of sheltered shores (Eckman 1996).

The second possibility is that larvae can respond quickly to cues for settlement, so that in wave-exposed, turbulent environments they are continually being brought into brief contact with possible sites for settlement. Denny (1988) explored the potential influences of turbulent flow to make educated guesses about the likelihood of larvae being able to make new contact with the surface of a rock once they reject a site for settlement. The model of turbulent flow analyzed by Denny (1988) certainly provided a mechanism by which larvae have opportunities to explore various possible sites for settlement.

Larvae are capable of attaching themselves very rapidly to sites that provide a positive stimulus. In high-energy environments, an understanding of settlement requires observing larvae as they encounter the substratum. Whether their exposure to surfaces includes exploratory behavior, or just a series of very brief contacts, must be determined.

As with most ecological disputes, the interesting question is not whether larval behavior is important or not, but under which conditions is larval behavior important. The "hydrodynamic limits" of some larvae are becoming understood (see Butman 1987; Abelson and Denny 1997 for reviews), with the expected result that under slow flow, behavior can be important. Where flow is faster, larvae act increasingly as passive particles (e.g., Mullineaux and Butman 1991; Jonsson et al. 1991).

Current views of larvae were summarized by Butman (1987) in her influential review. Larval behavior was most important as larvae near settlement; larger-scale dispersal processes are largely the result of passive transport. It should be emphasized, however, that in highly stratified flows, where behavior may influence dispersal, the role of larvae is not understood. Understanding behavior near the time of settlement is producing a more complex picture of the relationship between larvae and hydrodynamics.

Ultimately, understanding the behavior of larvae (and what influences the decision of larvae to settle in a given site) will allow integration of models about local supply and models about the actual numbers settling. Whether or not the numbers arriving at any site are actually related to the numbers settling is considered in the next section.

Is Settlement Correlated with Supply?

The processes of larval production, transport, and mortality combine to produce larval supply. It is possible that understanding supply is sufficient to explain variability in settlement. The evidence to examine the relationship between these variables is derived predominantly from studies of intertidal barnacles, where larval supply has been measured by pumping water samples (e.g., Grosberg 1982), or by cleverly designed integrated passive samplers (e.g., Yund et al. 1991). Within these studies, larval supply can be a good predictor of settlement (e.g., Grosberg 1982; Gaines et al. 1985; Minchin-

ton and Scheibling 1991), or poorly correlated (e.g., Miron et al. 1995). Even within the same population, larval supply may vary in its ability to predict settlement. For example, Miron et al. (1995) found that larval supply explained about 75% of variation in settlement of the barnacle *Semibalanus balanoides* at low levels of an intertidal shore in eastern Canada. At higher levels on the same shore, there was, however, little relationship.

As with other aspects of settlement, there may also be scale-dependent relationships. At larger scales, where passive transport may be involved, there should be a relationship between supply and settlement to a particular location. At very small scales, where larval behavior is important, supply and settlement may become decoupled and larval settlement may track the distribution of settlement cues (e.g., Raimondi 1991; Strathmann et al. 1981).

WHY IS THERE SUCH WASTE OF POTENTIAL RECRUITS?

Most authors from early discussions on the topic have been convinced that the phase of dispersal and development is very wasteful. Only a tiny proportion of the eggs or larvae released into the environment make it back to a suitable habitat for later life. The vast majority are assumed to be eaten by predators in the plankton or near the substratum when they are attempting to settle (Thorson 1950; Crisp 1964a). Others are carried away from suitable shallow or coastal habitats and are presumably lost because they cannot ever find a suitable place to settle. In addition, there has been considerable emphasis on the role of starvation of larvae as a major source of mortality (see, particularly, Leggett and DeBlois 1994). It is not known how often predation or starvation of any other process is the major source of mortality for larvae of any species. There is, however, widespread consensus that mortality of dispersive larvae is very great.

The issue is not to ask why have such a profligate waste, but rather to ask: what alternatives are there? Is it actually possible to avoid the waste? The most commonly advanced and probably the most currently convincing explanation for the widespread existence of such a wasteful mode of life as that used in the sea (and on land by many plants and insects) is the notion of "spreading the risk" (Reddingius and den Boer 1970). Widespread dispersal of larvae has the consequence that offspring have some probability of encountering a suitable patch of habitat somewhere. If, instead, the animals were all produced and retained locally (as done by the minority of coastal species that have direct development), there is a large risk that the patch of habitat will become unsuitable and therefore local populations will be extinguished. Disturbances due to storms, coastal uplift, waves, excessive periods of hot weather during low tide, floods from estuaries, and so on, will all act to make patches of habitat unsuitable. Over any long period of time, it can be expected that most, if not all, habitat will eventually become unsuitable, and therefore species that have depended on direct development have a greater chance of going extinct. In contrast, although the vast majority of the offspring are unsuccessful in any batch released into the sea by a broadcast developer, the probability is greater in the long run that some of the offspring will eventually find and be able to occupy a favorable piece of habitat.

Of necessity, when dealing with largely untestable evolutionary theories and predictions, it is always possible to generate quite contradictory models. Palmer and Strathmann (1981), among others, have suggested that greater distances spread by larvae do not confer short-term selective advantages for species where environmental variability is of similar spatial and temporal scales to the variations in fecundity and survival of adults of the species. The modeling on which this was based depended on assumptions, including that the distance dispersed was an increasing function of the time spent as larvae. Increasingly, this assumption must be called into question, given the new insights into oceanographic processes influencing larval spread (see the earlier comments about studies by Wing et al. 1995; Roughgarden et al. 1988; Swearer et al. 1999).

Habitat can become unsuitable because of variations in numbers surviving dispersive phases. There are known to be occasions when large numbers of potential competitors or predators may arrive in any patch because they are also operating with broadcast dispersal of offspring. As a result, frequencies and intensities of interactions among predators and prey or among competitors for resources will increase. Alternatively, from the point of view of animals such as filter-feeders that depend on an adequate supply of planktonic food arriving to their habitat, there may now be periods of little supply of food because at some times the dispersive larvae of species making up some of the plankton will be absent or in small numbers. For example, larvae of small rissoid gastropods living amongst beds of coralline algae can make up a substantial proportion of the diets of herring in some areas and at some times (Lebour 1921, 1934). If the gastropods fail to produce adequate larvae, the herring must find another food or go short of food. As a result, because of the widespread occurrence of dispersive stages of the life history, there are now many ecological and physical processes that can cause a piece of habitat to become unsuitable.

There has been some direct evidence to explore the paradox of some species being able to persist despite not having dispersive offspring. Thorson (1946, 1950) and Mileikovsky (1971) long ago described gradients in the proportion of species that have dispersive larvae. For example, in Antarctic waters, very few gastropods have dispersive larvae (Pearse et al. 1991). In contrast, in tropical seas, the great majority of gastropods have dispersive larval stages of life. There are also gradients with depth, and some types of animals (e.g., meiofauna) are predominantly direct developing (Coull and Bell 1979).

One explanation for these differences (apart from the risks associated with not spreading the offspring widely) is that there are habitats with little long-term disturbance. Deep-sea and Antarctic areas are supposedly examples of such places (Thorson 1950), although there can be argument about the validity of this explanation.

There is, however, some evidence for the nature of risk of extinction globally rather than locally in animals with direct development. Scheltema (1971, 1989) reasoned that having a dispersive stage of life history bestows advantages in terms of surviving when habitats are disturbed. Consequently, he predicted that during periods of frequent and widespread disturbance, species without dispersive stages should be more likely to go extinct than species with pelagic or other dispersive offspring. He tested this hypothesis by examining the mode of development of gastropods from before to after various geological upheavals. Many groups of gastropods leave tell-tale signs of the mode of development in the presence or absence of sculpturing on the earliest part of the coiled shell. This is the part laid down during larval life; most species with direct development have little or no sculpturing or pattern on the earliest part of the shell. Scheltema (1971, 1989) by patient search was able to locate specimens of fossil gastropods with the larval shell (the protoconch) sufficiently intact to allow determination of the mode of development. His results were clear-cut. Species with long-term planktonic development were far less restricted in their distribution due to long-term paleological alterations of habitat than were those with similar species with shorter-term dispersal. Similarly, Jablonski and Lutz (1983) reviewed rates of extinction and geographical spread of species for which the mode of development (i.e., long- or short-term dispersal) was identifiable. Gastropods with long-term larval dispersal tended to last for about twice as long in the fossil record (6 m.y. versus 3 m.y. and 4.4 m.y. versus 2.2 m.y. in two different assemblages). The former also occupied about twice the geographical area of the latter. So, the ability to disperse across large distances and therefore to recruit to widespread patches of habitat is important in determining the geographical (and historical) scales of existence of marine species.

Despite our desire to have large-scale models for the evolution of life histories among marine invertebrates, it should, nevertheless, be remembered that the modes of reproduction and type of life history shown by marine invertebrates in any small patch of habitat can be very different (Downes and Keough 1998). The terminology to describe mode of development is complex and variable (Levin and Bridges 1995) and only the simplest version will be used here to illustrate the point. On any patch of rocky shore in southeastern Australia, it is possible to find abundant species that have direct development [e.g., the predatory snails, *Bedeva hanleyi* (Anderson 1960) or *Lepsiella vinosa* and the starfish *Patiriella exigua* (Lawson-Kerrr and Anderson 1978)] and barnacles, such as *Tesseropora rosea* and *Tetraclitella purpurascens* (Anderson 1969) that produce larvae from eggs brooded within their shells. There are also snails that lay benthic egg-capsules from which emerge planktotrophic larvae with larval lives up to a few weeks [e.g., the limpets, *Siphonaria denticulata* (Creese 1980) and the snails, *Bembicium nanum* and *Nerita atramentosa* (Anderson 1961, 1962)], or larval lives that are short and the larvae are lecithotrophic (the starfish *Patiriella calcar*; Lawson-Kerr and Anderson 1978). There are also species that lay eggs directly into the sea and from which hatch planktotrophic larvae that swim around for at least two weeks [e.g., the limpet, *Siphonaria virgulata* (Creese 1980) and species that lay eggs directly into the sea, but the larvae are lecithotrophic and develop within a few days [the snail *Austrocochlea porcata* (Underwood 1974), the limpets *Cellana tramoserica* and *Patelloida alticostata* (Anderson 1966)] or only a few hours [the tunicate *Pyura stolonifera* (Anderson et al. 1976)]. Note that several of these species are closely related but have quite different modes of life history.

Finally, there are species in which the individuals demonstrate more than one mode of reproduction. For example, the anemone *Actinia tenebrosa* can breed by budding to produce genetically identical clones or by production of planktotrophic larvae (Ayre 1984). It is not easy to produce a grand unifying theory that allows for so much variation in any one habitat, particularly in species with similar phylogenetic origins and history.

Even so, although there is never any exactitude about the origins of different modes of life history and all arguments based on adaptive advantage are open to alternative interpretations, there is a consensus that much of what is seen is brought about by the great probability of going extinct because patches of occupiable habitat keep becoming unoccupiable due to disturbance and ecological crises. Only by shifting the larvae from one patch to another during the early, dispersive phase of life is it more likely that a species will persist despite the patchy nature of existence of suitable habitat.

MODELING DISPERSAL

A wide range of oceanographic features can transport larvae, and larval behavior can be important if larvae have the opportunity to move between bodies of water moving in different ways. Realizing that both components are important is not sufficient to make accurate predictions about links between populations. The two pieces of information must be combined. Because larval dispersal can rarely be observed directly, modeling is a useful alternative. An accurate model has the potential to predict at least relative numbers of larvae being transported to local populations. If accurate estimates of larval mortality can be incorporated, the model may be able to generate absolute numbers of larvae arriving at a locale.

To model larval dispersal, good physical oceanographic models are needed. The physical models must be able to predict accurately where passive particles will be transported. The models will require validation in the field, using direct measurements of currents. This is an important initial step for ecologists, who may need to choose between competing oceanographic models.

The complexity of the physical models varies widely, depending on the local environment. Production of an appropriate model may be very quick, if a model already exists, or very slow, for a poorly known, but complex situation (Keough and Black 1996). In relatively simple cases, tides and major, predictable currents may account for most movement of water, with little vertical stratification. In contrast, in complex situations, movements may be a complex mix of tides, local winds, coastal currents, and local geomorphology, resulting in a greatly stratified vertical flow.

To model dispersal, it must also be known where propagules enter the area. This information can be difficult to obtain if the organisms are widespread because many populations must be sampled to estimate their reproductive contributions.

The remaining question is how much of the biology of the larvae needs to be incorporated into the model. In most cases, the duration of the larval period must be specified along with estimates of planktonic mortality. A more interesting question is whether the behaviors described in the previous section really contribute to dispersal.

Modeling can be a useful way of approaching this question, if the distribution and abundance of late-stage larvae are also sampled. The predictions from models for dispersal can then be compared with the actual fates of larvae. Incorporating various aspects of larval behavior into the models should increase the ability to predict where larvae go.

PROCESSES NEGATIVELY AFFECTING SUCCESS OF SETTLEMENT: EXAMPLES FROM ROCKY SHORES

The outcome of the torrent of experimental studies on rocky shores from about 1970 onwards illustrates numerous processes that can affect whether or not larvae settle, settle and metamorphose, or manage to survive the first few days after arrival into the adult habitat. To illustrate each of these, consider first the widespread occurrence of pre-emptive competition for space. Much of the surface of a rocky shore is occupied by such things as encrusting algae and sessile animals. Some of these are known to be inimical to settlement of larvae of animals. For example, seaweeds can produce natural antifouling compounds that dissuade larvae from settling (Sieburth and Conover 1965). Corals can prevent settlement of barnacle larvae (Rittschoff et al. 1985). Without doubt, pre-emption of the surface reduces the likelihood that larvae will actually settle to recruit in areas occupied by pre-emptive competitors. These individuals can, however, go elsewhere to try their luck with another part of the habitat. In fact, there are cases where the chemistry of the benthic habitat provides warning to prevent settlement. The responses by the larvae are supposed to enhance the likelihood that larvae will settle in places where they are more likely to survive. Strathmann et al. (1981) showed that barnacles were less likely to settle where they could detect chemical cues indicating the presence of predators. In this case, the whole point is to ensure that the larvae move on to other places before settling, in complete contrast to larval responses to cues that act as stimulants for settlement (see above).

There are also processes that may influence the last stages of larval life or the earliest parts of the benthic existence. One of these is "whiplash" by algae, which has been shown in many parts of the world to prevent larval barnacles from successfully settling (Southward 1964; Dayton 1971; Hawkins

1983). The fronds of large fleshy algae sweep over the substratum, preventing larvae from attaching and settling. As a result, under the canopy of large plants, there is less chance of recruitment of species that are affected by such processes. Note, in passing, that demonstrating the reduced recruitment to be due to whiplash requires experimental manipulations to consider other processes such as increased predation around plants that provide shelter for predators; see Underwood (1999).

After larvae are settled and metamorphosed, the earliest stages of benthic life are subject to several disturbances. Some are physical, such as due to waves. These disturbances can be offset; for example, the snail *Littorina neritoides* wedges itself into tiny crevices in the rock and then swells its shell to fit tightly (Fretter and Manly 1977). Recruitment will be in greater numbers where the surface of the rock provides suitable crevices and holes.

In other cases, the newly settled, metamorphosing individuals are destroyed by disturbances caused by animals wandering across the substratum. The best-known cases concern "bulldozing" by limpets—a term probably coined by Dayton (1971). The grazing limpets wander across the shore and sweep up newly settled barnacles (Southward 1964; Dayton 1971) and limpets (Underwood et al. 1983) either by direct action of the feeding radula, or, more likely, by crushing the recruiting individuals or tearing them from the substratum as the grazer's foot sweeps over them.

These interactions are the final influences on larval existence and the first ecological processes affecting benthic existence. As such, they can influence the capacity of larvae that manage to settle to determine whether or not they are likely to recruit. Of course, there are many later processes of competition, disturbance, and predation that influence how many of the recruits will survive to any subsequent stage of life. These are, however, no longer part of the realm of supply-side processes, but are affected by its variation in the numbers that recruit, as described in the next section.

EXAMPLES OF CONSEQUENCES OF VARIATIONS IN SUPPLY OF RECRUITS TO ANALYSES OF ECOLOGICAL PROCESSES

The recent emphasis on supply-side ideas (or their rediscovery; see Young 1987) and on the processes and consequences of variability in numbers of recruits to any population or patch of habitat is important for all future ecological work in intertidal habitats. The crucial issue is that many ecological phenomena are routinely explained in terms of competitive interactions, predation, or disturbances as processes affecting numbers of animals and plants in any place or at any time. The supply of recruits (or the failure of recruits to arrive) is another important process (Connell 1985).

Invoking a model and assuming it to be correct is worthwhile only if no other model can realistically also explain the observations (see Underwood 1990, 1991 for details of the

logic for contrasting conceptual models in ecology). In many cases, such as the examples considered in the following sections, there can often be alternative models based on variations in supply of new individuals into a population; these must be eliminated before models based on events post-recruitment can be considered well supported by the available experimental evidence.

Missing Year-Classes

The size structure of marine populations is occasionally observed to consist of small (and young) individuals and large (old) individuals with no intermediate sizes in the population (as illustrated in Figure 7.1). Such a structure can be and has been explained by recruitment of juveniles followed by their failure to survive in some years, as they grow into the intermediate sizes. Mortality of cohorts has been attributed to inclement weather, as observed for whelks by Dayton (1971) and in many species in Britain following an exceptionally cold winter in the 1960s (Crisp 1964b). Alternatively, juveniles recruit, but are then consumed by their predators (or suc-

(A)

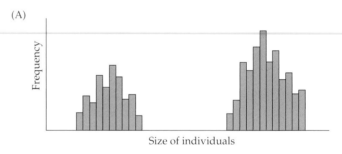

(B)

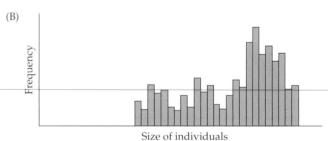

(C)

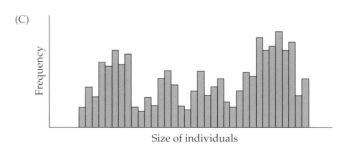

Figure 7.1 Illustration of missing size-classes in a population. (A) There are recently recruited juveniles and numerous adults, but no animals are of intermediate sizes. (B) There has been no recent recruitment, but previous cohorts have grown to intermediate sizes. (C) There are animals of intermediate sizes and a recent recruitment of small individuals.

cumb to diseases or competitors or disturbances), so that none of the intermediate sizes survives. This situation certainly occurs for some species in some areas of rocky shores (Dayton 1971; Paine 1974; Menge 1976). The existence of the larger animals is then attributed to survival and growth of the juveniles during periods of more benign weather or during periods when natural enemies are, for some reason, absent or less efficient, so that survival of the prey is good. An alternative scenario—that recruitment is occasionally excessive—is considered next. These notions were combined by Connell (1975) into an elegant model to explain recolonization by dominant species into patches of habitat from which they had been removed.

This sort of model is obviously a plausible explanation for the observed pattern of sizes. There are, however, other alternative models. Although less likely, it is possible that the animals simply grow so fast that they are not often observed while at the intermediate sizes. Suppose that animals recruit and then grow quickly to become adults in, say, three months. They then survive for long periods as adults. If the population is observed shortly after recruitment has occurred and more than three months since the previous recruitment, there will be only small or large animals present. It is quite trivial to determine whether this model has validity—frequent observations will demonstrate that animals are routinely arriving, growing, and surviving through the middle sizes.

The other alternative is the supply-side model. Animals usually recruit, grow through intermediate stages, and reach adult (large) sizes. In some years, there is no recruitment; the previously recruited cohorts grow up, but there is no replacement of animals in intermediate sizes; the smaller ones are missing and therefore cannot grow into the middle sizes. A subsequent episode of recruitment creates the observed pattern (Figure 7.1A). In such a population, the size-frequency distribution will change among the patterns shown in Figure 7.1, according to when the population is observed relative to the most recent recruitment (as will also occur in populations where intermediate sizes are eliminated in most years by mortality after routine recruitment).

In this example, the patterns of sizes can be explained by recruitment of juveniles followed by processes of competition, disease, disturbance, or predation that eliminate cohorts of individuals when they grow to intermediate sizes. The pattern can, however, also be explained by occasional failure to recruit. It is necessary *not* to assume that recruitment is persistent and subsequent mortality is the cause of the observed size frequencies. It is essential to test hypotheses derived from each model and thereby to eliminate the incorrect one. Thus, to depend on a model based on mortality after recruitment requires evidence that recruitment is regular and that the processes causing death of intermediate individuals are intense enough to eliminate them. Also, there must be evidence that these processes are sometimes absent (otherwise, there would never be adults!). During the absence of the causes of mortality of middle-sized animals, the recruits survive to become the adult cohort.

In contrast, the model based on failure to recruit at some times depends on there being evidence that, in some years, there is recruitment and then the recruits survive while growing through the middle sizes. Note that although presented as contrasting models, it is quite likely that the true explanation will be a combination of these two models (i.e., sometimes there are gaps in size-classes because of failures to recruit and sometimes because of mortality of the growing recruits).

Animals "Swamping" Their Predators

The converse of failures of recruitment (or inadequate recruitment) to maintain size-classes in a population is the arrival in any patch of habitat of excessively large numbers of recruits. Under these circumstances, the animals can "swamp" their predators—that is, they can arrive in sufficient numbers that predators do not consume them in a short period of time. For some species this has the consequence that the prey may then survive long enough to become invulnerable to the predators. For example, many species of barnacles can become relatively safe from predation if they grow large enough to have reached sizes beyond which the predators can kill them. So, in areas where the predators are whelks rather than very large generalist predators such as starfish, if barnacles can survive long enough to grow larger than the whelks can kill, they will persist for long periods.

Considerations of variations in recruitment also make it unlikely that the presence of excess prey can trigger a rapid numerical response by the whelks so that their numbers increase to capitalize on the available source of food. Although some whelks are direct developers (e.g., Spight 1975) and can produce relatively large numbers of offspring in some proportion to their numbers of adults, this process usually takes longer than does the growth of barnacles to a safe size. For other predators that have pelagic development, the numbers of their offspring arriving into a patch are also subject to the vagaries of tides, wind, and weather. So, recruitment back into any patch is not predictable in response to availability of prey there.

There are also interesting variations on this theme in terms of whether or not alternative prey arrive. Predatory whelks often have complex behaviors dictating which prey they are likely to choose to consume (Moore 1936; Murdoch 1969; Fairweather and Underwood 1983; Palmer 1984; Hughes and Burrows 1991). If a more preferred prey is abundant in any area, there can be increased survival of less preferred species of prey than would otherwise be the case. The whelk *Morula marginalba* eats barnacles of various species in preference to the limpet *Patelloida latistrigata* (Fairweather and Underwood 1983). By manipulating the numbers of barnacles recruiting into areas where whelks were feeding, Fairweather (1987) demonstrated that survival of limpets was less where barnacles were being removed than in areas where they were recruiting. So, the supply of recruits of one species can have profound influences on the surviving numbers of other species and therefore on the local structure of assemblages as a result of indirect processes (in the sense of Wootton 1993, 1994) such as predation, in addition to having direct effects.

There have been less formal accounts of other responses to different timing of recruitment. Thorson (1946) described the situation in which predatory brittle stars (*Amphiura* spp.) did not feed for two months while breeding. Several species of mollusks with short larval development bred during this period. The brittle stars had a longer period of development. As a consequence, the young mollusks could recruit and grow to a size where at least some of them would escape from the voracious predatory recruits of the brittle stars. If the mollusks recruited later, they would have been unable to avoid predators. This anecdote needs to be examined experimentally, but it indicates that the timing of recruitment can have profound influences on marine populations.

Outbreaks of Predators

Just as great recruitment of prey can swamp predators, unusually great recruitment of predators can result in outbreaks causing dramatic changes to assemblages of prey. Perhaps the most contentious such case can be seen in the outbreaks of the crown-of-thorns starfish *Acanthaster planci* on coral reefs, particularly those of the Great Barrier Reef in Australia. These outbreaks result in dramatic reductions in cover of corals on individual reefs and can spread from primary outbreaks, to cover large numbers of reefs. While large amounts of resources and many pages of journals have been devoted to the causes of outbreaks, the exact causes are not clear. Processes of settlement have been widely implicated as a cause, with contributions including fertilization kinetics (Benzie and Dixon 1994), unusually reduced larval mortality (Birkeland 1982), temperature tolerance during larval development (Johnson and Babcock 1994), dispersal (Black et al. 1995), and settling behavior (Johnson et al. 1991).

Marine introductions have recently become of considerable interest, as the extent of these introductions becomes publicized (Carlton and Geller 1993), together with the rapidity of their spread. Some of these species, such as the starfish *Asterias amurensis* in Tasmania have formed outbreaks. Given the current failure to control marine pests, understanding patterns of settlement, especially the initial spread of outbreaks, is a key requirement.

Competitive Interactions

There is no need to venture into the complex world of competitive interactions among marine species, which have been reviewed elsewhere (Connell 1983; Schoener 1983; Branch 1984, 1985; Underwood 1986, 1992). Some instances of hierarchies of competitive ability have been demonstrated experimentally in several parts of the world, for example overgrowth of barnacles by algae (Barnes and Powell 1950; Denley and Underwood 1979) and mussels (Dayton 1971; Paine 1974; Menge 1976).

Competition can, however, only occur where organisms share a resource (in the examples in the previous paragraph, the resource they need is space on the shore) and the resource is in short supply (Andrewartha and Birch 1954; Birch 1957). Resources can be in short supply for two major reasons. First, the absolute amount of resource available per capita fails. This often happens when resources are food and insufficient food grows in an area to support the numbers of consumers present. The alternative, which is probably more common in coastal marine habitats, is that the numbers of consumers of a resource arrive in excessive numbers compared with the availability of the resource. So, if there is sparse recruitment of such competitors as barnacles and mussels, competition will not occur, or will occur only in a few patches where there happen to be large densities of the competing species. Elsewhere, numbers are insufficient to occupy all of the space, and the resources are not then in short supply. Alternatively, if recruitment is intense for the various potentially competing species or for whichever of them dominates in a competitive struggle, there will be widespread competition throughout that part of their joint habitat. There are too many consumers of the resource for each animal to be able to obtain the quantity or quality of resource it needs.

Numerous examples of such situations were reviewed by Branch (1984) and Underwood (1992) for intertidal habitats and, more generally, by Connell (1983) and Schoener (1983). Reference to these reviews will identify the extraordinary range of resources for which competition can occur and the details of the processes by which it influences sizes, fecundities, and densities of the species involved.

This is sufficiently self-evident that it requires little more comment. Competitive interactions are obviously density-dependent, and one of the ways that density can be insufficient for competition to occur is that the numbers of individuals recruiting into the area are too small for resources to become saturated. The crucial issue is to remember that size of populations is not just held in check by disturbances and natural enemies, a point particularly emphasized by Andrewartha and Birch (1954), but can be kept small by lack of intense recruitment. In any study invoking competition, or making predictions about the outcomes of competitive interactions, it is important to remember that the predictability is limited by the degree to which the densities of the potential competitors can be predicted for any habitat or time.

There are "downstream" consequences of variations in recruitment as an influence on the likelihood or intensity of competitive interactions. For example, where numerous juveniles of a species of grazing gastropod arrive onto a shore, the available food may be in short supply. If small individuals have small needs for maintenance compared with the requirements of large individuals, competition for food can result in stunted growth of the juveniles and loss of tissue and eventual death of any pre-existing adults (Underwood 1976). Under normal circumstances, when food is not in short supply, adults can consume what they need for maintenance and reproduction; juveniles can consume what they need for maintenance and growth. When food is in short supply, reproduction is first in jeopardy for adults and growth ceases for juveniles. If food is not in sufficient availability for the remaining needs of individuals, adults will need more food per capita for maintenance of a larger body than is the case for smaller individuals. So, competition can be intense enough to prevent adults from surviving—they can no longer maintain their tissues. Clearly, the vagaries of numbers recruiting can have long-term influences on the survival and growth of individuals. Competition between size-classes is a particular form of intraspecific competition that results in potential for variations in ultimate size reached by adults and their capacity to breed. For many invertebrates, capacity to breed is determined largely by size of the body (e.g., Creese 1980; Hughes and Roberts 1980; Strathmann and Strathmann 1982; Stocker 1991). So, variations in supply of recruits can have different effects on an existing population depending on the sizes the individuals had previously reached in that habitat, and the availability of food (or other resources). Variations in supply can have variable outcomes for the subsequent reproductive success of the individuals in any habitat.

Geographical Patterns

Many species of marine animals and plant have geographic boundaries along coastlines that are not easily explained by prevailing patterns of weather or climate. Thus, although gradients of temperature are often invoked as explanations for the limitations of geographic distribution of organisms— probably starting with Orton (1920) and reviewed extensively by Ekman (1953) and Briggs (1974)—there are other alternatives that should be carefully considered and, if possible, eliminated from contention before accepting physiological or reproductive limitations to distribution.

As an example, Yamada (1977) investigated experimentally the proximate reasons for limitations of distribution of two species of intertidal littorinid snails. One of them (*Littorina sitkana*) has direct development and requires high-shore crevices to live in and in which to breed and lay eggs. Yamada (1977) argued that crevices were less available and predation by crabs in those crevices that were available would prevent *L. sitkana* from extending south of its natural geographical distribution. It was not clear what prevented the crabs from extending further north. In contrast, *L. planaxis,* when transplanted north of its usual range, could survive and grow. Yamada (1977) proposed that the usual northern limit of distribution is set by the fact that the snail breeds during times of the year when currents are mostly flowing to the south. Thus, larvae in the plankton are unable to move northwards. The limit of biogeographic range can be set by the prevailing pattern of supply of individuals and not the forces eliminating them after they arrive. This is an area of need for biogeographical research coupled with ecological studies of larval supply.

Such supply-side explanations are, in fact, widely invoked in discussion of biogeographic boundaries. The period of larval development sets the limit of how far most species can actually spread and therefore how much of the available habitat in the world they will actually occupy. So, the open spaces at the centers of large oceans are formidable barriers to geographic spread of species simply because many larvae do not persist long enough in the water column to have any chance of crossing over the open spaces to reach habitat on the other side. The period of development sets a limit on the possibility of recruiting to novel habitat. So, again, issues of recruitment dictate the large-scale patterns of distribution of many species and must be considered before more local explanations have any weight. Scheltema (1971, 1989) described a test of the hypothesis that opportunity to recruit across the Atlantic would be well correlated with the degree of interchange of populations. He proposed that species found on both sides of the Atlantic should have more frequent planktonic stages in the center of the ocean than is the case for species that are found on only one or the other side. The difficulties of catching many larvae made the data sparse. Nevertheless, there was a pattern that species with planktonic development of 2 to 6 weeks were seldom found on both sides of the Atlantic and their larvae were rare or absent from plankton hauls in the center of the ocean. In contrast, three-quarters of those species with very long larval lives, that is, 2 to 6 months or more, are found on both Atlantic coastlines and turn up relatively often in plankton samples in the center of the ocean. Obviously, the ability to recruit is the major determinant of distribution across the ocean basin. Processes acting after recruitment are apparently less important in terms of such large-scale distributions.

Further evidence for the failure of recruitment to increase geographical distributions is provided by the fate of organisms that are introduced by humans. It is difficult, if not impossible, to know what happens in cases in which there is an introduction, but the introduced species is unsuccessful at invading and subsequently disappears. For example, see the review by Simberloff (1981). Despite the bias this introduces into the data, there is widespread observation of the success of invasion by introduced coastal species (reviewed by Carlton 1989, 1996). This is strongly supportive of the idea that geographical distributions are often set by the lack of opportunity to recruit. Once this has been overcome by human intervention bringing the recruits into the new habitat, none of the physiological, competitive, predatory, or other interactions prevent them from becoming successfully established.

Conclusion

The extent to which previous explanations and models for various phenomena (size-structure, predictability of mortality due to predation, intensity of competition, and so on) are to be considered realistic is limited where supply-side alternatives have not simultaneously been examined. The challenge for ecological research is to incorporate models involving variations of recruitment and processes causing them. In some areas, this will require reevaluation of previously investigated scenarios. In other examples, the emphasis will need to shift to when, where, how often, and how widespread are the cases that can be explained by any particular process or combination of processes. Whatever the case, there is a great need to contrast possible supply-side explanations with those involving only the better-known and longer-studied ecological interactions after recruitment has occurred.

MODELING AND PREDICTING RECRUITMENT

As suggested in earlier sections, understanding dispersal has proceeded most effectively by combining empirical work with modeling, to try to deal with the difficulty of studying large-scale dispersal. In a similar way, examining the role of recruitment in local populations can be difficult because recruitment varies dramatically in time for most species, requiring empirical work to continue for long periods. In addition, larval supply is not yet generally amenable to the kinds of experimental manipulations that have proved so informative for later life history stages. Understanding the dynamics of metapopulations adds a requirement of a very large spatial scale for many species, creating further logistic difficulties.

One solution to this difficulty is to model the dynamics of populations and assemblages, allowing some mathematical consequences of variation in recruitment to be identified. The most detailed modeling has been done for populations, rather than assemblages, and for barnacles in the intertidal zone of rocky shores. These models, developed over the past 15 years by Roughgarden and her colleagues, began with population dynamic models for small sections of the shore, treating settlement as a random variable, with the number of settlers per unit area determined by the amount of free space, independent of the size or structure of the local population (Roughgarden et al. 1985). While these models will inevitably be simplifications, for example in the assumption of a simple relationship between free space and overall settlement (Pineda and Caswell 1997), they have generated several interesting results.

One of the most interesting has been the conclusion that qualitatively different population dynamics can result from overall differences in larval supply. When larval supply is small, not surprisingly, much space remains open. The population has a mixed age-structure and there can be long-term stability, as long as the rate of settlement does not vary dramatically through time. In contrast, at very intense settlement, space is quickly occupied and density-dependent processes are important. Most interestingly, the population becomes less stable through time, because dense aggregations of barnacles tend to disappear in large patches, creating large amounts of free space. For barnacles, hummocking—the formation of tall, relatively unstable clumps barnacles—resulting from effects of crowding on growth (Barnes and Powell 1950), provides an empirical mechanism for such patchy disappearance. Free space is then occupied by a single cohort of barnacles, which grow and senesce together, so the population goes through wild fluctuations.

These models have been expanded to link groups of local populations (Possingham and Roughgarden 1990) and to produce true metapopulation models (Roughgarden and Iwasa 1986). Most recently, models have incorporated local dynamics on the shore and larval transport models (Alexan-der and Roughgarden 1996; Shkedy and Roughgarden 1997). A further extension of modeling beyond metapopulations has considered the suggestion that variation in the importance of recruitment along the western coast of North America can be explained, at least in part, by variation in coastal oceanography, producing dynamics in which larvae are advected offshore in some coastal areas. Other sections of the coast have environments that promote onshore transport of larvae and therefore greater recruitment (Connolly and Roughgarden 1998).

Modeling has the potential to integrate large-scale phenomena and to develop real metapopulation approaches. At their best, models also combine empirical work that suggests appropriate ways to structure the model with the model producing estimates of parameters. This combined approach satisfies the key attribute identified by Chesson and Huntly (1997) of using empirical approaches to identify density dependence and using the models to explore the critical interaction between density-dependent and density-independent processes.

At present, modeling has been applied primarily to populations. Developing models that encompass interactions within local assemblages and the varied dispersal characteristics of members of an assemblage remains a daunting prospect.

CONCLUSION

The major purpose of this overview is to reinforce the notion that considering supply-side processes is an important part of understanding the ecology of marine animals and plants. It is not a basis for declaring that processes of recruitment are more or uniquely important. Determining whether or not recruitment is limiting to any species, in any habitat or time, is largely trivial. What matters is to determine the relative importance of variations in recruitment as they affect density-dependent processes such as competition, predator–prey interactions, and processes of recovery from disturbances. To have predictability about this recruitment requires much more research on the influences of success of fertilization and mechanics of transport of larvae. This is particularly necessary in near-coastal areas where local hydrology is very uncertain and "ship-based" oceanography probably has little direct relevance. Rates of larval mortality in the plankton must also be better understood in conjunction with much greater insight into the interactions and processes influencing survival of larvae.

Most studies to date, particularly the modeling so far, have focused on species with mid-term dispersal (over several weeks), generally on barnacles from rocky intertidal habitats. The degree to which these are representative of other types of animals, other types of development and periods of dispersal and other habitats is not known. It is, however, unlikely to be great.

It is also the case that understanding the roles of supply-side issues for whole assemblages is unlikely to be possible from the current focus on single species. This has already been demonstrated for modeling multispecies fisheries (e.g., Gulland and Garcia 1984). The species making up marine assemblages have very different life histories and very different patterns of larval production, dispersal and, therefore, supply. Fitting these together will be an important challenge for some time.

This is, however, a crucial challenge for marine ecologists, given that there is massive overexploitation of marine species, destruction of coastal habitats, introduction of exotic species, pollution of inshore waters, and potential shallow-water upheavals due to global warming and rises of sea level. The contribution of supply-side processes must be incorporated into any models (conceptual or mathematical) to be able to make useful and valid predictions about the management of these environmental issues. Without integration of the supply of individuals into ecological interpretations, ecology will not be offering its full potential as the primary science of environmental understanding.

ACKNOWLEDGMENTS

We each thank the Australian Research Council for grants to support the preparation of this chapter. Tony Underwood also acknowledges the support of the Centre for Research on Ecological Impacts of Coastal Cities, Dr. M. G. Chapman and Ms. V. Mathews in the preparation of the chapter. He also thanks Mick Keough and the editors for their considerable forbearance! Steve Gaines provided some very useful suggestions that have improved the chapter.

LITERATURE CITED

Abelson, A. and M. Denny. 1997. Settlement of marine organisms in flow. *Annu. Rev. Ecol. Syst.* 28: 317–339.

Alexander, S. E. and J. Roughgarden. 1996. Larval transport and population dynamics of intertidal barnacles: A coupled benthic/oceanic model. *Ecol. Monogr.* 66: 259–275.

Allison, G. W., J. Lubchenco and M. H. Carr. 1998. Marine reserves are necessary but not sufficient for marine conservation. *Ecol. Appl.* 8: S79–S92.

Anderson, D. T. 1960. The life-histories of marine prosobranch gastropods. *J. Malac. Soc. Austral.* 4: 16–29.

Anderson, D. T. 1961. The reproduction and early life history of the gastropod *Bembicium nanum* (Lam.)(Fam. Littorinidae). *Proc. Linn. Soc. N.S.W.* 86: 203–206.

Anderson, D. T. 1962. The reproduction and early life-histories of the gastropods *Bembicium auratum* (Quoy and Gaimard)(Fam. Littorinidae), *Cellana tramoserica* (Sowerby)(Fam. Patellidae) and *Melanerita melanotragus* (Smith)(Fam. Neritidae). *Proc. Linn. Soc. N.S.W.* 87: 62–68.

Anderson, D. T. 1966. The reproduction and early life-histories of the gastropods *Notoacmaea petterdi* (Ten.-Woods), *Chiazacmaea flammea* (Quoy and Gaimard) and *Patelloida alticostata* (Angas)(Fam. Acmaeidae). *Proc. Linn. Soc. N.S.W.* 90: 106–114.

Anderson, D. T. 1969. On the embryology of the cirripede crustaceans *Tetraclita rosea* (Krauss), *Tetraclita purpurascens* (Wood), *Chthamalus antennatus* (Darwin) and *Chamaesipho columna* (Spengler) and some considerations of crustacean phylogenetic relationships. *Philos. Trans. Roy. Soc. B* 256: 183–235.

Anderson, D. T., B. N. White and E. A. Egan. 1976. The larval development and metamorphosis of the Ascidians *Pyura praeputialis* (Heller) and *Pachydermatina pleurogona* (Herdman), family Pyuridae. *Proc. Linn. Soc. N.S.W.* 100: 205–217.

Andrewartha, H. G. and L. C. Birch. 1954. *The Distribution and Abundance of Animals*. University of Chicago Press, Chicago.

Ayre, D. J. 1984. The effects of sexual and asexual reproduction on geographic variation in the sea anemone *Actinia tenebrosa*. *Oecologia* 62: 222–229.

Ayre, D. J. 1990. Population subdivision in Australian temperate marine invertebrates: Larval connections versus historical factors. *Austral. J. Ecol.* 15: 403–412.

Barnes, H. and H. T. Powell. 1950. The development, general morphology and subsequent elimination of barnacle populations, *Balanus crenatus* and *Balanus balanoides*, after a heavy initial set. *J. Anim. Ecol.* 32: 107–127.

Benzie, J. A. H. and P. Dixon. 1994. The effects of sperm concentration, sperm:egg ratio, and gamete age on fertilization success in Crown-of-Thorns starfish (*Acanthaster planci*) in the laboratory. *Biol. Bull.* 186: 139–152.

Beverton, R. J. H. and S. J. Holt. 1957. *On the Dynamics of Exploited Fish Populations*. Ministry of Agriculture, Fisheries and Food, London.

Birch, L. C. 1957. The meanings of competition. *Amer. Nat.* 91: 5–18.

Birkeland, C. H. 1982. Terrestrial runoff as a cause of outbreaks of *Acanthaster planci* (Echinodermata: Asteroidea). *Mar. Biol.* 69: 175–185.

Black, K., P. Moran, D. Burrage and G. Death. 1995. Association of low-frequency currents and crown-of-thorns starfish outbreaks. *Mar. Ecol. Prog. Ser.* 125: 185–194.

Branch, G. M. 1984. Competition between marine organisms: Ecological and evolutionary implications. *Annu. Rev. Oceanogr. Mar. Biol.* 22: 429–593.

Branch, G. M. 1985. Competition: Its Role in Ecology and Evolution of Intertidal Communities. Transvaal Museum Monograph 4. In E. S. Vrba (ed.), *Species and Speciation*, pp. 97–104. Transvaal Museum, Pretoria, South Africa.

Briggs, J. C. 1974. *Marine Zoogeography*. McGraw Hill, New York.

Burton, R. S. 1983. Protein polymorphisms and genetic differentiation of marine invertebrate populations. *Mar. Biol. Lett.* 4: 193–206.

Butman, C. A. 1987. Larval settlement of soft-sediment invertebrates: The spatial scales of pattern explained by active habitat selection and the emerging role of hydrodynamical processes. *Annu. Rev. Oceanogr. Mar. Biol.* 25: 113–165.

Carlton, J. T. 1989. Man's role in changing the face of the ocean: Biological invasions and implications for conservation of near-shore environments. *Conserv. Biol.* 3: 265–273.

Carlton, J. T. 1996. Biological invasions and cryptogenic species. *Ecology* 77: 1653–1655.

Carlton, J. T. and J. B. Geller. 1993. Ecological roulette: The global transport of non-indigenous marine organisms. *Science* 261: 78–82.

Chamberlin, T. C. 1965. The method of multiple working hypotheses. *Science* 148: 754–759.

Chesson, P. and N. Huntly. 1997. The roles of harsh and fluctuating conditions in the dynamics of ecological communities. *Amer. Nat.* 150: 519–553.

Chia, F. -S., J. Buckland-Nicks and C. M. Young. 1984. Locomotion of marine invertebrate larvae: A review. *Can. J. Zool.* 62: 1205–1222.

Christiansen, F. B. and T. M. Fenchel. 1979. Evolution of marine invertebrate reproductive patterns. *Theor. Pop. Biol.* 16: 267–282.

Coe, W. R. 1956. Fluctuations in populations of littoral marine invertebrates. *J. Mar. Res.* 15: 212–232.

Connell, J. H. 1961a. Effects of competition, predation by *Thais lapillus* and other factors on natural populations of the barnacle *Balanus balanoides*. *Ecol. Monogr.* 40: 49–78.

Connell, J. H. 1961b. The influence of interspecific competition and other factors on the distribution of the barnacle *Chthamalus stellatus*. *Ecology* 42: 710–723.

Connell, J. H. 1975. Some mechanisms producing structure in natural communities: A model and evidence from field experiments.

In M. S. Cody and J. M. Diamond (eds.), *Ecology and Evolution of Communities*, pp. 460–490. Harvard University Press, Cambridge, MA.

Connell, J. H. 1983. On the prevalence and relative importance of interspecific competition: Evidence from field experiments. *Amer. Nat.* 122: 661–696.

Connell, J. H. 1985. The consequences of variation in initial settlement versus post-settlement mortality in rocky intertidal communities. *J. Exp. Mar. Biol. Ecol.* 93: 11–46.

Connolly, S. R. and J. Roughgarden. 1998. A latitudinal gradient in northeast pacific intertidal community structure—evidence for an oceanographically based synthesis of marine community theory. *Amer. Nat.* 151: 311–326.

Connolly, S. R. and J. Roughgarden. 1999. Increased recruitment of northeast Pacific barnacles during the 1997 El Nino. *Limnol. Oceanogr.* 44: 466–469.

Coull, B. C. and S. S. Bell. 1979. Perspectives in marine meiofaunal ecology. In R. J. Livingstone (ed.), pp. 189–216. *Ecological Processes in Coastal and Marine Ecosystems*, Plenum Press, New York.

Creese, R. G. 1980. Reproductive cycles and fecundities of two species of *Siphonaria* (Mollusca: Pulmonata) in south-eastern Australia. *Austral. J. Mar. Freshwat. Res.* 31: 37–48.

Crisp, D. J. 1964a. An assessment of plankton grazing by barnacles. In D. J. Crisp (ed.), *Grazing in Terrestrial and Marine Environments*, pp. 151–164. Blackwell, Oxford.

Crisp, D. J. 1964b. The effects of the severe winter of 1962–63 on marine life in Britain. *J. Anim. Ecol.* 33: 165–210.

Crisp, D. J. 1974. Factors influencing the settlement of marine invertebrate larvae. In P. T. Grant and A. N. Mackie (eds.), *Chemoreception in Marine Organisms*, pp. 177–215. Academic Press, London

Crisp, D. J. 1976. Settlement responses in marine organisms. In R. C. Newell (ed.), *Adaptation to Environment: Essays on the Physiology of Marine Animals*, pp. 83–124. Butterworth, London.

Davis, A. R. and A. J. Butler. 1989. Direct observations of larval dispersal in the colonial ascidian *Podoclavella moluccensis* Sluiter: Evidence for closed populations. *J. Exp. Mar. Biol. Ecol.* 127: 189–203.

Dayton, P. K. 1971. Competition, disturbance and community organization: The provision and subsequent utilization of space in a rocky intertidal community. *Ecol. Monogr.* 41: 351–389.

Denley, E. J. and A. J. Underwood. 1979. Experiments on factors influencing settlement, survival and growth of two species of barnacles in New South Wales. *J. Exp. Mar. Biol. Ecol.* 36: 269–293.

Denny, M. W. 1988. *Biology and the mechanics of the wave-swept environment*. Princeton University Press, Princeton, NJ.

Denny, M. W. and M. F. Shibata. 1989. Consequences of surf-zone turbulence for settlement and external fertilization. *Amer. Nat.* 134: 859–889.

DeVries, M. C., R. B. Forward and W. F. Hettler. 1995. Behavioural response of larval Atlantic menhaden to different rates of temperature change. *J. Fish. Biol.* 47: 1081–1095.

Downes, B. J. and M. J. Keough. 1998. Scaling of colonization processes in streams: Parallels and lessons from marine hard substrata. *Austral. J. Ecol.* 23: 8–26.

Eckman, J. E. 1996. Closing the larval loop: Linking larval ecology to the population dynamics of marine benthic invertebrates. *J. Exp. Mar. Biol. Ecol.* 200: 207–237.

Eckman, J. E., D. O. Duggins and A. T. Sewell. 1989. Ecology of understory kelp environments. I. Effects of kelps on flow and particle transport near the bottom. *J. Exp. Mar. Biol. Ecol.* 129: 173–187.

Eckman, J. E., D. O. Duggins and A. T. Sewell. 1990. Ecology of understory kelp environments. II. Effects of kelps on recruitment of benthic invertebrates. *J. Exp. Mar. Biol. Ecol.* 143: 27–45.

Eggleston, D. B., D. A. Armstrong, W. E. Elis and W. S. Patton. 1998. Estuarine fronts as conduits for larval transport: Hydrodynamics and spatial distribution of dungeness crab postlarvae. *Mar. Ecol. Prog. Ser.* 164: 73–82.

Ekman, S. 1953. *Zoogeography of the Sea*. Sedgwick and Jackson, London.

Fairweather, P. G. 1987. Experiments on the interaction between predation and the availability of different prey on rocky seashores. *J. Exp. Mar. Biol. Ecol.* 114: 261–274.

Fairweather, P. G. and A. J. Underwood. 1983. The apparent diet of predators and biases due to different handling times of their prey. *Oecologia* 56: 169–179.

Farrell, T. M., D. Bracher and J. Roughgarden. 1991. Cross-shelf transport causes recruitment to intertidal populations in central California. *Limnol. Oceanogr.* 36: 279–288.

Forward, R. B., J. S. Burke, D. Rittschof and J. M. Welch. 1996. Photoresponses of larval atlantic menhaden (brevoortia tyrannus latrobe) in offshore and estuarine waters—implications for transport. *J. Exp. Mar. Biol. Ecol* 199: 123–135.

Forward, R. B., J. Swanson, R. A. Tankersely and J. M. Welch. 1997. Endogenous swimming rhythms of blue crab, callinectes sapidus, megalopae—effects of offshore and estuarine cues. *Mar. Biol.* 127: 621–628.

Fretter, V. and R. Manly. 1977. Settlement and early benthic life of *Littorina neritoides* (L.) at Wembury, South Devon. *J. Moll. Stud.* 43: 255–262.

Gaines, S. D. and M. D. Bertness. 1992. Dispersal of juveniles and variable recruitment in sessile marine species. *Nature* 360: 579–580.

Gaines, S. D., S. Brown and J. Roughgarden. 1985. Spatial variation in larval concentrations as a cause of spatial variation in settlement for the barnacle, *Balanus glandula*. *Ecology* 67: 267–272.

Gaines, S. D. and J. Roughgarden. 1987. Fish in offshore kelp forests affect recruitment to intertidal barnacle populations. *Science* 235: 479–481.

Graham, K. R. and K. P. Sebens. 1996. The distribution of marine invertebrate larvae near vertical surfaces in the rocky subtidal zone. *Ecology* 77: 933–949.

Grimes, C. B. and M. J. Kingsford. 1996. How do riverine plumes of different sizes influence fish larvae—do they enhance recruitment? *Mar. Freshw. Res.* 47: 191–208.

Grosberg, R. K. 1982. Intertidal zonation of barnacles: The influence of planktonic zonation of larvae on vertical distribution of adults. *Ecology* 63: 894–899.

Gulland J. A. and S. Garcia. 1984. Observed patterns in multi-species fisheries. In R. M. May (ed.), *Exploitation of Marine Communities*, pp. 155–190. Springer-Verlag, Berlin.

Hawkins, S. J. 1983. Interactions of *Patella* and macroalgae with settling *Semibalanus balanoides* (L.). *J. Exp. Mar. Biol. Ecol.* 71: 55–72.

Hilborn, R. and C. J. Walters. 1992. *Quantitative Fisheries Stock Assessment: Choice, Dynamics and Uncertainty.* Chapman and Hall, London.

Hjort, J. 1914. Fluctuations in the great fisheries of northern Europe viewed in the light of biological research. *Rapp. P.-v. Reun. Cons. Perm. Int. Explor. Mer* 20: 1–228.

Hughes, R. N. and M. T. Burrows. 1991. Diet selection by dogwhelks in the field: An example of constrained optimization. *Anim. Behav.* 42: 47–55.

Hughes, R. N. and D. J. Roberts. 1980. Growth and reproductive rates of *Littorina neritoides* (L.) in North Wales. *J. Mar. Biol. Assoc. U. K.* 60: 191–199.

Jablonski, D. and R. A. Lutz. 1983. Larval ecology of marine benthic invertebrates: Paleobiological implications. *Biol. Rev.* 58: 21–89.

Jenkins, G. P., K. P. Black and M. J. Keough. 1999. The role of passive transport and the influence of vertical migration on the pre-settlement distribution of a temperate, demersal fish: Numerical model predictions compared with field sampling. *Mar. Ecol. Prog. Ser.* 184: 259–271.

Johnson, C. R., D. C. Sutton, R. R. Olson and R. Giddins. 1991. Settlement of crown-of-thorns starfish: Role of bacteria on surfaces of coralline algae and a hypothesis for deep-water recruitment. *Mar. Ecol. Prog. Ser.* 71: 143–162.

Johnson, L. G. and R. C. Babcock. 1994. Temperature and the larval ecology of the crown-of-thorns starfish, *acanthaster planci*. *Biol. Bull.* 187: 304–308.

Jones, G. P., M. J. Milicich, M. J. Emslie, and C. Lunow. 1999. Self-recruitment in a coral reef fish population. *Nature* 402: 802–804.

Jonsson, P. R. C., C. Andre and M. Lindegarth. 1991. Swimming behaviour of marine bivalve larvae in a flume boundary-layer flow: Evidence for near-bottom confinement. *Mar. Ecol. Prog. Ser.* 79: 67–76.

Keough, M. J. 1988. Benthic populations: Is recruitment limiting or just fashionable? *Proc. 6th Int. Coral Reef Symp.* 1: 141–148.

Keough, M. J. and K. P. Black. 1996. Predicting the scale of marine impacts: Understanding planktonic links between populations. In R. J. Schmitt and C. W. Osenberg (eds.), *The*

Design of Ecological Impact Studies: Conceptual Issues and Application in Coastal Marine Habitats, pp. 199–234. Academic Press, Orlando, FL.

Keough, M. J. and B. J. Downes. 1982. Recruitment of marine invertebrates: The role of active choices and early mortality. *Oecologia* 54: 348–352.

Keough, M. J. and P. T. Raimondi. 1995. Responses of settling invertebrate larvae to bioorganic films: Effects of different types of films. *J. Exp. Mar. Biol. Ecol.* 185: 235–253.

Kingsford, M. J. 1990. Linear oceanographic features: A focus for research on recruitment processes. *Austral. J. Ecol.* 15: 391–402.

Kingsford, M. J. and J. H. Choat. 1986. The influence of surface slicks on the distribution and onshore movement of small fish. *Mar. Biol.* 91: 161–171.

Lawson-Kerr, C. and D. T. Anderson. 1978. Reproduction, spawning and development of the starfish *Patiriella exigua* (Lamarck) (Asteroida: Asternidae) and some comparisons with *P. calcar* (LaMaru). *Austral. J. Mar. Freshw. Res.* 29: 45–53.

Lebour, M. V., 1921. The food of young clupeoids. *J. Mar. Biol. Assoc. U.K.* 12: 458–467.

Lebour, M. V., 1934. Rissoid larvae as food of the young herring. *J. Mar. Biol. Assoc. U.K.* 19: 523–539.

Leggett W. C. and E. M. DeBlois, 1994. Recruitment in marine fishes: Is it regulated by starvation and predation in the egg and larval stages. *Neth. J. Sea Res.* 32: 119–134.

Levin, L. A. and T. S. Bridges. 1995. Pattern and diversity in reproduction and development. In L. McEdward (ed.), *Ecology of Marine Invertebrate Larvae*, pp. 1–48. CRC Press, Boca Raton, FL.

Levitan, D. R. 1995. The ecology of fertilization in free-spawning invertebrates. In L. McEdward (ed.), *Ecology of Marine Invertebrate Larvae*, pp. 123–156. CRC Press, Boca Raton, FL.

Levitan, D. R. 1996. Predicting optimal and unique egg sizes in free-spawning marine invertebrates. *Amer. Nat.* 148: 174–188.

Levitan, D. R. and C. Petersen. 1995. Sperm limitation in the sea. *Trends Ecol. Evol.* 10: 228–231.

Lewin, R. 1986. Supply-side ecology. *Science* 234: 25–27.

Lindquist, N. and M. E. Hay. 1996. Palatability and chemical defense of marine invertebrate larvae. *Ecol. Monogr.* 66: 431–450.

Loosanoff, V. I. 1964. Variations in time and intensity of setting of the starfish *Asterias forbesi* in Long Island Sound during a twenty-five year period. *Biol. Bull.* 126: 423–439.

Loosanoff, V. I. 1966. Time and intensity of setting of the oyster, *Crassostrea virginica*, in Long Island Sound. *Biol. Bull.* 130: 211–227.

May, R. M., J. R. Beddington, C. W. Clark, S. J. Holt and R. M. Laws. 1979. Management of multispecies fisheries. *Science* 205: 267–277.

McGuinness, K. A., 1984. Communities of organisms on intertidal boulders: The effects of disturbance and other factors. PhD Dissertation, University of Sydney.

McGuinness, K. A. 1987. Disturbance and organisms on boulders. II. Causes of patterns in diversity and abundance. *Oecologia* 71: 420–430.

McShane, P., K. P. Black and M. G. Smith. 1988. Recruitment processes in *Haliotis rubra* (Mollusca: Gastropoda) and regional hydrodynamics in southeastern Australia imply localized dispersal of larvae. *J. Exp. Mar. Biol. Ecol.* 124: 175–203.

Mead, K. S. and M. W. Denny. 1995. The effects of hydrodynamic shear stress on fertilization and early development of the purple sea urchin, *Strongylocentrotus purpuratus*. *Biol. Bull.* 188: 46–56.

Meadows, P. S. and J. I. Campbell. 1972. Habitat selection by aquatic invertebrates. *Adv. Mar. Biol.* 10: 271–382.

Menge, B. A. 1976. Organization of the New England rocky intertidal community: Role of predation, competition and environmental heterogeneity. *Ecol. Monogr.* 46: 335–393.

Mileikovsky, S. A. 1971. Types of larval development in marine bottom invertebrates, their distribution and ecological significance: A reevaluation. *Mar. Biol.* 10: 193–213.

Minchinton, T. E. and R. E. Scheibling. 1991. The influence of larval supply and settlement on the population structure of barnacles. *Ecology* 72: 1867–1879.

Miron, G., B. Boudreau and E. Bourget. 1995. Use of larval supply in benthic ecology: Testing correlations between larval supply and larval settlement. *Mar. Ecol. Prog. Ser.* 124: 301–305.

Moore, H. B. 1936. The biology of *Purpura lapillus*. I. Shell-variation in relation to environment. *J. Mar. Biol. Assoc. U.K.* 21: 61–89.

Morgan, S. G. 1995a. Life and death in the plankton: Larval mortality and adaptation. In L. McEdward (ed.), *Ecology of Marine Invertebrate Larvae*, pp. 279–322. CRC Press, Boca Raton, FL.

Morgan, S. G. 1995b. The timing of larval release. In L. McEdward (ed.), *Ecology of Marine Invertebrate Larvae*, pp. 157–192. CRC Press, Boca Raton, FL.

Mullineaux, L. S. and C. A. Butman. 1991. Initial contact, exploration and attachment of barnacle (*Balanus amphitrite*) cyprids settling in flow. *Mar. Biol.* 110: 93–103.

Murdoch, W. W. 1969. Switching in general predators: Experiments on predator specificity and stability of prey populations. *Ecol. Monogr.* 39: 335–354.

Olson, R. R. 1983. Ascidian-*Prochloron* symbiosis: The role of larval photoadaptation in midday larval release and settlement. *Biol. Bull.* 165: 221–240.

Olson, R. R. 1985. The consequences of short-distance larval dispersal in a sessile marine invertebrate. *Ecology* 66: 30–39.

Orton, J. H. 1920. Sea temperature, breeding and distribution in marine animals. *J. Mar. Biol. Assoc. U.K.* 12: 339–366

Orton, J. H. 1937. Some inter-relationships between bivalve spatfalls, hydrography, and fisheries. *Nature* 140: 505.

Paine, R. T. 1966. Food web complexity and species diversity. *Amer. Nat.* 100: 65–75.

Paine, R. T. 1974. Intertidal community structure: Experimental studies on the relationship between a dominant competitor and its principal predator. *Oecologia* 15: 93–120.

Palmer, A. R. 1984. Prey selection of thaidid gastropods: Some observational and experimental field tests of foraging models. *Oecologia* 62: 162–172.

Palmer, A. R. and R. R. Strathmann. 1981. Scale of dispersal in varying environments and its implications for life histories of marine invertebrates. *Oecologia* 48: 308–318.

Pawlik, J. R. 1992. Chemical ecology of the settlement of benthic marine invertebrates. *Annu. Rev. Oceanogr. Mar. Biol.* 30: 273–335.

Pearse, J. S., J. B. McClintock and I. Bosch. 1991. Reproduction of Antarctic benthic marine invertebrates: Tempos, modes, and timing. *Amer. Zool.* 31: 65–80.

Phillips, B. F. and A. F. Pearce. 1997. Spiny lobster recruitment off Western Australia. *Bull. Mar. Sci.* 61: 21–41.

Pineda, J. 1991. Predictable upwelling and the shoreward transport of planktonic larvae by internal tidal bores. *Science* 253: 548–551.

Pineda, J. and H. Caswell. 1997. Dependence of settlement rate on suitable substrate area. *Mar. Biol.* 129: 541–548.

Possingham, H. P. and J. Roughgarden. 1990. Spatial population dynamics of a marine organism with a complex life cycle. *Ecology* 71: 973–985.

Raimondi, P. T. 1988. Settlement cues and determination of the vertical limit of an intertidal barnacle. *Ecology* 69: 400–407.

Raimondi, P. T. 1991. Settlement behaviour of *Chthamalus anisopoma* larvae largely determines the adult distribution. *Oecologia* 85: 349–360.

Reddingius, J. and P. J. den Boer. 1970. Simulation experiments illustrating stabilization of animal numbers by spreading of risk. *Oecologia* 5: 240–284.

Reed, C. G. 1991. Bryozoa. In A. C. Giese, J. S. Pearse and V. B. Pearse (eds.), *Reproduction of Marine Invertebrates*, Vol. 6, *Echinoderms and Lophophorates*, pp. 86–246. Boxwood Press, Pacific Grove, CA.

Rittschoff, D., I. R. Hooper, E. S. Branscomb and J. D. Costlow. 1985. Inhibition of barnacle settlement and behavior by natural products from whip corals, *Leptogorgia virgulata* (Lamarck, 1815). *J. Chem. Ecol.* 11: 251–263.

Roughgarden, J., S. D. Gaines and H. Possingham, 1988. Recruitment dynamics in complex life cycles. *Science* 241: 1460–1466.

Roughgarden, J. and Y. Iwasa. 1986. Dynamics of a metapopulation with space-limited subpopulations. *Theoret. Pop. Biol.* 29: 235–261.

Roughgarden, J., Y. Iwasa and C. Baxter. 1985. Demographic theory for an open marine population with space-limited recruitment. *Ecology* 66: 54–67.

Rumrill, S. S. 1990. Natural mortality of marine invertebrate larvae. *Ophelia* 32: 163–198.

Scheltema, R. S. 1971. Larval dispersal as a means of genetic exchange between geographically separated populations of shallow-water benthic marine gastropods. *Biol. Bull.* 140: 284–322.

Scheltema, R. S. 1989. On the children of benthic invertebrates: Their ramblings and migrations in time and space. In E. Spanier, Y. Steinberger and M. Luria (eds.), *Environmental Quality and Ecosystem Stability*, pp. 93–112. Israel Society for Ecology and Environmental Quality Sciences, Jerusalem.

Schoener, T. W. 1983. Field experiments on intraspecific competition. *Amer. Nat.* 122: 240–285.

Shanks, A. 1983. Surface slicks associated with tidally forced internal waves may transport larvae of benthic invertebrates and fishes shoreward. *Mar. Ecol. Prog. Ser.* 13: 311–315.

Shanks, A. L. 1995. Mechanisms of cross-shelf dispersal of larval invertebrates and fish. In L. McEdward (ed.), *Ecology of Marine Invertebrate Larvae*, pp. 323–368. CRC Press, Boca Raton, FL.

Shanks, A. L. 1998. Abundance of post-larval *Callinectes sapidus*, *Penaeus* spp., *Uca* spp. and *Libinia* spp. collected at an outer coastal site and their cross-shelf transport. *Mar. Ecol. Prog. Ser.* 168: 57–69.

Shkedy, Y. and J. Roughgarden. 1997. Barnacle recruitment and population dynamics predicted from coastal upwelling. *Oikos* 80: 487–498.

Sieburth, J. M. and J. T. Conover. 1965. Effect of tannins excreted from Phaeophyta on planktonic animal survival in tide pools. *Proc. Int. Seaweed Symp.* 5: 99–100.

Simberloff, D. 1981. Community effects of introduced species. In M. H. Nitecki (ed.), *Biotic Crises in Ecological and Evolutionary Time*, pp. 53–82. Academic Press, New York.

Sousa, W. P. 1979. Disturbance in marine intertidal boulder fields: The nonequilibrium maintenance of species diversity. *Ecology* 60: 1225–1239.

Sousa, W. P. 1980. The responses of a community to disturbance: The importance of successional age and species life histories. *Oecologia* 45: 72–81.

Southward, A. J. 1964. Limpet grazing and the control of vegetation on rocky shores. In D. J. Crisp (ed.), *Grazing in Terrestrial and Marine Environments*, pp. 265–273. Blackwell, Oxford.

Spight, T. M. 1974. Sizes of populations of a marine snail. *Ecology* 55: 712–729.

Spight, T. M. 1975. Factors extending gastropod embryonic development and their selective cost. *Oecologia* 21: 1–16.

Stocker, L. J. 1991. Effects of size and shape of colony on rates of fission, fusion, growth and mortality in a subtidal invertebrate. *J. Exp. Mar. Biol. Ecol.* 149: 161–175.

Strathmann, R. R., E. S. Branscomb and K. Vedder. 1981. Fatal errors in set as a cost of dispersal and the influence of intertidal flora on set of barnacles. *Oecologia* 48: 13–18.

Strathmann, R. R. and M. F. Strathmann. 1982. The relationship between adult size and brooding in marine invertebrates. *Amer. Nat.* 118: 91–101.

Styan, C. A. 1998. Polyspermy, egg size, and the fertilization kinetics of free-spawning marine invertebrates. *Amer. Nat.* 152: 290–297.

Svane, I. and C. M. Young. 1989. The ecology and behaviour of ascidian larvae. *Annu. Rev. Oceanogr. Mar. Biol.* 27: 45–90.

Swearer, S. E., J. E. Caselle, D. W. Lea and R. R. Warner, 1999. Larval retention and recruitment in an island population of a coral-reef fish. *Nature* 402: 799–802.

Tankersley, R. A. and R. B. Forward. 1994. Endogenous swimming rhythms in estuarine crab megalopae: Implications for flood-tide transport. *Mar. Biol.* 118: 415–423.

Tankersley, R. A., L. M. McKelvey and R. B. Forward. 1995. Responses of estuarine crab megalopae to pressure, salinity and light: Implications for flood tide transport. *Mar. Biol.* 122: 391–400.

Thompson, T. E. 1958. The natural history, embryology, larval biology and postlarval development of *Adalaria proxima* (Alder and Hancock) (Gastropoda: Opisthobrancia). *Philos. Trans. Roy. Soc. B* 242: 1–58.

Thorson, G. 1946. Reproduction and larval development of Danish marine bottom invertebrates. *Medd. Komm. Danm. Fisk. Havunder. Serie Plankton* 4: 1–523.

Thorson, G. 1950. Reproductive and larval ecology of marine bottom invertebrates. *Biol. Rev.* 25: 1–45.

Todd, C. D. and M. J. Keough. 1994. Larval settlement in hard substratum epifaunal assemblages: A manipulative field study of the effects of substratum filming and the presence of incumbents. *J. Exp. Mar. Biol. Ecol.* 181: 159–187.

Underwood, A. J. 1974. The reproductive cycles and geographical distribution of some common Eastern Australian prosobranchs (Mollusca: Gastropoda). *Austral. J. Mar. Freshwat. Res.* 25: 63–88.

Underwood, A. J. 1976. Food competition between age-classes in the intertidal neritacean *Nerita atramentosa* Reeve (Gastropoda: Prosobranchia). *J. Exp. Mar. Biol. Ecol.* 23: 145–154.

Underwood, A. J. 1986. The analysis of competition by field experiments. In J. Kikkawa and D. J. Anderson (eds.), *Community Ecology: Pattern and Process*, pp. 240–268. Blackwell, Melbourne.

Underwood, A. J. 1990. Experiments in ecology and management: Their logics, functions and interpretations. *Austral. J. Ecol.* 15: 365–389.

Underwood, A. J. 1991. The logic of ecological experiments: A case history from studies of the distribution of macro-algae on rocky intertidal shores. *J. Mar. Biol. Assoc. U. K.* 71: 841–866.

Underwood, A. J. 1992. Competition in marine plant–animal interactions. In D. M. John, S. J. Hawkins and J. H. Price (eds.), *Plant–Animal Interactions in the Marine Benthos*, pp. 443–475. Clarendon Press, Oxford.

Underwood, A. J. 1999. Physical distubances and their direct effect on an indirect effect: Responses of an intertidal assemblage to a severe storm. *J. Exp. Mar. Biol. Ecol.* 232: 125–140.

Underwood, A. J. and E. J. Denley. 1984. Paradigms, explanations and generalizations in models for the structure of intertidal communities on rocky shores. In D. R. Strong, D. Simberloff, L. G. Abele and A. Thistle (eds.), *Ecological Communities: Conceptual Issues and the Evidence*, pp. 151–180. Princeton University Press, Princeton, NJ.

Underwood, A. J. and P. G. Fairweather. 1989. Supply-side ecology and benthic marine assemblages. *Trends Ecol. Evol. Biol.* 4: 16–20.

Underwood, A. J., E. J. Denley and M. J. Moran. 1983. Experimental analyses of the structure and dynamics of mid-shore rocky intertidal communities in New South Wales. *Oecologia* 56: 202–219.

Vance, R. R. 1973a. More on reproductive strategies in marine benthic invertebrates. *Amer. Nat.* 107: 353–361.

Vance, R. R. 1973b. On reproductive strategies in marine benthic invertebrates. *Amer. Nat.* 107: 339–352.

Wing, S. R., L. W. Botsford, J. L. Largier and L. E. Morgan, 1995. Spatial structure of relaxation events and crab settlement in the northern California upwelling system. *Mar. Ecol. Prog. Ser.* 128: 199–211.

Wootton, J. T. 1993. Indirect effects and habitat use in an intertidal community: Interaction chains and interaction modifications. *Amer. Nat.* 141: 71–89.

Wootton, J. T. 1994. The nature and consequences of indirect effects in ecological communities. *Annu. Rev. Ecol. Syst.* 25: 443–466.

Yamada, S. B. 1977. Geographic range limitation of intertidal gastropods *Littorina sitkana* and *L. planaxis*. *Mar. Biol.* 39: 61–70.

Young, C. M. 1987. Novelty of "supply-side ecology." *Science* 235: 415–416.

Young, C. M. 1990. Larval predation by epifauna on temperate reefs: Scale, power and the scarcity of measurable effects. *Austral. J. Ecol.* 15: 413–426.

Young, C. M. 1995. Behavior and locomotion during the dispersal phase of larval life. In L. McEdward (ed.), *Ecology of Marine Invertebrate Larvae*, pp. 249–279. CRC Press, Boca Raton, FL.

Yund, P. O. 2000. How severe is sperm limitation in natural populations of free-spawners? *Trends Ecol. Evol. Biol.* 15: 10–13.

Yund, P. O., S. D. Gaines and M. D. Bertness. 1991. Cylindrical tube traps for larval sampling. *Limnol. Oceanogr.* 36: 1167–1177.

Zeldis, J. R. and J. B. Jillett. 1982. Aggregation of pelagic *Munida gregaria* (Fabricius)(Decapoda, Anomura) by coastal fronts and internal waves. *J. Plankt. Res.* 4: 839–857.

Zimmer-Faust, R. K. and M. N. Tamburri. 1994. Chemical identity and ecological implications of a waterborne, larval settlement cue. *Limnol. Oceanogr.* 39: 1075–1087.

chapter 8

Habitat Modification and Facilitation in Benthic Marine Communities

John F. Bruno and Mark D. Bertness

Most marine habitats are generated by the presence of either a single or a few habitat-modifying species. Familiar examples include kelp forests, mussel beds, oyster reefs, seagrass meadows, and coral reefs (Estes and Palmisano 1974; Orth 1977; Goreau et al. 1979; Suchanek 1979; Witman 1985; Zimmerman et al. 1989). These foundation species (*sensu* Dayton 1972) create a spatial refuge from environmental stress and/or predation, which can increase the fitness of individuals occupying the habitat and can positively affect populations of associated species (Huffaker 1958; Dayton 1975; Woodin 1978; Hay 1986). Such large-scale habitat modifiers also facilitate other species by increasing propagule retention and the availability of limiting resources (Eckman 1985; Eckman et al. 1989). Many associated species are only able to occupy the environment when a modifier reduces stress to tolerable levels, hence many foundation species have large positive effects on local species richness (Dayton 1975; Thompson et al. 1996). Such biologically generated habitats set the stage for a multitude of positive, neutral, and negative species interactions that drive many other ecological and evolutionary processes.

In this chapter we argue that the biological generation of habitats and the positive interactions that occur within them are fundamental processes across a wide range of benthic marine environments. Although we recognize that positive interactions play an important role in evolutionary processes such as speciation and extinction, our focus will be on their role in generating patterns that occur on ecological time scales. We begin by attempting to clarify definitions and by discussing semantic controversies related to habitat modification and facilitation. Next, we present a brief historical perspective of studies on this topic and ask why such research is less common than investigations of negative interactions such as pre-

dation. We then introduce some conceptual issues and models that make predictions about the conditionalities of facilitation. Some of these models are largely untested, so this section presents possible directions for future research. We conclude by suggesting how ecologists can apply what is known about habitat modification to marine conservation issues.

DEFINITIONS AND RELATED ISSUES

A habitat-modifying organism, broadly defined, significantly alters its local biotic and/or abiotic environment (of course in one sense this definition could include virtually any organism). Some habitat modifiers can substantially affect environmental conditions simply through their presence, such as seagrasses or mussels that reduce flow velocity or stabilize understory habitats (Orth 1977; Fonseca et al. 1982). Alternatively, they can modify habitats via their actions. Examples of this include consumers that remove common or large-prey species, such as sea urchins that control the abundance of macroalgae (Estes and Palmisano 1974). Jones et al. (1994, 1997) have called the process of habitat creation or modification "ecosystem engineering" and the organisms that modify the environment "ecosystem engineers" or bioengineers. They further distinguish between autogenic engineers, which change their environment via their physical presence, and allogenic engineers, which change the environment by transforming living or nonliving material from one physical state to another. Reactions to the efforts of Jones et al. to organize and clarify habitat modification terminology have been mixed. For example, in a recent editorial, Alper and others (Alper 1998) mistook the coining of the new terms for the creation of a "new concept" that compared well with the theory of natural selection and predator–prey theory. In contrast, other ecologists have had strong negative reactions to the new terminology and see it as redundant, unnecessary, and loaded with anthropomorphic connotations. In particular, Power (1997) has questioned the general use of the term *ecosystem engineering* because it implies purposeful intent. In our view, this is really not an issue for many marine habitat modifiers such as macrophytes and invertebrates that obviously never "intend" to do anything.

By ameliorating the environment, habitat modifiers can indirectly benefit other organisms. The response of associated or dependent species to modifier effects can range from trivial to dramatic. In general, we consider modifiers that positively affect a neighboring organism to be facilitators. The measured response parameter can be an individual trait such as reproductive output, biomass, or survivorship, or a population-level attribute such as population size or growth rate or even absolute presence or absence. Facilitation is analogous to a positive interaction, which is defined as an interaction that benefits at least one species, but does not negatively affect either species (Bronstein 1994; Bertness and Callaway 1994). Positive interactions include mutualisms and commensalisms and tightly coevolved, mutually obligate relationships as well as much looser, facultative interactions (Stachowicz, in press). Facilitation can also be viewed as a process that increases the amount of environment that meets the niche requirements of a species. Thus, by increasing habitable space, facilitators often increase the distributional range of dependent species at numerous spatial scales (Bertness and Callaway 1994; Bertness et al. 1999a).

Some facilitators dramatically impact entire communities by altering species composition or affecting community dynamics. These species have long been recognized by ecologists and termed *foundation species* (Dayton 1972), *keystone resource species* (Terborgh 1986), *keystone species* (Wilson and Agnew 1992), *keystone modifiers* (Bond 1993; Mills et al. 1993), *keystone facilitators* (Hacker and Gaines 1997), and *keystone engineers* (Jones at al. 1994). Despite its widespread use by ecologists, conservation biologists, resource managers, and politicians (Mills et al. 1993; Power and Mills 1995), the use of the term *keystone* to describe a habitat modifier/facilitator that has communitywide importance has become controversial. Power et al. (1996) proposed that influential species that constitute a high proportion of community biomass not be considered keystone species and instead be termed *dominants*. We suggest that designating the important habitat modifiers that form large structures (e.g., trees, grasses, kelp, corals, and bivalves) as dominants will not clarify their roles in communities, as this term carries an implied meaning of competitive suppression. The *American Heritage Dictionary's* (1994) definition of the verb *dominate* ("to control, govern, or rule, to enjoy a commanding position in or over") clearly carries an unintended connotation. Instead, we will use the term *foundation species* (Dayton 1972) to refer to influential yet large species that have a positive effect on community inhabitants. Although, as originally defined, foundation species also include-

ed herbivores and predators, we restrict the use of the term to include species that have a large effect on community structure by modifying environmental conditions, species interactions, and resource availability through their presence (e.g., kelps, grasses, mussels, and corals) and not their actions. As the term suggests, the initial presence of a foundation species is required before subsequent establishment by populations of other associated species. We refer to facilitators that have a large, *positive* effect on a community (e.g., by increasing species richness) through their actions as keystone facilitators. One example is sea otters, which by consuming urchins, maintain the cover of habitat-forming kelps in the northwest Pacific and, hence, indirectly facilitate numerous species associated with kelp forests (Estes and Palmisano 1974).

Our classification of the physical and biological factors that negatively affect organisms follows that of Menge and Sutherland (1987). Stress is defined as a fitness reduction of an individual or population in response to an extrinsic factor. We define *physiological stress* as the effect of factors, such as temperature or salinity, that can reduce the rates of biochemical reactions when their values are outside the optimal range of a specific organism. We define *physical stress* as the effect of abiotic factors that exert direct mechanical forces on organisms that result in tissue damage, removal, or burial. These two types of physical factors have collectively been termed "environmental stress" (Menge and Sutherland 1987). Biological factors that induce stress include competition, partial or complete consumption by a predator or herbivore, and biological disturbances that occur when the activities (e.g., burrowing) of one organism negatively affects another (Orth 1977). The limitation of resources, including food, light, metabolites, and living space, can also induce stress. Gradients of various factors that cause stress often run in opposing directions within a given habitat. Many of the models in this chapter and elsewhere in the literature make predictions about the unidirectional strength (i.e., the effect of species A on species B) or importance of facilitation and other processes relative to ambient environmental stress and consumer pressure. When interpreting such models, it is generally more appropriate to assume that the stress gradient depicts variation in the organismal response to a single factor (or variation of the factor itself), as opposed to a net or integrated measure of stress that considers all possible stress factors. Furthermore, the models presented in this chapter are more valid and useful when used to make predictions within a single habitat type instead of making comparisons among habitats (in which case habitat types are classified according to some subjective measure of inherent stress).

HISTORICAL PERSPECTIVE ON POSITIVE INTERACTIONS

Over the past 50 years, community ecologists in general and marine ecologists in particular have devoted most of their efforts to understanding the role of negative interactions (such as competition and predation) in regulating populations and in structuring communities (Jackson 1981; Keddy 1989; Peters 1991). As a result, experimental work on positive interactions is spotty, and in a surprising number of cases we know very little about the mechanisms and conditionalities of facilitation. Previous generations of ecologists viewed facilitation as an important community-level process and included it in models of community dynamics (e.g., Clements 1936). But the perceived importance of facilitation gradually diminished as Gleason's view of communities, which emphasized the importance of competition and chance events (Gleason 1926), emerged as the dominant ecological paradigm (Callaway 1995). This trend continued through the following decades, when small-scale studies of the effects of negative interactions and disturbance dominated marine ecology (e.g., Connell 1961, Paine 1974).

Is this still the case today? After all, in the past few years there have been undeniable advances and a growing interest in facilitation. We reviewed the abstracts from four of the last five years (1994, 1996–98) of the Western Society of Naturalists, a North American meeting with a focus on marine ecology. We found that only 13 of 646 studies addressed any kind of facilitative interaction (including studies of intracellular symbiosis), whereas 63 were of predation, 54 investigated propagule supply or recruitment, and 38 examined some aspect of disturbance (Table 8.1). An examination of abstracts from the last four meetings of the Benthic Ecology Society (1994–97) and recent publications in the prominent marine ecological journal *Marine Ecology Progress Series* (*MEPS*; 1994–97) are concordant with this pattern (Table 8.1). In fact, in *MEPS*, studies of fecal pellets nearly outnumbered those of facilitation! Overall, we found a 5:1:1 ratio of studies on predation:competition:facilitation. The 5:1 predation:facilitation ratio has been found by other authors who surveyed the general ecological literature (May and Seger 1986; Keddy 1989). However, we found a markedly reduced interest in competition among marine ecologists as compared to general ecological studies from previous decades. The previous focus on competition has been replaced by work on propagule dispersal and supply, biomechanics, and molecular genetics and phylogeny (Table 8.1).

So why are studies of facilitation still so much less common than those of other ecological processes? One explanation is simply the constraint of historical thought (Dayton 1984; Underwood and Denley 1984). Social and gender biases may also have influenced ecologists who principally view nature as a competitive arena analogous to a football stadium or market economy (Peters 1991). A number of practical considerations may also restrict investigations of facilitation. Manipulating large habitat modifiers such as kelp and forest trees has logistical and ethical constraints. Some important facilitations simply operate over too large a spatial and temporal scale, making experimental investigations difficult and costly (Bertness and Leonard 1997). A final explanation of the paucity of facilitation studies is based on a premise that we entirely reject: that positive interactions are too obvious to warrant se-

TABLE 8.1   Recent studies on selected topics in marine ecology.

Study Type	WSN Number	WSN %	Benthics Number	Benthics %	MEPS Number	MEPS %
Facilitation	9	1.4	41	3.4	27	2.2
Intracellular symbiosis	4	0.6	0	0	6	0.5
Predation, herbivory, parasitism	63	9.8	184	15.1	133	10.6
Propagule supply, dispersal, recruitment	54	8.4	149	12.3	76	6.1
Disturbance	38	5.9	83	6.8	53	4.2
Competition	17	2.6	33	2.7	15	1.2
Physiology	47	7.3	38	3.1	144	11.5
Genetics, phylogeny	53	8.2	51	4.2	32	2.6
Management, conservation, monitoring	55	8.5	31	2.6	35	2.8
Pollution and bioassay	11	1.7	48	4.0	45	3.6
Natural/life history	130	20.1	215	17.7	231	18.5
Morphology, biomechanics	55	8.5	35	2.9	14	1.1
Other	110	17.0	307	25.3	441	35.2
Total number of studies	646	100.0	1215	100.0	1252	100.0

Note: Data are from a review of annual meetings of two professional societies with a marine ecological focus (WSN = Western Society of Naturalists, 1994, 1996–98; Benthics = Benthics Ecology Society, 1994–97) and of publications in a marine ecological journal (MEPS = *Marine Ecology Progress Series*, 1994–96). Data for each study type were pooled across years for each source, and some studies were scored in more than one category.

rious study. Many ecological phenomena are obvious (Jackson 1981). For instance, the importance of predation in structuring rocky intertidal communities was suspected long before the development of experimental ecology (e.g., Ricketts and Calvin 1939). Only through repeated predator exclusions and removals at numerous locations were ecologists able to comprehend the complexities and importance of predators in rocky intertidal assemblages (Menge et al. 1994). In the following discussion, we argue that a similar approach toward positive interactions will lead to increased understanding of facilitation and its dependency on numerous extrinsic factors. We suggest that this will ultimately provide a more accurate view of the processes that structure communities.

BIOLOGICAL HABITAT GENERATION AND THE HIERARCHICAL ORGANIZATION OF MARINE COMMUNITIES

One of the difficulties of developing a community-level understanding of positive interactions is the vast scales across which they can operate. It can become conceptually murky when the communitywide effects of reef-building corals are considered simultaneously with any of the smaller-scale positive interactions that occur within reefs, such as when clean-

er wrasses remove parasites from groupers (Grutter 1996). Although most of the models in this chapter can be used to make predictions about both of these facilitations, it is important to recognize that they operate on very different spatial and temporal scales. The cleaner wrasse example, along with innumerable other smaller-scale facilitations, is essentially nested within and dependent on the larger-scale positive interaction (i.e., the creation/provision of the habitat by the presence of corals). We propose that most benthic marine communities can be viewed as hierarchical organizations because they are principally reliant on the presence of a foundation or habitat-forming species. Embedded within the framework generated by the foundation species (both spatially and temporally) are numerous smaller-scale species interactions that can be positive, neutral, or negative.

In many cases, the presence of a single foundation species is responsible for the generation of a given benthic habitat (see Figure 8.1 and Table 8.2). Other communities, such as salt marshes, coral reefs, and intertidal and subtidal algal communities, are primarily structured by a guild of foundation species (Hacker and Steneck 1990; Taylor and Cole 1994; Knowlton and Jackson, this volume; Pennings and Bertness, this volume). Results of investigations of facilitator redundancy (i.e., multiple facilitators that perform the same function) in such communities have been mixed. Many suggest that mor-

Figure 8.1 Photographs of common marine foundation species. From upper left: seagrass bed (photo J. Witman), mangroves forest (photo M. Bertness), coral reef (photo M. Bertness), cobble beach plant community (photo J. Bruno), salt marsh (photo R. Kneib).

TABLE 8.2 Examples of marine benthic biological habitat generation/whole-community facilitation.

Habitat	Foundation species	Mechanisms[a]	References
Cobble beach	*Spartina alterniflora* (grass)	3, 5	Bruno 2000a; Bruno and Kennedy 2000
Coral reef	Reef-building corals	1, 2, 3, 5, 6	Goreau et al. 1979; Abele 1984; Luckhurst and Luckhurst 1978; Reaka-Kudla 1997
Kelp forest	Giant kelps	2, 3, 5, 6	Estes and Palmisano 1974; Coyer 1979; Duggins et al. 1990; Carr 1989
Mangrove forest	Mangroves	1, 2, 5, 6	Rutzler and Feller 1996; Ellison and Farnsworth 1992
Mussel bed	Mussels (intertidal)	1, 2, 3, 4, 5, 6	Seed 1996, Suchanek 1986, Lohse 1993, Tokeshi and Romero 1995
	Mussels (subtidal)	1, 2, 5	Witman 1985
Oyster	Reef oysters	1, 2, 3, 5	Zimmerman et al. 1989
Salt marsh	Marsh grasses	2, 4	Vince et al. 1976; Bertness and Hacker 1994; Bertness and Yeh 1994; Rozas and Zimmerman 2000
Sand dune	Dune grasses	3, 4	Ehrenfeld 1990
Seagrass	Meadow seagrasses	1, 2, 3, 5, 6	Orth 1977; Heck and Orth 1980; Peterson et al. 1984; Stoner and Lewis 1985
Soft sediment	Polychaete worms	2, 3, 5, 6	Woodin 1978; Thisle and Eckman 1990; Schwindt 1997a

[a]Identified/proposed mechanisms of facilitation (other mechanisms may exist):

1 = general habitat creation and/or attachment site

2 = refuge from predation

3 = reduction of physical stress

4 = reduction of physiological stress

5 = enhancement of proagule supply or retention

6 = increased food supply

phological variation among facilitators causes different species within a guild to facilitate distinct species assemblages (e.g., seagrasses—O'Gower and Wacasey 1967; refs in Heck and Orth 1980; Stoner 1982; corals—Abele 1984; algae—Hacker and Steneck 1990; Taylor and Cole 1994; Levin and Hay 1996). Yet some studies have failed to find significant variation in the density or composition of associated species among facilitators (Eggleston et al. 1999). It is likely that the degree of facilitator redundancy is habitat-specific and dependent on the type of stress and mechanism of amelioration.

Marine foundation species generally form large aggregations (relative to the size of the organisms that they facilitate) through clonal propagation or gregarious settlement (Woodin 1978). The presence of foundation species dramatically increases the heterogeneity of the environment, often transforming a two-dimensional, featureless landscape into a complex, three-dimensional structure. This can have large impacts on multiple environmental parameters. For example, marine habitat modifiers often reduce flow velocity (Fonseca et al. 1982; Jackson and Winant 1983; Gambi et al. 1990; Leonard and Luther 1995). This in turn can stabilize the substrate (Orth 1977; Eckman et al. 1981; Bruno and Kennedy 2000), increase sedimentation and reduce substrate particle sizes (Orth 1977; Luckenbach 1986), retain propagules, and enhance settlement (Orth 1977; Eckman 1983, 1985; Smith and Witman 1999; Bruno 2000a). Flow modification can also increase or decrease turbulence, which can augment the delivery of food and critical metabolites by reducing the thickness of the diffusive boundary layer (Fonseca and Kentwor-

thy 1987; Dennison and Barnes 1988; Eckman et al. 1989; Gambi et al. 1990; Thisle and Eckman 1990; Irlandi and Peterson 1991; Worcester 1995; Shashar et al. 1996). In addition, an increase in the complexity of biologically generated habitats often reduces the foraging efficiency of consumers (Vince et al. 1976; Heck and Wetstone 1977; Crowder and Cooper 1982). This creates a partial to complete refuge from predators for many prey species, which can lead to coexistence and possibly to the stabilization or dampening of predator–prey population fluctuations (Huffaker 1958; Woodin 1978; Heck and Orth 1980; Crowder and Cooper 1982; Gosselin and Chia 1995). By shading the substrate surface, intertidal algae, mussels, and grasses can reduce substrate temperatures, increase moisture levels, and reduce desiccation-related stress (Dayton 1975; Hawkins 1981; Bertness and Yeh 1994; Gosselin and Chia 1995; Seed 1996; Leonard 1999). Finally, in many cases, foundation species simply provide a stable substrate on which other species can settle and live (Hacker and Madin 1991; Ellison and Farnsworth 1992).

Through these and many other mechanisms, foundation species can increase the fitness and population density of associated species (e.g. Eckman and Duggins 1991; Bologna and Steneck 1993). This effect is often cumulative, and in many cases local species diversity (i.e., total number of species present, *sensu* Rosenzweig 1995) is significantly greater when a foundation species is present. The strong positive effect of foundation species on species diversity has been demonstrated in both correlational and experimental investigations across a diverse array of communities (e.g., seagrass meadows—O'Gower and Wacasey 1967; Orth 1973, 1977; Heck and Wetstone 1977; Heck 1979; Stoner and Lewis 1985; soft-sediment habitats—Woodin 1978; Schwindt 1997a; Schwindt and Iribarne, in press; salt marsh habitats—Rozas and Zimmerman 2000; intertidal and subtidal mussel beds— Suchanek 1979; Witman 1985; Lohse 1993; Tokeshi and Romero 1995; intertidal and subtidal algae—Levin and Hay 1996; Thompson et al. 1996; kelp forests—Coyer 1979; Carr 1989; coral reefs—Luckhurst and Luckhurst 1978; Abele 1984; refs in Reaka-Kudla 1997; mangrove forests—refs in Ellison and Farnsworth, this volume; hydrothermal vent communities—refs in Etter and Mullineaux, this volume). As in tropical rainforests, where a huge portion of species diversity is made up by insects that live within the forest canopy (Erwin 1988), most species that inhabit marine communities are small secondary space holders dependent on a biogenic structure. For example, McCloskey (1970) documented 309 species larger than 0.2 mm associated with a single coral species (*Oculina arbuscula*). Likewise, Suchanek (1979) found 270 taxa inhabiting beds formed by the mussel *Mytilus californianus*. Although striking, these results are not exceptional (Reaka-Kudla 1997).

Although some infaunal species are obligate and can only live in association with a foundation species, many also live in adjacent space and habitats (Witman 1985; Lohse 1993). However, it is unclear whether populations of such facultative species found outside of their primary habitat are independently viable (i.e., they could be nonreproductive "sink populations"; e.g., Heck 1979). Other species can only survive in the environment in its unaltered state and will be displaced by the presence of a foundation species or other habitat modifiers (e.g., Dayton 1975; Eckman and Duggins 1991). Thus, despite the net positive effect on obligate and facultative-associated species, foundation species will also inevitably adversely affect other species. At small spatial scales, these effects are potentially large, and as many species that are facilitated could be displaced (Jones et al. 1997). In such a case, the modifiers would simply shift species composition (Dayton 1975). At a landscape or regional scale, however, foundation species usually increase habitat and species diversity because they only occupy small portions of the landscape (Jones et al. 1997).

Numerous abiotic and biotic factors can locally remove competitively dominant foundation species and thus prevent exclusion of other foundation species and nonfacilitative primary space holders (Dayton 1975; Sousa, this volume; Duffy and Hay, this volume). By regulating the size and spatial distribution of biologically generated habitats, these factors also control some of the most important aspects of the landscape, as perceived by obligate inhabitants. For example, an increase in the size of and a reduction in the distance between habitat patches (connectivity) can increase immigration and colonization rates and overall species richness (MacArthur and Wilson 1967; Hanski 1998). Physical disturbances generated by storms can limit the cover of mussel and seagrass beds, kelp forests, reef-building corals, and mangrove forests (Paine and Levin 1981; Woodley et al. 1981; Witman 1985;

Dayton et al. 1992; Fonseca and Bell 1998; Sousa, this volume). Foundation species can also be negatively impacted by other storm- and climate-related factors, including sedimentation/burial and changes in salinity and water temperature (Dayton and Tegner 1990; Woodley 1981; Glynn 1993). Predation is the biotic factor capable of limiting foundation species that has received the most attention. Examples of this include the removal of kelp forest by urchin grazing (Estes and Palmisano 1974), the consumption of reef-building corals by the predatory sea star *Acanthaster planci* (Glynn 1973), and the reduction of mussel and oyster cover by sea stars, lobsters, crabs, fish, and sea bird predators (Paine 1974; Feare and Summers 1986; Ojeda and Dearborn 1991). Because they regulate foundation species, these consumers have a large impact on the community and are usually referred to as keystone species (Power et al. 1996). Interestingly, the negative impact of predators on foundation and associated species is often mediated by an indirect positive interaction (Dayton 1972). For instance, predation by sea otters on sea urchins can maintain kelp cover (Estes and Palmisano 1974), many important Pacific corals are protected from *Acanthaster* predation by guard shrimp (Glynn 1976), and the consumption of algae by urchins in subtidal mussel beds and coral reefs benefits foundation species by removing potential competitors (Witman 1987; Hughes 1994; Stachowicz and Hay 1996). Likewise, epifaunal invertebrates on the roots of mangroves can prevent destructive boring by isopods (Ellison and Farnsworth 1990).

The positive interactions that occur within biologically generated habitats (i.e., between associated species) also have strong positive effects on individuals, populations, and whole communities. They operate through numerous mechanisms including the amelioration of physical and physiological stresses, the provision of a predation refuge (i.e., associational defenses, Hay 1986; Stachowicz and Hay 1999), and the reduction of threats from other natural enemies (Stachowicz and Hay 1996). Most of these positive interactions are interspecific, but they can also be intraspecific, such as when dense aggregations of conspecifics reduce environmental stress. For example, high densities of intertidal barnacles, mussels, and algae can greatly reduce thermal stress and enhance individual rates of growth and survival (Bertness and Leonard 1997; Bertness et al. 1999a). Like foundation species, these smaller-scale facilitators can be responsible for the presence of a species within a community (facilitative inclusion) or they can simply increase individual fitness or population density.

PREDICTABILITY OF POSITIVE INTERACTIONS

In addition to facilitative inclusion, there are negative interactions within most communities that can lead to competitive and predatory exclusion and other interactions that are neutral, at least in net outcome. There is currently a great need for theoretical advancements and empirical data that will increase our ability to predict when and where these different types of biotic interactions will affect populations and communities. Bertness and Callaway (1994) have proposed a model that predicts the relationship between stress and the frequency of two categories of positive interactions: habitat amelioration and associational defenses. The frequency of habitat amelioration is predicted to increase when environmental stress is high, whereas associational defenses increase when consumer pressure is high (also see Dayton 1975; Goldberg 1990). The Bertness–Callaway model is a consumer stress model (Menge and Olson 1990), which implicitly assumes that the intensity of environmental stress and consumer pressure are inversely related. This assumption is based on the idea that mobile consumers are more sensitive to environmental stress than their prey and that high levels of stress factors, including heat, waves, and low salinity, will reduce predator densities or foraging efficiencies (Menge 1978; Witman and Grange 1998). This assumption breaks down when predators are highly mobile and can seek refuge in less stressful microhabitats (Menge and Olson 1990), which in some cases can be provided by habitat modifiers (Dayton 1975; Connell 1990; Eckman and Duggins 1991; Bertness et al. 1999b). Therefore, in some circumstances the intensity of the environmental stress and predation are positively related, such as in salt marsh habitats where thermal stress and herbivory both increase with decreasing latitude (Pennings and Bertness, this volume).

Here we will consider a more general model that combines both types of facilitation. This model simply predicts that the strength or intensity of positive interactions increases with ambient stress, whether the source of stress is physical or biological or even resource limitation (Figure 8.2A). In areas of very low stress, the normally dependent species does not benefit from the presence of the facilitator. Hence, the model prediction is one-tailed: ambient stress will either have no effect on the strength of the facilitative interaction (the null case) or the strength will increase with ambient stress (alternative case).

Most species interactions consist of both facilitative and competitive components (Goldberg 1990; Callaway and Walker 1997; Holmgren et al. 1997; Brooker and Callaghan

1998). The Bertness and Callaway model also makes predictions about the strength of competition across a stress gradient. Their approach can be extended to consider how ambient stress affects the balance between facilitation and competition (Goldberg 1990; Callaway and Walker 1997). The basic prediction is that the net effect on the associated species will be negative and the competitive component of the interaction will be more intense (and more important) when environmental stress is low, whereas the opposite is expected when stress is high (Callaway and Walker 1997; Brooker and Callaghan 1998). Although there are some studies of plant–plant facilitations that support these predictions (e.g., Greenlee and Callaway 1996), we suspect that in many cases, the *strength* of the negative component of the interaction will remain constant over the entire stress gradient (Figure 8.2B). This is because the positive and negative components are often decoupled. For example, grasses facilitate smaller plants in salt marshes by shading the soil surface and reducing evaporation and thus levels of soil salinity (Bertness and Yeh 1994). There is a trade-off for the plants living within the grass matrix where light levels are significantly lower. However, the strength of this negative effect (competition for light) is constant across the salinity stress gradient and is independent of the intensity of the facilitative interaction (Rand 2000). Nonetheless, there are also many examples where the host or facilitator is thinned or partially removed by the stress it is reducing (e.g., high flow conditions damaging corals), and in such situations the strength of competition may indeed decrease with increasing stress. Unfortunately, studies that independently measure the relative strengths of the positive and negative components of species interactions are rare (but see Holzapfel and Mahall 1999), and currently there is not nearly enough data to make generalizations.

In contrast to the relationship between the *strength* of positive and negative interactions, the relative *importance* of the two usually will be inversely related (importance indicates the magnitude of the factor effect relative to the effect of all other factors under consideration). In fact, this is the ultimate outcome whether or not the strength of competition varies with stress, although the magnitude of the difference in im-

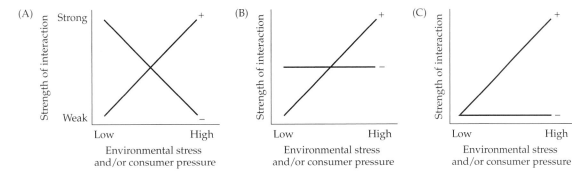

Figure 8.2 Conceptual models of the relationships between levels of ambient stress and the strength or intensity of facilitation (+) and competition (–).

Figure 8.3 The effects of the intertidal, canopy-forming algae *Ascophyllum nodosum* on invertebrate species at high and low tidal heights. Data are the percentage of one-way interactions for each demographic process that are positive, negative, and statistically neutral and are pooled responses for nine invertebrate species that are associated with *Ascophyllum* in northern New England. Data are from Bertness et al. 1999b.

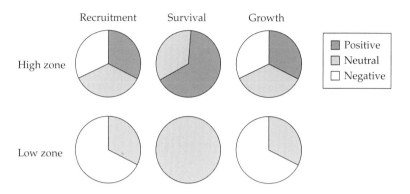

portation will be less if the strength of competition is constant (Figure 8.2). The difference between intensity and importance is not simply semantic, and failure to make this distinction, especially when the terms are used in predictive models, can lead to serious confusion (Weldon and Slauson 1986). After all, an interaction can be frequent and intense but unimportant, and vice versa (Menge and Sutherland 1987).

The strength of competition can also influence the net outcome or balance between facilitation and competition. When competitive intensity is high (Figure 8.2B), variation in the strength of facilitation across stress gradients will be masked and easily overlooked (Brooker and Callaghan 1998). This is the case in the zonation of plants across salt marsh landscapes (Bertness 1999). In this community, strong competitive dominance leads to distinct elevational zonation across the landscape and obscures the fact that positive interactions are required for many plant species to inhabit the environment (Pennings and Bertness, this volume). When the strength of competition is constant yet low (Figure 8.2C), facilitation is expected to have a much greater effect than competition when ambient stress is high, but the strength of both interaction types will be negligible and probably immeasurable when stress is low. Finally, direct negative effects through competition of the facilitator on the associated species are probably often small or completely absent when the interaction is between two species from different trophic levels or that have very different means of resource acquisition (e.g., macrophytes facilitating small invertebrates).

Some of the model predictions just discussed are supported by investigations in salt marsh and rocky intertidal habitats. In southern New England salt marshes, positive interactions among plants resulting from neighbor amelioration of elevated soil salinity predictably occur in physically harsh areas where salt accumulation is possible, but not in more physically benign zones (Bertness 1999). This leads to: (1) positive neighbor effects occurring predictably at some marsh elevations but not at others (Bertness and Hacker 1994); (2) secondary succession of large exposed bare patches closing by facilitation, whereas smaller bare patches close without facilitation (Bertness and Shumway 1993); and (3) predictable annual variation in the intensity of positive interactions due to variations in weather (Bertness, unpublished data). Similarly,

on New England rocky shores, the positive and negative effects of algal canopies on understory populations of barnacles, mussels, and snails vary predictably with tidal elevation and levels of heat and desiccation stress (Bertness et al. 1999b). At high elevations where the physiological stresses experienced by these organisms could potentially limit their abundance and distribution, the net effect of the canopy on recruitment, growth, and survivorship is positive (Figure 8.3). In contrast, at lower elevations where these stresses are much lower and less important, the net effect of the canopy on understory organisms shifts to neutral or negative (Figure 8.3). Likewise, Bertness et al. (1999a) found that intraspecific facilitation among barnacles in which dense aggregations prevent desiccation-related mortality were important at hotter southern sites (Rhode Island), especially in protected estuaries, but not at cooler northern sites (coastal Maine).

Predicting the strength of facilitation relative to ambient stress is useful, but the next step should be to determine how positive interactions relate to other factors. Initially, this can be accomplished by incorporating positive interactions into current models of community organization (e.g., Hacker and Gaines 1997). For instance, facilitation can be added to the Menge–Sutherland model (Menge and Sutherland 1976, 1987), which makes predictions about how the relative importance of predation, competition, and physical factors vary with environmental stress (Burnaford 1997; Bertness 1999). The purpose of this model in its original form (1976) was to depict how these factors "regulate" populations, but without considering factors that have positive effects (i.e., recruitment and facilitation), it can only address the mechanisms of population *limitation*. Assuming that recruitment of the basal or prey species is high, the Menge–Sutherland model (Figure 8.4A) predicts that predation pressure will decrease with increasing environmental stress (i.e., this is a consumer stress model). This inevitably leads to increased intensity and importance of competition as resources (e.g., space, light, food) become scarce. If stress increases still further, prey densities will eventually be reduced (as the source of stress becomes lethal), and competition will be replaced by physical factors as the most important mechanism of population limitation.

Incorporating positive interactions into the Menge–Sutherland model has a number of interesting effects (Fig-

(A) High recruitment
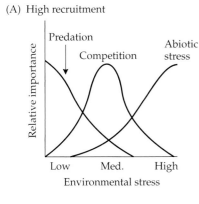

(B) High recruitment with facilitation: Case I

(C) High recruitment with facilitation: Case II
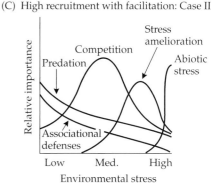

(D) Low recruitment
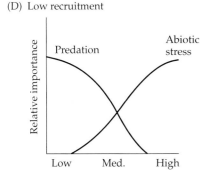

(E) Low recruitment with facilitation: Case I
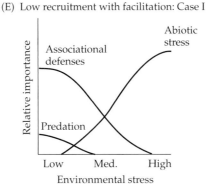

(F) Low recruitment with facilitation: Case II
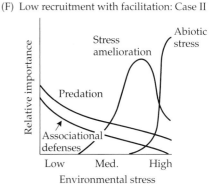

Figure 8.4 Conceptual models of community organization predicting the relative importance of predation, competition, abiotic stress, and two types of facilitation (amelioration of abiotic stress and associational defenses). In each figure, the importance of each factor is predicted in relation to ambient levels of abiotic stress (e.g., thermal stress, wave impacts, salinity, etc.). Figures A–C assume high levels of recruitment and D–F assume low recruitment of the basal (prey) taxa. A and D depict the original versions the environmental stress model in which facilitation was not considered (redrawn from Menge and Sutherland 1987).

Both types of facilitation were incorporated into B, C, E, and F. In case I with facilitation (B and E), the predation refuge provided through the associational defense is assumed to be nearly absolute and the amelioration of abiotic stress is an intraspecific facilitation that operates through dense aggregations. In case II with facilitation (C and F) the predation refuge is only partial. The reduction of abiotic stress in case II operates through an interspecific facilitation, which is expected to facilitate predators and increase predation intensity when stress is high.

ures 8.4B and 8.4C). First, stress amelioration, either by dense aggregations of conspecifics (figure 8.4B) or by an interspecific facilitator (Figure 8.4C), is predicted to increase population densities at medium-high to high levels of stress. Under these conditions, facilitation through the reduction of environmental stress will be the most important factor in determining population densities of the basal species. However, the actual mechanism of facilitation could be crucial because a large interspecific facilitator such as intertidal algae might also facilitate predators, which would in turn reduce prey densities (Figure 8.4C; Connell 1990; Burnaford 1997; Bertness et al. 1999b). Amelioration of environmental stress might still be important because it increases predation intensity and has an indirect negative effect on the prey. At some point, the facilitator will presumably no longer be able to effectively reduce environmental stress; thus, prey–population densities and the importance of facilitation will decrease, and physical factors will become important. But they do so at a much higher level of environmental stress relative to the Menge–Suther-

land model without facilitation (Figure 8.4B versus Figure 8.4A). Incorporating positive interactions is also predicted to increase the importance of competition from medium-high to high and from medium-low to the lowest stress levels. This is because the two types of facilitation increase prey densities in these ranges. However, at the maximum level of environmental stress, competition will still be weak or nonexistent because physical factors are expected to reduce densities.

When environmental stress is low and predators are abundant and unrestricted, associational defenses could reduce the intensity and importance of predation, resulting in increased prey densities (Figure 8.4B). However, the balance between the importance of predation and associational defenses is not entirely straightforward and is dependent on the biological details of the interaction. If the predation refuge is absolute, predators will rarely be able to consume the prey, although they may still affect densities or individual fitness (e.g., by affecting prey foraging behavior). If the refuge only reduces predator foraging efficiencies, the two curves will be much closer together, and predation and associational defenses might be equally important from medium to low stress.

A more recent version of the Menge–Sutherland model (1987) incorporates low recruitment of the basal or prey species into the model predictions (Figure 8.4D). The main effect of this modification is that intraspecific (or at least intraguild) competition is expected to be unimportant across the entire stress gradient (densities are never high enough for resources to become scarce). Intraspecific stress amelioration is also thought to be dependent on high levels of recruitment in order for group benefits to be conferred on individuals (Burnaford 1997; Leonard et al. 1999). Thus, when densities are low, conspecific buffering will do little to reduce stress, and physical factors will further reduce population densities (Figure 8.4E). In contrast, many interspecific facilitations will operate regardless of the recruitment levels of the facilitated species (assuming that the facilitator or host species is not reciprocally benefited by the associate). This type of facilitation will increase densities and reduce the importance of physical factors (at least up to the maximum stress levels) when recruitment is low and environmental stress is high (Figure 8.4F). Likewise, most interspecific associational defenses are also expected to operate when recruitment is low.

IMPORTANCE OF FACILITATOR TRAITS

The simple presence or absence of a facilitator in a habitat may tell us very little about its realized role, as individual and population traits of facilitators can largely determine their ability to modify the environment. For instance, the degree to which a foundation species reduces environmental stress and predation intensity may be largely dependent on the size or age of a local facilitator population (Woodin 1978). Smaller populations (or clonal aggregations) can generate edge effects (due greater perimeter to interior ratios) where stress is greater at patch edges. This could lead to small patches being essentially unmodified and consequently non-habitat for many species (Jackson and Winant 1983; Gambi et al. 1990; Irlandi 1997; Bruno and Kennedy 2000). For example, strong edge effects in seagrass beds where sediment size, stability and organic content, and predation intensity are only slightly modified at bed edges cause invertebrate growth rates, abundances, and diversity to peak in the center of beds (Orth 1977; Irlandi and Peterson 1991). Other traits, including the density and architectural complexity of facilitators, are also known to be important (Heck and Wetstone 1977; Woodin 1978). These traits can influence the effect that numerous modifiers (e.g., marsh grasses—Leonard and Luther 1995; seagrasses—Fonseca et al. 1982; Eckman 1987; Gambi et al. 1990; macroalgae—Eckman and Duggins 1991; Anderson 1994; corals—Dennsion and Barnes 1988; Bruno and Edmunds 1998) have on flow velocity and turbulence as well as on sediment particle size and on other related characteristics of the environment (Eckman 1983, 1987). Additionally, facilitator density, cover, and complexity can affect the degree to which predation intensity is reduced within biogenic habitats (Vince

et al. 1976; Heck and Wetstone 1977; Crowder and Cooper 1982; Peterson 1982; Stoner 1982). Changes in facilitator traits are also known to affect associate body size, growth rate, survivorship, and population density (Heck 1979; Peterson et al. 1984; Stoner and Lewis 1985; Hacker and Steneck 1990; Taylor and Cole 1994; Fonseca et al. 1996; Schwindt 1997b).

Although the relationship between local levels of stress (i.e., stress within modified space including environmental stress, predation intensity, and resource limitation) and facilitator traits may be simple and linear, it is likely that these relationships are more often complex and include both lower and upper thresholds (Figure 8.5A). Below such thresholds,

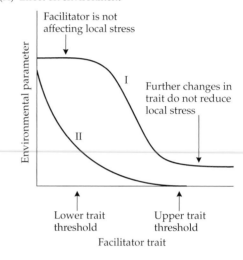

(A) Effect on environment

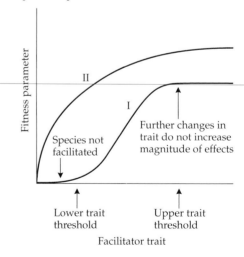

(B) Species response

Figure 8.5 Graphical model of relationships between a specific facilitator trait (e.g., size, density, morphology) and (A) local environmental stress or consumer pressure, and (B) the response of the facilitated or associated species (e.g., individual or population growth rate). Two hypothetical response curve shapes are presented for each. Response curve I in both figures includes lower and upper thresholds while II does not. The model assumes that the facilitator is not affected by the stress factor it ameliorates.

changes in facilitator traits would have no effect on the source of stress, and the environment would not be modified (Fonseca et al. 1996). For example, Gleason et al. (1979) found a nonlinear relationship between stem density of the intertidal grass *Spartina alterniflora* and the rate of sedimentation. Additionally, below a threshold of seagrass density, predation intensity by fish on invertebrates is not reduced (Heck and Orth 1980; Fonseca et al. 1996). The response of associated species is also likely to be complex for several reasons, including the fact that they are mediated through the association between the facilitator trait and the source of stress (i.e., facilitators only indirectly affect associated species). Many species display distinct thresholds to stressful factors like temperature (Glynn 1993; Urban 1994) and as long as the trait-dependent stress level continuously exceeds the tolerance of a given species, it cannot occupy the partially modified space (Figure 8.5B). The response curves of other species could be inversely related to the facilitator trait (as opposed to being positively related to the trait as in Figure 8.5B). In other words, some species might favor a slight modification over a greater reduction in stress (Eckman and Duggins 1991). For instance, in New England, lobsters prefer habitat edges, and their densities are highest at intermediate kelp bed sizes (Bologna and Steneck 1993). This is likely a common condition, as "stress" should usually be measured or defined on a species-by-species basis; it is not always a shared perspective or general attribute of the environment (a factor that induces stress in one species can be bliss to another).

Ambient stress could further complicate the predicted response of associated species by interacting with facilitator traits to determine the magnitude of the difference between modified and unmodified habitats. Increased ambient stress would require further change in the trait of interest for stress levels to remain constant within the modified environment (Figure 8.6). If the trait value is held constant, local stress will be higher in a location that has greater ambient stress. Increased ambient stress could also amplify edge effects, reducing the amount of modified area. In many cases, facilitators are not affected by the stressful factor they are mitigating (at least within the range of stress intensity that is reasonable to consider from the perspective of the organism being facilitated). For instance, consider the refuge from predation that reef-building corals (or many other foundation species) provide to numerous fish and invertebrates. Although corals can be consumed by their own predators, they typically are not affected by the predators of the associated species that utilize the refuge (Glynn 1976; Stachowicz and Hay 1999). In other cases, the facilitator trait will be affected, and if its modification efficiency is reduced, increased ambient stress would necessitate further change in the key attribute to compensate for this reduction. For example, high flow velocity can bend seagrass blades, which can diminish the ability of deformed blades to reduce local flow conditions (Fonseca et al. 1982; Gambi et al. 1990). In this example, if an associated species requires that the flow or turbulence within a bed be reduced to a certain degree, the morphological trait (e.g., blade stiffness

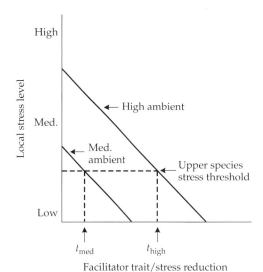

Figure 8.6 Graphical model of how the values of a facilitator trait (e.g., size, density, morphology) and ambient stress levels interact to determine local stress (stress within the modified environment). Source of stress could be biotic or abiotic. The relationship between local stress and the facilitator trait are depicted for two levels of ambient stress (medium and high). Increasing ambient stress from medium to high increases the facilitator trait value that must be reached (from t_{med} to t_{high}) to maintain stress below the upper stress threshold of a hypothetical dependent species. The model assumes that the facilitator is not affected by the stress factor it ameliorates.

or density) would have to increase further for the habitat requirements of that species to be met.

The relationship between a facilitator trait, local environmental stress, and the response of associated species can be illustrated by the results of a recent investigation of New England cobble beach plant communities. This community of annual and perennial halophytic plants is found in the middle to high intertidal zone of estuarine cobble beaches behind beds of the grass *Spartina alterniflora*. *Spartina* acts as a foundation species in this community by reducing water velocity, stabilizing the substrate (Bruno and Kennedy 2000), and enabling seedlings of dependent species to emerge and survive (Bruno 2000a; Kennedy and Bruno 2000). The degree to which *Spartina* reduces wave-related disturbance is strongly influenced by bed attributes. For example, there is an inverse log-log relationship between bed length and both average flow velocity and substrate stability behind beds (Figure 8.7). In Narragansett Bay, Rhode Island, most *Spartina* beds are small (< 25 m long) and unoccupied (Figure 8.8) (Bruno and Kennedy 2000). In contrast, the occupancy of beds > 40 m in length by at least one cobble beach plant species is 87% (Figure 8.8). Furthermore, there appears to be a threshold length of approximately 10–20 m below which beds are rarely occupied (Figure 8.8). Seed addition experiments have demonstrated that small beds remain unoccupied because they do not stabilize the substrate enough to meet the establishment requirements of seedlings of even the most tolerant species

(A) Average water velocity

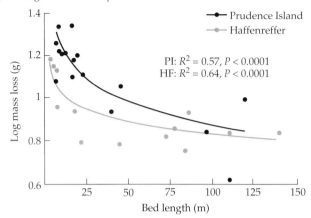

PI: $R^2 = 0.57$, $P < 0.0001$
HF: $R^2 = 0.64$, $P < 0.0001$

(B) Substrate stability

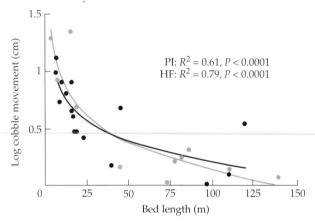

PI: $R^2 = 0.61$, $P < 0.0001$
HF: $R^2 = 0.79$, $P < 0.0001$

Figure 8.7 Relationship between length of *Spartina alterniflora* beds and two indices of wave-related disturbance at two sites in Narragansett Bay, RI (Haffenreffer and Prudence Island): (A) Water velocity, which was measured using the dissolution cylinder technique (1 cylinder/bed for 7 d). (B) Substrate stability measured as the mean net distance of movement by size-standardized cobbles (20 cobbles/bed over 7 d). Redrawn from Bruno and Kennedy (2000).

(Bruno and Kennedy 2000). These results suggested that limited propagule supply, increased extinction rates, or other factors often thought to reduce the occupancy and diversity of small patches were not responsible for the absence of associated plant species behind small *Spartina* beds.

The basic facilitator trait model (Figure 8.5B) can be expanded to predict trait effects on local species diversity. This diversity model predicts that a change in a facilitator trait that reduces stress and/or predation intensity will result in a greater number of species inhabiting a biologically generated habitat patch (Figure 8.9A; also see Heck and Orth 1980). The model assumes that there is variation among species in environmental tolerances or habitat requirements (i.e., some species are specialists whereas others are generalists). We will also initially assume that competitive exclusion does not reduce diversity when stress or disturbance is low. As in the single-species response model, the predictions of this community diversity model can be modified to account for different levels of ambient stress. When ambient stress is negligible, changes in a facilitator trait are unlikely to affect the number of species able to inhabit the patch (Figure 8.9A). However, increasing ambient stress to medium or high levels is predicted to depress the left side of the community diversity response curve well below the curve at low ambient stress. This is because low-stress specialist species are expected to be excluded when a facilitator is small, sparse, or young, and hence is unable to reduce stress (Heck and Wetstone 1977). Only generalist species will occupy the habitat under such conditions, and species diversity will be relatively low. In contrast, at high trait values, species diversity within the modified space should be similar at all ambient stress levels because the facilitator will largely negate the potentially stressful factor. Furthermore, when trait values are high, increased ambient stress could amplify diversity differences between modified and unmodified habitat. For instance, Witman (1985) found that the magnitude of the difference in diversity in and out of subtidal mussel beds was much greater after a drastic increase in predation intensity, which was largely ameliorated by the mussels. Species behavioral patterns surely complicate the model, as many fish and inver-

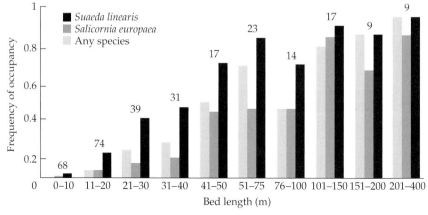

Figure 8.8 Frequency of occupancy of *Spartina alterniflora* generated habitat patches on New England cobble beaches by cobble beach plant species. Numbers above bars are sample sizes for each bed length class. Redrawn from Bruno and Kennedy (2000).

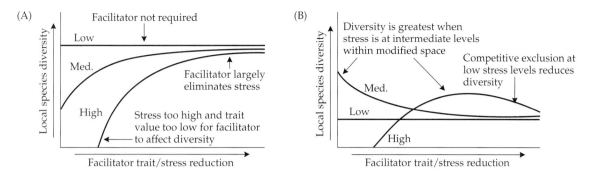

Figure 8.9 (A) Conceptual model of the hypothesized relationship between an important facilitator trait and species diversity within the modified space at three levels of ambient stress (low, medium, and high). More species are able to live in the biologically generated habitat as the trait value increases and local environmental stress is reduced. Increased ambient stress is predicted to depress the left side of the species diversity response curve. The source of stress can be a physical or physiological factor or consumer pressure. (B) Includes competitive exclusion, which is predicted to reduce local diversity when the stressful factor is completely ameliorated or when ambient stress is low.

tebrates would not occupy the habitat at low trait values even when the source of stress is absent (Woodin 1978; Hacker and Steneck 1990; Steele 1999). In this case, the species diversity response would follow the high ambient stress curve regardless of true ambient stress levels.

This model is supported by a number of descriptive and experimental studies. In numerous habitats including kelp forests, coral reefs, seagrass beds, mussel beds, and infaunal communities inhabiting intertidal and subtidal algae, the complexity of the structure generated by the foundation species is strongly related to the abundance and diversity of the associated species (Heck and Wetstone 1977; Luckhurst and Luckhurst 1978; Suchanek 1979; Stoner and Lewis 1985). It is thought that to a large degree, an inverse relationship between topographic complexity and predation intensity causes this relationship (Stoner and Lewis 1985; Irlandi 1997). Heck and Wetstone (1977) found that infaunal richness in seagrass beds was directly related to plant biomass (a proxy for complexity) and that rare species are only found in densely vegetated areas. Levin and Hay (1996) demonstrated the effect that the structure (i.e., density, height, and cover) of temperate, subtidal algae has on the diversity and abundance of associated fish. Likewise, the density of polychaete worms that stabilize soft-sediment habitats is directly related to the richness and abundance of associated infaunal species (Woodin 1978). Additionally, increases in algal chemical defenses against herbivory can increase the diversity of associated species (Hay et al. 1987; Hay et al. 1990; Hay and Fenical 1996). Finally, in New England cobble beach plant communities, *Spartina* bed length is related to plant species diversity, and plant species that are rare on a landscape scale are generally only found behind the longest beds (Bruno 2000b). This pattern could be caused by a number of related biogeographic effects (e.g., target effects, larger population sizes, etc.) (Rosenzweig 1995). However, manipulative field experiments have demonstrated that only

the longest *Spartina* beds reduce cobble size and stabilize the substrate to a degree that enables seedlings of rare species to emerge and survive (Bruno 2000b).

In some systems, interactions among associated species living within the modified space could lead to competitive exclusion or facilitative inclusion. Intermediate disturbance hypotheses (Connell 1978; Petraitis et al. 1989) predict that species diversity declines at the lowest levels of disturbance because some species are competitively excluded. Therefore, at the highest facilitator trait values (when stressful factors are nearly eliminated) competitive exclusion might be expected to decrease local species diversity. The facilitator trait–species diversity model could be modified to account for this possibility by extending and depressing the right side of the medium and high ambient stress curves (Figure 8.9B). Additionally, the diversity response at low ambient stress might be predicted to be below the response at intermediate stress levels (Figure 8.9B). Although they may help to reconcile the trait-diversity model with intermediate disturbance hypotheses, these modifications produce the seemingly unrealistic prediction that the reduction of stress and predation intensity via habitat modification can suppress diversity by enabling a highly competitive associated species to exclude other inhabitants. Predation pressure and environmental stress are thought to drive intense competition for biological refuges (e.g., competition for enemy free space, Price 1984; Buchheim and Hixon 1992). However, increasing spatial complexity is believed to decrease the overall importance of competition by isolating potential competitors from one another (Woodin 1978; Crowder and Cooper 1982) and is known to increase species diversity (Wallace 1890; Stoner and Lewis 1985). Furthermore, numerous comparative and experimental studies in a multitude of habitats have demonstrated the strong positive effect that habitat modifiers can have on local species diversity (e.g., Orth 1973; Heck 1979; Stoner 1983; Witman 1985; Thompson et al. 1996;

Tokeshi and Romero 1995; Schwindt 1997a; Bruno 2000a; Rozas and Zimmerman 2000; Schwindt and Iribarne, in press), yet intermediate disturbance hypotheses seem to predict that foundation species will reduce diversity when they ameliorate the environment.

We can think of a number of possible explanations for this apparent conflict. First, habitat modifiers may rarely reduce environmental stress and predation to a degree that allows competitively dominant species to displace other species. Likewise, competitive exclusion may be highly overrated as a process that can reduce species diversity on the scale of a habitat patch or site (Lawton 1984; Price 1984; Levine and D'Antonio 1999). Additionally, the increase in spatial complexity that usually accompanies the presence of a foundation species may offset any species losses due to competition. Finally, any reduction in species diversity due to competition could also be counteracted by facilitative inclusion by other facilitators living within the habitat. We suspect all of these explanations may be partially correct. Consequently, it may be justifiable to regard competition as a force that could potentially limit maximum diversity within biologically generated habitats (Coen et al. 1981; Abele 1984), although recognizing that in most situations, more species will be present when a facilitator provides refuge from environmental stress and predation than when it does not. In other words, the diversity increase resulting from facilitative inclusion appears to be greater in magnitude than the decrease due to exclusion, resulting in a significant net increase in species diversity within the space occupied and modified by a facilitator (Thompson et al. 1996).

CONSERVATION ISSUES

The loss of natural habitats due to the expansion and resource consumption of human civilization is a major conservation issue. In many respects, the study of habitat modification and facilitation is really an investigation of the basic habitat requirements of species. Consequently, the results of such studies are easily applicable to numerous problems that are routinely encountered in the conservation of many communities. In this section, we present two general lessons for the preservation of marine species and habitats based on our current understanding of positive interactions. First, the integral role that foundation species play in controlling community composition and richness should be explicitly incorporated into the design of marine reserves (Dayton 1972). Management plans and reserve designs based solely on the biology of an economically or aesthetically important species often fail to ensure the long-term presence of the foundation species upon which it may depend. A topical example is bottom trawling fisheries that often incidentally remove and destroy important habitat-modifying species, which can lead to the collapse of the targeted associated species (Watling and Norse 1998). The preservation of foundation species should be central to any conservation or restoration plan. As obvious as this may seem, there are still management plans (e.g.,

Roberts 1997) that target specific taxa and ignore their dependence on a foundation species.

Second, we need to recognize that simply preserving a foundation species will not necessarily also meet the habitat requirements of the associated species and hence the ultimate goal of preservation. This is why foundation species are generally poor candidates for protection under the endangered species act (ESA) when the motive is "umbrella" protection for a whole community. In such cases it would be relatively easy to meet the limited requirements of the ESA without indirectly benefiting any other species. An excellent illustration of the importance of trait-dependent facilitation to habitat restoration and species conservation is the case of the Sweetwater National Wildlife Refuge in San Diego, California. The Sweetwater marsh was created in 1985 as a restoration project designed to provide habitat for endangered species, including the federally listed clapper rail (Boyer and Zedler 1998; Malakoff 1998). The coarse, nutrient-poor soil upon which the marsh was built produced short-form cordgrass (*Spartina foliosa*). Unfortunately, clapper rails and other species only recognize tall-form cordgrass as habitat, and in this respect a very expensive project failed to meet its goal due to the trait-dependent nature of the cordgrass–clapper rail facilitation (Boyer and Zedler 1998).

The panacea of preservation through micromanagement implicitly assumes that fragmented or degraded habitats contain fewer species because colonization has become infrequent and extinction rates have increased. The hope is that we will be able to maintain populations of rare species and overall species richness in such habitats by periodically adding individuals. This strategy will fail if the alteration of attributes of foundation species such as size, density, morphology, and spatial arrangement renders them uninhabitable. However, we will rarely be able to foresee these problems unless we understand both the mechanisms and conditionalities of positive interactions.

SUMMARY

In this chapter we have argued that benthic marine habitats are largely formed by the presence of foundation species. These ubiquitous habitat modifiers indirectly facilitate the establishment and persistence of populations of numerous associated species by creating spatial refuges from environmental stresses and predation, by enhancing the supply and retention of propagules, and by increasing the supply of resources. Within biologically generated habitats, the net outcome of species interactions can be positive, neutral, or negative. Both foundation species and other facilitators can have large positive effects on local population densities and sizes, on species boundaries at many spatial scales, and on species composition and diversity. The strength and importance of positive interactions can be affected by a number of factors. In general, both parameters are predicted to increase with ambient environmental stress and predation intensity. Facilitator traits such as size, density, and morphological complexity can have a large effect on the ability of facilitators to modify habitat and to benefit other species. Additionally, ambient stress may often interact with facilitator traits to determine the magnitude of the difference between modified and unmodified space and the overall positive effect on individual species and local species diversity. Although much more work is needed, there are early indications that a number of landscape-scale patterns in marine communities could be driven largely by trait-dependent habitat modification and facilitation.

Despite their obvious and well-documented importance, positive interactions have received relatively little attention from ecologists and are rarely included in models of community organization or in discussions of factors thought to structure communities. Many of the models in this chapter remain largely untested and, for most positive species interactions, even the basic mechanisms of facilitation have not yet been determined. This is not simply a call for increased empirical work on facilitation, but an appeal for a more comprehensive approach to examining the role of habitat modifiers that consider the potential conditionalities of positive interactions. Such investigations will greatly increase our understanding of and ability to preserve and restore marine communities.

ACKNOWLEDGMENTS

Many of the ideas in this chapter originated during discussions with T. Rand, and we are very grateful for her help and inspiration. Several other friends also helped to clarify our thinking and to improve this chapter, including J. Ellis, N. Emery, C. Kennedy, J. Levine, and J. Stachowicz. The original research presented in this chapter was funded by a National Estuarine Research Reserve Graduate Fellowship and a National Science Foundation Dissertation Improvement Grant award to JFB, and National Science Foundation support to MDB.

LITERATURE CITED

Abele, L. G. 1984. Biogeography, colonization, and experimental community structure of coral-associated crustaceans. In D. R. Strong, D. Simberloff, L. G. Abele and A. B. Thistle (eds.), *Ecological Communities: Conceptual Issues and the Evidence*, pp. 123–137. Princeton University Press, Princeton, NJ.

Alper, J. 1998. Ecosystem "engineers" shape habitats for other species. *Science* 280: 1195–1196.

Anderson, T. W. 1994. Role of macroalgal structure in the distribution and abundance of a temperate reef fish. *Mar. Ecol. Prog. Ser.* 113: 279–290.

Bertness, M. D. 1999. *The Ecology of Atlantic Shorelines*. Sinauer Associates, Sunderland, MA.

Bertness, M. D. and R. Callaway. 1994. Positive interactions in communities. *Trends Ecol. Evol.* 9: 191–193.

Bertness, M. D. and S. D. Hacker. 1994. Physical stress and positive associations among marsh plants. *Amer. Nat.* 144: 363–372.

Bertness, M. D. and G. H. Leonard. 1997. The role of positive interactions in communities: Lessons from intertidal habitats. *Ecology* 78: 1976–1989.

Bertness, M. D. and S. W. Shumway. 1993. Competition and facilitation in marsh plants. *Amer. Nat.* 142: 718–724.

Bertness, M. D. and S. M. Yeh. 1994. Cooperative and competitive interactions in the recruitment of march elders. *Ecology* 75: 2416–2429.

Bertness, M. D., G. H. Leonard, J. Levine and J. Bruno. 1999a. Climate-driven interactions among rocky intertidal organisms caught between a rock and a hot place. *Oecologia* 120: 446–450.

Bertness, M. D., G. H. Leonard, J. M. Levine, P. R. Schmidt and A. O. Ingraham. 1999b. Testing the relative contribution of positive and negative interactions in rocky intertidal communities. *Ecology* 80: 2711–2726.

Bologna, P. A. X. and R. S. Steneck. 1993. Kelp beds as habitat for American lobster *Homarus americanus. Mar. Ecol. Prog. Ser* 100: 127–134.

Bond, W. J. 1993. Keystone species. In E. D. Schulze and H. A. Mooney (eds.), *Ecosystem Function and Biodiversity*, pp. 237–253. Springer-Verlag, Berlin.

Boyer, K. E. and J. B. Zedler. 1998. Effects of nitrogen additions on the vertical structure of a constructed cordgrass marsh. *Ecol. Appl.* 8: 692–705.

Bronstein, J. L. 1994. Conditional outcomes in mutualistic interactions. *Trends Ecol. Evol* 9: 214–217.

Brooker, R. W. and T. V. Callaghan. 1998. The balance between positive and negative plant interactions and its relationship to environmental gradients: A model. *Oikos.* 81: 196–207.

Bruno, J. F. 2000a. Whole-community facilitation through substrate stabilization by the intertidal grass *Spartina alterniflora. Ecology* 81: 1179–1192.

Bruno, J. F. 2000b. Macroecology of New England cobble beach plant communities. PhD Dissertation, Brown University, Providence, RI.

Bruno, J. F. and P. J. Edmunds. 1998. Metabolic consequences of phenotypic plasticity in the coral *Madracis mirabilis* (Duchassaing and Michelotti): The effect of morphology and water flow on aggregate respiration. *J. Exp. Mar. Biol. Ecol* 229: 187–195.

Bruno, J. F. and C. W. Kennedy. 2000. Reduction of wave-related disturbance in cobble beach habitats by *Spartina alterniflora* : Importance of patch size. *Oecologia* 122: 98–108.

Buchheim, J. R. and M. A. Hixon. 1992. Competition for shelter holes in the coral-reef fish *Acanthemblemaria spinosa* Metzelaar. *J. Exp. Mar. Bio. Ecol.* 164: 45–54.

Burnaford, J. L. 1997. A new model of community structure across environmental stress gradients: Relative roles of positive and negative interactions. Abstract: 1997 meeting of the Ecological Society of America, p. 230.

Callaway, R. 1995. Positive interactions among plants. *Bot. Rev.* 61: 306–349.

Callaway, R. M. and L. R. Walker. 1997. Competition and facilitation: A synthetic approach to interactions in plant communities. *Ecology* 78: 1958–1965.

Carr, M. H. 1989. Effects of macroalgal assemblages on the recruitment of temperate zone reef fishes. *J. Exp. Mar. Bio. Ecol.* 126: 59–76.

Clements, F. E. 1936. Nature and structure of climax. *J. Ecol.* 24: 252–284.

Coen, L. D., K. L. Heck and L. G. Abele. 1981. Experiments on competition and predation among shrimps of seagrass meadows. *Ecology* 62: 1484–1493.

Connell, J. H. 1961. The influence of interspecific competition and other factors on the distribution of the barnacle *Chthamalus stellatus. Ecology* 42: 710–723.

Connell, J. H. 1978. Diversity in tropical rain forests and coral reefs. *Science* 199: 1302–1310.

Connell, J. H. 1990. Apparent versus "real" competition in plants. In J. B. Grace and D. Tilman (eds.), *Perspectives on Plant Competition*, pp. 9–24. Academic Press, San Diego, CA.

Coyer, J. A. 1979. The invertebrate assemblage associated with *Macrocystis pyrifera* and its utilization as a food resource by kelp forest fishes. PhD Dissertation, University of Southern California, Los Angeles.

Crowder, L. B. and W. E. Cooper. 1982. Habitat structural complexity and the interaction between Bluegills and their prey. *Ecology* 63: 1802–1813.

Dayton, P. K. 1972. Toward an understanding of community resilience and the potential effects of enrichments to the benthos at McMurdo Sound, Antarctica. *Proceedings of the*

Colloquium on Conservation Problems in Antarctica, pp. 81–96.

Dayton, P. K. 1975. Experimental evaluation of ecological dominance in a rocky intertidal community. *Ecol. Monogr.* 45: 137–159.

Dayton, P. K. 1984. Processes structuring some marine communities: Are they general? In D. R. Strong, D. Simberloff, L. G. Abele and A. B. Thistle (eds.), *Ecological Communities: Conceptual Issues and the Evidence,* pp. 181–200. Princeton University Press, Princeton, NJ.

Dayton, P. K. and M. J. Tegner. 1990. Bottoms beneath troubled waters: Benthic impacts of the 1982–1983 El Niño in the temperate zone. In P. W. Glynn (ed.), *Global Ecological Consequences of the 1982–83 El Nino–Southern Oscillation,* pp. 433–504. Elsevier, Amsterdam.

Dayton, P. K., M. J. Tegner, P. E. Parnell and P. B. Edwards. 1992. Temporal and spatial patterns of disturbance and recovery in a kelp forest community. *Ecol. Monogr.* 62: 421–445.

Dennison, W. C. and D. J. Barnes. 1988. Effect of water motion on coral photosynthesis and calcification. *J. Exp. Mar. Biol. Ecol.* 115: 67–77.

Duggins, D. O., J. E. Eckman and A. T. Sewell. 1990. Ecology of understory kelp environments. II. Effects of kelps on recruitment on benthic invertebrates. *J. Exp. Mar. Biol. Ecol.* 143: 27–45.

Eckman, J. E. 1983. Hydrodynamic processes affecting benthic recruitment. *Limnol. Oceanogr.* 28: 241–257.

Eckman, J. E. 1985. Flow disruption by an animal-tube mimic affects sediment bacterial colonization. *J. Mar. Res.* 43: 419–435.

Eckman, J. E. 1987. The role of hydrodynamics in recruitment, growth, and survival of *Agropecten irradians* (L.) and *Anomia simplex* (D'Orbigny) within eelgrass meadows. *J. Exp. Mar. Biol. Ecol.* 106: 165–191.

Eckman, J. E. and D. O. Duggins. 1991. Life and death beneath macrophyte canopies: Effects of understory kelps on growth rates and survival of marine, benthic suspension feeders. *Oecologia* 87: 473–487.

Eckman, J. E., A. R. M. Nowell and P. A. Jumars. 1981. Sediment destabilization by animal tubes. *J. Mar. Res.* 39: 365–374.

Eckman, J. E., D. O. Duggins and A. T. Sewell. 1989. Ecology of understory kelp environments. I. Effects of kelps on flow and particle transport near the bottom. *J. Exp. Mar. Biol. Ecol.* 129: 173–187.

Eggleston, D. B., W. E. Elis, L. L. Ehterington, C. P. Dahlgren and M. H. Posey. 1999. Organism responses to habitat fragmentation and diversity: Habitat colonization by estuarine macrofauna. *J. Exp. Mar. Biol. Ecol.* 236: 107–132.

Ehrenfeld, J. G. 1990. Dynamics and processes of barrier island vegetation. Reviews in *Aquat. Sci.* 2: 437–480.

Ellison, A. M. and E. J. Farnsworth. 1990. The ecology of Belizean mangrove-root fouling communities. I. Epibenthic fauna are barriers to isopod attack of red mangrove roots. *J. Exp. Mar. Biol. Ecol.* 142: 91–104.

Ellison, A. M. and E. J. Farnsworth. 1992. The ecology of Belizean mangrove-root fouling communities: Patterns of epibiont distribution and abundance, and effects on growth. *Hydrobiologia.* 247: 87–98.

Erwin, T. 1988. The tropical forest canopy: The heart of biotic diversity. In E. O. Wilson and F. M. Peters (eds.), *Biodiversity,* pp. 123–129. National Academy Press, Washington, DC.

Estes, J. A. and J. F. Palmisano. 1974. Sea otters: Their role in structuring nearshore communities. *Science* 185: 1058–1060.

Feare, C. J. and R. W. Summers. 1986. Birds as predators on rocky shores. In P. G. Moore and R. Seed (eds.), *The Ecology of Rocky Coasts,* pp. 249–264. Columbia University Press, New York.

Fonseca, M. S. and S. S. Bell. 1998. Influence of physical setting on seagrass landscapes near Beaufort, North Carolina, USA. *Mar. Ecol. Prog. Ser.* 171: 109–121.

Fonseca, M. S. and W. J. Kenworthy. 1987. Effects of current on photosynthesis and distribution of seagrass. *Aquat. Bot.* 27: 59–78.

Fonseca, M. S., J. S. Fisher, J. C. Zieman and G. W. Thayer. 1982. Influence of the seagrass, *Zostera marina* L., on current flow. *Estuarine, Coastal, and Shelf Sci.* 15: 351–364.

Fonseca, M. S., D. L. Meyer and M. O. Hall. 1996. Development of planted seagrass beds in Tampa Bay, Florida, USA. II. Faunal components. *Mar. Ecol. Prog. Ser.* 132: 141–156.

Gambi, M. C., A. R. M. Nowell and P. J. Jumars. 1990. Flume observations on flow density dynamics in *Zostera marina* (eelgrass) beds. *Mar. Ecol. Prog. Ser.* 61: 159–169.

Gleason, H. A. 1926. The individualistic concept of the plant association. *Bull. Torrey Botanical Club* 53: 7–26.

Gleason, M. L., D. A. Elmer, N. C. Pien and J. S. Fisher. 1979. Effects of stem density upon sediment retention by salt marsh cord grass, *Spartina alterniflora* Loisel. *Estuaries* 2: 271–273.

Glynn, P. W. 1973. *Acanthaster:* Effect on coral reef growth in Panama. *Science* 180: 504–506.

Glynn, P. W. 1976. Some physical and biological determinants of coral community structure in the eastern Pacific. *Ecol. Monogr.* : 431–456.

Glynn, P. W. 1993. Coral reef bleaching: Ecological perspectives. *Coral Reefs* 12: 1–17.

Goldberg, D. E. 1990. Components of resource competition in plant communities. In J. B. Grace and D. Tilman (eds.), *Perspectives on Plant Competition,* pp. 27–49. Academic Press, San Diego, CA.

Goreau, T. F., N. I. Goreau and T. F. Goreau. 1979. Corals and coral reefs. *Sci. Amer.* 241: 124–136.

Gosselin, L. A. and F. S. Chia. 1995. Distribution and dispersal of early juvenile snails: Effectiveness of intertidal microhabitats as refuges and food sources. *Mar. Ecol. Prog. Ser.* 128: 213–223.

Greenlee, J. T. and R. M. Callaway. 1996. Abiotic stress and the relative importance of interference and facilitation in montane bunchgrass communities in western Montana. *Amer. Nat.* 148: 386–396.

Grutter, A. 1996. Parasite removal rates by the cleaner wrasse *Labroides dimidiatus. Mar. Ecol. Prog. Ser.* 130: 61–70.

Hacker, S. D. and S. D. Gaines. 1997. Some implications of direct positive interactions for community species diversity. *Ecology* 78: 1990–2003.

Hacker, S. D. and L. P. Madin. 1991. Why habitat architecture and color are important to shrimps living in pelagic *Sargassum:* Use of camouflage and plant-part mimicry. *Mar. Ecol. Prog. Ser.* 70: 143–155.

Hacker, S. D. and R. S. Steneck. 1990. Habitat architecture and the abundance and body-size-dependent habitat selection of a phytal amphipod. *Ecology* 71: 2269–2285.

Hanski, I. 1998. Metapopulation dynamics. *Nature* 396: 41–49.

Hawkins, S. J. 1981. The influence of season and barnacles on the algal colonization of *patella vulgata* exclusion areas. *J. Mar. Biol. Assoc.* 61: 1–15.

Hay, M. E. 1986. Associational plant defenses and the maintenance of species diversity: Turning competitors into accomplices. *Amer. Nat.* 128: 617–641.

Hay, M. E. and W. Fenical. 1996. Chemical ecology and marine biodiversity: Insights and products from the sea. *Oceanography* 9: 10–20.

Hay, M. E., J. E. Duffy and C. A. Pfister. 1987. Chemical defense against different marine herbivores: Are amphipods insect equivalents? *Ecology* 68: 1567–1580.

Hay, M. E., J. E. Duffy and W. Fenical. 1990. Host-plant specialization decreases predation on a marine amphipod: An herbivore in plant's clothing. *Ecology* 71: 733–743.

Heck, K. L., Jr. 1979. Some determinants of the composition and abundance of motile macroinvertebrate species in tropical and temperate turtlegrass (*Thalassia testudinum*) meadows. *J. Biogeogr.* 6: 183–200.

Heck, K. L., Jr. and R. J. Orth. 1980. Seagrass habitats: The roles of habitat complexity, competition and predation in structuring associated fish and motile macroinvertebrate assemblages. In V. S. Kennedy (ed.), *Estuarine Perspectives,* pp. 449–646. Academic Press, San Diego, CA.

Heck, K. L., Jr. and G. S. Wetstone. 1977. Habitat complexity and invertebrate species richness and abundance in tropical seagrass meadows. *J. Biogeogr.* 4: 135–142.

Holmgren, M., M. Scheffer and M. A. Huston. 1997. The interplay of facilitation and competition in plant communities. *Ecology* 78: 1966–1975.

Holzapfel, C. and B. E. Mahall. 1999. Bidirectional facilitation and interference between shrubs and annuals in the Mojave Desert. *Ecology* 80: 1747–1761.

Huffaker, C. B. 1958. Experimental studies on predation: Dispersion factors and predator-prey oscillations. *Hilgardia* 27: 343–383.

Hughes, T. P. 1994. Catastrophes, phase shifts, and large scale degradation of a Caribbean coral reef. *Science* 265: 1547–1551.

Irlandi, E. A. 1997. Seagrass patch size and survivorship of a infaunal bivalve. *Oikos* 78: 511–518.

Irlandi, E. A. and C. H. Peterson. 1991. Modification of animal habitats by large plants: Mechanisms by which seagrasses influence clam growth. *Oecologia* 87: 307–318.

Jackson, G. A. and C. D. Winant. 1983. Effect of a kelp forest on coastal currents. *Cont. Shelf Res.* 2: 75–80.

Jackson, J. B. C. 1981. Interspecific competition and species' distributions: The ghosts of theories and data past. *Amer. Zool.* 21: 889–901.

Jones, C. G., J. H. Lawton and M. Shachak. 1994. Organisms as ecosystem engineers. *Oikos* 69: 373–386.

Jones, C. G., J. H. Lawton and M. Shachak. 1997. Positive and negative effects of organisms as physical ecosystem engineers. *Ecology* 78: 1946–1957.

Keddy, P. A. 1989. *Competition*. Chapman and Hall, London.

Kennedy, C. W. and J. F. Bruno. 2000. Restriction of the upper vertical distribution of New England cobble beach plants by wave-related disturbance. *J. Ecol.* 88: 856–868.

Lawton, J. H. 1984. Non-competitive populations, non-convergent communities, and vacant niches: The herbivores of braken. In D. R. Strong, D. Simberloff, L. G. Abele and A. B. Thistle (eds.), *Ecological Communities: Conceptual Issues and the Evidence*, pp. 67–100. Princeton University Press, Princeton, NJ.

Leonard, G. H. 1999. Positive and negative effects of intertidal algal canopies on recruitment and survival of barnacles. *Mar. Ecol. Prog. Ser.* 178: 241–249.

Leonard, G. H., P. J. Ewanchuk and M. D. Bertness. 1999. How recruitment, intraspecific interactions, and predation control species borders in a tidal estuary. *Oecologia* 118: 492–502.

Leonard, L. A. and M. E. Luther. 1995. Flow hydrodynamics in tidal marsh canopies. *Limnol. Oceanogr.* 40: 1474–1484.

Levin, P. S. and M. E. Hay. 1996. Responses of temperate reef fishes to alterations in algal structure and species composition. *Mar. Ecol. Prog. Ser.* 134: 37–47.

Levine, J. M. and C. M. D'Antonio. 1999. Elton revisited: A review of evidence linking diversity and invasibility. *Oikos* 87: 15–26.

Lohse, D. P. 1993. The importance of secondary substratum in a rocky intertidal community. *J. Exp. Mar. Biol. Ecol.* 166: 1–17.

Luckenbach, M. W. 1986. Sediment stability around animal tubes: The roles of hydrodynamic processes and biotic activity. *Limnol. Oceanogr.* 31: 779–787.

Luckhurst, B. E. and K. Luckhurst. 1978. Analysis of the influence of substrate variables on coral reef fish communities. *Mar. Biol.* 49: 317–323.

MacArthur, R. H. and E. O. Wilson. 1967. *The Theory of Island Biogeography*. Princeton University Press, Princeton, NJ.

Malakoff, D. 1998. Restored wetlands flunk real-world test. *Science* 280: 371–372.

May, R. M. and J. Seger. 1986. Ideas in ecology. *Amer. Nat.* 74: 256–267.

McCloskey, L. 1970. The dynamics of the community associated with a marine scleractinian coral. *Int. Rev. Ges. Hydrobiol.* 55: 13–81.

Menge, B. A. 1978. Predation intensity in a rocky intertidal community: Effect of an algal canopy, wave action and desiccation on predator feeding rates. *Oecologia* 34: 17–35.

Menge, B. A. and A. M. Olson. 1990. Role of scale and environmental factors in regulation of community structure. *Trends Ecol. Evol.* 5: 52–57.

Menge, B. A. and J. P. Sutherland. 1976. Species diversity gradients: Synthesis of the roles of predation, competition, and temporal heterogeneity. *Amer. Nat.* 110: 351–369.

Menge, B. A. and J. P. Sutherland. 1987. Community regulation: Variation in disturbance, competition, and predation in relation to environmental stress and recruitment. *Amer. Nat.* 130: 730–757.

Menge, B. A., E. L. Berlow, C. A. Blanchette, S. A. Navarrete and S. B. Yamada. 1994. The keystone species concept: Variation in interaction strength in a rocky intertidal habitat. *Ecol. Monogr.* 64: 249–286.

Mills, L. S., M. E. Soulé and D. F. Doak. 1993. The keystone species concept in ecology and conservation. *BioScience* 43: 219–224.

O'Gower, A. K. and J. W. Wacasey. 1967. Animal communities associated with *Thalassia, Diplanthera,* and sand beds in Biscayne Bay. I. Analysis of communities in relation to water movements. *Bull. Mar. Sci.* 17: 175–210.

Ojeda, F. P. and J. H. Dearborn. 1991. Feeding ecology of benthic mobile predators: Experimental analyses of their influence in rocky subtidal communities of the Gulf of Maine. *J. Exp. Mar. Biol. Ecol.* 149: 13–44.

Orth, R. J. 1973. Benthic infauna of eelgrass, *Zostera marina,* beds. *Chesapeake Sci.* 14: 258–269.

Orth, R. J. 1977. The importance of sediment stability in seagrass communities. In B. C. Coull (ed.), *Ecology of Marine Benthos,* pp. 281–300. University of South Carolina Press, Columbia.

Paine, R. T. 1974. Intertidal community structure: Experimental studies on the relationship between a dominant competitor and its principal predator. *Oecologia* 15: 93–120.

Paine, R. T. and S. A. Levin. 1981. Intertidal landscapes. *Ecol. Monogr.* 51: 145–178.

Peters, R. H. 1991. *A Critique for Ecology.* Cambridge University Press, Cambridge.

Peterson, C. H. 1982. Clam predation by Whelks (*Busycon* spp.): Experimental tests of the importance of prey size, prey density, and seagrass cover. *Mar. Biol.* 66: 159–170.

Peterson, C. H., H. C. Summerson and P. B. Duncan. 1984. The influence of seagrass cover on population structure and individual growth of a suspension-feeding bivalve, *Mercenaria mercenaria. J. Mar. Res.* 42: 123–138.

Petraitis, P. S., R. E. Latham and R. A. Niesenbaum. 1989. The maintenance of species diversity by disturbance. *Quar. Rev. Biol.* 64: 393–418.

Power, M. E. 1997. Estimating the impacts of a dominant detritovore in a neotropical system. *Trends Ecol. Evol.* 12: 47–49.

Power, M. E. and L. S. Mills. 1995. The keystone cops meet in Hilo. *Trends Ecol. Evol.* 10: 182–184.

Power, M. E., D. Tilman, J. A. Estes, B. A. Menge, W. J. Bond, L. S. Mills, G. Daily, J. C.

Castilla, J. Lubchenco and R. T. Paine. 1996. Challenges in the quest for keystones. *BioScience* 46: 609–620.

Price, P. W. 1984. Communities of specialists: Vacant niches in ecological and evolutionary time. In D. R. Strong, D. Simberloff, L. G. Abele and A. B. Thistle (eds.), *Ecological Communities: Conceptual Issues and the Evidence,* pp. 510–523. Princeton University Press, Princeton, NJ.

Rand, T. A. 2000. Seed dispersal, habitat suitability and the distribution of halophytes across a salt marsh tidal gradient. *J. Ecol.* 88: 608–621.

Reaka-Kudla, M. 1997. The global biodiversity of coral reefs: A comparison with rain forests. In M. Reaka-Kudla, D. E. Wilson and E. O. Wilson (eds.), *Biodiversity II,* pp. 83–108. Joseph Henry Press, Washington, DC.

Ricketts, E. F. and J. Calvin. 1939. *Between Pacific Tides.* Stanford University Press, Stanford, CA.

Roberts, C. M. 1997. Connectivity and management of Caribbean coral reefs. *Science* 278: 1454–1457.

Rosenzweig, M. L. 1995. *Species Diversity in Space and Time.* Cambridge University Press, Cambridge.

Rozas, L. P. and R. J. Zimmerman. 2000. Small-scale patterns of nekton use among marsh and adjacent shallow nonvegetated areas of the Galveston Bay Estuary, Texas (USA). *Mar. Ecol. Prog. Ser.* 193: 217–239.

Rützler, K. and I. C. Feller. 1996. Caribbean mangrove swamps. *Sci. Amer.* 3: 94–99.

Schwindt, E. 1997a. Efecto de los agregados del poliqueto invasor *Ficopomatus enigmaticus* sobre el benthos en la laguna costera Mar Chiquita. Tesis, Universidad Nacional de Mar del Plata.

Schwindt, E. 1997b. Environmental heterogeneity generated by an introduced reef-forming polychaete *Ficopomatus enigmaticus* on a SW Atlantic coastal lagoon. *VII Congreso Latinoamericano de Ciencias del Mar, Santos, Brasil* 2: 426–427.

Schwindt, E. and O. O. Iribarne. In press. Settlement sites, survival and effects on benthos of an introduced reef-building polychaete in a SW Atlantic coastal lagoon. *Bull. Mar. Sci.*

Seed, R. 1996. Patterns of biodiversity in the macro-invertebrate fauna associated with mussel patches on rocky shores. *J. Mar. Biol. Assoc.* 76: 203–210.

Shashar, N., S. Kinane, P. L. Jokiel and M. R. Patterson. 1996. Hydromechanical boundary layers over a coral reef. *J. Exp. Mar. Biol. Ecol.* 199: 17–28.

Smith, F. and J. D. Witman. 1999. Species diversity in subtidal landscapes: Maintenance by physical processes and larval recruitment. *Ecology* 80: 51–69.

Stachowicz, J. J. In press. Mutualisms, positive interactions, and the structure of ecological communities. *BioScience.*

Stachowicz, J. J. and M. E. Hay. 1996. Facultative mutualism between an herbivorous crab and a coralline alga: Advantages of eating noxious seaweed. *Oecologia* 105: 377–387.

Stachowicz, J. J. and M. E. Hay. 1999. Reducing predation through chemically mediated camouflage: Indirect effects of plant defenses on herbivores. *Ecology* 80: 495–509.

Steele, M. A. 1999. Effects of shelter and predators on reef fishes. *J. Exp. Mar. Biol. Ecol.* 233: 65–79.

Stoner, A. W. 1982. The influence of benthic macrophytes on the foraging behavior of pinfish, *Lagodon rhomboides* (Linnaeus). *J. Exp. Mar. Biol. Ecol.* 58: 271–284.

Stoner, A. W. 1983. Distribution of fishes in seagrass meadows: Role of macrophyte biomass and species composition. *Fish. Bull.* 81: 837–846.

Stoner, A. W. and F. G. Lewis. 1985. The influence of quantitative and qualitative aspects of habitat complexity in tropical seagrass meadows. *J. Exp. Mar. Biol. Ecol.* 94: 19–40.

Suchanek, T. H. 1979. The *Mytilus californianus* community: Studies on the composition, structure, organization, and dynamics of a mussel bed. PhD Dissertation, University of Washington, Seattle.

Suchanek, T. H. 1986. Mussels and their role in structuring rocky shore communities. In P. G. Moore and R. Seed (eds.), *The Ecology of Rocky Coasts*, pp. 70–96. Columbia University Press, New York.

Taylor, R. B. and R. G. Cole. 1994. Mobile epifauna on subtidal brown seaweeds in northeastern New Zealand. *Mar. Ecol. Prog. Ser.* 115: 271–282.

Terborgh, J. 1986. Keystone plant resources in tropical forests. In M. E. Soulé (ed.), *Conservation Biology: The Science of Scarcity and Diversity*, pp. 330–344. Sinauer Associates, Sunderland, MA.

Thistle, D. and J. E. Eckman. 1990. The effect of a biologically produced structure on the benthic copepods of a deep-sea site. *Deep Sea Res.* 37: 541–554.

Thompson, R. C., B. J. Wilson, M. L. Tobin, A. S. Hill and S. J. Hawkins. 1996. Biologically generated habitat provision and diversity of rocky shore organisms at a hierarchy of spatial scales. *J. Exp. Mar. Biol. Ecol.* 202: 73–82.

Tokeshi, M. and L. Romero. 1995. Filling a gap: Dynamics of space occupancy on a mussel-dominated subtropical rocky shore. *Mar. Ecol. Prog. Ser.* 119: 167–176.

Underwood, A. J. and E. J. Denley. 1984. Paradigms, explanations and generalizations in models for the structure of intertidal communities on rocky shores. In D. R. Strong, D. Simberloff, L. G. Abele and A. B. Thistle (eds.), *Ecological Communities: Conceptual Issues and the Evidence*, pp. 151–180. Princeton University Press, Princeton, NJ.

Urban, H.-J. 1994. Upper temperature tolerance of ten bivalve species off Peru and Chile related to El Niño. *Mar. Ecol. Prog. Ser.* 107: 139–145.

Vince, S., I. Valiela, N. Backus and J. M. Teal. 1976. Predation by the salt marsh killifish *Fundulus heteroclitas* (L.) in relation to prey size and habitat structure: Consequence for prey distribution and abundance. *J. Exp. Mar. Biol. Ecol.* 23: 255–266.

Wallace, A. R. 1890. *The Malay Archipelago*. Dover, New York.

Watling, L. and E. A. Norse. 1998. Disturbance of the seabed by mobile fishing gear: A comparison to forest clearcutting. *Cons. Biol.* 12: 1180–1197.

Welden, C. W. and W. L. Slauson. 1986. The intensity of competition versus its importance: An overlooked distinction and some implications. *Quar. Rev. Biol.* 61: 23–43.

Wilson, J. B. and A. D. Agnew. 1992. Positive-feedback switches in plant communities. *Adv. Ecol. Res.* 23: 263–336.

Witman, J. D. 1985. Refuges, biological disturbance, and rocky subtidal community structure in *New England Ecol. Monogr.* 55: 421–445.

Witman, J. D. 1987. Subtidal coexistence: Storms, grazing, mutualism, and the zonation of kelps and mussels. *Ecol. Monogr.* 57: 167–198.

Witman, J. D. and K. R. Grange. 1998. Links between rain, salinity, and predation in a rocky subtidal community. *Ecology* 79: 2429–2447.

Woodin, S. A. 1978. Refuges, disturbance, and community structure: A marine soft-bottom example. *Ecology* 59: 274–284.

Woodley, J. D., and 17 others. 1981. Hurricane Allen's impact on Jamaican coral reefs. *Science* 214: 749–755.

Worcester, S. E. 1995. Effects of eelgrass beds on advection and turbulent mixing in low current and low shoot density environments. *Mar. Ecol. Prog. Ser.* 126: 223–232.

Zimmerman, R., T. Minello, T. Baumer and M. Castiglione. 1989. Oyster reef as habitat for estuarine macrofauna. NOAA Technical Memorandum NMFS–SEFC–249.

part II

Community Types

chapter 9

Rocky Intertidal Communities

Bruce A. Menge and George M. Branch

*L*ying between the low- and high-water tidemarks, inter-tidal habitats fringe the world's coasts, forming an almost one-dimensional "bathtub ring" that ranges in vertical extent from a few centimeters to more than 7 meters. On a map of the world, they occupy only the lines that outline the land masses. The modest proportion of the total earth surface occupied by these habitats, however, belies their importance both to science and to humankind. Scientifically, they have been disproportionately responsible for conceptual advances, especially in the field of community ecology. Rocky intertidal communities have been a cauldron of scientific ferment, and work in these habitats has steadily helped to "push the envelope" in developing the theory and understanding of community and ecosystem dynamics. As key components of nearshore coastal ecosystems, they are also critically important habitats for the future well-being of humankind, which, paradoxically, will bear full responsibility for their actual or potential degradation (Lubchenco 1998; Vitousek et al. 1997).

In this chapter, we focus on rocky intertidal habitats, emphasizing their role as a model ecosystem. Studies on rocky shores have provided rich insights into the interactions among the biota that dwell there. Their unique physical environment alternately exposes them to air and submerges them under the advancing ocean. This process creates steep environmental gradients, which both underlie the striking patterns of distribution and abundance seen on most rocky shores and help to explain these patterns. Several things conjoin to make rocky shores almost ideal outdoor "laboratories": steep vertical gradients, variable physical conditions over short distances, and the presence of organisms that are mostly sessile or sedentary, often reach high densities, are small in size, and are readily manipulated experimentally.

GENERAL PATTERNS ON ROCKY SHORES

Rocky intertidal habitats experience a wide range of physical conditions, including some of the most severe in the world (see Denny and Wethey, this volume). Extraordinary wave forces hammer rocky coastlines, raising obvious questions about the mechanisms that allow organisms to survive the pounding. Other important factors include the degree of immersion, which varies with an organism's level on the shore, thermal conditions, nutrient concentrations, and climate. Intertidal communities exist in conditions ranging from frequent to periodic freezing and ice abrasion (e.g., the shores of the northwestern Atlantic: Wethey 1985) to temperatures that thermally denature protein (e.g., the Pacific coast of Panama: Garrity 1984). Despite these extreme physical conditions, species interactions have often proved remarkably strong and important in determining patterns of distribution and abundance. In this sense, rocky shores are the "stage" upon which ecological "dramas" are played out, and physical conditions both provide the "ambience" and help direct the "plays."

Physical Environment

Rocky intertidal habitats are characterized by two dominant gradients in physical conditions. First, *wave exposure gradients* occur horizontally along the shore, typically being most severe at the tips of rocky headlands and gradually declining in severity toward more sheltered coves and bays. Communities occurring at the most exposed areas are on average pounded by much larger, more powerful waves and swells than are those in more sheltered areas. Headlands are not necessarily assaulted by giant waves continuously, of course, because oceanic environments are always in a state of flux and experience both stormy and calm periods. Nonetheless, at any given time and sea state, the forces imposed on wave-exposed headlands are always greater, and usually far greater, than wave forces in less exposed regions. These differences in wave forces have major and far-reaching consequences for the intertidal biota, with important direct (e.g., removing organisms) and indirect effects (e.g., altering interactions between organisms) to be discussed below.

Second, *tidal excursion gradients* occur vertically up and down the shore. As the tides recede and advance, the intertidal zone is first revealed, then covered up. These changes impose a sharp gradient of exposure to air, with high intertidal areas experiencing long periods of emersion (out of water), and low intertidal areas experiencing short periods of emersion. Thus, high intertidal biota must endure lengthy spells of exposure to air, sometimes experiencing both severe desiccation (drying out) and high thermal stress (heating up). It stands to reason that high intertidal biota should tolerate more severe conditions of heat and desiccation than low intertidal biota, and in fact this is generally what researchers observe when this hypothesis is tested (e.g., Roberts et al. 1997).

The combination of these two environmental gradients can produce a complex range of conditions in rocky intertidal habitats. For example, wave forces may limit the activity of mobile species, suggesting that greater activity (and stronger consequences of this activity, such as higher grazing or predation) will occur in more sheltered environments. However, a decline in wave force can also lead to an increase in thermal and desiccation stress because the intertidal habitat is moistened less reliably by wave splash and spray. Activity may thus also be limited in these more sheltered parts of the habitat. These considerations suggest that activity is likely to be greatest on shores of intermediate wave exposure; wave forces will be smaller, but there will still be sufficient splash and spray. We return to these issues and their ecological consequences later in this chapter.

There are, of course, other physical gradients in rocky intertidal environments. Sedimentation, for example, can occur at a higher rate in more sheltered habitats when the nearshore waters carry a high load of inorganic particles. Salinity may also vary, either vertically with seepage of fresh water from supratidal regions or horizontally in relation to riverine inputs. "Microgradients," or small-scale gradients of light, moisture, and temperature (around crevices or boulders, or under algal canopies, for example) are also common in rocky intertidal habitats. Quantification of such gradients and their ecological importance is, unfortunately, relatively lacking (but for an example, see Garrity 1984).

Patterns in the Biota of Rocky Shores

In general, community ecologists investigate *patterns, processes*, and *mechanisms* that describe or explain the composition and dynamics of populations of plants and animals interacting and persisting in a particular habitat. We first summarize some of the kinds of patterns that excite ecologists, present some examples from rocky intertidal environments, and then address the processes and mechanisms that underlie patterns on rocky shores.

DISTRIBUTION AND ABUNDANCE. Here, pattern, or *community structure*, is defined as observable regularity in such components as distribution and abundance, species diversity and composition, size, and trophic relationships. On rocky shores, community structure is particularly easy to see and quantify. Zonation, for example, is the pattern of distribution and abundance observable as successive bands of organisms as one moves from the low shore to the high shore. Zonation is perhaps the best-known pattern in rocky intertidal communities (Figure 9.1A–B). It occurs universally in rocky intertidal regions (Lewis 1964; Stephenson and Stephenson 1972), even where the tidal range is only a few tens of centimeters (e.g., the Swedish west coast: Johanneson 1989). As an example, on South African rocky shores, the highest levels support very few species, and littorinid snails are conspicuous, giving this band the name "*Littorina* zone." Below this, much of the mid-shore has abundant barnacles in the upper section and a mix of barnacles and macroalgae in the lower section, respectively called the Upper Balanoid and the Lower Balanoid zones. At the bottom of the shore, seaweeds may dominate the infratidal zone, giving way to kelp beds in the subtidal zone. Stephenson first coined these descriptive terms as part of his worldwide survey of zonation on rocky shores (Stephenson and Stephenson 1972). These zones are, however, modified by biogeographic changes as one moves around the South African coast. For instance, on the west coast (Figure 9.1D,E), subtidal kelp forests are a feature, barnacles are rare, and the limpet *Scutellastra* (formerly *Patella*) *argenvillei* occurs at such high densities low on wave-washed shores that it excludes most other organisms except encrusting corallines (Branch and Griffiths 1988). These biogeographic changes in zonation impose another, and larger-scale, pattern that also demands explanation.

Gradients in wave exposure provide an important backdrop against which community structure varies horizontally in space (Lewis 1964). Even over short distances, patterns of distribution and species composition can shift dramatically from wave-exposed headlands to nearby wave-sheltered coves, while still displaying sharp vertical zonation (e.g., Dayton 1971; Menge 1976). In wave-exposed areas in temperate North America (e.g., Figure 9.1A), the top of the shore is typically dominated by littorinid gastropods, followed by barnacles and, sometimes, foliose algae. Mid-shore zones often support mussels, and low-shore zones are occupied by a variety of invertebrates and/or algae, including mussels, barnacles, anemones, grazing molluscs, sea stars, kelps, and other seaweeds. At more sheltered sites, barnacles can still dominate high zones but may also be less abundant. In mid zones, mussels are reduced in abundance and often replaced as dominants by macrophytes (Figure 9.1B). In the low-shore zone, kelps decrease while turfy algae increase (Figure 9.1B; see also Menge and Farrell 1989). Similar patterns occur on rocky shores at temperate latitudes in many other regions of the world. In Britain, for example, mussels and barnacles, in-

Figure 9.1 (A, B) Zonation patterns at two sites on the New England coast, U.S.A. (A) A wave-exposed site, showing a high-shore barnacle zone (*Semibalanus balanoides*), and a mid- and low-shore mussel zone (*Mytilus edulis*). The mussels on the low shore are overlaid by a canopy of the kelp *Alaria esculenta*. (B) A less wave-exposed site, showing a high barnacle zone (*Semibalanus* again), a mid fucoid alga/bare zone (*Fucus vesiculosis, Ascophyllum nodosum*), and a low intertidal zone dominated by the turfy red alga *Chondrus crispus*. (C) The New Zealand sea star *Stichaster australis* can occur at high densities on wave-beaten shores, and controls the mussel *Perna canaliculus* in the low-shore zone. (D) On the west coast of South Africa, the limpet *Scutellastra argenvillei* depends on the subsidy it obtains from adjacent kelp beds to sustain extraordinarily high biomass. Competitive exclusion by the alien mussel *Mytilus galloprovincialis* (lower half of the photograph) poses a major threat to it. (E) Dense low-shore beds of *Scutellastra argenvillei* (right) exclude most organisms except encrusting corallines. However, a lush and diverse algal community develops within a month if these limpets are experimentally fenced out (left). (A–B from Wertheim 1984; C–E by G. M. Branch.)

terspersed with limpets, dominate exposed sites, and fucoid algae form dense stands in sheltered areas (e.g., Hartnoll and Hawkins 1985; Hawkins and Hartnoll 1983). In tropical regions, differences in wave action also lead to shifts in zonation patterns. In calmer areas, mussels and macrophytes are replaced as dominants by coralline algae and turfs up to a few centimeters in length (Menge and Farrell 1989). In some areas oysters and barnacles are common, but only occasionally form obvious zones like those seen at higher latitudes.

PATCHINESS. At smaller, within-zone spatial scales, patchiness of space-occupying organisms is another universally observed pattern in rocky intertidal communities. A classic example is the patches, or gaps, so commonly observed in mussel beds (e.g., Dayton 1971; Paine and Levin 1981) and algae (Dayton 1973). The level of patchiness can also vary, both in space and time, from virtually none to such extreme patchiness that there is no obvious zonal dominant. This latter case is termed a mosaic community (Menge et al. 1993).

SPECIES STRUCTURE. Biomass, species richness, and diversity all commonly vary predictably with height in the intertidal zone, progressively increasing as one moves downshore and peaking in the lowest zones, although this progression is sometimes interrupted by bands of dense low-shore grazers that abruptly reduce overall biomass and diversity (McQuaid and Branch 1985; and see Figure 9.1D,E). In the high-shore, mid-shore, and low-shore zones on the Pacific coast of Panama, Lubchenco et al. (1984) recorded the number of species of algae and invertebrates (species richness) at 8, 42, and 65 respectively. According to the Shannon-Wiener (*H'*) index, which reflects both species number and relative abundance, species diversity of sessile organisms in these zones increased 0.96 to 1.62 to 2.61.

SIZE AND MORPHOLOGY. The body size and morphology of intertidal organisms can also vary systematically in response to environmental conditions. For example, carnivorous whelks living in wave-sheltered areas commonly have thicker shells than do wave-exposed individuals of the same species (e.g., Ebling et al. 1964; Kitching and Lockwood 1974). The explanation for this is that shell-crushing predators such as crabs (which selectively consume thinner-shelled individuals) are more abundant and effective on sheltered shores. In comparison with temperate species, tropical gastropods are commonly larger and more heavily "armored," having thicker shells or heavier sculpturing that protects them against the more intense predation typical of the tropics (Vermeij 1978; Palmer 1979).

Size may also be influenced by physical factors. For example, the larger the organism, the greater the effect of drag as water passes over it. By measuring and modeling the forces imposed by water movement, Denny et al. (1985) have calculated the maximum sizes that various organisms can theoretically achieve in the face of wave action.

TROPHIC STRUCTURE. Trophic relationships in communities are commonly presented using food webs, which map out the feeding relationships among the species (e.g., Figure 9.2;

Pimm 1982). While useful in many respects, such diagrams are strictly descriptive and do not represent the dynamics of interactions among the species in the web, even if the links are quantitative (e.g., reflect the percentage of the diet made up by each prey species). Dynamics, such as the effect of predation by one species on another, must also include responses by both prey and predator, and can only be determined experimentally. Food webs also do not reflect non-trophic interactions (such as competition for space or facilitation).

Interaction webs are more useful tools for portraying community dynamics. They resemble food webs, but differ in including only those species involved in "strong" interactions (those producing a large effect on one or both interactors: e.g., Paine 1980, 1992; Menge and Sutherland 1987). They also cover both trophic and non-trophic interactions, and incorporate direct as well as indirect effects. Experiments are necessary to determine whether or not interactions are strong.

Observation of such patterns in communities raises an obvious question: What *are* the causes of community structure? Why are there sharp lower and upper boundaries of zones? What causes and maintains patchiness? What is the ecological significance of differences in size and morphology? What are the causes of variation in community structure? We cannot address all of these questions here, so our primary focus will be on the dynamics that underlie variations in patterns of spatial and trophic structure of rocky intertidal communities.

COMMUNITY DYNAMICS IN ROCKY INTERTIDAL COMMUNITIES

Both abiotic and biotic processes influence community structure (e.g., Menge and Sutherland 1987). Biotic factors include a wide range of direct species interactions, such as predation

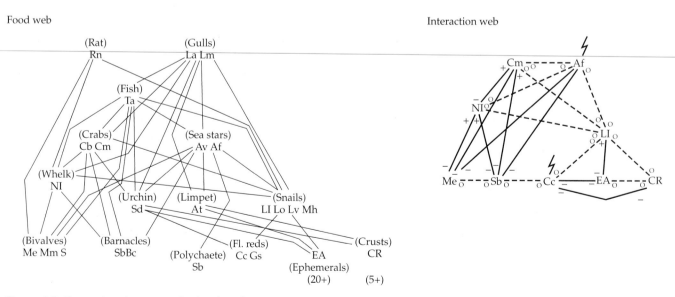

Figure 9.2 Comparison between a food web and an interaction web for the low-shore zone of New England. Thin lines in the food web indicate trophic links. Thick lines in the interaction web indicate strong effects, and dashed lines indicate weak links. The lightning-strike symbol indicates controlling effects of the physical environment. +, positive effect; –, negative effect, O, no effect. (After Menge and Sutherland 1987.)

(+−), herbivory (+−), parasitism (+−), intra- and interspecific competition (−−), mutualism (++), commensalism (+0), and amensalism (-0; sometimes called "biological disturbance"). (The signs indicate the nature of the effect on each interactor: + = positive effects, − = negative effects, and 0 = no effect.) These factors often act via interactions with other species in multispecies assemblages, and can lead to great complexity in community dynamics. Populations and communities can also change because of emigration and immigration—usually referred to as dispersal and recruitment (or settlement), at least for species with waterborne propagules.

The abiotic factors most likely to affect intertidal organisms include nutrients, habitat structure, light, salinity, and environmental stressors such as wave action or desiccation. Environmental stressors cause weakening or death due to changes in the environment. Nutrients (nitrate, nitrite, ammonium, phosphate, silicate, iron) are essential for photosynthesis by marine plants. They directly influence the abundance or composition of macroalgae, surfgrasses, and phytoplankton, and indirectly determine the productivity (the supply of live plant tissues and detritus) available to higher trophic levels. Habitat structure, specifically topographic complexity, can affect communities by providing a greater variety of microhabitats or by increasing the amount of refuge or shelter space.

All of these environmental factors vary in magnitude in space and time, thus establishing environmental gradients such as those described earlier. Wave action and exposure to air are relatively local gradients, varying at scales of centimeters to kilometers. Other gradients, such as those in nutrients and productivity, range over much larger scales. Nutrient and productivity gradients have been relatively unstudied in intertidal habitats, largely because it was assumed that they vary at such large scales that they are unlikely to influence the variation observed among intertidal communities within regions (Menge 1992). Recent work, however, shows the importance of these gradients at both local and regional scales (e.g., Bustamante et al. 1995a,b; Menge 1997a). Finally, gradients in habitat complexity tend to be irregular, ranging in scale from very localized variation in microtopography to entire coastlines. For example, some evidence suggests that diversity patterns can depend strongly on small-scale habitat complexity such as cracks and crevices (Menge et al. 1985; Hixon and Menge 1991). At the other extreme, the extent to which a coastline is broken up by deep indentations such as fjords or sounds can influence diversity by creating extensive areas of unique marine habitats with biotas largely distinct from that seen on open coasts.

Influence of Physical Factors

The effects that physical factors have on the patterns we perceive in community structure depend on their magnitude, duration, and frequency. If events are regular and predictable, organisms may be able to adapt to them. An obvious example is the rise and fall of tides. But other events may be more catastrophic because of their infrequency or severity.

One of the early researchers to appreciate the significance of this difference for rocky shore communities was Paul Dayton. He described how logs thrown ashore by waves eliminate clumps of organisms, creating a mosaic of different patches at different stages of succession (Dayton 1971). His insights were pursued by Sousa (1979a,b), who used intertidal boulder fields as a model system to explore the effects of disturbance. The frequency with which boulders are overturned, and therefore disturb communities, obviously depends on a combination of the strength of wave action and the sizes of the boulders themselves. Sousa showed that if disturbance is very intense and very frequent, the diversity of species drops dramatically. The greatest diversity is reached at some intermediate level of disturbance—a demonstration of the "intermediate disturbance hypothesis."

For many years, marine ecologists assumed that the structure of rocky intertidal communities was largely under physical control (e.g., Lewis 1964). Explanations for species distributions, for example, were sought through study of species' tolerances of waves, thermal stress, and desiccation. Many thought that species were prevented from living in particular zones because they could not tolerate the physical conditions there.

Several authors have shown that zonation is correlated with tolerance. Broekhuysen (1940) was one of the first to do so, demonstrating that the relative tolerances of six species of gastropods for extremes of salinity, water loss, and heat reflect their zonation, with high-shore species being "tougher" than low-shore ones. These early studies set a trend of focusing on the role of physical conditions as limiting factors at both upper and lower edges of the zonational ranges of species (e.g., Doty 1946; see also Underwood 1978). Despite many subsequent illustrations of such correlations, however, they are just that—correlations. Not until Wolcott (1973) monitored a North American assemblage of limpets over a period of 5 years did ecologists realize that physical factors seldom reach the extremes necessary to set limits by killing organisms, particularly for lower distributional limits. Most species live comfortably within their "zone of tolerance." Wolcott observed that only at the highest levels of the shore did physical conditions become lethal for adult limpets. He hypothesized that only there do organisms verge on unexploited resources, warranting their penetration farther upshore to capitalize on these, but incurring a greater risk of mortality because they will then be living at the edge of their tolerances. For species lower on the shore, there may be little benefit to moving upshore because this would place them in contact with higher-shore species that are better adapted to the stresses there. In other words, biotic processes may also set limits, either alone or with physical conditions.

Influence of Biotic Interactions

We now know that, while physical factors can indeed be important, they are only part of the story. Largely as a consequence of two influential studies, attention shifted dramatically in the 1960s toward the view that community patterns can be controlled by biotic factors. In 1961, Connell published two papers that elegantly and convincingly demonstrated that the lower limits of two zone-forming barnacles were set by species interactions. At Millport, Scotland, he found that interspecific competition for space determined the lower limit of the upper-shore barnacle, and that both intraspecific competition and predation by whelks determined the lower limit of the lower-shore barnacle (Connell 1961a,b). Five years later, Paine (1966) published the early results of a study on the Washington coast that clearly demonstrated that predation by a sea star maintains the lower limits of mid-shore mussel beds. Thus predation mediated patterns of species abundance, diversity, and composition in the low-shore community that normally lies below the mussels. Such studies of biological interactions touched off dramatic paradigm shifts, both in the ideas of ecology and in the ways of studying them, not only among marine ecologists but among theoretical, terrestrial, and freshwater researchers as well.

COMPETITION. Connell observed three major zones on the upper shore at Millport. The highest was a zone of the barnacle *Chthamalus stellatus*. Just below was a second zone of another, larger barnacle, *Semibalanus balanoides*, and below that, a fucoid algal zone. Previous observers had suggested that the sharp boundary between *Chthamalus* and *Semibalanus* reflected differential tolerances for desiccation, but Connell surmised that the boundary was due to the relative abilities of the barnacles to compete for space, in combination with differences in tolerance. He hypothesized that the lower limit of *Chthamalus* was determined by interspecific competition with *Semibalanus*, whereas the upper limit of *Semibalanus* was set by its intolerance of physical conditions higher on the shore.

Connell adopted a novel and extremely important approach in his investigation: he tested his hypothesis by performing field experiments. He fastened replicate stones to the rock in both the *Chthamalus* and the *Semibalanus* zones. To test the effect of *Semibalanus* on *Chthamalus*, he removed recruiting *Semibalanus* from half the stones (–*Semibalanus*) and allowed them to remain on the other half (+*Semibalanus*). On the +*Semibalanus* stones in the *Semibalanus* zone, *Chthamalus* were soon killed, being overgrown or crushed by the faster-growing *Semibalanus*. On the –*Semibalanus* stones, *Chthamalus* thrived, even growing faster there than in their normal high-shore zone. These results demonstrated not only that the absence of *Chthamalus* from the mid-shore was due to competitive exclusion (via the mechanism of overgrowth), but also that the environmental conditions there had positive, not negative, effects on *Chthamalus* growth. In a parallel study, using wire mesh cages to include (+whelk) or exclude whelks (–whelk), Connell (1961a) showed that predation by whelks set the lower limit of the *Semibalanus* zone. This classic study has long been prominent in virtually all general ecology textbooks, and is now widely known.

There are many other studies showing that competition for space can set zonation limits. In New England, Lubchenco (1980) demonstrated that interspecific competition sets the lower limit of fucoid algae. At many moderately sheltered sites, the mid-shore zone is dominated by *Fucus* spp., whereas the lower zone is dominated by the foliose red Irish moss alga, *Chondrus crispus*. Simple manipulative experiments (–*Fucus*, +*Fucus*) in the *Fucus* zone showed that Irish moss does not extend its range upward, even in the absence of *Fucus*. In contrast, removal of *Chondrus* allowed *Fucus* to spread downward into the *Chondrus* zone, where it persisted for at least 3 years. This is an example of competitive exclusion, acting via "preemptive exploitation": i.e., by individuals gaining prior access to a limiting resource and then using or exploiting it in a way that deters later arrivals. Occupation of space often falls into this category.

By contrast, some species control access to resources in a different way, by interfering directly with potential competitors, in a process (not surprisingly) called interference competition. An example is the territorial defense of patches of algae by some species of limpets and fish (Branch et al. 1992). By selectively removing competing algal species, territory holders create distinctly different assemblages of algae relative to areas outside their territories.

Many studies of competition on rocky intertidal shores focus on space, and indeed, this is the resource most often competed for by sessile organisms (Branch 1984). In the case of grazers, however, food supply is most frequently the limiting resource (for reviews, see Underwood 1979; Branch 1981; Branch 1984; Hawkins and Hartnoll 1983). Choat (1977), for instance, showed that removal of a high-shore limpet (*Lottia digitalis*) allowed the limpet species in the zone below (*L. strigatella*) to advance up the shore to make use of the food supply freed by its removal. This is one of the few documented cases in which an interspecific interaction sets the upper limits of zonation. As a general rule, upper limits appear to be set by physical factors, and lower limits by biological factors (Connell 1961a).

Studies in many other intertidal communities have documented other examples of competition and its effects on distribution, abundance, and body size. Thus, the key question is no longer "does competition occur?" but "under what conditions does it occur, and where and when is it important?" (e.g., Connell 1983; Schoener 1983).

PREDATION. When he first visited the outer coast of Washington in the early 1960s, Paine made several key observations. The first, and simplest, was that on wave-exposed shores, beds of the mussel *Mytilus californianus* always had a very sharp lower limit. Below this was a mixture of bare rock, scattered barnacles and anemones, and seaweeds, among which the ochre sea star *Pisaster ochraceus* was common. Like Connell, Paine was a good naturalist, and soon learned that mussels were a major component of the diets of these carnivores. Although *Pisaster* was not dominant in terms of numbers or biomass, Paine postulated that persistent predation by the sea stars could set a lower limit to the mussel bed.

To test this idea, he established plots with sea stars (+*Pisaster*) and without them (–*Pisaster*) on adjacent areas of the shore, removing all stars in the –*Pisaster* plots once to twice per month. Within a year, the mussel bed had begun to respond, and after 3 years, the bed had moved 2 meters down the shore, smothering and overgrowing all other sessile organisms in its path (Paine 1966, 1974). This experiment was later repeated on nearby Tatoosh Island, and there mussels persisted in the low zone of –*Pisaster* plots for over 25 years, while patterns of community structure in +*Pisaster* plots remained unchanged. Later, Paine (1971) undertook similar experiments in New Zealand, where he experimentally removed the sea star *Stichaster australis* and demonstrated almost identical responses from the mussel *Perna canaliculus* (see Figure 9.1C).

This investigation not only demonstrated that predation could determine the lower distributional limit of a dominant intertidal organism, in this case the mussel, but also made three important conceptual advances. First, this was one of the earliest experimental demonstrations of the predation hypothesis, which states that predation can control the diversity of species in a community (Paine 1966; Figure 9.3). By selectively feeding on a dominant competitor and thereby preventing competitive exclusion, predators can facilitate the coexistence of many species of both dominant and subordinate competitors. Overly severe predation can cause the local extinction of prey species, whereas in the absence of predation, competitive exclusion may run its course, reducing diversity by locally eliminating subordinate competitors.

Second, Paine's study established the concept of "keystone species," defined as a species that has a large effect on its community disproportional to its abundance (Paine 1969; Power et al. 1996; Figure 9.4). This idea has been exceptionally influential in the conceptual development of both community and applied ecology, where it has often occupied a central place in management decisions (Mills et al. 1993). Not all scientists are enamored of the concept, mainly because of the practical difficulties of quantifying what constitutes a "disproportionately large effect." Sloppiness in definition and application have also led some to question both its value as a tool in management and conservation biology and its value to ecological theory (Mills et al. 1993), but recent evaluations have helped to clarify these issues (Power et al. 1996).

Third, the *Pisaster–Mytilus* study was one of the first clear demonstrations of indirect effects, although little was made of this phenomenon until over a decade later. Indirect effects are defined as the effects of one species on a second, mediated through a third. They commonly result when species interact strongly through chains of pairwise interactions. In this case, *Pisaster* has a strong negative effect on mussels, and mussels have a strong negative effect on algae, which are abundant in the presence of *Pisaster*. Since *Pisaster* does not directly influence algae, high algal cover must be an indirect, positive effect of sea star predation on mussels (Figure 9.5).

A similar indirect effect of a large, relatively rare but charismatic predator was documented in Chile, in a warm temperate rocky intertidal community with a completely different cast of characters (Durán and Castilla 1989). On the wave-beaten Chilean coast, three zones are typical: a high-

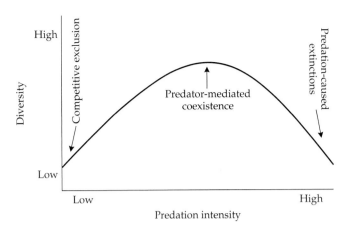

Figure 9.3 The predation hypothesis. With increasing predation, diversity increases to a maximum at some intermediate predation intensity, then declines. Low diversity results from competitive exclusion at low predation rates and predation-caused extinctions at high predation rates.

shore barnacle zone, a mid-shore mussel zone, and a low-shore macrophyte zone. The food web includes two relatively abundant, large sea stars, *Heliaster helianthus* and *Stichaster striatus*, and a large, abalone-like whelk, *Concholepas concholepas*, a consumer of mussels and barnacles. Paine et al. (1985) showed that, unlike the situation in Washington, the sea stars had weak, though measurable, effects on the mussels. However, predation by *Concholepas* had a much stronger effect—a surprising result arising from a study of the effects of human harvesting on intertidal species (Castilla and Durán 1985). Chileans consume vast quantities of limpets, sea ur-

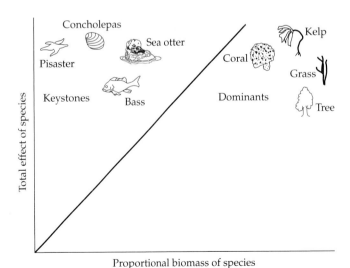

Figure 9.4 Diagram defining keystone predation. Keystone species have disproportionately large effects on their communities relative to their abundance (here, biomass), and thus lie above and to the left of the diagonal. Dominant species are the most abundant ones, and also have large effects on their communities, but their effects are not out of proportion to their abundance. (After Power et al. 1996.)

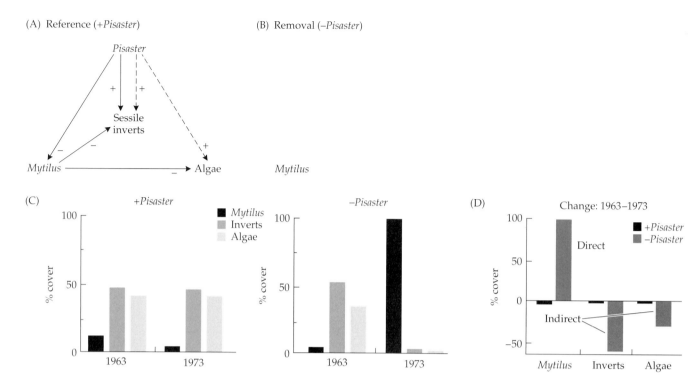

Figure 9.5 Indirect effects. (A) Interaction web showing direct (solid lines and indirect effects (dotted lines) of *Pisaster ochraceus* on mussels and seaweeds, respectively. (B) The effect on the interaction web of removing sea stars: mussels dominate. Only *Mytilus* is left. (C,D) A method of estimating the relative importance of the directversus indirect effects of sea stars. (C) Abundances of sessile organisms in the presence and absence of *Pisaster* in 1963, before sea star removal began, and 10 years later in 1973. (D) Changes in abundance: *Mytilus* increased in the absence of sea stars, which is a direct effect, and other sessile invertebrates and algae decreased in the absence of sea stars, which is an indirect effect. (After Paine 1974.)

chins, kelp, and *Concholepas* (termed "loco"), as well as many other marine organisms, and observations at sites with little human foraging suggested that harvesting had a strong effect on many intertidal species.

Castilla and his coworkers studied these effects by monitoring changes on a short stretch of coast that was fenced off as a Marine Protected Area (MPA). Within years of protecting the area, dramatic changes were evident. Mussels, previously the dominant space occupier on the upper shore, were largely replaced by barnacles. Loco abundance increased dramatically. Field observations confirmed that the decline in mussel abundance resulted from the increase in both the abundance and effect of the locos, which persisted even when the size structure of the loco population shifted from many small to few large individuals. While persistent, this pattern is clearly dependent on successful exclusion of human foragers from the MPA. Note that this case also illustrates the concepts of keystone species and indirect effects. The loco had, by far, the most dominant effect on the community, even though other, more abundant predators were present. Further, loco predation contravened a mussel monoculture and maintained striking differences in species composition and abundance.

Sometimes predation has more subtle effects. An example is the effect of whelk predation on zonation of the periwinkle *Oxystele variegata* in South Africa (McQuaid 1982). This snail exhibits a gradient in body size, with the largest individuals occurring highest on the shore, where they can largely escape predation by whelks. Because small individuals have a large surface area relative to volume, they suffer high mortality from desiccation in the high zone. Small snails are restricted to living lower on the shore, where desiccation is less intense. Although the ultimate causes of this differential zonation may be predation (low on the shore) and desiccation (higher on the shore), the size gradient is maintained behaviorally, and individuals transplanted above or below their "normal" zones migrate back to the "correct" ones with unerring accuracy and remarkable speed (McQuaid 1982).

These studies are but three of a host of similar ones showing the controlling effects of predation on rocky intertidal distribution patterns (see Table 9.1). Thus, at locations around the world, predators such as sea stars, whelks, crabs, eider ducks, and lobsters are known to have strong effects on the abundance and distribution of prey. As with competition, the question now is not so much "do predators have an effect?" but "where, and under what conditions do they have an effect?"

HERBIVORY.   As in most rocky intertidal habitats, tide pools are common along the New England coast. Lubchenco (1978) observed that at Nahant, Massachusetts, tide pools existed in three "states," dominated by the green alga *Enteromorpha in-*

TABLE 9.1   Additional studies showing effects of predators on distribution and abundance of prey in rocky intertidal communities.

Region	Predators	Prey	Effect	Reference
New Zealand North Island	*Stichaster australis* (sea star)	*Perna canaliculus* (mussel)	Limits mussel to upper mid zone on wave-exposed shores	(Paine 1971)
New Zealand North Island	*Neothais scalaris,* *Lepsiella scobina* (whelks)	*Chamaesipho brunnea,* *Epopella plicata* (barnacles)	Set lower limits to barnacle zones	(Luckens 1975)
New Zealand South Island	*Stichaster australis* (sea star)	*Mytilus galloprovincialis* (mussel)	Limits mussel to mid zone on wave-exposed shores	(Menge et al. 1999a)
East Australia Cape Banks	*Morula marginalba* (whelk)	*Tesseropora rosea* (barnacle), *Patelloida latistrigata* (limpet)	Reduced abundance of both barnacles and limpets	(Fairweather 1985; Fairweather and Underwood 1991)
So. California: Santa Catalina Island	*Panulirus interruptus* (lobster)	*Mytilus californianus,* *M. galloprovincialis* (mussels)	Eliminate mussels from sites of all exposures	(Robles 1987, 1997)
Oregon	*Pisaster ochraceus* (sea star)	*Mytilus californianus,* *M. trossulus* (mussels)	Restricts mussels to mid zone on wave-exposed shores	(Menge et al. 1994)
Washington	*Larus glaucescens* (gulls)	*Pollicipes polymerus* (barnacle)	Reduce gooseneck barnacle abundance, facilitating the main competitor for space (mussels *M. californianus*)	(Wootton 1993)
New Brunswick	*Somateria mollissima* (eider duck)	*Mytilus edulis* (mussel)	Reduce mussel abundance, cause shifts in relative abundance of competitors for space	(Hamilton 2000)
New England	*Nucella lapillus* (whelk)	*Mytilus edulis* (mussel)	Limits mussels to mid zone at intermediate sites, eliminates mussels in sheltered sites	(Menge 1976)
New England	*Nucella lapillus* (whelk), *Asterias* spp. (sea stars), *Carcinus maenas* (crab)	*Mytilus edulis* (mussel)	Restricts mussels to wave exposed shores in the low zone	(Lubchenco and Menge 1978)
Ireland	*Nucella lapillus* (whelk), *Marthasterias glacialis* (sea star), *Carcinus maenas* (crab)	*Mytilus edulis* (mussel)	Restricts mussels to wave-exposed shores	(Kitching et al. 1959)
Panama	Whelks, crabs, fishes (many spp.)	*Modiolus capax, Chama echinata,* *Balanus inexpectatus,* *Ostrea palmula* (bivalves)	Virtually eliminate non-refuging bivalves, barnacles, and other invertebrates	(Menge et al. 1986a,b)
South African West Coast	*Haematopus moquini* (oystercatcher)	*Scutellastra granularis* (limpet)	Reduces limpet abundance, promotes algal growth	(Hockey and Branch 1984)

testinalis ("green" pools), by the Irish moss *Chondrus crispus* ("red" pools), or by a mixture of the two ("mixed" pools). *Chondrus* pools had high densities of an introduced grazer, the periwinkle *Littorina littorea*, whereas *Enteromorpha* pools had virtually no grazers. Laboratory experiments had indicated that periwinkles preferred *Enteromorpha* to *Chondrus*, so Lubchenco surmised that the virtual absence of the green alga in red pools was a consequence of the high densities of *Littorina*.

She tested this hypothesis by transferring *Littorina* from red to green pools and monitoring the subsequent changes. Her experimental treatments were +*Chondrus* –*Littorina* (removal of periwinkles from red pools), +*Enteromorpha* +*Littorina* (addition of periwinkles to green pools), and untouched (control) red and green pools. Within 12 months, red pools from which periwinkles had been removed became dominated by *Enteromorpha*, which displaced Irish moss. In green pools to which periwinkles had been added, *Enteromorpha* was eliminated. In these +*Littorina* pools, however, the response by *Chondrus* was variable, and depended on whether or not crustose holdfasts of Irish moss were present. If *Chondrus* crusts were present, Irish moss increased from 0% to 50% cover within 12 months, but, evidently because the propagules of this alga recruit very slowly, no increases were observed even after 24 months if the crust was absent.

Similar strong effects of herbivores on abundances and distributions of algae have been documented frequently in rocky intertidal communities (e.g., reviews by Lubchenco and Gaines 1981; Gaines and Lubchenco 1982; Hawkins and Hartnoll 1983; Branch et al. 1992,: see also Benedetti-Cecchi and Cinelli 1993). Other studies have documented variable effects of grazers, with weak effects under some conditions and strong effects under others, all in the same community (e.g., Oregon coast: Gaines 1984; eastern Australia: Underwood and Jernakoff 1984; New England: Lubchenco 1986; Hong Kong: Williams 1993). Such variation indicates that, as in the case of competition and predation, we must address the issue of what factors underlie the differential influences of grazers.

FACILITATION.   The potential for one species to have positive effects on another has long been appreciated, especially as a mechanism in succession (e.g., Clements et al. 1926; Connell and Slatyer 1977). Facilitative interactions were often implicit in experimental studies on rocky shores (e.g., Menge 1995). For example, in Dayton's (1975) study of low intertidal community regulation, many species of foliose red algae died when canopy algal species were removed. He inferred that these species were dependent on the positive influence of the canopy species, presumably through the creation of cool, moist, low-stress conditions beneath the taller plants, and referred to the dependent species as an "obligate understory."

Until recently, however, compared with competition, predation, and physical disturbance, the effects of facilitation on community structure have received less attention. Bertness and colleagues, in particular, have documented a number of

cases demonstrating important community implications of direct positive effects. Using two mussel species (*Mytilus edulis* and *Geukensia demissa*) and two algal species (*Ascophyllum nodosum* and *Fucus distichus*), Bertness and Leonard (1997) tested the hypothesis that, under conditions of high thermal and desiccation stress, close proximity of conspecifics would increase survival and growth. They established high- and low-density treatments of each species in high (more stressful) and low (less stressful) intertidal zones. To manipulate stress levels within each zone, they shaded half of each density treatment in each zone. Consistent with the hypothesis, mussels in the high zone survived poorly in unshaded and low-density treatments. A similar but less striking trend was seen with *Ascophyllum*. With *Fucus*, high-zone results were qualitatively similar to those for mussels and *Ascophyllum*, but survival in the low zone was relatively poor, probably due to grazing or low light levels. The barnacle *Semibalanus balanoides* was similarly influenced by positive effects of high density under conditions of high stress in the same region (Bertness 1989). Comparable effects are likely to exist elsewhere, particularly in climates that impose chronic or periodic severe stress.

Research on positive effects is presently in its early, "discovery" stages. As a consequence, many questions remain unanswered. For most communities, we need to know if positive effects occur, under what conditions they occur, and ultimately, their relative importance.

Indirect Effects

The existence of indirect effects—the influence of one species on a second brought about by their joint interactions with a third—was first noted as unexpected or surprising outcomes of experiments investigating species interactions (e.g., Paine 1966, 1974; Dayton 1971; see above). The broader significance of indirect effects was underappreciated, however, until theorists (e.g., Holt 1977; Bender et al. 1984) helped to spur research to explicitly quantify their impact on community structure (see, e.g., Dungan 1986, 1987; Schmitt 1987; Wootton 1994). Key problems in the study of indirect effects include determining their frequency in natural communities, predicting where they will occur and identifying the conditions that foster them, and ultimately determining their importance relative to direct effects in structuring communities (Menge 1995).

As efforts to document indirect effects expanded, their variety seemed boundless. Among the consequences of such efforts were attempts to classify them. The categories proposed included Holt's (1977) "apparent competition" (in which two organisms indirectly affect each other negatively by affecting the abundance of a shared predator; see Figure 9.6). Keystone predation includes another kind of indirect effect (which could be termed "indirect facilitation" or "indirect commensalism"). Numerous other kinds of indirect effects have also been described (Menge 1995). Other efforts to impose order on this concept involved identifying qualitative categories of indirect effects (e.g., Miller and Kerfoot 1987; Strauss 1991;

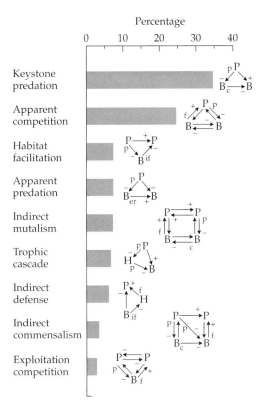

Figure 9.6 Types and frequencies of indirect effects found in 23 rocky intertidal interaction webs. Diagrams to the right of each bar show the form of each effect as an interaction web. P, predator; H, herbivore; B, basal species; p, predation; c, competition; f, provision of food; if, inhibition of feeding; er, enhancement of recruitment. (After Abrams et al. 1996 and Menge 1995.)

Wootton 1993).Two broad qualitative categories of indirect effects are recognized: density-mediated and trait-mediated (Abrams et al. 1996). Density-mediated indirect effects are transmitted through changes in the abundance of interactors, and trait-mediated indirect effects are transmitted through changes in behavior, physiology, or morphology (e.g., Wootton 1993).

EXAMPLES OF INDIRECT MUTUALISM AND INDIRECT FACILITATION. Indirect effects have been detected in virtually all systems investigated. For instance, in New South Wales, Australia, barnacles mediate competition between two limpets. High to moderate densities of barnacles can exclude the larger and competitively dominant limpet species, *Cellana tramoserica*. This promotes the survival of a smaller, subordinate limpet, *Patelloida latistrigata* (Creese 1982). Removal or thinning of barnacles escalates mortality of *Patelloida*. The whelk *Morula marginalba* indirectly encourages immigration of *Cellana* by preferentially feeding on barnacles, and barnacles indirectly promote algae by excluding *Cellana* (Fairweather et al. 1984).

Dungan (1986, 1987) revealed even more complex interactions when investigating indirect effects in a simple community in the upper Gulf of California. The interaction web for this system included a whelk, *Acanthina angelica*, a limpet, *Lottia strongiana*, a barnacle, *Chthamalus anisopoma*, and a brown algal crust, *Ralfsia pacifica*. Direct strong interactions documented in this study included predation by whelks on barnacles, grazing by limpets on algae, interspecific competition between barnacles and algae for space, and preemptive competition by barnacles over limpets (Figure 9.7). To discover the results of direct and indirect effects, Dungan established a 24-month experiment using 10×10 cm plots on the rock to which he applied one of four treatments: +whelks +limpets, +whelks −limpets, −whelks +limpets, and −whelks −limpets.

Acanthina had positive indirect effects on *Lottia* due to what can be termed an "indirect mutualism." The whelk increased the abundance of the limpet by reducing barnacle abundance, which led to increased algal abundance, thus providing more food for the limpet. Similarly, limpet grazing reduced algal cover, which freed the barnacle from competition, increasing its abundance and, in turn, allowing an increase in the whelk. Several other indirect effects were also apparent in Dungan's experiments (Dungan 1986, 1987; see Menge 1995; Appendix I, web 5). However, not all the indirect effects recorded were evident at all times, and in fact their existence became clear only as a result of experimental changes in abundances of the interactors.

Despite its seeming simplicity (four species), Dungan's food web included seven direct and seven indirect effects, five three-species interaction chains, and two four-species chains. In addition to indirect mutualisms, there were examples of indirect facilitation as well as other types of indirect effects. This complexity makes predictions about outcomes in complex species interactions difficult (but not impossible, as discussed below), because even apparently straightforward direct effects can be canceled by indirect effects that drive responses in an opposite direction. Experiments make a vital contribution to disentangling such interactions.

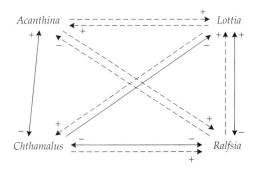

Figure 9.7 Direct and indirect effects in the northern Gulf of California rocky intertidal region. *Acanthina*, a whelk, preys on the barnacle *Chthamalus*, reducing its density (a negative effect). Other direct effects (solid arrows) are inhibition of feeding of the limpet *Lottia* by the barnacle, interspecific competition between the barnacle and the crustose alga *Ralfsia*, and grazing by the limpet on the alga. Many indirect effects result, as shown by the dashed arrows. (After Dungan 1986, 1987.)

Sometimes experiments reveal indirect effects that yield "surprises," producing an outcome contrary to intuition. For instance, Dethier and Duggins (1984) experimentally removed a large chiton, *Katharina tunicata*, from rocky shores in Washington, and might reasonably have expected that three species of coexisting limpets would respond positively to the absence of this presumed competitor for food. In fact, all three limpets declined radically as macroalgae proliferated, smothering their preferred microalgal food source. Thus, indirect facilitation of the limpets by *Katharina*, rather than direct competition, ruled the roost.

TYPES AND MAGNITUDES OF INDIRECT EFFECTS. As examples have accumulated, questions have arisen as to whether or not indirect effects show repeatable patterns. An analysis of studies from 23 rocky intertidal interaction webs identified nine general types of density-mediated indirect effects (see Figure 9.6; Menge 1995; Abrams et al. 1996). The two most common, by far, were keystone predation and apparent competition, and the least common was exploitation competition. The analysis also showed that when expressed per species, the number of both direct and indirect effects, and the number of interaction chains, increased with increasing species richness across the 23 webs. In other words, with increasing web diversity, each species interacted strongly with more species, was involved in more indirect effects, and was part of more interaction chains.

Many of the interaction webs in the survey were presented in sufficient detail that the relative importance of direct and indirect effects could be quantified. Using a standard protocol for estimating the size of each effect (see Figure 9.5), the survey showed that the relative magnitudes of community responses due to indirect effects were, on average, as great as those of direct effects (Menge 1995, 1997). Further, the magnitude of change due to indirect effects did not vary with web species richness, indicating that, at least at the community level, indirect effects caused a predictable amount of change, regardless of the diversity of the community.

ARE INDIRECT EFFECTS PREDICTABLE? Modelers investigating the influence of indirect effects on the dynamics of theoretical communities have suggested that, by introducing substantial uncertainty into the outcomes of species interactions, indirect effects could seriously compromise efforts to develop predictive models of community dynamics (e.g., Bender et al. 1984; Abrams 1987, 1992; Yodzis 1988). Potential problems include the following:

1. Indirect effects may take longer to appear than do direct effects and may thus be missed.

2. Indirect effects might produce relatively large changes and thus obscure direct effects.

3. Indirect effects produced by long interaction chains might be greater than those produced by short chains.

4. Because of multiple alternative interaction pathways with the potential for effects to cancel each other, the outcome of experimental treatments may be unpredictable.

5. Disentangling the contributions of direct and indirect effects might be difficult.

Empirical studies evaluating these concerns (Schoener 1993; Wootton 1994; Menge 1995, 1997) suggest that some of them are less serious than theory might suggest. Four of them (1, 2, 4, 5) can be addressed with data from field experiments. First, in relation to point 1, in most cases indirect effects appeared shortly after direct effects, and late indirect "surprises" were rare (Menge 1997). Second, the magnitude of indirect effects was either less than (Schoener 1993) or similar to (Menge 1995), not greater than, that of direct effects (point 2). Third, at least on a coarse scale, the magnitude of changes caused by indirect effects did not vary with the species richness of webs, which was itself related to the length of interaction chains (thus addressing point 3). This means that the magnitudes of indirect effects may be predictable (point 4; Menge 1995, 1997).

In a study aimed at predicting indirect effects, Wootton (1994) investigated the effects of gull predation on a rocky intertidal community dominated by mussels, gooseneck barnacles, limpets, and whelks, and observed large changes, some of which clearly were the result of indirect effects. Notably, whelks decreased in the absence of bird predation. To determine the direct interaction pathways that were most likely to have led to these changes, Wootton applied a statistical method called "path analysis." This method identifies the most likely of several alternative interaction chains that could produce the effects observed in the experiments. Once the most likely pathway was identified, Wootton tested its predictive capacity by using it to forecast the direct and indirect results of 11 separate species manipulations. The results were consistent with all 11 predictions of the most plausible web; none of the results were predicted by alternatives. Wootton's analysis thus successfully predicted indirect effects, further suggesting that multiple interaction pathways do not necessarily render indirect effects uncertain (point 4), and that direct and indirect effects can be disentangled (point 5). Despite this success, much effort and natural history knowledge was necessary to achieve sound predictions. Moreover, it is but a single example. Much work remains before the knotty problems posed by indirect effects can be fully worked out. |

Interaction Webs and Interaction Strengths

INTERACTION WEBS. Experimental ecologists have led the way toward rigorous investigation of species interactions and their impacts on communities. "Interaction webs" can be a powerful approach in determining the processes underlying patterns of community structure. This concept was first clarified in Paine's (1980) examination of three different approaches to understanding community dynamics, all based on knowledge of "linkages" between species in communities. The first of these, food webs, or diagrams of "who eats whom" are frequently and relatively easily documented, but are purely descriptive. As a consequence, efforts to infer dynamics from food (or "connectedness") webs are fraught with pitfalls (e.g., Polis 1991; Martinez 1991; Goldwasser and Roughgarden 1997).

A second approach examines patterns of energy flow or biomass, under the presumption that the magnitude of such flows and the species involved in the largest flows reflect the "importance" of particular species in community dynamics. While energy-flow webs indisputably do reflect an important aspect of community dynamics, they do not necessarily reveal the key processes that produce structure (Paine 1980). There are two main reasons for this. First, species may have impacts that are disproportionately larger than would be predicted from their contribution to energy flow. Thus, the importance of rare or small species may be "masked" by their misleadingly low contribution to energy transfer. Second, some important interactions cannot even by measured in terms of energy flow. For example, Velimirov and Griffiths (1979) have shown that the sweeping action ("whiplash"; Dayton 1971) of fronds of adult *Laminaria* in South African kelp beds maintains a grazer-free swathe around them, within which recruitment of kelp sporophytes is enhanced. This physical effect is unrelated to energy flow.

A third approach involves the development of what are now most often termed "interaction webs" (the "functional" webs of Paine 1980; see Menge and Sutherland 1987). As defined earlier, interaction webs reflect the results of experiments in communities, which determine the direction and magnitude of species interactions. Usually, these webs include only the interactions shown to have important effects on community structure (e.g., Figure 9.2B).

INTERACTION STRENGTH. The concept of "interaction strength" has different meanings depending on the context. Theoretical models, such as the Lotka–Volterra models of interspecific competition, include a coefficient, α_{ij}, which "measures how strong the interactions are…" (MacArthur 1972). This coefficient reflects the per-individual or "per capita" effect of one species *j* on another, species *i*. Similar coefficients are included in predator–prey models as well (e.g., Gotelli 1995). MacArthur (1972) also suggested a second meaning of interaction strength: interactions can be considered as strong if their "removal would produce a dramatic effect."

Despite its long history in ecology, the concept of interaction strength has only recently been explored by experimental field ecologists. Paine (1992), for example, quantified *per capita* interaction strengths in field enclosure/exclosure experiments involving herbivores (sea urchins, limpets and chitons) grazing on kelp sporelings. To determine the impacts of individual herbivore species Paine compared the densities of kelp sporelings that occurred in the complete absence of all herbivores to those occurring in the presence of single herbivore species (a measure of each species' effect). He estimated per capita effects by dividing by the number of individuals of each herbivore used in each treatment.

This analysis showed that *per capita* species interaction strengths varied among the seven species of this herbivore assemblage. Three "strong" interactors were identified. Sea urchins and a large chiton had large negative effects on algae. A smaller chiton had relatively large positive effects on kelp sporeling densities in one experiment and weak effects in another, showing interaction strength can vary within species (see also Ruesink 1998; Berlow 1999). The other four species had *per capita* effects indistinguishable from "no effect" and were therefore weak interactors.

Importantly, these studies have begun the process of testing the long-held notion that communities consist of a few strong, and many weak interactors (e.g., Paine 1980). More broadly, this approach offers a potentially powerful tool in distinguishing systems with weak predation from those with strong predation (Figure 9.8). Further, in systems with strong predation, this method should separate regimes affected by keystone predation (with predators having disproportionately greater effects on community structure than would be predicted by their abundance: Power et al. 1996), from regimes influenced by "diffuse" predation (defined as having strong predation impacts spread relatively evenly over several species: Figure 9.8). This approach, or variations on the same theme, has recently received increasing attention from researchers working with rocky intertidal communities (e.g.,

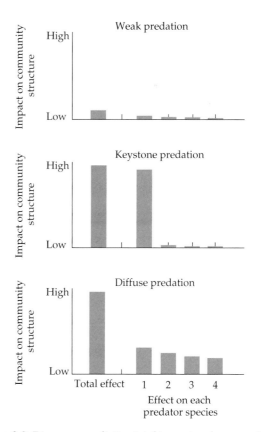

Figure 9.8 Diagrams predicting total impact and per-species impacts on community structure under weak predation, strong keystone predation and strong diffuse predation. With keystone predation, a single species is responsible for most change, while with diffuse predation, several species contribute to the large total effect.

Menge et al. 1994; Navarrete and Menge 1996; Wootton 1997; Ruesink 1998; Berlow 1999; Berlow et al. 1999).

Note, however, that species impacts will also vary with density. Regardless of how large its *per capita* effect, a single individual will never have the same impact as that of many individuals (e.g., Navarrete and Menge 1996). Thus, fuller understanding of interaction web dynamics will depend on knowledge of both *per capita* interaction strength, and population interaction strength or "species impacts" (Navarrete and Menge 1996; Berlow 1999; Sanford 1999).

INFLUENCE OF RECRUITMENT. Two aspects of larval biology powerfully influence population dynamics and community structure. The first is the behavior of larvae in selecting settlement sites, and the second relates to the quantities of larvae that recruit to the shore. A considerable body of work has shown that barnacle larvae have very specific requirements when they settle. The position of larvae in the water column (Grosberg 1982), the texture of the rock face (Crisp and Barnes 1954), the presence of conspecifics (Knight-Jones 1955; Minchinton and Scheibling 1993), and chemical cues from coexisting species (Raimondi 1988) are among many factors that play a role. Grosberg (1981) has shown that the presence of an aggressive space-competitor, the compound ascidian *Botryllus schlosseri*, discourages settlement of the larvae of many sessile species. An almost equal number of other species showed no preference, however, and settled equally on +*Botryllus* and –*Botryllus* plates. This example is particularly interesting because larvae avoiding *Botryllus* all belonged to species that were vulnerable to competitive overgrowth. Those that were not showed no selectivity. The example is powerful, because it involved a large number of taxonomically diverse species, and because the responses could be predicted *a priori* from a knowledge of vulnerability to competitive overgrowth. As a consequence, the result is probably broadly applicable.

The effect of a variable supply of new individuals on benthic populations has long been of interest in marine ecology (see reviews by Underwood and Denley 1984; Young 1987, 1990; Grosberg and Levitan 1992), and has been dubbed "supply-side ecology" (Lewin 1986). However, ecologists have only recently focused explicitly on the relative degree to which community structure is affected by settlement (defined as the act of colonization and metamorphosis by propagules: Connell 1985) and recruitment (defined as survival of settlers for some longer but usually arbitrary period of time: Connell 1985) vs. postrecruitment factors, such as predation and competition. Here we examine this issue in the context of rocky intertidal communities. Broader, more comprehensive treatments may be found elsewhere in this book (see Morgan, this volume; Underwood and Keough, this volume).

Most early research on the influence of recruitment dealt with barnacle populations and the impact of variable recruitment or settlement densities on adult density (e.g., Gaines and Roughgarden 1985; Connell 1985; Raimondi 1990). In central California, for instance, abundance of adult *Balanus*

glandula in the high zone varies from nearly complete coverage of the available rock surface at wave-exposed sites to low cover on more wave-sheltered sites (Gaines and Roughgarden 1985). Field measurements showed that rates of recruitment were up to 20x higher at wave-exposed sites compared to wave-sheltered sites. Abundance of adult barnacles also varied more at high vs. low density sites, evidently due to higher frequencies of predation at the site of high barnacle abundance (Gaines and Roughgarden 1985). The attraction of consumers to sites of high recruitment and an association between high adult densities of prey and high predation has been documented independently in several other intertidal communities (e.g., eastern Australia, Fairweather 1988a; Oregon, Menge et al. 1994; British Columbia, Robles et al. 1995).

Efforts to evaluate the relative effects of recruitment vs. postrecruitment factors on community structure have been limited. In a retrospective analysis of field experiments on rocky intertidal communities of New England and the Panamanian Pacific coast, the relative impact of the densities of barnacle and bivalve recruits on adult abundances was estimated (Menge 1991). Multivariate and multiple regression techniques suggested that, compared to postrecruitment processes (predation, interspecific competition), the contribution of recruitment to adult abundance patterns was small in New England, but large in Panama (Figure 9.9). These differences appeared dependent on differences in relative influences of recruitment and postrecruitment effects. High prey

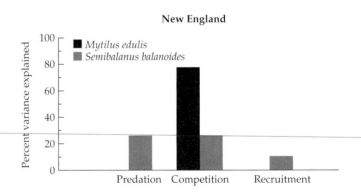

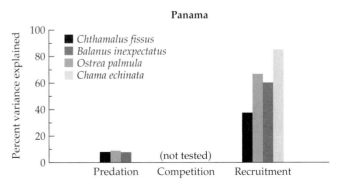

Figure 9.9 Proportion of variance explained by species interactions and recruitment in New England and Panama rocky intertidal zones. (After Menge 1991.)

recruitment over brief time periods in New England led rapidly to intense predation and competition, which overrode the impact of recruitment. Low prey recruitment occurring sporadically throughout the year dominated prey population dynamics in Panama by causing rapid increases in prey densities. Although predation also reduced densities rather rapidly, many predators in Panama lived subtidally and were thus relatively independent of intertidal prey. Thus, while predation was an important process in this system, prey densities were most strongly influenced by low and sporadic recruitment.

In another study in Nova Scotia, densities of barnacle settlers high on the shore were closely associated with adult density. Settler density lower on the shore, however, was unrelated to adult density. Minchinton and Scheibling (1993) attributed this difference to higher postrecruitment predation lower on the shore, which obliterated any pattern among treatments. This suggests that the importance of settlement (or recruitment) and postrecruitment processes were inversely related. Thus, settlement and/or recruitment can have a large effect on community structure when postrecruitment mortality is low, and a small effect when postrecruitment mortality is high.

These and other studies also strongly suggest that when recruitment is low, patterns of abundance and community structure may be more strongly influenced by the supply rate of new individuals than by agents of postrecruitment mortality. The generality of this pattern remains uncertain, however, and further research into this issue is needed. More fundamentally, the factors that underlie variation in settlement or recruitment rates, such as larval transport mechanisms or factors affecting larval survival, are poorly understood. Glimpses are emerging, however. For example, the negative relationship between an index of upwelling intensity and the recruitment of barnacle larvae (Roughgarden et al. 1988) is a strong indicator that offshore transport dictates barnacle densities via its effects on recruitment. Research into these and related problems should be a high priority in efforts to understand variation in community structure.

REGULATION OF ROCKY INTERTIDAL COMMUNITIES

Clearly, numerous factors can influence patterns of rocky intertidal community structure. Species interactions, larval biology and ecology, and physical environmental conditions can all be determinants of patterns of zonation, abundance, patchiness, and size structure. As we have seen, however, similar patterns can be explained by different factors (e.g., zonation can be due to desiccation, competition or predation). Conversely, different patterns can be caused by the same factor (predation can determine zonation and diversity patterns). Moreover, experiments suggest that different processes, such as predation or competition, can be important in some times or places but not in others. These considerations might give the impression that natural communities are "chaotic" in the

sense that they are so variable in pattern and process that they are impossible to understand. To scientists, however, such complexity presents a challenge: can we find order and predictability in what appears to be serious disorder? Below, we take up this challenge, and explore the ideas and evidence that might provide a broader environmental and ecological context in which seeming disorder can be placed. The goals of this endeavor are to predict under which conditions various processes are important, and the role that intertidal work has played in developing these models.

Models of Community Regulation

Several models have been proposed to explain how communities are regulated. The first significant conceptual model was that of Hairston, Smith, and Slobodkin (1960; hereafter HSS), and focused on trophic interactions. The idea advanced was simple: predators control the abundance of herbivores, preventing them from "overgrazing" or controlling plants. Plants are abundant as a consequence, and limited by resources not consumers. (Note that this postulate incorporates an indirect positive effect of predators on plants.) This was later termed the "green world" hypothesis (e.g., Pimm 1991) because it suggested that green plants dominated the Earth because of species interactions at higher trophic levels. Specific controlling factors were thus predicted to differ between trophic levels. At the top trophic level, competition for food controlled predators, but predation controlled herbivores at the middle level, and competition for space and/or light controlled plants at the bottom plant. HSS also inferred that, because organic matter was not observed to accumulate, detritivores were also limited by competition. This idea generated controversy (e.g., Ehrlich and Birch 1967; Murdoch 1966; Slobodkin et al. 1967), but at the time, insufficient appropriate evidence stymied efforts to resolve the debate. Nonetheless, this idea of "top-down" community regulation (i.e., that top predators ultimately regulate primary production) stimulated research into many issues such as community consequences of species interactions and plant defenses against herbivores, which are still of intense interest today.

The controversy continues (e.g., Hairston and Hairston 1993, 1997; Polis and Strong 1996) as ecologists debate the implicit assumptions of HSS that consumers are not omnivorous (i.e., their effects are limited to one trophic level), and that all food chains include three levels or, in aquatic systems, four levels (see Hairston and Hairston 1993; and a review in Persson et al. 1996). Studies on rocky intertidal shores have challenged the assumption that the number of trophic levels is fixed (Connell 1975; Menge and Sutherland 1976). In New England, for example, field experiments demonstrated that at wave-exposed headlands, predation was ineffective in controlling prey abundance (mussels and barnacles). In contrast, predation and grazing were strong at more sheltered sites. Consequently, prey abundances were controlled by competition for space and physical disturbance at wave-exposed sites, and by predation or grazing at wave-protected sites (Menge 1976; Menge and Sutherland 1976).

These results suggest that the number of trophic levels can be fewer or more than those suggested by HSS. Wave-exposed sites in New England, at least, had only one effective level (if macrophytes and sessile invertebrates are categorized as "basal species:" see Pimm 1982) or two levels (if sessile filter feeders are considered to be "herbivores"). Wave-protected sites had three levels in the mid-shore zone (carnivores, herbivores, basal species) and four levels in the low-shore zone (top carnivores in the form of crabs and sea stars, primary carnivores represented by whelks, herbivorous littorines, and basal species). These departures from the HSS model led to the development of "environmental stress" models of community regulation (Connell 1975; Menge and Sutherland 1976, 1987; see Figure 9.10).

Environmental Stress Models

Environmental stress models (hereafter termed ESMs) are fundamentally a modification of the top-down model. Their underlying presumption is that differences in community structure are not "chaotic," but are predictably related to "environmental stress." Environmental stress refers to physical processes or conditions that weaken organisms, and is imposed by extremes of, or rapid changes in physical factors or mechanical forces (Menge and Sutherland 1987). Stresses include physical stress, e.g., wave forces or cobble scour, and physiological stress, e.g., excessive heat or cold, or prolonged exposure to air. Both forms of stress can reach levels of severity at which they become lethal, in which case they result in the removal of biomass from the shore and are referred to as

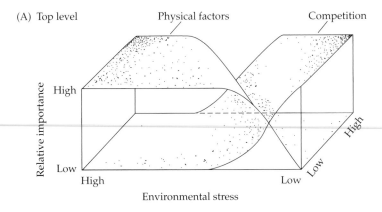

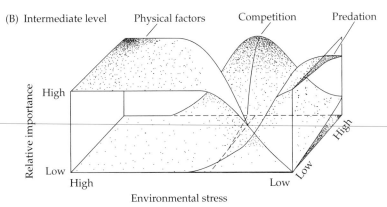

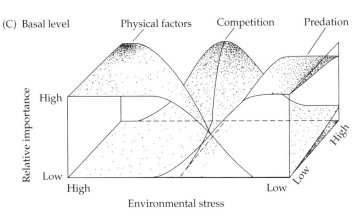

Figure 9.10 Predictions of an environmental stress model of community regulation. Relative importance, or the proportion of community variance explained by disturbance, competition, and predation is the y variable, magnitude of environmental stress is the x variable, and recruit density is the z variable. Predictions are shown for the top, intermediate and bottom (basal) trophic levels in a three-level system. Predictions are similar for intermediate and basal levels, except that intermediate (and top) consumers are more susceptible to stress, which shifts the curves describing the relative importances of each factor to the right, or low stress end of the gradient. Predation is unimportant for the top predator level, by definition. At the basal level with high recruitment, the model predicts that physical controlling effects are relatively more important at high stress, competition control is relatively more important at intermediate stress, and predation is relatively more important at low stress. Low recruitment removes competition as a strong factor in structuring communities. (After Menge and Sutherland 1987.)

"disturbances." It must be noted, however, that what constitutes an environmental stress for one species need not be so for another. For instance, strong wave action may inhibit grazers and predators, but be favorable for filter feeders. ESMs thus interpret variation in community structure as a consequence of predictable changes in the relative importance of species interactions and physical stress or disturbance (Figure 9.10). In highly stressful regions of an environmental gradient (e.g., wave-beaten headlands, high intertidal zones), community structure is predicted to be due mostly the direct effects of stress. In progressively less stressful regions, the model predicts that first competition and then predation (at least at lower trophic levels) will become the dominant structuring processes. This means that biological control will vary inversely with stress and that competition and predation will also be inversely related, at least when stress is relatively low (Figure 9.10).

Precisely these outcomes emerged from studies in the rocky intertidal of New England, (Menge 1976) in which cages were used to exclude predators from plots in the high, mid and low-shore. In the high zone, a single species of barnacle was the only dominant, because predators and other competitors were excluded by physical stress. In the mid and low zones at wave-exposed sites, predators still had no significant effects, but mussels won a competitive battle over barnacles. In the mid and low zones at wave-protected sites, habitats more benign than at wave-exposed sites, predators controlled mussels, preventing them from competitively excluding barnacles.

The intensity of recruitment can also have important effects on community structure. In most ESMs, recruitment is considered to act independently of environmental stress, and to have its greatest effect on competition intensity (Figure 9.10). Thus, with decreasing rates of recruitment, competition becomes less important at all levels of stress, and community structure is predicted to depend more on recruitment coupled with the direct effects of stress (at the high end of the environmental stress gradient) or with predation (at the low end).

STRESS-MODIFIED TOP-DOWN REGULATION. Although some tests for stress effects on species interactions have been inconclusive (e.g., Lively and Raimondi 1987), evidence consistent with ESMs has accumulated in marine (e.g., Menge 1976; Menge 1978a,b; Underwood 1985; Menge and Olson 1990; Fairweather 1988b; Leonard et al. 1998; Witman and Grange 1998) and non-marine settings (e.g., Louda and Collinge 1992; Arnott and Vanni 1993). In one study, Lubchenco (1986) investigated the impact of grazing and competition on early successional algae along a wave exposure gradient. Her experiments employed caging methods at sites of high, intermediate and low wave exposure, with results reported separately for winter (with generally higher wave forces) and summer (with generally lower wave forces). She compared three treatments: firstly, +grazers +algal competitors (uncaged controls and 'roof controls' consisting of cages that had a mesh roof but no side walls); secondly, –grazers +algal

competitors (cages excluding grazers); and thirdly, –grazers –algal competitors (exclosure cages with algal competition reduced). Using the proportion of replicates showing intense competition or herbivory, she estimated the relative magnitude of species interactions.

Her results are summarized in Figure 9.11 in the context of the ESM predictions for basal species at high recruitment rates. In winter, when environmental stress (wave turbulence) was highest, competition decreased with increasing wave exposure and grazing was low at all sites. In summer, with lower wave action, grazing increased in importance and competition decreased in importance at sites protected from strong wave action. Thus, for both grazer–algal interactions (Figure 9.11) and predator–prey interactions (Menge 1976, 1978a,b) on rocky shores of New England, consumer pressure decreased with increasing environmental harshness, and competition among lower trophic levels peaked at intermediate levels of environmental harshness. Both trends are consistent with ESM predictions.

RECRUITMENT-LIMITED TOP-DOWN REGULATION. Comp236ared to temperate shores, the tropical rocky shores of the Pacific coast of Panama initially seemed anomalous (Menge and Lubchenco 1981). Physical conditions during low tide can be persistently severe, with temperatures regularly exceeding 30°C and with highly desiccating conditions, especially during the dry season (December–March: Menge and Lubchenco 1981; Garrity 1984). These conditions create a sharp vertical gradient in environmental stress. Organisms in high zones experience severe thermal/desiccation stress while those on the low shore experience relatively benign conditions. Zones with abundant sessile biota are absent, and with

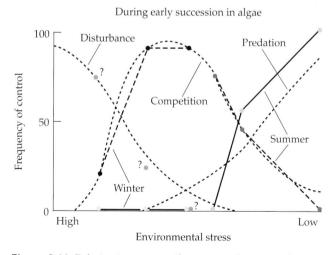

Figure 9.11 Relative importance (frequency of control) of disturbance, competition and grazing (predation) in controlling early successional algae under different levels of environmental stress in New England. (After Lubchenco 1986.) Solid lines with light dots indicate predation importance, and dashed lines with dark dots indicate competition importance, all at three sites differing in environmental stress. Dots with question marks suggest the magnitude of disturbance in winter.

the exception of algal crusts, abundances of most organisms are low. Closer study, however, revealed that invertebrates are very diverse on these shores (Menge et al. 1985), and trophic complexity is high (Menge et al. 1986b).

Do these differences in community structure arise from completely different ecological processes? Or do they simply depend on differences in effect or magnitude of the same processes as those documented in temperate areas? To address this issue, a complex field experiment was designed to test the effects of four different groups of consumers: two slow-moving groups—molluscan grazers and whelks; and two fast-moving consumers—crabs and fish in high, mid and low zones (Menge and Lubchenco 1981; Menge et al. 1986a,b). The total number of consumers in the food web was so high (>20 species) that single-species deletion experiments were unthinkable. Instead, the experiment was designed to evaluate the effects of most combinations of the four consumer groups.

In the low zone, with relatively benign physical conditions, predation had strong effects on community composition (Figure 9.12). In the absence of all four groups of consumers, abundance of sessile invertebrates reached dramatically higher levels than in their presence. Interestingly, treatments with 1, 2, or 3 groups present suggested that the impact of predation was roughly additive. That is, no single group seemed to include an overwhelmingly strong interactor, or keystone species. Their individual effects were similar, but in combination they had a strong effect, exemplifying diffuse predation (Figure 9.12), in contrast to the effects of keystone predators on temperate shores (compare with Figure 9.8). Despite this difference, however, community dynamics seemed to share an important characteristic with temperate communities. If predators were excluded or thinned, bivalves (mainly mussels and rock oysters) were on track to displace algal

crusts, barnacles, and algae and to eventually monopolize space on the rocks.

A second striking result of this experiment was how slowly the sessile invertebrate biota responded to the absence of predation (Menge 1991). In temperate communities, obvious responses are typically seen in < 10 months, whereas in Panama, equivalent responses took years. This slow response was probably due to very low rates of recruitment (e.g., barnacles recruited at densities of only 400/m² per year in Panama but 123,200/m² per year in New England: Menge 1991). Thus, in Panama, recruitment density strongly limited densities of sessile invertebrates in the low zone, and strong, persistent predation eliminated most prey that did manage to recruit. The few survivors were restricted to holes and crevices in the rock, where predation was less intense (Menge and Lubchenco 1981; Menge et al. 1985; Hixon and Menge 1991).

These results suggest that in the low zone in Panama, predation was the most important interspecific interaction affecting community structure. Since this community experiences relatively benign physical conditions and low recruitment, these results are consistent with the expectations of ESMs (Figure 9.10, lower right corner). In higher zones, physical stresses become progressively more important in structuring this community (e.g., Garrity and Levings 1981; Garrity 1984; Lubchenco et al. 1984; ref. Figure 9.10, lower left corner). Overall, the Panama study suggests that community structure depends on the same processes as in temperate zones, with two new insights: (1) strong predation can be diffuse, dependent on the combined effects of a diverse assemblage of consumers, and (2) low recruitment can virtually eliminate competition for space (see predictions in Underwood and Denley 1984; Menge and Sutherland 1987; Roughgarden et al. 1988).

Nutrient/Productivity Models

A second class of community regulation models focuses more on so-called "bottom-up" effects by incorporating the effects of a different environmental gradient, nutrients and productivity (e.g., Fretwell 1977, 1987; Oksanen et al. 1981). Nutrient/Productivity models (hereafter NPMs) propose that environments differ in the productivity of plants, which in turn depends mostly on underlying gradients of nutrients (Figure 9.13). In very unproductive habitats, production is so low that plants are sparse and herbivores cannot persist. With increasing productivity, plant production and abundance increase, leading first to intense competition for space among plants, and then, when food levels are capable of supporting resident herbivores, to increased grazing and reduced competition among plants. Still further increases in productivity allow the invasion and persistence of predators, which through the above logic, eventually control herbivore abundance, freeing plants from control by grazers. Note that this community state, with three trophic levels, yields the same predictions as the HSS model. Still greater increases in productivity could produce a system with four trophic levels. Thus, with increasing productivity, this NPM predicts an in-

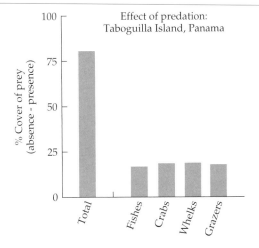

Figure 9.12 Total impact of predation, and separate impacts of four consumer groups in experiments in the rocky intertidal region of the Pacific coast of Panama. Predation was diffuse in this community. (After Menge 1986a.)

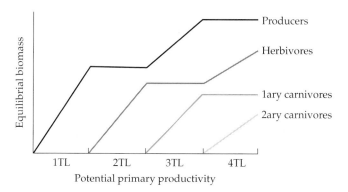

Figure 9.13 Predictions of the nutrient–productivity model with respect to changes in biomass by trophic level with increasing primary productivity. For the producer level, for example, the model predicts that biomass increases when only one trophic level is present, but biomass does not change when herbivores can persist (2 TL = 2 trophic levels) because increased productivity is balanced by increased consumption. Similar biomass changes occur with 3 and 4 trophic levels. (After Oksanen et al. 1981 and Leibold 1989.)

crease in the number of trophic levels, with increasing levels of plant biomass when there are 1, 3, and 5 trophic levels and constant plant biomass with 0 (i.e., plants are barely present), 2 and 4 trophic levels (Figure 9.13).

Productivity is, however, not always linked to the number of trophic levels in a simple manner, and the outcome of increasing productivity can have unexpected effects on grazer–plant interactions. Underwood and Jernakoff (1984) have shown that in the mid- to high-zones of shores in New South Wales (Australia), limpets and other grazers control algal growth by consuming sporelings. In the low zone, where productivity is highest, macroalgae are dominant. This is not because an extra trophic level is added in the form of predators that control the grazers, but rather because the higher growth rates of the algae themselves exclude grazers such as the limpet *Cellana tramoserica*. The mechanism is partly preemptive exploitation of space by the macroalgae (denying the limpets firm attachment) and partly because macroalgae outcompete microalgae (the limpet's main food supply).

Collectively, ESMs and NPMs emphasize contrasting viewpoints regarding whether regulation is "top-down" or "bottom-up." Top-down control refers to control of community structure by consumers (e.g., Hairston et al. 1960), whereas bottom-up control refers to control by conditions or processes (e.g., nutrients and plant productivity) at the basal trophic level (e.g., White 1978). More recently, however, most workers have stressed that these seeming alternatives are actually different aspects of an integrated "top-down/bottom-up" model (e.g., see Fretwell 1977, 1987; Oksanen et al. 1981; Persson et al. 1996 for general ideas; Menge 1992; Menge et al. 1997a; Leonard et al. 1998 for rocky intertidal communities). Efforts to extend and refine these models are ongoing, and recent additions have included models that involve the effects of omnivory (Menge et al. 1996; Polis and Strong

1996), "subsidies" in the form of material and energy inputs to communities from adjacent ecosystems (Bustamante et al. 1995a; Polis and Strong 1996), and the influence of positive interactions (Bertness and Callaway 1994).

BOTTOM-UP/TOP-DOWN CONTROL. Marine ecologists were slow to address the influence of bottom-up effects on rocky intertidal communities. Paradoxically, a major factor behind this neglect was the dramatic success of manipulative studies of the effects of species interactions on community pattern. A second factor was the spatial scales over which different processes vary. Thus, the effects of predation, competition, facilitation, wave forces, thermal stress and recruitment were all readily addressed at local scales (e.g., cm to 100s of m). The success of these investigations, combined with logistical and technological constraints and the assumption that nutrients, phytoplankton, and currents all varied at such large scales that among-site variability within a region was negligible, seemed to justify this neglect (e.g., Menge 1992).

Research in South Africa, however, began to contravene this view. One study showed that variation in nutrient input, such as that occurring in the vicinity of seabird colonies, could affect algal growth and biomass (Bosman et al. 1986; Bosman and Hockey 1986). The interactions involved were complex, involving both top-down and bottom-up effects. On islands, oystercatchers are abundant and decimate limpets (the major grazers), and algal cover increases as a result. Coupled with this, guano from other birds that roost and nest on the islands boosts the algal productivity. This increase in algal growth ripples through the community, increasing both growth rates and maximum sizes of limpets. Under such conditions, limpets can reach a size at which they are immune to avian predation, and their collective output of gametes per unit area exceeds that on the mainland even though their densities are lower. High algal cover also translates into a high abundance of algal-dwelling invertebrates, which sustain high numbers of other wading birds on the islands. The web is thus complex, with numerous indirect effects, and is dictated by both bottom-up (nutrient) and top-down (predation) effects (Branch et al. 1987).

Another study suggested that higher biomass of filter feeders and their carnivores on wave exposed shores was a consequence of high rates of detrital input from adjacent habitats (McQuaid and Branch 1985). This observation spurred a large-scale survey covering 5000 km of southern African coastline that showed that filter feeders on exposed shores reach biomasses of 10–50 times those in embayments (Bustamante and Branch 1996b). There are many possible reasons for this. On exposed shores, predation may be lower and recruitment higher, or alternatively, food supplies may be greater. Bustamante and Branch (1996a) showed that at exposed sites, concentrations of detrital food were twice those under sheltered conditions. Of greater importance, however, is the rate at which food is turned over. Modeling the inputs and turnover of food revealed that exposed shores could sustain a mussel biomass of 478 g (dry flesh mass) $\cdot$ m^{-2}; but sheltered shores only 23 g · m^{-2}. Both predicted values were comfortingly close to the actual means and ranges recorded in the field. This means that differences in food supply between exposed and sheltered shores alone could explain the contrasts in filter-feeder biomass. Differences in predation and recruitment may also exist, but food supply, a bottom-up factor, is clearly important.

This analysis also indicated that *in situ* productivity is insufficient to support the high biomasses of filter feeders on wave-beaten shores, suggesting that such areas depend on a subsidy of organic material. On the west coast of South Africa, much of this comes in the form of particulate kelp, and isotope analyses showed that 60–85% of the food of filter feeders comes from this source (Bustamante and Branch 1996a).

Building on these results, Bustamante and colleagues (Bustamante et al. 1995a,b) documented striking large-scale gradients of nutrients and primary productivity of benthic algae around the South Africa coast, spanning a distance of ~2500 km. The existence of strong upwelling on the west coast and weak or no upwelling on the east coast creates an oceanographic gradient of productivity. In the intertidal, concentrations of nutrients (especially nitrate and silicate) and the productivity of benthic algae also decreased clinally from west to south to east coasts (Figure 9.14A,B). Along these gradients, average biomass of both grazers and filter feeders also declined, and maximum shell length of a dominant grazer, the limpet *Patella*, increased with increasing intertidal primary productivity (Figure 9.15).

Despite the correlations between algal productivity and nutrients, invertebrate biomass, and maximum limpet size, calculations for the two most abundant limpets (*Scutellastra argenvillei* and *Cymbula granatina*) showed that *in situ* productivity was incapable of meeting their energetic needs. This led to the hypothesis that both are subsidized by having access to subtidal kelp (drift, in the case of *C. granatina*, and live kelp fronds for *S. argenvillei*). Evidence that limpet populations depend on this subsidy was obtained in field experiments that manipulated kelp inputs to these grazers. In the absence of kelp, survival (Figure 9.16) and body mass of these limpets declined sharply in comparison to limpets with normal supplies of kelp. By sustaining the phenomenally high biomasses of these limpets (the highest ever recorded anywhere for intertidal grazers—up to 771 g wet flesh · m^{-2}), bottom-up subsidies lead to top-down control of the *in situ* algae by these grazers. In the presence of limpets, macroalgae are absent or reduced to a thin coralline crust despite the high nutrient concentrations. These local-scale experiments, with the large-scale coastal correlations, strongly suggest that bottom-up factors can have important effects on community structure and dynamics in this rocky intertidal community.

A similar view of the importance of bottom-up effects on community structure has emerged from studies within an upwelling region on the Oregon coast. In this case, community structure in the low zone differed sharply at two sites separated by 80 km (Menge et al. 1994, 1997b). At wave-exposed areas on the low shore at each site, filter feeders dominated space at Strawberry Hill whereas macrophytes dominated space at Boiler Bay. Field experiments testing top-down effects were consistent with the idea that grazing influenced differences in algal cover. Grazing pressure was high at the site of low algal abundance (Strawberry Hill) and low at the site of high algal abundance (Boiler Bay), but predation pressure (and predator abundance) was positively associated with abundance of filter feeders (Menge et al. 1994, 1997a). Quantification of growth and recruitment rates of filter feeders (mussels and barnacles), however, suggested an alternative hypothesis to top-down control. Bottom-up processes (nutrients and phytoplankton) might differ between sites and underlie the positive association between filter-feeder abundance and predation. At Strawberry Hill, filter feeders grew faster, and mussel recruitment was higher, suggesting that predator abundance was positively correlated with prey abundance, and through a feedback loop, exerted stronger predation.

Intensive sampling of phytoplankton concentration (measured as planktonic Chlorophyll-a) and productivity at the two sites confirmed that Strawberry Hill had higher availability of filter-feeder food (Menge 1997a,b). Larger-scale sampling (over 380 km of coastline) suggested that these differences were representative of larger areas within the Oregon coast. That is, distinct regions of relatively high and low productivity of phytoplankton, both in the intertidal and over the continental shelf, occurred within the upwelling region along Oregon. Studies at up to 10 sites spanning a 300 km section of this coast indicated that the differences in filter-feeder growth observed between Boiler Bay and Strawberry Hill are broadly representative of larger stretches of coastline (Menge 2001). Satellite imagery and other evidence suggest that this "mesoscale" (10s to 100s of km) variation in near-shore oceanography and community dynamics may be ultimately a consequence of the variable influence of the margin of the continental shelf. Variable shelf width evidently alters offshore current patterns, leading to conditions that either concentrate or dilute larvae and phytoplankton . Thus, as in southern Africa, structure and dynamics of rocky intertidal communities along the Oregon coast can evidently depend on bottom-up processes interacting with top-down processes.

Other evidence from geographically distinct regions is also consistent with the view that rocky intertidal community structure is jointly dependent on the interaction between bottom-up and top-down effects (e.g., New England: Leonard et al. 1998; New Zealand: Menge et al. 1999). These results, and evidence for significant impacts of positive interactions on community structure (see above), support the view that further modification of models of community regulation is needed. These models, as yet undefined, should synthesize both the separate and interactive effects of species interactions (both positive and negative), rates of supply of recruits, environmental stress, and nutrients/productivity in relation to appropriate scales in space and time.

Predictability of Stresses and Disturbances

A picture of the circumstances under which factors such as competition, predation, recruitment and physical factors are

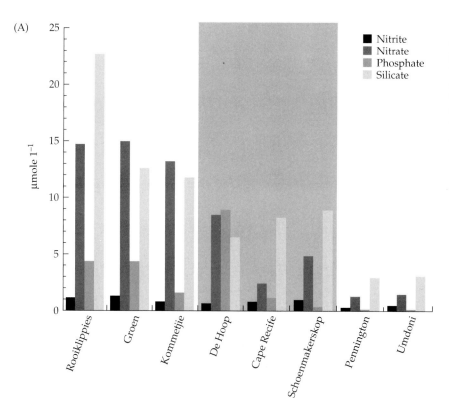

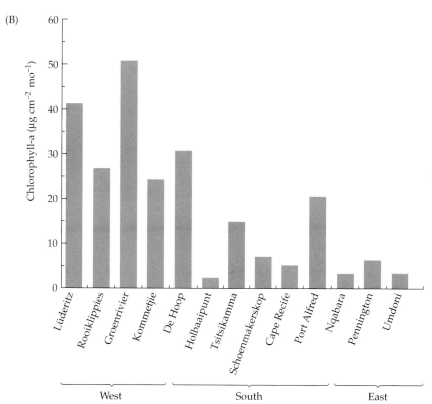

Figure 9.14 (A) Nutrient concentrations at sites on the west, south, and east coasts of South Africa. Nutrients are highest where upwelling is frequent on the west coast, and decrease away from this region. Sites on central coast are shaded. (B) Monthly production of chlorophyll *a* at 13 rocky intertidal sites on the west, south, and east coasts of South Africa. (After Bustamante et al. 1995a.)

most powerful is gradually emerging. Our grasp is firmest when stresses are predictable on the scale of the participating organisms' life spans. Branch et al. (1987) concluded that although intertidal shores experience formidable physical stresses, these are sufficiently predictable and frequent for or-

ganisms to adapt to them, and to evolve what Connell and Sousa (1983) call "resistance" to such perturbations. In turn, this allows strong biological interactions to develop and to play a dominant role in community dynamics. Rocky shores are dynamic, but nonetheless show constancy in species com-

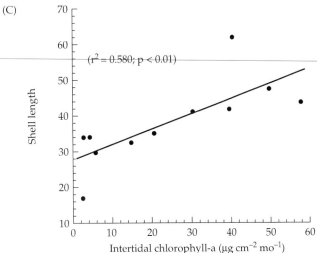

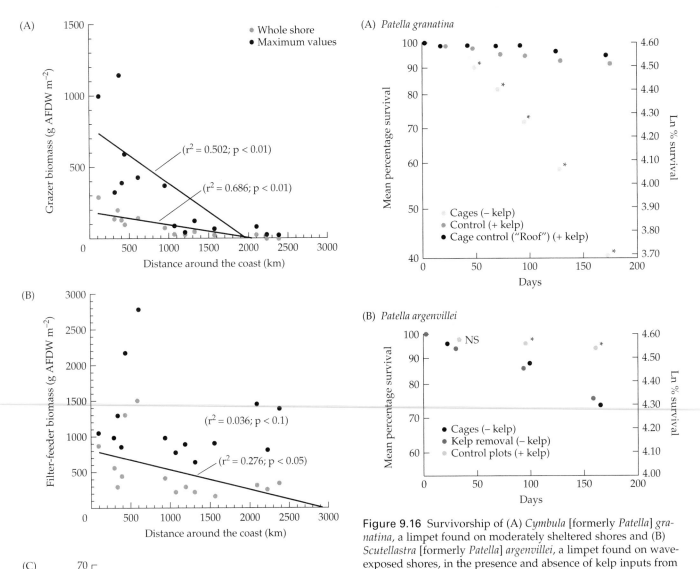

Figure 9.16 Survivorship of (A) *Cymbula* [formerly *Patella*] *granatina*, a limpet found on moderately sheltered shores and (B) *Scutellastra* [formerly *Patella*] *argenvillei*, a limpet found on wave-exposed shores, in the presence and absence of kelp inputs from adjacent habitats. (After Bustamante et al. 1995b.)

Figure 9.15 (A) Grazer biomass with distance from the most northerly site studied on the west coast of southern Africa. (B) Filter-feeder biomass with distance from the most northerly site studied on the west coast of southern Africa. (C) Maximum shell length of *Scutellastra* [formerly *Patella*] *granularis* in relation to intertidal primary productivity in South Africa. (After Bustamante et al. 1995a.)

position and relative abundance of dominants. Even when disturbed, rocky intertidal communities tend to return to a very similar condition ("adjustment stability"; see e.g., Connell and Sousa 1983).

However, rocky intertidal communities may be periodically struck by stochastic events such as freak flooding (Branch et al. 1990), disease (e.g., Lafferty and Kuris 1993) and harmful algal blooms (Mathews and Pitcher 1996) that decimate all but the most hardy elements of these communities. Although these are extreme, rare and unpredictable events, and thus can be beyond the adaptational limits of most organisms, their relative importance must be addressed. Many human-induced stresses and disturbances fall into this category because of both the recency and speed with which they have been introduced, and their rapid rates of change. There are, however, more subtle reasons why human activities break the ecological rules that apply to natural systems, and it is to these that we turn in the next section.

Community Stability and Conservation

Human impacts on rocky intertidal shores are diverse, and include pollution, overharvesting, introduction of exotic species, disturbance and the effects of climate change. On the plus side, impacts seldom alter the physical substratum of rocky shores, so that even if the overlying biota are disrupted, there is potential for recovery. This contrasts strongly with systems such as mangroves, estuaries and coral reefs, all powerfully dependent on the biological matrix that contributes to the physical structure. Their disturbance can destroy the whole fabric of the system, leading to prolonged or even irreversible effects. Many human impacts listed above are covered in Part Three of this volume, but research on rocky shores has contributed particularly to the understanding of some of them, and we touch on these here.

Introduced Species

Members of almost every phylum have been translocated to other parts of the world from their native environments. An estimated 10% of those arriving become established, some with major effects on local systems. The European shore crab *Carcinus maenas*, for example, has invaded the east and west coasts of North America, South Africa, Japan and Australia (Griffiths et al. 1992; Lafferty and Kuris 1996). It seems limited only by its preference for relatively sheltered shores. After introduction, its rate of spread ranges from 18 to 62 km.yr^{-1} (Grosholz 1996). An aggressive predator, its impact on prey species in some areas has been substantial, to the extent that it is often blamed for the demise of the soft-shell clam (*Mya arenaria)* fishery in New England and Nova Scotia (Moulton and Gustafson 1956). In one instance it may have caused a rapid evolutionary change in the morphology of an indigenous snail (Seely 1986). In another example, there is increasing concern that the introduction of alien phytoplankton in ballast water (Hallegraef 1993), or with shellfish used for mariculture, may trigger harmful algal blooms, some of which have caused mass mortality on rocky shores (e.g., Matthews and Pitcher 1996). In yet another case, the introduction of *Littorina littorea* has transformed intertidal algal community structure in New England and, as outlined above, its feeding preferences within tide pools tip the competitive balance away from fast-growing opportunistic green algae in favor of slower-growing *Chondrus crispus* (Lubchenco 1978).

The invasion of South African shores by the Mediterranean mussel *Mytilus galloprovincialis* is one of the most interesting cases, partly because its effects are so multiple and dramatic, and partly because they are modified by a range of biological factors and local conditions. The mussel was probably introduced in the early 1970s, as evidence from archaeological middens or field surveys for its prior occurrence is lacking (Griffiths et al. 1992). It has since expanded its range by about 115 km · yr^{-1}, and now forms dense mats on most exposed shores over nearly 2000 km of South Africa's west coast. More recently, *M. galloprovincialis* was deliberately introduced to the south coast of South Africa for mariculture

trials. There, its maximum distance of larval dispersal from source to settlement site was 80 km · yr^{-1}, but the dilution of larvae over this distance was so great that the adult beds effectively spread at a much lower rate: about 5 km · yr^{-1} (T. Phillips, pers. comm.). Relative to the indigenous ribbed mussel *Aulacomya ater*, it has twice the growth rate, three times the reproductive output, four times the filtration rate, and a higher tolerance for desiccation: all must contribute to its superiority as a competitor. Its success has led to a doubling of overall intertidal biomass on wave-exposed shores (Griffiths et al. 1992).

On the low-shore of wave-beaten west coast sites, *M. galloprovincialis* is gradually constricting the limpet *Scutellastra argenvillei* to small patches (Figure 9.1D), thereby reducing overall densities. This competitive interaction is moderated by wave action, *M. galloprovincialis* being favored by high wave action, whereas *S. argenvillei* are most dense where wave action is moderate (N. Steffani, pers. comm.). The dominant limpet on more sheltered shores, (*Cymbula granatina*) is unaffected by *M. galloprovincialis* because settlement and growth of the mussel are substantially lower in these habitats. On the mid-shore, *M. galloprovincialis* has transformed the zone, displacing the resident biota, including the ribbed mussel *A. ater*, the reef worm *Gunnarea capensis*, limpets and algae. Previously, for example, the mid zone was a mosaic of limpet-controlled patches of bare rock, algae and ribbed mussels. The smooth shell of *M. galloprovincialis* facilitates recruitment of *Scutellastra granularis*, increasing limpet density, but *M. galloprovincialis* excludes large adult limpets. Because large numbers of limpets recruit to the shells of *M. galloprovincialis*, algae are eliminated, and algal diversity drops in comparison with that in beds of the indigenous ribbed mussel.

Although *M. galloprovincialis* has been bad news for some species, its invasion has been good for others. The African Black Oystercatcher, *Haematopus moquini*, now has an altered but larger food supply (mussels), and has improved its rate of fledging success, with almost twice the number of birds now succeeding in rearing two chicks rather than the usual one (Griffiths et al. 1992). The effects of *M. galloprovincialis* are thus multiple, and operate via a range of processes: direct competition for space with algae and adult limpets, facilitation of limpet recruitment (thus increasing the magnitude of indirect effects on algae), and modification of energy flow and trophic pathways.

Climate Change

Marine biogeographic provinces are generally linked to sea temperature, so coastal biota should respond to global warming with shifts in distribution. One way of testing this potential effect is to monitor changes in communities at fixed sites over time. Barry et al. (1995; see also Sagarin et al. 1999) re-surveyed sites in Monterey Bay, California, repeating quantitative observations in the same plots used in 1931–33 by W. G. Hewatt. Over the intervening period, mean inshore sea temperatures had risen 0.75°C and maximum temperatures by 2.2°C. Of 45 species recorded, 32 had significantly changed in abundance. They could be divided into those whose distribution extended mainly South (into warmer waters), or North (into cooler waters), or were cosmopolitan. Eight out of nine southern-range species had increased in numbers over the 60 years and five of eight northern-range species had declined. Most cosmopolitan species had not changed, and of those that had, equal numbers increased and decreased. Although the lack of samples between 1931 and 1995 is a weakness in this study, this evidence is consistent with the idea that these biota have shifted northward, possibly in response to warming.

These results suggest that a gradual redistribution of species may result from the independent responses of species to climatic change. Sanford (1999) argued that if climate change alters species interactions, more rapid and dramatic alterations of rocky intertidal community structure are possible. After observing that the foraging activity of the keystone predator *Pisaster ochraceus* seemed to change drastically in concert with water temperature fluctuations associated with upwelling, Sanford (1999) initiated field experiments to test this effect. His experiment quantified the rate of mortality of mussels transplanted from mid to low zones with sea stars present (+sea stars) or absent (–sea stars). Five separate trials of the experiment were run from June through August 1997; during which there occurred three upwelling relaxations, one strong upwelling event and one weak upwelling event. Temperature decreases of only ~3°C were associated with sharp declines in rates of predation on mussels (Figure 9.17). Hence, if upwelling patterns are altered by global warming, changes in rocky intertidal community structure could occur through effects on keystone predation. For example, if upwelling decreases in magnitude or frequency, predation rates could remain consistently high instead of fluctuating. This could possibly shift the lower limit of the mussel bed to higher levels on the shore, thereby expanding the macrophyte-dominated low intertidal zone. Alternatively, if upwelling increases, predation rates might drop sharply, allowing invasion of the low zone by the competitively dominant mussel. As shown by Paine (1966, 1974), this would drastically lower species diversity and lead to major alterations in community dynamics.

Overharvesting

Rocky intertidal communities are incredibly vulnerable to overexploitation because most of the organisms are obvious, sessile and easily accessible during low tide. Nowhere in the world has this been more dramatically demonstrated than in Chile. Previously flourishing stocks of species such as key-hole limpets (*Fissurella* spp.) and 'loco' (*Concholepas concholepas*) have all but disappeared from intensely harvested areas, leading to drastic shifts in community structure and species composition (e.g., Durán and Castilla 1989).

When protected from harvesting, Chile's rocky shores support a wide diversity of giant key-hole limpets (which restrict the growth of algal beds), and locos become common enough to exert powerful direct and indirect effects on the entire community. In the presence of human harvesting, key-hole limpets and locos are scarce, and small limpets, algae, mussels and barnacles all flourish. The limpet *Siphonaria* and

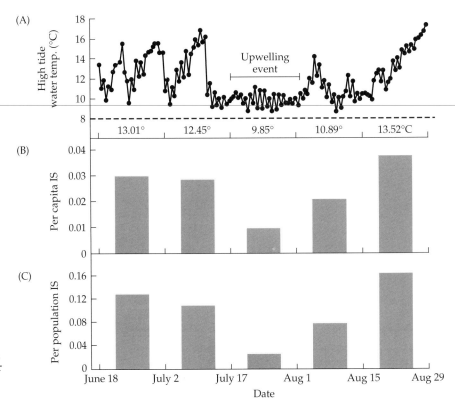

Figure 9.17 Changes in per-capita interaction strength (B) and population interaction strength (C) on the Oregon coast in summer 1997 during upwelling and non-upwelling events (A). (After Sanford 1999.)

the seaweed *Mazzaella* (formerly *Iridaea*) *laminarioides* increase, being freed from competition or grazing by keyhole limpets. The algae *Ulva* and *Porphyra* thrive in the absence of the competitively superior *Mazzaella*, but understory algae dependent on its shade diminish (Branch and Moreno 1994). In the absence of human harvesting, all these outcomes are reversed, with effects that cascade though the community, including an increase in the rate of parasitism of limpets by trematodes inside MPAs (Branch and Moreno 1994).

With the shifts documented by Barry et al. (1995) and Sanford (1999), the situation in Chile is a forceful demonstration of the importance of marine protected areas (MPAs) as reference sites (Hockey and Branch 1994). Without them we would not even have begun to grasp the magnitude of human harvesting, let alone the complexities of its effects.

The magnitude of the direct and indirect effects of harvesting have led some to suggest that they can impel communities into a new state (or "domain") in which they may remain for prolonged periods (and are thus regarded as "stable"), or from which they may even never return. Thus was born the concept graced with the name "alternate stable states" (e.g., Sutherland 1974). Obviously the implications are considerable. Populations may have only a certain amount of "resistance" to perturbation before they are altered beyond the normal limits of variability. Worse, there may be limits to their "adjustment stability," or their capacity to return to their original condition, even if the causes of change can be reversed.

Connell and Sousa (1983) questioned the validity of the concept of alternate (or multiple) stable states. They argued that there are virtually no examples consistent with the concept because the evidence fails for one of three reasons. (1) Observations have not been made for sufficiently long to test if the "new" or "alternate" state is stable. "Long enough" is considered to be at least one turnover of all individuals. (2) A condition cannot be considered stable if it has to be maintained by artificial means: i.e., human intervention. (3) If differences in physical conditions can explain why two states differ, they are not alternate stable states – rather, they are alternatives maintained by contrasting physical conditions.

Although there is no convincing evidence for alternate stable states in rocky intertidal communities, one rocky subtidal example satisfying these criteria has emerged since the critique by Connell and Sousa. Because it is unique, instructive, and based on processes commonly documented intertidally, we briefly summarize this example here.

Community structure in the shallow rocky subtidal of two adjacent islands on the west coast of South Africa is radically different (Branch et al. 1987). Malgas Island has dense populations of the rock lobsters *Jasus lalandii* but sparse mussel, grazer and whelk populations, and Marcus Island has no lobsters but dense mussel and whelk populations. Experiments at Malgas Island showed that shell-crushing lobsters are responsible for most features of community structure. Direct lobster predation virtually eliminates the weak-shelled black mussels (*Choromytilus meridionalis*), whelks (*Burnupena* spp.) and grazers. As an indirect consequence, seaweeds are abundant and a more weakly competitive but better defended (thicker-shelled) mussel (*Aulacomya ater*) is present. At Marcus Island, in the absence of lobster predation and despite the dense whelk population, *Choromytilus* forms dense, multi-layered beds that displace *Aulacomya* but support a range of small cryptic species. Grazers are common, and macroalgae consequently near-absent.

What maintains the differences? Controlled introductions of lobsters to Marcus Island revealed an extraordinary dynamic: the whelk *Burnupena papyracea*, occurring at enormous densities (>200 · m^{-2}), overwhelmed and consumed the rock lobsters within *minutes* of their introduction (Barkai and McQuaid 1988). As they increase in size, these whelks become coated with a toxic bryozoan, *Alcyonidium nodosum*, making them immune to lobster predation. At Marcus Island, whelks are extremely abundant and immune to lobster predation, allowing them to reverse the normal predator–prey relationship thereby excluding lobsters. At Malgas Island, however, whelks are scarce, subject to lobster predation and thus are a minor component of the community. Unfortunately, the origins of these strikingly different states are unknown.

Are these alternate stable states? Present evidence says yes (Castilla and Branch 1994). The differences have persisted for 17 years, are not artificially maintained since neither island is harvested, and no significant differences in physical conditions have been detected. Nonetheless, it seems unlikely that the special circumstances promoting alternate stable states at these two South African islands—interesting though they are—will ever be very common. The Chilean studies, for example, suggest that the alternative states occurring in the presence and absence of *loco* are labile, shifting relatively quickly from one to the other depending on rates of harvesting by humans. But even if the transformed Chilean rocky shore communities are not an "alternate stable state," it is obvious that they have been pushed beyond the limits of their normal resistance to change, and will not be restored without controls being placed on human activities. Regardless of the robustness of the concept of alternative stable states, overharvesting, with all its adverse direct and indirect effects, is short-sighted and unsustainable. Furthermore, the multiple changes wrought by the powerful biological interactions that can be unleashed by relatively simple changes make it abundantly clear that a purely single-species approach to managing living marine resources is not, and never has been, a viable strategy.

Are Human and Natural Impacts on Communities Qualitatively Different?

The interplay between humans and other organisms on rocky shores can be illustrated using the species interactions studied on the west coast of South Africa to explore how human effects differ from natural interactions (Dye et al. 1994; Figure 9.18). Under natural conditions, exploited species are buffered in some way. Limpets are eaten by oystercatchers, but some are always inaccessible or grow quickly to invulnerable sizes due to high algal productivity. Limpets con-

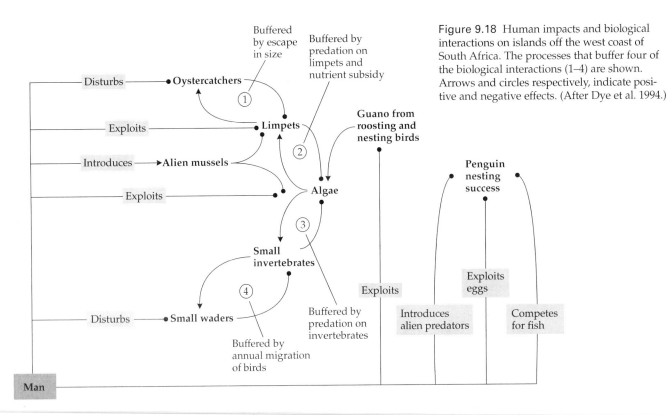

Figure 9.18 Human impacts and biological interactions on islands off the west coast of South Africa. The processes that buffer four of the biological interactions (1–4) are shown. Arrows and circles respectively, indicate positive and negative effects. (After Dye et al. 1994.)

sume algae, but their effect is muted because their numbers are held down by predation, and because guano input enhances algal productivity. Algae are also consumed by infaunal invertebrates, but the latter are reduced in number by predation by small wading birds. The impact of the birds is temporally variable, allowing recovery of prey populations, because most emigrate in winter.

Human impacts lack any of these subtle checks and balances. First, because human population density is relatively independent of rocky intertidal resources, overexploitation of intertidal populations has no negative demographic consequences for humans. Second, the lack of ecological feedback effects, and the short time scales over which human exploitation occurs, provide little or no opportunity for adaptations by exploited populations to the severe selective forces imposed by human depredations. Although a few species show signs of adapting (e.g., fished stocks have modified their life history characteristics by reproducing at a younger age), for the most part, the rates of human impacts are vastly greater than rates of adaptation of exploited species. Third, humans are supreme generalists. Because money and not energy is the basic currency, humans can simultaneously act as predator, competitor, amensal disturber, and introducer of "commensal" aliens. In South Africa (Figure 9.18) humans feed on penguin eggs, compete with penguins for food (fish), amensally alter habitat by removing guano (vital for penguin nesting), introduce alien predators, remove algal habitat, consume or sell limpets, and "inadvertently" disturb birds. Fourth, cheap long-range transport allows distant societies to

use resources that are not even wanted locally, so demands for resources are not dependent on the size of local human populations . Fifth, technology means that no resources ever have a refuge in time or space. None of the natural "escapes" exists for any prey. In all of these respects, therefore, human populations break the ecological rules by which natural systems operate.

FUTURE PROSPECTS

Research on rocky shore ecology and community dynamics is at a crossroad. Studies on rocky shores have unquestionably added profoundly to our knowledge, but generalizing our ideas and concepts to the point that we can be predictive remains an elusive goal. Can we achieve a level of knowledge that allows at least modestly successful predictions? If so, how should we proceed?

We suggest that progress toward a better predictive capacity will be stimulated by addressing three central issues. First, most prior research has been based at single localities, has been of short duration, and has often involved one or a few species. The results of such studies will be valid in the context in which they were done, but useful generalizations or extrapolations may be limited (Underwood and Denley 1984). Second, researchers often adopt polarized viewpoints (e.g., competition versus predation, or "my site is different from your site"), rather than seeking to identify the circumstances under which one view or another is most likely to be applicable. Third, many concepts have been uncritically accepted or worse, expanded and modified to suit almost any circumstance so that they cease to have meaning. Contemplate for a moment the range of meanings for "keystone species," or "stability," and their sometimes sloppy application or definition.

We suggest that ecological research should be done over sufficiently large scales in time and space to test their across-scale generality. The wider the range of conditions and the greater the diversity of species examined, the greater the likelihood that our conclusions will be robust. Only then will we be able to distinguish general vs. local rules. We emphasize that rules or phenomena that are specific to particular organisms, sites, communities, or habitats are not unimportant, and properly examined may tell us what processes or mechanisms lead to their being local. Such an analysis may, in fact, suggest general truths about processes and mechanisms. It is clear, nonetheless, that only by redirecting our efforts more explicitly toward the goal of obtaining information that allows evaluation of the level of generality can we hope to learn how predictive our science can become.

In addition, we need to critically test the ideas developed to explain the patterns that have emerged. Here, there is no substitute for experimentation (Connell 1972; Paine 1977; Underwood 1995), but complementary approaches can strengthen our attack. Keen observation of natural history, better quantification of environmental conditions and ecological processes, comparative studies, modeling, and phylogenetic, physiological and biochemical studies all add potential insight. Two particular needs in seeking broader, more synthet-

ic generalizations and deeper insights are to tighten and strengthen the interactions between theoreticians and experimentalists, on the one hand, and between experimentalists and more reductionistic scientists (geneticists, molecular biologists, and physiologists) on the other. We conclude by observing that, in our opinion, the uncertainties and rival views that currently exist in ecology in general, and marine intertidal ecology in particular, are not a sign of chaos. Rather, they are an indication of the vibrancy and rigor of the field, which is in large part a consequence of the exciting stage upon which intertidal ecologists can play. Our understanding of these awesome and dynamic communities has advanced dramatically in recent years, and we anticipate even more dramatic progress in the years to come.

ACKNOWLEDGMENTS

We thank Mark Bertness, Tess Freidenburg, Eric Sanford, and four anonymous reviewers for discussion and constructive critical comments on earlier drafts of the manuscript. This is contribution number 8 from PISCO, the Partnership for Interdisciplinary Studies of Coastal Oceans: A Long-Term Ecological Consortium funded by the David and Lucile Packard Foundation. Funding for GMB was provided by the National Research Foundation, the University of Cape Town and the South African Network for Coastal and Oceanographic Research.

LITERATURE CITED

Abrams, P. 1987. Indirect interactions between species that share a predator: Varieties of indirect effects. In W. C. Kerfoot and A. Sih (eds.), *Predation: Direct and Indirect Impacts on Aquatic Communities*, pp. 38–54. University Press of New England, Hanover, NH.

Abrams, P. 1992. Predators that benefit prey and prey that harm predators: Unusual effects of interacting foraging adaptations. *Amer. Nat.* 140: 573–600.

Abrams, P., B. A. Menge, G. G. Mittelbach, D. Spiller and P. Yodzis. 1996. The role of indirect effects in food webs. In G. A. Polis and K. O. Winemiller (eds.), *Food Webs: Integration of Pattern and Dynamics*, pp. 371–395. Chapman and Hall, New York.

Arnott, S. E. and M. J. Vanni. 1993. Zooplankton assemblages in fishless bog lakes: Influence of biotic and abiotic factors. *Ecology* 74: 2361–2380.

Barkai, A. and C. D. McQuaid. 1988. Predator–prey role reversal in a marine benthic ecosystem. *Science* 242: 62–64.

Barry, J. P., C. H. Baxter, R. D. Sagarin and S. E. Gilman. 1995. Climate-related, long-term faunal changes in a California rocky intertidal community. *Science* 267: 672–675.

Bender, E. A., T. J. Case and M. E. Gilpin. 1984. Perturbation experiments in community ecology: Theory and practice. *Ecology* 65: 1–13.

Benedetti-Cecchi, L. and F. Cinelli. 1993. Early patterns of algal succession in a midlittoral community of the Mediterranean Sea: A multifactorial experiment. *J. Exp. Mar. Biol. Ecol.* 169: 15–31.

Berlow, E. L. 1999. Strong effects of weak interactors in ecological communities. *Nature* 398: 330–334.

Berlow, E. L., S. A. Navarrete, C. J. Briggs, M. E. Power and B. A. Menge. 1999. Quantifying variation in the strengths of species interactions. *Ecology* 80: 2206–2224.

Bertness, M. D. 1989. Positive and negative density-dependent mortality and the population structure of *Semibalanus balanoides* in a sheltered bay habitat. *Ecology* 70: 257–268.

Bertness, M. D. and R. Callaway. 1994. Positive interactions in communities. *Trends Ecol. Evol.* 9: 191–193.

Bertness, M. D. and G. H. Leonard. 1997. The role of positive interactions in communities: Lessons from intertidal habitats. *Ecology* 78: 1976–1989.

Bosman, A. L. and P. A. R. Hockey. 1986. Seabird guano as a determinant of rocky intertidal community structure. *Mar. Ecol. Prog. Ser.* 32: 247–257.

Bosman, A. L., J. T Du Toit, P. A. R. Hockey and G. M. Branch. 1986. A field experiment demonstrating the influence of seabird

guano on intertidal primary production. *Estuarine, Coastal and Shelf Sci.* 23: 283–294.

Branch, G. M. 1981. The biology of limpets: Physical factors, energy flow and ecological interactions. *Oceanogr. Mar. Biol. Annu. Rev.* 19: 235–379.

Branch, G. M. 1984. Competition between marine organisms: Ecological and evolutionary implications. *Oceanogr. Mar. Biol. Annu. Rev.* 22: 429–593.

Branch, G. M. and C. L. Griffiths. 1988. The Benguela ecosystem Part V. The coastal zone. *Oceanogr. Mar. Biol. Annu. Rev.* 26: 395–486.

Branch, G. M. and C. A. Moreno. 1994. Intertidal and subtidal grazers. In R. W. Siegfried (ed.), *Rocky Shores: Exploitation in Chile and South Africa*, pp. 75–100. Springer-Verlag, New York.

Branch, G. M., A. Barkai, P. A. R. Hockey and L. Hutchings. 1987. Biological interactions: Causes or effects of variability in the Benguela ecosystem? *South African J. Mar. Sci.* 5: 425–445.

Branch, G. M., S. Eekhout and A. L. Bosman. 1990. Short-term effects of the 1988 Orange River floods on the intertidal rocky-shore communities of the open coast. *Trans. Roy. Soc. South Africa* 47: 331–354.

Branch, G. M., J. M. Harris, C. Parkins, R. H. Bustamante and S. Eekhout. 1992. Algal "gardening" by marine grazers: A comparison of the ecological effects of territorial fish and limpets. In D. M. John, S. J. Hawkins and J. H. Prices (eds.), *Plant–Animal Interactions in the Marine Benthos*, pp. 405–423. Clarendon Press, Oxford.

Broekhuysen, G. J. 1940. A preliminary investigation of the importance of desiccation, temperature and salinity as factors controlling the vertical distribution of certain intertidal marine gastropods in False Bay, South Africa. *Trans. Roy. Soc. South Africa* 28: 245–292.

Bustamante, R. H. and G. M. Branch. 1996a. The dependence of intertidal consumers on kelp-derived organic matter on the west coast of South Africa. *J. Exp. Mar. Biol. Ecol.* 196: 1–28.

Bustamante, R. H. and G. M. Branch. 1996b. Large scale patterns and trophic structure of southern African rocky shores: The roles of geographic variation and wave exposure. *J. Biogeogr.* 23: 339–351.

Bustamante, R. H., G. M. Branch and S. Eekhout. 1995a. Maintenance of an exceptional intertidal grazer biomass in South Africa: Subsidy by subtidal kelps. *Ecology* 76: 2314–2329.

Bustamante, R. H., G. M. Branch, S. Eekhout, B. Robertson, P. Zoutendyk, M. Schleyer, A. Dye, N. Hanekom, D. Keats, M. Jurd and C. McQuaid. 1995b. Gradients of intertidal primary productivity around the coast of South Africa and their relationships with consumer biomass. *Oecologia* 102: 189–201.

Castilla, J. C. and G. M. Branch. 1994. Exploitation of two critical predators: The gastropod *Concholepas concholepas* and the rocky lobster *Jasus lalandii*. In R. W. Siegfried (ed.), *Rocky Shores: Exploitation in Chile and South Africa*, pp. 101–130. Springer-Verlag, New York.

Castilla, J. C. and L. R. Duran. 1985. Human exclusion from the rocky intertidal zone of central Chile: The effects on *Concholepas concholepas* (Gastropoda). *Oikos* 45: 391–399.

Choat, J. H. 1977. The influence of sessile organisms on the population biology of three species of acmaeid limpets. *J. Exp. Mar. Biol. Ecol.* 26: 1–26.

Clements, F. E., J. Weaver and H. Hanson. 1926. *Plant Competition: An Analysis of The Development of Vegetation*. Carnegie Institute, Washington, DC.

Connell, J. H. 1961a. Effects of competition, predation by *Thais lapillus*, and other factors on natural populations of the barnacle *Balanus balanoides*. *Ecol. Monogr.* 31: 61–104.

Connell, J. H. 1961b. The influence of interspecific competition and other factors on the distribution of the barnacle *Chthamalus stellatus*. *Ecology* 42: 710–723.

Connell, J. H. 1972. Community interactions on marine rocky intertidal shores. *Annu. Rev. Ecol. Syst.* 3: 169–192.

Connell, J. H. 1975. Some mechanisms producing structure in natural communities: A model and evidence from field experiments. In M. L. Cody and J. M. Diamond (eds.), *Ecology and Evolution of Communities*, pp. 460–490. Belknap, Cambridge, MA.

Connell, J. H. 1983. On the prevalence and relative importance of interspecific competition: Evidence from field experiments. *Amer. Nat.* 122: 661–696.

Connell, J. H. 1985. The consequences of variation in initial settlement vs. post settlement mortality in rocky intertidal communities. *J. Exp. Mar. Biol. Ecol.* 93: 11–45.

Connell, J. H. and R. O. Slatyer. 1977. Mechanisms of succession in natural communities and their role in community stability and organization. *Amer. Nat.* 111: 1119–1144.

Connell, J. H. and W. P. Sousa. 1983. On the evidence needed to judge ecological stability or persistence. *Amer. Nat.* 121: 789–824.

Creese, R. J. 1982. Distribution and abundance of the acmaeid limpet *Patelloida latistrigata* and its interaction with barnacles. *Oecologia* 52: 85–96.

Crisp, D. J. and H. Barnes. 1954. The orientation and distribution of barnacles at settlement with particular reference to surface contour. *J. Anim. Ecol.* 23: 142–162.

Dayton, P. K. 1971. Competition, disturbance, and community organization: The provision and subsequent utilization of space in a rocky intertidal community. *Ecol. Monogr.* 41: 351–389.

Dayton, P. K. 1975. Experimental evaluation of ecological dominance in a rocky intertidal algal community. *Ecol. Monogr.* 45: 137–159.

Denny, M. N., Daniel, T. L. and M. A. R. Koehl. 1985. Mechanical limits to size in wave-swept organisms. *Ecol. Monogr.* 55: 69–102.

Dethier, M. N. and D. O. Duggins. 1984. An "indirect commensalism" between marine herbivores and the importance of competitive hierarchies. *Amer. Nat.* 124: 205–219.

Doty, M. S. 1946. Critical tide factors that are correlated with the vertical distribution of marine algae and other organisms along the Pacific coast. *Ecology* 27: 315–328.

Dungan, M. D. 1986. Three-way interactions: Barnacles, limpets, and algae in a Sonoran Desert rocky intertidal zone. *Amer. Nat.* 127: 292–316.

Dungan, M. L. 1987. Indirect mutualism: Complementary effects of grazing and predation in a rocky intertidal community. In W. C. Kerfoot and A. Sih (eds.), *Predation: Direct and Indirect Impacts on Aquatic Communities*, pp. 188–200. University Press of New England, Hanover, NH.

Duran, L. R. and J. C. Castilla. 1989. Variation and persistence of the middle rocky intertidal community of central Chile, with and without human harvesting. *Mar. Biol.* 103: 555–562.

Dye, A. H., G. M. Branch, J. C. Castilla and B. A. Bennett. 1994. Biological options for the management of the exploitation of intertidal and subtidal resources. In R. W. Siegfried (ed.), *Rocky Shores: Exploitation in Chile and South Africa*, pp. 131–154. Springer-Verlag, New York.

Ebling, F. J., J. A. Kitching, L. Muntz and C. M. Taylor. 1964. The ecology of Lough Ine XIII. Experimental observations of the destruction of *Mytilus edulis* and *Nucella lapillus* by crabs. *J. Anim. Ecol.* 33: 73–82.

Ehrlich, P. 1967. The "balance of nature" and "population control." *Amer. Nat.* 101: 97–107.

Fairweather, P. G. 1985. Differential predation on alternative prey, and the survival of rocky intertidal organisms in New South Wales. *J. Exp. Mar. Biol. Ecol.* 89:135–156.

Fairweather, P. G. 1988a. Predation can increase variability in the abundance of prey on seashores. *Oikos* 53: 87–92.

Fairweather, P. G. 1988b. Predation creates haloes of bare space among prey on rocky shores in New South Wales. *Austral. J. Ecol.* 13: 401–409.

Fairweather, P. G. and A. J. Underwood. 1991. Experimental removals of a rocky intertidal predator: Variations within two habitats in the effects of the prey. *J. Exp. Mar. Biol. Ecol.* 154:29–75.

Fairweather, P. G., A. J. Underwood, and M. J. Moran. 1984. Preliminary investigations of predation by the whelk *Morula marginalba*. *Mar. Ecol. Prog. Ser.* 17: 143–156.

Fretwell, S. D. 1977. The regulation of plant communities by food chains exploiting them. *Persp. Biol.Med.* 20: 169–185.

Fretwell, S. D. 1987. Food chain dynamics: The central theory of ecology? *Oikos* 50: 291–301.

Gaines, S. D. 1984. Herbivory and between-habitat diversity: The differential effectiveness of defenses in a marine plant. *Ecology* 66: 473–485.

Gaines, S. D. and J. Lubchenco. 1982. A unified approach to marine plant-herbivore interactions. II. Biogeography. *Annu. Rev. Ecol. Syst.* 13: 111–138.

Gaines, S. D. and J. Roughgarden. 1985. Larval settlement rate: A leading determinant of structure in an ecological community of the marine intertidal zone. *Proc. Natl. Acad. Sci. USA* 82: 3707–379.

Garrity, S. D. 1984. Some adaptations of gastropods to physical stress on a tropical rocky shore. *Ecology* 65: 559–574.

Garrity, S. D. and S. C. Levings. 1981. A predator-prey interaction between two physically and biologically constrained tropical rocky shore gastropods. *Ecol. Monogr.* 51:267–286.

Goldwasser, L. and J. Roughgarden. 1997. Sampling effects and the estimation of food-web properties. *Ecology* 78: 41–54.

Gotelli, N. J. 1995. *A Primer of Ecology*. Sinauer Associates, Sunderland, MA.

Griffiths, C. L., P. A. R. Hockey, C. Van Erkom Schurink and P. J. le Roux. 1992. Marine invasive aliens on South African shores: Implications for community structure and trophic functioning. *South African J. Mar. Sci.* 12: 713–722.

Grosberg, R. K. 1981. Competitive ability influences on habitat choice in marine invertebrates. *Nature* 290: 700–702.

Grosberg, R. K. 1982. Intertidal zonation of barnacles: The influence of planktonic zonation of larvae on vertical distribution of adults. *Ecology* 63: 894–899.

Grosberg, R. K. and D. Levitan. 1992. For adults only? Supply-side ecology and the history of larval biology. *Trends Ecol. Evol.* 7: 130–133.

Grosholz, E. D. 1996. Contrasting rates of spread for introduced species in terrestrial and marine systems. *Ecology* 77: 1680–1686.

Hairston, N. G. Jr. and N. G. Sr. Hairston. 1993. Cause–effect relationships in energy flow, trophic structure, and interspecific interactions. *Amer. Nat.* 142: 379–49.

Hairston, N. G. Jr. and N. G. Sr. Hairston. 1997. Does food web complexity eliminate trophic-level dynamics? *Amer. Nat.* 149: 1001–1007.

Hairston, N. G., F. E. Smith and L. B. Slobodkin. 1960. Community structure, population control, and competition. *Amer. Nat.* 94: 421–425.

Hallegraef, G. M. 1993. A review of harmful algal blooms and their apparent global increase. *Phycologia* 33: 79–99.

Hamilton, D. 2000. Direct and indirect effects of predation by common eiders and abiotic disturbance in an intertidal community. *Ecol. Monogr.* 70: 21–43.

Hartnoll, R. G and S. J. Hawkins. 1985. Patchiness and fluctuations on moderately exposed rocky shores. *Ophelia* 24: 53–63.

Hawkins, S. J. and R. G. Hartnoll. 1983. Grazing of intertidal algae by marine invertebrates. *Oceanogr. Mar. Biol. Annu. Rev.* 21: 195–282.

Hixon, M. A. and B. A. Menge. 1991. Species diversity: Prey refuges modify the interactive effects of predation and competition. *Theor. Pop. Biol.* 39: 178–200.

Hockey, P. A. R. and G. M. Branch. 1984. Oystercatchers and limpets: Impact and implications. A preliminary assessment. *Ardea* 72: 119–206.

Hockey, P. A. R. and G. M. Branch. 1994. Conserving marine biodiversity on the African coast: Implications of a terrestrial perspective. *Aquat. Cons. Mar. Freshw. Ecosyst.* 4: 345–362.

Holt, R. D. 1977. Predation, apparent competition, and the structure of prey communities. *Theor. Pop. Biol.* 12: 197–229.

Johanneson, K. 1989. The bare zone of Swedish rocky shores: Why is it there? *Oikos* 54: 77–86.

Kitching, J. A. and J. Lockwood. 1974. Observations on shell form and its ecological significance in thaisid gastropods of the genus *Lepsiella* in New Zealand. *Mar. Biol.* 28: 131–144.

Kitching, J. A., J. F. Sloan and F. J. Ebling. 1959. The ecology of Lough Ine. VIII. Mussels and their predators. *J. Anim. Ecol.* 28: 331–341.

Knight-Jones, E. W. 1955. The gregarious setting reaction of barnacles as a measure of systematic affinity. *Nature* 174: 266.

Lafferty, K. D. and A. M. Kuris. 1993. Mass mortality of abalone *Haliotis cracherodii* on the California Channel Islands: Test of epidemiological hypotheses. *Mar. Ecol. Prog. Ser.* 96: 239–248.

Lafferty, K. D. and A. M. Kuris. 1996. Biological control of marine pests. *Ecology* 77: 1989–2000.

Leibold, M. A. 1989. Resource edibility and the effects of predators and productivity on the outcome of trophic interactions. *Amer. Nat.* 134: 922–949.

Leonard, G. H., J. M. Levine, P. R. Schmidt and M. D. Bertness. 1998. Flow-driven variation in intertidal community structure in a Maine estuary. *Ecology* 79: 1395–149.

Lewin, R. 1986. Supply-side ecology. *Science* 234:25–27.

Lewis, J. R. 1964. *The Ecology of Rocky Shores.* English Universities Press, London.

Lively, C. M. and P. T. Raimondi. 1987. Desiccation, predation, and mussel-barnacle interactions in the northern Gulf of California. *Oecologia* 74: 304–309.

Louda, S. M. and S. K. Collinge. 1992. Plant resistance to insect herbivores: A field test of the environmental stress hypothesis. *Ecology* 73: 153–169.

Lubchenco, J. 1978. Plant species diversity in a marine intertidal community: Importance of herbivore food preference and algal competitive abilities. *Amer. Nat.* 112: 23–39.

Lubchenco, J. 1980. Algal zonation in a New England rocky intertidal community: An experimental analysis. *Ecology* 61: 333–344.

Lubchenco, J. 1986. Relative importance of competition and predation: Early colonization by seaweeds in New England. In J. M. Diamond and T. Case (eds.), *Community Ecology,* pp. 537–555. Harper & Row, New York.

Lubchenco, J. 1998. Entering the century of the environment: A new social contract for science. *Science* 279: 491–497.

Lubchenco, J. and S. D. Gaines. 1981. A unified approach to marine plant–herbivore interactions. I. Populations and communities. *Annu. Rev. Ecol. Syst.* 12: 405–437.

Lubchenco, J. and B. A. Menge. 1978. Community development and persistence in a low rocky intertidal zone. *Ecol. Monogr.* 48:67–94.

Lubchenco, J., B. A. Menge, S. D. Garrity, P. J. Lubchenco, L. R. Ashkenas, S. D. Gaines, R. Emlet, J. Lucas and S. Strauss. 1984. Structure, persistence, and role of consumers in a tropical rocky intertidal community (Taboguilla Island, Bay of Panama). *J. Exp. Mar. Biol. Ecol.* 78: 23–73.

Luckens, P. E. 1975. Predation and intertidal zonation of barnacles at Leigh, New Zealand. *N. Z. J. Mar. Freshw. Res.* 9: 355–378.

MacArthur, R. H. 1972. Strong, or weak, interactions? *Trans. Connecticut Acad. Arts Sci.* 44: 177–188.

Martinez, N. D. 1991. Artifacts or attributes? Effects of resolution on the Little Rock Lake food web. *Ecol. Monogr.* 61: 367–392.

Mathews, S. G. and G. C. Pitcher. 1996. Worst recorded marine mortality on the South African coast. In Y. Yasumoto, Y. Oshima and Y. Fukuyo (eds.), *Harmful and Toxic Algal Blooms,* pp. 89–92. Intergovernmental Oceanographic Commission of UNESCO.

McQuaid, C. D. 1982. The influence of desiccation and predation on vertical size gradients in populations of the gastropod *Oxystele variegata* (Anton) on an exposed rocky shore. *Oecologia* 53: 123–127.

McQuaid, C. D. and G. M. Branch. 1985. Trophic structure of rocky intertidal communities: Response to wave action and im-

plications for energy flow. *Mar. Ecol. Prog. Ser.* 22: 153–161.

Menge, B. A. 1976. Organization of the New England rocky intertidal community: Role of predation, competition and environmental heterogeneity. *Ecol. Monogr.* 46: 355–393.

Menge, B. A. 1978a. Predation intensity in a rocky intertidal community. Effect of an algal canopy, wave action and desiccation on predator feeding rates. *Oecologia* 34: 17–35.

Menge, B. A. 1978b. Predation intensity in a rocky intertidal community. Relation between predator foraging activity and environmental harshness. *Oecologia* 34: 1–16.

Menge, B. A. 1991. Relative importance of recruitment and other causes of variation on rocky intertidal community structure. *J. Exp. Mar. Biol. Ecol.* 146: 69–100.

Menge, B. A. 1992. Community regulation: Under what conditions are bottom-up factors important on rocky shores? *Ecology* 73: 755–765.

Menge, B. A. 1995. Indirect effects in marine rocky intertidal interactions webs: Patterns and importance. *Ecol. Monogr.* 65: 21–74.

Menge, B. A. 1997. Detection of direct versus indirect effects: Were experiments long enough? *Amer. Nat.* 149: 801–823.

Menge, B. A. 2001. Bottom-up : top-down determination of rocky intertidal shorescape dynamics. In press. In G. A. Polis, M. E. Power and G. R. Huxel (eds.), *Food Webs at the Landscape Level.* University of Chicago Press, Chicago, IL.

Menge, B. A. and T. M. Farrell. 1989. Community structure and interaction webs in shallow marine hard-bottom communities: Tests of an environmental stress model. *Adv. Ecol. Res.* 19: 189–262.

Menge, B. A. and J. Lubchenco. 1981. Community organization in temperate and tropical rocky intertidal habitats: Prey refuges in relation to consumer pressure gradients. *Ecol. Monogr.* 51: 429–450.

Menge, B. A. and A. M. Olson. 1990. Role of scale and environmental factors in regulation of community structure. *Trends Ecol. Evol.* 5: 52–57.

Menge, B. A. and J. P. Sutherland. 1976. Species diversity gradients: Synthesis of the roles of predation, competition, and temporal heterogeneity. *Amer. Nat.* 110: 351–369.

Menge, B. A. and J. P. Sutherland. 1987. Community regulation: Variation in disturbance, competition, and predation in relation to environmental stress and recruitment. *Amer. Nat.* 130: 730–757.

Menge, B. A., J. Lubchenco and L. R. Ashkenas. 1985. Diversity, heterogeneity and consumer pressure in a tropical rocky intertidal community. *Oecologia* 65: 394–405.

Menge, B. A., J. Lubchenco, L. R. Ashkenas and F. Ramsey. 1986a. Experimental separation of effects of consumers on sessile prey in the low zone of a rocky shore in the Bay of Panama: Direct and indirect consequences of food web complexity. *J. Exp. Mar. Biol. Ecol.* 100:225–269.

Menge, B. A., J. Lubchenco, S. D. Gaines and L. R. Ashkenas. 1986b. A test of the

Menge–Sutherland model of community organization in a tropical rocky intertidal food web. *Oecologia* 71: 75–89.

Menge, B. A., T. M. Farrell, A. M. Olson, P. van-Tamelen and T. Turner. 1993. Algal recruitment and the maintenance of a plant mosaic in the low intertidal region on the Oregon coast. *J. Exp. Mar. Biol. Ecol.* 170: 91–116.

Menge, B. A., E. L. Berlow, C. A. Blanchette, S. A. Navarrete and S. B. Yamada. 1994. The keystone species concept: Variation in interaction strength in a rocky intertidal habitat. *Ecol. Monogr.* 64: 249–286.

Menge, B. A., B. A. Daley and P. A. Wheeler. 1996. Control of interaction strength in marine benthic communities. In G. A. Polis and K. O. Winemiller (eds.), *Food Webs: Integration of Pattern and Dynamics*, pp. 258–274. Chapman and Hall, New York.

Menge, B. A., B. A. Daley, P. A. Wheeler, E. Dahlhoff, E. Sanford and P. T. Strub. 1997a. Benthic-pelagic links and rocky intertidal communities: Bottom-up effects on top-down control? *Proc. Natl. Acad. Sci. USA* 94: 14530–14535.

Menge, B. A., B. A. Daley, P. A. Wheeler and P. T. Strub. 1997b. Rocky intertidal oceanography: An association between community structure and nearshore phytoplankton concentration. *Limn. Oceanogr.* 42: 57–66.

Menge, B. A., B. A. Daley, J. Lubchenco, E. Sanford, E. Dahlhoff, P. M. Halpin, G. Hudson and J. L. Burnaford. 1999. Top-down and bottom-up regulation of New Zealand rocky intertidal communities. *Ecol. Monogr.* 69:297–330.

Miller, T. E. and W. C. Kerfoot. 1987. Redefining indirect effects. In W. C. Kerfoot and A. Sih (eds.), *Predation: Direct and Indirect Impacts on Aquatic Communities*, pp. 33–37. University Press of New England, Hanover, NH.

Mills, L. S., M. E. Soulé and D. F. Doak. 1993. The keystone-species concept in ecology and conservation. *BioScience* 43: 219–224.

Minchinton, T. E. and R. E. Scheibling. 1993. Free space availability and larval substratum selection as determinants of barnacle population structure in a developing rocky intertidal community. *Mar. Ecol. Prog. Ser.* 95: 233–244.

Moulton, J. M. and A. H. Gustafson. 1956. Green crabs and the distribution of quahogs. *Science* 123: 992.

Murdoch, W. W. 1966. "Community structure, population control, and competition"—a critique. *Amer. Nat.* 100: 219–226.

Navarrete, S. A. and B. A. Menge. 1996. Keystone predation and interaction strength: Interactive effects of predators on their main prey. *Ecol. Monogr.* 66: 409–429.

Oksanen, L., S. D. Fretwell, J. Arruda and P. Niemela. 1981. Exploitation ecosystems in gradients of primary productivity. *Amer. Nat.* 118: 240–261.

Paine, R. T. 1966. Food web complexity and species diversity. *Amer. Nat.* 100: 65–75.

Paine, R. T. 1969. A note on trophic complexity and community stability. *Amer. Nat.* 103: 91–93.

Paine, R. T. 1971. A short-term experimental investigation of resource partitioning in a New Zealand rocky intertidal system. *Ecology* 52: 1096–1106.

Paine, R. T. 1974. Intertidal community structure: Experimental studies on the relationship between a dominant competitor and its principal predator. *Oecologia* 15: 93–120.

Paine, R. T. 1977. Controlled manipulations in the marine intertidal zone, and their contribution to ecological theory. In *Changing Scenes in Natural Sciences, 1776–1976*, pp. 245–270. Special Publication 12. Academy of Natural Sciences, Philadelphia.

Paine, R. T. 1980. Food webs: Linkage, interaction strength and community infrastructure. *J. Anim. Ecol.* 49: 667–685.

Paine, R. T. 1992. Food-web analysis through field measurement of per capita interaction strength. *Nature* 355: 73–75.

Paine, R. T. and S. A. Levin. 1981. Intertidal landscapes: Disturbance and the dynamics of pattern. *Ecol. Monogr.* 51: 145–178.

Paine, R. T., J. C. Castilla and J. Cancino. 1985. Perturbation and recovery patterns of starfish-dominated intertidal assemblages in Chile, New Zealand, and Washington state. *Amer. Nat.* 125: 679–691.

Palmer, A. R. 1979. Fish predation and the evolution of gastropod shell sculpture: Experimental and geographic evidence. *Evolution* 33: 697–713.

Persson, L., J. Bengtsson, B. A. Menge and M. E. Power. 1996. Productivity and consumer regulation—concepts, patterns, and mechanisms. In G. A. Polis and K. O. Winemiller (eds.), *Food Webs: Integration of Pattern and Dynamics*, pp. 396–434. Chapman and Hall, New York.

Pimm, S. L. 1982. *Food Webs*. Chapman and Hall, London.

Pimm, S. L. 1991. *The Balance of Nature?* University of Chicago Press, IL.

Polis, G. A. 1991. Complex trophic interactions in deserts: An empirical critique of food-web theory. *Amer. Nat.* 138: 123–155.

Polis, G. A. and D. Strong. 1996. Food web complexity and community dynamics. *Amer. Nat.* 147: 813–846.

Power, M. E., D. Tilman, J. A. Estes, B. A. Menge, W. J. Bond, L. S. Mills, G. Daily, J. C. Castilla, J. Lubchenco and R. T. Paine. 1996. Challenges in the quest for keystones. *BioScience* 46: 609–620.

Raimondi, P. T. 1988. Settlement cues and determination of the vertical limit of an intertidal barnacle. *Ecology* 69:400–407.

Raimondi, P. T. 1990. Patterns, mechanisms, and consequences of variability in settlement and recruitment of an intertidal barnacle. *Ecol. Monogr.* 60: 283–309.

Robles, C. D. 1987. Predator foraging characteristics and prey population structure on a sheltered shore. *Ecology* 68:1502–1514.

Robles, C. D. 1997. Changing recruitment in constant species assemblages: Implications for predation theory in intertidal communities. *Ecology* 78:1400–1414.

Robles, C. D., R. Sherwood-Stephens, and M. Alvarado. 1995. Responses of a key intertidal predator to varying recruitment of its prey. *Ecology* 76: 565–579.

Roughgarden, J., S. D. Gaines and H. Possingham. 1988. Recruitment dynamics in complex life cycles. *Science* 241: 1460–1466.

Ruesink, J. L. 1998. Variation in per capita interaction strength: Thresholds due to nonlinear dynamics and nonequilibrium conditions. *Proc. Natl. Acad. Sci. USA* 95: 6843–6847.

Sagarin, R. D., J. P. Barry, S. E. Gilman and C. H. Baxter. 1999. Climate-related change in an intertidal community over short and long time scales. *Ecol. Monogr.* 69: 465–490.

Sanford, E. 1999. Regulation of keystone predation by small changes in ocean temperature. *Science* 283: 2095–2097.

Schmitt, R. J. 1987. Indirect interactions between prey: Apparent competition, predator aggregation, and habitat segregation. *Ecology* 68: 1887–1897.

Schoener, T. W. 1983. Field experiments on interspecific competition. *Amer. Nat.* 122: 240–285.

Schoener, T. W. 1993. On the relative importance of direct versus indirect effects in ecological communities. In H. Kawanabe, J. E. Cohen and K. Iwasaki (eds.), *Mutualism and Community Organization: Behavioral, Theoretical, and Food-Web Approaches*, pp. 365–411. Oxford University Press, New York.

Seely, R. H. 1986. Intense natural selection caused a rapid morphological transition in a living marine snail. *Proc. Natl. Acad. Sci. USA* 83: 6897–6901.

Slobodkin, L. B., F. E. Smith and N. G. Hairston. 1967. Regulation in terrestrial ecosystems, and the implied balance of nature. *Amer. Nat.* 101: 109–124.

Sousa, W. P. 1979a. Disturbance in marine intertidal boulder fields: The non-equilibrium maintenance of species diversity. *Ecology* 60: 1125–1239.

Sousa, W. P. 1979b. Experimental investigations of disturbance and ecological succession in a rocky intertidal community. *Ecol. Monogr.* 49: 227–254.

Stephenson, T. A. and A. Stephenson. 1972. *Life between Tidemarks on Rocky Shores.* Freeman, San Francisco, CA.

Strauss, S. Y. 1991. Indirect effects in community ecology: Their definition, study and importance. *Trends Ecol. Evol.* 6: 206–210.

Sutherland, J. P. 1974. Multiple stable points in natural communities. *Amer. Nat.* 108: 859–873.

Underwood, A. J. 1978. The refutation of critical tidal levels as determinants of intertidal communities on British shores. *J. Exp. Mar. Biol. Ecol.* 33: 261–276.

Underwood, A. J. 1979. The ecology of intertidal gastropods. *Adv. Mar. Biol.* 16: 111–210.

Underwood, A. J. 1985. Physical factors and biological interactions: The necessity and nature of ecological experiments. In P. G. Moore and R. Seed (eds.), *The Ecology of Rocky Coasts*, pp. 372–390. Hodder and Stoughton, London.

Underwood, A. J. 1995. Ecological research and (research into) environmental management. *Ecol. Appl.* 5: 232–247.

Underwood, A. J. and E. J. Denley. 1984. Paradigms, explanations and generalisations in models for the structure of intertidal communities on rocky shores. In D. R. Strong, Jr., D. Simberloff, L. G. Abele and A. B. Thistle (eds.), *Ecological Communities: Conceptual Issues and the Evidence*, pp. 151–180. Princeton University Press, Princeton, NJ.

Underwood, A. J. and P. Jernakoff. 1984. The effects of tidal height, wave-exposure, seasonality and rocky-pools on grazing and the distribution of intertidal macroalgae in New South Wales. *J. Exp. Mar. Biol. Ecol.* 75: 71–96.

Velimirov, B. and C. L. Griffiths. 1979. Wave-induced kelp movement and its importance for community structure. *Botanica Marina* 22: 169–172.

Vermeij, G. J. 1978. *Biogeography and Adaptation. Patterns of Marine Life*. Harvard University Press, Cambridge, MA.

Vitousek, P. M., H. A. Mooney, J. Lubchenco and J. M. Melillo. 1997. Human domination of Earth's ecosystems. *Science* 277: 494–499.

Wertheim, A. 1984. *The Intertidal Wilderness*. Sierra Club Books, San Francisco.

Wethey, D. S. 1985. Catastrophe, extinction, and species diversity: A rocky intertidal example. *Ecology* 66: 445–456.

Williams, G. A. 1993. Seasonal variation in algal species richness and abundance in the presence of molluscan herbivores on a tropical rocky shore. *J. Exp. Mar. Biol. Ecol.* 167: 261–275.

Witman, J. D. and K. R. Grange. 1998. Links between rain, salinity, and predation in a rocky subtidal community. *Ecology* 79: 2429–2447.

Wolcott, T. G. 1973. Physiological ecology and intertidal zonation in limpets (*Acmaea*): A critical look at "limiting factors. " *Biol. Bull.* 145: 389–422.

Wootton, J. T. 1993. Indirect effects and habitat use in an intertidal community: Interaction chains and interaction modifications. *Amer. Nat.* 141: 71–89.

Wootton, J. T. 1994. Predicting direct and indirect effects: An integrated approach using experiments and path analysis. *Ecology* 75: 151–165.

Wootton, J. T. 1997. Estimates and tests of per capita interaction strength: Diet, abundance, and impact of intertidally foraging birds. *Ecol. Monogr.* 67: 45–64.

Yodzis, P. 1988. The indeterminacy of ecological interactions as perceived through perturbation experiments. *Ecology* 69: 508–515.

Young, C. M. 1987. Novelty of "supply-side" ecology. *Science* 235: 415–416.

Young, C. M. 1990. Larval ecology of marine invertebrates: A sesquicentennial history. *Ophelia* 32: 1–48.

chapter 10

Soft-Sediment Communities

Hunter S. Lenihan and Fiorenza Micheli

Marine sediments cover over 80% of the ocean floor thus, creating one of the largest habitat types on earth. Organisms associated with soft sediments range in size from bacteria to bottom-feeding whales, but benthic biomass is dominated by macrofaunal (>0.5 mm) invertebrates, mainly various species of polychaete worms, crustaceans, echinoderms, and molluscs. These animals are morphologically and behaviorally adapted to live in the three-dimensional and fluid sedimentary environment. They also have profound influences on the physical, chemical, and biological structure of their sedimentary surroundings. The most outstanding feature of soft-sediment invertebrate communities is that individual abundance, biomass, and species composition vary greatly with both time and space.

Communities of soft-sediment organisms often provide important ecological goods and services (Peterson and Lubchenco 1997). For example, many fisheries target commercially valuable crabs, shrimps, and bivalves. Soft-sediment animals also recycle nutrients, detoxify pollutants, and represent important trophic links in coastal and estuarine ecosystems. For example, shallow-water species, including worms, amphipods, and clams eat allochthonous inputs of carbon and graze benthic algae and bacterial communities. In turn, the invertebrates are essential food for larger invertebrates (crabs, shrimps, and octopi), fishes, and marine mammals (sea otters, walrus, and gray whales) (Peterson and Quammen 1982; Fukuyama and Oliver 1985; Oliver and Slattery 1985; Kvitek et al. 1992; Micheli 1997). On exposed intertidal soft bottoms, birds and terrestrial mammals, including black bears, foxes, and raccoons, regularly forage (Botton 1984; Luckenbach 1984; Quammen 1984; Daborn et al. 1993; Peterson, in press; Figure 10.1). The profusion of benthic-pelagic and marine-terrestrial trophic links reveal that soft-sediment

communities provide important energy pathways in the marine coastal ecosystems (Tenore and Coull 1980; Grebmeier 1988, 1989; Graf et al. 1992).

Some of earliest quantitative ecological studies were conducted on marine soft-sediment communities by Petersen (1918, 1924), who was the first to describe species composition in terms of the relative abundance of individuals rather than just presence and absence (Nybakken 1997). Over the last 75 years, soft-sediment community ecology has evolved from simple observations of community composition to investigations of general mechanisms and processes that explain the distribution and abundance of species. We now recognize that soft-sediment ecosystems are driven by complex interactions among oceanographic processes, organic inputs and their utilization by benthic populations, and hydrodynamic and sedimentary conditions (Barry and Dayton 1991; Snelgrove and Butman 1994). Abiotic disturbances and biotic interactions also influence other processes in soft-sediment communities, especially recruitment, growth, survivorship, and fecundity (Peterson 1979; VanBlaricom 1982; Butman 1987; Ambrose 1991; Wilson 1991a; Woodin 1991; Bertness and Calloway 1994; Hall 1994; Olaffson et al. 1994; Bruno and Bertness, this volume).

Reviews of soft-sediment community ecology published during the last 50 years have covered a wide spectrum of ecological perspectives. Reviews have examined animal–sediment relationships (Gray 1974, 1981; Rhoads 1974; McCall and Tevesz 1982; and see Watling 1991), hydrodynamic processes (Nowell and Jumars 1984; Butman 1989; Barry and Dayton 1991), feeding behavior (Fauchald and Jumars 1977; Levinton 1977, 1979; Lopez and Levinton 1987; Jumars and Wheatcroft 1989; Lopez et al. 1989; Shimeta and Jumars 1991; Fréchette et al. 1993), and benthic-pelagic coupling (Mann 1980; Bonsdorff and Blomqvist 1993; Wildish and Kristman-

Temperate latitudes

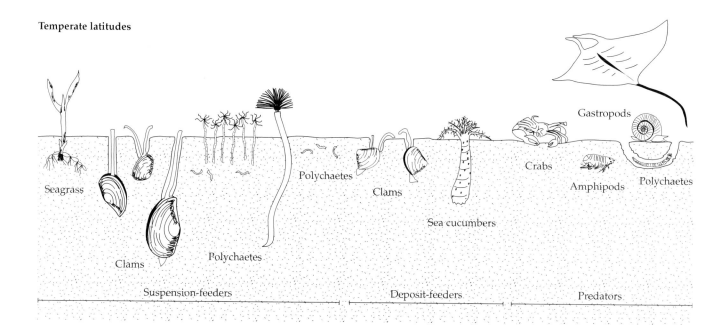

Polar latitudes

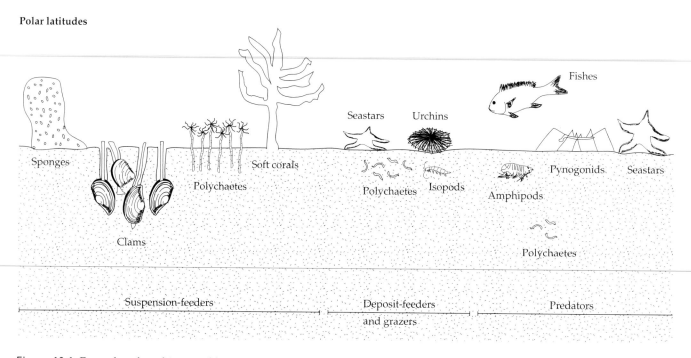

Figure 10.1 Examples of trophic assemblages in temperate and polar latitude marine soft-sediment habitats.

son 1997). One of the earliest reviews (Thorson 1950) analyzed settlement and recruitment processes. Other important reviews of soft-sediment systems have examined biotic interactions (Reise 1978, 1985; Kneib 1991; Peterson 1991; Sousa 1991), experimental methodology (Arntz 1977; Virnstein 1978; Dayton and Oliver 1980; Hurlberg and Oliver 1980; Peterson and Black 1994; Aronson and Heck 1995; Micheli 1996), and abiotic/biotic disturbances (Rhoads et al. 1978; Baker 1980; Capuzzo and Kester 1987; Hall 1994; Dayton et al. 1995; Newell et al. 1998). Here we draw on these reviews and many

other published papers to provide a general synthesis of the key biological and physical processes that regulate community composition and dynamics in the marine sedimentary environment.

Coastlines, coastal waters, estuaries, continental shelves, and the deep sea contain soft-sediment habitats. In this chapter, we concentrate on soft-sediment communities in all environments but the deep sea (see Etter and Mullineaux, this volume). The two major goals of our review are to establish the relative importance of different ecological processes operating at various spatial and temporal scales and to identify the most pressing questions in marine soft-sediment community ecology. After describing the general composition and biogeography of soft-sediment communities, we examine how pelagic and benthic primary productivity, and allochthonous inputs of organic matter influence secondary production in soft-sediment communities. We explore how organisms are influenced by and modify the physical and chemical properties of sediments, thereby creating community patterns. We review the role of recruitment in structuring communities and examine how biological interactions, specifically predation, competition, parasitism, and positive interactions (including ecosystem engineering), regulate communities. We discuss how biotic and abiotic disturbances affect community processes, including patterns of recolonization and community succession. Along the way, we attempt to identify major questions that should guide future research in marine soft-sediment habitats.

GENERAL COMMUNITY PATTERNS

There are an estimated 500 thousand to 10 million species of soft-sediment macrofauna worldwide (Snelgrove 1998). The actual number of species is unknown because only a small portion of the seafloor has been sampled. The dominant taxa are from the class Polychaeta, subphylum Crustacea, and phyla Echinodermata and Mollusca (Nybakken 1997). Cnidarians, such as soft corals and anthozoans, also inhabit soft bottoms. These animals live in intertidal (beaches, sand flats, and mudflats) and subtidal environments (estuaries, shallow offshore areas, and continental shelves), within (infauna) or on top (epifauna) of sediments and range in mobility from completely sessile to highly mobile. Soft-sediment invertebrates occupy almost every trophic level in marine ecosystems.

The most abundant macrofaunal group is composed of polychaete worms, which burrow through sediments or erect tube structures that innervate or protrude from sediments. Polychaetes filter-feed (suspension feeders) particles suspended in the water column, eat detritus (deposit feeders), prey on other organisms, or utilize various combinations of different feeding modes. The most abundant macrofaunal crustaceans are ostracodes, isopods, amphipods, tanaids, and decapods. Harpacticoid copepods, usually designated as meiofauna (<0.5 mm), can be as large as some juvenile and adult macrofauna and can be extremely abundant in some areas. Crustaceans burrow through sediments, swim or scurry across its surface, build tubes, and exhibit all forms of feeding modes, including scavenging and parasitism. Echinoderms, such as asteroids (sea stars), brittle stars, sand dollars, sea urchins, and sea cucumbers, usually live on or near the sediment surface and exhibit most feeding modes. Soft-sediment molluscs include predatory, scavenging, or deposit-feeding gastropods, nudibranchs, and octopi that move over surface sediments, and suspension- and deposit-feeding bivalve clams that bury into sediments, feeding with siphons exposed on the sediment surface. Many cnidarians, including anemones also live in soft sediments, some anchoring to buried worm tubes. Figure 10.2 provides examples of various trophic groups found in soft sediments in temperate latitude and polar environments.

Soft-sediment macrofauna are often divided into groups according to the life-history strategies they exhibit during the recolonization of disturbances to the seafloor. Opportunistic species (MacArthur 1960) are so named because they are usually pioneers that first occupy a disturbed patch. Their rapid

Figure 10.2 Examples of sediment destabilizing ("bioturbating") stabilizing soft-sediment invertebrates. (After Nybakken 1997.)

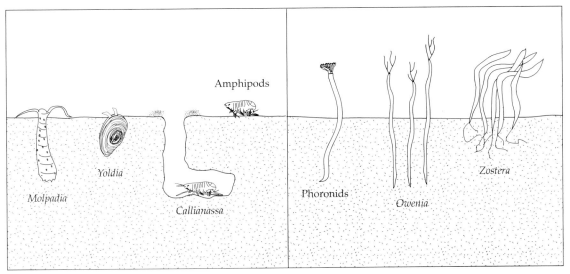

Sediment destabilizers
("bioturbators")

Sediment stabilizers

colonizing ability results from their life-history strategies. Opportunists are usually small, short-lived animals. They are often highly fecund, producing many eggs per female and several annual cohorts. Many opportunistic species have demersal, directly developing larvae that quickly colonize nearby sites (Grant 1981; Thistle 1981; see also Oliver 1984). Adults and juveniles of many opportunists readily emigrate from established populations and immigrate to disturbed patches (Levin 1981; Thrush et al. 1991; Commito et al. 1995). Other opportunistic species have planktonic larvae that are dispersed widely in high numbers (Grassle and Grassle 1974). These attributes permit opportunists to rapidly colonize proximal or remote disturbed areas in large numbers. Common species of opportunists are the polychaetes *Capitella capitata*, *Strebilospio benedictii*, *Scolelopis* spp., *Polydora* spp., and many from the dorvilleid group. Many nematodes, oligochaetes, and some molluscs, including the clams *Gemma gemma* and *Macoma* spp., and the gastropod *Hydrobia ulvae* also rapidly colonize disturbed areas.

Later successional species are represented by the bulk of soft-sediment taxon, but generally are larger, deeper living, and predatory or suspension-feeding species (Pearson and Rosenberg 1978). Most opportunistic species are poor competitors for food and space and do not possess advanced defenses against predators, so are easily displaced by the later-succession species (McCall 1977; Rhoads et al. 1978). Therefore, opportunistic species are often displaced by "transition" species with life-history traits intermediate between opportunists and late-successional species. The transition species are later replaced by species found in surrounding undisturbed patches, thereby completing a successional sequence.

Individual soft-sediment macrofauna often have dramatic impacts on sedimentary condition, including its organic content, morphology, grain size, water content, porosity, and chemical composition (Myers 1977a, b; Bender and Davis 1984; Weinberg 1988; Steward et al. 1992; 1996). In turn, changes in sedimentary properties caused by macrofauna often have dramatic impacts on community structure (Thayer 1983; Ricciardi and Bourget 1999). Consequently, soft-sediment macrofauna are often characterized by their effects on sediments. One group of animals, called sediment destabilizers or "bioturbators," cause sediments to move, be resuspended, or be eroded through their burrowing, digging, or feeding activities (see Figure 10.3). Bioturbators break up sediment aggregations, bury or resuspend surface sediments, and uncover, oxygenate, and irrigate deeper sediments. Bioturbation results from surface and subsurface movement, the excavation of burrows, and digging for prey by epifaunal or demersal predators (Gray 1974; Carney 1981; Rhoads and Boyer 1982; Thayer 1983). In contrast, sediment stabilizers are animals that create structures within or above the sediment surface that bind sediment or slow the flow of water, thereby baffling flow and decreasing hydrodynamic shear stress on the bottom (Fager 1964; Eckman et al. 1981; Fonseca et al. 1982; Luckenbach 1986). Baffling and reduced shear stress decreases sediment resuspension and creates higher deposi-

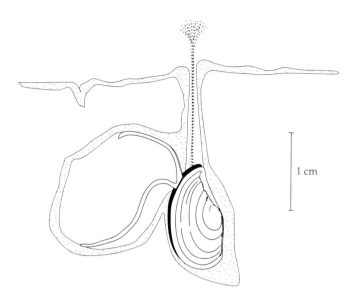

Figure 10.3 Example of a bioturbating infaunal clam (*Mya arenaria*). This animal deposit feeds and then ejects sediment onto the sediment surface (After Bender and Davis 1984.)

tion. Some sediment stabilizers also produce copious amounts of fecal pellets that bind or "pelletize" sediments thus increasing effective grain size and making the sediment surface more rigid. Another group of animals modifies subsurface sediments through irrigation, usually by creating tubes or burrows in which water is circulated, thereby flushing and oxygenating subsurface sediments and transporting metabolites and other chemical constituents (Hughes 1969; Aller and Yingst 1978; 1985).

Biogeography

The species composition of soft-sediment habitats varies substantially at large spatial scale across latitudes (Dayton 1990; Alongi 1990). Although most phyla and many families are represented at all latitudes, different phyla usually dominate at different latitudes. Nevertheless, the various trophic types (e.g., deposit feeders, scavengers, suspension feeders, algal grazers, and predators) are well represented worldwide, with taxonomically different but ecologically similar genera filling identical niches at different latitudes. All ancestors of most contemporary species probably originated from the circumtropical Tethys Sea and radiated poleward during the Miocene (Alongi 1990). This poleward movement of species is likely responsible for the considerable degree of longitudinal species homogeneity observed today within each latitude.

Latitudinal differences in benthic communities have been generated by evolutionary changes brought on by the movement, transport, isolation, and mixing of species caused mainly by ocean circulation patterns and tectonic activity. The proximal factors causing the evolutionary changes are mainly spatial and temporal variation in hydrographics (temperature, salinity, and dissolved oxygen concentration), hydrodynamics (horizontal and vertical mixing), primary production, geological processes affecting terrestrial runoff, Aeolian deposition, sedimentation, and many smaller-scale abiotic factors and biotic interactions. To date, we know relatively little about the oceanographic and ecological processes that have regulated communities over geological time scales (e.g., Tevesz and McCall 1983).

TROPICAL COMMUNITIES. The largest marine biogeographic region is the tropics, which contains about 40% of the world's open ocean area and 30% of the world's continental shelf areas. Temperate latitudes contain about 35% of the open ocean and 45% of the world's continental shelves, and polar latitudes contain the remaining 25% of both environments. The widest variations in soft-sediment faunal densities and the highest diversity of species occur in the tropics, coinciding with the greatest variety of microhabitats and environmental conditions (Alongi 1990). The highest levels of macroinvertebrate densities and production also occur in the tropics, especially near upwelling areas (Cushing 1988). However, very high abundances and production also occur in some temperate estuaries and Antarctic benthos (Barry and Dayton 1991).

As in other latitudes, tropical soft-sediment fauna varies with water depth and microhabitat. Intertidal habitats include sandy (quartz and/or carbonate) beaches, and sand and mudflats inhabited by *Donax* spp. (Bivalvia), *Emerita* spp. (Crustacea), various amphipods (e.g., haustorids), and polychaetes. Many of the same genera are found on temperate latitude beaches, but temperate beaches usually have greater faunal diversity, longer-lived species, and greater stability of faunal composition than tropical beaches (McLachlan and Jaramillo 1995). Tropical sand flats are dominated by gastropods such as *Cerithidea* spp., which is also common in temperate sand flats. Tropical mudflats support communities of various polychaete species (e.g., *Lumbrinereis*), fiddler crabs (*Uca* spp.), and gastropods (e.g., *Stenothyora* sp.). Temperate mudflats support many of the same phyla or ecological equivalents, for example the gastropod *Hydrobia* spp. Mean density and species diversity within estuaries and lagoons are usually lower in the tropics than at temperate latitudes because the tropical systems experience extremes in salinity, sedimentation, erosion, oxygen concentration, and nutrients associated with monsoons.

Many tropical plants and animals create biogenic structures in intertidal and subtidal areas inhabited by unique assemblages of invertebrate, fish, and algal species. Like temperate salt marshes, tropical marshes are inhabited by many species of polychaetes, epibenthic and infaunal molluscs, and crustaceans. Mangroves support infaunal communities as well as epibionts that encrust mangrove roots. Mangrove sediments support infaunal communities, which have relatively low abundance (<1000 individuals m^{-2}) due to the negative effects of polyphenolic compounds derived from mangrove roots and bark. Mangrove sediments generally have low interstitial dissolved oxygen concentrations caused by high deposition of organic matter. Tropical subtidal bottoms also contain a wide variety of biogenic structures, such as seagrass

(*Halodule* spp. and *Thalassia* spp.) beds, mangroves, coral reefs, algal stands, and polychaete reefs and tube mats that support a plethora of invertebrate and vertebrate species (Alongi 1990). Tropical subtidal soft sediments are usually dominated by decapod crustaceans, isopods, and bivalves, whereas in temperate latitudes, shallow-water sediments are often dominated by gastropods, clams, and polychaetes (Nybakken 1997). Sediments associated with coral reefs have very high total abundance (e.g., 3,115–43,690 m^{-2}) and species diversity of macroinvertebrates because they are protected within lagoons and are rich in micro- and macroalgae and plant detritus. In contrast, carbonate sediments are common in the tropics and support depauperate infaunal communities largely because this sediment type is either highly compacted (chalks), thereby preventing burrowing, or is very fine grained (oozes), thereby reducing oxygen diffusion. Carbonate sediments are usually dominated by epifauna and foraminiferans (Alongi 1990).

At all latitudes, temporal and spatial variability in community patterns on ecological time scales is driven mainly by variation in primary production, sediment type, disturbances, and biotic interactions. Due to high riverine inputs of organic materials, or, in other areas, high levels of benthic primary production resulting from high irradiance and water clarity, the tropics contain sediments that have the highest organic contents on earth (tropical lagoons and mud banks). Yet, carbonate sediments, present where nutrient availability is low, have the lowest organic carbon content and in situ primary production of any shallow-water sediment type (Alongi 1990). In general, tropical sediments have more mud and coral than other latitudes; temperate climates have more sand than other latitudes, and polar seas contain mostly gravel and rock, except in arctic regions subject to riverine deposition.

Community structure in the tropics is controlled by a suite of unique disturbances (see Table 10.1). In the wet tropics, the benthos is subjected to radical seasonal changes in salinity due to monsoonal rains and high levels of freshwater runoff from rivers, which also cause high sedimentation. In the dry tropics, where rainfall is sporadic, high temperatures, evaporation, and precipitation are major factors influencing intertidal and shallow subtidal habitats. In contrast, large-scale spatiotemperal differences in temperate benthos are driven largely by variation in pelagic and benthic primary production (Barry and Dayton 1991). Salinity and temperature extremes in the tropics also create highly stratified conditions leading to estuarine conditions in coastal waters and low oxygen concentrations near the seafloor in shallow water. In contrast, upwelling, storms, and tidal currents generated by tropical monsoons destroy stratification through mixing, thereby oxygenating bottom water and producing high rates of sediment deposition.

POLAR COMMUNITIES. Except for latitudinal position, low temperatures, and seasonal trends in sea ice and irradiance, soft-sediment communities of the Arctic and Antarctic vary dramatically (Dayton 1990). This is largely due to differences in

TABLE 10.1 Environmental and ecological factors influencing soft-sediment communities at different latitudes other than general level of primary production and sediment type.

		Polar	
Tropics	Temperate	Arctic	Antarctica
Coastal development	Coastal development	No permanent ice shelves	Permanent ice shelves
Fishing	Fishing	Little seasonality in pack ice	High seasonality in pack ice
Pollution	Nutrient loading	Limited connection with Pacific Ocean, but much larger connection with Atlantic Ocean	Free connection with major oceans
Monsoonal rains	Hypoxia/anoxia	Broad, shallow continental shelves	Deep, narrow continental shelves
High temperatures	Pollution	Pronounced stratification	No pronounced stratification
Hypersaline conditions	Biotic invasions	Low nutrient concentrations in euphotic zone	High nutrient levels in euphotic zone
Carbonate sedimentation/ compaction		Moderate primary production	Extremely high primary production
Low/variable oxygen concentrations		Riverine deposition of sediments	No riverine inputs of sediments (glacial)
Low/variable nutrient concentrations		Large recent changes in temperature	High degree of stability in marine climate (last 200 years)
Chemical defenses by plants			
Massive riverine sedimentation			
Formation/erosion of mudbanks			

physiography, evolutionary history, terrestrial influences, oceanographics, and primary production (Table 10.1). The Arctic Ocean is an enclosed basin and the Antarctic waters surround a continent. The Arctic Ocean has a constant influx of species from the Pacific Ocean and Atlantic Ocean through the restricted Bering (70 m depth) and Fran (400 m depth) Straits. In contrast, the Antarctic benthos has been isolated oceanographically for about 25 million years. Most paleoecologists now believe that Antarctic species have diverged from a relatively few original species. Continental shelves in the Arctic are wide and shallow and subjected to high levels of freshwater runoff causing stratification and estuarine conditions. In contrast, the Antarctic has narrow, deep shelves and no riverine runoff, and stratification is limited due to substantial wind and thermohaline mixing. High water clarity, mixing, and upwelling cause high primary production in Antarctic surface waters as well as substantial particle and organic carbon delivery to the shallow and deep benthos.

Variation in disturbance regimes also underlies much of the differences in benthic communities between the Arctic and Antarctic (Table 10.1). The Arctic benthos is subjected to a wider variety of disturbances than the Antarctic because of scouring from land-fast ice, extremes in salinity due to riverine runoff in summer (very low salinity), and the sinking of brine (salinity of 80–180 psu) produced during surface water freezing. Both polar systems are subjected to disturbances caused by grounding of icebergs (Lenihan and Oliver 1995; Conlan et al. 1998; Figure 10.4), but the Arctic benthos has a greater variety of biotic disturbances. The biological activities of fishes,

crabs, and bottom-feeding mammals (seals, walruses, and whales) disturb Arctic soft sediments, but similar disturbances are not found in the Antarctic ecosystem (Dayton 1990).

The Arctic marine ecosystem is divided into four major zones, the Beaufort Sea, Bering/Chukchi Seas, Soviet Arctic, and Eastern Canadian Arctic. Soft-sediment community composition differs greatly among these regions because of differences in climate, biotic invasions, riverine runoff (and, therefore, sedimentation, circulation, and primary production), and ice conditions (Dayton 1990). Nevertheless, soft-sediment fauna in each region is characterized by substantial depth zonation. Shallow areas (0–10 m) are usually very low in biomass and species richness due to scouring by land-fast ice. These depths often support chironomid larvae and highly mobile amphipod and isopod scavengers. At greater depths (10–30 m), biomass and species richness increase due to the presence of kelp, associated herbivorous species (mysids, amphipods, isopods, and euphausids), benthic fishes, suspension-feeding clams (*Hiatella* and *Mya* are common genera) and soft corals, and predatory crabs. Some areas support only sea urchins and coralline algae barrens. Offshore communities are characterized by ophiuroids, echinoderms, holoturians, crinoids, and scallops.

Unlike most other Arctic regions, the Bering/Chukchi Seas have very high primary production in the surface water that has been linked to high biomass in benthic communities (Grebmeier et al. 1988, 1989). For example, high primary production levels in the Chukchi Sea support large populations of clams, that, in turn, sustain a large walrus population (Oliver

Figure 10.4 Iceberg gouging of seafloor in the Arctic and Antarctic. This is a widespread disturbance influencing communities in polar latitudes. (From Conlan et al. 1998.)

et al. 1984). High primary production supports large beds of ampeliscid amphipods in the Bering Sea that, in turn, supports California grey whale populations (Oliver et al. 1985). High production in soft-sediment communities also sustains large tanner, king, and snow crab populations, which provide important fisheries. Arctic mammals eat about $9–10 \times 10^6$ metric tonnes of nekton and benthic spp. annually, which is about four times the catch of all commercial fisheries.

Communities with perhaps the highest macrofaunal abundance (>130,000 individuals m^{-2}) and biomass (> 1 kg m^{-2}) on earth are found in Antarctic soft sediments (Dayton and Oliver 1977; Dayton 1990). This is largely due to very high primary production, high rates of sinking of organic material due to mixing, physical stability caused by ice cover and no riverine runoff, and relatively low levels of biotic disturbances (i.e., Antarctica has no crabs, large fishes, skates, rays, sharks, or bottom-disturbing mammals). The flux of phytoplankton to the seafloor is so high in some places that it can sustain large populations of suspension feeders (e.g., siliceous sponges 3 m in diameter) in complete darkness. High fluxes of phytoplankton-derived organic matter to benthic communities is subsidized by ice algae (diatoms) that grow abundantly on the underside of sea ice and benthic diatoms. High primary production in general is caused by in large part by high irradiance (i.e., a lack of heavy snow cover) and nutrient availability.

Species diversity in the Antarctic is relatively high because of a high degree of endemism and subsequent species radiation. Unlike the Arctic, there is a characteristic circumcontinental fauna that is dominated by macroinvertebrate species. Soft-sediment communities are composed of many species of sponges, bivalves (<400 species), and cnidarians, although there are fewer polychaetes, crustaceans, and echinoderms than in the Arctic (Dayton 1990). Antarctic benthos varies spatially with changes in organic inputs and rates of sinking and upwelling, rather than exhibiting the dramatic depth zonation observed in Arctic (but see Dayton et al. 1969, 1970; Lenihan and Oliver 1995).

TEMPERATE COMMUNITIES. Most of the research in soft-sediment community ecology has been conducted in temperate latitudes community types. Early studies by Petersen (1918, 1924) conducted throughout north temperate seas to evaluate whether benthic animals supported commercial fish populations found that continental shelves were occupied by recurrent groups of invertebrate species. Petersen's work and similar studies that followed (Ford 1923; Davis 1925; Jones 1950) were synthesized by Thorson (1957), who recognized that similar sediment types and water depths throughout temperate latitudes were occupied by seven ecologically and taxonomically similar groups of species. Thorson called these "parallel bottom communities" after their dominant species. The seven community types were: (1) communities dominated by *Macoma* (Bivalvia) species, found in sheltered water to about 60 m depth; (2) *Tellina* (Bivalvia) communities found in shallow (< 7 m water depth), sandy bottoms; (3) *Venus* (Bivalvia) communities found in deeper (7–40 m), but still sandy, substrata; (4) *Abra* (Bivalvia) communities found in organic muds of estuaries and other sheltered habitats; (5) *Amphiura* (Polychaeta) communities found in muddy/silty sediments over a broad depth range (15–100 m); (6) *Maldana* (Polychaeta)/*Ophiura* (Ophiuroida) communities that replace *Abra* communities in soft muds; and (7) amphipod-dominated communities like the *Pontoporeia*/*Ampelisca* communities located patchily in muddy areas. The existence of such geographically discrete community types is now strongly doubted. More objective and quantitative sampling methods have shown that "typical" assemblages of species used to characterize specific community types usually grade smoothly into other species assemblages. Intermediate combinations of species are the rule rather than exception. For example, in sandy protected bays, *Macoma* communities often grade into Phoronid-Nudibranch dominated communities, which then grade into callianassid-shrimp dominated communities (Ronan 1978). In general, marine benthic species appear to be distributed in relation to the requirements and fate of individual species rather than as discrete assemblages sharing common responses to specific environmental conditions. Many other key examples of temperate soft-sediment community ecology are presented in the following discussion.

PRIMARY PRODUCTION AND BENTHIC COMMUNITIES

Marine benthic community processes depend heavily on the nature, amount, and predictability of organic carbon inputs and their utilization by benthic organisms. Generally, benthic secondary production is controlled by allochthonous inputs of organic matter, although energetic requirements can be supplemented with in situ benthic micro- and macroalgal primary production in shallow waters. Organic matter in the form of phytoplankton, or residual material (e.g., marine snow, zooplankton feces, and bacteria) generated by zooplankton grazing, decomposition, and other processes in the water column, are the major food source for most soft-sediment deposit feeders, suspension feeders, herbivores, and detritivores. The level of benthic primary production or supply of allochthonous organic material to the seafloor is usually a function of water column productivity, water depth, and various transport mechanisms (Barry and Dayton 1991; Dauwe et al. 1998).

Benthic-Pelagic Coupling

Over deeper portions of continental shelves, in situ benthic photosynthesis is missing and the soft-sediment animals are supported by pelagic production and by detritus originating from coastal areas (Grebmeier et al. 1988, 1989). Average input of organic carbon from the water column onto continental shelves in temperate latitudes is about 100 g C m^{-2} (<25 g C m^{-2} near edge of shelf and >300 g C m^{-2} in some upwelling zones). Important factors controlling the amount of material reaching the seafloor are (1) the depth of the water column, (2) the magnitude of pelagic production, and (3) the sinking rates and the intensity of vertical mixing (Barry and Dayton 1991). Pelagic primary production is spatially heterogeneous at the level of ocean basins: it varies with latitude, climate, and circulation patterns. There is usually strong temporal variability in primary production in temperate and polar latitudes, with the highest production occurring during spring blooms, when wind mixing, temperature, and light availability are highest (Parsons et al. 1984). Open tropical waters are less productive and temporally heterogeneous than temperate and polar waters because high thermal stratification in surface layers of tropical waters generally prevents the upwelling of nutrients from deep water (Lalli and Parsons 1993). Estuaries throughout the world support some of the highest primary production in marine waters mainly because they are shallow and have high nutrient inputs (Kennedy 1980).

On very large spatial scales (10,000 km^2), secondary production of soft-sediment communities is closely linked to the primary productivity in the overlying water column because the deposition of organic carbon (e.g., dead organisms and fecal material) to the seafloor provides plentiful food supplies (Pearson and Rosenberg 1978; Barry and Dayton 1991).

Macrofaunal biomass is usually low under central ocean gyres where primary production is low, but is high under mid-to-high latitude gyres and continental shelves where productivity is high. Macrofaunal biomass is often very high on continental shelves beneath upwelling zones, and in estuaries, where primary (and secondary) productivity in the water column is high (Thiel 1978; Kennedy 1980; Dunbar 1981; Grebmeier et al. 1988, 1989). In areas with high deposition of organic carbon, soft-sediment communities contain high densities of deposit-feeding species that support predatory and scavenging species. Suspension feeders are found in bottoms with both low and high supplies of organic matter, but usually in areas with relatively high flow speeds and delivery rates of suspended particles.

The linkage between water column productivity, organic carbon deposition, and macrofaunal secondary production is a form of benthic-pelagic coupling (Graf 1992). Dayton and Oliver (1977) studied one of the best examples of benthic-pelagic coupling in McMurdo Sound, Antarctica. They found that the biomass, abundance, and species diversity of soft-sediment communities within the usually ice-covered McMurdo Sound varied according to localized inputs of organic carbon. The organic carbon was produced in plankton blooms occurring in the nearby open waters of the Ross Sea. On the "eutrophic" side of McMurdo Sound, a region bathed by currents flowing in from the Ross Sea, there was high carbon input to the seafloor, resulting in high biomass and high species diversity in benthic communities (Table 10.2). Eutrophic regions of McMurdo Sound were characterized by communities with high densities of late-successional species, mostly deposit feeders, predators, and suspension feeders. Oligotrophic regions were bathed by nutrient-poor currents coming from the beneath the massive Ross Ice Shelf. Organic carbon input to the seafloor was low, resulting in depauperate benthic communities with relatively low species abundance and diversity. The oligotrophic communities were comprised of relatively low densities of species with opportunistic life histories and sparse populations of long-lived suspension feeders (clams and soft corals).

Benthic Primary Production

In shallow water depths (<150 m), soft-sediment animals graze micro- and macrobenthic algae. Benthic unicellular and filamentous algae can live on or in the surface layers of the sediment where the photic zone extends down to the substratum. There, production ranges about 0.2–1.3 g C m^{-2} per day in temperate latitudes, depending mainly on water clarity (MacIntyre et al. 1996). Mat-forming species are usually confined to relatively stable sediments, and sands support small microalgal species, especially diatoms and dinoflagellates, that attach to or live between sand grains. Macroalgal production is very high in some areas (e.g., kelp in temperate latitudes), and macroalgae provide food for a large suite of grazers, especially various species of amphipods and sea urchins (MacIntyre et al. 1996). However, grazing of macroalgae is often limited by the production of secondary metabolites that act as chemical defenses against herbivores (Hay

TABLE 10.2   Number of organisms in different microfaunal taxa per m². Data are from the Ross Sea and McMurdo Sound, Antarctica; the Gay Head–Bermuda transect (22); and two temperate embayments, one in California (23), the other in Massachusetts (24).

| Taxon | Gay Head—Bermuda transect | | McMurdo Sound | | | | | | | | Temperate embayments | |
| | | | West Sound | | | | McMurdo Sound | East Sound | | | | |
	D #1 (487 m)	G #1 (2086)	Ross Sea (74° 58'S, 170° 48'E) (500 m)	Garwood Valley (30 m)	Ferrar Glacier (30 m)	New Harbor (30 to 40 m)	Marble Point (30 m)	McMurdo Station Jetty (20 m)	Cape Armitage soft bottom (20 m)	Cape Armitage sponge mat (30 m)	Elkhorn Slough, Calif. (5 m)	Barnstable Harbor, Mass. (intertidal)
Ostracoda	0	0	70	18	110	132	6,586	948	55	4,354	21	0
Cumacea	7	6	40	55	367	885	2,150	31,548	12,950	937	41	0
Tanidacea	154	58	25	73	239	282	579	19,932	53,512	69,596	0	150
Isopoda	63	67	43	18	110	132	1,185	23,392	19,399	33,285	0	150
Amphipoda	507	123	56	184	294	207	3,059	11,728	9,975	8,432	14	43,350
Other arthropods	4	0	16	55	37	55	55	0	496	6,282	48	0
TOTAL ARTHROPODA	735	254	250	403	1,157	1,693	13,614	87,548	96,387	122,886	124	43,650
TOTAL MOLLUSCA	2,388	175	560	128	184	1,102	184	136	770	7,660	6,407	27,600
Polychaeta	4,956	1,418	1,070	1,598	3,896	4,718	27,142	11,276	52,134	9,500	9,506	9,050
Other vermes[a]	149	261	70	55	147	2,060	3,913	19,752	6,281	5,735	68,672	150
TOTAL VERMES	5,105	1,679	1,140	1,653	4,043	6,778	31,055	31,028	58,415	15,235	78,178	9,200
Echinodermata	32	31	8	0	0	0	0	0	0	0	0	0
Miscellaneous[b]	393	15	2	0	643	463	441	0	0	0	0	0
TOTAL	8,653	2,154	1,960	2,184	6,027	10,036	45,294	118,712	155,572	145,781	84,709	80,450
NUMBER OF SAMPLES	1	1	6	3	3	5	2	10	2	2	8	?

From Dayton and Oliver 1977. Depths at which samples were collected are in parentheses.

[a]"Other vermes" includes all other soft-bodied worms, such as Nemertea, *Edwardsia*, Phoronidae, and Oligochaeta.

[b]"Miscellaneous" includes Porifera, Bryozoa, Ascideae, and Cnidaria.

and Fenical 1989; and see Woodin et al. 1993). Benthic algae can usually photosynthesize over a much wider range of light intensities than planktonic species and rely in part on nutrient fluxes from sediments.

Benthic microalgae are grazed by meiofauna and macrofauna, including crustaceans, polychaetes, echinoderms, and gastropods. When resuspended by currents, algae and deposited organic matter can provide important food sources for suspension feeders (Bricelj et al. 1984; Muschenheim 1987; Emerson 1990). Benthic microalgae are also important food resources for deposit feeders. For example, the patchy distribution and growth rates of the deposit-feeding worm *Leitoscolopis fragilis* are associated with the patchy distribution of benthic diatoms (Bianchi and Rice 1988). Differences in light levels and grazing pressure by other infauna could not account for variation in the distribution of diatoms. Instead, positive interactions between the worm and diatoms explained their relationship. Diatoms were controlled by worm grazing and by ammonia flux from sediments. Ammonia flux was greater in patches of worms because worm excrement increased ammonia concentrations, the sediment grain size was greater due to bioturbation and fecal pellet production, and the sediment was more porous because it was constantly reworked. Therefore, diatom growth was greater among worms, and worm growth rates were higher in patches of high worm and diatom density.

ANIMAL–SEDIMENT RELATIONSHIPS

The characteristics of marine sediment, including its organic content, grain size, chemical properties, stability, and porosity, have major influences on benthic macrofauna. Early studies describing large-scale community patterns related community composition mainly to sediment grain size and/or carbon content (e.g., Petersen 1918, 1924; Ford 1923; Thorson 1957; Sanders 1958). These early studies prompted a plethora of successive studies that related soft-sediment community composition with sediment type (Rhoads and Young 1971; Gray 1974, 1981; Rhoads 1974; Thiel 1978; Whitlach 1977, 1981). We now realize that soft-sediment organisms also have profound influences on surrounding sediments through bioturbation (McCall 1977; Brenchley 1981), the creation of biogenic structures (Fager 1964; Bailey-Brock 1979; Eckman et al. 1981), and biogeochemical processes (Aller and Yingst 1978, 1985). We also recognize that physical factors, especially hydrodynamics, can control interactions between soft-sediment organisms and sedimentary conditions (Emerson 1990; Snelgrove and Butman 1994; Lenihan 1999).

Origin and Characteristics of Marine Sedimentary Habitats

The composition and distribution of marine sediments is determined by sedimentary sources, chemical binding and modification of minerals, hydrodynamic conditions, and biological activity. Marine sediments are composed mainly of loosely arranged inorganic particles, created from the deposi-

tion of terrigenous sediments and the siliceous or carbonate remains of plankton and nekton. Terrigenous and planktonic particles deposit in estuaries, on coastlines and continental shelves, and across the deep ocean. On continental slopes, accumulation of sediments often creates unstable masses that result in submarine slumps and turbidites (Kennett 1990). On wind- and wave-exposed coastlines, sediments create highly mobile sandy beaches and dunes (Brown and McLachlan 1990). Marine sediments range from fine muds, composed of particles less than 0.05 mm in diameter, to coarse sands, composed of particles up to 1.0 mm in diameter. The unconsolidated muddy and sandy particles are constantly set in motion by the movement of water and/or wind, thus creating dynamic habitats that change rapidly in their physical and chemical composition over both time and space (Dyer 1986).

On small spatial scales, the local distribution of sediments is largely determined by hydrodynamics, especially in shallow water (Miller et al. 1977; Grant 1983; Sternberg 1984; Grant and Madsen 1986). Horizontal flow across the bottom (boundary layer flow) creates hydrodynamic shear stress that lifts sediment into suspension, thus eroding sediment patches, depositing sediment elsewhere, and creating a seafloor that is topographically rough (Nowell and Jumars 1984; Figure 10.5). At low flow speeds, rates of sediment deposition are usually greater than rates of resuspension and transport, so the bottom is usually covered with muddy or fine sandy sediments. In moderate flow, fine sediments are lifted and resuspended above the bottom, and coarser sediments are left behind. In very high flow, whole sections of the bed are transported along the bottom (bedload transport) leaving behind bare substratum, deeper layers of hypoxic/anoxic sediment, or only large, heavy particles.

Over large spatial scales, variation in sediment deposition and hydrodynamics interact to create vastly different habitat types that are occupied by different groups of organisms. Water depth is also important, as it influences sedimentation patterns, hydrodynamic conditions, and, subsequently, the composition of local species (Sternberg 1984). In bays and lagoons there is usually a large supply of fine-grained sediments from creeks, rivers, and salt marsh habitat. Coastal embayments often contain intertidal mudflats that are characterized by slow-moving tidal currents that deposit mainly fine sedi-

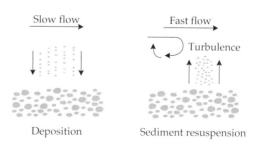

Figure 10.5 Effect of different flow speeds on sediment particles on soft bottoms. Deposition occurs in low flow, and sediments are resuspended in high flow.

ments (Kennedy 1980). Intertidal mudflats are habitat to small surface and subsurface deposit-feeding and / or tube-building polychaetes, deposit-feeding gastropods and bivalves, and bioturbators, such as hemichordates, sipunculids, and holothurians. These animals find plentiful organic carbon supplies in muddy sediments or in flux above sediments to grow and reproduce. In areas exposed to exposed currents and waves, such as intertidal sand flats and subtidal soft bottoms located offshore, sediments are more coarse and sandy than sediments in protected areas. These areas are exposed to faster flow speeds that resuspend and transport fine particles but leave larger grained sediments. Well-flushed sediments are often occupied by large, long-lived suspension-feeding clams that dig deeply into the shifting sediments, as well as sponges, hydroids, bryozoans, or sea lilies that use their fanlike tentacles to filter particles from the passing current. Coarse, wave-exposed sediments are also home to a myriad of mobile scavenging and predatory invertebrates, such as amphipods, starfish, crabs, and shrimp.

Biogeochemistry

Marine sediments can be kilometers thick, but all but the top few decimeters are inhospitable to organisms. As organic matter settles on the seafloor, it is buried by further sedimentation and decomposed by bacteria. Oxygen is used by aerobic bacteria where it is available, but where it is unavailable, bacteria utilize other oxidized inorganic and organic compounds (e.g., nitrates, sulfates, and phosphates), thus producing ammonia, hydrogen sulfide, ferrous ions, and other toxic reduced compounds and molecules (Fenchel and Riedl 1970). Anoxia and sulfides form in sediments where microbial oxygen consumption exceeds oxygen replenishment. Therefore, most marine sediments are too low in oxygen and too high in toxic chemicals for most soft-sediment invertebrates. However, many animals make the sediment habitable by irrigating subsurface sediments, and changing sediment grain size, porosity, stability, and deposition rate. Consequently, soft-

sediment residents change the profiles, fluxes, and diagenesis of chemicals in marine sediments.

Between aerobic surface sediments and deeper anaerobic sediments lies a zone of rapid chemical transition in which O_2, CO_2, NO_x, pH, and Eh (redox potential) change rapidly (Fenchel and Reidl 1970; Figure 10.6). This layer, called the redox potential discontinuity layer (RPD), is often delimited by changing sediment color from yellow, oxygenated sediment, to gray sediments where oxygen concentration drops and Eh changes rapidly, to a black, anoxic, and sulfidic layer. The depth of the RPD depends on the quantity of organic material available, the rate of decomposition, oxygen utilization and supply rates, grain size, and flow speed of water. On protected, muddy shores, where sediments are fine and little transport of water through sediments occurs, the RPD can be within a few mm of the sediment surface. In coarser-grained sediments, water easily penetrates sediments allowing oxygen to diffuse to depths of 30–50 cm, thereby replenishing oxygen utilized by the benthos through respiration.

Soft-sediment animals also greatly influence the chemical properties of sediments. For example, many deep-burrowing infauna live in subsurface sediments below the RPD layer (i.e., in anoxic sediments) primarily to escape predators. To maintain a sufficient oxygen supply, these animals must somehow irrigate their burrows by circulating water. Irrigation not only creates vertical and horizontal gradients in pore water oxygen levels, but it also produces a significant amount of spatial (and temporal) variability in the distribution of reduced and oxidized chemical compounds. For example, Aller and Yingst (1978) showed that the terebellid polychaete *Amphitrite ornata* (8–10 cm long) creates U-shaped burrows into which the worm draws oxygen. The supply of oxygen-rich water to subsurface sediments oxidizes reduced hydrogen and metal sulfides in the burrow walls and increases fluxes of NH_4^+, HPO_4^+, FeS, and other sulfates into the burrow water. Irrigation by *Amphitrite* also increases the rates and spatial heterogeneity of chemical fluxes to the overlying

Figure 10.6 Changes in physical and chemical properties of sediments across the redox discontinuity layer. (After Fenchel and Riedl 1970.)

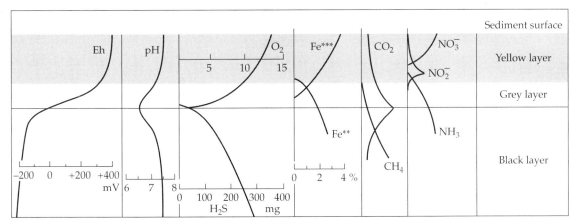

water column. Similarly, sediments in areas occupied by the irrigating and bioturbating polychaete worm *Heteromastus filiformis*, and bivalves *Macoma balthica* and *Tellina texana*, have 20–30% greater fluxes of NH_4^+ than areas without these species (Aller and Yingst 1985). Species that irrigate sediments also increase the abundance of aerobic bacteria in subsurface regions, thereby increasing food resources for many other meiofaunal and macrofaunal species (Fenchel 1978).

Sediment–Animal Interactions: A Shifting Paradigm

A major question in marine benthic ecology is whether sediment characteristics per se cause variability in soft-sediment communities or whether the many physical (e.g., hydrodynamics, disturbance, and sedimentation) and biological (e.g., bioturbation, stabilization, and chemical cycling) factors that underlie variation in sediment conditions ultimately drive community patterns. Many studies have correlated community composition with sediment characteristics. For example, Sanders (1958) examined the distribution of intertidal soft-sediment communities in Buzzards Bay, Massachusetts, and found that deposit feeders dominated mud and muddy sands, and suspension feeders dominated sandy sediments. Similar correlations were subsequently found in other locations (e.g., Whitlach 1977; Brown 1982). In a recent synthesis, Ricciardi and Bourget (1999) found strong correlation between intertidal sediment grain size and patterns of community composition on a global scale. Using regression analyses, Ricciardi and Bourget related variability in global patterns of intertidal soft-sediment community biomass to a suite of physical factors (air and water temperature, sediment grain size, intertidal slope, tide range and type, wave height, and exposure). Differences in grain size explained the largest percentage (44%) of total variance in intertidal soft-sediment communities. They also found that biomass peaked in temperate latitudes where suspension feeders were dominant (>30–60% of macrofaunal biomass). Although this synthesis does not explain causation of community patterns, it identifies their most important correlates.

Simple correlations between the spatial distribution of trophic groups (i.e., feeding modes) and sediment type provided the basis for a more mechanistic understanding of animal–sediment relationships. For example, Whitlach (1981) showed that the spatiotemporal variability in communities of deposit feeders was driven mainly by spatial and seasonal changes in total carbon content (TOC) of sediments. Species abundance was positively correlated with the amount of surficial organic carbon, and species diversity was positively correlated with the diversity of sediment and food particles (Figure 10.7).

One of the major paradigms in soft-sediment ecology concerns the relationship of trophic groups and sediment grain size. Using experimental manipulations of infauna in muddy Buzzards Bay, Massachusetts, Rhoads and Young (1970) showed that deposit feeders and suspension feeders rarely overlapped in space probably because resuspended sediments tended to clog the filtering apparati of suspension feed-

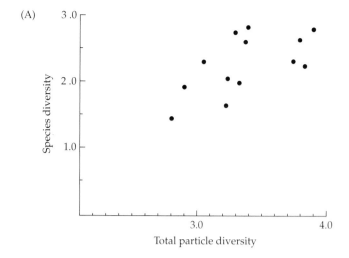

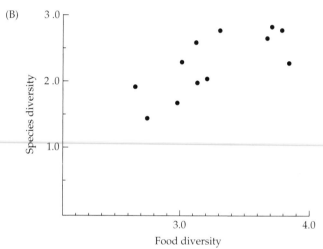

Figure 10.7 Relationships between deposit-feeder species density and sedimentary total particle diversity and food particle diversity. (After Whitlach 1981.)

ers and bury their newly settled larvae. They called this form of species interaction Trophic Group Amensalism (TGA) and proposed it as a general mechanism explaining trophic-group segregation shown in other studies (Rhoads and Young 1971; Rhoads 1974). Similar interactions among feeding guilds were hypothesized to drive community patterns in sandy sediments (Myers 1977b; Posey et al. 1991). The idea of TGA was expanded by Aller and Dodge (1974), who showed that the activity of deposit-feeding infauna in patches of carbonate sediments in tropical lagoons increased sediment suspension rates and loading, thereby reducing the growth and diversity of suspension feeders, including corals. TGA subsequently became a major paradigm of soft-sediment ecology.

Many studies provided counterexamples of TGA. For example, the deposit-feeding polychaete *Clymenella torquata* reduces the quantity of particulate organic matter at the sediment-water interface and increases concentrations of dissolved nutrients (nitrate, ammonia, silicate, and phosphate) in overlying water (Weinberg and Whitlach 1983). Increased fluxes of nutrients enhanced productivity of benthic microalgae, which when resuspended by current or bioturbation, increased the food supply and growth of the suspension-feeding clam *Gemma gemma*. Commito and Boncavage (1989) found that beds of suspension-feeding mussels (*Mytilus edulis*) on a soft bottom habitat facilitated the recruitment of the deposit-feeding oligochaete *Tubificoides* sp. by creating structural refuge from disturbance and predation. Based on previous studies and a group of manipulative experiments, Wilson (1981) refined the TGA hypothesis by showing that differences among species, including their relative and absolute body sizes, their relative mobility, and specific biological impacts on sediments, predict species distribution in soft sediments better than simple, general differences between trophic groups. Brenchley (1981), using a suite of elegant experiments (species exclusions and inclusions), also provided evidence that trophic-group segregation was due in large part to interspecific differences in relative mobility. She showed that species of suspension and deposit feeders bioturbate and resuspend sediments through their movement, thus reducing the density of tube-building species, but not other burrowers. Biotic sediment disturbances by mobile species caused a shift in the overall trophic composition of the community, specifically by increasing the relative numbers of suspension feeders and subsurface deposit feeders.

In a review of animal–sediment relationships, Snelgrove and Butman (1994) list four reasons why TGA may not be a universal process structuring soft-sediment invertebrate communities. First, many subsequent observations since Rhoads and Young (1970) do not support TGA because deposit and suspension feeders often co-occur. Second, many field studies have also shown that deposit feeders are not restricted to muddy sediments and suspension feeders to sandy sediments. Third, many clam and polychaete species are actually facultative suspension feeders that switch between deposit and suspension feeding depending on hydrodynamic conditions (Taghon et al. 1980; Levinton 1991; Peterson and Skilleter 1994). For example, *Macoma* spp. (Bivalvia) switch from deposit feeding to suspension feeding in high flow because most organic particles are suspended above the bottom (Levinton 1991). Therefore, categorizing animals into simple feeding groups is often incorrect. Finally, there is little evidence for the generalization that muddy sediments are detrimental to larval and adult suspension feeders in the presence of deposit feeders.

Snelgrove and Butman (1994) argue that associations between animal groups and sediment types are not caused by sediment characteristics per se but by physical processes that produce particular sedimentary conditions. They explained that boundary layer hydrodynamics are the most influential factors because they control, among other things, grain-size distribution, total sediment organic content (TOC), oxygen diffusion through sediments, and patterns of larval settlement and subsequently recruitment. For example, correlations between sediment grain size and macrofaunal distributions may often result from the passive settlement of both sediment particles and larvae. In contrast, TOC, which varies as function of flow speed and bottom topography, attracts many actively settling larvae and migrating adults of both deposit and suspension feeders (Lopez and Levinton 1987). The exchange of pore waters and subsequent profile of oxygen and sulfides in sediments is also closely related to the near-bed flow regime and the composition of the macrofaunal community (Ray and Aller 1985).

Physical processes associated with water flow apparently play a key role in structuring soft-sediment community at local scales, both directly and indirectly, through modification of the sediment characteristics and through their effects on behavior. For example, Grant (1983) compared the effects of tidal currents and biological activity (excavating by rays, sediment ingestion and defecation by a hemichordata, sediment displacement by a burrowing haustorid amphipod, and deposit feeding by an infaunal polychaete) on sediment reworking in a tidal sand flat. He showed that tidal forces had a much greater impact on bed transformations and sediment movement than biological processes on small and medium spatial scales. As discussed earlier, hydrodynamics also contribute to creating soft-sediment community patterns over regional scales by influencing both the patterns of primary productivity in the water column and the deposition of particulate organic carbon to the seafloor, and the transport and delivery of larvae to the seafloor.

RECRUITMENT

Understanding and predicting the spatial and temporal changes in natural populations and communities depends in part on understanding processes that regulate recruitment (Underwood and Denley 1984; Connell 1985; Gaines and Bertness 1992; Connolly and Roughgarden 1999). Recruitment is usually defined as the arrival of new individuals (recruits) to a population or community and has three components: supply of recruits, settlement, and recruit survival after an arbitrary period of time (usually hours to weeks). Recruits can be larvae, juveniles, or emigrating/immigrating adults (Palmer et al. 1996). Variability in recruitment can control community composition and dynamics for invertebrates in rocky intertidal habitats (Underwood and Denley 1984; Roughgarden et al. 1988; Gaines and Bertness 1992) as well as for fishes on coral reefs (Doherty and Williams 1988; Sale 1991) and in pelagic systems (Cushing 1971). A major question in benthic community ecology is, Does recruitment regulate the species composition and dynamics of soft-sediment communities (Olafsson et al. 1994)?

Many soft-sediment invertebrates have complex life cycles that include (sometimes multiple) planktonic larval stages that are transported in the water column (Young 1990; Eckman 1996) by currents. Planktonic larvae spend hours to weeks in the water column traveling only a few cm to thousands of km before settling to the seafloor and metamorphosing into juveniles. Still other species have direct development in which juveniles disperse from the adults, usually only over short distances (Palmer et al. 1996). Some infaunal poly-chaetes also reproduce asexually by releasing segments of their bodies that disperse and settle elsewhere (Oliver 1984). There are many subtle variations to these reproductive strategies (Young 1990), but all strategies provide a means of dispersal. Dispersal is also accomplished by the emigration and immigration of adults (Huffaker 1958; Committo et al. 1995).

Factors that govern recruitment in marine benthic invertebrates vary across spatial scales. However, hydrodynamics seem to be important at all scales. At very large spatial scales (100–1000 km), variation in larval availability to a given region results from spatial and temporal changes in ocean circulation patterns, vertical mixing, stratification, and turbulence (Eckman 1996). These factors control the geographic variation in the abundance, distribution, and survival of planktonic larvae and explain why different ocean basins and water depths support different community types. Hydrodynamic factors also control the direction and velocity of larval dispersal and the water depth at which they are transported, as well as their concentration and patchiness. If larvae are not transported to a suitable settlement site before some critical time limit, it may be too late for successful settlement and metamorphosis, as the larvae may starve (Young 1990). In addition, the longer larvae spend in the water column, the greater the probability of mortality due to predation, disease, or parasitism. Hydrodynamics also influence the growth and survival of planktonic larvae by influencing food availability (e.g., by controlling production and concentration of phytoplankton and organic matter), temperature, salinity, and the abundance of potential predators and competitors (Scheltema 1986).

Large-scale variation in larval distributions, recruitment patterns, and resulting community patterns are also caused by human activities. Larvae of many species are transported long distances in the ballast water of ships or associated with aquaculture species, such as oysters and mussels. Exotic species can reach remote regions where they establish themselves and sometimes drastically alter community structure (Stenek and Carlton, this volume). For example, when the Japanese oyster, *Crassostrea gigas,* and Atlantic oyster, *Crassostrea virginica,* were introduced to the west coast of the United States, several species of spionid polychaetes, the clam *Gemma gemma,* and tanaid crustaceans were also introduced. These species now dominate many intertidal soft-sediment habitats from Baja California, Mexico, to Washington (H. Lenihan, personal observations). Dense assemblages of the tube-building spionid worms and tanaids now provide an abundant food source for native rays and skates.

On a much smaller scale (mm to cm), recruitment is controlled largely by the interaction of hydrodynamics and larval behavior. Characteristics of flow near the seafloor, including velocity, turbulence, and their effects on particle transport, control whether larvae actually contact the sediment, remain where they first settle, and survive (Butman 1987; Eckman 1990). Where larvae come into contact with the bottom is often a function of horizontal and vertical flow velocity and larval swimming speed because many larvae either act as passive particles or swim too slowly to choose the actual settlement site (Hannan 1984). For many larvae, actual settlement is a matter of choice. Some larvae begin a swimming descent to the bottom in response to chemical cues (Pawlik 1992). Once larvae come into contact with the bottom, they choose to settle based on sediment grain size (Butman et al. 1988; Woodin 1991), food availability (Taghon et al. 1980), presence/absence of conspecifics or enemies (Highsmith 1982), and interactions among these factors (Pawlik and Butman 1993; Turner et al. 1995). Whether a larva actually remains at an optimal settlement site is dependent again on hydrodynamics (Butman et al. 1988). If the level of shear stress and drag on a larva or surrounding sediment is too great, the larva may tumble along the bottom or be resuspended. Flow can also transport sediments that bury and kill settling larvae.

Highsmith (1982) provided an elegant example of how various chemical, physical, and biological factors interact to influence the recruitment of the sand dollar *Dendraster excentricus* in shallow subtidal regions of the Washington coast of the United States. The sand dollar is a gregarious settler that recruits in higher numbers among adults than outside sand dollar beds. Sand dollar larvae are attracted to adults because of chemical cues the adults emit. Once near the adults, the larvae can easily settle and remain because the adults baffle flow. Survival and therefore recruitment is higher within conspecific beds than outside of them because the adults protect the larvae from potential predators and stabilize sediments. This interaction of larval behavior, hydrodynamics, and biotic elements maintains highly aggregated and patchy distributions of adult populations and helps determine the overall species composition of relatively large patches of subtidal soft bottoms.

At intermediate scales (m–km), hydrodynamic factors, sediment properties, and biotic interactions are all important in regulating recruitment. Flow velocity, flow direction, and turbulence strongly interact with the spacing of adults to determine the probability of gamete fertilization during spawning (Denny and Shibata 1989; Eckman 1996). Following fertilization, or release of larvae by adults, hydrodynamic factors, especially sea surface slope, tidal pressure gradients, surface stress from wind fields, bottom shear stress, vertical eddy diffusivity, and turbulent mixing, along with swimming behavior, control larval dispersal in the water column (Eckman 1996). During the settlement phase, hydrodynamics influence the concentration of larvae in flow (due to turbulent mixing), their delivery to seafloor (through horizontal and vertical transport), and their survival through the affects on organic material (food) deposition, sediment chemistry (e.g., concentrations and fluxes oxygen and hydrogen sulfide), and sediment movement. Geological and hydrodynamic conditions that control sediment deposition, grain-size distribution, porosity, and stability affect the spatial and temporal distribution of sediment types that, in turn, affect larval choice, growth, and survival. Other hydrodynamic factors, such as upwelling intensity, long shore currents, eddy formation around topographic features (e.g., headlands; Rankin et al. 1994), and variability of local circulation influence larval abundance, dispersal, and settlement on intermediate spatial scales. Smaller topographic features (e.g., worm tubes, burrow openings, and mollusc shells) also tend to increase settlement rates for many species because these structures create small-scale eddies that entrain and increase the vertical delivery of particles to the seafloor (Eckman et al. 1981; Snelgrove et al. 1993; Breitburg et al. 1995; Lenihan 1999). Finally, early postsettlement mortality is regulated in part by hydrodynamics as they control sediment movement, food availability, and grain size (Eckman 1983; 1996; Butman 1987; Roughgarden et al. 1988; Lenihan 1999).

Pre- and Postsettlement Processes: Which Dominate?

The relative importance of pre- or postsettlement processes in determining community variation on intermediate time and spatial scales is hotly debated. Olafsson et al. (1994) compared the relative importance of settlement, recruitment, and biotic interactions in soft-sediment communities and found that (1) the abundance of larvae in the water column is rarely correlated with settlement or recruitment patterns; and (2) populations and communities are rarely limited by rates of recruitment. Instead, they found that postsettlement processes, especially adult–larval interactions (Woodin 1978) and predation on juveniles and adults, "dominate the generation of population and community patterns in soft sediment habitats." However, work subsequent to Olafsson et al. (1994) has provided evidence that recruitment processes can regulate some populations and communities. For example, Peterson et al. (1996) showed that the availability of bay scallop (*Argopecten irradians*) larvae likely controlled the recruitment and reestablishment of scallops in hydrographically isolated bays in which all scallops were killed by exposure to a red tide. This represents one of the few examples of recruitment limitation in soft-sediment communities. Other examples are likely to emerge with time and greater research effort.

It is probably too soon to judge whether pre- and postsettlement processes control population and community structure because we know relatively little about either process. First, the term *recruitment* has a rather vague definition because one of its components—settlement—is very rarely measured in an accurate manner (Snelgrove and Butman 1994). Many studies assume that recruitment is directly related to larval settlement, which in turn is related to larval availability, when in fact this scenario is unlikely. Due to technical constraints, very few studies have actually measured the link between larval availability in the water column and settlement rates (but see Powers 1997). Therefore, we understand so little about presettlement processes that to compare their relative contributions with those of postsettlement processes (e.g., predation, competition, and disturbance), for which a large amount of information is available, is an equivocal undertaking. Second, to measure recruitment one needs to know the actual settlement rate of larvae. Without knowing settlement rate, postsettlement mortality cannot be estimated accurately.

Yet, settlement rate has rarely been measured in soft-sediment habitats (Olafsson et al. 1994), so quantifying levels of actual postsettlement mortality is impossible. Research is needed to examine the links between larval availability, settlement, and recruitment in varying environmental conditions and for different taxonomic groups.

Emerging Role of Postlarval Dispersal

Many theoretical and empirical studies have demonstrated that dispersal is fundamental in regulating population and community dynamics in natural populations (Huffaker 1958; Menge and Sutherland 1987; Gaines and Bertness 1992; Palmer et al. 1996). In marine systems, there is growing evidence that postsettlement dispersal of juveniles and adult soft-sediment animals is a common phenomenon responsible for a constant flux of animals in and out of sediment patches (Thrush et al. 1996). Unlike organisms inhabiting hard substrate habitats, soft-sediment animals appear to be in constant flux. For example, S. P. Powers (unpublished data) has estimated that up to 5% of the total number of adults within a population of small infaunal species are being transported in the water column at any given time. Commito et al. (1995) showed that some species, such as the clam *Gemma gemma*, which broods its young, rely exclusively on the movement of juveniles and adults within sediments for dispersal. Many other species rely on postsettlement dispersal. Studies of postsettlement dispersal processes are needed in soft-sediment community habitats, especially because infaunal communities are likely to vary substantially over intermediate spatiotemporal scales due entirely to postrecruitment dispersal dynamics. One important research need is to determine the role of hydrodynamic factors in regulating the distribution of species, sedimentary conditions (e.g., resuspension and bedload transport), and interactions between the two.

BIOTIC INTERACTIONS

Local biotic interactions play a key role in organizing soft-sediment marine communities. A plethora of studies have examined the effects of predation, competition, biotic disturbance, and habitat amelioration by habitat-forming organisms (e.g., seagrasses, salt marshes, and reef-building polychaetes and bivalves) on soft-sediment communities. Much less is known about the role of disease and parasitism and about how different types of biotic interactions act jointly to shape soft-sediment benthos. Together with physical disturbance, predation is probably the main process maintaining high variability in the distribution of organisms in marine soft sediments (Peterson 1979; Olafsson et al. 1994). In contrast, direct competition for space or food appears rarely important in soft-sediment marine communities. More commonly, species compete indirectly, through modification of the physical environment. A prevalent form of such biological disturbance is the enhanced mortality of newly settled individuals caused by bulldozing and sediment disturbance by adult deposit feeders. Finally, positive interactions, and particularly the modification of the physical environment by habitat-forming species, such as seagrasses, salt marsh plants, and biogenic reefs, can be powerful structuring forces in some communities. In the following sections, we review the available information on different types of biotic interactions among soft-sediment animals, specifically predation, competition, biotic disturbances, disease and parasitism, and positive interactions.

Predation

Predators often have large impacts on soft-sediment populations and communities (Peterson 1979; Reise 1985; Wilson 1991a). Predatory impacts tend to vary depending on the depth in the sediments at which organisms live and where predators are most efficient. Woodin (1983) classified predators of soft-sediment organisms into categories depending on their position and effects within sediments. *Surface predators*, such as many species of birds, crabs and fish, prey at or near the sediment surface consuming whole animals or only parts of their prey such as tentacles or siphons ("browsers" or "nippers"; deVlas 1979; Peterson and Quammen 1982). Surface predators can only consume shallow-living prey, and thus their feeding activity tends to depress abundances of shallow species but not of species that can burrow deeper in sediments (Virnstein 1977; Blundon and Kennedy 1982; Eggleston et al. 1992). *Burrowing predators*, such as some sea stars and nemertean worms, move down tubes and burrows of the prey to attack them. *Digging predators*, including some crabs, rays, and horseshoe crabs, excavate through the sediments to obtain their prey. Burrowing and digging predators have impacts deeper in sediments than do surface predators. In addition, digging predators influence communities indirectly by disrupting sediments and causing incidental mortality of nonprey species. For example, some large epibenthic predators (e.g., crabs, rays, sea stars, flatfish, and sea otters) that feed on deep-burrowing clams dig large pits that cause the incidental mortality of other infauna and contribute to spatial patchiness within infaunal communities.

Infaunal predators that live within sediments at all times can also play an important role in structuring soft-sediment communities (Ambrose 1986, 1991). For example, experimental manipulations conducted in tidal flats in Maine, showed that the large predatory polychaete *Nereis virens* causes reductions of 30–96% of other infaunal species (Commito 1982a; Ambrose 1984a, b). In contrast, a co-occurring predatory polychaete, *Glycera dibranchiata*, caused 40–75% increases in some infaunal taxa by negatively affecting the density of *N. virens* (Ambrose 1984b). Predator-prey interactions between epibenthic and infaunal predators can result in one of the few tritrophic food-web interactions documented for soft-sediment marine communities (Ambrose 1984a). For example, gulls feed preferentially on large infaunal predatory polychaetes, thereby keeping them in check and decreasing their impact on smaller members of the infaunal community (Ambrose 1984a, c; 1991).

Interactions among soft-sediment animals of different size classes and life-history stages apparently have important community impacts, especially on recruitment. Watzin (1983) found that macrofauna larval and juvenile recruits are in the same size category as meiofauna. Using a manipulative field experiment, she found that tubullarians and other meiofauna reduce the densities of juvenile spionid polychaetes and several other species of polychaete deposit feeders by preying on the new recruits. The effect of meiofaunal predators on macrofaunal recruitment was species specific. Meiofaunal presence had no negative effects on neried polychaetes, other predatory macrofaunal recruits, and bivalves, but increased the density of other infauna such as syllid polychaetes. Biotic interactions among different among life stages of organisms is probably important in determining community patterns, but has rarely been studied.

Different predatory guilds vary in their impacts depending on the depth in the sediments where they are able to feed; their day-night, tidal, and seasonal activity patterns; and their choice of different habitat types, prey species, and sizes (Quammen 1984; Wilson 1991a; Micheli 1997). Quammen (1984) conducted one of the few studies that has attempted to separate and directly compare effects of different predatory guilds on soft-sediment communities. Using cages designed to selectively exclude different predatory guilds, Quammen was able to separate the effects of birds, crabs, and fishes on tidal flat communities. Her results showed that crabs had the strongest impact on infaunal communities and fishes the least impact. The effects of birds were variable and depended on habitat type (i.e., sandy or muddy flats). Using cages with varying mesh size, Reise (1978) found that small predators, such as shrimp and gobid fishes, had stronger effects on infauna than large predators such as flatfish and birds.

To date, very few studies have focused on the foraging behavior of marine predators as a means of understanding the mechanisms causing variability in predatory impacts on benthic communities. Micheli (1997) investigated the foraging behavior of blue crabs, *Callinectes sapidus*, on the hard clam, *Mercenaria mercenaria*, in a North Carolina lagoon. She found that the impacts of blue crabs on clam populations varied among water depths, habitat types, and seasons because these factors controlled the density of clams and blue crabs and the avoidance behavior of blue crabs from crab-eating gulls. In particular, blue crabs preferred to feed within salt marsh vegetation than in unvegetated sand flats because the vegetation provided cover from the predatory birds. Thus, the spatial and temporal variabilities in the predatory impacts of crabs on infaunal prey were explained by the predators' foraging choices.

The impacts of predators are most commonly examined using cages or fences that exclude predators in a nonselective manner (i.e., exclusion studies) or by including some predators, particularly those that are expected to have the greatest impact on the community (i.e., inclusion studies) (reviewed by Olafsson et al. 1994). Analyses of caging experiments indicate that epibenthic predators can exert strong control on faunal abundance and biomass in intertidal and shallow-subtidal soft sediments (Peterson 1979). In 44% of the intertidal and shallow-subtidal studies synthesized by Olafsson et al. (1994), infaunal abundances increased by a factor of two or more following exclusion of large epibenthic predators. Similar results were observed in inclusion studies. Increased abundance following predator exclusion was less pronounced in deep- (> 2 m) than in shallow-water habitats (Olafsson et al. 1994). This result may indicate that predation is relatively more important in structuring soft-sediment communities in shallow than deep soft-sediment sediments.

The prevention of competitive exclusion is an important mechanism by which predation (and physical disturbance) maintains species diversity in communities inhabiting rocky substratum (Paine 1966; Dayton 1971; Connell 1975). Predators on hard substrata remove competitive dominants, thereby freeing space for the colonization of subdominants. In contrast, predators in soft sediments have no clear effect on species diversity; predation either decreases species richness or does not affect it (Peterson 1979). The lack of clear predation effects on diversity may be due to the absence of competitive exclusion in soft-sediment habitats (see section on Competition). In contrast to hard substratum, inferior competitors in soft sediments can find spatial refuge deeper in sediments, and so are not excluded from an area (reviewed by Olafsson et al. 1994). Predators appear to structure soft-sediment communities by directly removing prey, not through complex interactions involving competition for space.

General conclusions about the affects of predation in marine soft sediments are tainted by potential artifacts associated with using cages. Cages placed in unvegetated bottoms add structure to an otherwise structureless seafloor and, therefore, may influence infaunal communities by (1) decreasing hydrodynamic disturbances of sediments (Dayton and Oliver 1980; Levin 1984); (2) reducing current velocities, thereby enhancing larval settlement in cages (Hurlberg and Oliver 1980); (3) baffling flows and enhancing the deposition of fine organically rich particles that are food for and attract deposit feeders (Olafsson et al. 1994); and (4) by modifying animal behaviors, particularly in inclusion studies, where the incarceration of mobile consumers may induce behavioral artifacts (Hall et al. 1991). Partial cages, measurements of sediment grain-size composition and organic contents, and comparisons of experimental results across habitats characterized by different flow regimes have been used as means of teasing apart caging artifacts from actual effects of predators on infaunal communities (Olafsson et al. 1994). In general, these studies have concluded that most of the observed effects of caging on infaunal communities can be attributed to manipulation of predator access, but the assessment of caging artifacts is still incomplete (Hall et al. 1991).

Experimental manipulation of predator access to soft-sediment communities, for example by using cages, is the only way to establish a direct cause-effect relationship between predation and community changes of the infauna. However, results from manipulative experiments may be biased by caging artifacts (see previous). Moreover, caging experiments are typically conducted at scales of a few meters or less and

are maintained for a few weeks or months. Comparisons conducted across habitat types and over multiple years provide insight into processes occurring over greater and often more relevant spatiotemporal scales. However, between-habitat comparisons may also be confounded by a suite of factors and processes unique to each habitat in addition to structural complexity. Therefore, such broad comparisons and correlative studies do not allow one to establish cause-effect relationships. Example of such "natural experiments" are: (1) comparisons of predation effects between unvegetated soft sediments and adjacent biogenic habitats (e.g., Woodin 1978; Summerson and Peterson 1984); (2) correlative studies relating long-term trends in the abundance of predator and prey species (e.g., Beukema 1987); and (3) large-scale comparisons between areas with different abundances of predators (e.g., Kvitek et al. 1992).

Comparisons of predation effects between unvegetated soft-sediment communities and adjacent vegetated habitats (e.g., seagrass, salt marsh, and kelp) generally indicate that predators have a greater impact in the absence of biogenic structure, possibly because structure interferes with consumers' foraging efficiency. For example, variation in predator success likely explains lower abundance, biomass, and diversity of infaunal communities in unvegetated versus than in nearby seagrass meadows (Orth et al. 1984; Summerson and Peterson 1984). Increased infaunal abundance and biomass were also observed within patches of onuphid polychaete tube mimics than in surrounding, unstructured sediments because tubes interfere with foraging by portunid and horseshoe crabs (Woodin 1978). Thus, emergent vegetation and other biogenic structures appear to act as natural predator-exclusion "experiments" and produce enhanced infaunal abundance and diversity similar to what observed in caging experiments. Of course, deductions about the effects of predation inside and outside of structures are confounded by the effects structures have on hydrodynamics, sedimentation, larval settlement, and recruitment.

Long-term correlative studies have also provided indirect evidence that predators can control infaunal populations. One of the best examples comes from long-term (18 years) data from a Wadden Sea tidal flat, showing that the biomass of the polychaetes *Scolopls armiger* and *Heteromastus filiformis* tends to decrease in correspondence to biomass increases of their predator, the polychaete *Nephtys hombergii*, and vice versa (Beukema 1987). Seasonal or year-to-year variation in predation intensity may also occur because of episodic predation that accompanies the "stopover" of migratory birds and fishes or high-recruitment years of crustacean and fish predators (Orth 1975; Raffaelli and Milne 1987).

Episodic predation events can have significant consequences for infaunal populations and communities (Schneider and Harrington 1981; Raffaelli and Milne 1987; Wilson 1991b), although effects are often difficult to quantify using small-scale caging experiments because of high spatial and temporal variability in predation impacts (Sewell 1996). Sewell suggested using sampling designs developed for detecting environmental impacts (e.g., BACI) to study the impact of invasions by predators, such as the seasonal stopover of migratory shorebirds in intertidal flats. However, the effects of episodic predation by migratory species are sometimes so dramatic that methodology becomes nearly irrelevant. For example, seasonal migration of rays in Chesapeake Bay reworks large areas of the sediments causing dramatic destruction of seagrass habitat and reductions in infaunal organisms (Orth 1975). In summary, episodic predation events can play an important role in maintaining spatial and temporal variability of soft-sediment communities, though effects are often difficult to document.

Large-scale comparisons of community patterns between areas characterized by different abundance and composition of predatory guilds have also been used to establish predation impacts at regional scales. For example, Kvitek et al. (1992) documented the impacts of sea otter foraging on soft-sediment communities along a gradient of sea otter densities in the Gulf of Alaska. Sea otters had been eliminated from most of the Alaskan coastline through hunting but had recolonized the Aleutian islands following protection provided by the International Seal Fur Treaty and the reestablishment of populations through the introduction of breeding adults. By comparing community structure between areas with or without sea otters, Kvitek et al. showed that sea otters control infaunal abundance and biomass. Sea otter predation reduced abundance of infauna, particularly large clams, but there was little overall change in infaunal community structure. As observed in small-scale caging studies, sea otter predation does not lead to competitive replacement of species and decreased diversity.

In conclusion, predation appears to influence marine soft-sediment communities at different scales, from local to regional, although relatively few studies have examined regional effects. In addition, the impacts of predators are fairly similar across different studies and spatial scales. Predators commonly decrease the abundance, biomass, and sometimes diversity of infaunal and epifaunal organisms. Nevertheless, several questions concerning the community impacts of predators are still unanswered. Although there is little doubt that predation can influence soft-sediment communities, little is known about how general these effects are and how they vary as a function of recruitment levels, abiotic factors, and human disturbances.

Competition

Competition for space has been documented in some soft-sediment communities, such as dense assemblages of tube-building polychates, displacing burrowing infauna (Woodin 1976). However, competition for space does not play as important a role in structuring soft-sediment benthos as in other marine habitats, such as rocky bottoms and coral reefs (Peterson 1979, 1991). Organisms living in soft sediments occupy a three-dimensional space, thereby minimizing opportunities for direct competition for space by living at different depths within sediments (Peterson 1979). In addition, soft-sediment

animals rarely displace or kill subdominants because there is no physical leverage in soft sediments to pry or bulldoze a competitor. Soft-sediment infauna also do not commonly attain densities high enough to render space limiting (Peterson 1979, 1991). Densities may be high and space may become limiting within dense assemblages of tube-building suspension feeders (Woodin 1976; Levin 1981; Brenchley 1982). For example, the distribution of tubes of the spionid polychaete *Pseudopolydora paucibranchiata* is maintained through direct interference (Levin 1981). In addition, aggressive interactions between *Pseudopolydora* and other local tube-building infauna result in reduced foraging time for individuals in this community (Levin 1982).

Although intra- or interspecific competitive interactions rarely result in overgrowth and death of competitive inferiors in soft sediments, competitive interference often results in density-dependent migration and reduced feeding and growth. Density-dependent migration is common among mobile deposit feeders living on or just below the sediment surface. For example, Ambrose (1986) found that emigration rates of the deposit-feeding amphipod *Rhepoxynius abronius* increased with density. Levinton (1979) showed that the deposit-feeding snail *Hydrobia ventrosa* used floating as a means of dispersing as density increased. Experimental manipulations conducted in Barnstable Harbor, Massachusetts, showed that the native mud snail, *Ilyanassa obsoleta*, emigrates from areas of high densities of the introduced snail *Littorina littorea* (Brenchley and Carlton 1983). Few examples of direct interference exist among infaunal deposit feeders (but see Byers 2000). Experimental manipulations of bivalve densities conducted by Peterson (1977) showed that vertical zonation of bivalves in Mugu Lagoon, California, is driven by competition for space. Experimental removals and additions of individuals from different depths caused changes in the abundance of other species. However, density manipulations of other bivalve communities failed to provide any evidence for spatial competition in soft-sediment communities. Even at densities eight times greater than ambient densities there was no evidence of increased mortality or increased migration of recruits for the bivalves *Protothaca staminea* and *Chione undatella* (Peterson 1982). Instead, crowding caused reduced growth of these two clam species.

Exploitative competition is more common than direct competition for space in soft-sediment communities. Intra- and interspecific competition through depletion of food resources is particularly well documented for suspension-feeding bivalves living in intertidal and shallow flats (Peterson 1982; Carlson et al. 1984; Peterson and Black 1987). For example, field measurements conducted in western Australia and in the Gulf of Maine show that suspension-feeding bivalves living at low tidal heights on sand flats deplete phytoplankton from the water, thereby decreasing food availability for organisms living at higher tidal elevations (Carlson et al. 1984; Peterson and Black 1987, 1991). Reciprocal transplants of individuals between different elevations showed that food depletion resulted in decreased growth at high elevations

(Peterson and Black 1987). Exploitative competition of a common resource (e.g., phytoplankton) is also the most likely mechanism underlying reduced bivalve growth at high densities (Peterson 1982; Peterson and Black 1987, 1993).

Exploitative competition and food limitation also occurs among deposit feeders. A suite of laboratory experiments conducted with single species has shown that food addition results in increased growth and fecundity of individuals (reviewed by Olafsson et al. 1994). Evidence of effects on whole communities from food addition experiments conducted in the field is less conclusive, partly because of the difficulty in maintaining target levels of food supply to the benthos under field conditions (e.g., Dauer et al. 1982). Addition of detritus resulted in increased densities of oligochaetes in a subtidal site of the Baltic Sea (Olafsson 1989) and in increased growth of the snail *Hydrobia totteni* in an intertidal site in Long Island, New York (Levinton 1985). In contrast, food addition had no effect on an intertidal infaunal community in Cape Cod, Massachusetts (Wiltse et al. 1984). Addition of organic fertilizer had also no effect on a subtidal soft-sediment community (Dauer et al. 1982), but fertilizer may have been washed away from experimental plots by currents.

Soft-sediment communities appear to be food limited at large spatial and temporal scales. Many correlative studies relate enhanced food supply to greater production of benthic infaunal communities (reviewed by Olafsson et al. 1994). The most convincing evidence comes from the dramatic changes in benthic biomass associated with human activities, specifically fisheries exploitation and anthropogenic nutrient enrichment to coastal waters. In the mid-1970's, the anchovy fishery off Peru collapsed following sustained overfishing. It has been hypothesized that increases in the biomass of benthic communities have resulted from a decrease in the abundance of planktivorous anchovies and subsequent increases of phytoplankton deposition on the seafloor (Murphy 1972; Rowe 1981). Anthropogenic eutrophication of coastal waters can influence both total benthic biomass and community composition. For example, long-term monitoring data from intertidal and shallow flats in the Wadden, Baltic, and North Seas show trends for increased abundance and biomass of infaunal communities in correspondence with increased nutrient loadings and enhanced primary productivity in several areas (Reise 1982; Pearson and O'Barnett 1987; Beukema 1991). Increased abundance and biomass were generally driven by small deposit-feeding polychaetes that tended to increase their abundance relative to crustaceans and echinoderms.

In conclusion, although competition for space and direct interference among infaunal organisms do not appear to play important roles in structuring soft-sediment communities, exploitative competition for limiting food resources may be an important process controlling standing stocks and community composition of benthic macrofauna at a variety of spatial and temporal scales. Yet, food limitation and competition for phytoplankton or detritus do not seem to result in the disappearance of species from a community or to the death of individuals within a population. Food limitation commonly has more subtle effects, such as reduction of growth and reproductive output. The relatively minor role played by direct competition for space in soft-sediment communities may explain the lack of species replacements following either bottom-up changes in resource availability or top-down effects through predation.

Disease and Parasitism

A suite of micro- and macroparasites (*sensu* Anderson and May 1979), including viruses, bacteria, fungi, protozoans, nematodes, cestodes, acanthocephalans, rhizocephalans, and trematodes, infect soft-sediment animals (Kinne 1980, 1983; Rohde 1982; Sindermann 1990). Parasitic infections impact soft-sediment populations by causing mortality, reducing reproduction and growth, and altering host behavior. In contrast, the role of pathogens and parasite-host interactions in structuring soft-sediment marine communities is largely unknown. In fact, the potential community effects of parasites and pathogens are not even mentioned, or only briefly discussed, in most marine ecology reviews and textbooks (Sousa 1991).

Disease dynamics and population-level consequences of infection are well documented for some commercial species associated with marine soft sediments. For example, many studies have documented the spread of infection and impacts by the protozoan *Perkinsus marinus* that has decimated oyster populations and the oyster fishery in the eastern United States (Paynter and Burreson 1991; Ford and Tripp 1996). Recent experimental evidence has shown that the prevalence of infection and impacts on populations vary in response to fluctuations in environmental conditions (Lafferty and Kuris 1999; Lenihan et al. 1999). For example, Lenihan et al. (1999) found that exposure to multiple environmental stressors, including extremes of temperature, salinity, and low oxygen concentrations, influenced infection rates and intensity as well as growth and mortality of infected oysters.

The possible effects of parasitic infections in mediating species interactions and structuring whole communities are still largely speculative. One potential effect may occur because of alteration of adult–larval interactions and larval recruitment success (Sousa 1991). Infaunal clams, *Macoma balthica*, modify their behavior and tend to crawl on the surface instead of burrowing deep in the sediments when infected by trematode parasites (Swennen and Ching 1974). More intense surface activity by clams and the resulting sediment disturbance may increase larval mortality and negatively affect recruitment rates of other species (see Biotic Disturbances section). In addition, some predators, including birds and marine mammals, avoid infected individuals. For example, oystercatchers avoid infected *Macoma* (Hulscher 1973), and sea otters avoid clams infected by paralytic shell poisoning (PSP) as well as patches of clams containing infected individuals (Kvitek et al. 1991). Predator switching to alternative prey or prey patches may constitute another mechanism through which parasitic infections influence soft-sediment communities. However, these and other possible community effects of pathogens and parasites have not been rigorously documented.

Positive Interactions and Ecosystem Engineering

So far, we have reviewed studies focusing on the negative impacts of soft-sediment species on other components of these communities. Most ecological studies have highlighted the importance of predator-prey, competitive, or adult–larval interactions in structuring soft-sediment marine communities. These interactions are usually thought to have the most important and widespread influences on soft-sediment communities. However, theoretical (Connell and Slatyer 1977; DeAngelis et al. 1983; Abrams 1993; Bertness and Calloway 1994) and empirical (see following) research indicates positive interactions have far-reaching direct and indirect effects on community structure and dynamics. Positive interactions are defined as all nonconsumer interactions among two or more species that positively affect at least one of the species involved (Bertness and Calloway 1994). They include many forms of facultative and obligatory facilitations and mutualisms.

A common form of positive interactions in soft-sediment habitats is the generation, modification, or maintenance of habitat by certain facilitator species. Jones et al. (1994) has called these facilitator species "ecosystem engineers." Ecosystem engineers either directly or indirectly control the availability of resources to other organisms by causing changes in the physical state of biotic or abiotic materials and by changing energy flows (see Bruno and Bertness, this volume). Marine soft-sediment habitats have many ecosystem engineers, including mound-building and tube-building species; vegetation such as salt marsh, seagrass, and algae; and reef builders, such as oysters, mussels, polychaetes, and some molluscs. These organisms modify sediments (Fager 1964; Eckman et al. 1981; Luckenbach 1986) and ameliorate physical stress, such as dessication, burial, and oxygen stress (Hay 1981; Bertness and Grosholz 1985; Lenihan and Peterson 1998; Lenihan et al., in press). Through their physical presence, or the effects they have on hydrodynamics, ecosystem engineers can regulate the distribution and abundance of species (Hay 1981; Knieb 1984; Bertness and Hacker 1994); facilitate the settlement and recruitment of larvae (Eckman 1983; Eckman 1985; Bertness 1989; Lenihan 1999); and increase growth, survivorship, and fecundity (Lenihan 1999). Structural heterogeneity created by ecosystem engineers can both facilitate and provide refuge from predation (Micheli 1997). On small spatial scales, ecosystem engineers positively influence neighboring or closely associated species. On a large scale, ecosystem engineers positively influence environments by creating heterogeneity in the amount of engineered and unengineered environments (Bruno and Bertness, this volume).

Many aquatic plants are ecosystem engineers that regulate the distribution, abundance, and production of soft-sediment invertebrates. For example, communities within patches of seagrass (*Halodule* spp., *Zostera* spp., and *Thallasia* spp.) usually have higher total abundance and species diversity than communities in unvegetated sediments (Kikuchi 1966; Orth 1973; Orth 1977; Thayer et al. 1975; 1984; Reise 1977; Santos and Simon 1980; Stoner 1980). Summerson and Peterson (1984) found that seagrass beds in North Carolina estuaries contained 52 times the number of epibenthic animals and 3 times the number of infaunal animals than surrounding, unstructured sediments. Suspension feeders were most positively affected by seagrass. Several mechanisms explain increases in abundance and species diversity within the seagrass beds. First, the physical structure of the plants reduces predator efficiency. The blades, roots, and rhyzomes inhibit the movement, searching, and capturing ability of predators like fishes, crabs, shrimps, whelks, and rays (Nelson 1979; Heck and Thoman 1984; Summerson and Peterson 1984). Second, the plants hydrodynamically baffle flow, thereby increasing particle deposition and food availability. For example, the growth of the suspension-feeding clam (*Mercenaria mercenaria*) is greater in seagrass beds, partly because of increased availability of suspended organic particles (Kikuchi and Peres 1977; Peterson et al. 1984). Seagrass beds also positively influence associated species by reducing sediment transport and biotic disturbances. Irlandi and Peterson (1991) found that the growth and survival of *Mercenaria* was enhanced within seagrass because sediment disruption by whelks (a digging predator) and siphon nipping by fishes were reduced. Many of the positive interactions between seagrass and associated species have been described for other types of marine vegetation, mainly salt marshes (Micheli 1997) and algal beds (Hay 1986).

A common form of ecological engineering in soft sediments is accomplished by infaunal species that modify sediments thereby positively influencing local species density and diversity. For example, the deposit-feeding sea cucumber *Molpadia oolitica* lives head down in muddy sediments, ingesting sediments at depth and depositing fecal matter and undigested sediments on the surface. Through its feeding activity, *Molpadia* forms conical structures on the mud surface that are cemented by fecal matter and are more stable than the surrounding muds. Such stable substrate is suitable habitat for tube-building suspension-feeding polychaetes that are excluded from the surrounding shifting sediments (Rhoads and Young 1971). The presence of worm tubes, in turn, increases the accumulation of bacteria and microalgae that are food for many small gazers and deposit feeders (Alongi 1985; Eckman 1985). Another example is the clam *Cryptomya californica* that lives along the walls of *Callianassa californiensis* burrows (Peterson 1977). *Cryptomya* depend on this microhabitat and are mainly found in association with *Callianassa* burrows (Peterson 1977).

Biogenic structures such as polychaete tubes and mollusc shells also modify the physical environment in soft sediments and interfere with foraging efficiency of infaunal and epifaunal predators, thereby decreasing predation intensity on other species in the community. Polychaete tubes baffle water flows and may enhance passive accumulation of larvae (Eckman 1985). Levin (1991) suggested that agglutinating rhizopod protozoans play an important role in structuring deep-sea benthos. Large Foraminifera and Xenophyophorea create biogenic structures that provide stable habitat, refuge from predation, and elevation into faster flows and greater rates of food delivery. These structures and the surrounding sediments are colonized by a variety of meiofaunal and macrofaunal organisms (Levin 1991). Live bivalves and dead bivalve shells decrease predation rates on other bivalves and infaunal invertebrates in general. For example, shell debris decreases predation intensity on clams by interfering with the foraging of predatory crabs (Arnold 1984; Sponaugle and Lawton 1990). Similarly, Peterson and Black (1993) found that predation rates in a shallow sand flat in western Australia decreased with increasing densities of live bivalves because dense bivalve beds lowered the foraging efficiency of predatory sea stars.

Biogenic reef habitats are created in estuarine and shallow-water soft sediments by several ecological engineers, especially polychaetes, mussels, and oysters. These structures not only positively influence associated invertebrates and algae by increasing refuge and niche space, but also by ameliorating physical stress and enhancing resource availability (Bell et al. 1991). In estuaries worldwide, oysters form conspicuous hard-substrate biogenic reefs through the gregarious settlement of oyster larvae and subsequent accumulation of live and dead oyster shells. Oyster reefs increase local species diversity by providing complex structures on relatively monotonous sandy bottoms, thus increasing overall habitat heterogeneity. These reefs also provide structure to predatory crabs that can create halos of reduced infaunal densities around the habitat (Micheli and Peterson 1999). Oyster reefs also positively influence many local species (including oysters) by physically altering hydrodynamic conditions and reducing exposure to stressful hydrographic conditions (Lenihan 1999). Reefs are three-dimensional structures that provide substratum elevated above soft sediments that (1) increase local flow speeds by creating varying pressure gradients in flow streams; (2) produce local eddies and depositional environments; and (3) elevate fauna above bottom waters and sediments subject to hypoxia/anoxia that occurs when estuaries become stratified (Lenihan and Peterson 1998). Enhanced flow speeds in combination with eddy formation increase the delivery rate, settlement, and recruitment of oysters (Lenihan 1999) and benthic fishes (Breitburg et al. 1995). Enhanced flow also increases the growth, condition, and survival of oysters due to enhanced food availability and quality and reduced sediment deposition (Lenihan et al. 1996; Lenihan 1999). Reduced exposure to hypoxia/anoxia and increased flow also increased oyster growth, condition, and survival and was linked to decreased levels of parasitism (Lenihan et al. 1999). By enhancing flow speed and ameliorating oxygen stress, the structure of oyster reefs also regulated the density and species diversity of associated crustacean species and predator-prey dynamics between the crustaceans and assemblages of predatory fishes (Lenihan et al., in press).

In conclusion, there are several examples of positive interactions among soft-sediment organisms. Available evidence suggests that the provision of habitat by ecosystem engineers positively influences processes that regulate local invertebrate (and fish) populations and communities. The mechanisms by which ecosystem engineers positively regulate communities are varied and many, but the most common are the provision of colonization, niche, and refuge space; the enhancement of limiting resources; and the reduction of physical stress. The presence of ecosystem engineers thus creates patches of higher micro-, meio- and macrofaunal invertebrate abundance and diversity. Undoubtedly, many other forms of positive interactions and facilitation occur in soft sediments beside those associated with ecosystem engineers. However, in contrast with predator-prey and competitive interactions (Peterson 1979, 1991; Gray 1981; Reise 1985; Wilson 1991a; Olafsson et al. 1994), there has been no attempt to synthesize data and observations on the community effects of positive interactions and ecosystem engineering in soft sediments (but see Bertness and Calloway 1994). Thus, it is not known how pervasive positive interactions are and how their role in organizing communities compares with other types of biotic interactions.

DISTURBANCE. Disturbance is a major factor causing spatiotemporal variation in marine soft-sediment communities (Hall 1994). Disturbances are any discrete event in time that alters ecosystem, community, or population structure by directly removing individuals or by changing resource availability, substrate characteristics, or other physical conditions (Sousa 1984; Pickett and White 1985). Disturbances affect biological organization through death, injury, reduced/enhanced reproductive output, the provision of colonization space, or their influence on sedimentary properties, including chemistry. In soft sediments, disturbances are usually unevenly distributed in space and time, thereby creating spatiotemporal mosaics of patches of reduced animal densities experiencing different stages of community recovery (Johnson 1970, 1973). Disturbances are caused by a multitude of natural and anthropogenic agents and can be physical, biotic, or chemical in nature. Many disturbances have multiple direct and indirect impacts on communities of organisms (Myers 1995). Soft-sediment communities are commonly affected by disturbance events that vary in intensity, frequency, and spatial extent (Levin 1992; Thrush et al. 1996; Figure 10.8).

Biotic Disturbances

Feeding and movements of animals associated with marine soft sediments impact the associated communities not only through direct predation and interference, but also through modifications of the physical environment that result in decreased recruitment success, greater adult mortality, and lower growth for other species. Biotic disturbances are a ubiquitous feature of marine soft sediments and appear to play a major role in structuring soft-sediment communities. In particular, the hypothesis that adult invertebrates often decrease recruitment success of later colonizers has a long history in soft-sediment marine ecology and has motivated a plethora of investigations (Thorson 1966; Rhoads and Young 1970; Woodin 1976, 1991; Olafsson et al. 1994).

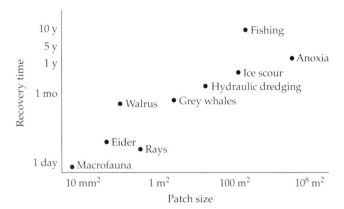

Figure 10.8 Scales of disturbances and recovery rate in soft sediments. Recovery rate is the time required for community composition in disturbed patch to resemble ambient, undisturbed patches. (M. Kaiser, unpublished data.)

ADULT–LARVAL INTERACTIONS. Mobile adults can cause mortality of newly settled individuals by disrupting sediments. Inhibition of recruitment at high densities of deposit feeders though ingestion and disturbance of settlers is the basis for one of the early models of community organization in marine soft sediments, the "trophic group amensalism" concept (Rhoads and Young 1970; Woodin 1976). A classic example of recruitment inhibition by a deposit feeder is the *Pontoporeia-Macoma* interaction in the Baltic Sea. The amphipod *Pontoporeia affinis* kills recruits of the clam *Macoma balthica* by disturbing sediments (Segersträle 1962; Elmgren et al. 1986). At high *Pontoporeia* densities, *Macoma* are usually absent (Segersträle 1962). This interaction most likely underlies long-term cycles in the covariation of these two species. *Pontoporeia* has high-recruitment years every 6–7 years, whereas in most years recruitment is low. *Macoma* oscillates in dominance with *Pontoporeia* abundance, attaining lower abundances during the high-recruitment years of the amphipod (Gray 1981). Negative effects of adult–larval interaction on recruitment may indeed be common. In a review of 54 separate experiments, Olafsson et al. (1994) found that 61% of studies revealed inhibition, 24% showed no effect, and 15% showed facilitation of recruitment by adults.

PREDATOR DISTURBANCES. Another common form of biotic disturbance to soft sediments is associated with the activity of predators. Many large epibenthic predators including some portunid crabs (Micheli 1997), fishes (Palmer 1988), rays (Thrush et al. 1991), walruses (Fukuyama and Oliver 1985), sea otters (Kvitek et al. 1992), and grey whales (Oliver et al. 1984; Oliver and Slattery 1985) dig pits in the sediments to obtain their infaunal prey. When excavating prey, predators also kill or remove most other infauna creating defaunated patches of sediments that are recolonized through migration from adjacent areas and larval settlement. In southern California, rays dig pits that tend to trap organic detritus, attract-

ing opportunistic, detritus-feeding invertebrates first and subsurface deposit feeders later in the recolonization sequence (VanBlaricom 1982). Depending on the time when pits are formed and on stochastic colonization events, pits may be colonized by different sets of species, thereby creating mosaics of infaunal communities of varying composition and maintaining high spatiotemporal variability (VanBlaricom 1982). Oliver and Slattery (1985) have documented similar patchy disturbances and recolonization sequences for gray-whale feeding pits in the Bering Sea. The creation of feeding pits that vary in size from a few cm² to 100s m² is a common process structuring soft-sediment communities. Thus, biotic disturbances contribute to maintaining high spatial patchiness and temporal variability of soft-sediment communities over small (e.g. adult–larval interactions) to mesoscales (e.g., feeding pits of large predators).

Abiotic Physical Disturbances

Abiotic physical disturbances are caused by a multitude of natural and anthropogenic agents. The mechanical forces of physical disturbances crush, remove, and injure soft-sediment animals or alter sediment properties by removing, delivering, or disrupting sediment. Physical disturbances are also caused by extreme changes in temperature, salinity, or oxygen concentration. Following, we discuss several of the most common natural and human-induced disturbances in marine soft sediments.

WAVE DISTURBANCES. Waves are a continual disturbance that influences community structure and dynamics over large and small scales on beaches and continental shelves. Waves affect communities mainly by shifting, resuspending, and depositing sediments. Waves also dislodge and transport animals, sometimes defaunating one area and repopulating another (Hall 1994). Waves create sand ripples that can migrate across the bottom over m–km. Migrating ripples can cause short-term, small-scale (cm) changes in the density of amphipods because these are forced to constantly emerge and rebury in the migrating sediment waves (McLachlan and Hesp 1984). Overall, waves have a major influence on the distribution of surface sediments on continental shelves (Dyer 1986).

The influence of wave disturbance on the bottom is depth dependent because wave energy and the size of wave orbitals decreases exponentially with water depth. Consequently, the community impacts of waves decreases with water depth and can cause zonation in infaunal communities in the shallow subtidal areas, usually within the first 20–30 m. Oliver et al. (1980) reported wave-induced infaunal community zonation in subtidal regions off sandy beaches in central California. At depths below 14 m, the fauna were mostly polychaetes that lived in permanent tubes or burrows. In contrast, animals located shallower than 14 m were small, mobile deposit feeders (mainly crustaceans) that actively burrowed within the sediments. They argued that this community zonation resulted from depth-dependent wave disturbance that prevented tube builders and commensal animals from maintaining dwellings in shallow water (unless they were protected from wave disturbance). They also showed that depth of the transition between the mobile species community and tube mat community increased with increasing wave intensity.

Wave impacts are strongest during storms. Storm waves are most effective in shallow water (0–25 m), but can transport sediment at rates of 1000 kg m^{-2} d^{-1} even at 100-m water depth (Hall 1994). Thistle et al. (1991) documented how benthic storms off Nova Scotia can erode sediment and remove meiofaunal crustaceans (isopods and harpacticoid copepods) at 4280 m deep. In shallower water, many solitary macrofauna and large patches of tube-building species and clams can be removed by storm waves (Eagle 1973). Storm waves can also deposit sediment and resuspend particulate food matter for animals (Bock and Miller 1995). For example, a major storm can produce a bed of sediment several cm thick at 20 m deep and several mm thick at 40 m deep (Hall 1994). The relatively few studies that have documented the biological effects of storms in soft sediments show that storm waves have a major influence on community composition, especially over short time periods. If storms are large enough, entire communities can be removed from large area along with surface sediments (McCall 1977; but see Posey et al. 1996).

Some species have evolved reproductive strategies that take advantage of wave disturbances. Barry (1989) found that a tube-dwelling sabellid polychaete in Southern California persisted because individuals timed their reproductive output to coincide with storm events, which removed competing species. More importantly, the worms maximized their reproductive output during storms because the probability of future reproduction was reduced because of future storm disturbance. In contrast, many other studies have reported that intermittent recruitment events and physical disturbances, such as that produced by waves, cause instability in the structure of soft-sediment communities over longer time periods (e.g., Eagle 1975; McCall 1977).

ICE DISTURBANCES. Ice disturbance in polar latitudes, specifically bottom gouging by grounded icebergs and anchor-ice formation and uplift, influence the structure of soft-sediment invertebrate communities (Dayton et al. 1969; Dayton 1989; Dayton 1990; Lenihan and Oliver 1995). Conlan et al. (1998) calculated that 149,000 km of coastline in the Arctic and Antarctica are impacted by iceberg scouring, thus indicating that icebergs are the most important benthic disturbance in shallow polar waters. In the Arctic and Antarctica, icebergs run aground in water up to 500 m deep, although most scours are found in water depths less than 70 m (Barnes and Lien 1988; Lien et al. 1989). The keels of icebergs create gouges up to 1375 m wide, 10.5 m deep, and several km in length (see Figure 10.4; Lewis and Blasco 1990). On the deep seafloor, large gouges may take millennia to disappear (Josenhans and Woodworth-Lynas 1988). Icebergs remove sediments, creating large troughs and pits, as well as tall berms of displaced sediment that reach 5 m in height. Icebergs uproot, crush, dis-

place, plough, and bury soft-sediment organisms over large areas of the seafloor in polar latitudes. Conlan et al. (1998) found that the communities within iceberg scours in the High Canadian Arctic were dominated by small polychaetes of the family Spionidae, Capitellidae, Phyllodocidae, and Dorvilleidae (Figure 10.9). The communities within scours also contained highly mobile, surface-dwelling scavenging species, including lissianassid amphipods and buccinid gastropods. The scavengers were usually found eating the abundant clams (*Mya truncata* and *Serripes groenlandicus*) that had been displaced and damaged by the passing iceberg. In contrast, communities outside of iceberg scours contained higher species diversity, biomass, and abundances of deeper burrowing, long-lived clams, soft-bodied suspension feeders (e.g., sipunculids, infaunal anemones, sea cucumbers, soft corals, and solitary tunicates) than communities in scours.

FISHING DISTURBANCES. Commercial fishing causes one of the most widespread physical disturbances to the ocean floor (Hall 1994; Dayton et al. 1995; Figure 10.8). Fishing for demersal fishes, crabs, and shrimps is conducted on the soft-sediment seafloor in very shallow to deep water (1200 m deep) using beam and otter trawls. The total amount of soft-bottom area impacted by trawling is staggering. For example, 35% of the Baltic Sea and 71% of the Danish North Sea are apparently trawled at least once a year. Large sections off the northeastern United States and other areas are trawled 3–7 times per year. Fishermen also dredge sediments for clams and other shellfish mainly in shallow water and intertidal areas. In addition, the seafloor is also dredged to extract gravel and other aggregate materials for use as construction materials.

Trawls impact the bottom by resuspending sediment, leveling biogenic structures, and crushing or otherwise injuring animals (Watling and Norse 1998). Beam trawls are the biggest and heaviest types of gear, sometimes extending 12 m in width and weighing 10 metric tons. Each pull of the dredge along the bottom can last for up to 16 km. Otter trawls are smaller (3–5 m in width), but are often pulled up to 24 km. The total area of the seafloor affected by one pull of an otter trawl can exceed 144,000 m^2 (Churchill 1989). Trawl gear penetrates deeper into soft muds than into hard-packed sands. For example, otter trawls can penetrate about 1 cm into coarse sand, resuspending 39 kg sec^{-1}, and 4 cm into muddy sand, resuspending 112 kg sec^{-1} (Churchill 1989). Otter trawls have been reported to penetrate sediments up to 16 cm deep and dredges up to 30 cm (Dayton et al. 1995).

Trawling and dredging have both direct and indirect impacts on soft-sediment communities (Bergmun and Hup 1992; Dayton et al. 1995; Engel and Kvitek 1995; Watling and Norse 1998; Lenihan and Peterson 1998). Both types of bottom fishing cause considerable direct incidental mortality of nontarget species. Populations of long-lived species can be nearly or completely destroyed. For example, trawling reduced echinoderm, polychaete, and mollusc populations by 10–65% in one study (Bergman and Hup 1992). Other studies have reported complete mortality of the clam *Arctica islandica*

(A)

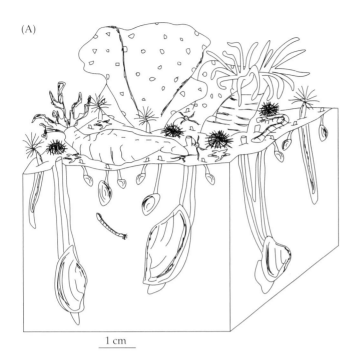

1 cm

(B)

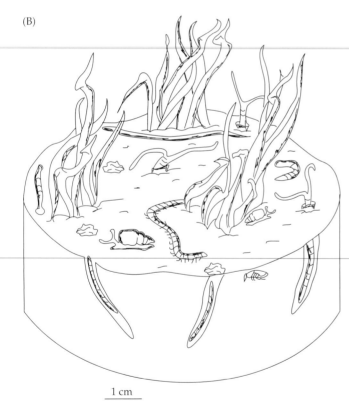

1 cm

Figure 10.9 Stylized representation of the community changes caused by iceberg scouring in the eastern Canadian Arctic (18 m water depth). (A) Community is in an unscoured area. Community is characterized by high biomass, abundance, and species diversity. Biomass is dominated by long-lived, deep-burrowing clams and algae. (B) Community is in an area scoured by icebergs within one year of the scouring event. Community is characterized by low biomass, abundance, and species diversity. Community is dominated by opportunistic polychaetes and surface-dwelling scavengers and deposit feeders. (Redrawn from Conlan et al. 1998.)

caused in part by consumption of damaged individuals by scavenging cod and other predators (Dayton et al. 1995). Even a 25% reduction in populations of long-lived species is extremely serious if the species has episodic recruitment and is exposed to trawling several times a year (Dayton et al. 1995). In almost every case in which a long-lived suspension-feeding group is eliminated by bottom fishing, there is a shift to a habitat dominated by small deposit-feeding polychaetes. Once the deposit feeders become established, they can resist recovery by suspension feeders by consuming and burying potential recruits (Dayton et al. 1995). Therefore, trawling and dredging can have long-lasting influences on ecological processes over large areas of the seafloor.

The indirect effects of trawling are as serious as direct effects and include altered sedimentary characteristics and increased turbidity that kills suspension feeders, like scallops, clams, and slow-growing deep-water corals (e.g., *Lophelia* sp.). Sediment transport caused by trawling also buries and kills epifaunal invertebrates, like bryozoans and sponges, that create beds that are important nurseries for fishes (Dayton et al. 1995). Mortality of epifaunal animals has severe implications for benthic food webs and community composition because epifauna influences hydrodynamics, sediment characteristics, and patterns of larval settlement. When trawling for shrimp, flatfish, and crabs in estuaries, fishermen can degrade and damage biogenic reefs created by polychaetes and oysters (Reise 1982; Rothschild et al. 1994; Lenihan and Peterson 1998). Dredging for clams within seagrass (*Zostera marina*) beds also has negative impacts on other commercially valuable fishery species such as the bay scallop (*Argopecten irradians*) because it destroys large patches of the seagrass habitat on which scallops depend (Peterson et al. 1987). Biogenic structures found within estuaries and in shallow water are usually constructed by and support species with high commercial and ecological value in estuarine and coastal marine ecosystems. Thus, their degradation and destruction by commercial fishing has detrimental effects on fisheries and on a suite of ecological processes.

Chemical Disturbances

Another significant anthropogenic disturbance in marine soft-sediment habitats is chemical contamination. Although huge amounts of contaminants enter ocean ecosystems annually, detecting their complex ecological impacts is difficult (Schmitt and Osenberg 1996). Anthropogenic contaminants benefit some organisms as food or nutrients, but more commonly negatively affect benthic communities by causing acute injury and mortality or chronic, long-term, low-level damage that reduces growth, fecundity, and survival (Underwood and Peterson 1988). The most common types of pollutants released into the marine environment are nutrients, especially nitrogen compounds (Paerl 1985), organic material (i.e., carbon enrichment; Pearson and Rosenberg 1978), hydrocarbons (Suchanek 1993), and organochlorine compounds, especially PCBs (Baker 1980). Although we do not understand many of the indirect ecological impacts of contaminants, we have a good understanding of their direct effects on soft-sediment communities.

KITROGEN LOADING. The release of nitrogen may have the largest spatial impact of any pollutant because it exists in a multitude of forms (e.g., NO_x and NH^x) and enters the ocean over large spatial scales via atmospheric deposition and riverine runoff (Paerl 1985). Anthropogenic nitrogen inputs readily enter marine food webs because they are commonly a limiting resource for primary production. In coastal systems, increases in primary production caused by N-loading results in eutrophication (excess production of organic carbon) and alteration of phytoplankton community composition (Micheli 1999, and references therein). Increased primary production and subsequent increases in the deposition of organic material (plankton parts, marine snow, and fecal pellets) to the seafloor result in increased biological oxygen demand (BOD) of microbial communities and resulting hypoxia (<2 mg O_2 L^{-1})/anoxia (0 mg O_2 L^{-1}) (see Peterson and Estes, this volume). Hypoxia/anoxia can cause large-scale community changes, especially the mass mortality of sessile species and exodus of mobile species (Tenore 1972; Diaz and Rosenberg 1995; Lenihan et al., in press). Shifts in phytoplankton species composition, especially an overabundance of toxic dinoflagellates (red tides), also influence soft-sediment communities by killing suspension feeders and mobile predators (Paerl 1985).

ORGANIC ENRICHMENT. Inputs of organic material from sewage outfalls, industrial and municipal effluents (e.g., wood pulp mills and seaweed and seafood processing plants), and rivers are a biologically significant form of anthropogenic chemical contamination in coastal systems (NRC 1993). Organic carbon is primarily a food source for benthic organisms, especially deposit feeders, but when disposed of in large amounts can cause a complex of chemical, physical, and biological changes that negatively influence soft-sediment communities. The most obvious impact of carbon loading is an increase in BOD and associated hypoxia/anoxia in bottom water and sediments. This phenomenon is similar to that caused by nitrogen loading and eutrophication.

In their classic review of organic enrichment, Pearson and Rosenberg (1978) synthesized the spatial and temporal community responses to localized organic enrichment from a variety of systems. Their graphical model illustrates that the abundance, biomass, and species richness of communities along organic enrichment gradients exhibit consistent patterns (Figure 10.10). In contrast, the responses of epifaunal communities did not show consistent patterns. In the immediate vicinity of a discharge of organic material (or immediately after the discharge in a temporal gradient), sediments are devoid of infauna mainly due to burial, oxygen stress, and the production of hydrogen sulfide. The first species encountered along a gradient are low numbers of small opportunistic species, very often the polychaete *Capitella capitata*. Accordingly, both biomass and species number is depressed

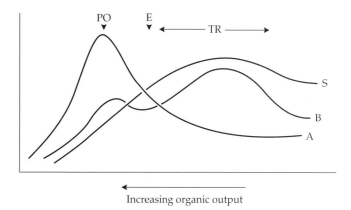

Figure 10.10 Changes in community total abundance (A), biomass (B), and species richness (S) in time or space along an organic enrichment gradient. PO represents the peak in abundance of opportunistic species. (From Pearson and Rosenberg 1978.)

in this loading zone. Farther along the gradient, the number of species begins to increase slowly to an ecotone point, after which species number and biomass increases towards an asymptote, but total abundance falls. Ecotone communities have extremely abundant populations of opportunistic species but are low in species number. These communities also represent the first of two peaks in biomass. After the ecotone community, a transition community appeared that consists of semiopportunistic species (common fauna: polychaetes *Tharyx* and various spionids, surface deposit-feeding crustaceans, including isopods and cumaceans). The transition community had lower abundances, but greater biomass than the ecotone community. After the transition community, biomass and species number generally decreased to background levels. Maximum biomass occurred in the area of the gradient where organic enrichment of the sediments was sufficient to provide a rich food source, but not high enough to cause serious oxygen depletion. In general, organic enrichment favors deposit feeders over suspension feeders potentially because of TGA, but certainly because of changes in sedimentary and hydrodynamic conditions.

HYDROCARBON CONTAMINATION. Human activities result in the annual discharge of about 3.8 billions liters of hydrocarbon compounds to marine ecosystems (Suchanek 1993). Hydrocarbon contamination results from oil spills, petroleum exploration and refinement, sewage outfalls, and other sources. Natural sources of hydrocarbons include oil seeps and the breakdown of organic matter. The ecological impact of acute, short-term exposure to hydrocarbon contaminants, including toxic aromatic compounds and less toxic but mechanically debilitating oils and tars, causes mortality and injury to marine soft-sediment animals (NRC 1993). Chronic long-term, low-level exposure to hydrocarbons is more common than acute exposure (Boesch and Rabalais 1987; Carney 1981). However, the ecological effects of chronic exposure to hydrocarbons are more difficult to evaluate than acute exposure because impacts are usually sublethal (Kennicutt et al. 1996). In addition, the effects of hydrocarbons are hard to separate from the effects of other toxic compounds and organic material that are often associated with hydrocarbon discharges. For example, petroleum products or by-products from exploration (i.e., oil rig wastes) usually contain toxic metals and organic compounds (Swartz et al. 1986; Olsgard and Gray 1995; Kennicutt et al. 1996). Municipal sewage outfalls also discharge mixtures of hydrocarbons, toxins, and organic matter.

The covariance of pollutant types around hydrocarbon sources and sewage outfalls commonly causes confounding in the spatial patterns of contamination and community responses, making it difficult to determine what factors, or interaction of factors, are responsible for any observed biological responses (Peterson et al. 1996). The trouble lies in the fact that the confounding varies with each system, thereby necessitating site-specific and costly forms of pollution monitoring, control, abatement, and other management efforts. To address the problem of confounded pollution patterns, Peterson et al. (1996) proposed a synthetic model of the responses of benthic invertebrates to different contaminant types. Due to their longevity, sessile lifestyles, feeding modes, and ecological significance, soft-sediment invertebrates provide an excellent template for tracking the biological impacts of marine pollutants. Although individual species within a higher taxon vary greatly in their sensitivity to contaminants, the responses of benthic communities to contamination are detectable at higher taxonomic levels (Warwick and Clarke 1993). For macrofauna, detection is possible at the level of phyla and family, and for meiofauna, usually at the level of family. These differences in the responses of higher taxon appear to be caused by differences in the responses to the major classes of pollutants, toxic contaminants, and organic enrichment. The most common pattern observed in areas exposed to toxic compounds (metals, hydrocarbons, and organics) is the lack of echinoderms and crustaceans, especially amphipods and some groups of harpacticoids copepods. In laboratory bioassay tests, these animals are highly susceptible to toxic compounds (Lenihan et al. 1995). In contrast, organic enrichment is usually associated with increases in the abundance of deposit-feeding polychaetes, oligochaets, and nematodes. If these patterns are truly caused by variation in the levels of toxic compounds and organic enrichment, relatively simple monitoring schemes of higher taxon may provide a mean of teasing apart the impacts of the common anthropogenic pollutants and improving management.

Community Succession Following Disturbance

Following disturbances, defaunated patches often undergo a recovery process that varies temporally with the size and type of disturbance (see Figure 10.8). If disturbances are small, rare, or weak, the recovery processes will likely be fast, and disturbed areas will be transient features in the habitat and have only very localized effects (Probert 1984; Hall 1994).

When disturbances are large, intense, or frequent, biological recovery is usually slow. Large-scale disturbances can create large-scale patchiness in community composition, patterns of community zonation, and ecological changes over large areas of the seafloor (Oliver et al. 1980; Diaz and Rosenberg 1995; Conlan et al. 1998).

Recovery processes in soft-sediment communities are characterized by a succession of community types, usually beginning with the appearance of opportunistic species and progressing to the reestablishment of an assemblage that is similar to the surrounding (or ambient) community. The speed and form of succession is dependent primarily on the habitat type, species composition of the surrounding communities, the local disturbance regime, and interactions among these factors (Zajac and Whitlach 1982a, b; Zajac et al. 1998). In physically stable environments, succession is often initiated by opportunistic species that appear soon (hrs–days) after a disturbance, either through the dispersal of adults and juveniles from the surrounding community or from the settlement of planktonic larvae (Pearson and Rosenberg 1978; Lenihan and Oliver 1995). The ratio of planktonic larvae to dispersing adults/juveniles among colonizers is thought to depend on spatial scale (Thrush 1991). As patch size increases, so should the proportion of species with pelagic larvae because increasing dispersal distances increase the immigration time of benthic dispersers. Most opportunistic species are surface and shallow subsurface deposit feeders that bioturbate and irrigate the top few mm of sediment, thereby oxygenating subsurface sediments, altering grain size, reducing sulfide concentrations, or creating biotic structures (tubes, mounds, or sediment pellets). The alteration of sediment conditions allows other species that are less tolerant of toxic conditions or unstable and unstructured sediments to colonize the patch. This type of community succession is a positive interaction referred to as facilitation (Connell and Slatyer 1997) and is thought to be common in soft sediments (Gallagher et al. 1983). Rhoads et al. (1978) graphically described facilitation in a soft-sediment community following defaunation resulting from the deposition of sediment and organic matter (see Figure 10.11). Similar successional sequences are observed in many systems in both physically and chemically disturbed sediments (Hall 1994).

Community recovery in high stress environments (e.g., shallow, windy basins with sandy bottoms) also depends heavily on the scale of the disturbance and the species composition and abundance of the ambient communities. Recolonization of patches in high-stress environments is usually carried out by dispersing adults and larvae from the ambient community that are transported in sediments along the bottom or in suspension above the bottom (Commito et al. 1995; Thrush et al. 1996; Zajac et al. 1998). However, scale-dependent changes of colonization mode also likely occur (Zajac et al. 1998). Thrush et al. (1996) found that the recovery time of communities in sediment patches defaunated by wind-generated waves is relatively slow (>9 mo) overall and increases

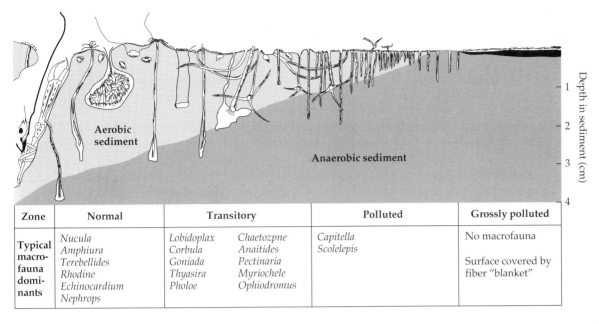

Zone	Normal	Transitory		Polluted	Grossly polluted
Typical macro-fauna domi-nants	*Nucula* *Amphiura* *Terebellides* *Rhodine* *Echinocardium* *Nephrops*	*Lobidoplax* *Corbula* *Goniada* *Thyasira* *Pholoe*	*Chaetozpne* *Anaitides* *Pectinaria* *Myriochele* *Ophiodromus*	*Capitella* *Scolelepis*	No macrofauna Surface covered by fiber "blanket"

Figure 10.11 Illustration representing temporal or spatial changes in a soft-sediment community located along a temporal or spatial gradient in organic enrichment. (Redrawn from Pearson and Rosenberg 1978.)

with the size of the patch. It took longer for dispersing animals to immigrate to the central areas of larger patches than smaller patches. It also took longer for recovery to occur in patches where tube mats were removed. Waves and other physical disturbances can uproot tube mats made by polychaetes and other species. Tube structures, even in high wave energy environments, can stabilize sediments (VanBlaricom 1982). Therefore, sediments in patches where tubes are dislodged are more readily resuspended, transported, and deposited. Sediment movement causes a continual flux of potential colonists in and out of the patch, whereas burial and scouring by sediments kill or force the emigration of colonists. Therefore, the removal of ecosystem engineers like tube builders can prolong succession and the reestablishment of the community.

Interplay of Biotic Interactions and Disturbances

Disturbances cause physical stress to soft-sediment organisms in many different forms. Bruno and Bertness (this volume) have devised a set of conceptual models to describe the interplay of biotic interactions and abiotic factors along gradients of physical stress related to disturbances. The models are based partly on the models of Menge and Sutherland (1976, 1987). Applying the general results of these models to soft-sediment communities is one means of synthesizing our understanding how biotic interactions influence community structure and dynamics. Bruno and Bertness' models predict that the relative role of positive interactions, predation, and competition change with physical stress. In extreme physical

conditions, such as wave-beaten shores, continental slopes experiencing slumping, and in tropical mudbanks, all forms of biotic interactions probably play minor roles in community regulation. Organisms persist if they are adapted to sediment movement and related disturbances (scouring, resuspension, burial, or hypoxia). Disturbances create free space for colonization, thereby favoring opportunistic species or postlarval dispersers. In moderate levels of environmental stress, facilitation by ecosystem engineers has high relative importance. Biogenic structures created by facilitators bind sediment, reduce scour and resuspension, and increase organism survival, thereby allowing the persistence of species. However, facilitation may also benefit predators, thereby increasing the relative importance of consumer pressure, and increase overall density, thus potentially increasing competitive interactions. The most complex interplay of biotic interactions probably occurs under moderate levels of environmental stress. The relative importance of different biotic interactions is also likely to show high between-site and temporal variability. Finally, at low levels of biotic stress, higher densities of many species can persist because they are not removed by physical disturbances. Therefore, the importance of competition and predation in regulating population and community dynamics are likely to increase. In low-stress systems, ecosystem engineers play a smaller role because their ability to ameliorate physical stress is less critical. Associational defenses (e.g., chemical defenses of plants and animals) are likely to increase in relative importance in environments experiencing low environmental stress.

Summary

In this chapter we have identified many of the key factors that regulate soft-sediment communities. We have shown that the relative importance of each factor and interactions among factors changes with the spatiotemporal scale being considered and levels of environmental stress. At relatively small spatial (mm–m) and temporal (sec–hrs) scales, biotic disturbance patterns of larval settlement (driven mainly by behavior) and animal–sediment relationships appear most important. Although large-scale differences in the distribution and survival of larvae ultimately regulate the species composition of communities, variation in larval settlement driven by hydrodynamic factors and recruitment determines the initial distribution of species at mesocales (m–km; days–months) scales. Substantial evidence indicates that postsettlement biotic interactions (especially predation, competition, and facilitation) occurring on relatively small spatial and temporal scales are more important than variation in settlement and recruitment patterns in regulating community structure, although this is still hotly debated. In addition, positive interactions by species such as ecosystem engineers can greatly influence settlement and recruitment. At relatively large spatial and temporal scales, abiotic environmental factors represent the highest level of organization within ecosystems in which other factors are usually subordinate (O'Neill et al. 1986; Barry and Dayton 1991). Oceanographics, physiography, and hydrodynamics ultimately control oceanographic conditions (temperature, salinity, water-column stability) and most biological activities (Legendre and Demers 1984; Barry and Dayton 1991). Large-scale abiotic and biotic factors (e.g., primary production) regulate the availability of organic carbon (mainly from allochthonous sources), which largely controls the distribution of soft-sediment species and population production. Nevertheless, small-scale hydrodynamic factors (flow and turbulence and resulting sedimentation patterns) can control the availability of organic carbon and therefore biological activity on smaller spatial and temporal scales.

One approach to understanding the interplay between various processes that shape communities is to conduct broad syntheses using data from a variety of locations and periods in time (e.g., Warwick and Clarke 1993; Micheli 1999; Ricciardi and Bourget 1999). Broad comparisons of community patterns along gradients of productivity, natural or anthropogenic disturbances, and abundance of predators or recruits represent a promising approach for producing generalizations and predictions about soft-sediment community patterns and responses to environmental change (e.g., Pearson and Rosenberg 1978; Swartz et al. 1986). Another approach to achieving this goal entails using general ecological theory that has been developed and tested primarily in the terrestrial environment (Bruno and Bertness, this volume). To date, research on marine soft-sediment communities has been primarily data driven. This empirical approach has generated a profound awareness of unique features of different assemblages and of the great variability in community patterns. However, it is often difficult to identify the most important and general processes regulating these communities. Models of population and community dynamics (May 1974; Murdoch 1994; Roughgarden 1998) provide a framework for investigating the role of different processes in shaping soft-sediment marine communities and predicting the impacts of anthropogenic and environmental change.

Our ability to recognize, explain, and predict changes in soft-sediment communities caused by natural and anthropogenic factors is also hampered by a relatively poor understanding of the mechanisms that drive ecological processes. For example, we are relatively ignorant about interactions among soft-sediment associated species. It is difficult to directly observe individual behavior, larval, and species interactions and to track individuals and populations through time. We are still frustrated by potentially important experimental artifacts, especially the modification of sediments during experimental manipulations and restriction of the movements of individuals when using tethers or inclusion/exclusion cages. These logistical difficulties hinder our ability to uncover mechanisms that result in observed patterns of population and community variation. There is a great need to develop methods that will allow direct behavioral observations of individuals and populations over time and to provide easier measurements of growth, survival, feeding, and reproductive rates.

Conservation and Management Issues

Human activities cause disturbances in soft-sediment habitats that have impacts at a variety of spatiotemporal scales. The largest and most intense physical disturbances are probably caused by bottom fishing. Trawling and dredging kills and injures sessile and mobile invertebrate species, degrades and destroys biogenic habitat, and modifies sediment characteristics over large portions of the ocean floor (Watling and Norse 1998). In many cases, soft sediments recover from fishing disturbances within several years. However, many areas are fished repeatedly, thereby preventing community recovery. At present, we know little about how fisheries and other dredge-related disturbances affect trophic links between benthic and pelagic communities. Nutrient-loading (especially nitrogen) and related changes in phytoplankton production and hypoxia/anoxia represent another form of large-scale disturbance in soft-sediment communities. Although the acute impacts of other pollutants such as oil and toxic chemical spills may affect a smaller area of the seafloor than do fishery disturbances and nitrogen-related disturbances, their chronic, long-term ecological impacts impacts are potentially more pervasive. Further effort is needed to determine the impact of contaminants on marine systems largely to provide enough political will to reduce inputs. In general, although we often recognize the immediate impact of human physical and biological disturbances, rarely have the wider ecosystem impacts been identified.

Acknowledgments

We thank Mark Hay, Mark Bertness, and Steve Gaines for inviting us to contribute to this excellent and timely book. We thank Stacy Kim, Bill Murdoch, John Oliver, Pete Peterson, and Sean Powers for ideas and encouragement. We also thank Leah Akins, Mark Bertness, Joel Fodrie, and two anonymous reviewers for helping to improve the manuscript. Support for H.S.L. was provided by NSF grant OPP-537338.

Literature Cited

Abrams, P. A. 1993. Effect of increased productivity on the abundances of trophic levels. *Amer. Nat.* 141: 351–371.

Aller, R. C. and R. E. Dodge. 1974. Animal–sediment relations in a tropical lagoon, Discovery Bay, Jamaica. *J. Mar. Res.* 32: 209–232.

Aller, R. C. and J. Y. Yingst. 1978. Biogeochemistry of tube-dwellings: a study of the sedentary polychaete *Amphitrite ornata* (Leidy). *J. Mar. Res.* 36: 201–254.

Aller, R. C. and J. Y. Yingst. 1985. Effects of the marine deposit-feeders *Heteromastus filiformis* (Polychaeta), *Macoma balthica* (Bivalvia), and *Tellina texana* (Bivalvia) on averaged sedimentary solute transport, reaction rates, and microbial distributions. *J. Mar. Res.* 43: 615–645.

Alongi, D. M. 1985. Microbes, meiofauna, and bacterial productivity on tubes constructed by the polychaete *Capitella capitata*. *Mar. Ecol. Prog. Ser.* 23: 207–208.

Alongi, D. M. 1990. The ecology of tropical soft-bottom benthic ecosystems. *Oceanogr. Mar. Biol. Annu. Rev.* 28: 381–496.

Ambrose, W. G., Jr. 1984a. Role of predatory infauna in structuring marine soft-bottom communities. *Mar. Ecol. Prog. Ser.* 17: 109–115.

Ambrose, W. G., Jr. 1984b. Influence of residents on the development of a marine soft-bottom community. *J. Mar. Res.* 42: 633–654.

Ambrose, W. G., Jr. 1984c. Influences of predatory polychaetes and epibenthic predators on the structure of a soft-bottom community in a Maine estuary. *J. Exp. Mar. Biol. Ecol.* 81: 115–145.

Ambrose, W. G., Jr. 1986. Experimental analysis of density dependent emigration of the amphipod *Rhepoxynius abronius*. *Mar. Behav. Physiol.* 12: 209–216.

Ambrose, W. G., Jr. 1991. Are infaunal predators important in structuring marine soft-bottom communities? *Amer. Zool* 31: 849–860.

Anderson, R. M. and R. M. May. 1979. Population biology of infectious diseases. *Nature* 280: 361–367.

Arnold, W. S. 1984. The effects of prey size, predator size and sediment composition on the rate of predation of the blue crab, *Callinectes sapidus* Rathbun, on the hard clam, *Mercenaria mercenaria* (Linne'). *J. Exp. Mar. Ecol. Biol.* 80: 207–219.

Arntz, W. E. 1977. Results and problems of an unsuccessful benthos cage predation experiment (western Baltic). In B. F. Keegan et al. (eds.), *Biology of Benthic Organisms*, pp. 31–44. Pergamon Press, Oxford.

Arntz, W. E., T. Brey and V. A. Gallardo. 1979. Antarctic zoobenthos. *Oceanogr. Mar. Biol. Annu. Rev.* 32: 241–304.

Aronson, R. B. and K. L. Heck, Jr. 1995. Tethering experiments and hypothesis testing in ecology. *Mar. Ecol. Prog. Ser.* 121: 307–309.

Bailey-Brock, J. H. 1979. Sediment trapping by chaetopterid polychaetes on a Hawaiian fringing reef. *J. Mar. Res.* 37: 643–656.

Baker, R. A. (ed.). 1980. *Contaminants in Sediments*. University of Michigan Press, Ann Arbor, MI.

Barnes, P. W. and R. Lien. 1988. Icebergs rework shelf sediments to 500 m off Antarctica. *Geology* 16: 1130–1133.

Barry, J. P. 1989. Reproductive response of a marine annelid to winter storms: An analog to fire adaptation in plants? *Mar. Ecol. Prog. Ser.* 54: 99–107.

Barry, J. P. and P. K. Dayton. 1991. Physical heterogeneity and the organization of marine communities. In J. Kolasa and S. T. A. Pickett (eds), *Ecological Heterogeneity*, pp. 270–320. Springer-Verlag, New York.

Bell, S. S., E. D. McCoy and H. R. Mushinsky (eds.). 1991. *Habitat Structure: The Physical Arrangement of Objects in Space*. Chapman and Hall, London.

Bender, K. and W. R. Davis. 1984. The effect of feeding by *Yoldia limatula* on bioturbation. *Ophelia* 23: 91–100.

Bergman, M. J. N. and M. Hup. 1992. Direct effects of beam trawling on macrofauna in a sandy sediment in the southern North Sea. ICES. *J. Mar. Sci.* 49: 5–11.

Bertness, M. D. 1989. Intraspecific competition and faciliation in a northern acorn barnacle population. *Ecology* 70: 257–268.

Bertness, M. D. and R. Callaway. 1994. Positive interactions in communities. *Trends Ecol. Evol.* 9: 191–193.

Bertness, M. D. and E. Grosholz. 1985. Population dynamics of the ribbed mussel, *Guekensia demissa*: The cost and benefits of an aggregated distribution. *Oecologia* 67: 192–204.

Bertness, M. D. and S. D. Hacker. 1994. Physical stress and positive associations among marsh plants. *Amer. Nat.* 144: 363–372.

Beukema, J. J. 1987. Influence of the predatory polychaete *Nephtys hombergii* on the abundance of other polychaetes. *Mar. Ecol. Prog. Ser.* 40: 95–101.

Beukema, J. J. 1991. Changes in composition of bottom fauna of a tidal flat area during a period of eutrophication. *Mar. Biol.* 111: 293–301.

Bianchi, T. S. and D. L. Rice. 1988. Feeding ecology of *Leitoscoloplos fragilis*. II. Effects of worm density on benthic diatom production. *Mar. Biol.* 99: 123–131.

Blundon, J. A. and V. S. Kennedy. 1982. Refuges for infaunal bivalves from blue crab, *Callinectes sapidus* (Rathbun), preda-

tion in Chesapeake Bay. *J. Exp. Mar. Biol. Ecol.* 65: 67–81.

Bock, M. J. and D. C. Miller. 1995. Storm effects on particulate food resources on an intertidal sandflat. *J. Exp. Mar. Biol. Ecol.* 187: 81–101.

Boesch, D. F. and N. N. Rabalais (eds.). 1987. *Long-Term Environmental Effects of Offshore Oil and Gas Development*. Elsevier, New York.

Bonsdorff, E. and E. M. Blomqvist. 1993. Biotic coupling on shallow water soft bottoms- examples from the northern Baltic Sea. *Oceanogr. Mar. Biol. Annu. Rev.* 31: 153–176.

Botton, M. L. 1984. Effects of Laughing Gull and shorebird population on the intertidal fuana at Cape May, New Jersey Estuar. *Coast. Shelf Sci.* 18: 209–220.

Breitburg, D. L., M. A. Palmer and T. Loher. 1995. Larval distributions and the spatial patterns of settlement of an oyster reef fish: Response to flow and structure. *Mar. Ecol. Prog. Ser.* 125: 45–60.

Brenchley, G. A. 1981. Disturbance and community structure: An experimental study of bioturbation in marine soft-sediment environments. *J. Mar. Sci.* 39: 767–790.

Brenchely, G. A. 1982. Mechanisms of spatial competition in marine soft-bottom communities. *J. Exp. Mar. Biol. Ecol.* 60: 17–33.

Brenchley, G. A. and J. T. Carlton. 1983. Competitive displacement of native mud snails by introduced periwinkle in the New England intertidal zone. *Biol. Bull.* 165: 543–558.

Bricelj, C. J. V. M., R. E. Malouf and C. DeQuillfeldt. 1984. Growth of juvenile *Mercenaria mercenaria* and the effect of resuspended bottom sediments. *Mar. Biol.* 84: 167–173.

Brown, B. 1982. Spatial and temporal distribution of a deposit-feeding polychaete on a heterogeneous tidal flat. *J. Exp. Mar. Biol. Ecol.* 65: 213–227.

Brown, A. C. and A. McClachlan. 1990. *Ecology of Sandy Shores*. Elsevier, Amsterdam.

Butman, C. A. 1987. Larval settlement of soft-sediment invertebrates: The spatial scales of pattern explained by active habitat selection and the emerging role of hydrodynamical processes. *Oceanogr. Mar. Biol. Annu. Rev.* 25: 113–165.

Butman, C. A. 1989. Sediment-trap experiments on the importance of hydrodynamical processes in distributing settling larvae in near-bottom waters. *J. Exp. Mar. Biol. Ecol.* 134: 37–88.

Butman, C. A., J. P. Grassle and C. M. Webb. 1988. Substrate choices made by marine larvae settling in still water and in a flume flow. *Nature* 333: 771–773.

Byers, J. E. 2000. Competition between two estuarine snails: Implications for invasions of exotic species. *Ecology* 81: 1225–1239.

Capuzzo, J. M. and D. R. Kester (eds). 1987. *Oceanic Processes in Marine Pollution.* R. E. Krieger Publishing Co., Malabar, FL.

Carlson D. J., D. W. Townsend, A. L. Hilyard and J. F. Eaton. 1984. Effect of an intertidal mudflat on plankton of the overlying water column. *Can. J. Fish. Aquat. Sci.* 41: 1523–1528.

Carney, R. S. 1981. Bioturbation and biodeposition. In A. J. Boucot (ed.), *Principles of Benthic Marine Paleoecology,* pp 357–399. Academic Press, New York.

Churchill, J. H. 1989. The effect of commercial trawling on sediment resuspension and transport over the middle Atlantic Bight continental shelf. *Cont. Shelf Res.* 9: 841–864.

Commito, J. A. 1982a. Importance of predation by infaunal polychaetes in controlling the structure of a soft-bottom community in Maine, USA. *Mar. Biol.* 68: 77–81.

Commito, J. A. 1982b. Effects of *Lunatia heros* predation on the population dynamics of *Mya arenaria* and *Macoma balthica* in Maine, USA. *Mar. Biol.* 69: 187–193.

Commito, J. A. and W. G. Ambrose, Jr. 1985. Multiple trophic levels in soft-bottom communities. *Mar. Ecol. Prog. Ser.* 26: 289–293.

Commito, J. A. and E. M. Boncavage. 1989. Suspension-feeders and coexisting infauna: An enhancement counter-example. *J. Exp. Mar. Biol. Ecol.* 125: 33–42.

Commito, J. A., C. A. Currier, L. R. Kane, K. A. Reinsel and I. M. Ulm. 1995. Dispersal dynamics of the bivalve *Gemma gemma* in a patchy environment. *Ecol. Monogr.* 65: 1–20.

Conlan, K. E., H. S. Lenihan, R. G. Kvitek and J. S. Oliver. 1998. Ice scour disturbance to benthic communities in the Canadian High Arctic. *Mar. Ecol. Prog. Ser.* 166: 1–16.

Connell, J. H. 1975. Some mechanisms producing structure in natural communities: A model and some evidence from field experiments. In M. L. Cody and J. M. Diamond (eds.), *Ecology and Evolution of Communities,* pp. 460–490. Belknap Press, Cambridge, MA.

Connell, J. H. 1985. The consequences of variation in initial settlement vs. post-settlement mortality in rocky intertidal communities. *J. Exp. Mar. Biol. Ecol.* 93: 11–45.

Connell, J. H. and R. O. Slayter. 1977. Mechanisms of succession in natural communities and their role in community stability and organization. *Amer. Natur.* 111: 1119–1144.

Connolly, S. R. and J. Roughgarden. 1999. Theory of marine communities: Competition, predation, and recruitment-dependent interaction strength. *Ecol. Monogr.* 63: 277–296.

Cushing, D. H. 1971. The dependence of recruitment on parent stock in different groups of fisheries. *J. Cons. Int. Explor. Mer.* 33: 340–362.

Cushing, D. H. 1988. The study of stock and recruitment. In J. A. Gulland (ed.), *Fish Population Dynamics,* pp. 105–128. Wiley, New York.

Daborn, G. R., C. L. Amos, M. Brylinksy, H. Christian, G. Drapeau, R. W. Faas, J. Grant, B. Long, G. M. E. Perillo and M. C. Piccolo. 1993. An ecological cascade effect: Migratory birds affect stability of intertidal sediments. *Limnol. Oceanogr.* 38: 225–231.

Dauer, D. M., R. M. Ewing, G. H. Tourtellotte, W. T. Harlan, J. W. Sourbeer and H. R. Barker, Jr. 1982. Predation, resource limitation, and the structure of benthic infaunal communities of the lower Chesapeake Bay. *Internationale Revue der Gesamten Hydrobiologie* 67: 477–489.

Dauwe, B. M. J. Herman and C. H. R. Heip. 1998. Community structure and biotrubation potential of marcofauna at four North Sea stations with contrasting food supply. *Mar. Ecol. Prog. Ser.* 173: 67–83.

Davis, F. M. 1925. Quantitative studies on the fauna of the sea bottom. No. 2. Results of the investigations in the Southern North Sea. 1921–1924. *Fish. Invest. Series ll.* 8: 1–50.

Dayton, P. K. 1971. Competition, disturbance and community organization: The provision and subsequent utilization of space in a rocky intertidal community. *Ecol. Monogr.* 41: 351–389.

Dayton, P. K. 1989. Interdecadal variation in an Antarctic sponge and its predators from oceanographic climate shifts. *Science* 245: 1484–1486.

Dayton, P. K. 1990. Polar benthos. In W. O. Smith (ed.), *Polar Oceanography, Part B: Chemistry, Biology, and Geology,* pp. 631–685. Academic Press, London.

Dayton, P. K. and J. S. Oliver. 1977. Antarctic soft-bottom benthos in oligotrophic and eutrophic environments. *Science* 197: 55–58.

Dayton, P. K. and J. S. Oliver. 1980. An evaluation of experimental analyses of population and community patterns in benthic marine environments. In K. R. Tenore and B. C. Coull (eds.), *Marine Benthic Dynamics,* pp. 93–120. University of South Carolina Press, Columbia.

Dayton, P. K., G. A. Robilliard, R. T. Paine and L. B. Dayton. 1969. Anchor ice formation in McMurdo Sound, Antarctica, and its biological effects. *Science* 163: 273–274.

Dayton, P. K., G. A. Robilliard and R. T. Paine. 1970. Benthic faunal zonation as a result of anchor ice at McMurdo Sound, Antarctica. In M. W. Holdgate (ed), *Antarctic Ecology,* pp. 244–258. Academic Press, London.

Dayton P. K., S. F. Thrush, M. T. Agardy and R. J. Hofman. 1995. Environmental effects of marine fishing. *Aquat. Conserv.* 5: 205–232.

DeAngelis, D. L. 1983. *Current Trends in Foodweb Theory.* Oak Ridge National Laboratory, Oak Ridge, TN.

Denny, M. W. and M. F. Shibata. 1989. Consequences of surf-zone turbulence for settlement and eternal fertilization. *Amer. Natur.* 134: 859–889.

DeVlas, J. 1979. Annual food intake by plaice and flounder in a tidal flat area in the Dutch Wadden Sea with special reference to consumption of regenerating parts of macrobenthic prey. *Neth. J. Sea Res.* 13: 117–153.

Diaz, R. J. and R. Rosenberg. 1995. Marine benthic hypoxia: A review of its ecological effects and the behavioral responses of benthic macrofauna. *Oceanogr. Mar. Biol. Annu. Rev.* 33: 245–303

Doherty, P. J. and D. McB. Williams. 1988. The replenishment of coral reef fish populations. *Oceanogr. Mar. Biol. Annu. Rev.* 26: 487–551.

Dunbar, R. B. 1981. Sedimentation and the history of upwelling and climate in high fertility areas of the northeastern Pacific Ocean. Ph. D. Thesis, University of California at San Diego.

Dyer, K. R. 1986. *Coastal and Estuarine Sediment Dynamics.* John Wiley, Chichester, England.

Eagle, R. A. 1973. Benthic studies in the south east of Liverpool Bay. *Estuar. Coast. Shelf Sci.* 1: 285–299.

Eagle, R. A. 1975. Natural fluctuations in a soft bottom benthic community. *J. Mar. Biol. Assoc. U. K.* 55: 865–878.

Eckman, J. E. 1983. Hydrodynamic processes affecting benthic recruitment. *Limnol. Oceanogr.* 28: 241–257.

Eckman, J. E. 1985. Flow disruption by an animal-tube mimic affects sediment bacterial colonization. *J. Mar. Res.* 43: 419–435.

Eckman, J. E. 1990. A model of passive settlement by planktonic larvae onto bottoms of differing roughness. *Limnol. Oceanogr.* 35: 887–901.

Eckman, J. E. 1996. Closing the larval loop: Linking larval ecology to the population dynamics of marine benthic invertebrates. *J. Exp. Mar. Biol. Ecol.* 200: 207–237.

Eckman, J. E., A. R. M. Nowell and P. A. Jumars. 1981. Sediment destabilization by animal tubes. *J. Mar. Res.* 37: 437–457.

Eggleston, D. B., R. N. Lipcius and A. H. Hines. 1992. Density-dependent predation by blue crabs upon infaunal clam species with contrasting distribution and abundance patterns. *Mar. Ecol. Prog. Ser.* 85: 55–68.

Elmgren, R., S. Ankar, B. Marteleur and G. Ejdung. 1986. Adult interference with postlarvae in soft sediments: The *Pontoporeia-Macoma* example. *Ecology* 67: 827–836.

Emerson, C. W. 1990. Influence of sediment disturbance and water flow on the growth of the soft-shell clam, *Mya arenaria* L. *Can. J. Fish. Aquat. Sci.* 47: 1655–1663.

Engel, J. and R. G. Kvitek. 1995. Effects of otter trawling on a benthic community in Monterey Bay National Marine Sanctuary. *Conserv. Biol.* 12: 1204–1214.

Fager, E. W. 1964. Marine sediments: Effects of tube-building polychaetes. *Science* 143: 356–359.

Fauchald, K. and P. A. Jumars. 1979. The diet of worms: A study of polychaete feeding guilds. *Oceanogr. Mar. Biol. Annu. Rev.* 17: 193–28.

Fenchel, T. 1978. The ecology of micro- and meiobenthos. *Annu. Rev. Ecol. Syst.* 9: 99–121.

Fenchel, T. and R. J. Riedl. 1970. The sulfide system: New biotic community underneath the oxidized layer in marine sand bottoms. *Mar. Biol.* 7: 255–268.

Fielman, K. T., S. A. Woodin, M. D. Walla and D. E. Lincoln. 1999. Widespread occurrence of natural halogenated organics among temperate marine infauna. *Mar. Ecol. Prog. Ser.* 181: 1–12.

Fonseca, M. S., J. S. Fisher, S. Zieman and G. W. Thayer. 1982. Influence of seagrass (*Zostera marina*) on current flow. *Estuar. Coast. Shelf Sci.* 15: 351–361.

Ford, E. 1923. Animal communities of the level sea bottom in the waters adjacent to Plymouth. *J. Mar. Biol. Assoc. U. K.* 13: 164–224.

Ford, S. E. and M. R. Tripp. 1996. Diseases and defense mechanisms. In V. S. Kennedy et al. (eds.), *The Eastern Oyster* Crassostrea virginica, pp. 581–660. Maryland Sea Grant Publications, College Park, MD.

Fréchette, M., D. Lefaivre and C. A. Butman. 1993. Bivalve feeding and the benthic boundary layer. In R. Dame (ed.), *Bivalve Filter Feeding in Estuarine and Coastal Ecosystem Processes*, pp. 325–369. NATO ASI Series Vol. 633. Springer, Berlin.

Fukuyama, A. K. and J. S. Oliver. 1985. Sea star and walrus predation on bivalves in Norton Sound, Bering Sea, Alaska. *Ophelia* 24:17–36.

Gaines, S. D. and M. D. Bertness. 1992. Dispersal of juveniles and variable recruitment in sessile marine species. *Nature.* 360: 579–580.

Gallagher, E. D., P. A. Jumars and D. D. Trueblood. 1983. Facilitation of soft-bottom benthic succession by tube builders. *Ecology* 64: 1200–1216.

Graf, G. 1992. Benthic-pelagic coupling: A benthic review. *Oceanogr. Mar. Biol. Annu. Rev.* 30: 149–190.

Grant, J. 1981. Sediment transport and disturbance on an intertidal sandflat: Infuanal distribution and recolonization. *Mar. Ecol. Prog. Ser.* 6: 249–255.

Grant, J. 1983. The relative magnitude of biological and physical sediment reworking in an intertidal community. *J. Mar. Res.* 41: 673–689.

Grant, W. D. and O. S. Madsen. 1986. The continental-shelf bottom boundary layer. *Annu. Rev. Fluid Mech.* 18: 265–305.

Grassle, J. F. and J. P. Grassle. 1974. Opportunistic life histories and genetic systems in marine benthic polychaetes. *J. Mar. Res.* 32: 253–284.

Gray, J. S. 1974. Animal–sediment relationships. *Oceanogr. Mar. Biol. Annu. Rev.* 12: 223–261.

Gray, J. S. 1981. *The Ecology of Marine Sediments.* Cambridge University Press, Cambridge.

Grebmeier, J. M., C. P. McRoy and H. M. Feder. 1988. Pelagic-benthic coupling on the shelf of the northern Bering and Chukchi Seas. I. Food supply and biomass. *Mar. Ecol. Prog. Ser.* 48: 57–67.

Grebmeier, J. M., H. M. Feder and C. P. McRoy. 1989. Pelagic-benthic coupling on the shelf of the northern Bering and Chuckchi Seas. ll. Benthic community structure. *Mar. Ecol. Prog. Ser.* 51: 253–269.

Hall, S. J. 1994. Physical disturbance and marine benthic communities: Life in unconsolidated sediments. *Oceanogr. Mar. Biol. Annu. Rev.* 32: 179–239.

Hall, S. J., D. Raffaelli and W. R. Turrell. 1991. Predator caging experiments in marine systems: A re-examination of their value. *Amer. Natur.* 136: 657–672.

Hannon, C . A. 1984. Planktonic larvae may act like passive particles in turbulent near-bottom flows. *Limnol. Oceanogr.* 29: 1108–1116.

Hay, M. E. 1981. The functional morphology of turf-forming seaweeds: Persistence in stressful habitats. *Ecology* 52: 739–750.

Hay, M. E. 1986. Associational plant defenses and the maintenance of species diversity: Turing competitors into accomplices. *Amer. Natur.* 128: 617–641.

Hay, M. E. and W. Fenical. 1989. Marine plant–herbivore interactions: The ecology of chemical defenses. *Annu. Rev. Ecol. Syst.* 19: 111–145.

Heck, K. L., Jr. and T. A. Thoman. 1984. The nursery role of seagrass meadows in the upper and lower reaches of the Chesapeake Bay. *Estuaries* 7: 70–92.

Highsmith, R. C. 1982. Induced settlement and metamorphosis of sand dollar (*Dendraster excentricus*) larvae in predator-free sites: Adult sand dollar beds. *Ecology* 63: 329–337.

Huffaker, C. B. 1958. Experimental studies on predation: Dispersion factors and predator–prey oscillations. *Hilgardia* 27: 343–383.

Hughes, R. N. 1969. A study of feeding in *Scrobicularia plana. J. Mar. Biol. Assoc. U. K.* 49: 805–823.

Hulscher, J. B. 1973. Burying-depth and trematode infection in *Macoma balthica. Neth. J. Sea Res.* 6: 141–156.

Hurlberg, L. W. and J. S. Oliver. 1980. Caging manipulations in marine soft-bottom communities: Importance of animal interactions or sedimentary habitat modifications. *Can J. Fish. Aquat. Sci.* 37: 1130–1139.

Irlandi, E. A. and C. H. Peterson. 1991. Modification of animal habitat by large plants: Mechanisms by which seagrasses influence clam growth. *Oecologia* 87: 307–318.

Johnson, R. G. 1970. Variation in diversity within benthic communities. *Amer. Nat.* 104: 285–300.

Johnson, R. G. 1973. Conceptual models of benthic marine communities. In T. J. M. Schopf (ed.), *Models in Paleobiology*, pp. 631–685. Freeman and Cooper, San Francisco.

Jones, C. G., J. H. Lawton and M. Shachak. 1994. Organisms as ecosystem engineers. *Oikos* 69: 373–386.

Jones, N. S. 1950. Marine bottom communities. *Biol. Rev.* 25: 283–313.

Josenhans, H. and C. M. T. Woodworth-Lynas. 1988. Enigmatic linear furrows and pits on the upper continental slope, northwest Labrador Sea: Are they sediment furrows or feeding traces? *Mar. Sed. Atl. Geol.* 24: 149–155.

Jumars, P. A. and A. R. M. Nowell. 1984. Effects of benthos on sediment transport: difficulties with functional grouping. *Cont. Shelf. Res.* 3: 115–130.

Jumars, P. A. and R. A. Wheatcroft. 1989. Responses of benthos to changing food quantity and quality, with a focus on deposit feeding and bioturbation. In W. H. Berger et al. (eds.), *Productivity of the Oceans: Present and Past*, pp. 235–253. Wiley, New York.

Kennedy, V. S. 1980. *Estuarine Perspectives.* Academic Press, New York.

Kennett, G. 1990. *Marine Geology.* Academic Press, New York.

Kennicutt, M. C. II, P. N. Booth, T. L. Wade, S. T. Sweet, R. Rezak, F. J. Kelly, J. M. Brooks, B. J. Presly and D. A. Wiesenberg. 1996. Geochemical patterns in sediments near off-shore production platforms. *Can. J. Fish. Aquat. Sci.* 53: 2554–2566.

Kikuchi, T. 1966. An ecological study on animal communities of the *Zostera marina* belt in Tomioka Bay: Amakusa, Kyushu. *Publ. Amakusa Mar. Biol. Lab.* 1: 1–106.

Kikuchi, T. and J. M. Peres. 1977. Animal communities in seagrass beds: A review. In C. P. McRoy and C. Helfferich (eds.), *Seagrass Ecosystems: A Scientific Perspective*, pp. 147–193. Dekker, New York.

Kinne, O. (ed.) 1980. *Diseases of Marine Animals.* Vol. I. *General aspects, Protozoa to Gastropoda.* Wiley, New York.

Kinne, O. (ed.) 1983. *Diseases of Marine Animals.* Vol. II. *Introduction, Bivalvia to Scaphopoda.* John Wiley & Sons, New York.

Kneib, R. T. 1984. Patterns of invertebrate distribution and abundance in the intertidal salt marsh: Causes and questions. *Estuaries* 7: 392–412.

Kneib, R. T. 1991. Indirect effects in experimental studies of marine soft-sediment communities. *Am. Zool.* 31: 874–885.

Kvitek, R. G., A. R. DeGange and M. K. Beitler. 1991. Paralytic shellfish poisoning toxins mediate feeding behavior of sea otters. *Limnol. Oceanogr.* 36: 393–404.

Kvitek, R. G, J. S. Oliver, A. R. DeGange and B. S. Anderson. 1992. Changes in Alaskan soft-bottom prey communities along a gradient in sea otter predation. *Ecology* 73: 413–428.

Lalli, C. M. and T. R. Parsons. 1993. *Biological Oceanography: An Introduction.* Butterworth-Heinemann, Oxford.

Lafferty, K. D. and A. M. Kuris. 1999. How environmental stress affects the impacts of parasites. *Limnol. Oceanogr.* 44: 925–931.

Legendre, L. and S. Demers. 1984. Towards a dynamical biological oceanography and limnology. *Can. J. Fish. Aquat. Sci.* 41: 2–19.

Lenihan, H. S. 1999. Physical–biological coupling on oyster reefs: How habitat structure influences individual production. *Ecol. Monogr.* 69: 1–23.

Lenihan, H. S. and J. S. Oliver. 1995. Anthropogenic and natural disturbances to marine benthic communities in Antarctica. *Ecol. Appl..* 5: 311–326.

Lenihan, H. S. and C. H. Peterson. 1998. How habitat degrdation through fishery disturbance enhances the impacts of hypoxia on oyster reefs. *Ecol. Appl.* 8: 128–140.

Lenihan, H. S., K. A. Kiest, K. E. Conlan, P. N. Slattery, B. H. Konar and J. S. Oliver. 1995. Patterns of survival and behavior of marine invertebrates exposed to contaminated sediments from McMurdo Station, Antarctica. *J. Exp. Mar. Biol. Ecol.* 192: 233–255.

Lenihan, H. S., F. Micheli, S. W. Shelton and C. H. Peterson. 1999. The influence of multiple environmental stressors on susceptibility to parasites: An experimental determination with oysters. *Limnol. Oceanogr.* 44: 910–924.

Lenihan, H. S., C. H. Peterson and J. M. Allen. 1996. Does flow also have a direct effect on growth of active suspension feeders: An experimental test with oysters. *Limnol. Oceanogr.* 41: 1359–1366.

Lenihan, H. S., C. H. Peterson, J. E. Byers. G. H. Grabowski, G. W. Thayer and D. R.

Colby. In press. Cascading of habitat degradation: Oyster reefs invaded by refugee fishes escaping stress. *Ecol. Appl.*

Levin, L. A. 1981. Dispersion, feeding behavior and competition in two spionid polychaetes. *J. Mar. Res.* 39: 99–117.

Levin, L. A. 1982. Intereference interactions among tube dwelling polychaetes in a dense infaunal assemblage. *J. Exp. Mar. Biol. Ecol.* 65: 107–119.

Levin, L. A. 1984. Life history and dispersal patterns in a dense infaunal polychaete assemblage: Community structure and response to disturbance. *Ecology* 65: 1185–1200.

Levin, L. A. 1991. Interactions between metazoan and large, aglutinating protozoans: Implications for the community structure of deep-sea benthos. *Amer. Zool* 31: 886–900.

Levin, S. A. 1992. The problem of pattern and scale in ecology. *Ecology* 73: 1943–1967.

Levinton, J. S. 1977. Ecology of shallow water deposit feeding communities, Quissett Harbor, Massachusetts. In B. Coull (ed.), *Ecology of Marine Benthos*, pp. 191–227. University of South Carolina Press, Columbia.

Levinton, J. S. 1979. The effect of density upon deposit-feeding populations: Feeding and floating of *Hydrobia ventrosa* Montagu (Gastropoda: Prosobranchia). *Oecologia* 43: 27–39.

Levinton, J. S. 1985. Complex interactions of a deposit feeder with its resources: Roles of density, a competitor, and detrital addition in the growth and survival of the mudsnail *Hydrobia totteni. Mar. Ecol. Prog. Ser.* 22: 31–40.

Levinton, J. S. 1991. Variable feeding behavior in three species of *Macoma* (Bivalvia: Tellinacea) as a response to water flow and sediment transport. *Mar. Biol.* 110: 375–383.

Lewin, R. 1986. Supply-side ecology. *Science* 234: 25–27.

Lewis, C. F. M. and S. M. Blasco. 1990. Character and distribution of sea-ice and iceberg scours. In J. I. Clark (ed.), *Workshop on Ice Scouring and Design of Offshore Pipelines, Calgary, Alberta, April 18–19, 1990*, pp. 57–101. Canada Oil and Gas Lands Administration, Energy, Mines, and Resources, Calgary.

Lien, R., A. Solheim, A. Elverhii and K. Rokoengen. 1989. Iceberg scouring and sea bed morphology on the eastern Weddell Sea shelf, Antarctica. *Polar Res.* 7: 43–57.

Lopez, G. R. and J. S. Levinton. 1987. Ecology of deposit-feeding animals in marine sediments. *Quart. Rev. Biol.* 62: 235–260.

Lopez, G. R., G. Taghon and J. S. Levinton. 1989. Ecology of marine deposit feeders. Lecture notes on coastal and estuarine studies 31. Springer, New York.

Luckenbach, M. W. 1984. Biogenic structure and foraging by five species of shorebirds (Charadrii). *Estuarine, Coastal and Shelf Sci.* 19: 691–696.

Luckenbach, M. W. 1986. Sediment stability and animal tubes: The role of hydrodynamic processes and biotic activity. *Limnol. Oceanogr.* 31: 779–787.

MacArthur, R. 1960. On the relative abundance of species. *Amer. Natur.* 94: 25–34.

MacIntyre, H., G, Richard and D. C. Douglas. 1996. Mircophytonbenthos: The ecological role of the "Secret Garden" of unvegetated, shallow-water marine habitats. I. Distribution, abundance, and primary production. *Estuaries* 19: 186–201.

Mann, K. H. 1980. Benthic secondary production. In R. S. K. Barnes and K. H. Mann (eds.), *Fundamentals of Aquatic Ecosystems*, pp. 103–118. Blackwell Scientific Publications, Oxford.

May, R. M. 1974. *Stability and Complexity in Model Ecosystems*. Princeton University Press, Princeton, NJ.

McCall, P. L. 1977. Community patterns and adaptive strategies of the infaunal benthos of Long Island Sound. *J. Mar. Res.* 35: 221–266.

McCall, P. L. and M. J. S. Tevesz (eds.). 1982. *Animal–Sediment Relations*. Plenum Press, New York.

McLachlan, A. and P. Hesp. 1984. Faunal response to morphology and water circulation of a sandy beach with cusps. *Mar . Ecol. Prog. Ser.* 19: 133–144.

McLachlan, A. and E. Jaramillo. 1995. Zonation on sandy beaches. *Oceanogr. Mar. Biol. Annu. Rev.* 33: 305–335.

Menge, B. A. and J. P. Sutherland. 1976. Species diversity gradients: Synthesis of the roles of predation, competition, and temporal heterogeneity. *Amer. Natur.* 110: 351–369.

Menge, B. A. and J. P. Sutherland. 1987. Community regulation: Variation in disturbance, competition, and predation in relation to gradients of environmental stress and recruitment. *Amer. Natur.* 130: 730–757.

Micheli, F. 1996. Predation intensity in estuarine soft bottoms: Between-habitat comparisons and experimental artifacts. *Mar. Ecol. Prog. Ser.* 141: 295–302.

Micheli, F. 1997. Effects of predators foraging behavior on patterns of prey mortality in marine soft bottoms. *Ecol. Monogr.* 67: 203–224.

Micheli, F. 1999. Eutrophication, fisheries, and consumer-resource dynamics in marine pelagic ecosystems. *Science* 285: 1396–1398.

Micheli, F. and C. H. Peterson. 1999. Estuarine vegetated habitats as corridors for predator movement. *Cons. Biol.* 13: 869–881.

Miller, D. C., I. N. McCave and P. D. Komar. 1977. Threshold of sediment motion under unidirectional currents. *Sedimentology* 24: 507–527.

Mills, E. L. 1969. The community concept in marine zoology, with comments on continua and instability in some marine communities: A review. *J. Fish. Res. Bd. Can.* 26: 1415–1428.

Murdoch, W. W. 1994. Population regulation in theory and practice. *Ecology* 75: 271–287.

Murphy, G. I. 1972. Fisheries in upwelling regions—with special reference to Peruvian waters. *Geoforum* 11: 63–71.

Muschenheim, D. K. 1987. The dynamics of near-bed seston flux and suspension-feeding benthos. *J. Mar. Res.* 45: 473–496.

Myers, A. C. 1977a. Sediment processing in a marine subtidal sandy bottom community. I. Physical aspects. *J. Mar. Res.* 35: 609–632.

Myers, A. C. 1977b. Sediment processing in a marine subtidal sandy bottom community. II. Biological consequences. *J. Mar. Res.* 35: 633–647.

Myers, N. 1995. Environmental unknowns. *Science* 269: 358–360.

National Research Council. 1993. Managing wastewater in coastal urban areas. National Academy Press, Washington, DC.

Nelson, W. G. 1979. An analysis of structural pattern in an eelgrass (*Zostera marina*) amphipod community. *J. Exp. Mar. Biol. Ecol.* 39: 231–264.

Newell, R. C., L. J. Seiderer and D. R. Hitchcock. 1998. The impact of dredging works in coastal waters: A review of the sensitivity to disturbance and subsequent recovery of biological resources on the sea bed. *Oceanogr. Mar. Biol. Annu. Rev.* 36: 127–178.

Nowell, A. R. M. and P. A. Jumars. 1984. Flow environments of aquatic benthos. *Annu. Rev. Ecol. Syst.* 15: 303–328.

Nybakken, J. W. 1997. *Marine Biology: An Ecological Approach*. Benjamin Cummings, Menlo Park, CA.

Olaffsson, E. B. 1989. Contrasting influences of suspension-feeding and deposit-feeding populations of *Macoma balthica* on infaunal recruitment. *Mar. Ecol. Prog. Ser.* 55: 171–179.

Olaffsson, E. B., C. H. Peterson and W. G. Ambrose, Jr. 1994. Does recruitment limitation structure populations and communities of macro-invertebrates in marine soft sediments: The relative significance of pre- and post-settlement processes. *Oceanogr. Mar. Biol. Annu. Rev.* 32: 65–109.

Oliver, J. S. 1984. Selection for asexual reproduction in an Antacrtic polychaete worm. *Mar. Ecol. Prog. Ser.* 19: 33–38.

Oliver, J. S. and R. G. Kvitek. 1984. Side-scan sonar records and diver observations of the gray whale (*Eschrictus robustus*) feeding grounds. *Biol. Bull.* 167: 264–269.

Oliver, J. S. and P. N. Slattery. 1985. Destruction and opportunity on the seafloor: Effects of gray whale feeding. *Ecology* 66: 1965–1975.

Oliver, J. S., P. N. Slattery, L. W. Hulberg and J. W. Nybakken. 1980. Relationships between wave disturbance and zonation of benthic invertebrate communities along a subtidal high energy beach in Monterey Bay, California. *Fish. Bull.* 78: 437–454.

Oliver, J. S., P. N. Slattery, M. A. Silberstein and E. F. O'Connor. 1984. Gray whale feeding on dense ampeliscid amphipod communities near Bamfield, British Columbia. *Can. J. Zool.* 62: 41–49.

Olsgard, F. and J. S. Gray. 1995. A comprehensive analysis of the effects of offshore oil and gas exploration and production on the benthiccommunities of the Norwegian continental shelf. *Mar. Ecol. Prog. Ser.* 122: 277–306.

O'Neill, R. V., D. L. DeAngelis, J. B. Wade and T. F. H. Allen. 1986. *Hierarchial Concept of Ecosystems*. Princeton University Press, Princeton, NJ.

Orth, R. J. 1973. Benthic fauna of eelgrass, *Zostera marina*, beds. *Chesapeake Sci.* 14: 258–269.

Orth, R. J. 1975. Destruction of eelgrass, *Zostera marina*, by the cownose ray, *Rhinoptera bona-*

sus, in the Chesapeake Bay. *Chesapeake Sci.* 16: 205–208.

Orth, R. J. 1977. The importance of sediment stability in seagrass communities. In B. C. Coull (ed.), *Ecology of Marine Benthos*, pp. 281–300. University of South Carolina Press, Columbia.

Orth, R. J., K. L. Heck and J. van Montfrans. 1984. Faunal communities in seagrass beds: A review of the influence of plant structure and prey characteristics on predator–prey relationships. *Estuaries* 7: 339–350.

Paerl, H. W. 1985. Enhancement of marine primary production by nitrogen-enriched acid rain. *Nature* 315: 747–749.

Paerl, H. W., J. L. Pinckney, J. M. Fear, B. L. Peierls. 1998. Ecosystem responses to internal and watershed organic matter loading: Consequences for hypoxia in the eutrophying Neuse River Estuary, North Carolina, USA. *Mar. Ecol. Prog. Ser.* 166: 17–25.

Paine, R. T. 1966. Food web complexity and species diversity. *Amer. Nat.* 100: 65–75.

Paine, R. T and S. A. Levin. 1981. Intertidal landscapes: Disturbance and the dynamics of pattern. *Ecol. Monogr.* 51: 145–178.

Palmer, M. A. 1988. Epibenthic predators and marine meiofauna: A review of conceptual models explaining passive transport and active emergence with implications for recruitment. *Ecology* 69: 1251–1259.

Palmer, M. A, J. D. Allan and C. A. Butman. 1996. Dispersal as a regional processes affecting the local dynamics of marine and stream benthic invertebrates. *Trends Ecol. Evol.* 11: 322–326.

Parsons, T. R., M. Takahashi and B. Hargrave. 1984. *Biological Oceanographic Processes.* Pergamon Press, New York, NY.

Pawlik, J. R. 1992. Chemical ecology of the settlement of benthic marine invertebrates. *Oceanogr. Mar. Biol. Annu. Rev.* 30: 273–335.

Pawlik, J. R. and C. A. Butman. 1993. Settlement of a marine tube worm as a function of current velocity: Interacting effects of hydrodynamics and behavior. *Limnol. Oceanogr.* 38: 1730–1740.

Pawlik, J. R., C. A. Butman and V. R. Starczak. 1991. Hydrodynamic facilitation of gregarious settlement of a reef-building tube worm. *Science* 251: 421–424.

Paynter, K. T. and E. M. Burreson. 1991. Effects of *Perkinsus marinus* infection in the eastern oyster, *Crassostrea virginica*: Disease development and impact on growth rate at different salinities. *J. Shellfish Res.* 10: 425–431.

Pearson, T. H. and P. R. O'Barnett. 1987. Long-term changes in benthic populations in some West European coastal areas. *Estuaries* 10: 220–226.

Pearson, T. H. and R. Rosenberg. 1978. Macrobenthic succession in relation to organic enrichment and pollution of the marine environment. *Oceanogr. Mar. Biol. . Rev.* 16: 229–311.

Petersen, C. G. J. 1918. The sea bottom and its production of fish food. A survey of the work done in connection with the valuation of the Danish waters from 1883–1917. *Rap. Danish Biol. Stat.* 25: 1–62.

Petersen, C. G. J. 1924. A brief survey of the animal communities in Danish waters. *Amer. J. Sci. Ser.* 57: 343–354.

Peterson, C. H. 1977. Competitive organization of the soft bottom macrobenthic communities of southern California lagoons. *Mar. Biol.* 43: 343–359.

Peterson, C. H. 1979. Predation, competitive exclusion, and diversity on soft-sediment benthic communities of estuaries and lagoons. In R. J. Livingston (ed.), *Ecological Processes in Coastal Marine Systems*, pp. 233–264. Plenum Press, New York.

Peterson, C. H. 1982. The importance of predation and intra- and interspecific competition in the population biology of two infaunal suspension-feeding bivalves, *Protothaca staminea* and *Chione undatella*. *Ecol. Monogr.* 52: 437–475.

Peterson, C. H. 1991. Intertidal zonation of marine invertebrates in sand and mud. *Amer. Sci.* 70: 236–249.

Peterson, C. H. 2001. The "Exxon Valdez" oil spill in Alaska: Acute, indirect and chronic effects on the ecosystem. *Adv.in Mar. Biol.* 39: 1–103.

Peterson, C. H. and R. Black. 1987. Resource depletion by active suspension feeders on tidal flats: Influence of local density and tidal elevation. *Limnol. Oceanogr.* 32: 143–166.

Peterson, C. H. and R. Black. 1991. Preliminary evidence for progressive sestonic food depletion in incoming tide over a broad tidal sand flat. *E. Coast. Shelf Sci.* 32: 405–413.

Peterson, C. H. and R. Black. 1993. Experimental tests of the advantages and disadvantages of high density for two coexisting cockles in a Southern Ocean lagoon. *J. Anim. Ecol.* 62: 614–633.

Peterson, C. H. and R. Black. 1994. An experimentalist's challenge: When artifacts of intervention interact with treatment. *Mar. Ecol. Prog. Ser.* 111: 289–297.

Peterson, C. H. and J. Lubchenco. 1997. On the value of marine ecosystem services. In G. C. Daily (ed.), *Nature's Services: Societal Dependence on Natural Ecosystems*, pp. 177–194. Island Press, Chapel Hill, NC.

Peterson, C. H. and M. L. Quammen. 1982. Siphon nipping: Its importance to small fishes and its impact on growth of the bivalve *Protothaca staminea* (Conrad). *J. Exp. Mar. Biol. Ecol.* 63: 249–268.

Peterson, C. H. and G. A. Skilleter. 1994. Control of foraging behavior of individuals within an ecosystem context: The clam Macoma balthica, flow environment, and siphon-cropping fishes. *Oecologia* 100: 256–267.

Peterson, C. H., H. C. Summerson and P. B. Duncan. 1984. The influence of seagrass cover on population structure and individual growth rate of a suspension-feeding bivalve, *Mercenaria mercenaria*. *J. Mar. Res.* 42: 123–148.

Peterson, C. H., H. C. Summerson and S. R. Fegley. 1987. Ecological consequences of mechanical harvesting of clams. *Fish. Bull.* 85: 281–298.

Peterson, C. H., M. C. Kennicutt II, R. H. Green, P. Montagna, D. E. Harper, Jr., E. N. Powell and P. F. Roscigno. 1996. Ecological consequences of environmental perturbations associated with offshore hydrocarbon production: A perspective on long-term exposure in the Gulf of Mexico. *Can. J. Fish. Aquat. Sci.* 53: 2637–2654.

Pickett, S. T. A. and P. S. White. 1985. *The Ecology of Natural Disturbance and Patch Dynamics.* Academic Press, New York.

Pilskaln, C. H., J. H. Churchill and L. M. Mayer. 1998. Resuspension of sediment by bottom trawling in the Gulf of Maine and potential geochemical consequences. *Conserv. Biol.* 12: 1223–1229.

Posey, M. H., B. R. Dumbauld and D. A. Armstrong. 1991. Effects of a burrowing mud shrimp, *Upogebia pugettensis* (Dana), on abundances of macro-infauna. *J. Exp. Mar. Biol. Ecol.* 148: 283–294.

Posey, M., W. Lindberg, T. Alphin and F. Vose. 1996. Influence of storm disturbance on an offshore benthic community. *Bull. Mar. Sci.* 59: 523–529.

Powers, S. P. 1997. Recruitment of soft-bottom benthos. Ph. D. Thesis, Texas A&M University, College Station.

Powers, S. P. Supply side ecology and soft-bottom benthic community structure: Does water column supply of larvae correspond to adult population dynamics? *Mar. Ecol. Prog. Ser.* In review.

Probert, P. K. 1984. Disturbance, sediment stability, and trophic structure of soft-bottom communities. *J. Mar. Res.* 42: 893–921.

Quammen, M. L. 1984. Predation by shore birds, fish, and crabs on invertebrates on intertidal mudflats: An experimental test. *Ecology* 65: 529–537.

Raffaelli, D. and H. Milne. 1987. An experimental investigation of the effects of shore-bird and flatfish predation on estuarine invertebrates. *E. Coast. Shelf Sci.* 24: 1–13.

Rankin, K. L., L. S. Mullineaux and W. R. Geyer. 1994. Recruitment of gem clams (*Gemma gemma*) near a headland wake. *Estuaries* 17: 655–667.

Ray, A. J. and R. C. Aller. 1985. Physical irrigation of relict burrows: Implications for sediment chemistry. *Marine Geology* 62: 371–379.

Reise, K. 1978. Experiments on epibenthic predation in the Wadden Sea. *Helgo. Wiss. Meeresunters.* 31: 55–101.

Reise, K. 1982. Long-term changes in the macrobenthic invertebrate fauna of the Wadden Sea: Are polychaetes about to take over? *Neth. J. Sea Res.* 16: 29–36.

Reise, K. 1985. *Tidal Flat Ecology.* Springer-Verlag, Berlin.

Rhoads, D. C. 1974. Organism–sediment relations on the muddy sea floor. *Oceanogr. Mar. Biol. Annu. Rev.* 12: 263–300.

Rhoads, D. C. and L. F. Boyer. 1982. The effects of marine benthos on physical properties of sediments: A successional perspective. In P. L. McCall and M. J. S. Tevesz (eds.), *Animal–Sediment Relations*, pp. 3–52. Plenum Press, New York.

Rhoads, D. C. and D. K. Young. 1970. The influence of deposit feeding organisms on sediment stability and community structure. *J. Mar. Res.* 28: 150–178.

Rhoads, D. C. and D. K. Young. 1971. Animal–sediment relations in Cape Cod Bay, Massachusetts. II. Reworking by *Molpadia oolitica. Mar. Biol.* 11: 255–261.

Rhoads, D. C., P. L. McCall and J. Y. Yingst. 1978. Disturbance and production on the estuarine seafloor. *Amer. Sci.* 66: 577–586.

Ricciardi, A. and E. Bourget. 1999. Global patterns of macroinvertebrate biomass in marine intertidal communities. *Mar. Ecol. Prog. Ser.* 185: 21–35.

Rohde, K. 1982. *Ecology of Marine Parasites.* University of Queensland Press, St. Lucia.

Ronan, T. E., Jr. 1978. Food resources and the influence of spatial pattern on feeding in the phoronid *Phoronopsis viridis. Biol. Bull.* 154: 472–484.

Rothschild, B. J., J. S. Ault, P. Goulletquer and M. Heral. 1994. Decline of the Chesapeake Bay oyster population: A century of habitat destruction and overfishing. *Mar. Ecol. Prog. Ser.* 111: 29–39.

Roughgarden, J. 1998. *The Primer of Ecological Theory.* Prentice Hall, Upper Saddle River, NJ.

Roughgarden, J., S. D. Gaines and H. Possingham. 1988. Recruitment dynamics in complex life cycles. *Science* 241: 1460–1466.

Rowe, G. T. 1981. The benthic processes of coastal upwelling ecosystems. In F. A. Richards (ed.), *Coastal Upwelling,* pp. 464–471. American Geophysical Union, Washington, DC.

Sale, P. F. 1991. Habitat structure and recruitment in coral reef fishes. In S. S. Bell, E. D. McCoy and H. R. Mushinsky (eds.), *Habitat Structure: The Physical Arrangement of Objects in Space,* pp. 196–234. Chapman and Hall, London.

Sanders, H. L. 1958. Benthic studies in Buzzards Bay. l. Animal–sediment relationships. *Limnol. Oceanogr.* 3: 245–258.

Scheltema, R. S. 1986. On dispersal and planktonic larvae of benthic invertebrates: An eclectic overview and summary of problems. *Bull. Mar. Sci.* 39: 290–322.

Schmitt, R. J. and C. W. Osenberg (eds.). 1996. *Detecting Ecological Impacts: Concepts and Applications in Coastal Habitats.* Academic Press, San Diego, CA.

Schneider, D. C. and B. A. Harrington. 1981. Timing of shorebird migration in relation to prey depletion. *Auk* 98: 801–811.

Segerstrále, S. G. 1962. Investigations on Baltic populations of the bivalve *Macoma balthica* (L.). Part II. What are the reasons for the periodic failure of recruitment and scarcity of *Macoma* in the deep waters of the inner Baltic? *Commentat. Biol. Soc. Scient. Fenn.* 24: 1–26.

Sewell, M. A. 1996. Detection of the impact of predation by migratory shorebirds – an experimental test in the Fraser River Estuary, British Columbia. *Mar. Ecol. Prog. Ser.* 144: 23–40.

Shimeta, J. and P. A. Jumars. 1991. Physical mechanisms and rates of particulate capture by suspension-feeders. *Oceanogr. Mar. Biol. Annu. Rev.* 29: 191–257.

Sindermann, C. J. 1990. *Principal Diseases of Marine Fish and Shellfish.* Vol. 2. *Diseases of Marine Shellfish.* Academic Press, New York.

Snelgrove, P. V. R. 1998. The biodiversity of macrofaunal organisms in marine sediments. *Biodiver. Conserv.* 7: 1123–1132.

Snelgrove, P. V. R. and C. A. Butman. 1994. Animal–sediment relationships revisited: Cause versus effect. *Oceanogr. Mar. Biol. Annu. Rev.* 32: 111–177.

Snelgrove, P. V. R., C. A. Butman and J. P. Grassle. 1993. Hydrodynamic enhancement of larval settlement in the bivalve *Mulinia lateralis* and the polychaete *Capitella* Sp. 1 in microdepositional environments. *J. Exp. Mar. Biol. Ecol.* 168: 71–109.

Sousa, W. P. 1984. The role of disturbance in natural communities. *Annu. Rev. Ecol. Syst.* 15: 353–391.

Sousa, W. P. 1991. Can models of soft-sediment community structure be complete without parasites? *Amer. Zool* 31: 821–830.

Sponaugle, S. and P. Lawton. 1990. Portunid crab predation on juvenile hard clams: Effects of substrate type and prey density. *Mar. Ecol. Prog. Ser.* 67: 43–53.

Sternberg, R. W. 1984. Sedimentation processes on continental shelves. In B. U. Haq and J. D. Milliman (eds.), *Marine Geology and Oceanography of Arabian Sea and Coastal Pakistan,* pp. 137–157. Van Nostrand and Reinhold, New York.

Steward, C. C., J. Pinckney, Y. Piceno and C. R. Lovell. 1992. Bacterial numbers and acitivity, microbial biomass, and productivity, and meiofaunal distribution in sediments naturally contaminated with biogenic bromophenols. *Mar. Ecol. Prog. Ser.* 90: 61–71.

Steward, C. C., S. C. Nold, D. B. Ringelberg, D. C. White and C. R. Lovell. 1996. Microbial biomass and community structures in the burrows of bromophenol producing and non-producing marine worms and surrounding sediments. *Mar. Ecol. Prog. Ser.* 133: 149–165.

Stoner, A. W. 1980. The role of seagrass biomass in the organization of the benthic macrofaunal assemblages. *Bull. Mar. Sci.* 30: 537–551.

Suchanek, T. H. 1993. Oil impacts on marine invertebrate populations and communities. *Amer. Zool* 33: 510–523.

Suchanek, T. H. 1994. Temperate coastal marine communities—biodiversity and threats. *Amer. Zool* 34: 100–114.

Summerson, H. C. and C. H. Peterson. 1984. Role of predation in organizing benthic communities of a temperate-zone seagrass bed. *Mar. Ecol. Prog. Ser.* 15: 63–77.

Swartz, R. C., F. A. Cole, D. W. Schultz and D. W. DeBen. 1986. Ecological changes in the Southern California Bight near a large sewage outfall: Benthic conditions in 1980 and 1983. *Mar. Ecol. Prog. Ser.* 31: 1–13.

Swennen, C. and H. L. Ching. 1974. Observation on the trematode *Parvatrema affinis,* causative agent of crawling tracks of *Macoma balthica. Neth. J. Sea Res.* 8: 108–115.

Taghon, G. L., A. R. M. Nowell and P. A. Jumars. 1980. Induction of suspension feeding in spionid polychaetes by high particulate fluxes. *Science* 210: 562–564.

Tenore, K. R. 1972. Macrobenthos of the Pamlico River estuary, North Carolina. *Ecol. Monogr.* 42: 51–69.

Tenore, K. R. and B. C. Coull. 1980. *Marine Benthic Dynamics.* The Belle W. Baruch Library in Marine Science No. 11. University of South Carolina Press, Columbia.

Tevesz, M. J. S. and P. L. McCall (eds.). 1983. *Biotic Interactions in Recent and Fossil Benthic Communities.* Plenum Press, New York.

Thayer, C. W. 1983. Sediment-mediated biological disturbance and the evolution of marine benthos. In M. J. S. Tevesz and P. L. McCall (eds.), *Biotic Interactions in Recent and Fossil Benthic Communities,* pp. 479–625. Plenum Press, New York.

Thayer, G. W., S. M. Adams and M. W. LaCroix. 1975. Structural and functional aspecys of recently established *Zostera marina* community. In L. E. Conin (ed.), *Estuarine Research,* Vol I: *Chemistry, Biology, and the Estuarine System,* pp. 518-540. Academic Press, New York.

Thayer, G. W., W. J. Kenworthy and M. S. Fonseca. 1984. The Ecology of Eelgrass Meadows of the Atlantic Coast: A Community Profile. U. S. Fish Wildl. Serv. FWS/OBS–84/02.

Thiel, H. 1978. Benthos in upwelling regions. In R. Boje and M. Tomzack (eds.), *Upwelling Ecosystems,* pp. 124–138. Springer-Verlag, New York.

Thistle, D. S. 1981. Natural physical disturbance and communities of marine soft-bottoms. *Mar. Ecol. Prog. Ser.* 6: 223–281.

Thistle, D. S., C. Ertman and K. Fauchald. 1991. The fauna of the HEBBLE site: Patterns in standing stock and sediment-dynamic effects. *Mar. Geol.* 99: 413–422.

Thorson, G. 1950. Reproductive and larval ecology of marine bottom invertebrates. *Biol. Rev.* 25: 1–45.

Thorson, G. 1957. Bottom communities (sublittoral and shallow shelf). In *Treatise on Marine Ecology and Paleoecology,* Vol. I. Geol. Soc. Amer., Memoir 67: 461–534.

Thorson, G. 1966. Some factors influencing the recruitment and establishment of marine benthic communities. *Neth. J. Sea Res.* 3: 267–293.

Thrush, S. F. 1991. Spatial patterns in soft-bottom communites. *Trends Ecol. Evolut.* 6: 75–79.

Thrush, S. F., R. D. Pridmore, J. E. Hewitt and V. J. Cummings. 1991. Impact of ray feeding disturbances on sandflat macrobenthos: Do communities dominated by polychaetes or shellfish respond differently? *Mar. Ecol. Prog. Ser.* 69: 245–252.

Thrush, S. F., R. D. Pridmore and J. E. Hewitt. 1994. Impacts on soft-sediment macrofuana: The effects of spatial variation on temporal trends. *Ecol. Appl.* 4: 31–41.

Thrush, S. F., R. B. Whitlach, R. D. Pridmore, J. E. Hewitt, V. J. Cummings and M. R. Wilkinson. 1996. Scale-dependent recolonization: The role of sediment stability in a dynamic sandflat habitat. *Ecology* 77: 2472–2487.

Turner, S. J., S. F. Thrush, R. D. Pridmore, J. E. Hewitt, V. J. Cummings and M. Maskery.

1995. Are soft-sediment communities stable? An example from a windy harbour. *Mar. Ecol. Prog. Ser.* 120: 219–230.

Underwood, A. J. and E. J. Denley. 1984. Paradigms, explanations, and generalizations in models for the structure of intertidal communities on rocky shores. In D. R. Strong, Jr., D. Simberloff, L. G. Abele and A. B. Thistle (eds.), *Ecological Communities: Conceptual Issues and Evidence,* pp. 151–180. Princeton University Press, Princeton, NJ.

Underwood, A. J. and C. H. Peterson. 1988. Towards an ecological framework for investigating pollution. *Mar. Ecol. Prog. Ser.* 46: 227–234.

VanBlaricom, G. R. 1982. Experimental analyses of structural regulation in a marine sand community exposed to ocean swell. *Ecol. Monogr.* 52: 283–305.

Virnstein, R. W. 1977. The importance of predation by crabs and fishes on benthic infauna in Chesapeake Bay. *Ecology* 58: 1199–1217.

Virnstein, R. W. 1978. Predator caging experiments in soft sediments: Caution advised. In M. L. Wiley (ed.), *Estuarine Interactions,* pp. 261–273. Academic Press, New York.

Warwick, R. M. and K. R. Clarke. 1993. Comparing the severity of disturbance: A meta-analysis of marine macrobenthic community data. *Mar. Ecol. Prog. Ser.* 92: 221–231.

Watling, L. 1975. Analysis of structural variations in a shallow estuarine deposit-feeding community. *J. Exp. Mar. Biol. Ecol.* 19: 275–313.

Watling, L. 1991. The sedimentary milieu and its consequences for resident organisms. *Amer. Zool* 31: 789–796.

Watling, L. and E. A. Norse. 1998. Disturbance of the seabed by mobile fishing gear: A comparison to forest clearcutting. *Conserv. Biol.* 12: 1180–1197.

Watzin, M. C. 1983. The effects of meiofuana on settling macrofuana: Meiofuana may structure meiofuanal communities. *Oecologia* 59: 163–166.

Weinberg, J. R. 1988. Detritus on sediment surface enhances growth of *Clymenella torquata,* a head-down feeding, tubicolous polychaete. *Ophelia* 29: 187–197.

Weinberg, J. R. and R. B. Whitlatch. 1983. Enhanced growth of a filter-feeding bivalve by a deposit-feeding polychaete by means of nutrient regeneration. *J. Mar. Res.* 41: 557–569.

Whitlatch, R. B. 1977. Seasonal changes in the community structure of the macrobenthos inhabiting the intertidal sand and mud flats of Barnstable Harbor, Massachusetts. *Biol. Bull.* 152: 275–294.

Whitlatch, R. B. 1981. Animal–sediment relationships in intertidal marine benthic habitats: Some determinants of deposit-feeding species diversity. *J. Exp. Mar. Biol. Ecol.* 53: 31–45.

Wildish, D. and D. Kristmanson. 1997. *Benthic Suspension Feeders and Flow.* Cambridge University Press, Cambridge.

Wilson, W. H., Jr. 1981. Sediment-mediated interactions in a density populated infaunal assemblage: Effects of the polychaete Abarenicola pacifica. *J. Mar. Res.* 39: 735–748.

Wilson, W. H. 1991a. Competition and predation in marine soft-sediment communities. *Annu. Rev. Ecol. Syst.* 21: 221–241.

Wilson, W. H. 1991b. The foraging ecology of migratory shorebirds in marine soft-sediment communities: The effects of episodic predation on prey populations. *Amer. Zool.* 31: 840–848.

Wiltse, W. I., K. H. Foreman, J. M. Teal and I. Valiela. 1984. Effects of predators and food resources on the macrobenthos of salt marsh creeks. *J. Mar. Res.* 42: 923–942.

Woodin, S. A. 1976. Adult-larval interactions in dense infaunal assemblages: Patterns of abundance. *J. Mar. Res.* 34: 25–41.

Woodin, S. A. 1978. Refuges, disturbance, and community structure: A marine soft-bottom example. *Ecology* 59: 274–284.

Woodin, S. A. 1983. Biotic interactions in recent marine sedimentary environments. In M. J. S. Tevesz and P. L. McCall (eds.), *Biotic Interactions in Recent and Fossil Benthic Communities,* pp. 3–38. Plenum Press, New York.

Woodin, S. A. 1991. Recruitment and infauna: Positive or negative cues? *Amer. Zool* 31: 797–807.

Woodin, S. A., R. L. Marinelli and D. E. Lincoln. 1993. Allelochemical inhibition of recruitment in a sedimentary assemblage. *J. Chem. Ecol.* 19: 517–530.

Young, C. M. 1990. Larval ecology of marine invertebrates: A sesquicentennial history. *Ophelia* 32: 1–48.

Zajac, R. N. and R. B. Whitlatch. 1982a. Responses of estuarine infuana to disturbance. I. Spatial and temporal variation of initial recolonization. *Mar. Ecol. Prog. Ser.* 10: 1–14.

Zajac, R. N. and R. B. Whitlatch. 1982b. Responses of estuarine infuana to disturbance. II. Spatial and temporal variation of succession. *Mar. Ecol. Prog. Ser.* 10: 15–27.

Zajac, R. N., R. B. Whitlatch and S. F. Thrush. 1998. Recolonization and succession in soft-sediment infuanal communities: The spatial scale of controlling factors. *Hydrobiologia* 375/376: 227–240.

chapter 11

Salt Marsh Communities

Steven C. Pennings and Mark D. Bertness

Salt marshes form along coastlines where disturbance from water motion and ice is moderate enough to allow the accumulation of sediments and the growth of angiosperms (Chapman 1960). In the United States, salt marshes are the dominant intertidal habitat along the east and Gulf coasts (Figure 11.1) (Chapman 1960; Reimold 1977; Mitsch and Gosselink 1993). In contrast, salt marshes are rare on the west coast because heavy surf, a narrow continental shelf, and mountainous terrain limit suitable habitat along most of the coastline (MacDonald and Barbour 1974; MacDonald 1977a,b). Worldwide, salt marshes are found at almost all latitudes, but are largely replaced by mangrove forests in the tropics (Chapman 1960, 1974, 1975; Costa and Davy 1992).

Marsh development can follow several courses (Clark and Patterson 1985; Adam 1990; Mitsch and Gosselink 1993). Marshes can overlay terrestrial habitats, indicating that the marshes moved upland as sea levels rose (Redfield 1965, 1972; Rampino and Sanders 1981; Montague and Wiegert 1990). Other marshes have expanded over previously subtidal habitats by trapping sediments, colonizing sediments deposited by severe storms, or colonizing sediments that have been lifted into the intertidal zone by rising coastlines (Ranwell 1964a,b; Ferren 1985; Osgood et al. 1995; Allison 1996; Olff et al. 1997). In either of these marsh development scenarios, the resulting marsh is inhabited both by organisms with terrestrial origins, such as angiosperms, insects, birds, and mammals, and by organisms with marine origins, such as algae, molluscs, crustaceans, and fish.

Like coral reefs, seagrass beds, and mangroves, salt marsh habitats are biogenic communities that exist largely because of the success of the foundation species that build and maintain them. Moreover, like other intertidal habitats that are routinely exposed to both marine and terrestrial conditions, marsh habitats are physically stressful for residents of both marine and terrestrial origins. The biogenic nature and formidable physical stresses of salt marsh habitats are key features in understanding the community ecology of these common and important habitats.

WHY STUDY MARSHES?

Salt marshes are of interest to ecologists because they are fairly simple communities, display striking community patterns across strong gradients in physical stress, and are relatively easy to manipulate. As a result, they are good model systems in which to study how physical and biological factors interact to create pattern in natural communities. Moreover, because salt marshes occur across a wide range of latitudes, they are ideal for examining links between climate and community structure (Pennings and Bertness, 1999).

Understanding salt marshes is also important for practical reasons. Marshes provide a variety of ecosystem services to humanity, sheltering coasts from erosion, filtering sediments and nutrients from the water column, and supporting fisheries (Turner 1976; Turner and Boesch 1988; Dreyer and Niering 1995; Bertness 1999). Salt marshes may also someday provide crops of the future that can be irrigated with seawater along arid coasts (O'Leary et al. 1985; Glenn et al. 1991). Nonetheless, the loss of marsh acreage to human development can approach 80% in developed countries (Dreyer and Niering 1995). Understanding how marsh communities function will be necessary to properly protect and restore them. In particular, to protect salt marshes from global climatic changes such as rising sea levels and alterations in CO_2, nutrient, and temperature regimes, we must learn enough about marsh community organization and function to predict how marshes

(A)

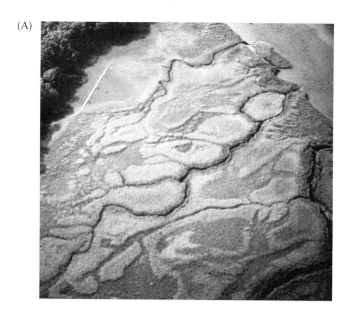

(B)

(C)

(D)

(E)

(F)

Figure 11.1 (A) Keenan Field marsh (Sapelo Island, Georgia). (B) Salt pan in a Sapelo Island marsh. (C) Oyster reefs in a Georgia marsh. (D) Rumstick Cove marsh (Rhode Island).

(E) Wrack cover in a New England marsh. (F) Feral horses grazing on barrier island marshes.

Scope of This Chapter

Salt marshes have long been of interest to ecologists, who have produced a rich literature that includes many books and monographs (Chapman 1960; Ranwell 1972; Pomeroy and Wiegert 1981; Adam 1990; Coultas and Hsieh 1997). More specific reviews are available that focus on particular geographic regions (e.g., Beeftink 1966, 1977; MacDonald and Barbour 1974; Chapman 1977; MacDonald 1977a,b; Adam 1978; Seliskar and Gallagher 1983; Stout 1984; Ferren 1985; Teal 1986; Montague and Wiegert 1990; Wiegert and Freeman 1990; Bertness 1992; Costa and Davy 1992), on particular organisms or concepts important in salt marsh systems (e.g., Nixon 1981; Drake 1989; Newell 1993, 1996; Kneib 1997; Ungar 1998), or on restoration (Josselyn et al. 1990; Matthews and Minello 1994; Zedler 1995, 1996a,b). Most previous overviews of salt marsh research, however, have had a strong ecosystem focus, reflecting the seminal work on nutrient dynamics and energy flow that has been done in marsh systems (e.g., Teal 1962; Odum and de la Cruz 1967; Valiela and Teal 1979a,b). Here we focus on the much less studied community ecology of salt marshes, and review the physical and biotic forces that generate patterns in these systems. We begin by describing the physical stresses and disturbances that occur across salt marsh landscapes, creating the template for marsh communities. We then examine the roles that competition for resources, habitat modification by marsh organisms, and consumers play in generating the distributions and abundances of plants and animals across salt marsh communities. Throughout this chapter we point out weaknesses in our understanding of salt marsh communities and suggest avenues for future research. Our geographic coverage is admittedly biased toward marshes on the east coast of North America due to our familiarity with this region, and because these marshes have been more extensively studied than marshes elsewhere.

Physical Stress

Although salt marshes are highly productive (Turner 1976), they are also physically stressful habitats. Marsh plants and animals must cope with both tidal flooding and high salinity. Geographic variation in the spatial pattern and severity of these physical stresses appears to be responsible for considerable large-scale variation in marsh communities.

Flooding

Salt marsh soils are periodically flooded by the tides (Figure 11.2). Decomposition of organic matter in waterlogged soils rapidly depletes available oxygen and leads to anoxic soils (Ponnamperuma 1972; Mausbach and Richardson 1994). The chemistry of waterlogged soils differs from that of well-drained soils in numerous ways, but probably the most important are the lack of available oxygen and the production of toxic sulfides (Ponnamperuma 1972; Drake 1989; Adam 1990; Pezeshki 1997). Both factors vary across tidal elevation. Because tide height varies on a lunar cycle, high-marsh soils are flooded less frequently than low-marsh soils, and the water table has several days to drop following each period of flooding (Bertness et al. 1992b). As a result, high-marsh soils typically are less waterlogged and have higher redox potentials (i.e., have more oxygen) than low-marsh soils (Bertness and Ellison 1987; Adam 1990; Bertness 1991b; Pennings and Callaway 1992). An exception to this generalization occurs adjacent to creekbanks. Creekbank soils exchange water both on the marsh surface and through creek channels, and as a result of increased drainage have higher redox and lower sulfide levels than do soils more distant from creeks (Chapman 1960; Howes et al. 1981; Adam 1990; Howes and Goehringer 1994).

Wetland plants have both architectural and metabolic adaptations to cope with waterlogged soils. Most plants that live in waterlogged soils have adventitious roots near the soil surface to facilitate root oxygenation. For example, smooth cordgrass (*Spartina alterniflora*), which dominates frequently flooded salt marsh habitats on the Atlantic coast of North America, has surface roots in the top 2–3 cm of the soil that help oxygenate the deeper roots (Anderson 1974). Plants that dominate waterlogged soils also typically have well-developed aerenchyma tissue, a system of air passages extending from aboveground to belowground parts that allows oxygen to diffuse passively to the roots (Ponnamperuma 1972; Armstrong 1979). Some marsh plants can facultatively respond to waterlogged soils by increasing aerenchyma size (Seliskar 1985, 1987). In addition, many marsh plants also have well-developed anaerobic metabolic pathways, which reduce their dependence on root oxygenation (Mendelssohn et al. 1981; King et al. 1982).

The intertidal nature of salt marsh habitats also constrains the distributions of animals, but the direction of the stress gradient differs between aquatic and terrestrial species. In either case, marsh animals must either tolerate or avoid alternating periods of submergence and emergence (Teal 1962; Daiber 1977). Large fish and crustaceans may move onto the marsh surface at high tide but retreat to creeks when the tide falls, whereas small fish and crustaceans may remain on the marsh surface at low tide by taking refuge in pools or wet mud (Daiber 1977; Kneib 1984, 1997). Similarly, mobile insects, mammals, and birds may feed on the marsh at low tide but retreat to terrestrial habitats when the tide rises, whereas less mobile invertebrates may climb to the top of plants to escape the rising tide, or may tolerate periods of submergence (Daiber 1977; Foster 1983; Fell et al. 1991).

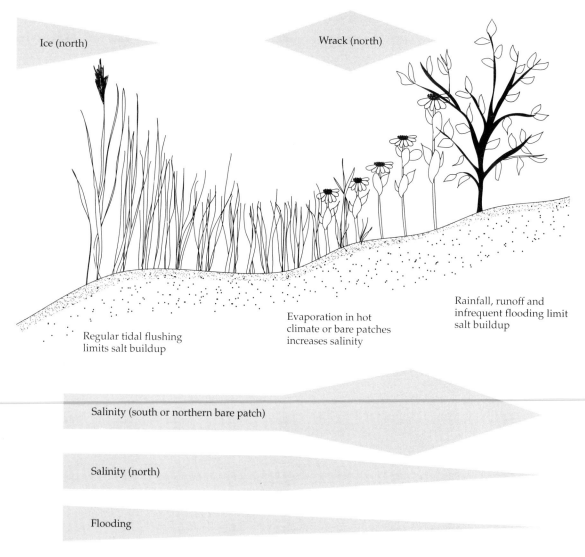

Figure 11.2 Importance of common disturbances and physical stresses across a generic salt marsh profile.

Both the range and predictability of tides vary geographically (Figure 11.3, Ranwell 1972; Davy and Costa 1992). Marshes on the east coast of the United States typically experience two tides a day with a range of 2–3 m. In contrast, tides on the Gulf coast have a range of only 20–40 cm, and flooding patterns are primarily driven by variation in atmospheric pressure and wind direction (Stout 1984). As a result, both the timing and duration of flooding are unpredictable. Whether such geographic variation in tidal flooding drives variation among marsh communities is an issue that deserves increased attention. Early correlative studies suggested that both the productivity and elevational range of dominant marsh plants might increase with tidal range (Odum and Fanning 1973; Steever et al. 1976; McKee and Patrick 1988). However, patterns of production may have been driven by other factors correlated with tidal range (Turner 1976), and many microtidal marshes can be highly productive (Costa 1988). Thus, although it is reasonable to hypothesize that tidal flooding

patterns should affect both the ecosystem functioning and community structure of salt marshes, these links remain to be clearly demonstrated.

The intensity of flooding in many marshes is currently changing due to rising or falling sea levels. Rising sea levels are leading to changes in the plant community and/or the loss of marsh acreage in many areas of the United States (Stevenson et al. 1986; Warren and Niering 1993; Grace and Ford 1996; Ford and Grace 1998a; Gough and Grace 1998a). In contrast, relative sea level is falling in Canada along Hudson Bay due to isostatic uplift, and marshes are undergoing a succession to terrestrial plant communities (Hik et al. 1992).

Salinity

Because salt marshes are flooded by seawater, they are also salty. Salt affects plants both indirectly, by lowering the soil water potential and thereby making it difficult for plants to take up water, and directly, by damaging cellular processes

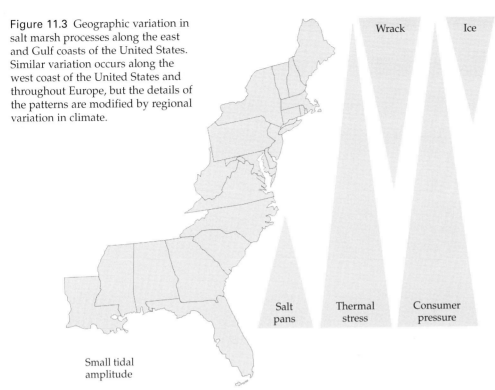

Figure 11.3 Geographic variation in salt marsh processes along the east and Gulf coasts of the United States. Similar variation occurs along the west coast of the United States and throughout Europe, but the details of the patterns are modified by regional variation in climate.

Wrack   Ice

Mild climate, slow decompostition, peaty soils
Ice limits low marsh development
Seasonal plant growth
Intense wrack disturbance
Moderate soil salinities
Salinity limits plants primarily in bare patches

Hot climate, fast decomposition, little peat
Year-round plant growth, detritivores abundant
High soil salinities
Increased presence of salt-tolerant plants
Increased importance of salinity in plant zonation
Increased consumer pressure
Greater plant defenses

Salt pans   Thermal stress   Consumer pressure

Small tidal amplitude

(Poljakoff-Mayber 1975; Drake 1989). Most angiosperms have a very limited ability to tolerate salt, and the species richness of wetland floras drops dramatically from freshwater to salt marshes (Odum 1988; Odum and Hoover 1988). Even among salt marsh plants, there is considerable variation in salt tolerance, which may preclude some species from inhabiting saltier parts of marshes (Pearcy and Ustin 1984; Rozema et al. 1985; Rozema and Van Diggelen 1991; Bertness et al. 1992a). Seeds and seedlings are particularly vulnerable to salt stress, and the successful establishment of salt marsh plants by seeds is commonly limited to brief periods following heavy rains and/or flooding with fresh water (Chapman 1975; Zedler and Beare 1986; Bertness et al. 1992a; Shumway and Bertness 1992; Ungar 1995; Allison 1996). Similarly, marine invertebrates must have well-developed osmoregulatory mechanisms to tolerate the highly variable salinities found in salt marshes, and variation among species in osmoregulatory capabilities is often proposed to explain differences in their distributions (Teal 1958; Daiber 1977; Mitsch and Gosselink 1993).

Salt marsh plants and animals have several strategies to deal with high soil salinities. To maintain an osmotic potential lower than that of pore water, marsh plants typically accumulate salts and other solutes in their tissues. Since high salt concentrations can be detrimental to plant metabolism, however, high osmotic vascular pressure is often achieved at least in part by organic solutes such as sugars and proline (Flowers et al. 1977, 1986; Rozema et al. 1985). To manage tissue salt concentrations, many plants increase in succulence, exclude salt at the roots, excrete salt through salt glands in the leaves, or shed leaves with high salt concentrations (Poljakoff-Mayber 1975; Rozema et al. 1981; Hacker and Bertness 1995b; Mitsch and Gosselink 1993; Dawes 1998). Compared with their subtidal counterparts, marine invertebrates found in salt marshes typically have excellent osmoregulatory abilities and can tolerate a wide range of salinities (Gross 1964; Daiber 1977; Kneib 1984; Anger 1995).

Soil salinity levels vary across marsh elevations, but the shape of this salt gradient varies geographically (see Figures 11.2, 11.3). Salt concentrations in the soil are moderated by tidal input and flushing at low elevations, and by freshwater input from rain and upland sources at the terrestrial border (Chapman 1974; Adam 1990). At intermediate marsh elevations, salts can be concentrated by evapotranspiration, and may reach concentrations several times that of seawater (Adam 1990; Davy and Costa 1992). Because evapotranspiration is more intense at lower latitudes, salt marshes at low latitudes are typified by a hump-shaped salinity pattern, with highest salinities at intermediate elevations (Adam 1990; Pennings and Bertness 1999). Similar hump-shaped salinity patterns may occur in marshes at moderate latitudes that experience little summer rainfall (Mahall and Park 1976b; Jefferies et al. 1979; Davy and Smith 1985). In contrast, salinity in salt marshes at high latitudes typically declines monotonically from the water's edge to the terrestrial border (Pennings and Bertness 1999). As a consequence of their higher salinities, low-latitude marshes are characterized by a more salt-tolerant flora than high-latitude marshes (Pennings and Bertness 1999).

High soil salinities in low-latitude marshes also lead to the development of salt pans, permanent bare areas lacking plant cover (Chapman 1960; Basan and Frey 1977; Adam 1990; Pennings and Bertness 1999). Salt pans typically are well drained, have extremely high soil salinities, usually in excess of 100 ppt, and are fringed by an extremely salt-tolerant flora (Stout 1984; Callaway et al. 1990; Wiegert and Freeman 1990; Clewell 1997; Nomann and Pennings 1998; Pennings and Richards 1998). The literature has often confused what we call salt pans with salt ponds (or pannes), which are depressed, poorly drained areas in high-latitude marshes where tidal water pools and concentrates through evaporation (Chapman 1940; Miller and Egler 1950; Pethick 1974; Boston 1983; Ewing 1983). The formation of salt ponds is driven primarily by the presence of sunken areas in the peat. Low-latitude salt pans are a distinct phenomenon, the extreme expression of the elevated soil salinities typical of low-latitude salt marshes (Pennings and Bertness 1999).

Despite the general pattern of higher salinities at lower latitudes, salinity in any one geographic region can be highly variable. Soil salinity drops and rises as the marsh undergoes cycles of tidal wetting and drying, and temporarily decreases following heavy rains or flooding with fresh water (Zedler and Beare 1986; Adam 1990; Allison 1996). If rainfall is highly seasonal, as in Mediterranean climates, salinity gradients may differ markedly between the wet and dry seasons (Zedler 1982; Callaway et al. 1990). In Mediterranean-climate marshes, short-lived winter annual plants commonly exploit a window of low salinity created in the high marsh by winter rains, and variations in rainfall between years may lead to dominance by different winter annuals that vary in their salt tolerance (Callaway et al. 1990; Callaway and Sabraw 1994).

PHYSICAL STRESS AND VARIATION IN PLANT SIZE

Variations in flooding and salinity across marsh landscapes are responsible for generating gradients in the sizes of many marsh plants (Valiela et al. 1978; Antlfinger 1981; Seliskar 1985a,b; Bertness et al. 1992b; Clewell 1997; Pennings and Richards 1998). Most research on these size gradients has focused on the cordgrass *Spartina alterniflora*.

Shore-level size gradients are a striking feature of *Spartina alterniflora* populations from New England to Florida (Valiela et al. 1978; Mendelssohn 1979a; Howes et al. 1981). *Spartina* reaches heights of 2 m or more at low-marsh elevations and along creekbanks, but is often less than 30 cm tall at intermediate marsh elevations. Most evidence suggests that cordgrass growth forms are largely a phenotypic response to variation in edaphic conditions (Anderson and Treshow 1980; Mendelssohn et al. 1982). Plants grow well on the seaward border of low-marsh habitats, where the soil is well drained and the accumulation of sulfides and salts is limited. At higher marsh elevations, soil drainage is reduced, leading to anoxic soils and elevated sulfide and salinity levels. These conditions limit nitrogen uptake and stunt plant growth (Howes et al. 1981, 1986; King et al. 1982; Mendelssohn 1979b). Adding nutrients or artificially draining short-form cordgrass stands increases

plant height (Valiella and Teal 1974; Gallagher 1975; Valiela et al. 1978; Mendelssohn 1979a; Wiegert et al. 1983), and decreasing the drainage of tall-form cordgrass stands decreases plant height (Bertness 1985). Variation in the size of many other species of salt marsh plants is probably also mediated by edaphic conditions (de la Cruz et al. 1981; Seliskar 1985a; Thompson et al. 1991; Bertness et al. 1992b; Pennings and Richards 1998; Pennings and Moore, in press).

While it is reasonable to suspect that genetic differentiation might occur along the strong edaphic gradients found in marsh landscapes, evidence for a genetic component to the height forms of cordgrass is mixed (Thompson et al. 1991; Clewell 1997). Some studies have found no evidence of a genetic basis for cordgrass growth forms (Shea et al. 1975), whereas others have found a strong genetic component (Stalter and Batson 1969; Gallagher et al. 1988). In the sea oxeye (*Borrichia frutescens*), Antlfinger (1981) found evidence of modest genetic differentiation along a salinity gradient. With a few exceptions (Silander 1979, 1984, 1985; Silander and Antonovics 1979; Davy and Smith 1985; Eppley et al. 1998; Ayres et al. 1999), we have a poor understanding of how genetic differentiation contributes to the structure and dynamics of marsh plant communities, and studies exploring genetic differentiation at local, regional, and latitudinal spatial scales would be extremely valuable.

DISTURBANCE

Natural disturbances by ice, floating debris, herbivores, fire, and sediments play an important role in the dynamics of marsh plant communities. Disturbance in marshes is particularly severe at high latitudes, where winter ice can heavily erode marsh soils and the highly seasonal climate leads to the production of abundant plant debris, or wrack, which can smother and kill marsh plants. Low-latitude marshes, in contrast, are not heavily influenced by either of these predictable annual disturbances.

Ice Disturbance

High-latitude marshes worldwide are subject to ice disturbance, which can destroy large areas of low-marsh vegetation and raft intact marsh chunks to new locations (see Figure 11.2; Adam 1990). For example, in southern New England, ice sheets up to 30 cm thick can cover intertidal marsh habitats during severe winters (Figure 11.4; Redfield 1972). These ice sheets can freeze to waterlogged low-marsh soils, which may be lifted free in large, intact portions during high tides (Redfield 1972; Richard 1978; Roberts and Robertson 1986). If rafted to the high marsh, they can kill underlying vegetation. If rafted to lower elevations, they can form the nucleus of new marsh growth, but rafted marsh plants and animals commonly die from physical stress, competition, or predation if transported below their natural elevation (Richard 1978; Hardwick-Witman 1985).

Ice damage is responsible for strong geographic patterns in salt marsh structure (see Figure 11.3). At high latitudes, as

Figure 11.4 Winter ice in a New England marsh.

in Arctic Alaska, Atlantic Canada, and northern New England, ice damage is so severe that it limits the development of the low marsh, which is continually in a state of recovery, with plants colonizing scoured lower elevations (Johnson 1920; MacDonald 1977b; Gordon and Desplanque 1983; Adam 1990). At moderate latitudes, as in southern New England, ice damage is less severe, and while often important in low-marsh habitats, is not always conspicuous. At lower latitudes, ice disturbance is not an important factor, and uninterrupted sediment deposition can lead to the development of characteristic "levees," or elevated seaward edges of marshes (Wiegert and Freeman 1990).

Wrack Disturbance

A chronic disturbance in New England marshes is the burial of vegetation by rafts of floating dead plant material, or "wrack" (Reidenbaugh and Banta 1982; Hartman et al. 1983; Bertness and Ellison 1987; Valiela and Rietsma 1995). Wrack mats can often be 100–1000 m² in area and 10–30 cm thick, and can completely kill underlying vegetation if they remain stationary for most of a growing season. In contrast to ice disturbance, wrack disturbance is most severe at high-marsh elevations (see Figure 11.2). At low-marsh elevations, wrack is constantly moved by tides, and is less likely to stay in place long enough to kill vegetation (Bertness and Ellison 1987; Valiela and Rietsma 1995). Wrack disturbance is also promoted by the presence of tall vegetation, which can trap and concentrate floating wrack (Hackney and Bishop 1981; Bertness and Yeh 1994; Pennings and Richards 1998).

At larger spatial scales, wrack deposition depends upon wrack production, wind direction, and water flow patterns. Thus, within a geographic region, there is considerable marsh-to-marsh variation in the intensity of wrack disturbance (Valiela and Rietsma 1995; Brewer and Bertness 1996; Brewer et al. 1998). Variation among marshes in the history of wrack disturbance is reflected in the morphology of gap-colonizing

plants such as *Distichlis spicata* (Brewer and Bertness 1996) and in the plant community composition (Brewer et al. 1998).

Wrack disturbance also varies along the east coast of the United States because of latitudinal variation in plant phenology (see Figure 11.3). In the north, large amounts of wrack are produced as a consequence of the seasonal growth pattern of the marsh plants. Plants in New England marshes grow from May to September, but in the late fall, after setting seed, perennials reallocate their aboveground resources to belowground organs (Valiela et al. 1978; Ellison et al. 1986). This leaves dead aboveground skeletons that often collapse and are rafted away by tides. In contrast to this seasonal primary production in New England, production of marsh grass south from the Carolinas may slow during the winter months, but does not stop. Dead material is produced throughout the year as individual leaves and stems die back, and much of it decomposes in place (Turner 1976; Wiegert and Freeman 1990; Newell 1993, 1996). As a result, wrack mats in southern marshes are small and rare compared with those in northern marshes, and the area of marsh disturbed by wrack is modest (Wiegert and Freeman 1990; Pennings and Richards 1998).

Various types of floating debris can disturb marshes in different parts of the world. In Dutch, English, and Australian marshes, *Spartina* wrack can be an important disturbance agent, as it is in New England (Ranwell 1961, 1964b; Beeftink 1975, 1977; Boston 1983). In marshes in the Pacific Northwest of the United States, disturbance from floating logs can be important (Seliskar and Gallagher 1983; Vince 1985). Marshes can also be disturbed by material such as seagrass blades or seaweeds originating from nearby subtidal systems (Beeftink 1977; Seliskar and Gallagher 1983; Adam 1990; S. C. Pennings, pers. obs.).

Other Sources of Disturbance

Other sources of disturbance in marshes include foraging by consumers, fire, and sedimentation. Feeding by geese on plant rhizomes can heavily disturb the upper 20 cm of soil and reduce large areas of vegetation to bare mud (Lynch et al. 1947; Smith and Odum 1981; Cargill 1984; Jefferies 1988; Iacobelli and Jefferies 1991; Hik et al. 1992). Heavy foraging by geese, nutria, and wild boar can reduce vertical accretion of marsh surfaces, contributing to loss of marsh acreage in areas of subsiding coastlines or maintaining intertidal habitats in areas of rising coastlines (Jefferies 1988; Ford and Grace 1998a; Hik et al. 1992; Miller et al. 1996). Mudflat amphipods in England bury seeds and uproot seedlings of the annual *Salicornia europaea* and limit its expansion to lower elevations (Gerdol and Hughes 1993). In some California marshes the parasitic plant *Cuscuta* can create bare areas in vegetation and trigger secondary succession (Pennings and Callaway 1996).

Fire may be an important disturbance agent in areas where extensive stands of marsh become dry enough to burn (Turner 1987; Taylor et al. 1994; Ford and Grace 1998b; Bortolus and Iribarne 1999). The severity of disturbance caused by fire depends markedly on whether only aboveground or both aboveground and belowground plant biomass burns (Baldwin and Mendelssohn 1998).

Sedimentation can also be an important source of disturbance in marshes (Gough and Grace 1998b). Marshes along geologically young mountainous coastlines, such as the coast of California, can receive large amounts of eroded sediment during heavy winter rainstorms, which can create new marsh habitats and increase the elevation of established marshes (Zedler 1982; Ferren 1985; Allison 1996). On geologically older coastlines dominated by accumulated sediments, such as the east coast of North America, strong storms can move large amounts of sediment onshore, burying marshes (Rejmanek et al. 1988).

RECOVERY FROM DISTURBANCE EVENTS

Secondary succession in salt marshes is initiated when any of the disturbances described above kill vegetation. Secondary succession of marsh vegetation has been best studied in New England, where colonization of bare soils following wrack disturbance is driven by a predictably varying combination of competitive and facilitative interactions (Figure 11.5).

In low-marsh habitats in New England, anoxic soils limit most marsh plants, and secondary succession simply involves the clonal reinvasion of *Spartina alterniflora*, the only plant capable of thriving in low-marsh habitats (Hartman et al. 1983; Hartman 1988). In more species-rich higher marsh habitats, however, secondary succession is a more complicated process. Initial invasion of high-marsh bare patches is by fugitive plants, which are uncommon in undisturbed vegetation. Over a period of 2–3 years, these fugitive plants are gradually outcompeted by zonal dominants (Bertness and Ellison 1987; Ellison 1987b; Bertness 1991a; Bertness et al. 1992a; Brewer et al. 1997, 1998).

Invasion of disturbance-generated bare patches occurs by either seed or clonal growth. The most common seed-dispersed fugitive in New England is the annual glasswort *Salicornia europaea*, whose seeds stick to wrack and are commonly transported with wrack to new patches, as are skeletons of adult plants with seeds still attached (Ellison 1987b). Other common fugitive plants, such as *Atriplex patula*, *Limonium nashii*, and *Solidago sempervirens* also invade patches by seed. The spikegrass *Distichlis spicata* is the most important clonally invading fugitive plant. It occurs at low densities in undisturbed vegetation in high-marsh habitats, but dramatically increases in abundance following wrack disturbance (Bertness and Ellison 1987; Brewer et al. 1997, 1998). Spikegrass often dominates recently disturbed habitats because it is resistant to disturbance mortality and is able to invade bare patches rapidly through clonal growth (Bertness and Ellison 1987; Brewer and Bertness 1996). Invasion of bare patches by *Distichlis* may also be promoted by high nutrient availability (Valiela and Teal 1974; Levine et al. 1998) due to reduced uptake by plants and release of nutrients from decomposing wrack (Valiela et al. 1984).

Soil salinities often rise in bare patches due to increased evaporation caused by the lack of shading by vegetation (Bertness et al. 1992a). High soil salinities can preclude most seedling establishment, and only extremely salt-tolerant species, such as *Salicornia europaea*, germinate and grow in the saltiest bare patches (Shumway and Bertness 1992; Brewer et al. 1998). Hypersaline bare patches can also limit the vegetative colonization of clonal perennial plants that are not salt-tolerant. In southern New England, neither *Spartina patens* nor *Juncus gerardi*, which dominate high-marsh habitats, is capable of rapidly invading patches with high soil salinities (Bertness 1991a). Spikegrass (*Distichlis spicata*), however, is capable of invading even extremely salty patches because of its high salt tolerance and physiological integration among ramets (Bertness 1991a; Shumway 1995). Ramets invading bare patches are released from competition with the surrounding turfs, but must rely on water transported to them by their clone-mates in dense vegetation that are not salt-stressed (Shumway 1995; Brewer and Bertness 1996). In southeastern U.S. marshes, the ramets of several marsh plant species invading hypersaline salt pans similarly depend upon support from parent clones (Pennings and Callaway 2000).

Positive interactions mediate secondary succession in hypersaline bare patches. The initial invaders of these patches can facilitate further invasion because they shade the soil, ameliorate hypersaline soil conditions, and thus create conditions conducive to the invasion of less salt-tolerant, but competitively dominant, plants (Bertness 1991a). Because facilitated secondary succession in bare patches depends on soil conditions, facilitation is important only in the colonization of the more stressful patches, and factors that influence potential salt accumulation predictably affect mechanisms of patch colonization (Bertness 1991a; Bertness and Shumway 1993). Small patches that are relatively shaded and thus not prone to salt buildup are colonized competitively without facilitation, whereas succession in larger, saltier patches is facilitated (Shumway and Bertness 1994). Moreover, since the potential for salt buildup in bare patches is a function of tidal flooding frequency, whether patches close by competition or facilitation is also a function of marsh elevation (Brewer et al. 1997).

In southeastern U.S. marshes, wrack mats are relatively small and rare, and the effects of wrack disturbance are modest (see Figure 11.3; Wiegert and Freeman 1990; S. C. Pennings, pers. obs.). The light wrack mats often found in southeastern marshes may in fact benefit vegetation in physically stressful habitats, both by providing nutrients and by shading the soil and thereby limiting salt accumulation (Pennings and Richards 1998). When disturbances do occur, however, facilitated colonization of bare space might be more prevalent in southeastern than northeastern U.S. marshes, because southern marshes experience a hotter climate and have correspondingly saltier soils (Pennings and Bertness 1999).

The mechanisms driving secondary succession following disturbance have not been studied as thoroughly in other parts of the world, or in response to disturbances other than wrack. Observations suggest that wrack disturbance in English and Dutch marshes increases plant diversity by releasing *Scirpus*, *Aster*, *Atriplex*, and other species from competition with *Spartina*, aiding their dispersal to disturbed patches,

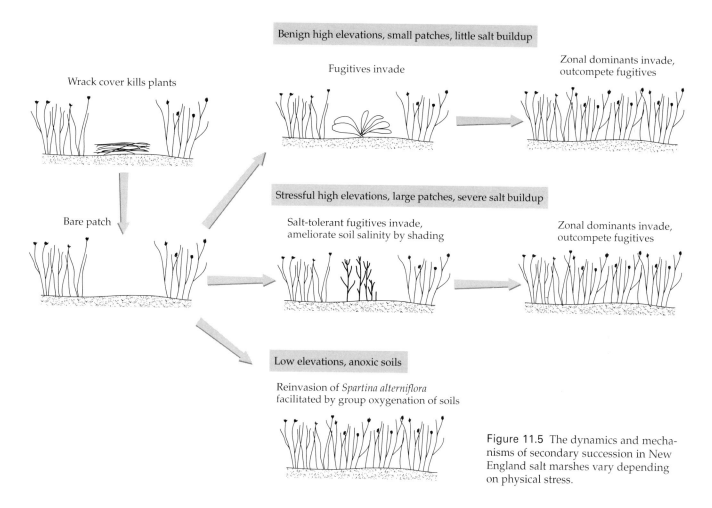

Benign high elevations, small patches, little salt buildup

Wrack cover kills plants

Fugitives invade

Zonal dominants invade, outcompete fugitives

Bare patch

Stressful high elevations, large patches, severe salt buildup

Salt-tolerant fugitives invade, ameliorate soil salinity by shading

Zonal dominants invade, outcompete fugitives

Low elevations, anoxic soils

Reinvasion of *Spartina alterniflora* facilitated by group oxygenation of soils

Figure 11.5 The dynamics and mechanisms of secondary succession in New England salt marshes vary depending on physical stress.

and/or fertilizing the soil (Ranwell 1961, 1964b, 1972; Beeftink 1975, 1977). Secondary succession following severe herbivory by birds in arctic and subarctic marshes has been hypothesized to be influenced by reduced soil elevation due to erosion (Jefferies 1988), increased soil salinity due to reduced plant cover (Iacobelli and Jefferies 1991), and increased nutrient levels due to input of bird feces (Bazely and Jefferies 1985). Regrowth of burned *Spartina* marshes in Argentina may be inhibited by heavy crab herbivory on tender new shoots (Bortolus and Iribarne 1999).

COMPETITION

Competition is one of the most conspicuous processes that structures salt marsh communities. Many marsh plants and sessile animals live in dense aggregations, in which intraspecific competition regulates individual survival, size, and morphology. Interspecific competition, operating across sharp gradients of physical stress, is one of the primary mechanisms creating the strong spatial segregation or zonation patterns of plant species in salt marsh communities.

Intraspecific Competition

Many common salt marsh plants typically form dense monospecific stands on marsh landscapes, which have strong intraspecific competitive effects on further recruitment and on the morphology of resident plants. The dense stands of clonal and solitary plants common in marsh plant communities typically suppress seed germination and the survival of seedlings (Bertness and Ellison 1987; Metcalfe et al. 1986; Ellison 1987b; Bertness et al. 1992a; Shumway 1992; Bertness and Yeh 1994; Baldwin and Mendelssohn 1998). Even when seeds do germinate, intraspecific competition among seedlings often leads to density-dependent variation in survival or growth (Ellison 1987a; Ungar 1992; Bertness and Yeh 1994). Seedling survival in dense marsh plant stands is typically low, and most marsh plants respond to variations in density by altering their morphology. At low densities, individuals have thicker, stronger stems and attain high biomass, whereas at high densities, individuals have thinner, weaker stems, are tall and slender, and attain low biomass (Ellison 1987a; Ellison and Niklas 1988; Harley and Bertness 1996). The top-heavy plants that develop at high densities invest so little in structural support that they become dependent on their neighbors for physical support to prevent toppling (Harley and Bertness 1996). While crowding clearly has many costs to marsh plants, we will argue below that the high plant densities typical of most marsh habitats and the pervasiveness of dense clonal morphologies in marsh plants are probably due to the group benefits plants receive by ameliorating the physical stresses of these habitats.

Similar effects of intraspecific crowding have been documented in sessile marsh invertebrates. In the ribbed mussel

(*Geukensia demissa*), for example, which typically occurs in highly aggregated clumps in salt marshes (Kuenzler 1961; Bertness and Grosholz 1985), individuals grow more slowly and often have deformed shells at high densities, suggesting severe competition for food and space. At high densities, however, juvenile mussels are less vulnerable to mortality from ice, predators, and suffocation in the mud, and these benefits of an aggregated distribution outweigh the costs (Bertness and Grosholz 1985; Lin 1991; Stiven and Gardner 1992). Oyster beds probably have similar costs and benefits to individuals (Dame 1996), but their group dynamics have not been scrutinized.

Intraspecific competition is also important for many of the mobile animals that inhabit marshes. Fiddler crabs compete for burrows, which they use at high tides to escape their predators (Crane 1975; Hyatt and Salmon 1978; Bertness and Miller 1984). Deposit-feeding snails and worms deplete their food sources at high densities (Levinton and Lopez 1977; Levinton 1981; Hylleberg 1975). High densities of planthoppers deplete their marsh grass food supply and then develop into dispersing individuals (Denno et al. 1985, 1986, 1991). Even the juvenile fish that utilize the marsh surface for food and shelter deplete resources enough to limit the growth of successive cohorts (Kneib 1993).

Interspecific Competition and Plant Zonation

Salt marsh communities worldwide are characterized by striking elevational plant zonation (Chapman 1974). Older ideas that these zonation patterns represented successional sequences have largely been discounted (Davy and Costa 1992); instead, these zonation patterns appear to be driven by interspecific competition acting across gradients in waterlogging and salinity (Pielou and Routledge 1976; Russell et al. 1985; Ungar 1998). However, experimental studies of marsh plant zonation have been done at a very limited number of locations, making it difficult to know how general our understanding of marsh plant zonation is. Our current understanding suggests that the mechanisms of zonation may differ between high-latitude and low-latitude marshes, and between marshes with different levels of nutrient input.

Zonation of salt marsh plants is best understood in New England, where the interactions between all the zonal dominant plants have been quantified (Figure 11.6). In these marshes, *Iva frutescens* outcompetes *Juncus gerardi* at the terrestrial border of marshes, displacing it to lower elevations (Bertness and Hacker 1994). In turn, *Juncus gerardi* competitively displaces *Spartina patens* to lower elevations (Bertness 1991a). Finally, *Spartina patens* displaces *Spartina alterniflora* to the lowest marsh habitats (Bertness 1991b). These species differ in their ability to oxygenate their roots in anoxic soils (Mendelssohn 1979a; Gleason 1980; Gleason and Zieman 1981), and each dies if transplanted to elevations lower than where it normally occurs (Bertness and Ellison 1987; Bertness 1991a,b; Bertness et al. 1992b). In contrast, each species is fully capable of living at elevations higher than where it normally occurs if competitors are absent. For example, smooth cordgrass (*Spartina alterniflo-*

ra) commonly invades high-marsh habitats after disturbances (Miller and Egler 1950; Bertness and Ellison 1987), and when transplanted to the high marsh without neighbors, does as well or better than it does at low-marsh elevations (Bertness 1991b). Yet this cordgrass does not normally invade vegetated high-marsh habitats, and is outcompeted and dies if transplanted to high-marsh habitats with neighbors (Bertness and Ellison 1987; Bertness 1991b). Thus, in New England salt marshes, the lower limit of each dominant species is set primarily by its ability to tolerate flooding, and the upper limit of each species is set primarily by competition. Very similar results have come from studies of plant zonation in Alaskan marshes (Snow and Vince 1984), freshwater marshes (Grace and Wetzel 1981; Grace 1985), and lakeshores (Keddy 1989).

The processes leading to the elevational zonation of salt marsh plants at low latitudes appear to be more complex (see Figure 11.6). In mid- to low-latitude marshes, elevated high-marsh soil salinities can result from increased solar radiation or, in Mediterranean climates, from low summer rainfall. These high salinities may combine with competition to limit low-marsh plants from moving to higher elevations (Mahall and Park 1976a,b; Zedler and Beare 1986; Covin and Zedler 1988), and may be equally as or more important than flooding in limiting plants that occur above the peak in salinity from moving to lower marsh zones (Pennings and Bertness 1999). As a result, competition may displace plants either to low, regularly flooded habitats or to high, extremely salty habitats (Pennings and Callaway 1992). For example, in southern California, the upper limit of *Salicornia virginica* is set by a combination of competition from *Arthrocnemum subterminale* and the extremely high salinities found in the upper end of the *Arthrocnemum* zone (Pennings and Callaway 1992). *Arthrocnemum* is precluded from the lower part of the *Salicornia* zone by intolerance to flooding, but would grow well in the upper end of the *Salicornia* zone were it not competitively displaced to higher, saltier habitats by *Salicornia* (Pennings and Callaway 1992). Recent work in Georgia suggests that a similarly complex interaction between flooding, salinity, and competition is responsible for plant zonation patterns in southeastern U.S. salt marshes (S. C. Pennings, pers. obs.).

While climate may influence the processes generating the zonation of marsh plants by affecting physical stress gradients across marshes, factors that influence the competitive relations of dominant marsh plants may also strongly affect marsh zonation patterns. In particular, if competitive dominance among marsh plants is determined by access to nutrients, plant zonation patterns may differ among marshes with different levels of nutrient input (Levine et al. 1998). For example, experimental additions of nitrogen to New England salt marshes reversed the competitive hierarchy among marsh plants, allowing *Spartina alterniflora* and *S. patens* to expand to higher marsh elevations than normal, and leading to an increased abundance of the usually rare *Distichlis spicata* within its normal elevational range (Levine et al. 1998). The likely mechanism for these results was a switch from belowground competition for nutrients to aboveground competition for

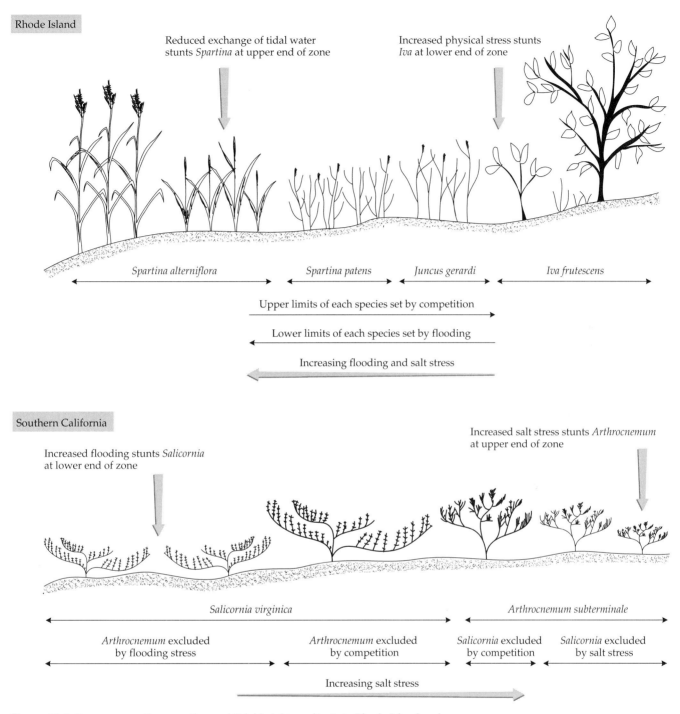

Figure 11.6 Processes creating zonation and tidal height gradients in Rhode Island and southern California salt marshes.

light once nutrients were present in excess. Shifts in the composition of salt marsh plant communities following fertilization have also been observed in England and southern California (Jefferies and Perkins 1977; Covin and Zedler 1988), suggesting that nutrient-based shifts in the competitive dominance of marsh plants may be common. An important implication of these findings is that eutrophication in estuaries may have marked effects on marsh plant community struc-

ture by shifting the competitive balance among plants and consequently altering the zonation and species composition of plant communities (Levine et al. 1998).

Salt marsh animals also vary in abundance across marsh habitats, but their zonation patterns are rarely abrupt (Kneib 1984; Daiber 1977). Interspecific competition among salt marsh animals has been documented (e.g., Willason 1981; Brenchley and Carlton 1983; Stiling et al. 1991; Denno and

Roderick 1992), but there is little evidence that competition is typically important in determining their zonal distributions (Vince et al. 1976; Kneib 1984). This conclusion may reflect a lack of attention, since most salt marsh animals are hidden among plants or in the mud, their distributions are hard to observe without extensive sampling, and relatively few experimental studies of salt marsh animals have been done (Kneib 1984). Alternatively, it may be, as in many other habitats (Strong 1984), that competition is relatively unimportant in determining the distributions of small, mobile animals that live associated with dominant spaceholders, and that their distributions are instead determined by a combination of physical stress, availability of food (e.g., Davis and Gray 1966; Denno 1977), and predation.

HABITAT MODIFICATION

One of the most basic features of salt marsh communities is that, like coral reefs, seagrass beds, and kelp and mangrove forests, they are biogenic habitats built and maintained by resident organisms. Jones et al. (1994) suggested using the term "ecosystem engineering" to focus attention on critical, but often overlooked, non-trophic roles organisms can play in communities by altering the availability of resources or providing other organisms with habitat. Because physical stresses in marshes are potentially limiting, and because many marsh organisms can ameliorate these stresses, modification of the habitat by resident marsh organisms is a pervasive and critical process mediating the structure and organization of salt marsh communities (Figure 11.7).

Habitat Modification by Plants

Salt marsh communities would not exist without halophytic (salt-loving) plants capable of invading and thriving in the often anoxic sediments found on shorelines where salt marshes develop. On the east coast of North America, the cordgrass *Spartina alterniflora* is the pioneer species that initially invades shoreline sediments and facilitates sediment accumulation and the formation of salt marsh habitats. Similar pioneer marsh plants are found in all geographic regions of the world where salt marshes are common (Chapman 1974). These foundation species (*sensu* Dayton 1974) literally create marsh habitats by stabilizing shoreline substrate, buffering the shoreline from wave stress, and providing refuges from predation and physical stress for other marsh organisms (Ranwell 1972; Bruno 2000; Bruno and Kennedy 2000). Without these foundation species, marsh communities would be limited to narrow bands fringing the high intertidal zone, and would occupy only a fraction of their current acreage.

SUBSTRATE STABILIZATION AND WAVE BUFFERING. The stabilization of sediments and amelioration of wave stress that occurs when vascular marsh plants invade shorelines has long been considered a crucial early step in marsh development (Ranwell 1972; Chapman 1974). The roots and rhizomes of colonizing marsh plants bind sediments together, limiting substrate mobility, while aboveground biomass slows water movement, increasing sedimentation and limiting hydrodynamic stresses on shorelines. Recent work on cobble beach plant communities in southern New England has elegantly

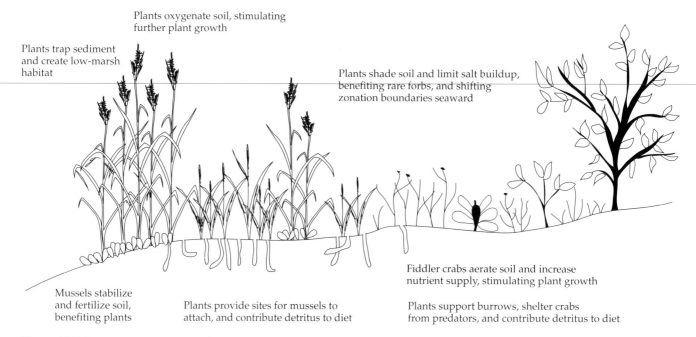

Plants oxygenate soil, stimulating further plant growth

Plants trap sediment and create low-marsh habitat

Plants shade soil and limit salt buildup, benefiting rare forbs, and shifting zonation boundaries seaward

Mussels stabilize and fertilize soil, benefiting plants

Plants provide sites for mussels to attach, and contribute detritus to diet

Fiddler crabs aerate soil and increase nutrient supply, stimulating plant growth

Plants support burrows, shelter crabs from predators, and contribute detritus to diet

Figure 11.7 Positive interactions in salt marshes. Mussel–plant interactions are most obvious at low elevations in northeastern marshes and at intermediate elevations in southeastern marshes.

demonstrated the role played by pioneer plants in ameliorating stresses during the early stages of marsh development (Bruno 2000, Bruno and Kennedy 2000). On these cobble beaches, establishment of *Spartina alterniflora* is necessary for the colonization of all other members of the plant community and for continued marsh development. Similar positive effects of neighbors may occur in lakeshore plant communities at sites exposed to heavy wave action (Wilson and Keddy 1986; Twolan-Strutt and Keddy 1996).

The effect that substrate stabilization can have in a novel system has been powerfully illustrated by repeated introductions of *Spartina alterniflora* to new habitats. *Spartina alterniflora* was introduced to Europe around the turn of the twentieth century. It has crossed with native *S. maritima* to create hybrid species, which have occupied vast areas of mud flats, eradicating previous systems and dramatically altering the hydrology of local estuaries (Beeftink 1966, 1977; Ranwell 1964a,b, 1972; Gray and Benham 1990). *S. alterniflora* and *S. anglica* have been introduced to China, where they are systematically used to protect shorelines and reclaim land from the sea (Mitsch and Gosselink 1993). Finally, *S. alterniflora* is currently invading the west coast of North America and hybridizing with native *Spartina foliosa* (MacDonald 1977b; Callaway and Josselyn 1992; Daehler and Strong 1995, 1996, 1997; Anttila et al. 1998). *S. alterniflora* and hybrid forms are colonizing large expanses of mudflats and converting them, through substrate stabilization and increased sedimentation, to higher-elevation cordgrass monocultures at the expense of native mudflat organisms. In each case, the introduction of *Spartina* spp. has dramatically altered the hydrology, topography, species composition, and food web of the estuary.

SUBSTRATE OXYGENATION. Marsh plants may also modify soils by increasing their oxygen levels. As already discussed, most marsh plants capable of living in anoxic soils transport oxygen to their roots through aerenchyma tissue. Some of this oxygen leaks from the roots and oxygenates the surrounding rhizosphere (Teal and Kanwisher 1966; Howes et al. 1981; Armstrong 1979; Armstrong et al. 1985; Sorrell and Armstrong 1994; but see Bedford et al. 1991; Bedford and Bouldin 1994; Howes and Teal 1994). Additionally, water uptake by roots to replace losses due to transpiration draws the water table down and further introduces oxygen into the soil (Dacey and Howes 1984; Howes and Teal 1994; Morris and Whiting 1985).

The amelioration of low soil oxygen levels is a common positive interaction among marsh plant neighbors at low-marsh elevations (Howes et al. 1981, 1986; Bertness 1991b). For example, the success of *Spartina alterniflora* in anoxic soils is facilitated by group benefits. Cordgrass seedlings and small plants have higher growth and survival rates in the high marsh in the absence of competitors than they do in the low marsh, but in contrast, large cordgrass stands are more productive in the low marsh than in the high marsh (Bertness and Ellison 1987; Bertness 1991b). This size-dependent success in the low marsh results from group benefits of rhizos-

phere oxygenation. Cordgrass seedlings and small plants are unable to oxygenate low-marsh soils successfully, but large cordgrass stands have a communal effect on soil oxygen levels, resulting in enhanced growth (Bertness 1991b). This growth leads to further rhizosphere oxygenation and a positive feedback loop between soil oxygen levels and plant production (Howes et al. 1981, 1986; de la Cruz et al. 1989).

Patterns of clumping of non-aerenchymous plants around aerenchymous plants in waterlogged habitats suggest that similar positive interactions are common between plants in bogs, dune slacks, and salt marshes (Castellanos et al. 1994; Callaway 1995). In laboratory experiments, aerenchymous plants from dune slacks (Schat 1984) and freshwater wetlands (Callaway and King 1996) have been shown to oxygenate soils and improve the growth of neighboring plants that lack well-developed aerenchyma.

SUBSTRATE SHADING AND SALINITY AMELIORATION. Plant shoots can also have important effects on marsh soils by shading the soil and limiting the potential accumulation of salts. As discussed earlier, soil salinities are limited by regular tidal flushing at low elevations, and at the highest elevations adjacent to uplands, by rain and runoff (Chapman 1939). At intermediate elevations, where salt accumulations are possible, plant shading often plays a major role in limiting evaporation of surface pore water and the resultant increase in soil salinity (Ganong 1903; Chapman 1940; Zedler 1982; Iacobelli and Jefferies 1991; Bertness et al. 1992a; Srivastrava and Jefferies 1996). A major consequence of this feedback between plants and soil salinity is that plants can buffer one another from salinity stress.

The role of feedbacks between plants and soil salinities has been most thoroughly examined in New England marshes. In these marshes, both the marsh elder, *Iva frutescens*, and the black rush, *Juncus gerardi*, which dominate intermediate elevations, benefit from their neighbors ameliorating salt stress. *Iva* and *Juncus* are both relatively intolerant of high soil salinities, and their seedling recruitment, as well as the survival of adults in salty habitats, is dependent on the presence of neighbors (Bertness and Hacker 1994; Bertness and Yeh 1994; Hacker and Bertness 1995b). The moderating effect of perennial turfs on soil salinities is also largely responsible for the high plant species diversity of intermediate marsh elevations in New England marshes, and is essential to support marsh insect food webs (Hacker and Bertness 1996, 1999; Hacker and Gaines 1997). Most of the forbs common at intermediate elevations in New England marshes die if neighbors are removed (Hacker and Bertness 1999), and the herbivore food chains dependent on them subsequently collapse (Hacker and Bertness 1996).

The importance of salinity-mediated positive interactions among plants in salt marshes is probably widespread, but has rarely been studied outside of New England. At high elevations in southern California salt marshes, the perennial *Arthrocnemum* facilitates the survival and growth of winter annuals by increasing soil moisture and reducing soil salinity through shading (Callaway 1994). Moreover, the common occurrence of permanent salt pans in low-latitude salt marshes worldwide (Chapman 1960; Zedler 1984; Wiegert and Freeman 1990; Clewell 1997; Dawes 1998) suggests that, in hotter climates with increased evaporation, the importance of these feedbacks may increase until the ability of plants to ameliorate soil salinities is overwhelmed and salinities rise beyond the point permitting plant survival (Pennings and Bertness 1999).

PROVIDING REFUGE FROM CONSUMERS. In addition to benefiting marsh organisms by buffering them from physical stresses, marsh plants can also provide them refuge from their enemies (Shanholtzer 1974). Foraging by predatory crabs (West and Williams 1986; Micheli 1997) and fish (Vince et al. 1976; Kneib 1993) is limited in most high-marsh habitats both by reduced flooding duration and by dense marsh vegetation that prevents access and limits mobility (Kneib 1984, 1991, 1997). Many juvenile fish, crustaceans, and molluscs consequently use high-marsh habitats as nurseries (Vince et al. 1976; Kneib 1993). Palatable marsh plants are also commonly protected when hidden from their consumers in dense marsh vegetation (Ellison 1987b; Hacker and Bertness 1993; Rand 1999).

Habitat Modification by Animals

While plants modify marsh habitats by ameliorating harsh physical conditions and providing habitats for marsh organisms, many filter-feeding and deposit-feeding animals modify marsh habitats by converting resources from one state to another.

FERTILIZATION AND SUBSTRATE STABILIZATION BY FILTER FEEDERS. Salt marsh plants are generally nitrogen-limited (Valiela 1995) and vulnerable to disturbances (Redfield 1972). Bivalve filter feeders can alleviate both of these stresses. Sessile filter feeders increase nutrient availability to plants by transferring nutrient-rich particulate material from the water column to the soil (Jordan and Valiela 1982). Both ribbed mussels (*Geukensia demissa*) and oysters (*Crassostraea virginica*) can form dense beds of hundreds to thousands of individuals per square meter in low-marsh habitats. These beds buffer marshes from erosion and are capable of processing much of the water entering the marsh system every tide cycle, depositing large amounts of particulate matter on the sediment as feces and pseudofeces (Kraeuter 1976; Jordan and Valiela 1982; Newell and Krambeck 1995; Dame 1996). Conversely, marsh filter feeders benefit from associating with plants, which provide attachment sites and contribute food in the form of detritus. The relationship between the ribbed mussel (*Guekensia demissa*) and smooth cordgrass (*Spartina alterniflora*) in southern New England marshes is a good example of these interactions. In southern New England, ribbed mussels are often found in dense (300–1500 individuals/m²) beds on the seaward edge of marshes, attached to cordgrass roots and to one another. These dense aggregations are the product of the gregarious settlement of larvae and survivorship advantages of individuals in groups (Bertness and Grosholz 1985). These mussel beds increase cordgrass growth by providing the

cordgrass with nutrients as well as by reducing erosion and disturbance to cordgrass stands through the strength of their communal attachment to the substrate and by stimulating cordgrass root production (Bertness 1984).

Mussels reciprocally benefit from the presence of plants. Without cordgrass stems to crawl up on, mussels are more vulnerable to predation and suffocation from burial in the mud (Bertness and Grosholz 1985). Moreover, detritus derived from vascular plant material is an important component of the diet of mussels (Stiven and Kuenzler 1979; Kreeger et al. 1988; Langdon and Newell 1990).

The potential importance of mussel–plant interactions in marsh communities changes latitudinally along the east coast of the United States. Dense beds of ribbed mussels are restricted to marshes from Chesapeake Bay to southern New England. Farther north, winter ice scour limits mussel bed formation (Hardwick-Witman 1985), and south of Chesapeake Bay, predation by blue crabs restricts mussels to dense clumps of individuals at high elevations (Lin 1989; Stiven and Gardner 1992). In southeastern marshes, mussel clumps are often conspicuously demarcated by localized areas of increased sediment deposition and cordgrass height (Kuenzler 1961; Smith and Frey 1985).

Potentially important positive associations between vascular plants and sessile filter feeders appear to be widespread in coastal marine habitats (see Reusch et al. 1994 for seagrass beds and Ellison et al. 1996 for mangrove forests). Intertidal oyster reefs have been suggested to benefit marsh plants just as mussels do (Dame 1996). Oyster–plant interactions were probably more important in the past, when oysters were more abundant, than they currently are. Intertidal oyster beds were common in colonial times as far north as southern New England, but now are found only in southern marshes, due to overharvesting, disease, and eutrophication (Dame 1996).

SOIL MODIFICATION BY BURROWING CRABS. Like filter-feeding bivalves, burrowing crabs can also modify the quality of marsh soils and benefit plants. Burrowing crabs from the genera *Uca*, *Sesarma*, and *Armases* are among the most characteristic animals of salt marsh communities, reaching densities greater than 100/m² (Teal 1958, 1962; Basan 1979; Montague 1980). Crab burrowing benefits marsh plants by increasing oxygen penetration into otherwise anoxic soils, stimulating the decay and recycling of belowground debris, and increasing nutrient availability. Conversely, plants positively affect crabs by supporting burrows in soft sediments, providing a detrital food source, and protecting the crabs from predators.

The best-studied crab–plant interaction in salt marshes is the interaction between fiddler crabs (*Uca* spp.; Figure 11.8) and cordgrass (*Spartina alterniflora*). Fiddler crabs are the most common burrowing crabs in western Atlantic salt marshes, and their burrowing has large impacts on marsh sediments. Fiddler crab burrows can be very abundant (>200/m²), are often up to 30 cm deep, and can have a high turnover rate (Montague 1980; Katz 1980; Bertness and Miller 1984; Mouton and Felder 1996). As a result of their burrow-

Figure 11.8 Mud fiddler crab *Uca pugnax.*

ing and sediment reworking, fiddler crabs increase soil drainage, oxygen levels, and the decomposition of belowground plant debris, as well as enhancing soil nitrogen levels with their waste products (Teal and Kanwisher 1961; Montague 1980, 1982; Bertness 1985). Experimental manipulations of fiddler crab burrows have demonstrated that crabs can enhance cordgrass production and flowering (Montague 1982; Bertness 1985), but that crab effects differ among marsh zones as a function of burrow density and edaphic stress (Bertness 1985; Nomann and Pennings 1998).

Crabs, in turn, benefit from the presence of plants. In soft sediments, cordgrass stems and roots structurally support fiddler crab burrows, reducing burrow maintenance costs (Bertness and Miller 1984). Cordgrass detritus is an important food source for fiddler crabs (Haines and Montague 1979; Robertson and Newell 1982; Genoni 1985; Currin et al. 1995). Finally, shading by marsh plants may protect fiddler crabs from predators (Nomann and Pennings 1998) and keep the sediments that fiddler crabs feed on free of seaweeds.

Positive feedbacks between burrowing crabs and marine vascular plants appear to be widespread in temperate wetlands where plant success is potentially limited by waterlogged soil conditions (Montague 1982; Bertness 1985; Smith et al. 1991; Bortolus and Iribarne 1999). Nevertheless, since crab activity is temperature dependent, and since marsh crab diversity and densities generally increase with decreasing latitude (Crane 1943; Abele 1992), crabs probably have their most dramatic effects on substrate conditions and plants at lower latitudes (Montague 1982).

THE ROLE OF CONSUMERS IN SALT MARSH COMMUNITIES

Salt marshes can be extremely productive systems, with aboveground primary production often reaching 2000 g/m^2/year (Marinucci 1982; Dame 1989). Most of this production enters detrital food chains rather than being consumed directly by herbivores. However, herbivores do have an effect on plant biomass and community structure in many marsh systems. Predators, in general, exert strong effects on prey populations, typically driving them into refuge habitats. The high primary production and refuge from predators found in salt marshes makes them important nursery grounds for many marine species.

Detritivores

Salt marsh food webs have long been thought to be detritus-based (Teal 1962). Typical estimates suggest that only 5–10% of the carbon fixed by marsh halophytes is eaten by herbivores (Smalley 1960; Teal 1962; Mann 1972; Nixon and Oviatt 1973; Valiela and Teal 1979b; Pfeiffer and Wiegert 1980). Instead, most of the vascular plant production of marshes dies, is attacked by microbes, and only then reaches invertebrate detritivores, deposit feeders, and filter feeders (Lopez and Levinton 1987; Haines 1977; Haines and Montague 1979; Cammen 1980; Newell 1993). Many of these consumers also gain a substantial part of their nutrition from consuming microalgae (Haines 1977, 1979; Haines and Montague 1979; Peterson et al. 1985; Page 1997; Boschker et al. 1999).

The detrital link in marsh grass food webs has been most thoroughly examined with the cordgrass *Spartina alterniflora* in the southern marshes of Georgia (Newell 1993, 1996). In these marshes, cordgrass grows year-round and routinely produces senescent leaves, which remain attached to living plants as they undergo initial decay (Newell et al. 1998). Standing dead leaves are heavily colonized by fungi, and are then shredded by invertebrates such as the snail *Littoraria irrorata* and the amphipod *Uhlorchestia spartinophila*, which break the leaves into small fragments that fall to the marsh surface (Newell et al. 1985; Newell 1993, 1996). *Littoraria* and *Uhlorchestia* are found on freestanding dead plants, and their diets consist in part of fungi and partially decomposed plant cells (Newell and Bärlocher 1993; Bärlocher and Newell 1994a,b; Covi and Kneib 1995; Kneib et al. 1997). *Littoraria* migrates up and down cordgrass stems with the tide, at least partially to forage on recently wetted dead plant material, which is most easily processed (Newell 1996). Detrital particles that fall to the soil surface are further decomposed by bacteria (Howarth and Teal 1979; Newell 1993, 1996) and become a large part of the diets of a variety of marsh consumers, including deposit feeders such as fiddler crabs and snails and filter feeders such as mussels and oysters (Haines 1976; Haines and Montague 1979; Marinucci 1982; Rietsma et al. 1982). Experimental studies of cordgrass detritus have shown that its availability can mediate individual and population growth of marsh crabs, snails, and bivalves (Stiven and Kuenzler 1979; Genoni 1985).

The chemical composition of plant litter and its palatability to detritivores changes during decomposition through leaching and microbial processing (Valiela et al. 1984; Buchsbaum et al. 1991; Newell 1996). The palatability of cordgrass detritus to consumers (the snails *Littoraria irrorata* and *Melampus bidentatus* and the amphipods *Orchestia grillis* and *Uhlorchestia spartinophila*) is affected by phenolic compounds such as ferulic acid, by nitrogen content, and possibly by toughness (Valiela et al. 1979, 1984; Valiela and Rietsma 1984; Rietsma et al. 1988; Bärlocher and Newell 1994a,b; Graça et al. 2000).

Although much is known about detrital processes, many gaps in our knowledge remain (Newell 1993, 1996; Newell and Porter, in press). For example, relatively little is known about the decomposition of plants other than *Spartina alterniflora* and *Juncus roemerianus*, or about detrital processes in locations other than the east coast of North America (but see Buth and de Wolf 1985; Buth and Voesenek 1987). Two observations suggest that there is considerable geographic variation in detrital processes. First, in contrast to low-latitude marshes, primary production in high-latitude marshes is seasonal, and much of the aboveground production can be transported as wrack away from its source, potentially decoupling the production of detritus from its availability to consumers (Newell 1993). Second, a major detritivore specialist that shreds dead leaves in low-latitude marshes, *Littoraria irrorata*, does not occur in high-latitude marshes, and other shredders may be less common at higher latitudes. Since different shredding organisms affect decomposition dynamics in different ways (Graça et al. 1999), the nature of the detritus-based food chain probably differs at low and high latitudes.

Early interest in marsh production and detrital processes was motivated by suggestions that salt marshes, like seagrass beds, might export large amounts of detrital material to adjacent habitats (the "outwelling hypothesis"). In John Teal's seminal study of energy flow in a Georgia salt marsh (Teal 1962), he estimated that 40% of cordgrass production was exported from the marsh, supplying fixed carbon and nutrients to other marine habitats. Subsequent studies (Woodwell et al. 1977; Pomeroy and Wiegert 1981) supported this conclusion, leading to the idea that marshes were vital habitats for estuarine food chains (Odum and De la Cruz 1967; Woodwell et al. 1977; Odum 1978). This hypothesis, however, has not proved to be robust (Haines 1977, 1979; Chalmers et al. 1985). Marshes vary in their export/import characteristics as a function of primary production levels, marsh morphology, oceanographic conditions, and marsh age, and consequently, some marshes are exporters and others are primarily importers (Odum 1978; Odum et al. 1979; Nixon 1981; Dame 1994, 1996).

Even if marshes do not export detritus, they still may contribute to the production of nearby habitats (Turner 1976; Haines 1979; Turner and Boesch 1988). Kneib (1997, in press) has suggested that "trophic relays" are critical in transforming marsh primary production into secondary production in adjacent, energetically subsidized habitats. Trophic relays occur when small consumers and/or juveniles of large consumers tap the detritivore/algal food chain in marshes. Since larger nekton are increasingly constrained to subtidal habitats, marsh production is progressively transferred to lower elevations through ontogenetic shifts in habitat use and through predation events. The net result is a transfer of organic matter from the marsh to larger and larger organisms—initially fish and crustaceans, but ultimately their bird and cetacean top predators—that primarily occupy estuarine and nearshore habitats rather than the intertidal marsh.

Herbivores

Although herbivores usually remove only a modest proportion of the angiosperm production in salt marshes, it would be a mistake to conclude that they are not important in regulating community structure. A wide range of herbivores as well as parasitic plants have been shown to affect the distributions and abundances of marsh plants. Some of these effects are subtle and easily overlooked, but others are quite dramatic.

Insects are the most ubiquitous herbivores on most contemporary marshes. While insect herbivory does not typically influence the distributions and abundances of plants that dominate marshes (Smalley 1960; Nixon and Oviatt 1973; Daehler and Strong 1995; Olmstead et al. 1997), it may be important in mediating the distributions of plants that live at low densities scattered throughout the dominant plant matrix (Ellison 1987a; Foster 1984; Rand 1999). Insects can also be important flower and seed predators on marsh plants (Bertness et al. 1987; Ellison 1991; Bertness and Shumway 1992; Davy et al., in press), and thus may affect the recruitment dynamics of some marsh plants.

In contrast to the subtle effects of insects, birds and large mammals can be extremely important herbivores in some marsh systems, sometimes consuming large areas of marsh vegetation. Foraging by geese can denude large tracts of marsh (Lynch et al. 1947; Smith and Odum 1981; Kerbes et al. 1990), and grazing by muskrats, nutria, and ungulates can strongly affect plant species distribution patterns and production (Lynch et al. 1947; Shanholtzer 1974; Turner 1987; Ford and Grace 1998a). Large mammalian herbivores may have been common in prehistoric North American marshes and may have played a major role in the vegetation dynamics of marshes before the arrival of humans (Levin et al., unpub.).

Crabs and snails may be more important consumers of marsh plants than has been traditionally recognized. Marsh crabs may be capable of consuming large amounts of cordgrass under certain conditions (Crichton 1960; Pfeiffer and Wiegert 1981; Bortolus and Iribarne 1999), but it is not clear how often they are important. Recent work with the marsh periwinkle *Littoraria* has revealed that it can exert surprisingly strong top-down control on cordgrass production (Silliman and Zieman, in press). Although *Littoraria* is a detritivore, its grazing damages healthy plant tissue and causes it to senesce, and the snails subsequently consume the decomposing plant tissue (Silliman and Zieman, in press).

Thus, the traditional view of salt marshes as detritus-based systems, which minimized interest in the effects of herbivores on marsh plant communities, may have been misleading. Herbivores may play a larger role in the community structure of many marshes than is generally recognized.

HERBIVORE FOOD PREFERENCES. Herbivores do not attack plants at random, but usually focus on preferred species. Plant chemistry, toughness, and nitrogen levels are important determinants of herbivore food preferences. Extracts of a variety of marsh plants have been shown to deter feeding by insects, crabs, and geese (Kraft and Denno 1982; Buchsbaum et al. 1984; Pennings et al. 1998; E. L. Siska and S. C. Pennings, unpub.), suggesting the presence of unpalatable secondary metabolites. In the case of *Spartina alterniflora*, these are probably simple phenolic compounds such as ferulic and coumeric acid, which also play a role in the palatability of decomposing litter. Secondary metabolites have been isolated from a variety of salt marsh plants (e.g., Kagan and Mabry 1969; Herz et al. 1972; Miles et al. 1977; Chiji et al. 1978; Seaman 1982; Arakawa et al. 1983; Geslin and Verbist 1985; Delgado et al. 1992), but their actual role in plant palatability has not been explicitly tested.

Plant toughness may also deter potential marsh plant herbivores. Many marsh herbivores prefer to feed on softer leaves (Kraft and Denno 1982; Krischik and Denno 1990; Pennings et al. 1998), although geese are potentially able to eat extremely tough plant material (Lynch et al. 1947). Silica is present in many marsh plants, but its role in deterring marsh herbivores remains to be unequivocally demonstrated (Pennings et al. 1998). Marsh plants are also often covered with salt excretions or have salty vascular fluids, which might cause water regulation problems for consumers, but both brant geese and wharf crabs prefer saltier foods rather than avoiding them (Summers et al. 1993; Pennings et al. 1998).

The nutrient status of plants can also influence their attractiveness to herbivores. Salt marsh herbivores commonly prefer, and grow better on, fertilized as compared with unfertilized plants (Vince et al. 1981; Denno et al. 1986; Rossi and Strong 1991; Olmstead et al. 1997; Rossi et al. 1996; Rossi and Stiling 1998), suggesting that foliar nitrogen concentration and quality is important to their feeding preferences (Parsons and de la Cruz 1980). Fertilizing plants, however, also induces rapid growth and changes the C:N balance, raising the possibility that other factors, such as toughness and secondary metabolite concentrations, may differ between fertilized and unfertilized plants (Vince et al. 1981; Rossi and Stiling 1998). Moreover, nitrogen content alone is usually a poor predictor of patterns of preference among different plant species (Buchsbaum et al. 1984; Buchsbaum and Valiela 1987; Amat et al. 1991; Pennings et al. 1998; but see Summers et al. 1993).

Few studies have examined the relative importance of different types of herbivore defenses in marsh plants. Buchsbaum et al. (1984) concluded that secondary chemistry was more important than nitrogen content in determining the feeding preferences of Canada geese for different plants in a New England salt marsh, but nitrogen content explained feeding preferences among plants that lacked chemical defenses (Buchsbaum and Valiela 1987). Brant geese in England preferentially fed on plants that were high in the amino acid proline and in chloride, but low in tannins (Summers et al. 1993). In contrast, plant toughness was more important than plant chemistry or nitrogen content in determining the feeding preferences of the wharf crab *Armases cinereum* in Georgia (Pennings et al. 1998). Clearly, more comparative studies are needed to understand marsh plant defenses and their effectiveness against different herbivores. Different defenses may have evolved to deal with different herbivores—or even for reasons unrelated to herbivore pressure—but we simply do not know enough about herbivory in marsh systems to speculate about these relationships.

COMMUNITY EFFECTS OF HERBIVORY. Given that marsh herbivores discriminate among plant species, and that some can strongly depress preferred species, the potential exists for herbivores to alter plant community composition. While insects do not appear to affect the dominant marsh plants strongly, geese and mammalian herbivores can, when common, have large effects on the dominant plants of the marsh, and can strongly affect plant production, succession, species composition, and zonation patterns.

The effects of insects on marsh plant communities are generally subtle and often mediated by associational defenses (*sensu* Atsatt and O'Dowd 1976) . Herbivorous beetles can be common at high-marsh elevations, but feed very little on the clonal turfs that usually dominate these habitats. Beetles often specialize on rarer plants that live within the dense clonal turf matrix. Beetle herbivory has been shown to be capable of preventing *Salicornia europaea*, the seaside goldenrod (*Solidago sempervirens*), and the arrow plant (*Atriplex patula*) from inhabiting bare patches where they are released from neighborhood competition (Ellison 1987b; Hacker and Gaines 1997; Rand 1999). These plants survive best when they are surrounded by less palatable vegetation, ostensibly since they are not detected by beetle herbivores. Similar associational defenses have been suggested to protect *Triglochin* from herbivory by brant geese when it is rare and embedded in stands of less preferred plants (Mulder and Ruess 1998). In English marshes, the density of *Salicornia europaea* declines and the density of *Suaeda maritima* increases near dense stands of *Atriplex portulacoides*, ostensibly because a lepidopteran herbivore of *Atriplex* secondarily feeds on *Salicornia*, thereby releasing *Suaeda* from competition (Davy et al., in press).

In contrast to insects, geese can have dramatic effects on the distributions and abundances of the numerically dominant clonal turfs that characterize most salt marsh landscapes. Foraging by migrating flocks of geese can create disturbances that trigger secondary succession, change the relative abundances of plant species by altering competitive relations, and alter nutrient cycling by reducing litter production and increasing deposition of nutrient-rich feces (Jefferies 1988; Hik et al. 1992; Mulder and Ruess 1998). The effects of goose herbivory are best known in Canadian subarctic marshes, where snow goose herbivory is predictable and intense and can increase plant production in a simple positive feedback loop. In these systems, goose grubbing for rhizomes increases production of the grasses *Puccinellia* and *Carex* by thinning stands, reducing plant competition, and fertilizing soils through deposition of feces (Cargill and Jefferies 1984; Bazely and Jefferies 1985; Jefferies 1988). Grazing in these habitats maintains the high-marsh community in an early state of succession similar to that found in the low marsh because the preferred early-succession graminoids are more tolerant of heavy grazing and trampling than are late-succession dicots (Bazely and Jefferies 1986; Jefferies 1988; Hik et al. 1992).

A similar positive feedback between grazing and vegetation quality occurs between brant geese and marsh plants in Europe. Brant geese preferentially consume young leaves, and their foraging maintains a high proportion of young leaves in stands of *Plantago* and *Puccinellia* (Prins et al. 1980; Rowcliffe et al. 1998). Moreover, foraging by brant geese retards succession toward dense stands of *Puccinellia* and maintains a community dominated by *Salicornia*—a favored food plant—and new-growth *Puccinellia* (Summers et al. 1993; Rowcliffe et al. 1998). These positive feedback loops between geese and plants are not universal, however. When geese forage selectively on rare plants, their effects on preferred plants may be negative rather than positive, and overgrazing by geese can entirely destroy marsh habitats (Esselink et al. 1997; Mulder and Ruess 1998).

Most information on the effects of large mammalian grazers on marsh systems comes from studies of livestock. Marshes in North America and Europe have historically been heavily used for livestock grazing and hay production (Ganong 1903; Beeftink 1975; Adam 1978; Looijen and Bakker 1987; Olff et al. 1997). The effects of livestock on vegetation are greatest on the high marsh because livestock avoid softer low-marsh sediments (Ranwell 1961; Kiehl et al. 1996). Sheep grazing on an English marsh negatively affected *Spartina*, the favored diet, and *Atriplex*, which is facilitated by *Spartina* litter, but favored *Puccinellia*, presumably because it was released from competition (Ranwell 1961). Similarly, sheep grazing in Denmark and Germany maintained a low-biomass community dominated by *Puccinellia*, which is tolerant of grazing and trampling, and *Salicornia* and *Suaeda*, which are poor competitors; whereas the absence of grazers led to a high-biomass community dominated by *Halimione* (Jensen 1985; Kiehl et al. 1996). Cattle grazing can also dramatically reduce vegetation biomass and promote the existence of competitively inferior species (Bakker 1985). Cattle grazing in the Netherlands may remove competitively dominant plants that suppress plants favored by geese, such that cattle maintain habitat favorable to geese (Olff et al. 1997; Huisman and Olff 1998).

The best-studied large grazing mammals in North American marshes are the feral horse populations on barrier islands off the southeastern coast. In colonial America, the introduction of ungulates to barrier islands by European explorers and immigrants was a common practice, and the feral horse populations of these islands are remnants of those introductions. Grazing on *Spartina alterniflora* and *S. patens* by these horses can be severe, particularly in the high marsh, and may influence plant species composition by reducing plant cover and selectively removing competitively dominant plants (Shanholtzer 1974; Turner 1987; Wood et al. 1987; Furbish and Albano 1994). Trampling of soft marsh sediments by horses may be as important as actual removal of vegetation by grazing (Turner 1987). Recent work on Shackleford Bank, North Carolina (P. S. Levin, unpub. data), has shown that horse herbivory and trampling can combine to shift marsh communities from cordgrass-dominated systems with high fish production to more open systems with reduced cover and fewer resident fish. P. S. Levin (unpub. data) has speculated that prehistoric large mammal grazing may have had similar effects on Pleistocene marshes, suggesting that our contemporary view of marshes as highly productive, detritus-based

nursery grounds may apply only to marshes after humans drove large mammalian grazers to extinction in North America. This idea deserves further attention.

In recent decades, population increases of the introduced nutria (*Myocaster coypus*), a large herbivorous rodent from South America, have led to intense herbivory in many marshes along the Gulf coast of the United States (Lowery 1974; Taylor et al. 1994; Ford and Grace 1998b; Gough and Grace 1998b). Nutria can remove over 50% of aboveground plant biomass in certain situations, and their feeding strongly suppresses some species (e.g., *Scirpus* spp.) while strongly favoring others (e.g., *Cyperus* spp.), presumably by releasing them from competition (Taylor et al. 1994; Taylor and Grace 1995; Ford and Grace 1998a,b; Gough and Grace 1998a). In addition to the effects of direct herbivory and competitive release, changes in the accumulation of litter due to nutria grazing may affect plant species diversity and nutrient cycling (Ford and Grace 1998a; Gough and Grace 1998b). Deer, rabbits, and wild boar probably also have effects on marsh vegetation (Ranwell 1961; Mesléard 1994; Ford and Grace 1998a; Gough and Grace 1998a,b; S. C. Pennings, pers. obs.), but these have not been well studied.

Parasitic plants such as *Cuscuta* and *Agalina*, which use host plants to obtain water and nutrients, potentially limit the abundance and distribution of their host plants, are common in some marsh systems, and can have community effects that parallel those of herbivores. In southern California marshes, dodder (*Cuscuta salina*) preferentially attacks *Salicornia virginica* over other marsh plants (Pennings and Callaway 1996). Dense patches of *Cuscuta* depress cover of *Salicornia* by up to 90%, indirectly favoring *Limonium* and *Frankenia*, and initiating a vegetation cycle that ends with *Salicornia* reinvading and outcompeting other plants. *Cuscuta* also tips the competitive balance between *Salicornia* and *Arthrocnemum*, altering the zonation pattern of these plants (Callaway and Pennings 1998).

The nature of plant–herbivore interactions in salt marshes probably varies geographically, but this has not been well studied (but see Denno and Grissell 1979; Denno et al. 1996). Biogeographic theory has long suggested that consumer pressure has historically been greatest at low latitudes and that this pressure should have selected for increased prey defenses (MacArthur 1972; Vermeij 1978; Coley and Aide 1991). We tested this hypothesis with salt marsh plants along the east coast of North America, and our results strongly supported the hypothesis that low-latitude plants are less palatable than high-latitude plants. When given a choice between northeastern and southeastern conspecific plants, thirteen species of herbivores consistently preferred to eat northern over southern individuals of all ten plant species studied (Pennings et al., in press). These results suggest that we are just beginning to scratch the surface in our understanding of plant–herbivore interactions in marsh plant communities.

Predators

Predation plays a conspicuous role in marsh communities by restricting prey to high-marsh elevations, where they are less vulnerable. The refuge from predators that marshes provide, along with their high food production, make them important marine nursery grounds and heightens their conservation value. Predators dictate the abundances and distributions of marsh organisms ranging from interstitial meiofauna such as nematodes and harpacticoid copepods to large molluscs and fish. Most of the predation pressure on marsh organisms comes from fish and crabs, but birds and mammals can also be important.

Predation on small invertebrates—nematodes, copepods, polychaetes, anemones, and others—that inhabit the top few centimeters of marsh sediments is intense. In marshes along the east coast of the United States, grass shrimp and killifish are extremely abundant predators that forage intensively on sediments during high tide. Their foraging can limit the size, distribution, and abundance of small invertebrates across marsh habitats, as well as limiting them to spatial and temporal refuges (Bell et al. 1978; Bell 1980; Posey and Hines 1991). As a result, many small invertebrates are found in abundance only at high-marsh elevations and among dense vegetation, where predation pressure is reduced (Bell 1980).

Predatory crabs and fish also limit the distributions and abundances of their larger prey (Vince et al. 1976; Micheli 1997; Kneib 1997). Predation by crabs and large fish is most intense at lower elevations and in marshes with extensive networks of tidal creeks because dense vegetation and reduced foraging time limit the predators' access to the high marsh (Kneib 1984, 1994; Lin 1989). As a result, prey are often most abundant in mid- to high-marsh zones, limited at the low end of their distributions by predation and at the high end by desiccation (Kneib 1984, 1997; West and Williams 1986). Predation by blue crabs in southeastern U.S. marshes restricts ribbed mussels to high elevations, where they have reduced feeding time (Lin 1989; Seed 1980; Stiven and Gardner 1992), excludes marsh periwinkles from habitats where they cannot migrate out of the water during high tides to avoid being eaten (Hamilton 1976; Schindler et al. 1994), and probably also forces many sluggish infaunal organisms to live in association with marsh grass roots or other predator refuges. Since blue crabs themselves are vulnerable to being eaten by birds, blue crab foraging is focused on the seaward edge of the marsh, which is both accessible to crabs at high tide and provides them with cover from their enemies (Micheli 1997). Predation by killifish restricts juvenile fish and a variety of invertebrates, such as the snail *Melampus bidentatus* and amphipods, to the high marsh or to dense stands of cordgrass (Vince et al. 1976; Van Dolah 1978; Kneib 1987, 1997; Posey and Hines 1991). Similarly, predation on marsh mussels and oysters limits them to living in dense aggregations in which they are protected from predation (Bertness and Grosholz 1985; Stiven and Gardner 1992; Dame 1996). Since high-marsh habitats are physically stressful to marine species, and high densities carry the cost of increased intraspecific competition, predation in marshes forces many prey organisms to live in habitats where their growth is limited (Vince et al. 1976). As many invertebrates

and fish grow, however, they reach a refuge in size from predation and move to lower marsh elevations (Vince et al. 1976; Kneib 1987).

Terrestrial predators such as raccoons and wading birds such as rails, egrets, and herons also feed on molluscs, decapods, and fish in marshes (Oney 1954; Daiber 1977; Petit and Bildstein 1987; Watts 1988; Frix et al. 1991; Ens et al. 1993). Their effects on prey populations, however, are not well known. Behavioral observations suggest that the foraging behavior of blue and fiddler crabs is constrained by avoidance of exposure to bird predators (Ens et al. 1993; Micheli 1997; Nomann and Pennings 1998). The burrowing lifestyle of fiddler and wharf crabs (*Uca, Sesarma* and *Armases* spp.) also appears to be largely driven by predators. Although these crabs utilize burrows to reduce moisture loss, especially when molting (Crane 1975), they also retreat into burrows to avoid predators (Daiber 1977; Frix et al. 1991).

Predation pressure in salt marshes varies temporally and spatially, but neither of these phenomena has been closely examined. Marshes are used by many species of nekton only seasonally (Kneib 1984, 1991, in press; Kneib and Knowlton 1995). Predation is generally most intense in the warm summer months, while during the winter months crab and fish predators are inactive and predation pressure is relaxed (West and Williams 1986; Lin 1990; Stiven and Gardener 1992; Micheli 1997). How seasonal variation in predation affects prey populations has only rarely been examined (Kneib and Knowlton 1995).

Predation pressure in salt marshes, as in other marine habitats (Vermeij 1978), probably increases at low latitudes, although such variations have not been well documented. This latitudinal variation deserves more attention because it implies that there may be latitudinal variation in the use of marshes as predator refuges and in the importance of marshes as nurseries. Woodin (1976) argued that higher predation rates in soft-sediment habitats on the east coast of North America lead to vastly different benthic assemblages south versus north of Cape Cod. Variation in blue crab predation in marshes along the Atlantic coast of North America also suggests a latitudinal gradient. In New England, crab predation on marsh mussels is restricted to smaller individuals, particularly solitary individuals, and the seaward borders of marshes are often covered by dense mussel beds (Bertness and Grosholz 1985). In the marshes of the Carolinas and Georgia, however, blue crabs eat more and larger mussels, and as a result, crab predation drives mussels out of the low marsh and restricts them to high-density, high-intertidal refuges (Lin 1989; Stiven and Gardner 1992). Mud crabs also are important predators in southeastern U.S. marshes (Seed 1980; Lin 1990), but do not appear to have much of an effect in the north (M. D. Bertness, pers. obs.).

Conclusions

Salt marshes are characterized by strong gradients in physical factors that provide a template for community organization and structure. Biological interactions and physical stresses operate across this template to generate striking plant and animal zonation patterns. Competition among the foundation plant species that conspicuously structure these communities usually results in the displacement of competitively inferior plants to physically stressful portions of the template, while competitively superior plants monopolize physically benign portions of the template. Plant competition clearly plays a prominent role in structuring these communities. Habitat modification by plants and animals, however, is just as important a force in these habitats, since without many of the positive feedbacks between plant and animal cover and the stability, oxygen level, and salinity of the substrate, many marsh organisms simply could not tolerate the stresses of these habitats.

Physical disturbances, resource levels, and climate all strongly affect spatial patterns across marsh communities. Disturbances of different types can kill vegetation, disrupt competitive interactions, and trigger secondary succession. Resource supplies may alter the outcome of competitive encounters, and climate influences the shape of the stress gradient, or physical template, on which marsh communities are built.

Consumers also play a large role in generating spatial patterns across marsh communities by restricting prey populations to refuges. Since most marsh systems have detritus-based food webs, herbivores do not typically limit plant species distributions, but large mammal and bird herbivores do play this role in some marsh systems. Predators are important in most marsh communities because they limit prey to living at high elevations, in burrows, or in dense aggregations.

While we clearly have a good grasp of many of the basic processes that drive patterns in marsh communities, there is still much to learn. One of the biggest problems is that our understanding of marsh systems is based on a limited number of studies in an even more limited number of study systems. This makes suspect our understanding of the generality of the processes driving marsh community structure and severely constrains our understanding of geographic variation in pattern and process. It is also unclear whether or not our understanding of marsh systems based on the results of small-scale experiments can be scaled up to explain marsh communities at large spatial scales. Community-level studies of marsh systems are needed from different parts of the world and at larger spatial scales to address these issues.

Some very basic questions about the structure and organization of salt marsh communities, such as how marsh age or location along estuarine salinity gradients influences marshes, also remain to be answered. While it is widely believed that marshes develop when critical foundation species colonize appropriate habitats and ameliorate physical stresses (Ranwell 1972), the roles of physical stresses and biotic interactions in marsh community shifts during marsh development are not well known. Moreover, salt and freshwater marshes are typically treated as different habitats, when they are clearly similar communities along an environmental continuum (Odum 1988; Wilson et al. 1996). How the processes that determine pattern in marsh communities change across estuarine gradients has rarely been experimentally addressed

and is another large hole in our understanding of how marsh communities work.

The role of propagule supply in influencing process and pattern in marsh communities has also received little attention. The distributions of some marsh plants are known to be dictated by seed supply patterns (Rand 2000), but we don't know how common this is. Moreover, although larval supply commonly influences the abundances and distributions of shallow-water marine invertebrates with planktonic larvae (Gaines and Roughgarden 1985), the implications of this finding have rarely been explored in marsh systems (but see Willason 1981; O'Connor 1993). Larval supply could dictate the within- and between-marsh abundances and distributions of the crabs, bivalves, and snails that strongly modify marsh habitats or that are important marsh consumers, and so could have strong repercussions on the spatial distributions of feedbacks and the intensity of biological interactions across marsh communities.

How genetic adaptation to local conditions influences proximate ecological processes that shape marsh communities is largely unexplored, but may be particularly important in developing a predictive understanding of salt marsh communities at global spatial scales. If, for example, natural selection acting across large biogeographic spatial scales affects the ability of marsh organisms to deal with physical stresses, competitive ability or consumer defenses, predictions about the dynamics of marsh communities across large spatial scales based on our understanding of local marshes could be incorrect.

Links between the community ecology of marshes and ecosystem properties, such as nursery ground and nutrient filtering functions, have not been rigorously examined in spite of their potential importance. While these functions are typically assumed for all marshes, the structure and organization of marsh communities, which varies markedly from place to place, likely mediates the quality and quantity of services provided.

Finally, increasing anthropogenic impacts on the environment demand that we study how marshes will respond to global change. This chapter discussed community impacts of eutrophication and sea level rise. Other issues that deserve increased attention include the effects of rising CO_2 levels (Arp et al. 1993), rising temperatures (Pennings and Bertness 1999), and introduced species (Daehler and Strong 1995, 1996, 1997; Amsberry et al. 2000).

As coastal marshes continue to be destroyed and altered by anthropogenic impacts, our grasp of their community dynamics becomes more and more critical. Without a mechanistic understanding of the processes that generate patterns in marsh communities and the consequences of these patterns, we will not be capable of predicting how our remaining marshes will respond to further change, or confident of successfully restoring them.

Acknowledgments

Our work in coastal salt marshes has been supported by the National Science Foundation, the National Institute for Global Environmental Change, the National Geographic Society, and Sea Grant. We thank A. Bortolus, C. S. B. Costa, A. M. Ellison, R. T. Kneib, D. J. Moore, S. Y. Newell, E. L. Siska and W. Sousa for helpful comments on the manuscript. This is contribution number 837 from the University of Georgia Marine Institute. Illustrations by S. C. Pennings and K. Benoit. Photographs by M. D. Bertness, R. T. Kneib, C. L. Richards and J. Waage.

LITERATURE CITED

Abele, L. G. 1992. A review of the grapsid crab genus *Sesarma* (Crustacea: Decapoda: Grapsidae) in America, with the description of a new genus. Smithsonian Contributions to Zoology No. 527.

Adam, P. 1978. Geographical variation in British saltmarsh vegetation. *J. Ecol.* 66: 339–366.

Adam, P. 1990. *Saltmarsh Ecology.* Cambridge University Press, Cambridge.

Allison, S. K. 1996. Recruitment and establishment of salt marsh plants following disturbance by flooding. *Amer. Midl. Nat.* 136: 232–247.

Amat, J. A., B. Garcia-Criado and A. Garcia-Ciudad. 1991. Food, feeding behaviour and nutritional ecology of wintering greylag geese *Anser anser. Ardea* 79: 271–282.

Amsberry, L., M. A. Baker, P. J. Ewanchuk and M. D. Bertness. 2000. Clonal integration and the expansion of Phragmites australis. *Ecol. Appl.* 10: 1110–1118.

Anderson, C. E. 1974. A review of structures of several North Carolina salt marsh plants. In R. J. Reimold and W. H. Queen (eds.), *Ecology of Halophytes*, pp. 307–344. Academic Press, New York.

Anderson, C. E. and M. Treshow. 1980. A review of environmental and genetic factors that affect *Spartina alterniflora* height forms. *Estuaries* 3: 168–176.

Anger, K. 1995. The conquest of freshwater and land by marine crabs: Adaptations in life-history patterns and larval bioenergetics. *J. Exp. Mar. Biol. Ecol.* 193: 119–145.

Antlfinger, A. E. 1981. The genetic base of microdifferentiation in natural and experimental populations of *Borrichia frutescens* in relation to salinity. *Evolution* 35: 1056–1068.

Anttila, C. K., C. C. Daehler, N. E. Rank and D. R. Strong. 1998. Greater male fitness of a rare invader (*Spartina alterniflora*, Poaceae) threatens a common native (*Spartina foliosa*) with hybridization. *Amer. J. Bot.* 85: 1597–1601.

Arakawa, Y., H. Chiji and M. Izawa. 1983. Structural elucidation of two new chromones isolated from glasswort (*Salicornia europaea* L.). *Agric. Biol. Chem.* 47: 2029–2033.

Armstrong, W. 1979. Aeration in higher plants. *Adv. Bot. Res.* 7: 225–332.

Armstrong, W., E. J. Wright, S. Lythe and T. J. Gaynard. 1985. Plant zonation and the effects of the spring-neap tidal cycle on soil aeration in a Humber salt marsh. *J. Ecol.* 73: 323–339.

Arp, W. J., B. G. Drake, W. T. Pockman, P. S. Curtis and D. F. Whigham. 1993. Interactions between C_3 and C_4 salt marsh plant species during four years of exposure to elevated atmospheric CO_2. *Vegetatio* 104/105: 133–143.

Atsatt, P. R. and D. J. O'Dowd. 1976. Plant defense guilds. *Science* 193: 24–29.

Ayres, D. A., D. Garcia-Rossi, H. G. Davis and D. R. Strong. 1999. Extent and degree of hybridization between exotic (*Spartina alterniflora*) and native (*Spartina foliosa*) cordgrass (Poaceae) in California, USA determined by RAPDs. *Molec. Ecol.* 8: 1179–1186.

Bakker, J. P. 1985. The impact of grazing on plant communities, plant populations and soil conditions on salt marshes. *Vegetatio* 62: 391–398.

Baldwin, A. H. and I. A. Mendelssohn. 1998. Response of two oligohaline marsh communities to lethal and nonlethal disturbance. *Oecologia* 116: 543–555.

Bärlocher, F. and S. Y. Newell. 1994a. Growth of the saltmarsh periwinkle *Littoraria irrorata* on fungal and cordgrass diets. *Mar. Biol.* 118: 109–114.

Bärlocher, F. and S. Y. Newell. 1994b. Phenolics and proteins affecting palatability of *Spartina* leaves to the gastropod *Littoraria irrorata*. *Mar. Ecol. PSZNI* 15: 65–75.

Basan, P. B. 1979. Classification of low marsh habitats in a Georgia salt marsh. *Georgia J. Sci.* 37: 139–154.

Basan, P. B. and R. W. Frey. 1977. Actual-palaeontology and neoichnology of salt marshes near Sapelo Island, Georgia. *Geol. J. Special Issue No. 9*: 41–70.

Bazely, D. R. and R. L. Jefferies. 1985. Goose faeces: A source of nitrogen for plant growth in a grazed salt marsh. *J. Appl. Ecol.* 22: 693–703.

Bazely, D. R. and R. L. Jefferies. 1986. Changes in the composition and standing crop of salt-marsh communities in response to the removal of a grazer. *J. Ecol.* 74: 693–706.

Bedford, B. L. and D. R. Bouldin. 1994. Response to the paper "On the difficulties of measuring oxygen release by root systems of wetland plants," by B. K. Sorrell and W. Armstrong. *J. Ecol.* 82: 185–186.

Bedford, B. L., D. R. Bouldin and B. D. Beliveau. 1991. Net oxygen and carbon-dioxide balances in solutions bathing roots of wetland plants. *J. Ecol.* 79: 943–959.

Beeftink, W. G. 1966. Vegetation and habitat of the salt marshes and beach plains in the south-western part of the Netherlands. *Wentia* 15: 83–108.

Beeftink, W. G. 1975. The ecological significance of embankment and drainage with respect to the vegetation of the south-west Netherlands. *J. Ecol.* 63: 423–458.

Beeftink, W. G. 1977. The coastal salt marshes of western and northern Europe: An ecological and phytosociological approach. In V. J. Chapman (ed.), *Wet Coastal Ecosystems*, pp. 109–155. Elsevier, Amsterdam.

Bell, S. S. 1980. Meiofauna-macrofauna interactions in a high salt marsh habitat. *Ecol. Monogr.* 50: 487–505.

Bell, S. S., M. C. Watzin and B. C. Coull. 1978. Biogenic structure and its effect on the spatial heterogeneity of meiofauna in a salt marsh. *J. Exp. Mar. Biol. Ecol.* 35: 99–107.

Bertness, M. D. 1984. Ribbed mussels and *Spartina alterniflora* production in a New England salt marsh. *Ecology* 65: 1794–1807.

Bertness, M. D. 1985. Fiddler crab regulation of *Spartina alterniflora* production on a New England salt marsh. *Ecology* 66: 1042–1055.

Bertness, M. D. 1991a. Interspecific interactions among high marsh perennials in a New England salt marsh. *Ecology* 72: 125–137.

Bertness, M. D. 1991b. Zonation of *Spartina patens* and *Spartina alterniflora* in a New England salt marsh. *Ecology* 72: 138–148.

Bertness, M. D. 1992. The ecology of a New England salt marsh. *Amer. Sci.* 80: 260–268.

Bertness, M. D. 1999. *The ecology of Atlantic shorelines*. Sinauer Associates, Sunderland, MA.

Bertness, M. D. and A. M. Ellison. 1987. Determinants of pattern in a New England salt marsh plant community. *Ecol. Monogr.* 57: 129–147.

Bertness, M. D. and E. Grosholz. 1985. Population dynamics of the ribbed mussel, *Geukensia demissa*: The costs and benefits of an aggregated distribution. *Oecologia* 67: 192–204.

Bertness, M. D. and S. D. Hacker. 1994. Physical stress and positive associations among marsh plants. *Amer. Nat.* 144: 363–372.

Bertness, M. D. and T. Miller. 1984. The distribution and dynamics of *Uca pugnax* (Smith) burrows in a New England salt marsh. *J. Exp. Mar. Biol. Ecol.* 83: 211–237.

Bertness, M. D. and S. W. Shumway. 1992. Consumer driven pollen limitation of seed production in marsh grasses. *Amer. J. Bot.* 79: 288–293.

Bertness, M. D. and S. W. Shumway. 1993. Competition and facilitation in marsh plants. *Amer. Nat.* 142: 718–724.

Bertness, M. D. and S. M. Yeh. 1994. Cooperative and competitive interactions in the recruitment of marsh elders. *Ecology* 75: 2416–2429.

Bertness, M. D., C. Wise and A. M. Ellison. 1987. Consumer pressure and seed set in a salt marsh perennial plant community. *Oecologia* 71: 190–200.

Bertness, M. D., L. Gough and S. W. Shumway. 1992a. Salt tolerances and the distribution of fugitive salt marsh plants. *Ecology* 73: 1842–1851.

Bertness, M. D., Wikler, K. and T. Chatkupt. 1992b. Flood tolerance and the distribution of *Iva frutescens* across New England salt marshes. *Oecologia* 91: 171–178.

Bortolus, A. and O. Iribarne. 1999. Effects of the SW Atlantic burrowing crab *Chasmagnathus granulata* on a *Spartina* salt marsh. *Mar. Ecol. Prog. Ser.* 178: 79–88.

Boschker, H. T. S., J. F. C. de Brouwer and T. E. Cappenberg. 1999. The contributions of macrophyte-derived organic matter to microbial biomass in salt-marsh sediments: Stable carbon isotope analysis of microbial biomarkers. *Limnol. Oceanogr.* 44: 309–319.

Boston, K. G. 1983. The development of salt pans on tidal marshes, with particular reference to south-eastern Australia. *J. Biogr.* 10: 1–10.

Brenchley, G. A. and J. T. Carlton. 1983. Competitive displacement of native mud snails by introduced periwinkles in the New England intertidal zone. *Biol. Bull.* 165: 543–558.

Brewer, J. S. and M. D. Bertness. 1996. Disturbance and intraspecific variation in the clonal morphology of salt marsh perennials. *Oikos* 77: 107–116.

Brewer, J. S., J. M. Levine and M. D. Bertness. 1997. Effects of biomass removal and elevation on species richness in a New England salt marsh. *Oikos* 80: 333–341.

Brewer, J. S., J. M. Levine and M. D. Bertness. 1998. Interactive effects of elevation and burial with wrack on plant community structure in some Rhode Island salt marshes. *J. Ecol.* 86: 125–136.

Bruno, J. F. 2000. Facilitation of cobble beach plant communities through habitat modification by *Spartina alterniflora*. *Ecology* 81: 1179–1192..

Bruno, J. F. and C. W. Kennedy. Reduction of wave-related disturbance in cobble beach habitats by *Spartina alterniflora*. *Oecologia* 122: 98–108.

Buchsbaum, R. and I. Valiela. 1987. Variability in the chemistry of estuarine plants and its effect on feeding by Canada geese. *Oecologia* 73: 146–153.

Buchsbaum, R., I. Valiela and T. Swain. 1984. The role of phenolic compounds and other plant constituents in feeding by Canada geese in a coastal salt marsh. *Oecologia* 63: 343–349.

Buchsbaum, R., I. Valiela, T. Swain, M. Dzierzeski and S. Allen. 1991. Available and refractory nitrogen in detritus of coastal vascular plants and macroalgae. *Mar. Ecol. Prog. Ser.* 72: 131–143.

Buth, G. J. C. and L. de Wolf. 1985. Decomposition of *Spartina anglica*, *Elytrigia pungens* and *Halimione portulacoides* in a Dutch salt marsh in association with faunal and habitat influences. *Vegetatio* 62: 337–355.

Buth, G. J. C. and L. A. C. J. Voesenek. 1987. Decomposition of standing and fallen litter of halophytes in a Dutch salt marsh. In A. H. L. Huiskes, C. W. P. M. Blom and J. Rozema (eds.), *Vegetation between Land and Sea*, pp. 146–162. Dr. W. Junk, Dordrecht.

Callaway, J. C. and M. N. Josselyn. 1992. The introduction and spread of smooth cordgrass (*Spartina alterniflora*) in south San Francisco Bay. *Estuaries* 15: 218–226.

Callaway, R. M. 1994. Facilitative and interfering effects of *Arthrocnemum subterminale* on winter annuals. *Ecology* 75: 681–686.

Callaway, R. M. 1995. Positive interactions among plants. *Bot. Rev.* 61: 306–349.

Callaway, R. M. and L. King. 1996. Temperature-driven variation in substrate oxygena-

tion and the balance of competition and facilitation. *Ecology* 77: 1189–1195.

Callaway, R. M. and S. C. Pennings. 1998. Impact of a parasitic plant on the zonation of two salt marsh perennials. *Oecologia* 114: 100–105.

Callaway, R. M and C. S. Sabraw. 1994. Effects of variable precipitation on the structure and diversity of a California salt marsh community. *J. Vegetation Sci.* 5: 433–438.

Callaway, R. M., S. Jones, W. R. Ferren, Jr. and A. Parikh. 1990. Ecology of a mediterranean-climate estuarine wetland at Carpinteria, California: Plant distributions and soil salinity in the upper marsh. *Can. J. Bot.* 69: 1139–1146.

Cammen, L. M. 1980. The significance of microbial carbon in the nutrition of the deposit feeding polychaete, *Nereis succinea*. *Mar. Biol.* 61: 9–20.

Cargill, S. M. 1984. The effects of grazing by lesser snow geese on the vegetation of a sub-arctic salt marsh. *J. Appl. Ecol.* 21: 669–686.

Cargill, S. M. and R. L. Jefferies. 1984. Nutrient limitation of primary production in a sub-arctic salt marsh. *J. Appl. Ecol.* 21: 657–668.

Castellanos, E. M., M. E. Figueroa and A. J. Davy. 1994. Nucleation and facilitation in saltmarsh succession: Interactions between *Spartina maritima* and *Arthrocnemum perenne*. *J. Ecol.* 82: 239–248.

Chalmers, A. G., R. G. Wiegert and P. L. Wolf. 1985. Carbon balance in a salt marsh: Interactions of diffusive export, tidal deposition and rainfall-caused erosion. *Est. Coast. Shelf Sci.* 21: 757–771.

Chapman, V. J. 1939. Studies in salt-marsh ecology. Sections IV and V. *J. Ecol.* 27: 160–201.

Chapman, V. J. 1940. Studies in salt-marsh ecology. Sections VI and VII. Comparison with marshes on the east coast of North America. *J. Ecol.* 28: 118–152.

Chapman, V. J. 1960. *Salt Marshes and Salt Deserts of the World*. Leonard Hill Limited, London.

Chapman, V. J. 1974. Salt marshes and salt deserts of the world. In R. J. Reimold and W. H. Queen (eds.), *Ecology of Halophytes*, pp. 3–19. Academic Press, New York.

Chapman, V. J. 1975. The salinity problem in general, its importance, and distribution with special reference to natural halophytes. In A. Poljakoff-Mayber and J. Gale (eds.), *Plants in Saline Environments*, pp. 7–24. Springer-Verlag, New York.

Chapman, V. J. 1977. *Wet Coastal Ecosystems*. Elsevier, Amsterdam.

Chiji, H., T. Aiba and M. Izawa. 1978. Isolation and identification of two 2,3-unsubstituted chromones from glasswort (*Salicornia europaea* L.). *Agric. Biol. Chem.* 42: 159–165.

Clark, J. S. and W. A. Patterson III. 1985. The development of a tidal marsh: Upland and oceanic influences. *Ecol. Monogr.* 55: 189–217.

Clewell, A. F. 1997. Vegetation. In C. L. Coultas and Y.-P. Hsieh (eds.), *Ecology and Management of Tidal Marshes: A Model from the Gulf*

of Mexico, pp. 77–109. St. Lucie Press, Delray Beach, FL.

Coley, P. D. and T. M. Aide. 1991. Comparison of herbivory and plant defenses in temperate and tropical broad-leaved forests. In P. W. Price, T. M. Lewinsohn, G. W. Fernandes and W. W. Benson (eds.), *Evolutionary Ecology in Tropical and Temperate Regions*, pp. 25–49. John Wiley & Sons, New York.

Costa, C. S. B. 1988. Production ecology of *Scirpus maritimus* in southern Brazil. *Ciencia e Cultura: Journal of the Brazilian Association for the Advancement of Science* 50: 273–280.

Costa, C. S. B. and A. J. Davy. 1992. Coastal salt marsh communities of Latin America. In U. Seeliger (ed.), *Evolutionary Ecology in Tropical and Temperate Regions: Coastal Plant Communities of Latin America*, pp. 179–199. Academic Press, San Diego.

Coultas, C. L. and Y.-P. Hsieh. 1997. *Ecology and Management of Tidal Marshes: A Model from the Gulf of Mexico*. St. Lucie Press, Delray Beach, FL.

Covi, M. P. and R. T. Kneib. 1995. Intertidal distribution, population dynamics and production of the amphipod *Uhlorchestia spartinophila* in a Georgia, USA, salt marsh. *Mar. Biol.* 121: 447–455.

Covin, J. D. and J. B. Zedler. 1988. Nitrogen effects on *Spartina foliosa* and *Salicornia virginica* in the salt marsh at Tijuana Estuary, California. *Wetlands* 8: 51–65.

Crane, J. 1943. Display, breeding and relationships of fiddler crabs (Brachyura, genus *Uca*) in the northeastern United States. *Zoologica* 28: 217–223.

Crane, J. 1975. *Fiddler Crabs of the World*. Princeton University Press, Princeton, NJ.

Crichton, O. W. 1960. Marsh crab, intertidal tunnel-maker and grass-eater. *Estuarine Bull.* 5: 3–10.

Currin, C. A., S. Y. Newell and H. W. Paerl. 1995. The role of standing dead *Spartina alterniflora* and benthic microalgae in salt marsh food webs: Considerations based on multiple stable isotope analysis. *Mar. Ecol. Prog. Ser.* 121: 99–116.

Dacey, J. W. H. and B. L. Howes. 1984. Water uptake by roots controls water table movement and sediment oxidation in short *Spartina* marsh. *Science* 224: 487–489.

Daehler, C. C. and D. R. Strong. 1995. Impact of high herbivore densities on introduced smooth cordgrass, *Spartina alterniflora*, invading San Francisco Bay, California. *Estuaries* 18: 409–417.

Daehler, C. C. and D. R. Strong. 1996. Status, prediction and prevention of introduced cordgrass *Spartina* spp. invasions in Pacific estuaries, USA. *Biol. Conserv.* 78: 51–58.

Daehler, C. C. and D. R. Strong. 1997. Reduced herbivore resistance in introduced smooth cordgrass (*Spartina alterniflora*) after a century of herbivore-free growth. *Oecologia* 110: 99–108.

Daiber, F. C. 1977. Salt marsh animals: Distributions related to tidal flooding, salinity and vegetation. In V. J. Chapman (ed.), *Wet Coastal Ecosystems*, pp. 79–108. Elsevier, Amsterdam.

Dame, R. F. 1989. The importance of *Spartina alterniflora* to Atlantic Coast estuaries. *Rev. Aquat. Sci.* 1: 639–660.

Dame, R. F. 1994. The net flux of materials between marsh-estuarine systems and the sea: The Atlantic coast of the United States. In W. J. Mitsch (ed.), *Global Wetlands: Old World and New,* pp. 295–302. Elsevier Science, The Netherlands.

Dame, R. F. 1996. *Ecology of Marine Bivalves: An Ecosystem Approach.* CRC Press, Boca Raton, FL.

Davis, L. V. and I. E. Gray. 1966. Zonal and seasonal distribution of insects in North Carolina salt marshes. *Ecol. Monogr.* 36: 275–295.

Davy, A. J. and C. S. B. Costa. 1992. Development and organization of saltmarsh communities. In U. Seeliger (ed.), *Coastal Plant Communities of Latin America,* pp. 157–178. Academic Press, San Diego.

Davy, A. J. and H. Smith. 1985. Population differentiation in the life-history characteristics of salt-marsh annuals. *Vegetatio* 61: 117–125.

Davy, A. J., C. S. B. Costa, A. M. Proudfoot, A. R. Yallop and M. Mohamed. In press. Biotic interactions in plant communities of saltmarshes. In T. Harris and B. Sherwood (eds.), *British Saltmarshes.* Linnean Society/Samara Publishing, London.

Dayton, P. K. 1974. Experimental evaluation of ecological dominance in a rocky intertidal algal community. *Ecol. Monogr.* 54: 253–289.

Dawes, C. J. 1998. *Marine Botany,* 2nd ed. John Wiley & Sons, New York.

de la Cruz, A., C. T. Hackney and J. P. Stout. 1981. Aboveground net primary productivity of three Gulf Coast marsh macrophytes in artificially fertilized plots. In B. J. Neilson and L. E. Cronin (eds.), *Estuaries and Nutrients,* pp. 437–445. Humana Press, Clifton.

de la Cruz, A., C. T. Hackney and N. Bhardwaj. 1989. Temporal and spatial patterns of redox potential (Eh) in three tidal marsh communities. *Wetlands* 9: 181–190.

Delgado, G., M. Y. Ríos, L. Colín, P. E. García and L. Alvarez. 1992. Constituents of *Borrichia frutescens. Fitoterapia* 63: 273–275.

Denno, R. F. 1977. Comparison of the assemblages of sap-feeding insects (Homoptera-Hemiptera) inhabiting two structurally different salt marsh grasses in the genus *Spartina. Environ. Entomol.* 6: 359–372.

Denno, R. F. and E. E. Grissell. 1979. The adaptiveness of wing-dimorphism in the salt marsh-inhabiting planthopper, *Prokelisia marginata* (Homoptera: Delphacidae). *Ecology* 60: 221–236.

Denno, R. F. and G. K. Roderick. 1992. Density-related dispersal in planthoppers: Effects of interspecific crowding. *Ecology* 73: 1323–1334.

Denno, R. F., L. W. Douglass and D. Jacobs. 1985. Crowding and host plant nutrition: Environmental determinants of wing-form in *Prokelisia marginata. Ecology* 66: 1588–1596.

Denno, R. F., L. W. Douglass and D. Jacobs. 1986. Effects of crowding and host plant nutrition on a wing-dimorphic planthopper. *Ecology* 67: 116–123.

Denno, R. F., G. K. Roderick, K. L. Olmstead and H. G. Döbel. 1991. Density-related migration in planthoppers (Homoptera: Delphacidae): The role of habitat persistence. *Amer. Nat.* 138: 1513–1541.

Denno, R. F., G. K. Roderick, M. A. Peterson, A. F. Huberty, H. G. Döbel, M. D. Eubanks, J. E. Losey and G. A. Langellotto. 1996. Habitat persistence underlies intraspecific variation in the dispersal strategies of planthoppers. *Ecol. Monogr.* 66: 389–408.

Drake, B. G. 1989. Photosynthesis of salt marsh species. *Aquat. Bot.* 34: 167–180.

Dreyer, G. D. and W. A. Niering. 1995. *Tidal Marshes of Long Island Sound.* Connecticut College Arboretum Bulletin 34.

Ellison, A. M. 1987a. Density-dependent dynamics of *Salicornia europaea* monocultures. *Ecology* 68: 737–741.

Ellison, A. M. 1987b. Effects of competition, disturbance, and herbivory on *Salicornia europaea. Ecology* 68: 576–586.

Ellison, A. M. 1991. Ecology of case-bearing moths (Lepidoptera: Coleophoridae) in a New England salt marsh. *Environ. Entomol.* 20: 857–864.

Ellison, A. M. and K. J. Niklas. 1988. Branching patterns of *Salicornia europaea* (Chenopodiaceae) at different successional stages: A comparison of theoretical and real plants. *Amer. J. Bot.* 75: 501–512.

Ellison, A. M., M. D. Bertness and T. Miller. 1986. Belowground dynamics of the salt marsh cordgrass, *Spartina alterniflora. Amer. J. Bot.* 73: 1548–1554.

Ellison, A. M., E. J. Farnsworth and R. R. Twilley. 1996. Facultative mutualism between red mangroves and root-fouling sponges in Belizean mangal. *Ecology* 77: 2431–2444.

Ens, B. J., M. Klaasen and L. Zwarts. 1993. Flocking and feeding in the fiddler crab (*Uca tangeri*): Prey availability as risk-taking behavior. *Neth. J. Sea Res.* 31: 477–494.

Eppley, S. M., M. L. Stanton and R. K. Grosberg. 1998. Intrapopulation sex ratio variation in the salt grass *Distichlis spicata. Amer. Nat.* 152: 659–670.

Esselink, P., G. J. F. Helder, B. A. Aerts and K. Gerdes. 1997. The impact of grubbing by greylag geese (*Anser anser*) on the vegetation dynamics of a tidal marsh. *Aquat. Bot.* 55: 261–279.

Ewing, K. 1983. Environmental controls in Pacific Northwest intertidal marsh plant communities. *Can. J. Bot.* 61: 1105–1116.

Fell, E. P., K. A. Murphy, M. A. Peck and M. L. Recchia. 1991. Re-establishment of *Melampus bidentatus* and other macroinvertebrates on a restored impounded tidal marsh: Comparison of populations above and below the impoundment dike. *J. Exp. Mar. Biol. Ecol.* 15: 33–48.

Ferren, W. R., Jr. 1985. Carpinteria salt marsh. Environment, history, and botanical resources of a southern California estuary. Publication no. 4. The Herbarium, Department of Biological Sciences, University of California, Santa Barbara.

Flowers, T. J., P. F. Troke and A. R. Yeo. 1977. The mechanism of salt tolerance in halophytes. *Ann. Rev. Plant Physiol.* 28: 89–121.

Flowers, T. J., M. A. Hajibagheri and N. W. J. Clipson. 1986. Halophytes. *Q. Rev. Biol.* 61: 313–337.

Ford, M. A. and J. B. Grace. 1998a. Effects of vertebrate herbivores on soil processes, plant biomass, litter accumulation and soil elevational changes in a coastal marsh. *J. Ecol.* 86: 974–982.

Ford, M. A. and J. B. Grace. 1998b. The interactive effects of fire and herbivory on a coastal marsh in Louisiana. *Wetlands* 18: 1–8.

Foster, W. A. 1983. Activity rhythms and the tide in a saltmarsh beetle *Dicheirotrichus gustavi. Oecologia* 60: 111–111.

Foster, W. A. 1984. The distribution of the sea-lavender aphid *Staticobium staticis* on a marine saltmarsh and its effect on host plant fitness. *Oikos* 42: 97–104.

Frix, M. S., M. E. Hostetler and K. L. Bildstein. 1991. Intra- and interspecies differences in responses of Atlantic sand (*Uca pugilator*) and Atlantic marsh (*U. pugnax*) fiddler crabs to simulated avian predators. *J. Crust. Biol.* 11: 523–529.

Furbish, C. E. and M. Albano. 1994. Selective herbivory and plant community structure in a mid-Atlantic salt marsh. *Ecology* 75: 1015–1022.

Gaines, S. and J. Roughgarden. 1985. Larval settlement rate: A leading determinant of structure in an ecological community of the marine intertidal zone. *Proc. Natl. Acad. Sci. USA* 82: 3707–3711.

Gallagher, J. L. 1975. Effect of an ammonium nitrate pulse on the growth and elemental composition of natural stands of *Spartina alterniflora* and *Juncus roemerianus. Amer. J. Bot.* 62: 644–648.

Gallagher, J. L., G. F. Somers, D. M. Grant and D. M. Seliskar. 1988. Persistent differences in two forms of *Spartina alterniflora*: A common garden experiment. *Ecology* 69: 1005–1008.

Ganong, W. F. 1903. The vegetation of the Bay of Fundy salt and diked marshes: An ecological study. *Bot. Gaz.* 36: 161–186, 280–302, 350–367, 429–455.

Genoni, G. P. 1985. Food limitation in salt marsh fiddler crabs *Uca rapax* (Smith) (Decapoda: Ocypodidae). *J. Exp. Mar. Biol. Ecol.* 87: 97–110.

Gerdol, V. and R. G. Hughes. Effect of the amphipod *Corophium volutator* on the colonisation of mud by the halophyte *Salicornia europaea. Mar. Ecol. Prog. Ser.* 97: 61–69.

Geslin, M. and J.-F. Verbist. 1985. Flavonoides de *Salicornia europaea. J. Nat. Prod.* 48: 111–111.

Gleason, M. L. 1980. Influence of tidal inundation on internal oxygen supply of *Spartina alterniflora* and *Spartina patens.* Ph.D. dissertation, University of Virginia, Charlottesville.

Gleason, M. L. and J. C. Zieman. 1981. Influence of tidal inundation on internal oxygen supply of *Spartina alterniflora* and *Spartina patens. Est. Coast. Shelf Sci.* 13: 47–57.

Glenn, E. P., J. W. O'Leary, M. C. Watxon, T. L. Thompson and R. O. Kuehl. 1991. *Salicornia bigelovii* Torr.: An oilseed halophyte for seawater irrigation. *Science* 251: 1065–1067.

Gordon, D. C., Jr. and C. Desplanque. 1983. Dynamics and environmental effects of ice in the Cumberland Basin of the Bay of Fundy. *Can. J. Fish. Aquat. Sci.* 40: 1331–1342.

Gough, L. and J. B. Grace. 1998a. Effects of flooding, salinity and herbivory on coastal plant communities, Louisiana, United States. *Oecologia* 117: 527–535.

Gough, L. and J. B. Grace. 1998b. Herbivore effects on plant species density at varying productivity levels. *Ecology* 79: 1586–1594.

Graça, M. A., S. Y. Newell and R. T. Kneib. 2000. Grazing rates of organic matter and living fungal biomass of decaying *Spartina alterniflora* by three species of salt-marsh invertebrates. *Mar. Biol.* 136: 281–289.

Grace, J. B. 1985. Juvenile vs. adult competitive abilities in plants: Size-dependence in cattails (*Typha*). *Ecology* 66: 1630–1638.

Grace, J. B. and M. A. Ford. 1996. The potential impact of herbivores on the susceptibility of the marsh plant *Sagittaria lancifolia* to saltwater intrusion in coastal wetlands. *Estuaries* 19: 13–20.

Grace, J. B. and R. G. Wetzel. 1981. Habitat partitioning and competitive displacement in cattails (*Typha*): Experimental field studies. *Amer. Nat.* 118: 463–474.

Gray, A. J. and P. E. M. Benham. 1990. *Spartina anglica*—a research review. ITE research publication no. 2. Natural Environment Research Council, HMSO, London.

Gross, W. J. 1964. Trends in water and salt regulation among aquatic and amphibious crabs. *Biol. Bull.* 127: 447–466.

Hacker, S. D. and M. D. Bertness. 1995a. A herbivore paradox: Why salt marsh aphids live on poor-quality plants. *Amer. Nat.* 145: 192–210.

Hacker, S. D. and M. D. Bertness. 1995b. Morphological and physiological consequences of a positive plant interaction. *Ecology* 76: 2165–2175.

Hacker, S. D. and M. D. Bertness. 1996. Trophic consequences of a positive plant interaction. *Amer. Nat.* 148: 559–575.

Hacker, S. D. and M. D. Bertness. 1999. Experimental evidence for factors maintaining plant species diversity in a New England salt marsh. *Ecology* 80: 2064–2073.

Hacker, S. D. and S. D. Gaines. 1997. Some implications of direct positive interactions for community species diversity. *Ecology* 78: 1990–2003.

Hackney, C. T. and T. D. Bishop. 1981. A note on the relocation of marsh debris during a storm surge. *Est. Coast Shelf Sci.* 12: 621–624.

Haines, E. B. 1976. Relation between the stable carbon isotope composition of fiddler crabs, plants and soils in a salt marsh. *Limnol. Oceanogr.* 21: 880–883.

Haines, E. B. 1977. The origins of detritus in Georgia salt marsh estuaries. *Oikos* 29: 254–260.

Haines, E. B. 1979. Interactions between Georgia salt marshes and coastal waters: A changing paradigm. In R. J. Livingston (ed.), *Ecological Processes in Coastal and Marine Systems*, pp. 35–46. Plenum Press, New York.

Haines, E. B. and C. L. Montague. 1979. Food sources of estuarine invertebrates analyzed using $^{13}C/^{12}C$ ratios. *Ecology* 60: 48–56.

Hamilton, P. V. 1976. Predation on *Littorina irrorata* by *Callinectes sapidus. Bull. Mar. Sci.* 26: 401–409.

Hardwick-Witman, M. N. 1985. Biological consequences of ice rafting in a New England salt marsh community. *J. Exp. Mar. Biol. Ecol.* 87: 283–298.

Harley, C. D. G. and M. D. Bertness. 1996. Structural interdependence: An ecological consequence of morphological responses to crowding in marsh plants. *Funct. Ecol.* 10: 654–661.

Hartman, J. M. 1988. Recolonization of small disturbance patches in a New England salt marsh. *Amer. J. Bot.* 75: 1625–1631.

Hartman, J. M., H. Caswell and I. Valiela. 1983. Effects of wrack accumulation on salt marsh vegetation. Proceedings of the 17th European Marine Biology Symposium. *Oceanologica Acta*, Brest, France, pp. 99–102.

Herz, W., S. V. Bhat and V. Sudarsanum. 1972. Sesquiterpene lactones and flavones of *Iva frutescens. Phytochemistry* 11: 1829–1831.

Hik, D. S., R. L. Jefferies and A. R. E. Sinclair. 1992. Foraging by geese, isostatic uplift and asymmetry in the development of salt-marsh plant communities. *J. Ecol.* 80: 395–406.

Howarth, R. W. and J. M. Teal. 1979. Sulfate reduction in a New England salt marsh. *Limnol. Oceanogr.* 24: 999–1011.

Howes, B. L and D. D. Goehringer. 1994. Porewater drainage and dissolved organic carbon and nutrient losses through the intertidal creekbanks of a New England salt marsh. *Mar. Ecol. Prog. Ser.* 114: 289–301.

Howes, B. L. and J. M. Teal. 1994. Oxygen loss from *Spartina alterniflora* and its relationship to salt marsh oxygen balance. *Oecologia* 97: 431–438.

Howes, B. L., R. W. Howarth, J. M. Teal and I. Valiela. 1981. Oxidation-reduction potentials in a salt marsh: Spatial patterns and interactions with primary production. *Limnol. Oceanogr.* 26: 350–360.

Howes, B. L., J. W. H. Dacey and D. D. Goehringer. 1986. Factors controlling the growth form of *Spartina alterniflora*: Feedbacks between above-ground production, sediment oxidation, nitrogen and salinity. *J. Ecol.* 74: 881–898.

Huisman, J. and H. Olff. 1998. Competition and facilitation in multispecies plant-herbivore systems of productive environments. *Ecol. Lett.* 1: 25–29.

Hyatt, G. W. and M. Salmon. 1978. Combat in the fiddler crabs *Uca pugilator* and *U. pugnax*: A quantitative descriptive analysis. *Behaviour* 65: 184–221.

Hylleberg, J. 1975. Selective feeding by *Arenicola pacifica* with notes on *Arenicola vagabunda* and a concept of gardening in lugworms. *Ophelia* 14: 113–137.

Iacobelli, A. and R. L. Jefferies. 1991. Inverse salinity gradients in coastal marshes and the death of stands of *Salix*: The effects of grubbing by geese. *J. Ecol.* 79: 61–73.

Jefferies, R. L. 1988. Vegetational mosaics, plant-animal interactions and resources for plant growth. In L. D. Gottlieb and S. K. Jain (eds.), *Plant Evolutionary Biology*, pp. 341–369. Chapman and Hall, London.

Jefferies, R. L. and N. Perkins. 1977. The effects on the vegetation of the addition of inorganic nutrients to salt marsh soils at Stiffkey, Norfolk. *J. Ecol.* 65: 867–882.

Jefferies, R. L., A. J. Davy and T. Rudmik. 1979. The growth strategies of coastal halophytes. In R. L. Jefferies and A. J. Davy (eds.), *Ecological Processes in Coastal Environments*, pp. 243–268. Blackwell Scientific Publications, Oxford.

Jensen, A. 1985. The effect of cattle and sheep grazing on salt-marsh vegetation at Skallingen, Denmark. *Vegetatio* 60: 37–48.

Johnson, D. J. 1920. *Shoreline Processes and Shoreline Development.* Columbia University Press, New York.

Jones, C. G., J. H. Lawton and M. Shachak. 1994. Organisms as ecosystem engineers. *Oikos* 69: 373–386.

Jordan, T. E. and I. Valiela. 1982. The nitrogen budget of the ribbed mussel, *Geukensia demissa*, and its significance in nitrogen flow in a New England salt marsh. *Limnol. Oceanogr.* 27: 75–90.

Josselyn, M., J. Zedler and T. Griswold. 1990. Wetland mitigation along the Pacific coast of the United States. In J. A. Kusler and M. E. Kentula (eds.), *Wetland Creation and Restoration: The Status of the Science*, pp. 3–36. Island Press, Washington DC.

Kagan, J. and T. J. Mabry. 1969. Isorhamnetin 3-*O*-rutinoside, the flavonoid pigment in *Batis maritima. Phytochemistry* 8: 325–326.

Katz, L. C. 1980. Effects of burrowing by the fiddler crab, *Uca pugnax* (Smith). *Est. Coast Mar. Sci.* 11: 233–237.

Keddy, P. A. 1989. *Competition.* Chapman & Hall, London.

Kerbes, R. H., P. M. Kotanen and R. L. Jefferies. 1990. Destruction of wetland habitats by lesser snow geese: A keystone species on the west coast of Hudson Bay. *J. Appl. Ecol.* 27: 242–258.

Kiehl, K., I. Eischeid, S. Gettner and J. Walter. 1996. Impact of different sheep grazing intensities on salt marsh vegetation in northern Germany. *J. Veg. Sci.* 7: 99–106.

King, G. M., M. J. Klug, R. G. Wiegert and A. G. Chalmers. 1982. Relation of soil water movement and sulfide concentration to *Spartina alterniflora* production in a Georgia salt marsh. *Science* 218: 61–63.

Kneib, R. T. 1984. Patterns of invertebrate distribution and abundance in the intertidal salt marsh: Causes and questions. *Estuaries* 7: 392–412.

Kneib, R. T. 1987. Predation risk and use of intertidal habitats by young fishes and shrimp. *Ecology* 68: 379–386.

Kneib, R. T. 1988. Testing for indirect effects of predation in an intertidal soft-bottom community. *Ecology* 69: 1795–1805.

Kneib, R. T. 1991. Indirect effects in experimental studies of marine soft-sediment communities. *Amer. Zool.* 31: 874–885.

Kneib, R. T. 1993. Growth and mortality in successive cohorts of fish larvae within an estuarine nursery. *Mar. Ecol. Prog. Ser.* 94: 115–127.

Kneib, R. T. 1994. Spatial pattern, spatial scale, and feeding in fishes. In D. J. Stouder, K. L.

Fresh and R. J. Feller (eds.), *Theory and Application in Fish Feeding Ecology*, pp. 171–185. The Belle W. Baruch Library in Marine Science, no. 18. University of South Carolina Press, Columbia.

Kneib, R. T. 1997. The role of tidal marshes in the ecology of estuarine nekton. *Oceanogr. Mar. Biol. Ann. Rev.* 35: 163–220.

Kneib, R. T. In press. Salt marsh ecoscapes and production transfers by estuarine nekton in the southeastern U.S. In Kreeger and Wienstein (eds.), *Concepts and Controversies in Tidal Marsh Ecology*. Kluwer, Dordrecht.

Kneib, R. T. and M. K. Knowlton. 1995. Stage-structured interactions between seasonal and permanent residents of an estuarine nekton community. *Oecologia* 103: 425–434.

Kneib, R. T., S. Y. Newell and E. T. Hermeno. 1997. Survival, growth and reproduction of the saltmarsh amphipod *Uhlorchestia spartinophila* reared on natural diets of senescent and dead *Spartina alterniflora* leaves. *Mar. Biol.* 128: 423–431.

Kraeuter, J. N. 1976. Biodeposition by salt-marsh invertebrates. *Mar. Biol.* 35: 215–223.

Kraft, S. K. and R. F. Denno. 1982. Feeding responses of adapted and non-adapted insects to the defensive properties of *Baccharis halimifolia* L. (Compositae). *Oecologia* 52: 156–163.

Kreeger, D. A., C. J. Langdon and R. I. E. Newell. 1988. Utilization of refractory cellulosic carbon derived from *Spartina alterniflora* by the ribbed mussel *Geukensia demissa*. *Mar. Ecol. Prog. Ser.* 42: 171–179.

Krischik, V. A. and R. F. Denno. 1990. Patterns of growth, reproduction, defense, and herbivory in the dioecious shrub *Baccharis halimifolia* (Compositae). *Oecologia* 83: 182–190.

Kuenzler, E. J. 1961. Structure and energy flow of a mussel population in a Georgia salt marsh. *Limnol. Oceanogr.* 6: 191–204.

Langdon, C. J. and R. I. E. Newell. 1990. Utilization of detritus and bacteria as food sources by two bivalve suspension-feeders, the oyster *Crassostrea virginica* and the mussel *Geukensia demissa*. *Mar. Ecol. Prog. Ser.* 58: 299–310.

Levine, J. M., J. S. Brewer and M. D. Bertness. 1998. Nutrients, competition and plant zonation in a New England salt marsh. *J. Ecol.* 86: 285–292.

Levinton, J. S. 1981. Nutrition and food limitation of deposit feeders. I. The role of microbes in the growth of mud snails (Hydrobiidae). *J. Mar. Res.* 39: 531–545.

Levinton, J. S. and G. R. Lopez. 1977. A model of renewable resources and limitation of deposit-feeding benthic populations. *Oecologia* 31: 177–190.

Lin, J. 1989. Influence of location in a salt marsh on survivorship of ribbed mussels. *Mar. Ecol. Prog. Ser.* 56: 105–110.

Lin, J. 1990. Mud crab predation on ribbed mussels in salt marshes. *Mar. Biol.* 107: 103–109.

Lin, J. 1991. Predator-prey interactions between blue crabs and ribbed mussels living in clumps. *Est. Coast. Shelf Sci.* 32: 61–69.

Looijen, R. C. and J. P. Bakker. 1987. Utilization of different salt-marsh plant communities by cattle and geese. In A. H. L. Huiskes,

C. W. P. M. Bloom and J. Rozema (eds.), *Vegetation between Land and Sea*, pp. 52–64. Dr. W. Junk, Dordrecht.

Lopez, G. R. and J. S. Levinton. 1987. Ecology of deposit-feeding animals in marine sediments. *Q. Rev. Biol.* 2: 235–260.

Lowery, G. H., Jr. 1974. *The Mammals of Louisiana and Its Adjacent Waters.* Louisiana State University Press, Baton Rouge.

Lynch, J. J., T. O'Neil and D. W. Lay. 1947. Management significance of damage by geese and muskrats to Gulf coast marshes. *J. Wildl. Mgmt.* 11: 50–76.

MacArthur, R. H. 1972. *Geographical Ecology: Patterns in the Distribution of Species.* Harper and Row, New York.

MacDonald, K. B. 1977a. Coastal salt marsh. In M. G. Barbour and J. Major (eds.), *Terrestrial Vegetation of California*, pp. 263–294. John Wiley and Sons, New York.

MacDonald, K. B. 1977b. Plant and animal communities of Pacific North American salt marshes. In V. J. Chapman (ed.), *Wet Coastal Ecosystems*, pp. 167–191. Elsevier, Amsterdam.

MacDonald, K. B. and M. G. Barbour. 1974. Beach and salt marsh vegetation of the North American Pacific coast. In R. J. Reimold and W. H. Queen (eds.), *Ecology of Halophytes*, pp. 175–233. Academic Press, New York.

Mahall, B. E. and R. B. Park. 1976a. The ecotone between *Spartina foliosa* Trin. and *Salicornia virginica* L. in salt marshes of northern San Francisco Bay. I. Biomass and production. *J. Ecol.* 64: 421–433.

Mahall, B. E. and R. B. Park. 1976b. The ecotone between *Spartina foliosa* Trin. and *Salicornia virginica* L. in salt marshes of northern San Francisco Bay. II. Soil water and salinity. *J. Ecol.* 64: 793–809.

Mann, K. H. 1972. Macrophyte production and detritus food chains in coastal waters. *Mem. Ist. Ital. Idrobiol.* 29 (Suppl.): 353–383.

Marinucci, A. C. 1982. Trophic importance of *Spartina alterniflora* production and decomposition to the marsh-estuarine system. *Biol. Conserv.* 22: 35–58.

Matthews, G. A. and T. J. Minello. 1994. Technology and success in restoration, creation, and enhancement of *Spartina alterniflora* marshes in the United States. Vols. 1 and 2. NOAA Coastal Ocean Program Decision Analysis Series no. 2. NOAA Coastal Ocean Office, Silver Spring, MD.

Mausbach, M. J. and J. L. Richardson. 1994. Biogeochemical processes in hydric soil formation. *Curr. Top. Wetl. Biogeochem.* 1: 68–127.

McKee, K. L. and W. H. Patrick, Jr. 1988. The relationship of smooth cordgrass (*Spartina alterniflora*) to tidal datums: A review. *Estuaries* 11: 143–151.

Mendelssohn, I. A. 1979a. The influence of nitrogen level, form and application method on the growth response of *Spartina alterniflora* in North Carolina. *Estuaries* 2: 106–112.

Mendelssohn, I. A. 1979b. Nitrogen metabolism in the height forms of *Spartina alterniflora* in North Carolina. *Ecology* 60: 574–584.

Mendelssohn, I. A., K. L. McKee and M. T. Postek. 1982. Sublethal stresses controlling

Spartina alterniflora productivity. In B. Gopal, R. T. Turner, W. G. Wetzel and D. F. Whigham (eds.), *Wetlands: Ecology and Management*, pp. 223–242. National Institute of Ecological International Scientific Publications, Jaipur, India.

Mendelssohn, I. A., K. L. McKee and W. H. Patrick. 1991. Oxygen deficiency in *Spartina alterniflora* roots: Metabolic adaptation to anoxia. *Science* 214: 439–441.

Mesléard, F. 1994. Agricultural abandonment in a wetland area: Abandoned ricefields in the Camargue, France—can they be of value for conservation? *Environ. Conserv.* 21: 354–357.

Metcalfe, W. S., A. M. Ellison and M. D. Bertness. 1986. Survivorship and spatial development of *Spartina alterniflora* Loisel. (Gramineae) seedlings in a New England salt marsh. *Ann. Bot.* 58: 249–258.

Micheli, F. 1997. Effects of predator foraging behavior on patterns of prey mortality in marine soft bottoms. *Ecol. Monogr.* 67: 203–224.

Miles, D. H., J. Bhattacharyya, N. V. Mody, J. L. Atwood, S. Black and P. A. Hedin. 1977. The structure of juncusol, a novel cytotoxic dihydrophenanthrene from the estuarine marsh plant *Juncus roemerianus*. *J. Amer. Chem. Soc.* 99: 618–620.

Miller, D. L., F. E. Smeins and J. W. Webb. 1996. Mid-Texas coastal marsh change (1939–1991) as influenced by lesser snow goose herbivory. *J. Coast. Res.* 12: 462–476.

Miller, W. B. and F. E. Egler. 1950. Vegetation of the Wequetequock-Pawcatuck tidal marshes, Connecticut. *Ecol. Monogr.* 20: 143–172.

Mitsch, W. J. and J. G. Gosselink. 1993. *Wetlands*, 2nd ed. Van Nostrand Reinhold, New York.

Montague, C. L. 1980. A natural history of temperate western Atlantic fiddler crabs (genus *Uca*) with reference to their impact on the salt marsh. *Contrib. Mar. Sci.* 23: 25–55.

Montague, C. L. 1982. The influence of fiddler crab burrows and burrowing on metabolic processes in salt marsh sediments. In V. S. Kennedy (ed.), *Estuarine Comparisons*, pp. 283–301. Academic Press, New York.

Montague, C. L. and R. G. Wiegert. 1990. Salt marshes. In R. L. Myers and J. J. Ewel (eds.), *Ecosystems of Florida*, pp. 481–516. University of Central Florida Press, Orlando.

Morris, J. T. and G. J. Whiting. 1985. Gas advection in sediments of a South Carolina salt marsh. *Mar. Ecol. Prog. Ser.* 27: 187–194.

Mouton, E. C., Jr. and D. L. Felder. 1996. Burrow distributions and population estimates for the fiddler crabs *Uca spinicarpa* and *Uca longisignalis* in a Gulf of Mexico salt marsh. *Estuaries* 19: 51–61.

Mulder, C. P. H. and R. W. Ruess. 1998. Effects of herbivory on arrowgrass: Interactions between geese, neighboring plants, and abiotic factors. *Ecol. Monogr.* 68: 275–293.

Newell, S. Y. 1993. Decomposition of shoots of a salt-marsh grass. *Adv. Microb. Ecol.* 13: 301–326.

Newell, S. Y. 1996. Established and potential impacts of eukaryotic mycelial decomposers in marine/terrestrial ecotones. *J. Exp. Mar. Biol. Ecol.* 200: 187–206.

Newell, S. Y. and F. Bärlocher. 1993. Removal of fungal and total organic material from decaying cordgrass leaves by shredder snails. *J. Exp. Mar. Biol. Ecol.* 171: 39–49.

Newell, S. Y. and C. Krambeck. 1995. Responses of bacterioplankton to tidal inundations of a saltmarsh in a flume and adjacent mussel enclosures. *J. Exp. Mar. Biol. Ecol.* 190: 79–95.

Newell, S. Y. and D. Porter. In press. Microbial secondary production from saltmarsh-grass shoots, and its known and potential fates. In Kreeger and Wienstein (eds.), *Concepts and Controversies in Tidal Marsh Ecology.* Kluwer.

Newell, S. Y., R. D. Fallon, R. M. Cal Rodriguez and L. C. Groene. 1985. Influence of rain, tidal wetting and relative humidity on release of carbon dioxide by standing-dead salt-marsh plants. *Oecologia* 68: 73–79.

Newell, S. Y., T. L. Arsuffi and L. A. Palm. 1998. Seasonal and vertical demography of dead portions of shoots of smooth cordgrass in a south-temperate saltmarsh. *Aquat. Bot.* 60: 325–335.

Nixon, S. W. 1981. Between coastal marshes and waters: A review of twenty years of speculation and research on the role of salt marshes in estuarine productivity and water chemistry. In P. Hamilton and K. B. MacDonald (eds.), *Estuarine and Coastal Processes*, pp. 437–525. Plenum Press, New York.

Nixon, S. W. and C. A. Oviatt. 1973. Ecology of a New England salt marsh. *Ecol. Monogr.* 43: 463–498.

Nomann, B. E. and S. C. Pennings. 1998. Fiddler crab-vegetation interactions in hypersaline habitats. *J. Exp. Mar. Biol. Ecol.* 225: 53–68.

O'Connor, N. J. 1993. Settlement and recruitment of the fiddler crabs *Uca pugnax* and *U. pugilator* in a North Carolina, USA, salt marsh. *Mar. Ecol. Prog. Ser.* 93: 227–234.

Odum, E. P. and A. de la Cruz. 1967. Particulate organic detritus in a Georgia salt marsh-estuarine system. In G. H. Lauff (ed.), *Estuaries*, pp. 383–385. AAAS Publication 83, Washington, DC.

Odum, E. P. and M. E. Fanning. 1973. Comparison of the productivity of *Spartina alterniflora* and *Spartina cynosuroides* in Georgia coastal marshes. *Bull. Ga. Acad. Sci.* 31: 1–12.

Odum, W. E. 1978. The importance of tidal freshwater wetlands in coastal zone management. In *Coastal Zone '78: Symposium on Technical, Environmental, Socioeconomic and Regulatory Aspects of Coastal Zone Management*, pp. 1196–1203. American Society of Civil Engineers, New York.

Odum, W. E. 1988. Comparative ecology of tidal freshwater and salt marshes. *Ann. Rev. Ecol. Syst.* 19: 147–176.

Odum, W. E. and J. K. Hoover. 1988. A comparison of vascular plant communities in tidal freshwater and saltwater marshes. In D. D. Hook, W. H. McKee, Jr., H. K. Smith, J. Gregory, V. G. Burrell, Jr., M. R. DeVoe, R. E. Sojka, S. Gilbert, R. Banks, L. H. Stozy, C. Brooks, T. D. Matthews and T. H. Shear (eds.), *The Ecology and Management of Wetlands*, vol. 1: *Ecology of Wetlands*, pp. 526–534. Croom Helm, London.

Odum, W. E., J. S. Fisher and J. C. Pickral. 1979. Factors controlling the flux of particulate organic carbon from estuarine wetlands. In R. J. Livingston (ed.), *Ecological Processes in Coastal and Marine Systems*, pp. 69–80. Plenum Press, New York.

O'Leary, J. W., E. P. Glenn and M. C. Watson. 1985. Agricultural production of halophytes irrigated with seawater. *Plant Soil* 89: 311–321.

Olff, H., J. De Leeuw, J. P. Bakker, R. J. Platerink, H. J. Van Wijnen and W. De Munck. 1997. Vegetation succession and herbivory in a salt marsh: Changes induced by sea level rise and silt deposition along an elevational gradient. *J. Ecol.* 85: 799–814.

Olmstead, K. L., R. F. Denno, T. C. Morton and J. T. Romeo. 1997. Influence of *Prokelisia* planthoppers on amino acid composition and growth of *Spartina alterniflora*. *J. Chem. Ecol.* 23: 303–321.

Oney, J. 1954. *Final Report: Clapper Rail Survey and Investigation Study.* Georgia Game and Fish Commission.

Osgood, D. T., M. C. F. V. Santos and J. C. Zieman. 1995. Sediment physio-chemistry associated with natural marsh development on a storm-deposited sand flat. *Mar. Ecol. Prog. Ser.* 120: 271–283.

Page, H. M. 1997. Importance of vascular plant and algal production to macro-invertebrate consumers in a southern California salt marsh. *Est. Coast. Shelf Sci.* 45: 823–834.

Parsons, K. A. and A. A. de la Cruz. 1980. Energy flow and grazing behavior of conocephaline grasshoppers in a *Juncus roemerianus* marsh. *Ecology* 61: 1045–1050.

Pearcy, R. W. and S. L. Ustin. 1984. Effects of salinity on growth and photosynthesis of three California tidal marsh species. *Oecologia* 62: 68–73.

Pennings, S. C. and M. D. Bertness. 1999. Using latitudinal variation to examine effects of climate on coastal salt marsh pattern and process. *Current Topics in Wetland Biogeochemistry* 3: 100–111.

Pennings, S. C. and R. M. Callaway. 1992. Salt marsh plant zonation: The relative importance of competition and physical factors. *Ecology* 73: 681–690.

Pennings, S. C. and R. M. Callaway. 1996. Impact of a parasitic plant on the structure and dynamics of salt marsh vegetation. *Ecology* 77: 1410–1419.

Pennings, S. C. and R. M. Callaway. 2000. The advantages of clonal integration under different ecological conditions: A community-wide test. *Ecology* 81: 709–716.

Pennings, S. C. and D. Moore. In press. Zonation of shrubs in western Atlantic salt marshes. *Oecologia.*

Pennings, S. C. and C. L. Richards. 1998. Effects of wrack burial in salt-stressed habitats: *Batis maritima* in a southwest Atlantic salt marsh. *Ecography* 21: 630–638.

Pennings, S. C., T. H. Carefoot, E. L. Siska, M. E. Chase and T. A. Page. 1998. Feeding preferences of a generalist salt-marsh crab: Relative importance of multiple plant traits. *Ecology* 79: 1968–1979.

Pennings, S. C., E. L. Siska and M. D. Bertness. In press. Latitudinal differences in plant palatability in Atlantic coast salt marshes. *Ecology.*

Peterson, B., R. Howarth and R. Garritt. 1985. Multiple stable isotopes used to trace the flow of organic matter in estuarine food webs. *Science* 227: 1361–1363.

Pethick, J. S. 1974. The distribution of salt pannes on tidal salt marshes. *J. Biogeogr.* 1: 57–62.

Petit, D. R. and K. L. Bildstein. 1987. Effect of group size and location within the group on the foraging behavior of white ibises. *Condor* 89: 602–609.

Pezeshki, S. R. 1997. Photosynthesis and root growth of *Spartina alterniflora* in relation to root zone aeration. *Photosynthetica* 34: 107–114.

Pfeiffer, W. J. and R. G. Wiegert. 1981. Grazers on *Spartina* and their predators. In L. R. Pomeroy and R. G. Wiegert (eds.), *The Ecology of a Salt Marsh*, pp. 87–112. Springer-Verlag, New York.

Pielou, E. C. and R. D. Routledge. 1976. Salt marsh vegetation: Latitudinal gradients in the zonation patterns. *Oecologia* 24: 311–321.

Poljakoff-Mayber, A. 1975. Morphological and anatomical changes in plants as a response to salinity stress. In A. Poljakoff-Mayber and J. Gale (eds.), *Plants in Saline Environments*, pp. 97–117. Springer-Verlag, New York.

Pomeroy, L. R. and R. G. Wiegert. 1981. *The Ecology of a Salt Marsh.* Springer-Verlag, New York.

Ponnamperuma, F. N. 1972. The chemistry of submerged soils. *Adv. Agron.* 24: 29–95.

Posey, M. H. and A. H. Hines. 1991. Complex predator-prey interactions within an estuarine benthic community. *Ecology* 72: 2155–2169.

Prins, H. H. Th., R. C. Ydenberg and R. H. Drent. 1980. The interaction of brent geese *Branta bernicla* and sea plantain *Plantago maritima* during spring staging: Field observations and experiments. *Acta Bot. Neerl.* 29: 585–596.

Rampino, M. R. and J. Sanders. 1981. Episodic growth of Holocene tidal marshes in the northeastern United States: A possible indicator of eustatic sea level fluctuations. *Geology* 9: 63–67.

Rand, T. A. 1999. Effects of environmental context on the susceptibility of *Atriplex patula* to attack by herbivorous beetles. *Oecologia* 121: 39–46.

Rand, T. 2000. Seed dispersal habitat suitability and the distribution of halophytes across a salt marsh tidal gradient. *J. Ecol.* 88: 608–621.

Ranwell, D. S. 1961. *Spartina* salt marshes in southern England. I. The effects of sheep grazing at the upper limits of *Spartina* marsh in Bridgwater Bay. *J. Ecol.* 49: 325–340.

Ranwell, D. S. 1964a. *Spartina* salt marshes in southern England. II. Rate and seasonal pattern of sediment accretion. *J. Ecol.* 52: 79–94.

Ranwell, D. S. 1964b. *Spartina* salt marshes in southern England. III. Rates of establishment, succession and nutrient supply at Bridgwater Bay, Somerset. *J. Ecol.* 52: 95–105.

Ranwell, D. S. 1972. *Ecology of Salt Marshes and Sand Dunes.* Chapman and Hall, London.

Redfield, A. C. 1965. Ontogeny of a salt marsh. *Science* 147: 50–55.

Redfield, A. C. 1972. Development of a New England salt marsh. *Ecol. Monogr.* 42: 201–237.

Reidenbaugh, T. G. and W. C. Banta. 1982. Origin and effects of tidal wrack in a Virginia salt marsh. *Gulf Res. Rep.* 6: 393–401.

Reimold, R. J. 1977. Mangals and salt marshes of eastern United States. In V. J. Chapman (ed.), *Wet Coastal Ecosystems*, pp. 157–166. Elsevier Scientific, Amsterdam.

Rejmanek, M., C. Sasser and G. W. Peterson. 1988. Hurricane-induced sediment deposition in a Gulf Coast marsh. *Est. Coast. Shelf Sci.* 27: 217–222.

Reusch, T. B. H., A. R. O. Chapman and J. P. Gröger. 1994. Blue mussels *Mytilus edulis* do not interfere with eelgrass *Zostera marina* but fertilize shoot growth through biodeposition. *Mar. Ecol. Prog. Ser.* 108: 265–282.

Richard, G. A. 1978. Seasonal and environmental variation in sediment accretion in a Long Island salt marsh. *Estuaries* 1: 29–35.

Rietsma, C. S., I. Valiela and A. Sylvester-Serianni. 1982. Food preferences of dominant salt marsh herbivores and detritivores. *P.S.Z.N.I. Mar. Ecol.* 3: 179–189.

Rietsma, C. S., I. Valiela and R. Buchsbaum. 1988. Detrital chemistry, growth and food choice in the salt-marsh snail (*Melampus bidentatus*). *Ecology* 69: 261–266.

Roberts, B. A. and A. Robertson. 1986. Salt marshes of Atlantic Canada: Their ecology and distribution. *Can. J. Bot.* 64: 455–467.

Robertson, J. R. and S. Y. Newell. 1982. Experimental studies of particle ingestion by the sand fiddler crab *Uca pugilator* (Bosc). *J. Exp. Mar. Biol. Ecol.* 52: 1–21.

Rossi, A. M. and P. Stiling. 1998. The interactions of plant clone and abiotic factors on a gall-making midge. *Oecologia* 116: 170–176.

Rossi, A. M. and D. R. Strong. 1991. Effects of host-plant nitrogen on the preference and performance of laboratory populations of *Carneocephala floridana* (Homoptera: Cicadellidae). *Environ. Entomol.* 20: 1349–1355.

Rossi, A. M., B. V. Brodbeck and D. R. Strong. 1996. Response of xylem-feeding leafhopper to host plant species and plant quality. *J. Chem. Ecol.* 22: 653–671.

Rowcliffe, J. M., A. R. Watkinson and W. J. Sutherland. 1998. Aggregative responses of brent geese on salt marsh and their impact on plant community dynamics. *Oecologia* 114: 417–426.

Rozema, J. and J. Van Diggelen. 1991. A comparative study of growth and photosynthesis of four halophytes in response to salinity. *Acta Oecologica* 12: 673–681.

Rozema, J., H. Gude and G. Pollak. 1981. An ecophysiological study of the salt secretion of four halophytes. *New Phytol.* 89: 201–217.

Rozema, J., P. Bijwaard, G. Prast and R. Broekman. 1985. Ecophysiological adaptations of coastal halophytes from foredunes and salt marshes. *Vegetatio* 62: 499–521.

Russell, P. J., T. J. Flowers and M. J. Hutchings. 1985. Comparison of niche breadths and overlaps of halophytes on salt marshes of differing diversity. *Vegetatio* 61: 171–178.

Schat, H. 1984. A comparative ecophysiological study on the effects of waterlogging and submergence on dune slack plants: Growth, survival and mineral nutrition in sand culture experiments. *Oecologia* 62: 279–286.

Schindler, D. E., B. M. Johnson, N. A. MacKay, N. Bouwes and J. F. Kitchell. 1994. Crab/snail size-structured interactions and salt marsh predation gradients. *Oecologia* 97: 49–61.

Seaman, F. C. 1982. Sesquiterpene lactones as taxonomic characters in the Asteraceae. *Bot. Rev.* 48: 121–592.

Seed, R. 1980. Predator-prey relationships between the mud crab *Panopeus herbstii*, the blue crab, *Callinectes sapidus* and the Atlantic ribbed mussel *Geukensia* (= *Modiolus*) *demissa*. *Est. Coast. Mar. Sci.* 11: 445–458.

Seliskar, D. M. 1985a. Effect of reciprocal transplanting between extremes of plant zones on morphometric plasticity of five plant species in an Oregon salt marsh. *Can. J. Bot.* 63: 2254–2262.

Seliskar, D. M. 1985b. Morphometric variations of five tidal marsh halophytes along environmental gradients. *Amer. J. Bot.* 72: 1340–1352.

Seliskar, D. M. 1987. The effects of soil moisture on structural and biomass characteristics of four salt marsh plants. *J. Exp. Bot.* 38: 1193–1202.

Seliskar, D. M. and J. L. Gallagher. 1983. The ecology of tidal marshes of the Pacific Northwest coast: A community profile. FWS/OBS-82/32. U.S. Fish and Wildlife Service, Division of Biological Services, Washington, D.C.

Shanholtzer, G. F. 1974. Relationship of vertebrates to salt marsh plants. In R. J. Reimold and W. H. Queen (eds.), *Ecology of Halophytes*, pp. 463–474. Academic Press, New York.

Shea, M. L., R. S. Warren and W. A. Niering. 1975. Biochemical and transplantational studies of the growth form of *Spartina alterniflora* on Connecticut salt marshes. *Ecology* 56: 461–466.

Shumway, S. W. 1995. Physiological integration among clonal ramets during invasion of disturbance patches in a New England salt marsh. *Ann. Bot.* 76: 225–233.

Shumway, S. W. and M. D. Bertness. 1992. Salt stress limitation of seedling recruitment in a salt marsh plant community. *Oecologia* 92: 490–497.

Shumway, S. W. and M. D. Bertness. 1994. Patch size effects on marsh plant secondary succession mechanisms. *Ecology* 75: 564–568.

Silander, J. A., Jr. 1979. Microevolution and clone structure in *Spartina patens*. *Science* 203: 658–660.

Silander, J. A., Jr. 1984. The genetic basis of the ecological amplitude of *Spartina patens*. III. Allozyme variation. *Bot. Gaz.* 145: 569–577.

Silander, J. A., Jr. 1985. The genetic basis of the ecological amplitude of *Spartina patens*. II. Variance and correlation analysis. *Evolution* 39: 1034–1052.

Silander, J. A., Jr. and J. Antonovics. 1979. The genetic basis of the ecological amplitude of *Spartina patens*. I. Morphometric and physiological traits. *Evolution* 33: 1114–1127.

Silliman, B. R. and J. C. Zieman. In press. Top-down control of *Spartina alterniflora* production by periwinkle grazing in a Virginia salt marsh. *Ecology*.

Smalley, A. E. 1960. Energy flow of a salt marsh grasshopper population. *Ecology* 41: 785–790.

Smith, J. M. and R. W. Frey. 1985. Biodeposition by the ribbed mussel *Geukensia demissa* in a salt marsh, Sapelo Island, Georgia. *J. Sed. Petrol.* 55: 817–828.

Smith, T. J. III, K. G. Boto, S. D. Frusher and R. L. Giddins. 1991. Keystone species and mangrove forest dynamics: The influence of burrowing by crabs on soil nutrient status and forest productivity. *Est. Coast. Shelf Sci.* 33: 419–432.

Smith, T. J. III and W. E. Odum. 1981. The effects of grazing by snow geese on coastal salt marshes. *Ecology* 62: 98–106.

Snow, A. and S. Vince. 1984. Plant zonation in an Alaskan salt marsh. II. An experimental study of the role of edaphic conditions. *J. Ecol.* 72: 669–684.

Sorrell, B. K. and W. Armstrong. 1994. On the difficulties of measuring oxygen release by root systems of wetland plants. *J. Ecol.* 82: 177–183.

Srivastava, D. S. and R. L. Jefferies. 1996. A positive feedback: Herbivory, plant growth, salinity, and the desertification of an Arctic salt-marsh. *J. Ecol.* 84: 31–42.

Stalter, R. and W. T. Batson. 1969. Transplantation of salt marsh vegetation, Georgetown, South Carolina. *Ecology* 50: 1087–1089.

Steever, E. Z., R. S. Warren and W. A. Niering. 1976. Tidal energy subsidy and standing crop production of *Spartina alterniflora*. *Est. Coast. Mar. Sci.* 4: 473–478.

Stevenson, J. C., L. G. Ward and M. S. Kearney. 1986. Vertical accretion in marshes with varying rates of sea level rise. In D. A. Wolfe (ed.), *Estuarine Variability*, pp. 241–259. Academic Press, Orlando, FL.

Stiling, P., B. V. Brodbeck and D. R. Strong. 1991. Population increases of planthoppers on fertilized salt-marsh cord grass may be prevented by grasshopper feeding. *Florida Entomol.* 74: 88–97.

Stiven, A. E. and S. A. Gardner. 1992. Population processes in the ribbed mussel *Geukensia demissa* (Dillwyn) in a North Carolina salt marsh tidal gradient: Spatial pattern, predation, growth and mortality. *J. Exp. Mar. Biol. Ecol.* 160: 81–102.

Stiven, A. E. and E. J. Kuenzler. 1979. The response of two salt marsh molluscs, *Littorina irrorata* and *Geukensia demissa*, to field manipulations of density of *Spartina* litter. *Ecol. Monogr.* 49: 151–171.

Stout, J. P. 1984. The ecology of irregularly flooded salt marshes of the northeastern Gulf of Mexico: A community profile. U.S. Fish and Wildlife Service Biol. Rep. 85 (7.1).

Strong, D. R. 1984. Exorcising the ghost of competition past: Phytophagous insects. In D. R. Strong, D. Simberloff, L. G. Abele and A. B. Thistle (eds.), *Ecological Communities: Conceptual Issues and the Evidence*, pp. 28–41. Princeton University Press, Princeton, NJ.

Summers, R. W., J. Stansfield, S. Perry, C. Atkins and J. Bishop. 1993. Utilization, diet and diet selection by brent geese *Branta bernicla bernicla* on salt-marshes in Norfolk. *J. Zool. Lond.* 231: 249–273.

Taylor, K. L. and J. B. Grace. 1995. The effects of vertebrate herbivory on plant community structure in the coastal marshes of the Pearl River, Louisiana, USA. *Wetlands* 15: 68–73.

Taylor, K. L., J. B. Grace, G. R. Guntenspergen and A. L. Foote. 1994. The interactive effects of herbivory and fire on an oligohaline marsh, Little Lake, Louisiana, USA. *Wetlands* 14: 82–87.

Teal, J. M. 1958. Distribution of fiddler crabs in Georgia salt marshes. *Ecology* 39: 185–193.

Teal, J. M. 1962. Energy flow in the salt marsh ecosystem of Georgia. *Ecology* 43: 614–624.

Teal, J. M. 1986. The ecology of regularly flooded salt marshes of New England: A community profile. U.S. Fish and Wildlife Service Biol. Rep. 85(7.4).

Teal, J. M. and J. Kanwisher. 1961. Gas exchange in a Georgia salt marsh. *Limnol. Oceanogr.* 6: 388–399.

Teal, J. M. and J. Kanwisher. 1966. Gas transport in the marsh grass, *Spartina alterniflora*. *J. Exp. Bot.* 17: 13–37.

Thompson, J. D., T. McNeilly and A. J. Gray. 1991. Population variation in *Spartina anglica* C. E. Hubbard. II. Reciprocal transplants among three successional populations. *New Phytol.* 117: 129–139.

Turner, M. G. 1987. Effects of grazing by feral horses, clipping, trampling, and burning on a Georgia salt marsh. *Estuaries* 10: 54–60.

Turner, R. E. 1976. Geographic variations in salt marsh macrophyte production: A review. *Contrib. Mar. Sci.* 20: 47–68.

Turner, R. E. and D. F. Boesch. 1988. Aquatic animal production and wetland relationships: Insights gleaned following wetland loss or gain. In D. D. Hook, W. H. McKee, Jr., H. K. Smith, J. Gregory, V. G. Burrell, Jr., M. R. DeVoe, R. E. Sojka, S. Gilbert, R. Banks, L. H. Stozy, C. Brooks, T. D. Matthews and T. H. Shear (eds.), *The Ecology and Management of Wetlands*, vol. 1: *Ecology of Wetlands*, pp. 25–39. Croom Helm, London.

Twolan-Strutt, L. and P. A. Keddy. 1996. Above- and belowground competition intensity in two contrasting wetland plant communities. *Ecology* 77: 259–270.

Ungar, I. A. 1992. The effect of intraspecific competition on growth, reproduction, and survival of the halophyte *Spergularia marina*. *Int. J. Plant Sci.* 15: 421–424.

Ungar, I. A. 1995. Seed germination and seed-bank ecology in halophytes. In J. Kigel and G.

Galili (eds.), *Seed Development and Germination*, pp. 599–628. Marcel Dekker, New York.

Ungar, I. A. 1998. Are biotic factors significant in influencing the distribution of halophytes in saline habitats? *Bot. Rev.* 64: 176–199.

Valiela, I. 1995. *Marine Ecological Processes*. Springer-Verlag, New York.

Valiela, I. and C. S. Rietsma. 1984. Nitrogen, phenolic acids, and other feeding cues for salt marsh detritivores. *Oecologia* 63: 350–356.

Valiela, I. and C. S. Rietsma. 1995. Disturbance of salt marsh vegetation by wrack mats in Great Sippewissett Marsh. *Oecologia* 102: 106–112.

Valiela, I. and J. M. Teal. 1974. Nutrient limitation in salt marsh vegetation. In R. J. Reimold and W. H. Queen (eds.), *Ecology of Halophytes*, pp. 547–563. Academic Press, New York.

Valiela, I. and J. M. Teal. 1979a. Inputs, outputs and interconversions of nitrogen in a salt marsh ecosystem. In R. L. Jefferies and A. J. Davy (eds.), *Ecological Processes in Coastal Environments*, pp. 399–414. Blackwell Scientific Publications, Oxford.

Valiela, I. and J. M. Teal. 1979b. The nitrogen budget of a salt marsh ecosystem. *Nature* 280: 652–656.

Valiela, I., J. M. Teal and W. G. Deuser. 1978. The nature of growth forms in the salt marsh grass *Spartina alterniflora*. *Amer. Nat.* 112: 461–470.

Valiela, I., L. Koumjian, T. Swain, J. M. Teal and J. E. Hobbie. 1979. Cinnamic acid inhibition of detritus feeding. *Nature* 280: 55–57.

Valiela, I., J. Wilson, R. Buchsbaum, C. Rietsma, D. Bryant, K. Foreman and J. Teal. 1984. Importance of chemical composition of salt marsh litter on decay rates and feeding by detritivores. *Bull. Mar. Sci.* 35: 261–269.

Van Dolah, R. F. 1978. Factors regulating the distribution and population dynamics of the amphipod *Gammarus palustris* in an intertidal salt marsh community. *Ecol Monogr.* 48: 191–217.

Vermeij, G. J. 1978. *Biogeography and Adaptation: Patterns of Marine Life*. Harvard University Press, Cambridge, MA.

Vince, S. W. 1985. Revegetation dynamics in an Alaskan coastal marsh. *Estuaries* 8: 124A.

Vince, S. W., I. Valiela, N. Backus and J. M. Teal. 1976. Predation by the salt marsh killifish *Fundulus heteroclitus* (L.) in relation to prey size and habitat structure: Consequences for prey distribution and abundance. *J. Exp. Mar. Biol. Ecol.* 23: 255–266.

Vince, S. W., I. Valiela and J. M. Teal. 1981. An experimental study of the structure of herbivorous insect communities in a salt marsh. *Ecology* 62: 1662–1678.

Warren, R. S. and W. A. Niering. 1993. Vegetation change on a northeast tidal marsh: Interaction of sea-level rise and marsh accretion. *Ecology* 74: 96–103.

Watts, B. D. 1988. Foraging implications of food usage patterns in yellow-crowned night-herons. *Condor* 90: 860–865.

West, D. L. and A. H. Williams. 1986. Predation by *Callinectes sapidus* (Rathbun) within *Spartina alterniflora* (Loisel) marshes. *J. Exp. Mar. Biol. Ecol.* 100: 75–95.

Wiegert, R. G. and B. J. Freeman. 1990. Tidal salt marshes of the southeast Atlantic coast: A community profile. U.S. Fish and Wildlife Service Biol. Rep. 85(7.29).

Wiegert, R. G., A. G. Chalmers and P. F. Randerson. 1983. Productivity gradients in salt marshes: The response of *Spartina alterniflora* to experimentally manipulated soil water movement. *Oikos* 41: 1–6.

Willason, S. W. 1981. Factors influencing the distribution and coexistence of *Pachygrapsus crassipes* and *Hemigrapsus oregonensis* (Decapoda: Grapsidae) in a California salt marsh. *Mar. Biol.* 64: 125–133.

Wilson, J. B., W. McG. King, M. T. Sykes and T. R. Partridge. 1996. Vegetation zonation as related to the salt tolerance of species of brackish riverbanks. *Can. J. Bot.* 74: 1079–1085.

Wilson, S. D. and P. A. Keddy. 1986. Measuring diffuse competition along an environmental gradient: Results from a shoreline plant community. *Amer. Nat.* 127: 862–869.

Wood, G. W., M. T. Mengak and M. Murphy. 1987. Ecological importance of feral ungulates at Shackleford Banks, North Carolina. *Amer. Midl. Nat.* 118: 236–244.

Woodin, S. A. 1976. Adult-larval interactions in dense infaunal assemblages: Patterns of abundance. *J. Mar. Res.* 34: 25–41.

Woodwell, G. M., D. E. Whitney, C. A. S. Hall and R. A. Houghton. 1977. The Flax Pond ecosystem study: Exchanges of carbon in water between a salt marsh and Long Island Sound. *Limnol. Oceanogr.* 22: 833–838.

Zedler, J. B. 1982. The ecology of southern California coastal salt marshes: A community profile. FWS/OBS-81/54. U.S. Fish and Wildlife Service, Division of Biological Services, Washington, D.C.

Zedler, J. B. 1995. Salt marsh restoration: Lessons from California. In J. Cairns, Jr. (ed.), *Rehabilitating Damaged Ecosystems*, pp. 75–95. Lewis Publishers, Boca Raton, FL.

Zedler, J. B. 1996a. Coastal mitigation in southern California: The need for a regional restoration strategy. *Ecol. Appl.* 6: 84–93.

Zedler, J. B. 1996b. Ecological issues in wetland mitigation: An introduction to the forum. *Ecol. Appl.* 6: 33–37.

Zedler, J. B. and P. A. Beare. 1986. Temporal variability of salt marsh vegetation: The role of low-salinity gaps and environmental stress. In D. A. Wolfe (ed.), *Estuarine Variability*, pp. 295–306. Academic Press, Orlando, FL.

chapter 12

Seagrass Community Ecology

Susan L. Williams and Kenneth L. Heck, Jr.

*F*or a long time, seagrass communities remained largely unstudied by ecologists, probably because seagrasses usually exist at depths requiring the use of SCUBA. Uniformly green and almost impenetrably dense, seagrass beds hide the life teeming within them very well. The 1970s brought an explosion of research, and the abundance of organisms within seagrass communities became widely acknowledged among marine scientists. Why seagrass beds should support such abundant life became a major research question concerning habitat utilization and function, including trophic support, refuge from predation, recruitment, and provision of nursery areas. This question has dominated seagrass community ecology and is the framework for this chapter.

Within the general question of habitat utilization and function, we chose to focus on several specific topics in marine community ecology to highlight significant contributions from seagrass studies. First, some of the most comprehensive analyses of detrital food webs originated from seagrass beds, along with salt marshes. At least half of the prodigious primary production of seagrasses enters the food chain as detritus. Seagrass studies helped to establish stable isotopes as food web tracers in ecology. Second, seagrass studies demonstrated that inconspicuous but highly productive and palatable microalgae provide an important source of food for consumers. Third, seagrass beds provide some examples of apparently rare marine trophic cascades, where the primary control of the community clearly resides in the effects of higher-order trophic levels. Fourth, seagrass studies have contributed greatly to understanding how structural complexity in the habitat influences the distribution and abundance of organisms. Fifth, recent experimental manipulations in seagrass beds have provided examples of the complex nature of ecological interactions between native and non-native species.

Until recently, knowledge about marine non-native species has been limited primarily to their distribution, abundance, and perhaps origin, and ecological interactions have only been hypothesized (Steneck and Carlton, this volume).

Finally, seagrass communities provide some of the most comprehensive examples of the acid test of ecological understanding—marine habitat restoration. Seagrass community research is driven increasingly by the accelerating loss of seagrass habitat and associated species of economic value and, in the United States, the legislative mandate to mitigate intentional loss of seagrass ecosystems (Orth and Moore 1983; Robblee et al. 1991; Walker and McComb 1992; Short and Wyllie-Echeverria 1996). Ecologists need to understand the community consequences of seagrass decline. Mechanistic understanding of the community is required for effective mitigation and restoration and to achieve ecological functions (e.g., primary production, trophic support) that are equivalent to those in the seagrass beds replaced, that is, functional equivalency. What kinds of functions lead to the biological wealth of relatively undisturbed seagrass beds?

INTRODUCTION TO SEAGRASS COMMUNITIES

Our description of seagrass communities will be brief because excellent references exist (McRoy and Helferrich 1977; Phillips and McRoy 1980; Phillips 1984; Thayer et al. 1984; Larkum et al. 1989; Zieman and Zieman 1989). Seagrasses are clonal marine flowering plants and occur in shallow soft-sediment habitats along the shores of bays and estuaries throughout most of the world. The notable exceptions are the surfgrasses (*Phyllospadix* spp.) and *Amphibolis* spp., which grow on hard substrata. There are between 50–60 seagrass species in the families Hydrocharitaceae and Potamogetonaceae. Seagrasses are primarily subtidal, but they can extend also into the intertidal zone. In subtropical and tropical meadows, several seagrass species typically coexist. Although temperate meadows in the northern hemisphere tend to be dominated by a single genus, either *Zostera* (eelgrass) in sediments or *Phyllospadix* (surfgrass) on rocks in the north Pacific, a careful observer will find that even these beds are not monospecific (Figure 12.1). *Ruppia maritima* (widgeongrass or ditch grass) frequently coexists with eelgrass on a seasonal or perennial basis, depending on the locale. Up to three species of surfgrass intergrade across the depth distribution of surfgrass beds in North America and, depending on the substratum, can be mixed with eelgrass at some sites. On the northeast coast of Japan, five species of eelgrass occur, each with a distinct growth form, and up to three species (e.g., *Zostera marina, Z. caulescens,* and *Z. caespitosa*) can be found in a bed (Aioi and Komatsu 1996; Iizumi 1996; S. Williams pers. obs.).

All seagrass beds also include many kinds of algae. Algal epiphytes use seagrass leaves and rhizomes as substrata and include microscopic and small filamentous forms as well as larger blades and corticated thalli. For example, Humm (1964) reported 113 species of algal epiphytes on turtlegrass (*Thalassia*) in Biscayne Bay, Florida, and Ballantine and Humm recorded 66 epiphytic algal species in a seagrass bed on the west coast of Florida (1975). The epiphytes composed from

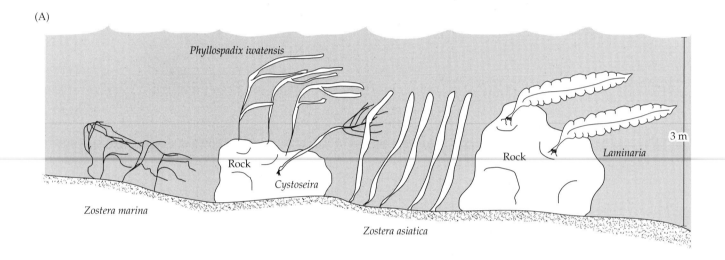

(A)

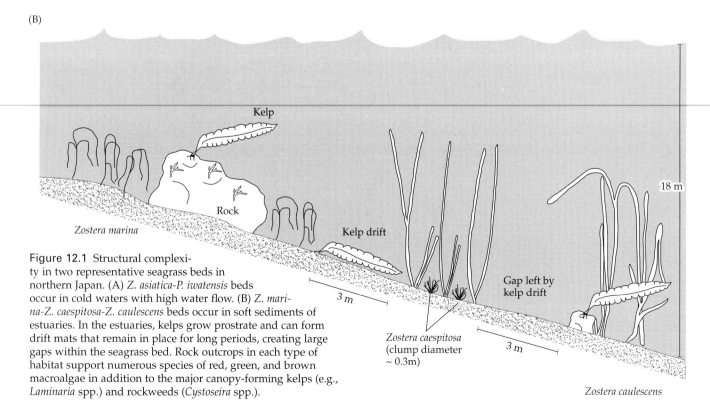

(B)

Figure 12.1 Structural complexity in two representative seagrass beds in northern Japan. (A) *Z. asiatica-P. iwatensis* beds occur in cold waters with high water flow. (B) *Z. marina-Z. caespitosa-Z. caulescens* beds occur in soft sediments of estuaries. In the estuaries, kelps grow prostrate and can form drift mats that remain in place for long periods, creating large gaps within the seagrass bed. Rock outcrops in each type of habitat support numerous species of red, green, and brown macroalgae in addition to the major canopy-forming kelps (e.g., *Laminaria* spp.) and rockweeds (*Cystoseira* spp.).

25–45% of the local algal flora. Free-living macroalgae (as well as periphytic forms) grow from rocks and shells. In temperate beds, large canopy-forming rockweeds (*Cystoseira*, Fucales) and kelps (*Egregia*, *Laminaria*), as well as surfgrass, grow on numerous small (few m²) rock outcrops. In tropical seagrass beds, over a dozen species of siphonous green algae (Caulerpales), which grow from rhizoids anchored in the sediments, form a major component of the community. Attached macroalgae often break off and form large, drifting clumps and mats that are important components in the community. The common macroalgae in drift mats alone represented 13 species of green, brown, and red seaweeds in one study (Williams Cowper 1978). Although the seagrass canopies strongly attenuate light, benthic microalgae also occur commonly in seagrass communities.

Animals in every major Phylum occur within seagrass beds. Animals pack the complex belowground mat of seagrass roots and rhizomes and live attached to or closely associated with the leaves or drift macroalgae (Figure 12.2). More mobile snails, crabs, and fishes cruise through or above the leaf canopy. Seagrass beds also support large populations of migrating waterfowl such as herbivorous swans, ducks, and geese, and predatory wading birds and diving ducks. Raptors such as bald eagles and ospreys feed over the beds. Large vertebrate grazers such as green turtles, dugongs, and manatees rely on seagrass beds for food and habitat; some of these species are threatened or endangered. The majority of the commercially valuable marine species in the United States are found in seagrass communities at some stage in their life histories.

SEAGRASSES AND THE DISTRIBUTION AND ABUNDANCE OF ASSOCIATED ORGANISMS

Seagrass beds harbor higher numbers of animal species and individuals than other marine soft-bottom communities (McRoy and Helferrich 1977) and also support exceptionally high rates of secondary productivity (Pihl-Baden and Pihl 1984; Fredette et al. 1990; Valentine and Heck 1993; Heck et al. 1995). The question of why this should be so fostered research on major aspects of seagrass habitat function, including trophic support, refuge from predation, recruitment, and

Figure 12.2 Pathways of energy flux among major consumer groups in Caribbean seagrass meadows. (Redrawn after Ogden 1980.)

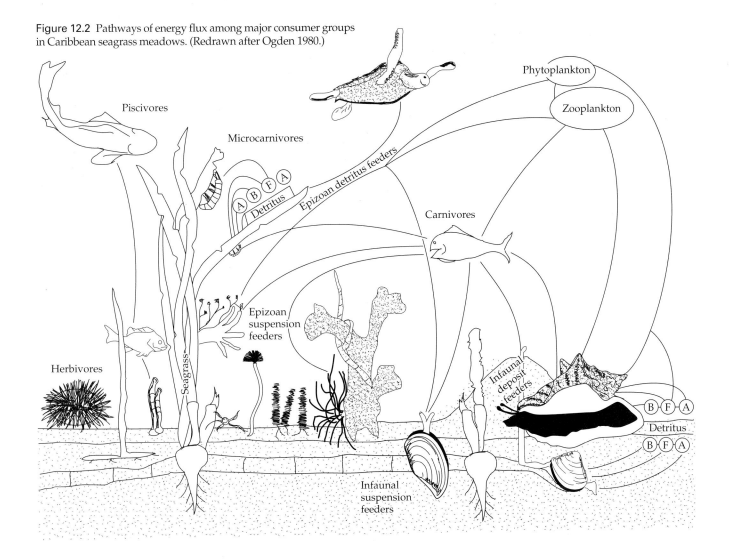

provision of nursery areas. This research has broadened the understanding of how marine plants and animals interact. Herbivory has dominated the study of marine plant-animal interactions, and seagrass studies certainly have contributed to this topic. Extending beyond herbivory, seagrass studies have provided some of the best examples of nontrophic interactions, both positive and negative (e.g., fertilization, bioturbation), that also control the distribution and abundance of associated organisms.

Trophic Support

The prodigious primary production of seagrass ecosystems, reaching up to 8 g C/m²/d for seagrasses alone (Zieman and Wetzel 1980), is a major aspect of their ecological and economic importance (McRoy and Helferrich 1977; Phillips and McRoy 1980; Larkum et al. 1989). Leaves can grow over 1 cm/d in many cases (Ogden and Ogden 1982; Erftemeijer et al. 1993) and are continuously shed and replaced. Studies of the fate of this primary production have contributed to marine ecology in several major ways. First, the importance of macrophyte detritus as trophic support was quantified. The early debate over whether the detritus itself, or the associated bacteria, was the main source of trophic support for detritivores was resolved in the favor of both in part by studies on the assimilation of eelgrass detritus (Adams and Angelovic 1970; Tenore 1975). Seagrasses have high C:N ratios (Atkinson and Smith 1983), large amounts of structural carbohydrates, and phenolic compounds that reduce their nutritional value relative to many algae (Nicotri 1980), but not salt marsh plants (Buchsbaum et al. 1984). Although many animals directly consume seagrass leaves (McRoy and Helferrich 1977; Ogden 1980; Thayer et al. 1984; Williams 1988; Valentine and Heck 1991), the proportion of leaf biomass production of seagrasses that enters the food web via grazing is typically less than 50% (Cebrián and Duarte 1998).

Belowground seagrass production has not been considered in seagrass trophic support. Although rhizomes grow slowly relative to leaves, the belowground biomass can be an order of magnitude greater than the leaf biomass, thus representing a significant sink for photosynthate (Pangallo and Bell 1988; Powell et al. 1989; Williams 1990; Kenworthy and Schwarzschild 1998). Although rhizomes have high caloric values (Birch 1975), we know of no reports of infauna grazing the living roots and rhizomes. Instead, belowground seagrass production might represent a major source of detritus for infaunal consumers. Belowground biomass forms detritus as the older distal end dies and is replaced by the terminal rhizome meristem (Tomlinson 1974).

The importance of detritus in seagrass beds was inferred for a long time because of the sheer amount of detritus formed and the biomass and dominance of detritivores in seagrass beds (Petersen and Boyson Jensen 1911; Howard 1982). Seagrass ecosystems thus provided a model to analyze detrital food webs using stable isotopic ratios. Confirmation of the source of plant detritus is difficult because it is basically unidentifiable once in a consumer's gut. However, detritus retains the unique stable isotope signature laid down by the plant's physiology, and thus stable isotopes can be used to differentiate the source of the primary production at successively higher levels in the food web. Stable isotope analysis of seagrass food webs confirmed that seagrasses provided a major source of organic matter for detritivores, but mixed diets were also common (Thayer et al. 1978; Fry and Parker 1979; McConnaughey and McRoy 1979; Fry et al. 1983; Nichols et al. 1985). Stable isotopes also helped in determining situations where other primary producers become more important (Stephenson et al. 1986). Stable isotope ratios provided a valuable tracer for shrimp migrations and feeding areas and helped identify the functional importance of seagrass beds as feeding grounds for commercial species (Fry 1981; Zieman et al. 1984b; Loneragan et al. 1997). Utilization of seagrass detritus by large invertebrates in the deep sea was elucidated through stable isotopic analyses (Suchanek et al. 1985). Ruckelshaus et al. (1993) combined isotopic analyses with measures of food quality and quantity to challenge the paradigm that the suspended pool of organic particles in estuaries is a well-mixed "soup" for filter feeders. Instead, habitat patches (e.g., mudflats, channels in salt marshes, eelgrass beds, or neritic zones) locally differed in the quality and quantity of suspended food particles. These differences were realized in the growth of filter-feeders, including the mussel *Mytilus galloprovencialis*, which grew best in eelgrass habitat (Ruckelshaus et al. 1993).

Studies of the fate of primary production in seagrass beds also contributed to a growing understanding that inconspicuous microalgae are very productive and important sources of high-quality food for benthic marine consumers (Fry 1984; Kitting et al. 1984; Moncreiff et al. 1992). In comparison to seagrass beds, the trophic importance of algal epiphytes in kelp beds and other macroalgal systems is poorly understood (Brawley and Fei 1987). In these systems, stable isotope analyses cannot be used as successfully to identify the relative trophic importance of small algae because their isotopic signatures overlap with those of the macroalgae.

The primary production of algal epiphytes can represent a substantial component of the total primary production of a seagrass bed, sometimes matching or exceeding that of the seagrasses (Morgan and Kitting 1984; Mazella and Alberte 1986; Thom 1990a). Epiphytic algae are an important determinant of epifauna abundance (Hall and Bell 1988; Edgar 1990). Typically comprising diatoms and other unicellular species as well as small filaments (Coleman and Burkholder 1995), algal epiphytes can have low biomass that belies their trophic significance (Jernakoff et al. 1996). Algal epiphytes have very high biomass-specific rates of primary production and can replace their standing stock within a few days (Borum 1987; Sand-Jensen and Borum 1991). In addition, the biomass represents higher nutritional quality for consumers (Zimmerman et al. 1979), being relatively rich in nitrogen and low in structural carbohydrates compared to seagrasses and macroalgae and the detritus they form (Nicotri 1980; Klumpp et al. 1989; Duarte 1992; Enríquez et al. 1993).

Epiphytes also apparently lack the phenolic compounds found in seagrasses that can inhibit grazing on living and recently dead leaves (Harrison 1982). Although very few studies have directly assessed the nutritional content of epiphytes (Nichols et al. 1985, 1986), data for diatoms and other microalgae or small filamentous species should be representative of similar epiphyte species. Most of the mesoconsumers such as caprellids and gammarids are small enough to select algae from the epiphyte matrix, which also includes sediment particles and detritus (Harrison 1977; Zimmerman et al. 1979; Caine 1980; Howard 1982; Kitting et al. 1984). Because consumers select algae from the matrix, values for organic content, proteins, and carbohydrates derived from the intact matrix probably underestimate its nutritional quality for the meso- and micrograzers.

Trophic Interactions

Although the focus on detrital food webs might predominate in seagrass ecology, it was always apparent that seagrass vegetation and the associated community could be controlled by herbivores because of dramatic examples of overgrazing by large invertebrates such as sea urchins (Camp et al. 1973; Valentine and Heck 1991) and vertebrates such as birds, sea turtles, and marine mammals (Thayer et al. 1982a,b). Despite these dramatic examples, there has been a tendency to treat herbivore control of seagrasses as an anomaly. It has been argued that a historically important top predator was missing (in the case of sea urchins) or that the environment represented some otherwise "special case." In fact, these "special cases" might better represent seagrass communities of the past when large herbivorous vertebrates (waterfowl, manatees, sea turtles) were numerous (Jackson 1997).

In addition to controlling the distribution and abundance of seagrasses, animals also influence the population biology of clonal seagrasses. The influence of herbivores on the population biology of seagrasses represents a relatively unexplored research area, but one with some interesting parallels to terrestrial ecosystems such as grasslands with intense grazing. Physiological integration within a seagrass clone (Harrison 1978; Iizumi and Hattori 1982; Tomasko and Dawes 1989a; Pedersen and Borum 1993) helps it withstand grazing. When photosynthetic tissues are removed, physiological readjustments occur among leaves, leaf shoots, and rhizomes (Dawes and Lawrence 1979; Dawes et al. 1979; Tomasko and Dawes 1989b). After adjustment, the remaining ungrazed shoots can exhibit increased rates of photosynthesis and production of nitrogen-rich young leaves. The new growth is higher-quality forage for sea turtles, which repeatedly return to feed on it (Bjorndal 1980; Thayer et al. 1982b, 1984; Zieman et al. 1984a). Because internal adjustments to grazing cannot be sustained indefinitely, there is a broad range of plant responses to grazing intensity. For example, heavy grazing by sea turtles (Williams 1988), sea urchins (Heck and Valentine 1995), and dugongs (Preen 1995) can lead to reduced seagrass standing crop, and intense grazing during fall and winter can lead to local disap-

pearance of seagrasses (Greenway 1974; Heck and Valentine 1995). However, intermediate levels of grazing can stimulate the production of new shoots and areal productivity, especially during periods of high growth (Valentine et al. 1997). Similarly, seven seagrass species in a variety of locations, subjected to a one-time experimental cropping of up to 100% of the aboveground shoot biomass, showed little evidence of negative effects on regrowth rates. Instead, regrowth rates at the highest levels of cropping were often greater than those with lower rates of biomass removal (Cebrián et al. 1998). Just as noted in terrestrial systems (McNaughton 1983; Belsky 1986; Huntley 1991; Herms and Mattson 1992), there is a continuum of seagrass responses to grazing pressure, ranging from negligible effects on shoot production at low intensity, to stimulatory effects at intermediate intensity and negative effects at high intensity. Although the ability of seagrasses to withstand grazing pressure appears to be related to the amount of belowground rhizome storage capacity (Dawes and Lawrence 1979; Dawes et al. 1979; Heck and Valentine 1995; Cebrián et al. 1998), this needs to be substantiated by experiments.

Animals also can influence the sexual reproduction of seagrasses. Polychaetes inhabiting eelgrass inflorescences (Hellwig-Armonies 1988) prey upon flowers and seeds (M. Herndon, pers. com.). Although there are few published studies on seagrass seedling recruitment in the field, seed predators can limit seedling recruitment (Fishman and Orth 1996). Although herbivores defoliate seagrasses, they also can exert a positive effect on seagrass population growth rates, persistence, and, conceivably, genetic diversity. Animals, by creating gaps in the canopy, can enhance the recruitment of seagrass; seed germination and seedling survival for *Zostera* spp. are significantly higher in gaps (Ewanchuk 1995, Peterken and Conacher 1997, Williams, unpubl. data).

The view that seagrass communities are not controlled by consumers recently achieved the status of a paradigm, with the advent of declines in seagrass vegetation (Orth and Moore 1983; Short et al. 1986; Robblee et al. 1991; Cambridge and McComb 1992; Short and Wyllie-Echeverria 1996) and the search for causes. Seagrasses require large quantities of light to support their rapid growth rates (McRoy and McMillan 1977; Kenworthy and Haunert 1991). When the attenuation of light increases as phytoplankton and epiphytes bloom under eutrophication or as sedimentation increases, seagrass distribution and abundance is clearly reduced (Dennison et al. 1993; Short et al. 1995; Moore et al. 1996; Olesen 1996). Hence, emphasis has been placed on physico-chemical control of seagrass communities. However, the issue is more complex and interesting when subtle biological interactions between seagrasses, shading epiphytes, herbivores, and perhaps top predators are considered. Mesoherbivores clearly can control the growth of seagrass leaves by removing epiphytes (Neckles et al.1993; Williams and Ruckelshaus 1993; reviewed by Jernakoff et al. 1996), and thus can mitigate the negative effects of increasing eutrophication. Grazers similarly can control macroalgae that bloom in response to eutrophication (Hauxwell et al. 1998). Epiphyte-grazer interactions need to be incorporated in models devised as management tools to predict seagrass distribution (Wetzel and Neckles 1986; Williams and Ruckelshaus 1993). Models promised for management are often based primarily on water column attenuation of light or water column nutrient concentrations. These models will be less useful where mesograzers control epiphytes.

Furthermore, the assumption that epiphyte-associated declines in seagrasses are due to bottom-up control by eutrophication needs to be evaluated against alternative hypotheses. For example, the papers cited in the preceding paragraph indicate that mesograzers can and do control epiphyte biomass. Mesograzers can exhibit nonlinear functional responses to increased resource availability (Nelson 1997), although the numerical responses are poorly known. In addition, Edgar (1993), after estimating food consumption by amphipods and gastropods, concluded that mesograzers are probably food-limited in Australian seagrass meadows. This raises the question of why mesograzers do not respond sufficiently to the eutrophication-induced algal proliferation to ultimately reestablish grazer control. An alternative to the conventional wisdom of bottom-up control of seagrasses in eutrophic environments may provide the explanation that overfishing of top predators might lead to a cascading effect in which epiphytes are released from grazing when small fishes increase and in turn control the abundance of meso- and microherbivores, such as isopods, caprellids, and amphipods (Figure 12.3). Data in partial support of this alternative hypothesis have recently been published (Heck et al. 2000), and confirmatory evidence for trophic cascades from freshwater macrophyte beds (Bronmark et al. 1992; Martin et al. 1992; McCollum et al. 1998) suggests that it deserves serious consideration.

In developing a general understanding of trophic interactions and community structure (e.g., Paine 1980; Polis 1994; Polis and Strong 1996), seagrass communities with their great diversity and abundance of organisms offer promising but unexplored model systems. On a gradient of primary production (Oksanen et al. 1981), they represent high end-point members. As discussed above, the wide variation between the relative importance of detritus versus living plants in supporting food webs should be useful in evaluating the effects of detritus and omnivory on trophic structure. There is exceptional functional diversity at the primary producer level because seagrasses themselves vary in nutritional value (Birch 1975; Irving et al. 1988), and they are associated with many different forms of algae, as we discussed previously. Epiphytes take on greater significance in seagrass beds than in other marine communities. This plant diversity can facilitate coexistence among very similar species of sea urchin consumers (Keller 1983). The combination of vascular plants and diverse forms of algae might also explain why seagrass beds not only support most of the kinds of animals found in the rocky, intertidal seaweed beds and unvegetated soft sediments, but also sea turtles, sirenians, and waterfowl not typically found in these other communities.

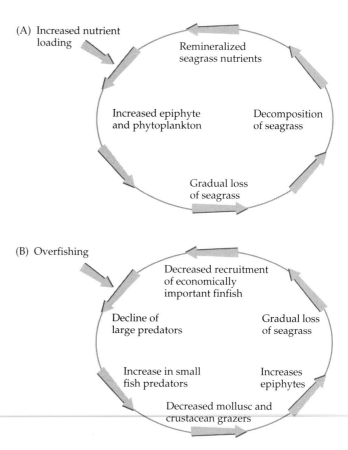

Figure 12.3 Models for the separate effects of increased nutrient loading (A) and overfishing (B) on seagrass ecosystems. Overfishing is hypothesized to initiate cascading trophic effects that lead to algal overgrowth and seagrass loss. The combined effects are expected to lead to accelerated seagrass loss.

Nursery and Refuge Function

Seagrass meadows support populations of invertebrates and small fishes that are substantially more abundant (often by an order of magnitude or more) than on nearby unvegetated substrata (Orth 1977; Virnstein et al. 1983; Orth et al. 1984; Heck et al. 1997). This is especially true of epifauna, but characteristic of infauna as well. In addition, because many of these animals are present as juveniles, seagrass beds often are described as "nursery grounds," (or said to play a "nursery role" in coastal waters), where nursery grounds are understood to be places where young animals survive and grow at exceptionally high rates (see Kikuchi 1980; Thayer et al. 1984; Zieman and Zieman 1989). The "nursery grounds" concept forms the primary basis for the protection and conservation of seagrass habitats, which are declining worldwide (Hinrichsen 1998). As such, it is being subjected to increasing scrutiny and, as noted following, there are inconsistencies in the existing data.

However, there is strong and consistent experimental evidence that seagrasses provide protection for a variety of small invertebrates from actively foraging fish predators (see reviews by Orth et al. 1984; Heck and Crowder 1991) and that increasing amounts of vegetation provide increasing refuge from predators. Nevertheless, there is considerable variation in the protective function of vegetation among seasons and years (Heck and Wilson 1987), among seagrass species, and among individual suites of predators and prey in precisely how vegetation affects the outcome of predator-prey interactions (Heck and Crowder 1991). Most often there is threshold density of vegetation that is necessary before a significant reduction in predation effectiveness is noted, and different seagrass species provide varying amounts of protection, depending on the species-specific visual acuities, sizes, and behavior of predator and prey taxa (Heck and Crowder 1991; Orth 1992). The only published exception to this relationship showed that increasing vegetation density did not hinder the effectiveness of an ambush predator, the seahorse *Hippocampus erectus*, foraging on small caridean shrimp (James and Heck 1994). This result verified an earlier hypothesis that the success of ambush predators, in contrast to what was known about active foragers, might not be negatively affected by increasing seagrass biomass (Heck and Orth 1980). The rationale for the hypothesized difference between ambushers and active foragers was that prey would have increasing difficult times detecting the presence of ambushers as seagrass biomass increased, and at some point the advantage of inhabiting seagrass would switch from prey to predator.

Although fewer studies have investigated the form of the relationship between belowground biomass and the protection received by infaunal seagrass associates, the existing evidence, although published some time ago, suggests that the root-rhizome complex does reduce predator success (reviewed by Orth et al. 1984).

Given the nearly universal acceptance of the "nursery grounds" concept, it is somewhat surprising that there is only equivocal evidence that organisms grow at accelerated rates in seagrass habitats than elsewhere. In fact, nearly half the comparisons of invertebrate and fish growth rates in seagrass and on unvegetated substrate have found either no significant difference among substrata or significantly greater growth on unvegetated substrata (Heck et al. 1997). Included in the taxa studied are organisms as diverse as suspension-feeding bivalves, predatory penaeid shrimp and portunid crabs, and several species of small predatory fishes, indicating that these results are not taxon-specific. Therefore, the evidence for the role of food in the nursery grounds concept is far less compelling than the role of seagrass as shelter from predation.

In addition, there is a growing recognition that commercially important species in some areas do not appear to rely on seagrass meadows as important nursery grounds. For example, there are few commercially important species in Cape Cod waters that appear to rely heavily on seagrass nursery habitats (Heck et al. 1989; Heck et al. 1995). Similarly, there is little evidence for a significant seagrass nursery function in temperate Australia (Edgar and Shaw 1995; Gillanders and Kingsford 1996). At present the evidence for the seagrass "nursery grounds" concept seems to come consistently from

warm subtropical and tropical latitudes and to be much less obvious in temperate and boreal latitudes. This may be explained by the existence of latitudinal gradients in predation pressure, with higher rates characteristic of tropical regions (cf. Bertness et al. 1981; Menge and Lubchenco 1981; Heck and Wilson 1987). Such higher predation rates may strongly select for shelter occupation in tropical taxa and may also lead to competition for hiding places among taxa at great risk to predation. Although competition for access to seagrass habitat and escape from predation has been demonstrated among seagrass-associated caridean shrimps (Coen et al. 1981; Tayasu et al. 1996), competition has been investigated very infrequently among seagrass animal associates and remains a fertile area for study.

Nontrophic Interactions between Plants and Animals

Seagrass communities provide ecologists with numerous opportunities in which to study nontrophic interactions between plants and animals and also the indirect effects, sensu Wooten (1994) and Menge (1995), of ecological interactions. Nontrophic interactions between seagrasses and animals also can exert major control over the distribution and growth of seagrasses. Well before recent emphasis on ecosystem engineers (Jones et al. 1994), it was known from seagrass studies that faunal feeding and burrowing could limit the distribution and growth of seagrasses and associated macroalgae (Ogden et al. 1973; Orth 1975; Suchanek 1983; Williams et al. 1985; Valentine et al. 1994). Mussels growing within seagrass beds can alleviate nutrient limitation of seagrass growth (Reusch et al. 1994; Reusch and Williams 1998; Peterson and Heck 1999). Mussels filter organic matter in the water column and transfer it to the sediments as feces and pseudofeces, which after remineralization increase porewater nutrients for seagrasses. Mussel-seagrass interactions are complex, because the same mussels can affect seagrasses in negative ways, depending on the densities of both interactors, the habitat structure, and the season. Eventually, mussels can replace seagrass beds, particularly in the face of frequent disturbances of seagrasses, because mussels can recruit and grow much more rapidly than seagrasses. Even without disturbance, mussel recruitment into seagrass beds can be so strong at times that the seagrass canopy collapses and eventually degrades (Sewell 1996, Williams, pers. obs.). Another indirect but potentially major influence of suspension feeders in seagrass beds is their potential to mediate deleterious phytoplankton-seagrass interactions in eutrophic estuaries (Lemmens et al. 1996).

INFLUENCE OF HABITAT STRUCTURE ON THE DISTRIBUTION AND ABUNDANCE OF ORGANISMS

Seagrass beds are structurally complex habitats (Robbins and Bell 1994), and this complexity exists at various spatial scales. Kelp beds and salt marshes also have complex habitat structure, but we argue that seagrass meadows are exceptional among vegetation-dominated marine habitats. First, seagrasses add structure to both the above- and belowground habitat. Aboveground, structural complexity is afforded by different leaf morphologies within a bed, for example, straplike (e.g., *Zostera, Thalassia, Posidonia*), cylindrical (*Syringodium*), ovoid (*Halophila decipiens*), or clustered (*Amphibolis*). Leaf lengths can also vary; *Zostera marina* varies from a few cm to over 4 m within and among beds. *Zostera caulescens* achieves lengths of nearly 7 m (Aioi et al. 1998; see Figure 12.1). Reproductive shoots add structure because they branch more highly than the vegetative shoots of many species. Such differences in morphology result in quantitative differences in canopy height, area biomass, shoot density, and surface area:volume or SA/biomass ratios. Belowground, rhizomes and roots enmesh to create a solid mat that can extend meters into the sediments. The belowground habitat is structured vertically because the rhizomes of different species occupy relatively distinct layers in the sediment, with the larger species extending deeper (Williams 1990).

The prolific growth of macroalgae and epiphytes adds another element of structural complexity to seagrass beds. Neither seaweed beds nor salt marshes are noted in the literature for the prolific growth of epiphytic algae. Tidal exposure limits the development of algae in salt marshes. Kelps and rockweeds are relatively free of epiphytes compared to seagrasses. Rockweeds shed their outer cell walls and epiphytes on a regular basis, and algal cell wall characteristics or chemicals also might account for the difference in epiphyte development.

There are numerous reports of how grazers and bioturbators, humans anchoring boats, and drifting mats of macroalgae create gaps in seagrass beds. Similar observations are rarer from seaweed-dominated habitats and salt marshes, with the exceptions of disturbances from logs washing ashore in the intertidal and of decomposing wrack mats in salt marshes. Finally, at the largest spatial scale, currents configure seagrass vegetation and soft sediments to create numerous meadow configurations of different vertical relief and ranging from relatively continuous meadows to "leopard skin" patterns. Following, we describe seagrass habitat complexity in detail.

Animals encounter different habitat structure at many spatial scales within a seagrass bed (Table 12.1). At the scale of individual leaf shoots, animals encounter a gradient of epiphytic algal cover increasing toward the leaf tips (Nagle 1968). In moving only a few mm, an animal can encounter an order of magnitude difference in epiphytic algal biomass (Hall and Bell 1988). Over a few cm, animals can encounter different seagrass species as well as epiphytic, benthic, and drifting macroalgae (Figure 12.4, Figure 12.5). The additional structure of rhizophytic seaweeds (Figure 12.6) in the tropics influences the distribution of crustaceans within the seagrass bed. For example, *Penicillus* harbors an order of magnitude more crustaceans than *Halodule* (Stoner 1985). Larger animals moving over many meters also encounter a very heterogeneous environment because the aboveground seagrass biomass is patchily distributed, with a standard deviation typi-

Figure 12.4 A *Thalassia*-dominated bed in the Caribbean (3–5 m water depth). *Thalassia* leaves range between 30–60 cm in height and are encrusted with calcareous red algal crusts. The bed is mixed with *Syringodium, Halimeda*, and epiphytes over a scale of a few cm. *Halodule* is common, but not shown in this photograph.

cally twice the mean (Phillips and McRoy 1980, Figure 12.7). Small gaps are created by bioturbation (Suchanek 1983; Williams et al. 1985, Matsumasa et al. 1992; Valentine et al. 1994), and the vegetation is interrupted by macroalgal and mussel mats (Valentine and Heck 1993; Bell et al. 1995; Holmquist 1997). Large grazers such as dugongs, sea turtles, and geese create mosaics of large areas of leaf shoots cropped

Figure 12.5 A bed of surfgrass (*Phyllospadix torreyi*) in southern California. Long fronds of the rockweed *Cystoseira* (Fucales) are evident at the top left of the photograph. Rocks are also covered with a variety of smaller red and brown seaweeds of different morphologies.

TABLE 12.1   Variation in the structural complexity of seagrass beds is evident at many scales.

Scale	Structures	Characteristics	Variable	Range[a]	Reference
mm²	Single leaves	Microalgal cover	Biomass	10×	Hall & Bell 1988
cm²	Leaf shoots	Macroalgal epiphytes			
		Leaf ramet spacing			
		Rhizome packing			
		Shape of leaf, rhizome, thallus			
		No. leaves in shoot			
		Increased epiphytes at tip			
	Algal thalli				
m²	Aboveground	Leaf canopy	Leaf area	4× within species	McRoy & McMillan 1977
			Leaf biomass	10× within species	McRoy & McMillan 1977
				1000× among spp.	McRoy & McMillan 1977
			Canopy height	10× among spp.	
		Seaweeds			
		Drift algal mats	Biomass	100×	Bell et al. 1995
	Belowground	Vertical rhizome layering			
patch/gap[b]		Grazing scars	Diameter	>10× (turtles)	Ogden et al. 1983
		Bioturbation pits	Diameter	8× (stingray pits)	Valentine et al. 1994
		Callianasid shrimp mounds	No./m²	16×	Suchanek 1983
		Rocky outcrops with large seaweeds			
		Seagrass patches	Diameter		
km²	Coastal system	Patch configuration	Bed height/ length	20× (*Zostera*)	Fonseca et al. 1983
			Diameter	500× (*Cymodocea*)	Duarte & Sand-Jensen 1990

[a]*Range* refers to the magnitude of variation in the listed variable that can be encountered at the given scale.
[b]*Patch* refers to a vegetated area; *gap* refers to an unvegetated area.

to, or nearly to, the substratum (Thayer et al. 1984). Physical disturbances such as currents and storms create gaps that cover hundreds of meters (Patriquin 1975; Fonseca et al. 1983; Marbá and Duarte 1995). Humans rival or exceed nature in fragmenting the seagrass landscape by ripping up plants with boat propellers and anchors and by dredging and filling (Thayer et al. 1975; Zieman 1976; Williams 1988).

If the structure of habitat is important to the distribution of organisms at least at some scale, then differences among seagrass species should be reflected in their associated communities (Jernakoff and Nielsen 1998). This prediction assumes that other important parameters, for example, epiphytic food production or predation, are similar. An important research challenge is to test for the effects of parameters that covary with habitat structure. That acknowledged, habitat structure seems to be an important influence on the distribution of organisms within seagrass beds. Evidence for the importance of structure alone comes from studies showing that artificial leaves

support a community of epiphytes and mobile fishes and decapods similar in biomass and species composition to ones associated with natural leaves (Silberstein et al. 1986; Virnstein and Curran 1986; Hall and Bell 1988; Sogard 1989). Seagrass-produced chemicals inhibitory to epiphytes (Harrison 1982; Harrison and Durance 1985) apparently play a minor role in influencing the community.

Individual species clearly differentiate seagrass habitat structure based on leaf shoot length, density, or surface area. Stoner (1980) experimentally determined that amphipods differentiate among seagrass structure based on surface area rather than qualitative aspects of leaf shoot morphology. When *Thalassia*, *Halodule*, and *Syringodium* were offered to amphipods in equal biomass, amphipods preferred *Halodule* with its high SA/volume ratio. Amphipods were equally distributed among the three seagrasses when presented in equal surface area. Two species of pipefish select naturally long *Posidonia* or *Zostera* over clipped leaves, and males of one

Figure 12.6 Rhizophytic algae are common in tropical seagrass beds. Two species from the Caribbean: *Halimeda incrassata* (left) and *Penicillus capitatus* (right), both attached to their mass of rhizoids. The maximum aboveground height is around 20 cm.

species and both sexes of the other selected dense seagrass over experimentally thinned plots (Steffe et al. 1989). Pipefish of one species had significantly fuller guts in dense seagrass, suggesting that they captured their principal prey of copepods more efficiently there. This observation is consistent with the work of Thistle et al. (1984) on harpacticoid copepod abundance. Thistle et al. also applied an experimental ap-

proach to understanding the influence of seagrass structure on harpacticoid copepod abundance. Using live *Syringodium* leaf shoots, mimics, and sediment controls with no structure, they found that copepod abundance and the biomass of bacterial food were higher around leaves and mimics, but there was no difference between them. Thus, the structure of the seagrass, not the release of dissolved organic substrate for bacterial growth, was critical to copepods and their food source. The authors hypothesized that the effect was due to a change in the water flow around the structures. Their hypothesis was supported later by experiments using tube mimics in flumes (Eckman 1985). Around nearby tubular structures such as seagrass leaf shoots, the viscous and diffusional sublayers within the boundary layer are thinner, thereby enhancing the flux of solutes to microbes near the structures. This is just one example of how seagrass structure can change water flow patterns and influence the distribution of animals.

Heterogeneity within seagrass patches can enhance the abundance and secondary production of associated animals. Drift algal mats result in local increases in faunal species and numbers, presumably through provision of additional resources and by increased dispersal of mat-associated animals into the seagrass bed (Virnstein and Howard 1987a, b; Holmquist 1997). However, if mats remain stationary too long and become anoxic, they have the potential to cause the loss of the seagrass (Holmquist 1997). Upright macroalgae (Heck 1979; Stoner and Lewis 1985), sponges and ascidians (Heck and Orth 1980), and mussel patches (Valentine and Heck 1993) within seagrass meadows lead to an enhanced abundance and even secondary production of associated fauna.

Organisms also respond to the larger landscape formed by mosaics of seagrasses patches and gaps. Mobile predators on infauna should be distributed predictably at the edges of a bed where the rhizome mat with associated animals is less dense and thus easier to penetrate. This relationship is upheld for stingrays (Ogden 1980; Valentine et al. 1994) and juveniles of the commercially valuable California halibut (Kramer 1990, pers. com.). The seagrass landscape also affects the growth and survival of bivalve species (Irlandi 1994; Irlandi et al. 1995; Reusch 1998a; Reusch and Williams 1999), copepod recruitment (Bell and Hicks 1991), the recruitment and survival of an epibiotic macroalga (Inglis 1994), and the accumulation of drift algae (Bell et al. 1995). Researchers are just beginning to study the underlying mechanisms for these landscape-scale patterns.

Studies in seagrass beds probably have contributed more to our understanding of the specific ways in which habitat structure influences individual organisms than studies in other benthic habitats. Nonetheless, a major research gap remains: How does habitat structure influence the structure of the associated community? As discussed previously, most of the seagrass studies focus on a single species rather than the community. Is habitat structure a better predictor of seagrass community structure than food availability or predation, which strongly influence community structure in the deep-

Fig. 12.7 Patch and gap structure is demonstrated in a bed of *Halophila decipiens* in the Caribbean (20–30 m water depth). Mounds of callianasid shrimps are visible every few m. The bed contains 7 species of the rhizophytic alga *Caulerpa* and also *Halimeda* and *Penicillus*.

sea or rocky intertidal? Habitat structure hypothetically could be the most important determinant of seagrass community structure because it influences both food availability and predation. However, tight correlations between seagrass structural attributes (density, leaf area, canopy height) and community structure and secondary production unfortunately are not very evident (Heck 1979; Virnstein et al. 1984; Bell and Westoby 1986a, b; Virnstein and Howard 1987a, b; Worthington et al. 1992). It would be useful for seagrass management if a few attributes of seagrass vegetation were good predictors of community structure and secondary production. A few such structural predictors could render evaluation of the performance of seagrass mitigations and restorations more cost effective. Recently, Parker et al. (in preparation) determined that the diversity and production of a temperate seagrass epifaunal community depended more on the composition, particularly the morphologies, of the vegetation than on plant diversity per se. Structural complexity both within (density, biomass, leaf area, canopy height) and among (e.g., patch-gap structure) seagrass beds contribute to shaping the community, but the relative contributions of each are incompletely understood. To our knowledge, no appropriate data set exists for a multivariate analysis of the influence of different types and scales of habitat structure on community structure. An experiment that varies structure across the scales is needed but would be very labor intensive.

Community Responses to Seagrass-Induced Alterations in Water Flow Regimes

Along with predation, the dynamic relationship between seagrass beds and the water flow regime is invoked frequently to explain the observed differences both between seagrass and adjacent communities and among different seagrass communities. Seagrass landscapes are molded by water flow; beds become increasingly fragmented as water flows faster, eroding the sediments and belowground biomass (Fonseca et al. 1983). Some mobile organisms such as fishes and pink shrimps are predictably more abundant within low energy, more continuous seagrass beds (Bell et al. 1994; Murphy and Fonseca 1995). Within low-energy beds, these organisms might have reduced costs of mobility and foraging. The sediments have more organic matter that might be important in supporting prey populations.

Within the seagrass canopy, friction with leaf shoots extracts momentum from the flowing water so that the mean water flow speed is slower, mass transport is reduced, and sedimentation of small particles is increased (Burrell and Schubel 1977; Fonseca et al. 1982; Ackerman and Okubo 1993). The exact relationships between seagrass density, canopy height, water depth, seagrass bed dimensions, and various aspects of the water flow regime (mean speeds, variance in speed or turbulence, scales of turbulence, shear stress, mixing, and mass transport) are largely unknown and undoubtedly complex (Fonseca and Fisher 1986; Gambi et al. 1990; Worchester 1995; Koch and Gust 1999). Proper quantification of these relationships is difficult. To date, flumes have

not been scaled appropriately for naturally long seagrass leaves, and leaves interfere with field flow sensors, a problem that needs to be resolved. Regardless of a limited quantitative understanding of fluid dynamics in seagrass beds, studies have demonstrated that modification of the flow regime by the seagrass canopy can affect the distribution and abundance of associated organisms, through influences on recruitment or dispersal and/or food supply (Thistle et al. 1984; Eckman 1985; Irlandi and Peterson 1991; Inglis 1994; Bell et al. 1995).

Patterns in the relative abundances of specific animals in seagrass beds with different structure and compared to adjacent unvegetated areas have been explained in light of how seagrass canopies influence recruitment processes through modifying hydrodynamic regimes (Peterson 1986; Eckman 1987; Orth 1992; Grizzle et al. 1996). Recruitment represents the net balance between the flux of larvae into the seagrass bed and the loss of newly settled larvae due to resuspension, assuming competent larvae are passively distributed. The flux increases both with higher larval concentration and higher water flow speeds (lateral advection) into the seagrass beds (Table 12.2). As larvae encounter surfaces on route to their preferred adult habitat (leaves, sediments), shear stress determines whether the larvae will be resuspended from each surface. Both advection and shear stress decrease as water flow slows, as it does as the number of leaf shoots increase in the canopy, but their effects might act in opposition (Table 12.2). Eckman (1987) concluded that advection, thus larval flux, was the dominant influence on bivalves settling on the leaves, because more settled in areas of lower shoot density where flow speeds were higher. In contrast, Peterson (1986) concluded the "baffling" effect of the seagrass shoots resulted in increased adult abundances of *Mercenaria mercenaria* in seagrass sediments, although factors affecting post-settlement survival were equally important in explaining the magnitude of the enhancement. For *Mercenaria*, low shear stress at the bottom of the canopy can be inferred as the overriding hydrodynamic control on recruitment of the clam. For benthic settlers like clams, increased shear stress at the unsuitable leaf surface should facilitate reentry into the water column, but decreased shear stress at the sediments should result in higher settlement due to reduced erosion of settlers. Epiphyte cover complicates the picture by increasing turbulence at the leaf surface (Koch 1994). Finally, geochemical cues for settlement, for example, ammonium concentrations (Woodin et al. 1998), are patchy on very local scales around individual shoots. This is because shoots redirect water flow and create pressure gradients that change the advective flux of dissolved substances from the sediments (Nepf and Koch 1999). Recruitment is a function of the combined hydrodynamic influences at each step on route to the adult habitat of an organism. Determining which step is the most critical one is a major research question. To this end, a sophisticated hydrodynamic settlement-recruitment model, analogous to ones developed for the unvegetated benthos (Denny and Shibata 1989; Gross et al. 1992; Eckman et al. 1994), would help

TABLE 12.2   Influence of hydrodynamics on larval recruitment in seagrass meadows.

Hydrodynamic Effects	Hypothetical Influence on Recruitment	Evidence
CANOPY		
Reduces flow speeds	Reduced larval flux	Higher settlement in sparse canopies[1]
Reduces shear stress	Reduced resuspension of settlers on leaf; increased settlement of epiphytic organisms; increased settlement of benthos on unsuitable habitat	
	Reduced resuspension of settler in sediments; increased settlement of benthos	Higher settlement in seagrass vs. sand[2]
EPIPHYTES		
Increase leaf shear stress[3]	Increased resuspension of settlers on leaf; reduced settlement of epiphytic organisms; decreased settlement of benthos on unsuitable habitat	
"Monami" (canopy waving)	Increased larval flux[4]	

[1]Eckman 1987
[2]Peterson 1986
[3]Koch 1994
[4]Grizzle et al. 1996

Note: Recruitment is a function of the larval flux and the loss of new settlers due to resuspension. Larval flux is the rate that larvae intercept the substratum, which in turn is a function of larval concentration and mainstream water flow speed.

test the degree to which recruitment reflects the physical environment in a seagrass bed.

If most soft-bottom marine communities are not limited by the supply of propagules or larvae (Olafsson et al. 1994), then the supply of critical resources might be a more important influence on the abundances of organisms in seagrass beds. Nutrients and CO_2 are critical resources for algal epiphytes (Sand-Jensen et al. 1985), just as food is to filter and suspension feeders. Compared to many marine communities, most seagrass communities exist in relatively sheltered environments, with measured freestream flow speeds often less than 0.4 m/s. Sessile organisms within and below the canopy experience even slower flow speeds (references cited previously). Hypothetically, these organisms are subject to physiological limitation by the flux of critical resources. The supply of resources to many organisms within seagrass beds depends on the freestream water flow regime, the hydrodynamics at the water-organism boundary, the ambient resource concentration, and the resource acquisition capacity of the organism. Food flux for suspension feeders increases with water flow speeds, and active suspension feeders are less likely to deplete their food when the boundary layer is thinner under higher flow speeds (Fréchette et al. 1993). Flow speeds in most estuarine seagrass habitats are too slow to reduce particle capture by feeding structures. Beyond these generalizations, it is difficult to predict how the growth of organisms that depend on water flow for food delivery will vary with leaf shoot densities or seagrass patch size. This is illustrated by the wide variation in results from studies of bivalve growth in seagrass beds versus adjacent soft sediments

or among different leaf shoot densities (Kerswill 1949; Peterson et al. 1984; Eckman 1987; Peterson and Beal 1989; Coen and Heck 1991; Irlandi and Peterson 1991; Reusch and Williams 1998). Bivalve growth can increase, decrease, or not change as a function of seagrass cover and flow regimes. Increased growth within slower flow inside the canopy hypothetically reflects the depositional environment that entrains advected food particles (Peterson et al. 1984; Irlandi and Peterson 1991). In addition to food advected into the seagrass bed, these bivalves can utilize suspended benthic microalgae growing within the bed (Judge et al. 1993). What matters to the organism is the food delivered to its feeding ambit. Exactly where the animal resides will be important in determining how water flow affects food delivery. Where food concentrations are very high and densities of filter feeders are relatively low, we would predict that hydrodynamic effects on growth will be minor.

Until both food resources and hydrodynamics are quantified more precisely, the relationships between seagrass cover, water flow modification, and secondary production will not be resolved. To this end, Reusch and Williams (1999) found that the growth of the mussel *Musculista senhousia* in eelgrass beds was proportional to rates of horizontal advection, which decreased as eelgrass patch size increased. The hypothesis that the mussel was limited by a reduced flux of phytoplankton into the eelgrass bed was supported by measurements of reduced chlorophyll concentrations next to and just above the mussels compared to outside the canopy. This hypothesis was verified subsequently when mussels grew faster when experimentally supplemented in situ with phytoplankton (Allen

1999). We believe this is the first *direct* demonstration that the growth and survival of bivalves living in seagrass beds, and indeed in the benthos in general, can be limited by food.

Food availability, whether produced locally or advected in, is apparently important, but is only part of the story. For most of the bivalves studied, predation, which varies with seagrass structure, also had a significant effect on growth due to both direct effects and indirect ones wherein the presence of a predator limited feeding (Coen and Heck 1991; Irlandi and Peterson 1991; Pohl et al. 1991; Reusch 1998b).

Linkages among Marine Communities

Seagrass communities can be linked to other marine communities in striking ways through the movement of animals and the export of large quantities of slowly decaying organic matter. Nightly migrations of French and white grunts from their daytime shelter among Caribbean reef corals to adjacent seagrass beds where they feed results in the transfer of nutrients back to the corals, whose growth is thereby increased (Meyer et al. 1983). Fishes living in close association with mangroves or migrating between them and seagrass beds apparently derive most of their trophic support from the seagrass beds (Marguillier et al. 1997). And, we can't resist including this probably unimportant but droll example of trophic transfer from a seagrass community to the squirrels that forage on detached eelgrass leaves in the harbor of Morro Bay, California (Roest 1993).

Seagrass beds export large quantities of leaves that are continuously replaced (Zieman et al. 1979; Josselyn et al. 1983; Bach et al. 1986). Because the leaves are buoyed by internal air channels and are refractory to decomposition, they can be transported far from their origin. A careful look at many deep-sea benthic photographs reveals the presence of seagrass leaves that provide both habitat and trophic support for deep-sea animals (Suchanek et al. 1985). Closer to shore, detrital seagrass mats serve as localized hot spots of secondary production (Vetter 1995). These linkages emphasize that degradation of nearshore seagrass beds can have far-reaching consequences for other marine communities.

Ecological Interactions between Native and Non-Native Marine Species

Many marine communities have been invaded by non-native species (Steneck and Carlton, this volume), and there is concern that these species might reduce natural levels of biodiversity (Butman and Carlton 1995). In general, manipulative experiments rarely have been used to elucidate the ecological interactions between native and invading species (Kareiva 1996). As an exception to this, seagrass studies have contributed to the understanding that the ecological effects of invading species are complex and not always deleterious (Harrison 1987; Posey 1988; Sewell 1996; Zimmerman et al. 1996; Ceccherelli and Cinelli 1997; Reusch and Williams 1998, 1999). The invasion of *Zostera japonica* in the Pacific Northwest re-

gion of North America in the 1950s afforded the opportunity to study the effects of an invading species on seagrass communities. *Z. japonica* invaded intertidal mudflats located mostly above the upper tidal limit of native *Z. marina*, which was displaced only slightly during the invasion. By modifying the physical structure of the habitat, *Z. japonica* changed the community structure in mostly positive ways, for example, increasing species richness and the abundance of common species, although the abundance of some species declined or did not change (Harrison 1987; Posey 1988). *Z. japonica* also provided waterfowl with increased feeding ground and was easier to access and handle and had higher food quality than *Z. marina* (Baldwin and Lovvorn 1994). The changes were predictable from the ways that seagrasses in general structure the associated community, as discussed above.

Interactions between native *Zostera marina* and the non-native infauna mussel *Musculista senhousia* are more complicated. In the 1920s, *M. senhousia* invaded an astonishing variety of habitats on the west coast of the United States. *M. senhousia* can occur at densities > 15,000 individuals/m² in eelgrass beds in southern California, and the abundances of the two species is negatively correlated. The outcome of their interaction is a complicated function of relative plant and animal densities, seasonal shifts in the limiting factor for eelgrass growth, the structure of the eelgrass landscape, food availability for the mussel, and the presence of native gastropod predators (Reusch and Williams 1998, 1999; Reusch 1998b; Allen 1999; Williams and Ebert, unpubl.). The overriding influences are the patch structure of the habitat and food availability. In dense continuous meadows, the mussel starves because of the reduction in water flow, and thus phytoplankton flux into the meadow. Where eelgrass is sparse and patchy, the mussel can achieve densities sufficient to inhibit leaf growth rates. At all densities, the mussel inhibits the growth of eelgrass rhizomes and expansion of the meadow. Over time, the mussel is predicted to win because it recruits extremely well, grows fast and can preempt any habitat where eelgrass, slow to recruit and recover, is disturbed.

Range expansions of a limpet (*Tectura depicta*) and an anemone (*Bunodeopsis* sp.) from warmer waters into more northern eelgrass beds in California have contributed to recent and severe declines in eelgrass (Figure 12.8; Sewell 1996; Zimmerman et al. 1996). Both species are cryptogenic, that is, their origin is uncertain. The sudden appearance in Monterrey Bay of the limpet, which is typically found in southern California, is assumed to be in response to ocean warming. The anemone, misidentified for years, is known from tropical locales. Its distribution in San Diego eelgrass beds could represent either a range expansion in response to ocean warming or an introduction. The limpet catastrophically overgrazed its habitat. The anemone blooms in summers to cover virtually all eelgrass leaves, blocking light and causing the canopy to collapse, leading to eelgrass death. Such occurrences of new interactions between eelgrass and animals highlight that, although in general the kinds of interactions between seagrasses and introduced species can be predicted

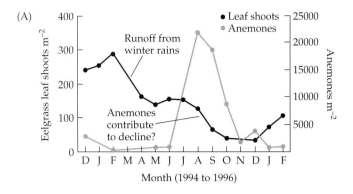

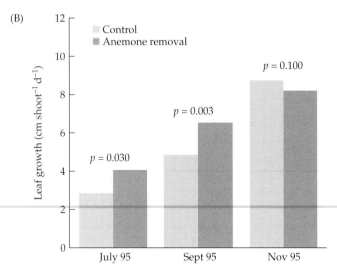

Figure 12.8 Effects of the cryptogenic anemone, *Bunodeopsis* sp., on eelgrass in San Diego, California. (A) Declines in eelgrass leaf shoot density (mean ± se, *n* = 40) coincide with summer increases in anemone density (mean, *n* = 20) in Mission Bay, San Diego. (B) Mean daily eelgrass leaf growth in three experimental removals of the anemones from eelgrass leaves (*n* = 4 treatments in July and September and 6 in November; experiments lasted 8–14 days). Probability levels from an analysis of covariance with leaf width as the covariate. Nonsignificant results of anemone removals in November were attributed to anemone densities that were 75% lower than in earlier experiments. (Data from Sewell 1996.)

from existing knowledge about seagrass communities, there are going to be surprises.

RESTORATION ECOLOGY

Seagrasses, along with mangroves and salt marshes, fall under the legislative mandate of the U.S. Clean Water Act, and thus their deliberate removal must be mitigated. As a result, much research has been devoted to restoration of seagrass ecosystems. Much of this research has been technique-driven and has lead to an understanding of the environmental parameters necessary to support seagrass growth (Fonseca et al. 1988). Here, we will focus on the community-level aspects of seagrass restoration. Establishment of community functions, particularly trophic support, is a primary goal of restoration, but one dif-

ficult to achieve. Designing seagrass beds to maximize functional equivalency requires an exacting knowledge of the mechanisms that result in a particular community and level of secondary production. As described above, ecologists understand the attributes, primarily structural, of the seagrass vegetation that control the distribution and abundance of specific organisms far better than those that influence community structure. Not surprisingly, one species will increase and another decrease as a function of leaf shoot density. This specific knowledge is very useful if mitigation or restoration is directed toward a target species, such as the scallop *Argopecten irradians* (Smith et al. 1989); however, most projects are directed toward community properties such as species diversity and total abundance.

Although there have been numerous seagrass mitigation and restoration projects (Fonseca et al. 1988; Thom 1990b), the results of the required monitoring of community development reside primarily in the gray literature. In the limited published studies, two approaches have been taken to assess the functionality of mitigated or restored beds. First, the community structure (number and density of individuals, number of taxa, species diversity indices) was compared in natural versus planted beds (Homziak et al. 1982; McLaughlin et al. 1983; Fonseca et al. 1990; Fonseca et al. 1996). Trajectories for community development were produced as a function of leaf shoot density (except in McLaughlin et al. 1983). The abundance and diversity of organisms, particularly mobile ones, became similar to natural areas relatively early after planting and, in some cases, before the vegetation had developed fully.

The second approach to evaluating functional equivalency has involved assessing the survival or production of a single species in transplanted versus natural beds (Smith et al. 1989; Bell et al. 1993; Clements et al. 1994). In these studies, the production of animal tissue was used as a measure of equivalency. Both arm regeneration rates for a brittle star and estimated biomass production for a polychaete were greater in transplanted beds of relatively young age (~ 2 years).

The authors just listed pointed out that only young beds were evaluated for functional equivalency. Brown-Peterson et al. (1993) compared 31-year-old seagrass beds that had colonized dredge spoils and suggested that fish community structure differed between these older beds and natural ones. The replicates for one bed type were located at a site physically different from the site for the other bed type, a problem that is common in restoration research. Unless restorations and mitigations are part of an adaptive management program of experimental design and hypothesis testing or are strictly research projects (Bell et al. 1993), they present ecologists with numerous problems of pseudoreplication. The development of restored or mitigated seagrass beds is a successional process (Bell et al. 1993; Montalvo et al. 1997), but unfortunately, seagrass succession has focused primarily on the development of vegetation and nutrient cycling processes (Williams 1990; Pedersen et al. 1997) to the exclusion of the associated animal community.

Studies on the functional equivalency of planted seagrass beds reveal major uncertainties in seagrass community ecology. Although leaf shoot density and perhaps canopy cover can be reasonable predictors of community structure on the scale of a single seagrass bed, the relationship of seagrass vegetation to secondary production is unresolved (Smith et al. 1989; Bell et al. 1993; Clements et al. 1994). Although it is generally assumed that high seagrass primary production supports high secondary production (e.g., Petersen and Boyson Jensen 1911), this relationship needs to be evaluated with more rigor. The study of Lubbers et al. (1990) in natural submersed vascular plant beds in the Chesapeake Bay provides a start. Fish biomass was a positive function of plant biomass. Of greater relevance, overall fish production was higher in vegetated versus nonvegetated sites and tracked seasonal changes in plant biomass changes, and fish guts were fuller. The increased production was largely attributable to higher growth rates, not higher biomass. The diets of several fishes shifted to epifauna in vegetation from infauna in unvegetated areas. Infauna are presumably harder for fishes to find.

Understanding the relationship of secondary to primary production is crucial not only for restoring seagrass beds but also for determining whether declines in fisheries are the result of, or merely correlated with, seagrass declines. This issue is difficult and requires an understanding of population demography and dynamics. Knowing population growth rates would help determine whether changes in numbers of organisms in planted seagrass beds merely reflect a redistribution of biomass from elsewhere. Attainment of functional equivalency will depend to some unknown degree on source populations and their proximity (e.g., Bell and Hicks 1991). A demographic approach to evaluating functional equivalency can help elucidate when immigration is important (Bell et al. 1993). In general, benthic marine ecologists have not linked how demographic changes in the populations that interact in a community ultimately lead to changes in community structure.

and thus radically changing the community. Why epiphytes can escape mesograzer control remains a major research question. Herbivores also influence seagrass physiology and demography, but these aspects deserve more study. Primary production exported from seagrass beds provides important linkages to other nearshore and offshore communities.

Another prevailing influence on seagrass communities is the complex above- and belowground structure of the vegetation. In other marine communities, experiments have verified that competition, predation, recruitment, or food flux control community structure. In seagrass beds, each of these very important processes is strongly modulated by the vegetation structure. The leaf canopy and the associated epiphyte community modify the hydrodynamic regime in very striking, complex ways. Spatial heterogeneity, for example, in the form of macroalgal mats or patches of filter feeders, increases the primary and secondary productivity in seagrass beds. Although ecologists understand the responses of many different species to seagrass habitat structure at a variety of scales, they have not been able to generalize about how habitat complexity influences community structure beyond knowing that with more vegetation, the numbers of individuals and species increase.

Seagrass beds are very susceptible to human influences. Seagrass declines occur when algae overgrow them. Eutrophication has been implicated in algal overgrowth, but this hypothesis needs to be tested against the alternative that the removal of top predators results in algal overgrowth. Introductions of animal species new to a seagrass community have significant, primarily negative effects on seagrasses. In contrast, when non-native seagrass vegetation is introduced to a locale, the overall abundance of other organisms in the community tends to increase. Restoration of seagrass beds offers a unique opportunity to determine how the associated community develops and also to perform controlled manipulations of the structural complexity to test for its influence on community structure.

SUMMARY

The high primary production of seagrass beds and the diversity of primary producers is a major factor of importance for the associated animal communities. Although most of this production enters food webs as detritus, herbivory nonetheless is an important process in seagrass beds. Herbivores can control the distribution and abundance of seagrasses directly as well as indirectly by controlling algal epiphytes. Epiphytic microalgae are more notable than in many other vegetated marine communities because of their role in trophic support and because of their propensity for overgrowing seagrasses

ACKNOWLEDGMENTS

Mark Denny and Jim Eckman kindly reviewed the section on hydrodynamics. Bruce Nyden provided the photographs and digital images. We thank Aaron Ellison and another (anonymous) reviewer. SLW was supported in part by the National Sea Grant Program on Non-Indigenous Species (#NA66RGO477). KLH was supported in part by a grant form the Environmental Protection Agency to the Alabama Center for Estuarine Studies (ACES). Contribution #294 from the Coastal and Marine Institute, San Diego State University and #323 from the Dauphin Island Sea Lab.

LITERATURE CITED

Ackerman, J. D. and A. Okubo. 1993. Reduced mixing in a marine macrophyte canopy. *Func. Ecol.* 7: 305–309.

Adams, S. M. and J. W. Angelovic. 1970. Assimilation of detritus and its associated bacteria by three species of estuarine animals. *Chesapeake Sci.* 11: 249–254.

Aioi, K. and T. Komatsu. 1996. A preliminary report on the recovery process of *Zostera marina* in Otsuchi Bay, northern Japan, after disturbance by large atmospheric depressions. In J. Kuo, R. C. Phillips, D. I. Walker and H. Kirkman (eds.), *Seagrass Biology: Proceedings of an International Workshop*, pp. 319–322.

Aioi, K., T. Komatsu and K. Morita. 1998. The world's longest seagrass, *Zostera caulescens* from northeastern Japan. *Aquat. Bot.* 61: 87–93.

Allen, B. J. 1999. Native eelgrass, *Zostera marina*, mediates growth and reproduction of an introduced marine bivalve through food limitation. MS Thesis, San Diego State University.

Atkinson, M. J. and S. V. Smith. 1983. C: N: P ratios of benthic marine plants. *Limnol. Oceanogr.* 28: 568–574.

Bach, S. D., G. W. Thayer, and M. W. LaCroix. 1986. Export of detritus from eelgrass (*Zostera marina*) beds near Beaufort, North Carolina, USA. *Mar. Ecol. Prog. Ser.* 28: 265–278.

Baldwin, J. R. and J. R. Lovvorn. 1994. Expansion of seagrass habitat by the exotic *Zostera japonica*, and its use by dabbling ducks and brant in Boundary Bay, British Columbia. *Mar. Ecol. Prog. Ser.* 103: 119–127.

Ballantine, D. and H. J. Humm. 1975. Benthic algae of the Anclote estuary. I. Epiphytes of seagrass leaves. *Florida Sci.* 38: 150–162.

Bell, J. D. and M. Westoby. 1986a. Importance of local changes in leaf height and density to fish and decapods associated with seagrasses. *J. Exp. Mar. Biol. Ecol.* 104: 249–274.

Bell, J. D. and M. Westoby. 1986b. Variation in seagrass height and density over a wide spatial scale: Effects on common fish and decapods. *J. Exp. Mar. Biol. Ecol.* 104: 275–295.

Bell, S. S. and G. R. F. Hicks. 1991. Marine landscapes and faunal recruitment: A field test with seagrasses and copepods. *Mar. Ecol. Prog. Ser.* 73: 61–66.

Bell, S. S., L. A. J. Clements and J. Kurdziel. 1993. Production in natural and restored seagrasses: A case study of a macrobenthic polychaete. *Ecol. Appl.* 3: 610–621.

Bell, S. S., M. O. Hall and M. S. Fonseca. 1994. Evaluation of faunal and floral attributes of seagrass beds in high and low energy regimes: A geographic comparison. In K. R. Dyer and R. J. Orth (eds.), *Changes in Fluxes in Estuaries*, pp. 267–272. Olsen and Olsen, Denmark.

Bell, S. S., M. O. Hall and B. D. Robbins. 1995. Toward a landscape approach in seagrass beds: Using macroalgal accumulation to address questions of scale. *Oecologia* 104: 163–168.

Belsky, A. J. 1986. Does herbivory benefit plants? A review of the evidence. *Amer. Nat.* 127: 870–892.

Bertness, M. D., S. D. Garrity and S. C. Levings. 1981. Predation pressure and gastropod foraging: A tropical–temperate comparison. *Evolution* 35: 995–1007.

Birch, W. R. 1975. Some chemical and calorific properties of tropical marine angiosperms compared with those of other plants. *J. Appl. Ecol.* 12: 201–212.

Bjorndal, K. A. 1980. Nutrition and grazing behavior of the green turtle, *Chelonia mydas. Mar. Biol.* 56: 147–154.

Borum, J. 1987. Dynamics of epiphyton on eelgrass (*Zostera marina* L.) leaves: Relative roles of algal growth, herbivory, and substratum turnover. *Limnol. Oceanogr.* 32: 986–992.

Brawley, S. H. and X. G. Fei. 1987. Studies of mesoherbivory in aquaria and in an unbarricaded mariculture farm on the Chinese coast. *J. Phycol.* 23: 614–623.

Bronmark, C. S., P. Klosiewski and R. A. Stein. 1992. Indirect effects of predation in a freshwater, benthic food chain. *Ecology* 73: 1662–1673.

Brown-Peterson, N. J., M. S. Peterson, D. A. Rydene and R. W. Eames. 1993. Fish assemblages in natural versus well-established recolonized seagrass meadows. *Estuaries* 16: 177–189.

Buchsbaum, R., I. Valiela and T. Swain. 1984. The role of phenolic compounds and other plant constituents in feeding by Canada geese in a coastal marsh. *Oecologia* 63: 343–349.

Burrell, D. C. and J. R. Schubel. 1977. Seagrass ecosystem oceanography. In C. P. McRoy and C. Helfferich (eds.). *Seagrass Ecosystems: A Scientific Perspective*, pp. 195–232. Dekker, New York.

Butman, C. A. and J. Carlton, eds. 1995. *Understanding marine biodiversity: A research agenda for the Nation*. National Research Council, National Academy Press, Washington, DC.

Caine, E. A. 1980. Ecology of two littoral species of caprellid amphipods (Crustacea) from Washington, USA. *Mar. Biol.* 56: 327–335.

Cambridge, M. L. and A. J. McComb. 1992. Seagrass degradation in Australian coastal waters. *Mar. Poll. Bull.* 25: 191–195.

Camp, D. K., S. P. Cobb and J. F. Van Breeveld. 1973. Overgrazing of seagrasses by a regular urchin, *Lytechinus variegatus. BioScience* 23: 37–38.

Cebrián, J. and C. M. Duarte. 1998. Patterns in leaf herbivory on seagrasses. *Aquat. Bot.* 60: 67–82.

Cebrián, J., C. M Duarte, N. S. R. Agawin and M. Merino. 1998. Leaf growth response to simulated herbivory: A comparison among seagrass species. *J. Exp. Mar. Biol. Ecol.* 220: 67–81.

Ceccherelli, G. and F. Cinelli. 1997. Short-term effects of nutrient enrichment of the sediment and interactions between the seagrass *Cymodocea nodosa* and the introduced green

algal *Caulerpa taxifolia* in a Mediterranean bay. *J. Exp. Mar. Biol. Ecol.* 217: 165–177.

Clements, L. A. J., S. S. Bell and J. P. Kurdziel. 1994. Abundance and arm loss of the infaunal brittlestar *Ophiophragmus filograneus* (Echinodermata: Ophiuroidea), with an experimental determination of regeneration rates in natural and planted seagrass beds. *Mar. Biol.* 121: 97–104.

Coen, L. D. and K. L. Heck, Jr. 1991. The interacting effects of siphon nipping and habitat on bivalve (*Mercenaria mercenaria* (L.)) growth in a subtropical seagrass (*Halodule wrightii* Ashers.) meadow. *J. Exp. Mar. Biol. Ecol.* 145: 1– 13.

Coen, L. D., K. L. Heck, Jr. and L. G. Abele. 1981. Experiments on competition and predation among shrimps of seagrass meadows. *Ecology* 62: 1484–1493.

Coleman, V. L. and J. M. Burkholder. 1995. Response of microalgal epiphyte communities to nitrate enrichment in an eelgrass (*Zostera marina*) meadow. *J. Phycol.* 31: 36–43.

Dawes, C. J. and J. M. Lawrence. 1979. Effects of blade removal on the proximate composition of the rhizome of the seagrass *Thalassia testudinum* Banks ex König. *Aquat. Bot.* 7: 255–266.

Dawes, C. J., K. Bird, M. Durako, R. Goddard, W. Hoffman and R. McIntosh. 1979. Chemical fluctuations due to seasonal and cropping effects on an algal-seagrass community. *Aquat. Bot.* 6: 79–86.

Dennison, W. C., R. J. Orth, K. A. Moore, J. C. Stevenson, V. Carter, S. Kollar, P. W. Bergstrom and R. A. Batuik. 1993. Assessing water quality with submersed aquatic vegetation. *BioScience* 43: 86–94.

Denny, M. W. and M. F. Shibata. 1989. Consequences of surf-zone turbulence for settlement and external fertilization. *Amer. Nat.* 134: 859–889.

Duarte, C. M. 1992. Nutrient concentration of aquatic plants: Patterns across species. *Limnol. Oceanogr.* 37: 882–889.

Duarte, C. M. and K. Sand–Jensen. 1990. Seagrass colonizaiton: Patch formation and patch growth in *Cymodocea nodosa. Mar. Ecol. Prog. Ser.* 65: 193–200.

Eckman, J. E. 1985. Flow disruption by an animal-tube mimic affects sediment bacterial colonization. *J. Mar. Res.* 43: 419–435.

Eckman, J. E. 1987. The role of hydrodynamics in recruitment, growth, and survival of *Argopecten irradians* (L.) and *Anomia simplex* (D'Orbigny) within eelgrass meadows. *J. Exp. Mar. Biol. Ecol.* 106: 165–191.

Eckman, J. E., F. E. Werner and T. F. Gross. 1994. Modelling some effects of behavior on larval settlement in a turbulent boundary layer. *Deep-Sea Res.* 41: 185–208.

Edgar, G. J. 1990. Population regulation, population dynamics and competition amongst mobile epifauna associated with seagrass. *J. Exp. Mar. Biol. Ecol.* 144: 205–234.

Edgar, G. J. 1993. Measurement of the carrying capacity of macrophytic habitats using a metabolic-rate based index. *Oecologia* 95: 115–121.

Edgar, J. W. and C. Shaw. 1995. The production and trophic ecology of shallow-water fish assemblages in Southern Australia I. Species richness, size-structure and production of fishes in Western Port, Victoria. *J. Exp. Mar. Biol. Ecol.* 194: 53–81.

Enríquez, S., C. M. Duarte and K. Sand-Jensen. 1993. Patterns in decomposition rates among photosynthetic organisms: The importance of detritus C: N: P content. *Oecologia* 94: 457–465.

Erftemeijer, P. L. A., R. Osinga and A. E. Mars. 1993. Primary production of seagrass beds in South Sulawesi (Indonesia): A comparison of habitats, methods and species. *Aquat. Bot.* 46: 67–90.

Ewanchuk, P. J. 1995. Population growth of eelgrass (*Zostera marina* L.): The relative importance of sexual versus asexual reproduction. MS Thesis, San Diego State University.

Fishman, J. and R. J. Orth. 1996. Effects of predation on *Zostera marina* L. seed abundance. *J. Exp. Mar. Biol. Ecol.* 198: 11–26.

Fonseca, M. S. and J. S. Fisher. 1986. A comparison of canopy friction and sediment movement between four species of seagrass with reference to their ecology and restoration. *Mar. Ecol. Prog. Ser.* 29: 15–22.

Fonseca, M. S., J. S. Fisher, J. C. Zieman and G. W. Thayer. 1982. Influence of the seagrass, *Zostera marina* L., on current flow. *Estuarine and Coastal Shelf Sci.* 15: 351–364.

Fonseca, M. S., J. C. Zieman, G. W. Thayer and J. S. Fisher. 1983. The role of current velocity in structuring eelgrass (*Zostera marina*) meadows. *Estuarine and Coastal Shelf Sci.* 17: 367–380.

Fonseca, M. S., W. J. Kenworthy and G. W. Thayer. 1988. Restoration and management of seagrass systems: A review. In D. D. Hook, W. H. McKee, Jr., H. K. Smith, J. Gregory, V. G. Burrell, Jr., M. R. DeVoe, R. E. Sojka, S. Gilbert, R. Banks, L. H. Stolzy, C. Brooks, T. D. Matthews and T. H. Shear (eds), *The Ecology and Management of Wetlands, Vol. 2. Management, Use and Value of Wetlands*, pp. 353–368. Timber Press, Portland, OR.

Fonseca, M. S., W. J. Kenworthy, D. R. Colby, K. A. Rittmaster and G. W. Thayer. 1990. Comparisons of fauna among natural and transplanted eelgrass *Zostera marina* meadows: Criteria for mitigation. *Mar. Ecol. Prog. Ser.* 65: 251–264.

Fonseca, M. S., D. L. Meyer and M. O. Hall. 1996. Development of planted seagrass beds in Tampa Bay, Florida, USA. II. Faunal components. *Mar. Ecol. Prog. Ser.* 132: 141–156.

Fréchette, M., D. Lefaivre and C. A. Butman. 1993. Bivalve feeding and the benthic boundary layer. In R. F. Dame (ed.), *Bivalve Filter Feeders in Estuarine and Coastal Ecosystem Processes*, pp. 325–369. NATO ASI Series, Vol. G 33. Springer-Verlag, Berlin.

Fredette, T. J., R. J. Diaz, J. van Montfrans and R. J. Orth. 1990. Secondary production within a seagrass bed (*Zostera marina* and *Ruppia maritima*) in lower Chesapeake Bay. *Estuaries* 13: 431–440.

Fry, B. 1981. Natural stable carbon isotope tag traces Texas shrimp migrations. *Fish. Bull.* 79: 337–345.

Fry, B. 1984. ^{13}C/^{12}C ratios and the trophic importance of algae in Florida *Syringodium filiforme* seagrass meadows. *Mar. Biol.* 79: 11–19.

Fry, B. and P. L. Parker. 1979. Animal diet in Texas seagrass meadows: Del ^{13}C evidence for the importance of benthic plants. *Estuarine, Coastal, and Mar. Sci.* 8: 499–509.

Fry, B., R. S. Scalan and P. L Parker. 1983. ^{13}C/^{12}C ratios in marine food webs of the Torres Strait, Queensland. *Austral. J. Mar. Freshw. Res.* 34: 707–715.

Gambi, M. C., Nowell, A. R. M. and P. A Jumars. 1990. Flume observations on flow dynamics in *Zostera marina* (eelgrass) beds. *Mar. Ecol. Prog. Ser.* 61: 159–169.

Gilanders, B. M. and M. J. Kingsford. 1996. Elements in otoliths may elucidate the contribution of estuarine recruitment to sustaining coastal reef populations of a temperate reef fish. *Mar. Ecol. Prog. Ser.* 141: 13–20.

Greenway, M. 1976. The grazing of *Thalassia testudinum* in Kingston Harbour, Jamaica. *Aquat. Bot.* 2: 117–126.

Grizzle, R. E., F. T. Short, C. R. Newell, H. Hoven and L. Kindblom. 1996. Hydrodynamically induced synchronous waving of seagrasses: 'Monami' and its possible effects on larval mussel settlement. *J. Exp. Mar. Biol. Ecol.* 206: 165–177.

Gross, T. F., F. E. Werner and J. E. Eckman. 1992. Numerical modeling of larval settlement in turbulent bottom boundary layers. *J. Mar. Res.* 50: 611–642.

Hall, M. O. and S. S. Bell. 1988. Response of small motile epifauna to complexity of epiphytic algae on seagrass blades. *J. Mar. Res.* 116: 613–630.

Hall, M. O. and S. S. Bell. 1993. Meiofauna on the seagrass *Thalassia testudinum*: Population characteristics of harpacticoid copepods and associations with algal epiphytes. *Mar. Biol.* 116: 137–146.

Harrison, P. G. 1977. Decomposition of macrophyte detritus in seawater: Effects of grazing by amphipods. *Oikos* 28: 165–169.

Harrison, P. G. 1978. Patterns of uptake and translocation of ^{14}C by *Zostera americana* Den Hartog in the laboratory. *Aquat. Bot.* 5: 93–97.

Harrison, P. G. 1982. Control of microbial growth and of amphipod grazing by water-soluble compounds from leaves of *Zostera marina*. *Mar. Biol.* 67: 225–230.

Harrison, P. G. 1987. Natural expansion and experimental manipulation of seagrass (*Zostera* spp.) abundance and the response of infaunal invertebrates. *Estuarine and Coastal Shelf Sci.* 24: 799–812.

Harrison, P. G. and C. D. Durance. 1985. Reductions in photosynthetic carbon uptake in epiphytic diatoms by water-soluble extracts of leaves of *Zostera marina*. *Mar. Biol.* 90: 117–119.

Hauxwell, J., J. McClelland, P. J. Behr and I. Valiella. 1998. Relative importance of grazing and nutrient controls of macroalgal biomass in three temperate shallow estuaries. *Estuaries* 21: 347–360.

Heck, K. L., Jr. 1979. Some determinants of the composition and abundance of motile macroinvertebrate species in tropical and temperate turtlegrass (*Thalassia testudinum*) meadows. *J. Biogeogr.* 6: 183–200.

Heck, K. L., Jr. and L. B. Crowder. 1991. Habitat structure and predator–prey interactions in vegetated aquatic ecosystems. In S. S. Bell, E. D. McCoy and E. R. Mushinsky (eds.), *Habitat Structure of Objects in Space*, pp. 281–299. Chapman and Hall, London.

Heck, K. L., Jr., and R. J. Orth. 1980. Seagrass habitats: The roles of habitat complexity, competition and predation in structuring associated fish and motile macroinvertebrate assemblages. In V. S. Kennedy (ed.), *Estuarine Perspectives*, pp. 449–464. Academic Press, New York.

Heck, K. L., Jr. and J. F. Valentine. 1995. Sea urchin herbivory: Evidence for long-lasting effects in subtropical seagrass meadows. *J. Exp. Mar. Biol. Ecol.* 189: 205–217.

Heck, K. L., Jr. and K. A. Wilson. 1987. Predation rates of decapod crustaceans in latitudinally separated seagrass communities: A study of spatial and temporal variation using tethering techniques. *J. Exp. Mar. Biol. Ecol.* 107: 87–100.

Heck, K. L., Jr., K. W. Able, M. P. Fahay and C. T. Roman. 1989. Fishes and decapod crustaceans of Cape Cod eelgrass meadows: Species composition, seasonal abundance patterns and comparison with unvegetated substrates. *Estuaries* 12: 59–65.

Heck, K. L., Jr., K. W. Able, C. T. Roman and M. P. Fahay. 1995. Composition, abundance, biomass and production of macrofauna in a New England estuary: Comparison among eelgrass meadows and other nursery habitats. *Estuaries* 18: 379–389.

Heck, K. L., Jr., D. A. Nadeau and R. Thomas. 1997. The nursery role of seagrass beds. *Gulf of Mex. Sci.* 1: 50–54.

Heck, K. L., Jr., J. R. Pennock, L. D. Coen and S. A. Sklenar. 2000. Effects of nutrient enrichment and small predator density on seagrass ecosystems: An experimental assessment. *Limnol. Oceanogr.* 45: 1041–1057.

Hellwig-Armonies, M. 1988. Mobile epifauna on *Zostera marina*, and infauna of its inflorescences. *Helgo. Meeres.* 42: 329–337.

Herms, D. A. and W. J. Mattson. 1992. The dilemma of plants: To grow or defend. *Quart. Rev. Biol.* 67: 283–335.

Hinrichsen, D. 1998. *Coastal Waters of the World, Trends, Threats, and Strategies.* Island Press, Washington, DC.

Holmquist, J. G. 1997. Disturbance and gap formation in a marine benthic mosaic: Influence of shifting macroalgal patches on seagrass structure and mobile invertebrates. *Mar. Ecol. Prog. Ser.* 158: 121–130.

Homziak, J., M. S. Fonseca and W. J. Kenworthy. 1982. Macrobenthic community structure in a transplanted eelgrass (*Zostera marina*) meadow. *Mar. Ecol. Prog. Ser.* 9: 211–221.

Howard, R. K. 1982. Impact of feeding activities of epibenthic amphipods on surface-fouling of eelgrass leaves. *Aquat. Bot.* 14: 91–97.

Humm, H. J. 1964. Epiphytes of the sea grass, *Thalassia testudinum*, in Florida. *Bull. Mar. Sci. Gulf Carib.* 14: 306–341.

Huntley, N. 1991. Herbivores and the dynamics of communities and ecosystems. *Annu. Rev. Ecol. Syst.* 22: 477–503.

Iizumi, H. 1996. Temporal and spatial variability of leaf production of *Zostera marina* L. at Otsuchi, northern Japan. In J. Kuo, R. C. Phillips, D. I. Walker and H. Kirkman (eds.), *Seagrass Biology: Proceedings of an International Workshop*, pp. 143–148.

Iizumi, H. and K. Hattori. 1982. Growth and organic production of eelgrass (*Zostera marina* L.) in temperate waters of the Pacific coast of Japan. III. The kinetics of nitrogen uptake. *Aquat. Bot.* 12: 245–256.

Inglis, G. J. 1994. Contrasting effects of habitat structure on the recruitment and mortality of an epibiotic macroalga. *Oecologia* 99: 352–365.

Irlandi, E. A. 1994. Large- and small-scale effects of habitat structure on rates of predation: How percent coverage of seagrass affects rates of predation and siphon nipping on an infaunal bivalve. *Oecologia* 98: 176–183.

Irlandi E. A. and C. H. Peterson. 1991. Modification of animal habitat by large plants: Mechanisms by which seagrasses influence clam growth. *Oecologia* 87: 307–318.

Irlandi, E. A, W. G. Ambrose, Jr. and B. A. Orlando. 1995. Landscape ecology and the marine environment: How spatial configuration of seagrass habitat influences growth and survival of the bay scallop. *Oikos* 72: 307–313.

Irving, D. W., V. A. Breda, R. Becker and R. M. Saunders. 1988. Anatomy and composition of *Zostera marina* L. : A potential new crop. *Ecol. Food Nutrition* 20: 263–274.

Jackson, J. B. C. 1997. Reefs since Columbus. *Proc. 8th Internat. Coral Reef Symp.* 1: 97–106.

James, P. L. and K. L. Heck, Jr. 1994. The effects of habitat complexity and light intensity on ambush predation within a simulated seagrass habitat. *J. Exp. Mar. Biol. Ecol.* 176: 187–200.

Jernakoff, P. and J. Nielsen. 1998. Plant–animal associations in two species of seagrasses in Western Australia. *Aquat. Bot.* 60: 359–376.

Jernakoff, P., A. Brearley and J. Nielsen. 1996. Factors affecting grazer-epiphyte interactions in temperate seagrass meadows. *Oceanogr. Mar. Biol. Annu. Rev.* 34: 109–162.

Jones, C. G., J. H. Lawton and M. Shchak. 1994. Organisms as ecosystem engineers. *Oikos* 69: 373–386.

Josselyn, M. N., G. M. Cailliet, T. M. Niesen, R. Cowen, A. C. Hurley, J. Connor and S. Hawes. 1983. Composition, export and faunal utilization of drift vegetation in the Salt River submarine canyon. *Estuarine and Coastal Shelf Sci.* 17: 447–465.

Judge, M. L., L. D. Coen and K. L. Heck, Jr. 1993. Does *Mercenaria mercenaria* encounter elevated food levels in seagrass beds? Results from a novel technique to collect suspended food resources. *Mar. Ecol. Prog. Ser.* 92: 141–150.

Kareiva, P. 1996. Developing a predictive ecology for non-indigenous species and ecological invasions. *Ecology* 77: 1651–1652.

Keller, B. D. 1983. Coexistence of sea urchins in seagrass meadows: An experimental analysis of competition and predation. *Ecology* 64: 1581–1598.

Kenworthy, W. J. and D. E. Haunert (eds.). 1991. *The Light Requirements of Seagrasses: Proceedings of a Workshop to Examine the Capability of Water Quality Criteria, Standards and Monitoring Programs to Protect Seagrasses.* NOAA Technical Memorandum NMFS–SEFC–287.

Kenworthy, W. J. and A. C. Schwarzschild. 1998. Vertical growth and short-shoot demography of *Syringodium filiforme* in central Florida Bay. *Mar. Ecol. Prog. Ser.* 173: 25–37.

Kenworthy, W. J., J. C. Zieman and G. W. Thayer. 1982. Evidence for the influence of seagrasses on the benthic nitrogen cycle in a coastal plain estuary near Beaufort, North Carolina (USA). *Oecologia* 54: 152–158.

Kerswill, C. J. 1949. Effects of water circulation on the growth of quahogs and oysters. *J. Fish. Res. Bd. Can.* 7: 545–551.

Kikuchi, T. 1980. Faunal relationships in temperate seagrass beds. In R. C. Phillips and C. P. McRoy (eds.), *Handbook of Seagrass Biology: An Ecosystem Perspective*, pp. 153–172. Garland STPM Press, New York.

Kitting, C. L., B. Fry and M. D. Morgan. 1984. Detection of inconspicuous epiphytic algae supporting food webs in seagrass meadows. *Oecologia* 62: 145–149.

Klumpp, D. W., R. K. Howard and D. A. Pollard. 1989. Trophodynamics and nutritional ecology of seagrass communities. In Larkum, A. W. D., A. J. McComb and S. A. Shepherd (eds.), *Biology of Seagrass: A Treatise on the Biology of Seagrasses with Special Reference to the Australian Region*, pp. 153–172. Elsevier, Amsterdam.

Koch, E. W. 1994. Hydrodynamics, diffusion-boundary layers and photosynthesis of the seagrasses Thalassia *testudinum* and *Cymodocea nodosa. Mar. Biol.* 118: 767–776.

Koch, E. W. In press. Preliminary evidence on the interdependent effect of currents and porewater geochemistry on *Thalassia testudinum* Banks ex König seedlings. *Aquat. Bot.*

Koch, E. W. and G. Gust. 1999. Water flow in tide and wave dominated beds of the seagrass *Thalassia testudinum. Mar. Ecol. Prog. Ser.* 184: 63–72.

Kramer, S. H. 1990. Distribution and abundance of juvenile California halibut, *Paralichthys californicus*, in shallow waters of San Diego County. *Fish. Bull.* 174: 99–126.

Larkum, A. W. D., A. J. McComb and S. A. Shepherd (eds.). 1989. *Biology of Seagrass: A Treatise on the Biology of Seagrasses with Special Reference to the Australian Region.* Elsevier, Amsterdam.

Lemmens, J. W. T. J., G. Clapin, P. Lavery and J. Cary. 1996. Filtering capacity of seagrass meadows and other habitats of Cockburn Sound, Western Australia. *Mar. Ecol. Prog. Ser.* 143: 187–200.

Loneragan, N. R., S. E. Bunn and D. M. Kellaway. 1997. Are mangroves and seagrasses sources of organic carbon for penaeid prawns in a tropical Australian estuary? A multiple stable-isotope study. *Mar. Biol.* 130: 289–300.

Lubbers, L., W. R. Boynton and W. M. Kemp. 1990. Variations in structure of estuarine fish communities in relation to abundance of submersed vascular plants. *Mar. Ecol. Prog. Ser.* 65: 1–14.

Marbá, N. and C. M. Duarte. 1995 Coupling of seagrass (*Cymodosea nodosa*) patch dynamics to subaqueous dune migration. *J. Ecol.* 83: 381–389.

Marguillier, S., G. van de Velde, F. Dehairs, M. A. Heminga and S. Rajagopal. 1997. Trophic relationships in an interlined mangrove–seagrass ecosystem as traced by del ^{13}C and del ^{15}N. *Mar. Ecol. Prog. Ser.* 151: 115–121.

Martin, T. H., L. B. Crowder, C. F. Dumas and J. M. Burkholder. 1992. Indirect effects of fish on macrophytes in Bays Mountain Lake: Evidence for littoral trophic cascade. *Oecologia* 89: 476–481.

Matsumasa, M. S. Takeda, S. Poovachiranon and M. Murai. 1992. Distribution and shape of *Dotilla mycrtiroides* (Brachyura: Ocypodidae) burrow in the seagrass *Enhalus acoroides* zone. *Benthos Res.* 43: 1–9.

Mazella, L. and R. S. Alberte. 1986. Light adaptation and the role of autotrophic epiphytes in primary production of the temperate seagrass, *Zostera marina* L. *J. Exp. Mar. Biol. Ecol.* 100: 165–180.

McCollum, E. W., L. B. Crowder and S. A. McCollum. 1998. Complex interactions of fish, snails, and littoral zone periphyton. *Ecology* 79: 1980–1994.

McConnaughey, T. and C. P. McRoy. 1979. ^{13}C label identifies eelgrass (*Zostera marina*) carbon in an Alaskan estuarine food web. *Mar. Biol.* 53: 263–269.

McLaughlin, P. A., S. -A. F. Treat and A. Thorhaug. 1983. A restored seagrass (*Thalassia*) bed and its animal community. *Environ. Conserv.* 10: 247–254.

McNaughton, S. J. 1983. Compensatory plant growth as a response to herbivory. *Oikos* 40: 329–336.

McRoy, C. P. and C. Helfferich (eds.). 1977. *Seagrass Ecosystems: A Scientific Perspective.* Dekker, New York.

McRoy, C. P. and C. McMillan. 1977. Productivity and physiological ecology of seagrasses. In McRoy, C. P. and C. Helfferich (eds), *Seagrass Ecosystems: A Scientific Perspective*, pp. 53–88. Dekker, New York.

Menge, B. A. 1995. Indirect effects in marine rocky intertidal interaction webs: Patterns and importance. *Ecol. Monogr.* 65: 21–74.

Menge, B. A. and J. Lubchenco. 1981. Community organization in temperate and tropical rocky intertidal habitats: Prey refuges in relation to consumer pressure gradients. *Ecol. Monogr.* 51: 429–450.

Meyer, J. L., E. T. Schultz and G. S. Helfman. 1983. Fish schools: An asset to corals. *Science* 220: 1047–1049.

Montalvo, A. M., S. L. Williams, K. J. Rice, S. L. Buchmann, C. Cory, S. N. Handel, G. P. Nabhan, R. Primack and R. H. Robichaux.

1997. Restoration biology: A population biology perspective. *Res. Ecol.* 5: 277–290.

Moncrieff, C. A., M. J. Sullivan and A. E. Daehnick. 1992. Primary production dynamics in seagrass beds of Mississippi Sound: The contributions of seagrass, epiphytic algae, sand microflora and phytoplankton. *Mar. Ecol. Prog. Ser.* 87: 161–171.

Moore, K. A., H. A. Neckles and R. J. Orth. 1996. *Zostera marina* (eelgrass) growth and survival along a gradient of nutrients and turbidity in the lower Chesapeake Bay. *Mar. Ecol. Prog. Ser.* 142: 247–259.

Morgan, M. D. and C. L. Kitting. 1984. Productivity and utilization of the seagrass *Halodule wrightii* and its attached epiphytes. *Limnol. Oceanogr.* 29: 1066–1076.

Murphy, P. L. and M. S. Fonseca. 1995. Role of high and low energy seagrass beds as nursery areas for *Penaeus duorarum* in North Carolina. *Mar. Ecol. Prog. Ser.* 121: 91–98.

Nagle, J. S. 1968. Distribution of epibiota of macroepibenthic plants. *Cont. Mar. Sci.* 13: 105–144.

Neckles, H. A., R. L. Wetzel and R. J. Orth. 1993. Relative effects of nutrient enrichment and grazing on epiphyte-macrophyte (*Zostera marina* L.) dynamics. *Oecologia* 93: 285–295.

Nelson, T. A. 1997. Epiphyte–grazer interactions on *Zostera marina* (Anthophyta: Monocotyledones): Effects of density on community function. *J. Phycol.* 33: 743–752.

Nepf, H. M. and E. W. Koch. 1999. Vertical secondary flows in submersed plant-like arrays. *Limnol. Oceanogr.* 44: 1072–1080.

Nichols, P. D., D. W. Klumpp and R. B. Johns. 1983. Lipid components of the epiphyte material, suspended particulate matter and cultured bacteria from a seagrass, *Posidonia australis*, community as indicators of carbon source. *Comp. Biochem. Physiol.* 80B: 315–325.

Nichols, P. D., D. W. Klumpp and R. B. Johns. 1985. A study of food chains in seagrass communities III. Stable carbon isotope ratios. *Austral. J. Mar. Freshw. Res.* 36: 683–690.

Nichols, P. D., D. W. Klumpp and R. B. Johns. 1986. Lipid components and utilization in consumers of a seagrass community: An indication of carbon source. *Comp. Biochem. Physiol.* 83B: 103–113.

Nicotri, M. E. 1980. Factors involved in herbivore food preference. *J. Exp. Mar. Biol. Ecol.* 42: 13–26.

Ogden, J. C. 1980. Faunal relationships in Caribbean seagrass beds. In R. C. Phillips and C. P. McRoy (eds.), *A Handbook of Seagrass Biology: An Ecosystem Perspective*, pp. 173–198. Garland STPM Press, New York.

Ogden, J. C. and N. B. Ogden. 1982. A preliminary study of two representative seagrass communities in Palau, Western Caroline Islands (Micronesia). *Aquat. Bot.* 12: 229–244.

Ogden, J. C., R. A. Brown and N. Salesky. 1973. Grazing by the echinoid *Diadema antillarum* Philippi: Formation of halos around West Indian patch reefs. *Science* 182: 715–717.

Ogden, J. C., L. Robinson, K. Whitlock, H. Daganhardt and R. Cebula. 1983. Diel foraging patterns in juveline green turtles (*Chelonia*

mydas L.) in St. Croix, United States Virgin Islands. *J. Exp. Mar. Biol. Ecol.* 66: 199–205.

Oksanen, L., S. D. Fretwell, J. Arruda and P. Niemala. 1981. Exploitation ecosystems in gradients of primary productivity. *Amer. Nat.* 118: 240–261.

Ólafsson, E. B., C. H. Peterson and W. G. Ambrose Jr. 1994. Does recruitment limitation structure populations and communities of macro-invertebrates in marine soft sediments: The relative significance of pre- and post-settlement processes. *Oceanogr. Mar. Biol. Annu. Rev.* 32: 65–109.

Olesen, B. 1996. Regulation of light attenuation and eelgrass *Zostera marina* depth distribution in a Danish embayment. *Mar. Ecol. Prog. Ser.* 134: 187–194.

Orth, R. J. 1975. Destruction of eelgrass, *Zostera marina*, by the cownose ray, *Rhinoptera bonasus*, in the Chesapeake Bay. *Chesapeake Sci.* 16: 205–208.

Orth, R. J. 1977. The importance of sediment stability in seagrass communities. In B. C. Coull (ed.), *Ecology of Marine Benthos*, pp. 281–300. University of South Carolina Press, Columbia.

Orth, R. J. 1992. A perspective on plant–animal interactions in seagrasses: Physical and biological determinants influencing plant and animal abundance. In D. M. John, S. J. Hawkins and J. H Price (eds.), *Plant–Animal Interactions in the Marine Benthos*, pp. 247–164. Systematics Association Special Vol. 46. Clarendon Press, Oxford.

Orth, R. J. and K. A. Moore. 1983. Chesapeake Bay: An unprecedented decline in submerged aquatic vegetation. *Science* 222: 51–53.

Orth, R. J., K. L. Heck, Jr. and J. V. Montfrans. 1984. Faunal communities in seagrass beds: A review of the influence of plant structure and prey characteristics on predator–prey relationships. *Estuaries* 7: 339–350.

Paine, R. T. 1980. Food webs: Linkage, interaction strength and community infrastructure. *J. Anim. Ecol.* 49: 667–685.

Pangallo, R. A. and S. S. Bell. 1988. Dynamics of the aboveground and belowground structure of the seagrass *Halodule wrightii*. *Mar. Ecol. Prog. Ser.* 43: 297–301.

Parker, J. D., J. E. Duffy and R. J. Orth. In review. Experimental tests of plant diversity on epifaunal diversity and production in a temperate seagrass bed. *Ecology*.

Patriquin, D. G. 1975. 'Migration' of blowouts in seagrass beds at Barbados and Carriacou, West Indies, and its ecological and geological implications. *Aquat. Bot.* 1: 163–189.

Pedersen, M. F. and J. Borum. 1993. An annual nitrogen budget for a seagrass *Zostera marina* population. *Mar. Ecol. Prog. Ser.* 101: 169–177.

Pedersen, M. F., C. M. Duarte and J. Cebrián. 1997. Rates of changes in organic matter and nutrient stocks during seagrass *Cymodocea nodosa* colonization and stand development. *Mar. Ecol. Prog. Ser.* 159: 29–36.

Peterken, C. J. and C. A. Conacher. 1997. Seed germination and recolonisation of *Zostera capricorni* after grazing by dugongs. *Aquat. Bot.* 59: 333–340.

Petersen, C. G. J. and R. Boyson Jensen. 1911. Valuation of the sea. *Rep. Dan. Biol. Stat.* 20: 3–81.

Peterson, B. J. and K. L. Heck, Jr. 1999. The potential for suspension feeding bivalves to increase seagrass productivity. *J. Exp. Mar. Biol. Ecol.* 240: 37–52.

Peterson, C. H. 1986. Enhancement of *Mercenaria mercenaria* densities in seagrass beds: Is pattern fixed during settlement season or altered by subsequent differential survival? *Limnol. Oceanogr.* 31: 200–205.

Peterson, C. H. and B. F. Beal. 1989. Bivalve growth and higher order interactions: Importance of density, site, and time. *Ecology* 70: 1390–1404.

Peterson, C. H., H. C. Summerson and P. B. Duncan. 1984. The influence of seagrass cover on population structure and individual growth rate of a suspension-feeding bivalve, *Mercenaria mercenaria*. *J. Mar. Res.* 42: 123–138.

Phillips, R. C. 1984. *The Ecology of Eelgrass Meadows in the Pacific Northwest: A Community Profile*. U.S. Fish and Wildlife Service, FWS/OBS–84/24, Washington, DC.

Phillips, R. C., and C. P. McRoy (eds.). 1980. *Handbook of Seagrass Biology: An Ecosystem Perspective*. Garland STPM, New York.

Pihl-Baden, S. and L. Pihl. 1984. Abundance, biomass and production of motile epibenthic fauna in *Zostera marina* (L.) meadows, western Sweden. *Ophelia* 23: 65–90.

Pohl, D. G., V. M. Bricelj and Z. García-Esquivel. 1991. The eelgrass canopy: An above-bottom refuge from benthic predators for juvenile bay scallops *Argopecten irradians*. *Mar. Ecol. Prog. Ser.* 74: 47–59.

Polis, G. A. 1994. Food webs, trophic cascades and community structure. *Austral. J. Ecol.* 19: 121–136.

Polis, G. A. and D. R. Strong. 1996. Food web complexity and community dynamics. *Amer. Nat.* 147: 813–846.

Posey, M. H. 1988. Community changes associated with the spread of an introduced seagrass, *Zostera japonica*. *Ecology* 69: 974–983.

Powell, G. V. N., W. J. Kenworthy and J. W. Fourqurean. 1989. Experimental evidence for nutrient limitation of seagrass growth in a tropical estuary with restricted circulation. *Bull. Mar. Sci.* 44: 324–340.

Preen, A. R. 1995. Impacts of dugong foraging on seagrass habitats: Observational and experimental evidence for cultivation grazing. *Mar. Ecol. Prog. Ser.* 124: 201–213.

Reusch, T. B. H. 1998a. Differing effects of eelgrass *Zostera marina* on recruitment and growth of associated blue mussels *Mytilus edulis*. *Mar. Ecol. Prog. Ser.* 167: 149–153.

Reusch, T. B. H. 1998b. Native predators contribute to invasion resistance to the non-indigenous bivalve *Musculista senhousia* in southern California, USA. *Mar. Ecol. Prog. Ser.* 170: 159–168.

Reusch, T. B. H. and S. L. Williams. 1998. Variable responses of native eelgrass *Zostera marina* to a non-indigenous bivalve *Musculista senhousia*. *Oecologia* 113: 428–441.

Reusch, T. B. H. and S. L. Williams. 1999. Macrophyte canopy structure and the success of an invasive marine bivalve. *Oikos* 84: 398–416.

Reusch, T. B. H., A. R. O. Chapman and J. P. Gröger. 1994. Blue mussels *Mytilus edulis* do not interfere with eelgrass *Zostera marina* but fertilize shoot growth through biodeposition. *Mar. Ecol. Prog. Ser.* 108: 65–282.

Robbins, B. D. and S. S. Bell. 1994. Seagrass landscapes: A terrestrial approach to the marine subtidal environment. *Trends Ecol. Evol.* 9: 301–304.

Robblee, M. B., T. R. Barber, P. R. Carlson, Jr., M. J. Durako, J. W. Fourqurean, L. K. Muehlstein, D. Porter, L. A. Yarbro, R. T. Zieman and J. C. Zieman. 1991. Mass mortality of the tropical seagrass *Thalassia testudinum* in Florida Bay (USA). *Mar. Ecol. Prog. Ser.* 71: 297–299.

Roest, A. I. 1993. Ground squirrels feeding on eelgrass. *Calif. Fish Game* 79: 85–86.

Ruckelshaus, M. H., R. C. Wissmar and C. A. Simenstad. 1993. The importance of autotroph distribution to mussel growth in a well-mixed temperate estuary. *Estuaries* 16: 898–912.

Sand-Jensen, K. and J. Borum. 1991. Interactions among phytoplankton, periphyton, and macrophytes in temperate freshwaters and estuaries. *Aquat. Bot.* 41: 137–175.

Sand-Jensen, K., N. P. Revsbech and B. B. Jørgensen. 1985. Microprofiles in epiphyte communities on submerged macrophytes. *Mar. Biol.* 89: 55–62.

Sewell, A. T. 1996. Eelgrass growth and abundance in an urban estuary: The negative effects of anemone coverage. MS Thesis, San Diego State University.

Short, F. T. and S. Wyllie-Echeverria. 1996. Natural and human-induced disturbance of seagrasses. *Environ. Conserv.* 23: 17–27.

Short, F. T., A. C. Mathieson and J. I. Nelson. 1986. Recurrence of the eelgrass wasting disease at the border of New Hampshire and Maine, USA. *Mar. Ecol. Prog. Ser.* 29: 89–92.

Short, F. T., D. M. Burdick and J. E. Kaldy III. 1995. Mesocosm experiments quantify the effects of eutrophication on eelgrass, *Zostera marina*. *Limnol. Oceanogr.* 40: 740–749.

Silberstein, K., A. W. Chiffings, A. J. McComb. 1986. The loss of seagrass in Cockburn Sound, Western Australia: III. The effect of epiphytes on productivity of *Posidonia australis* Hook. *Aquat. Bot.* 24: 355–371.

Smith, I., M. S. Fonseca, J. A. Rivera and K. R. Rittmaster. 1989. Habitat value of natural versus recently transplanted eelgrass, *Zostera marina* for the bay scallop, *Argopecten irradians*. *Fish. Bull.* 87: 189–196.

Sogard, S. M. 1989. Colonization of artificial seagrass by fishes and decapod crustaceans: Importance of proximity to natural eelgrass. *J. Exp. Mar. Biol. Ecol.* 133: 15–37.

Steffe, A. S., M. Westoby and J. D. Bell. 1989. Habitat selection and diet in two species of pipefish from seagrass: Sex differences. *Mar. Ecol. Prog. Ser.* 55: 23–30.

Stephenson, R. L., F. C. Tan and K. H. Mann. 1986. Use of stable carbon isotope ratios to compare plant material and potential con-

sumers in a seagrass bed and a kelp bed in Nova Scotia, Canada. *Mar. Ecol. Prog. Ser.* 30: 1–7.

Stoner, A. W. 1980. Perception and choice of substratum by epifaunal amphipods associated with seagrasses. *Mar. Ecol. Prog. Ser.* 3: 105–111.

Stoner, A. W. 1985. *Penicillus capitatus*: An algal island for macrocrustaceans. *Mar. Ecol. Prog. Ser.* 26: 279–287.

Stoner, A. W. and F. Graham Lewis, III. 1985. The influence of quantitative and qualitative aspects of habitat complexity in tropical sea-grass meadows. *J. Exp. Mar. Biol. Ecol.* 94: 19–40.

Suchanek, T. H. 1983. Control of seagrass communities and sediment distribution by *Callianassa* (Crustacea, Thalassinidea) bioturbation. *J. Mar. Res.* 41: 281–298.

Suchanek, T. H., S. L. Williams, J. C. Ogden, D. K. Hubbard and I. P. Gill. 1985. Utilization of shallow-water seagrass detritus by Caribbean deep-sea macrofauna: Del ^{13}C evidence. *Deep-Sea Res.* 32: 201–214.

Tayasu, I., N. Shigesada, H. Mukai and H. Caswell. 1996. Predator-mediated coexistence of epiphytic grass shrimps that compete for refuges. *Ecol. Model.* 84: 1–10.

Tenore, K. R. 1975. Detrital utilization by the polychaete, *Capitella capitata*. *J. Mar. Res.* 33: 261–274.

Thayer, G. W., D. A. Wolfe and R. B. Williams. 1975. The impact of man on seagrass systems. *Amer. Sci.* 63: 289–296.

Thayer, G. W., P. L. Parker, M. W. LaCroix and B. Fry. 1978. The stable carbon isotope ratio of some components of an eelgrass, *Zostera marina*, bed. *Oecologia* 55: 1–12.

Thayer, G. W., K. A. Bjorndal, J. C. Ogden, S. L. Williams and J. C. Zieman. 1982a. Role of large herbivores in seagrass communities. *Estuaries* 7: 351–376.

Thayer, G. W., D. W. Engel and K. A. Bjorndal. 1982b. Evidence for short-circuiting of the detritus cycle of seagrass beds by the green turtle, *Chelonia mydas*. *J. Exp. Mar. Biol. Ecol.* 62: 173–183.

Thayer, G. W., M. S. Fonseca and E. Pendleton. 1984. *The Ecology of Eelgrass Meadows of the Atlantic Coast: A Community Profile*. FWS/OBS–84/02. U.S. Department of the Interior, Washington, DC.

Thistle, D., J. A. Reidenauer, R. H. Findlay and R. Waldo. 1984. An experimental investigation of enhanced harpacticoid (Copepoda) abundances around isolated seagrass shoots. *Oecologia* 63: 295–299.

Thom, R. M. 1990a. Spatial and temporal patterns in plant standing stock and primary production in a temperate seagrass system. *Bot. Mar.* 33: 497–510.

Thom, R. M. 1990b. A review of eelgrass (*Zostera marina* L.) transplanting projects in the Pacific Northwest. *Northwest Environmental Journal* 6: 121–137.

Tomasko, D. A. and C. J. Dawes. 1989a. Evidence for physiological integration between shaded and unshaded short shoots of *Thalassia testudinum*. *Mar. Ecol. Prog. Ser.* 54: 299–305.

Tomasko, D. A. and C. J. Dawes. 1989b. Effects of partial defoliation on remaining intact leaves in the seagrass *Thalassia testudinum* Banks ex Konig. *Bot. Mar.* 32: 235–240.

Tomlinson, P. B. 1974. Vegetative morphology and meristem dependence- the foundation of productivity in seagrasses. *Aquaculture* 4: 107–130.

Valentine, J. F. and K. L. Heck Jr. 1991. The role of sea urchin grazing in regulating subtropical seagrass meadows: Evidence from field manipulations in the northern Gulf of Mexico. *J. Exp. Mar. Biol. Ecol.* 154: 215–230.

Valentine, J. F. and K. L. Heck Jr. 1993. Mussels in seagrass meadows: Their influence on macroinvertebrate abundance and secondary production in the northern Gulf of Mexico. *Mar. Ecol. Prog. Ser.* 96: 63–74.

Valentine, J. F., K. L. Heck, Jr., P. Harper and M. Beck. 1994. Effects of bioturbation in controlling turtlegrass (*Thalassia testudinum* Banks *ex* König) abundance: Evidence from field enclosures and observations in the Northern Gulf of Mexico. *J. Exp. Mar. Biol. Ecol.* 178: 181–192.

Valentine, J. F., K. L. Heck Jr., J. Busby and D. Webb. 1997. Experimental evidence that herbivory increases shoot density and productivity in a subtropical turtlegrass (*Thalassia testudinum*) meadow. *Oecologia* 112: 193–200.

Vetter, E. W. 1995. Detritus-based patches of high secondary production in the nearshore benthos. *Mar. Ecol. Prog. Ser.* 120: 251–262.

Virnstein, R. W. and M. C. Curran. 1986. Colonization of artificial seagrass versus time and distance from source. *Mar. Ecol. Prog. Ser.* 29: 279–288.

Virnstein, R. W. and R. K. Howard. 1987a. Motile epifauna of marine macrophytes in the Indian River Lagoon, Florida. I. Comparisons between drift algae and three species of seagrasses. *Bull. Mar. Sci.* 41: 1–12.

Virnstein, R. W. and R. K. Howard. 1987b. Motile epifauna of marine macrophytes in the Indian River Lagoon, Florida. II. Comparisons between three species of seagrasses from adjacent beds. *Bull. Mar. Sci.* 41: 13–26.

Virnstein, R. W., P. S. Mikkelsen, K. D. Cairns and M. A. Capone. 1983. Seagrass beds versus sand bottoms: The trophic importance of their associated benthic invertebrates. *Florida Sci.* 46: 363–381.

Virnstein, R. W., W. G. Nelson, F. Graham Lewis III and R. K Howard. 1984. Latitudinal patterns in seagrass epifauna: Do patterns exist, and can they be explained? *Estuaries* 7: 310–330.

Walker, D. I. and A. J. McComb. 1992. Seagrass degradation in Australian coastal waters. *Mar. Poll. Bull.* 25: 191–195.

Wetzel, R. L. and H. A. Neckles. 1986. A model of *Zostera marina* L. photosynthesis and growth: Simulated effects of selected physical–chemical variables and biological interactions. *Aquat. Bot.* 26: 307–323.

Williams, S. L. 1988. *Thalassia testudinum* productivity and grazing by green turtles in a highly disturbed seagrass bed. *Mar. Biol.* 98: 447–455.

Williams, S. L. 1990. Experimental studies of Caribbean seagrass bed development. *Ecol. Monogr.* 60: 449–469.

Williams, S. L. and M. H. Ruckelshaus. 1993. Effects of nitrogen availability and herbivory on eelgrass (*Zostera marina*) and epiphytes. *Ecology* 74: 904–918.

Williams, S. L., V. A. Breda, T. W. Anderson and B. B. Nyden. 1985. Growth and sediment disturbances of *Caulerpa* spp. (Chlorophyta) in a submarine canyon. *Mar. Ecol. Prog. Ser.* 21: 275–281.

Williams Cowper, S. L. 1978. The drift algae community of seagrass beds in Redfish Bay, Texas. *Cont. Mar. Sci.* 21: 125–132.

Woodin, S. A., R. L. Marinelli and S. M. Lindsay. 1998. Process-specific cues for recruitment in sedimentary environments: Geochemical cues? *J. Mar. Res.* 52: 535–558.

Wooten, J. T. 1994. Predicting direct and indirect effects: An integrated approach using experiments and path analysis. *Ecology* 75: 151–165.

Worcester, S. E. 1995. Effects of eelgrass beds on advection and turbulent mixing in low current and low shoot density environments. *Mar. Ecol. Prog. Ser.* 126: 223–232.

Worthington, D. G., D. J. Ferrell, S. E. McNeill and J. D. Bell. 1992. Effects of the shoot density of seagrass on fish and decapods: Are correlations evident over large spatial scales? *Mar. Biol.* 112: 139–146.

Zieman, J. C. 1976. The ecological effects of physical damage from motor boats on turtle grass beds in southern Florida. *Aquat. Bot.* 2: 127–139.

Zieman, J. C. and R. G. Wetzel. 1990. Productivity in seagrasses: Methods and rates. In R. C. Phillips and C. P. McRoy (eds.), *Handbook of Seagrass Biology: An Ecosystem Perspective*, pp. 87–116. Garland STPM Press, New York.

Zieman, J. C. and R. T. Zieman. 1989. *The Ecology of the Seagrass Meadows of the West Coast of Florida: A Community Profile*. U.S. Fish and Wildlife Service Biological Report 85, Washington, DC.

Zieman, J. C., G. W. Thayer, M. B. Robblee and R. T. Zieman. 1979. Production and export of seagrasses from a tropical bay. In R. J. Livingston (ed.), *Biological Processes in Coastal and Marsh Systems*, pp. 21–33. Plenum Press, New York.

Zieman, J. C., R. L. Iverson and J. C. Ogden. 1984a. Herbivory effects on *Thalassia testudinum* leaf growth and nitrogen content. *Mar. Ecol. Prog. Ser.* 15: 151–158.

Zieman, J. C., S. A. Macko and A. L. Mills. 1984b. Role of seagrasses and mangroves in estuarine food webs: Temporal and spatial changes in stable isotope composition and amino acid content during decomposition. *Bull. Mar. Sci.* 35: 380–392.

Zimmerman, R., R. Gibson and J. Harrington. 1979. Herbivory and detritivory among gammaridean amphipods from a Florida seagrass community. *Mar. Biol.* 54: 41–47.

Zimmerman, R. C., D. G. Kohrs and R. S. Alberte. 1996. Top-down impact through a bottom-up mechanisms: The effect of limpet grazing on growth, productivity and carbon allocation of *Zostera marina* L. (eelgrass). *Oecologia* 107: 560–567.

chapter *13*

Rocky Subtidal Communities

Jon D. Witman and Paul K. Dayton

*T*he foundation of experimental marine ecology is based on research conducted on rocky intertidal shores (Hatton 1938; Connell 1961; Paine 1966). Studies of this ecotone between land and sea have produced important theories and conceptual models used to guide the understanding of other ecological systems. Here, we shift the focus from the intertidal fringe of the ocean (Menge and Branch, this volume) to subtidal habitats along the submerged coastlines of continents and islands.

Imagine that you were able to pull on the bedrock of the rocky intertidal zone, stretch it until it was a 20 to 100 m long span of continuous rock, and then submerge it in the ocean. You would have created a typical slope in the rocky subtidal zone. It is a vast region, orders of magnitude larger than the global area occupied by rocky intertidal habitats. Naturally, less is known about the ecology of rocky subtidal communities than their intertidal counterparts (Figure 13.1), largely because subtidal habitats are less accessible than intertidal ones. Although the number of experimental studies conducted in subtidal habitats is increasing rapidly, rocky subtidal ecology is in more of a descriptive phase than intertidal ecology, as basic patterns of community structure are unknown from many subtidal regions of the world. Nonetheless, recurring patterns of community structure, common mechanisms of community regulation and predictable gradients of environmental and biotic factors have been identified across the large landscapes of the rocky subtidal zone.

The goal of this chapter is to make the ecology of the rocky subtidal zone more accessible by comparing patterns of community structure, environmental gradients, and physical and biotic processes creating the structure of subtidal communities to the better-known rocky intertidal system. Where possible, we address the extent to which models of community or-

ganization based on intertidal systems apply to rocky subtidal communities. Because ecological processes are scale-dependent (Steele 1978; Dayton and Tegner 1984a; Wiens 1989; Jackson 1991), we divide the chapter into a consideration of local processes, for example, those occurring primarily on a spatial scale of meters to a few kilometers, and mesoscale processes (few km to hundreds of km spatial scale) influencing subtidal community structure. Of course, the separation by scale is for convenience only, as processes at both spatial scales interact to produce the dynamics of local communities. In addition to reviewing the published literature, we introduce two working hypotheses that may be conceptually significant. One predicts the relation between predation impact and the return time of environmental stress, whereas the other posits a relation between depth and the extent of connectivity among subtidal populations. We point out that these are simply hypotheses that need to be rigorously tested. Our aim here is not to propagate dogma, but rather to attempt to organize observations in a conceptual framework that points to directions for future research. In addition to the need to expand the spatial scale of subtidal research, we highlight the need for research over long time scales, as infrequent events can create persistent patterns in subtidal communities.

For the purposes of this chapter, we consider rocky subtidal habitats to be any benthic habitat composed of hard substrate from the intertidal/subtidal fringe down to the upper limit of the deep sea (200 m; Etter and Mullineaux, this volume). This includes sloping bedrock ledges, offshore banks and pinnacles, cobble and boulder fields, and rock walls in Arctic, Antarctic, temperate, and tropical regions, but excludes carbonate reefs constructed by corals (Knowlton and Jackson, this volume). Our focus is largely on communities of

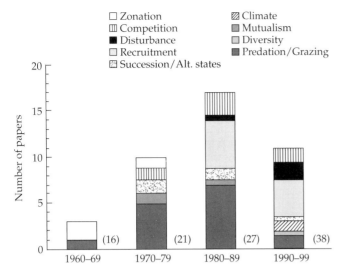

Figure 13.1 Bar graph of temporal trends in the processes studied by rocky subtidal ecologists and published in *Ecology* or *Ecological Monographs* from 1960 to 1999. The classification was made by the major processes investigated with multiple processes in a single paper represented as a proportion of 1.0. For example, in a paper on the effects of competition and predation in a subtidal community the Competition and Predation/Grazing categories would each receive a score of 0.5. Early descriptive papers on the zonation of subtidal algae or invertebrates were classified as Zonation. The number of papers published in the same decade on rocky intertidal communities appears in parentheses for comparison. Note the trend from the dominance of Predation/Grazing studies to investigations of Recruitment processes.

sessile invertebrates and plants that create the habitat of the hard substrate seafloor. In particular, we concentrate on rocky subtidal environments of open coastal habitats (e.g., nonestuarine), as these are the systems we know best.

A simple comparison of the number of papers on rocky intertidal versus subtidal communities published in *Ecology* and *Ecological Monographs* over the past 40 years reveals the dominance of intertidal contributions to marine ecology. In the early formative years (1960–1979) of marine community theory, intertidal contributions outnumbered subtidal ones by eight to one in the 1960ss and greater than 2:1 in the 1970s (Figure 13.1). After an increase in subtidal publications in the 1980s, the gap has widened to 3.3:1 over the past decade. Subtidal ecosystems are likely to remain less understood than intertidal ones well into the new millennium, but there is an urgent need to better understand how they function from both theoretical and applied standpoints, considering that most ecological impacts of fisheries, threats to marine biodiversity, and conservation efforts of marine reserves will occur in habitats below the tides (Witman and Sebens 1992; Dugan and Davis 1993; Norse 1993; Dayton et al. 1995; Steneck and Carlton, this volume).

The same review of the rocky subtidal literature revealed temporal trends in the most common processes investigated

(Figure 13.1). After an initial focus on algal or invertebrate zonation in the 1960s, investigations of consumer pressure (predation and or grazing) clearly dominated the rocky subtidal literature in these two journals for the next 20 years (1970–1989). A renewed emphasis on recruitment as a cause of patterns of distribution was reflected in the relatively large number of papers on recruitment during the 1980s (Figure 13.1). The last decade was marked by a pronounced shift from studies of consumer pressure to papers on recruitment phenomena in rocky subtidal habitats. The scarcity of papers on mutualism in rocky subtidal communities reinforces Bertness and Callaway's (1994) assertion that the influence of positive interactions on community structure has been largely overlooked. It is interesting to note that only two papers concern the influence of climatic factors on the structure of rocky subtidal communities (Figure 13.1).

PATTERNS OF COMMUNITY STRUCTURE

Two worldwide divisions of the rocky subtidal or sublittoral zone have been recognized from temperate regions: (1) the infralittoral zone, a shallow zone dominated by macroalgae that extends as deep as there is light for photosynthesis (Golikov and Scarlato 1968; Dayton 1975), and (2) the circalittoral zone, a region below the macroalgal zone dominated by sessile and mobile invertebrates (Peres and Molinier 1957; Hiscock and Mitchell 1980). The term *subtidal zone* thus refers generally to the infralittoral and circalittoral zones.

Within the infralittoral zone, the overall composition of the community is greatly influenced by the slope of the rock bottom and the nature of the substrate. Horizontal and gently sloping substrates are generally dominated by macroalgae, whereas vertical rock walls are covered by epifaunal invertebrates (Figure 13.2A; Pequenat 1964; Lundalv 1971; Velimirov et al. 1977; Witman et al. 1980; Hulbert et al. 1982; Sebens 1985, 1986; Vance 1978; Witman and Sebens 1988; Mathieson et al. 1991; Bruno and Witman 1996; Uriz et al. 1998; Witman and Grange 1998). Substrate angle is therefore a fundamental determinant of local community structure, that is, dominance by algae versus invertebrates (Figure 13.3). This is partly attributed to higher light levels on horizontal than on vertical surfaces (Witman and Cooper 1983; Baynes 1999), which create a more favorable environment for the growth and survival of macroalgae on flat and sloping rock surfaces than on vertical walls (Harris and Irons 1982; Sebens 1985). Higher sedimentation on horizontal surfaces and selection for the more shaded rock wall habitats by photonegative invertebrate larvae are other important factors contributing to differences in community structure by substrate angle (Witman and Cooper 1983). In addition, there is circumstantial evidence that vertical and overhanging wall habitats in the rocky subtidal zone are more sheltered from physical and biological disturbance than the broad expanses of habitats on horizontal to sloping rock surfaces. This hypothesis was formulated by Witman and Cooper (1983), who suggested that populations of brachiopods in horizontal rock surface habitats experienced higher rates of biological disturbance from fish predation than those on adjacent vertical cliffs (rock walls) in the Gulf of Maine. Similarly, rates of patch creation in monitored quadrats indicated that the biogenic substrata that the larval brachiopods settled on were more vulnerable to physical disturbance in horizontal than in vertical habitats. Communities on very steep or overhanging walls may be less susceptible to sea urchin predation because urchins have difficulty attaching onto some steep rock slopes encrusted by invertebrates (Sebens 1985). Horizontal versus vertical comparisons weren't the focus of Vance's (1988) long-term studies of epifaunal communities off southern California (15 m depth), but his conclusion that predation and disturbance played a minor role in determining the high taxonomic diversity there is in line with results from the Gulf of Maine. Cliffs on land have been similarly considered as refuges from natural and anthropogenic disturbance for the plant communities inhabiting them (Larson et al. 1999a). These terrestrial rock walls support ancient trees and apparently represent the largest tract of undisturbed old growth forest east of the Mississippi (Larson et al. 1999b). More experimental work needs to be conducted in the subtidal zone, however, to evaluate the hypothesis that vertical wall communities generally experience lower levels of disturbance than those on horizontal substrata.

The distribution and abundance of species in this template of community structure based on substrate angle is modified by grazing, predation, competition, recruitment, disturbance, water flow, and sedimentation, which are discussed in greater detail following. Sessile invertebrates do occur on nonvertical substrates, as horizontal and gently sloping rock surfaces are encrusted by colonial invertebrates (Jackson 1977; Estes and Duggins 1995) and aggregations of solitary invertebrates such as mussels (Paine 1976a; Velimirov et al. 1977), but the large differences in invertebrate cover between horizontal and vertical surfaces is one of the most striking and general features of rocky subtidal communities worldwide. In temperate regions, the abundance of sessile invertebrates on horizontal-sloping substrata increases with depth as the abundance of erect and turfing macroalgae decreases. This "depth emergence" phenomenon has been quantified from sites in the Gulf of Maine where the density of brachiopods on horizontal surfaces doubled between 33 and 42 m (Witman et al. 1980; Hulbert et al. 1982; Witman and Cooper 1983) and the percent cover of sponges increased fourfold between 28 and 45 m (Witman and Sebens 1988) One effect of the depth emergence phenomenon is that differences in invertebrate community structure on horizontal and vertical rock surfaces diminish with depth. In this depth range (> 30 m) of the circalittoral zone, predation (Witman and Cooper 1983; Witman 1998), recruitment (Sebens et al. 1988), flow (Leichter and Witman 1997), and combined effects of flow, sedimentation, and spatial competition (Genovese 1996; Genovese and Witman 1999) all play important roles in determin-

ing community differences over small spatial scales. Heterogeneous patterns of substrate distribution such as those created by cobble and boulder fields at any depth impose a patch structure on epifaunal communities characterized by smaller-scale spatial variability than on continuous expanses of bedrock.

Because kelp are largely absent from the tropics (Luning 1985; Dayton 1985) and other erect macroalgae are less abundant in general, the ecotone between the infralittoral and circalittoral zone is less conspicuous in tropical rocky subtidal communities than in temperate ones (Figure 13.2B). On rocky subtidal slopes in the tropics, such as on rock walls in the eastern Caribbean islands, on rock islands of Palau, or in the granitic islands of the Seychelles, the high light environments of horizontal-sloping surfaces tend to be dominated by scleractinian corals and octocorals, rather than kelp of the temperate zone, with encrusting invertebrates more common on vertical surfaces. Ahermatypic corals such those in the genus *Tubastrea* are a typical component of rock wall communities in the tropics (Witman 1992).

Large brown algae in the order Laminariales and Fucales are often the community dominants of the infralittoral zone in temperate regions down to 10–25 m depth (Neushel 1967; Kain 1969; Shepard and Womersley 1970; North 1971; Dayton 1975, 1985; Velimirov et al. 1977; Duggins 1980; Field et al. 1980; Choat and Schiel 1982; Santileces and Ojeda 1984; Witman 1985, 1987; Johnson and Mann 1988; Mathieson et al. 1991; Bologna and Steneck 1993). Kelp, if present, create an upper canopy, with an understory of foliose red and green algae (Figure 13.3). The scale of the kelp canopy varies from tall forests of vegetation in beds of giant kelp, *Macrocystis pyrifera*, *Nereocystis lutkeana,* or *Ecklonia maxima*, extending 5 to 20 m above the bottom to low beds of *Laminaria* and *Agarum,* a meter or less tall (Figures 13.2, 13.3). Noncanopy (prostate) kelps are also an important component of Pacific and Atlantic kelp beds. Much of the primary space on the rocks in the kelp-dominated zone is covered by crustose coralline algae (Sears and Cooper 1978; Steneck 1986). Macroalgae can reduce the abundance of large sessile invertebrates on horizontal surfaces either via preemptive or interference competition for space (Velimirov and Griffiths 1979; Witman 1987). Superior competitive ability of macroalgae on nonvertical rocky surfaces may displace sessile invertebrates to rock walls and is likely a key factor contributing to the disjunct distribution of macroalgae and invertebrates by substrate angle in the temperate zone. Kelps may have the opposite effect of increasing the abundance of small mobile invertebrates on horizontal surfaces because the interstices of kelp holdfasts are inhabited by abundant polychaetes, brittle stars, and gastropods (Moore 1973; Velimirov et al. 1977).

The sessile epifauna of the circalittoral zone is largely composed of suspension feeding invertebrates such as sponges, anthozoans, octocorals, gorgonians, bryozoans, ascidians, brachiopods, sea cucumbers, and ahermatypic corals (Figure 13.3; Zenkevitch 1963; Dayton et al. 1974; Konnecker 1977;

(A) Gulf of Maine

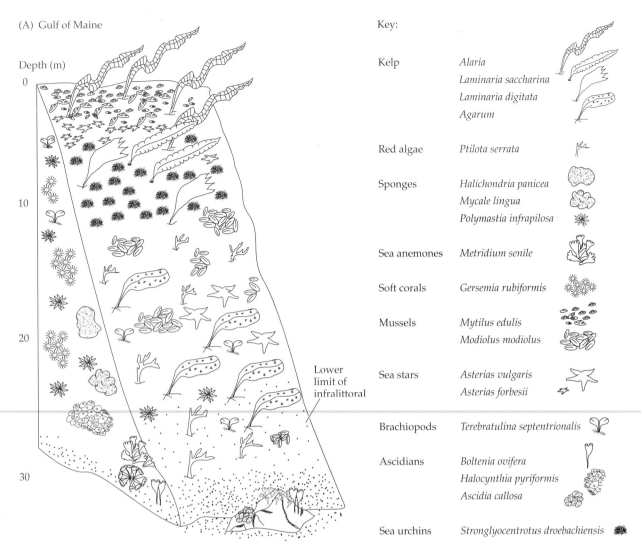

Key:

Kelp	*Alaria*
	Laminaria saccharina
	Laminaria digitata
	Agarum
Red algae	*Ptilota serrata*
Sponges	*Halichondria panicea*
	Mycale lingua
	Polymastia infrapilosa
Sea anemones	*Metridium senile*
Soft corals	*Gersemia rubiformis*
Mussels	*Mytilus edulis*
	Modiolus modiolus
Sea stars	*Asterias vulgaris*
	Asterias forbesii
Brachiopods	*Terebratulina septentrionalis*
Ascidians	*Boltenia ovifera*
	Halocynthia pyriformis
	Ascidia callosa
Sea urchins	*Stronglyocentrotus droebachiensis*

Figure 13.2 A comparison of rocky subtidal zonation in the cold temperate zone versus the tropics. (A) A typical wave-exposed site in the Gulf of Maine, such as Murray Rock, Monhegan Island, or Boone Island, showing communities on a sloping rock shelf (front slope) versus a vertical rock wall (left-side diagram) down to a depth of 33 m. The lower limit of the algal dominated infralittoral zone extends to ~ 25 m, as indicated by shotgun kelp *Agarum cribosum* on the slope. A shallow bed of laminarian kelp is truncated at about 10–15 m depth by sea urchin grazing (see Figure 13.3). Dense carpets of blue mussel recruits can cover the substrate down to ~ 5 m depth. Not shown in the upper 10 m of the slope community is an understory of red algal turf. Beds of horse mussels, *Modiolus modiolus*, are a conspicuous feature of slopes at 10–20 m depth. Note that macroalgae are absent from vertical rock walls, which are covered by soft corals, sponges, ascidians, and aggregations of the sea anemone *Metridium senile* in the deeper zone. (B) Subtidal zonation at a wave-exposed side of an island in the Galapagos, such as Roca Sin Nombre or

Hiscock and Mitchell 1980; Sebens 1986; Witman and Sebens 1988). The sessile invertebrates create the vertical relief of the circalittoral zone in addition to occupying primary space on the substratum. Although not as tall as kelp forests, the major vertical structure of the deep subtidal community may consist of trees and fans of cnidaria such as gorgonians, antipatharians, and hydrocorals and flexible aggregations of anemones, in addition to beds of stalked ascidians and mounding and finger-shaped sponges (Figures 13.2, 13.3). Erect species creating vertical habitat structure and aggregating species defining the horizontal dimensions of patches are examples of foundation species (*sensu* Dayton 1972). Subtidal foundation species play important roles as habitat modifiers principally by altering patterns of water movement (Jackson and Winant 1983; Patterson 1984; Eckman et al. 1989), which subsequently influences food and larval supply (Genin et al. 1986; Eckman and Duggins 1991; Wildish and Kristmanson 1997; Gill and Coma 1998) and by providing refuges from predation (Witman 1985; Stachowicz and Hay 1999; Bruno and Bertness, this volume).

(B) Galapagos

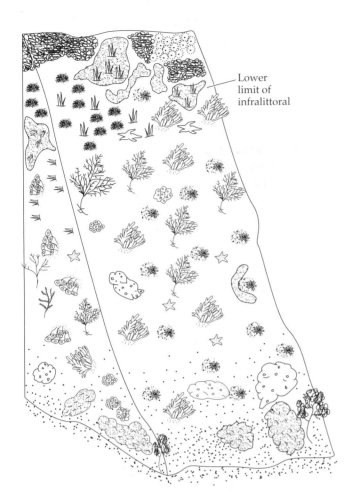

Lower limit of infralittoral

Key:

Algae	Red algal turf
Sponges	Red encrusting sponge
Sea anemones	*Anthopleura sp.*
Hydroids	*Lytocarpus sp.*
Gorgonians	*Pacifigorgia sp.*
	Muricea californica
	Lophogorgia sp.
Black corals	*Antipathes panamaensis*
	Antipathes galapagensis
Corals	*Tubastrea sp.*
Barnacles	*Megabalanus galapaganus*
	Balanus trigonus
Sea urchins	*Eucidaris thouarsii*
	Tripneustes depressus
Sea star	*Nidorellia armata*
Ascidians	*Pyura sp.*
	Leptoclinides sp.

Daphne Minor. The infralittoral zone is much shallower in the tropics, here ending at ~ 5 m depth. Note that sea fans (gorgonians) and black corals have replaced the kelp of the temperate subtidal—the major species forming the vertical structure of the community. Boring sea urchins (*Eucidaris*) increase the spatial complexity of the substrate by excavating holes on both sloping and shelves and vertical rock walls. Small aggregations of the ahermatypic coral *Tubastrea* sp. are more abundant on vertical than on horizontal-sloping rock faces. In general, differences in community structure between horizontal-sloping rock surfaces and vertical rock walls tend to be less conspicuous in the tropical rocky subtidal. Barnacles are an important component of rocky subtidal communities in the Galapagos, where they are preyed on by fish, crabs, and lobsters (not to scale). Depth variation in the physical and biological factors shaping community structure at sites like these is shown in Figures 13.4 and 13.7.

Although zonation is usually described along a vertical gradient such as elevation, there is considerable variation in the abundance of foundation species such as mussels, kelp, ascidians, and gorgonians in the horizontal dimension, either parallel to shore or along an isobath at an offshore reef (Velimirov et al. 1977; Dayton et al. 1984; Underwood et al. 1991; Smith and Witman 1999). The scale of the along isobath transition from one major habitat patch to another varies from several meters for sessile invertebrates and small kelp patches up to tens of kilometers for large kelp beds. Thus, rocky subtidal communities may be viewed as a mosaic of habitat patches that changes somewhat predictably with depth.

Rocky subtidal zonation has been described from South Africa (Field et al. 1980), New Zealand (Grange et al. 1981; Choat and Schiel 1982; Witman and Grange 1998; Smith 1999), Chile (Santileces 1991), the Northeast Pacific (Neushel 1967), the Sea of Japan (Golikov and Scarlato 1968), and the Northeast (Earll and Erwin 1983) and Northwest Atlantic (Witman 1985, 1987; Mathieson et al. 1991). We take a conceptual approach here and attempt to synthesize information about local and mesoscale processes causing patterns of subtidal community structure.

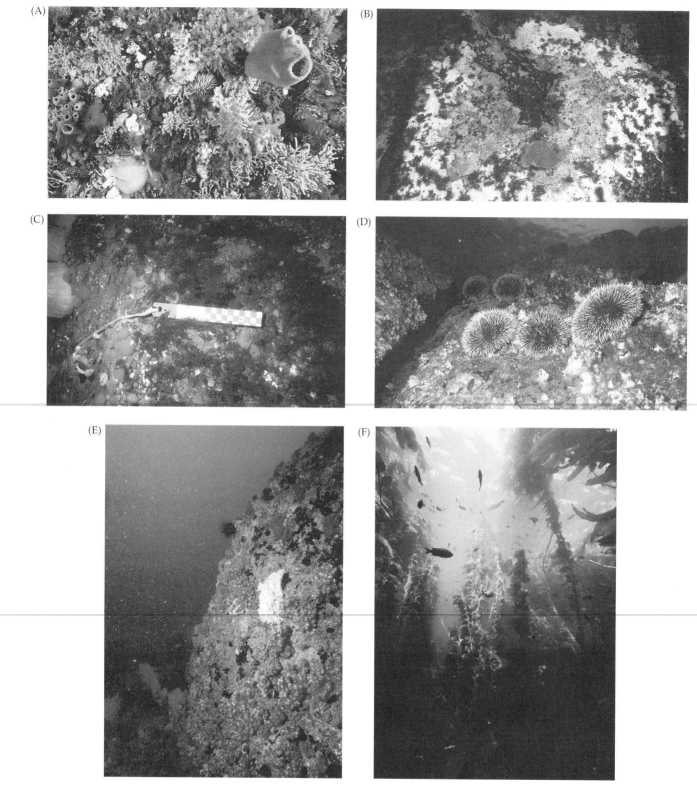

Figure 13.3 Some representative rocky subtidal communities. (A) A diverse, space-limited community of sponges, anemones, gorgonians, and ascidians on a rock wall at 12 m depth off the Cape Peninsula, South Africa. (B) The effects of kelp whiplash (*Agarum cribosum*; see Figure 13.2A) on the sponge *Halichondria*, in the Gulf of Maine. Kelp is in the center of the area lacking sponge cover. (C) The abrupt transition in community structure at the junction of horizontal and vertical substrata. Horizontal-sloping surfaces are dominated by red algae, whereas vertical walls are dominated by sessile invertebrates including ascidians and sea anemones. (D) Sea urchins (*Tripneustes*) clearing epifaunal invertebrates at 7 m depth, Roca Gordon, Galapagos Islands (see the data in Figure 13.8). (E) Rock slope at 12–15 m depth in the Seychelles Islands (lower left) is covered by soft corals (*Nepthyea, Dendronepthyea*) and the ahermatypic coral *Tubastrea*. (Photos by J. Witman.) (F) A forest of giant kelp, *Macrocystis pyrifera*, off southern California. (Photo by E. Hanauer.)

LOCAL SCALE PROCESSES

Environmental Gradients

As shown in Figure 13.4, the physical regime shows striking variation above and below mean low water on rocky shores.

TEMPERATURE. Steep thermal gradients occur from high to low elevations in the rocky intertidal zone, where high thermal stress at mid to high intertidal elevations are a major source of mortality for barnacles (Connell 1961; Wethey 1984) and snails (Garrity and Levings 1981; Etter 1988). Heat stress is diminished in the low intertidal due to more frequent tidal immersion, inundation by waves (Bustamente et al. 1997), and covering by macroalgae (Bertness et al. 1999) low on the rocky shore.

Temperature variability in the subtidal zone is governed by the interaction between solar warming of surface waters and the degree of vertical mixing of cold, deeper waters (Svedrup et al. 1942). Mixing is dependent on the strength of tides, wind, and the density stratification of the water column. A thermocline of decreasing temperature with depth is created as the surface of the ocean is warmed by the sun. The steepness of the thermocline and its fluctuations determine the magnitude of temperature variation in the subtidal zone and, consequently, thermal stress to algae and invertebrates (Figures 13.4, 13.5). The depth of the thermocline varies seasonally (months) and over shorter time periods due to tidal phenomena (hours). Below the surface, from the intertidal/subtidal fringe down to a depth of 2 m and beyond, the water column is well mixed and often turbulent due to wave action (Riedl 1970). Such turbulent mixing generally prevents shallow waters in the temperate subtidal from heating to stressful levels except during El Niño events (Figure 13.5; Glynn 1988).

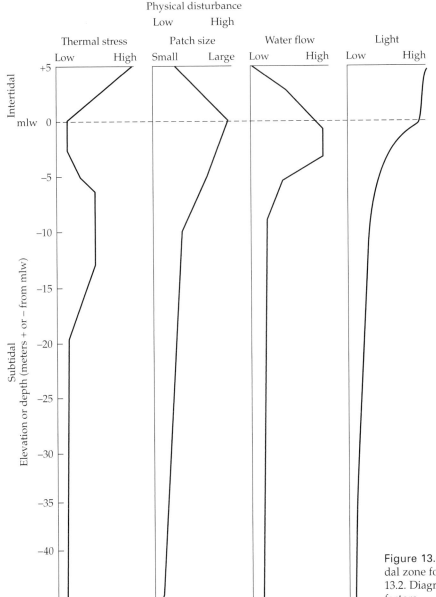

Figure 13.4 Environmental gradients in the rocky subtidal zone for typical wave-exposed sites depicted in Figure 13.2. Diagram shows the relative levels of parameters or factors.

Figure 13.5 Representative temperature profiles for the water column overlying wave-exposed rocky subtidal sites in the Gulf of Maine and in the Galapagos. Profile (A), taken off Machias Seal Island in August 1994, shows a steep thermocline between the surface and 13 m depth. Profiles in (B) were conducted at Daphne Minor (solid line) and Roca Gordon sites in May 1999. Note shallow layer of warm water down to 2–5 m and evidence of a smaller thermocline beginning at 20–23 m. Rocky subtidal organisms may be thermally stressed in the shallow zone (~ 3 to 18 m depth) when the thermocline is upwelled and downwelled. In the tropics, deeper dwelling organisms (i.e., 15–25 m) may be subjected to cold-water stress when the deep thermocline is upwelled.

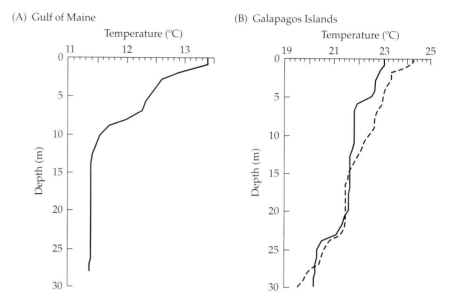

In temperate seas, abrupt thermoclines develop as the water column is stratified from late spring–autumn. The thermocline is located in the shallow zone (approximately 3–12 m depth) of coastal regions (Figures 13.4, 13.5). Large temperature variation may occur in this depth range as the thermocline is upwelled or downwelled. Consequently, thermal stress may increase along the 3–12 m depth range in temperate rocky subtidal habitats along open coasts (Figures 13.4, 13.5). Thermal stress is unlikely at depths below the thermocline except in internal wave regimes where large (10°C) temperature fluctuations occur at 28–35 m depth over short time periods (10 min.; Witman et al. 1993) or during periods of intense upwelling. We suggest that the typical pattern for open coastlines is, therefore, decreasing thermal stress with depth below the lower boundary of the thermocline (Figure 13.4). Because strong tidal mixing can prevent thermal stratification of the water column, the pattern shown in Figure 13.4 would be less common in tidal straits and estuaries. Representative temperature profiles of the water column overlying a tropical rocky subtidal region such as the Galapagos Islands shows a thin lens of warm water at the surface and shallow thermoclines between 1–15 m depth (Figure 13.5). Temperature is often nearly isothermal over mid-depths with a second thermocline demarcating the boundary between deep, cool water and the warmer mid-water column. Benthic organisms living at warm shallow depths in the tropical rocky subtidal may be thermally stressed when this deep (> 23 m), cool water is upwelled. In the Galapagos, Glynn and Wellington (1983) observed a rapid upwelling of the thermocline from 21 m to 11 m depth in 10 minutes. Shepard et al. (1992) noted an inverse relation between the distribution of soft corals and upwelling regions in the Arabian Sea, suggesting that cool, upwelled water may limit their ability to dominate hard substrata. On the western coast of South Africa, water temperature can drop 9°C in 7 hours during upwelling of the Benguela current (Branch and Branch 1981), resulting in mass mortalities of fish in some cases. It's possible that benthic invertebrates are also negatively impacted by rapid upwelling of cold water in the rocky subtidal off the west coast of South Africa.

Thermoclines are additionally important to benthic plants and sessile invertebrates because they affect the supply of nutrients and phytoplankton. It is a central tenant of oceanography that the thermocline tends to restrict the diffusion of cooler nutrient-rich water into the photosynthetic zone (Mann and Lazier 1996). Kelps are especially dependent on the availability of nutrients, especially nitrogen. Indeed, nutrients are a key variable controlling the large-scale biogeography of kelps, and there are very strong inverse correlations between temperature and nutrients (Waldron and Probyn 1992; Dayton et al. 1999). Thus, in many systems, physical mechanisms such as breaking internal waves (Zimmerman and Kremer 1984) and wind-driven upwelling (Branch and Griffiths 1988) that bring the nutrients locked below the thermocline up into the kelp habitat are important to the kelp populations. Where upwelling is a predictable, seasonal feature of the environment, kelp ecosystems tend to be much less limited by nutrients, and in such systems biological interactions can be very important to the structure of the kelp populations (Dayton 1985; Chapman 1986; Branch and Griffiths 1988; Luning and Asmus 1991). The thermocline also influences phytoplankton distributions, as maximum concentrations of phytoplankton are often greatest at the base of the thermocline in temperate seas (Cullen 1982). The influence of these Subsurface Chlorophyll Maximum (SCM) layers on the rocky subtidal benthos is little studied, but this topic deserves more attention, as SCMs can increase the growth rates of benthic suspension feeders (Witman et al. 2000) by increasing the supply of phytoplankton to the bottom (Witman et al. 1993).

PHYSICAL DISTURBANCE: VARIATION ALONG DEPTH GRADIENTS. Physical disturbance from wave action or wave-borne projectiles peaks at the low tide fringe of the rocky intertidal (Figure

13.4; Dayton 1971; Paine and Levin 1981; Shanks and Wright 1986), where the greatest amount of patch space is opened up (Paine and Levin 1981; Connell and Keough 1985). The highest physical disturbance is created by breaking waves in the intertidal and shallow subtidal zones (Figure 13.4; Denny 1995). Such disturbance gradually decreases with depth from the turbulent surface of the ocean because wave energy decreases with depth (Denny 1988). Disturbance-produced patches in the Gulf of Maine rocky subtidal were an order of magnitude larger at 8 m than at 45 m (Witman 1998). Here, the largest patches (1.0–1.5 m^{-2} area) were created by boulders flipped during the 1978 "groundhog gale" down to a depth of 8 m at the Isles of Shoals. Much smaller patches (order of 0.03 m^{-2} area) are routinely created in this depth range in the Gulf of Maine when kelp and horse mussels overgrown by kelp are dislodged during storms (Witman 1987). Further evidence of decreasing physical disturbance with depth comes from an unusually severe storm that caused catastrophic mortality of kelp and sessile invertebrates down to a 22 m depth off southern California in 1988 (Dayton et al. 1989). The physical disturbance was far more severe at the 8 m site where the algal and invertebrate communities were sandblasted off the conglomerate bedrock bottom, than at the 22 m site (Dayton et al. 1989). In tropical rock wall communities, the amount of patch space generated by hurricanes predictably decreased from 4 to 12 m depth after Hurricane Gilbert, but did not decrease one year later following Hurricane Hugo (Witman 1992). This nonintuitive result occurred because species with "disturbance vulnerable" high drag morphologies, such as erect colonies of fire coral, mound-shaped sponges, and protruding gorgonians, were dislodged from the shallow site during the first hurricane and hadn't regrown by the time that the "hurricane of the century" (Hugo) struck 53 weeks later (Witman 1992).

Scouring by ice is a major agent of physical disturbance in polar benthic communities that also decreases with depth, although ice disturbance effects often extend deeper into the subtidal than wave-induced disturbance (Dayton et al. 1969; Keats et al. 1985; Dayton 1989; Conlan et al. 1998; Heine 1989). In the Antarctic, disturbance from anchor ice creates huge barren areas (km^2) from the shallow subtidal down to a depth of 33 m that are devoid of attached macrofauna (Dayton et al. 1969). In addition to scouring, erect invertebrates in this depth zone are frozen into the anchor ice and floated off the substrate (Dayton et al. 1969; Dayton 1989). Iceberg impact creates patches several m^{-2} area on rock walls in the South Shetland Islands, Antarctica (F. Smith, personal communication), and likely creates far larger patches like those over 30 m in diameter recently reported from soft substrate habitats in the Antarctic (Peck et al. 2000). Ice disturbance apparently impacts smaller areas of rocky subtidal communities in the Arctic where it gouges 10–30 m^2 areas of ledge and restricts the distribution of kelp (*Laminaria, Agarum, Alaria*) to depressions in the rock slope or to depths beyond 12 m, which is below the influence of ice (Heine 1989). One community pattern associated with frequent and intense disturbance from ice is that the shallow polar habitats are kept in

early stages of succession and at low levels of species diversity (Dayton et al. 1969; Keats et al. 1985; Heine 1989; Dayton et al. 1994).

Overall, the general trend of decreasing disturbance from storms, landslides, and lava flows with depth suggests that deep subtidal communities have greater persistence stability (numerical constancy) than shallow communities that are frequently interrupted by physical disturbance. This was the case with horse mussel populations along an 8–30 m depth gradient in the northwest Atlantic where the 18 and 30 m populations experienced no mortality from the storm dislodgment that greatly impacted shallow (8 m) populations over a five-year period (Witman 1985). Other support for greater persistence stability of deep populations comes from solitary ascidians monitored for over a decade at sites off Sweden (Svane 1984). Deep sponge- dominated communities in the Mediterranean showed similar persistence over the long term (e.g., > 5 yrs.; Pansini and Prozato 1990). Turnover of space in the lower physical disturbance regimes of the deep rocky subtidal occurs when sessile species are removed by consumers, disease, or natural mortality (Dayton et al. 1974; Witman 1998; Smith 1999). Although the persistence stability of deep (≥ 30 m) communities tends to be greater than shallow (< 12 m) ones, once disturbed, deep communities probably take longer to recover than shallow ones, due to comparatively lower recruitment and growth rates in deep subtidal habitats (see following).

PHYSICAL DISTURBANCE AND SUBTIDAL PATCH DYNAMICS. At any depth, the trajectory of colonization and recovery of disturbance-produced patches may be predicted by theory. Connell and Keough (1985) and Sousa (1985) defined two types of disturbances based on the spatial extent of the disturbance as it relates to recolonization and recovery. Type I disturbances result in the death of some residents, leaving a patch bounded by survivors usually of the same assemblage. Type II disturbances are much larger and result in patches isolated from existing assemblages. Recovery from Type I disturbances relies on vegetative growth and asexual budding, some settlement from fast-growing opportunistic species (which may soon disappear), short-lived larvae from adjacent areas, longlived from distant areas, and immigration of mobile adults. Type II disturbances are very large relative to the local dispersal, and they select for opportunistic, dispersing species, both adults and larvae. Type II succession is more stochastic because it depends on long-distance dispersal of species that tend to be highly variable over time. Dislodged adults or fragments may be transported for unusually long distances during storms to colonize Type II patches (Peck et al., 2000).

Predictions about the mode of recolonization for Type I patches (Connell and Keough 1985), although logical, may not always obtain for communities of epifaunal invertebrates in the subtidal zone. For example, colonization of small Type I (20–40 cm^2) patches created by nudibranch predation on sea anemones and natural mortality of sponges in deep (30 m) rock wall communities in the Gulf of Maine occurred by planktonic recruitment of bryozoans, serpulid polychaetes, and ascidians (Witman 1998). Over a three-year period, none of the patches were closed by vegetative encroachment of the thinly encrusting sponge, *Hymedesmia*, sp. 3, which surrounded the patches and dominated the wall community (Witman and Sebens 1990; Witman 1998). This specific example raises the issue that Type I patches may not be closed by asexual spread as predicted (Connell and Keough 1985) when the patch is surrounded by slow-growing species, such as sponges (Ayling 1983). Linear Markov models are being used to simulate the dynamics of these deep communities of sponges, anemones, bryozoans, and ascidians in the Gulf of Maine (Hill et al., in preparation). The model, which was constructed by following transitions of 13 species in a ten-year time series, reveals that patch succession is primarily controlled by colonization and that species diversity is most sensitive to changes from a sponge-dominated state (Hill et al., in preparation).

Ecologists have long understood the importance of local (usually Type I) disturbances in creating mosaics of patches in different successional stages. At the same time, much more massive disturbances such as hurricanes (Woodley et al. 1981), landslides, or other large-scale catastrophes appear to have much more general impacts by overwhelming the quilt work of small-scale patches. Lava flows and landslides are such catastrophic disturbances that create large Type II patches in the rocky subtidal zone. For land-based volcanoes, this extreme form of physical disturbance undoubtedly decreases along the depth gradient in places such as Iceland and the Galapagos Islands. Landslides are a very important disturbance to rocky subtidal communities in New Zealand fiords (K. Grange, personal communication; Smith and Witman 1999), along the coast of central California (Konar and Roberts 1996), and in southeast Alaska (D. Duggins, personal communication). One landslide in Doubtful Sound, New Zealand, impacted a broad area approximately 300 m across and at least 20 m deep on vertical walls (F. Smith and J. Witman, unpublished observations). There was a lot of small-scale heterogeneity within the large landslide patch, however, as large scoured areas were interspersed with smaller debris and sediment-covered outcrops protruding from the walls. We are unaware of any tests of Connell and Keogh's (1985) predictions about Type II patch colonization for rocky subtidal communities.

The different types of large-scale physical disturbances in California kelp forests include major El Niños that are associated with severe nutrient depletions, which selectively kill the dominant *Macrocystis pyrifera* (Figure 13.3), possibly allowing the expansion of subdominant understory species, and storms of various intensities that have species-specific impacts on kelp species. The relative impacts of these disturbances were evaluated in southern California by Dayton et al. (1992) after a decade that included one of the strongest El Niños of the century and perhaps the strongest storm in 200 years. They asked whether the large-scale episodic events are more important than the more typical biological processes

structuring the community. They found that the massive disturbances disrupted the patch structure, and the succession was disrupted by lag effects such as the preemption of space by ephemeral algae and the loss of drift algae that normally feeds sea urchins with subsequent outbreaks of sea urchin fronts that overgrazed all the algae, resulting in larger denuded patches. The temporary loss of small fish that eat crustacea resulted in outbreaks of amphipod grazing. Despite these extreme perturbations, original marked patches recovered within a few months. The implication was that the kelp patches were extremely resilient and that residual effects from surviving gametophytes and tiny sporophytes were very important. Although this conclusion is true, a strong La Niña and oceanographic climate shift that involved the strengthening of the nutrient-rich California current followed these disturbances (Dayton et al. 1999). One component of La Niña is that there tends to be more nutrients in the coastal surface waters; these increased nutrients selectively enhanced the *Macrocystis* surface canopy, and this resulted in a much stronger absorption of the light that once went to the bottom. Thus, after surviving all the storms, grazing, and nutrient stress of the El Niño, a simple increase in nutrients allowed the expression of competitive dominance that finally eliminated the patch structure. Although we have discussed the roles of episodic disturbance, episodic, "bottom-up" nutrient forcing can result in rare competitive impacts that might last as long as the disturbance-driven changes (Dayton et al. 1999).

Many of these disturbance-mediated patterns also occur in other kelp forests around the world, but another type of interaction occurs in the Northwest Atlantic, where Witman (1987) described a situation in wave-exposed habitats that included a three-way relationship between kelps, sea urchins, and mussels in which the mussels furnish important substratum for the kelps, but are vulnerable to wave action. A positive interaction between the horse mussels and sea urchins enabled the mussels to coexist with kelp in the shallow zone (Witman 1987). The interaction was a facultative mutualism where the mussel beds provided a refuge from predation for the urchins and the urchins grazed the kelp off mussels, decreasing their mortality from dislodgment. In a more protected northwest Atlantic habitat, Johnson and Mann (1988) report a more ephemeral situation with a strong competitive dominant *Laminaria longicruris* that tends to be short lived, resulting in periodic outbreaks rather than large-scale competitive dominance, as was found for *Macrocystis*. Unfortunately, we lack data on patch structure and patch longevity for this system, especially as they relate to environmental heterogeneity in space and time.

FLOW. It was recognized early on that water movement played a paramount role in rocky shore ecology (Kitching 1939; Kitching 1941; Kitching et al. 1952). Pequenat (1964) was one of the first to recognize the important influence of flow on the subtidal zonation of epifaunal invertebrates. He found that the shallow tops (9–12 m depth) of siltstone reefs off southern California supported the highest densities of invertebrates, suggesting that this pattern was due to a high availability of suspended food at the reef top, where flow was highest. Some of Pequenat's insights into the population and community effects of flow-enhanced food supply are still being tested in the subtidal (Hiscock 1983, 1985; Sebens 1984; Genin et al. 1986; Duggins 1988; Eckman et al. 1989; Lesser et al. 1994; Leichter and Witman 1997; Genovese and Witman 1999) and in the low intertidal zone (Sanford et al. 1994; Leonard et al. 1998). Riedl (1971) classified the many influences of water movement on benthic organisms into primary limiting effects that directly impact the survival of organisms exposed to high hydrodynamic forces and secondary limiting effects involving the transport of nutrients, gases, and food. Tertiary effects of water movement are associated with the movement of the benthic substrate (i.e., sediment and rock) and the influence of flow on predation and grazing. Riedl (1971) asserted that the premier role of flow is as a transport medium, which is likely true, as flow-mediated transport influences benthos across a broad spectrum of spatial scales. Many studies since have underscored the importance of primary flow effects, as large hydrodynamic forces affect the distribution of benthos by dislodging mussels and other invertebrates (Paine and Levin 1981; Witman and Suchanek 1984; Denny et al. 1985; Witman 1987) and kelp (Dayton 1975; Field et al. 1980). In a particularly illuminating book chapter, Hiscock (1983) outlined many of the beneficial and antagonistic effects of flow on subtidal communities in the British Isles. Flow effects on suspension feeding invertebrates in particular are treated extensively in a book by Wildish and Kristmanson (1997).

The velocity of flowing water decreases with depth in the rocky subtidal on wave-exposed open coasts from the surge zone at the intertidal–subtidal fringe where maximal velocities may exceed 11.0 m · s^{-1} (Denny et al. 1985) and 3.0 m · s^{-1} at 1–3 m depth (Figure 13.6; Hiscock 1983; Alfaro 1994; J. Witman and C. Siddon, unpublished data). Water movement in the shallowest subtidal is turbulent, consisting of strong shoreward and seaward flows superimposed on alongshore currents (Riedl 1971; Denny 1988; Mann and Lazier 1996). Hiscock (1976) described a pronounced decrease in

wave-induced water velocity as a function of depth to 60 m by estimating near-bed (bottom) velocity from surface velocity data. Water velocity decreased by a factor of 30 between 5 and 60 m depth for large swells and by a factor of 25 between 5 and 30 m depth for a low swells (~ 0.3 m high; Hiscock 1976). In the shallow subtidal of the Gulf of Maine, maximum

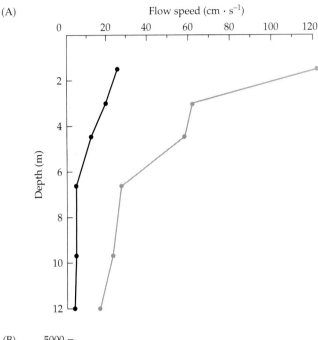

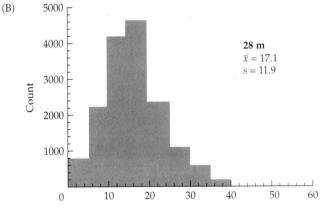

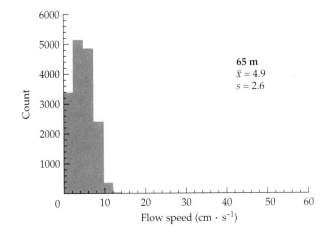

Figure **13.6** Depth variation in flow speed at Halfway Rock, Gulf of Maine. Solid circles are mean values of 5 min. recordings sampling at 10 hertz with an acoustic flow probe (Sontek, model ADV). Shaded circles connected by dotted lines represent the maximum flow speeds. Note decreasing mean and maximum flow speed with depth. Probe head was positioned 3 centimeters above the rock bottom. (B) A 3.5-fold increase in average free-stream flow speed (0.5 m above the substrate) at the peak (28 m depth) versus the lower slope (65 m depth) of Ammen Rock Pinnacle, central Gulf of Maine. This pattern of increased flow over topographically high regions of hard substrate is typical of steep rock slopes, banks, and fjord sills. Flow recorded by electromagnetic current meters (InterOcean model S4) at 1 hertz for 24 hours in August 1993. Means ($\bar{x}$) and standard deviations (s) are reported.

velocities of 1.7 to 3.8 m · s⁻¹ were estimated (Witman 1987) using dynamometers designed by Denny (1982). These storm-generated forces were measured at 8 m depth at the same height off the bottom (5 cm) as large invertebrates. The same dynamometers indicated that average maximum velocities of 2.5 m · s⁻¹ at 4 m depth were 2.6-fold higher than at 12 m depth in wave-exposed Caribbean rock wall habitats (Witman 1992). Flow speeds as high as 10–11 m · s⁻¹ can occur at 18 m depth during exceptional (once in 200 years) storms along the coast of San Diego, California (Dayton et al. 1989). A typical decrease in horizontal flow velocity with depth is illustrated in Figure 13.6A for a calm day off southern New England. Alfaro (1994) measured an even more striking 35-fold decrease in average flow speed with depth from 2–3 m to 10–12 m depth at Bird Rock off southern California. Unless the deep habitat is located in a narrow inlet with strong tidal flow, or on a topographically high area of the bottom such as the top of a bank, rocky pinnacle, or fjord sill, flow velocities in the benthic boundary layer of deep rocky subtidal environments (> 30 m depth) are rarely above a few centimeters per second (Hiscock 1983; Leichter and Witman 1997; Genovese and Witman 1999).

Bottom topography modulates large- and small-scale currents (Wolanski and Hamner 1988) greatly affecting flow velocity at the level of the benthic community (Wildish and Kristmanson 1997). Like deep seamounts (Genin et al. 1986), flow speed increases as water flows over the tops of pinnacles, banks, and sills (Stanton and Pickard 1981; Sebens et al. 1988; Figure 13.6B). Such high flow habitats like Ammen Rock Pinnacle in the central Gulf of Maine, Cordell and Tanner Banks off California, and fjord sills in New Zealand are usually dominated by dense assemblages of suspension feeding invertebrates (Lewbell et al. 1981; Witman and Sebens 1988; F. Smith, personal communication). These communities are "structured by flow" in the sense that flow may increase the flux of larvae to the substrate and enhance the abundance of benthic suspension feeders via recruitment, or increase the coverage of suspension feeders on the substrate by increasing the flux of particulate food and DOM, thereby enhancing the growth of suspension feeders. These mechanisms were dubbed the "larval pathway" and the "food pathway" in a key paper by Genin et al. (1986). Lesser et al. (1994) found evidence of the food pathway effect in high-flow habitats for passive suspension feeders (anemones), but not for active suspension feeders (mussels), suggesting that the food pathway effect may be predictable by the guild (e.g., active or passive) of suspension feeder and the range of flow velocity. Segregation among active and passive suspension feeders by flow habitat occurs where passive forms occupy elevated locations on the tops of hydroid stalks or short rock walls and active ones occupy lower flow environments at the base of these structures (Hughes 1975; Leichter and Witman 1997). In high-flow habitats at the peak of Ammen Rock Pinnacle (28–35 m depth), Genovese and Witman (1999) found no evidence of the flow enhanced "food pathway" effect for an active suspension feeding encrusting bryozoan compared to

habitats at the same depth in the coastal Gulf of Maine. There was, however, enhanced growth of both passive and active suspension feeders transplanted hundreds of meters of distance at these offshore pinnacles from low-flow habitats at 50 m to high flow at 28 and 35 m (Witman et al. 2000). Enhanced growth in this case is due to greater food particle supply at the peaks versus the lower slopes of pinnacles caused by the combined effects of increased horizontal currents at the top and the vertical displacement of a plankton maxima (Subsurface Chlorophyll Maximum) layer by internal waves (Witman et al. 1993; Witman et al. 2000). It is possible that the "larval pathway effect" may contribute to high abundance of bryozoans at the top of these pinnacles because a fouling panel experiment conducted for a year along a 30–90 m depth gradient at this site showed significantly higher recruitment at the top versus the bottom of Ammen Rock pinnacle (Sebens et al. 1988). Dense communities of suspension-feeding epifauna may "self-organize" in the sense that the structures they create modify flow to restrict larval dispersal (Wildish and Kristmanson 1997; Gill and Coma 1998), which may influence patterns of species richness on scales of 300–600 m⁻² (Smith and Witman 1999).

Possibly the most comprehensive treatment of flow effects on rocky subtidal communities has been conducted in kelp beds. Pioneering work by Jackson and Winant (1983) and Jackson (1984) showed that forests of giant kelp, *Macrocystis,* off southern California reduced flow velocity by as much as 54% compared to control sites lacking kelp. The consequences of such dramatic flow reduction by kelp for benthic communities via the food and larval pathways were not experimentally tested until Eckman and Duggins investigated the effects of understory kelps (*Agarum fimbriatum*) in San Juan Islands of Washington State (Eckman et al. 1989; Duggins et al. 1990; Eckman and Duggins 1991; Duggins and Eckman 1994). The *Agarum* kelp beds were considerably smaller than giant *Macrocystis,* as the *Agarum* canopy projected at most a meter above the rock surface in the wave-protected tidal straits (Eckman et al. 1989). Using clever methods to measure particle deposition and mass flux, they found that the *Agarum* beds reduced particle transport from the water column and decreased mass transport by half relative to sites lacking kelp (Eckman et al. 1989). Subsequent experiments at 7 to 11 m depth in this system tested the consequences of flow reduction by kelp for the growth of suspension-feeding invertebrates. They revealed that mussels (*Mytilus edulis*), barnacles (*Balanus glandula*) and a serpulid polychaete all grew faster beneath the kelp canopy (Eckman and Duggins 1991). Efforts to separate the influence of flow reduction by *Agarum* beds from increased food supply (kelp detritus) to identify the mechanisms responsible for invertebrate growth differences in and out of the kelp beds proved challenging, as only one of six suspension-feeding species grew faster in kelp bed mimics (Duggins and Eckman 1994). This experiment contributed an important perspective on the spatial scale of the kelp detritus effect, however, as kelp patches on the order of 10 m² were likely too small to increase the supply of kelp detritus in the immediate area (Duggins and Eckman 1994). In the strong tidal currents of this subtidal region, kelp detritus is probably exported farther than the 5–10 m distance separating natural kelp beds and kelp bed mimics (Duggins and Eckman 1994).

SEDIMENTATION. Sedimentation is inversely related to water movement and consequently increases with depth in rocky subtidal habitats (Gulliksen 1982; Figure 13.6) and with flow reduction in kelp beds (Eckman and Duggins 1991). Increased sedimentation on hard substrates may be responsible for the decline in the cover of suspension-feeding invertebrates below 50 m in the Gulf of Maine (Witman and Sebens 1988) and below 40 m in New Zealand fjords (K. Grange, personal communication). Due to runoff from the land, sedimentation onto rocky substrates is higher in the coastal zone than offshore, where it may reduce the growth and survival of coastal populations of encrusting bryozoans (Genovese 1996; Genovese and Witman 1999). On smaller spatial scales of local sites, differences in sedimentation can alter the diversity and distribution of algal assemblages colonizing shallow subtidal rocky shores of the Mediterranean (Airoldi and Cinelli 1997; Airoldi 1998). This work showed that susceptibility to sedimentation is species-specific and may therefore affect diversity by changing competitive interactions (Airoldi and Cinelli 1997). Generally, more attention needs to be given to the influence of sedimentation on community structure in the rocky subtidal zone.

LIGHT. Total light intensity shows a near-exponential decrease with depth (Figure 13.4). Variation in light transmission in the marine environment has been reviewed extensively by Jerlov (1970), Luning and Dring (1979), and Drew (1983). Underwater irradiance levels are commonly used to define the lower depth limit of macroalgae in general (Neushel 1967) and the depth limits of major taxonomic groups of algae. Red algae penetrate deeper into the subtidal than brown algae (Sears and Cooper 1978; Vadas and Steneck 1989; Mathieson et al. 1991). As shown by early work on European species of laminarian kelp in the UK (Kain 1971), Helgoland (Luning and Dring 1979), and the Mediterranean (Drew 1974), the lower limit of the Laminariales occurs at 0.7 to 1.4 % of surface irradiance. Like some terrestrial plant communities, light intensity within a given depth underwater may be highly variable due to movement of the canopy (Wing et al. 1993). Light reduction occurs under manufactured structures as well as under kelp forests (Duggins et al. 1990;Glasby 1999) where it can play an important role in determining epifaunal community structure (Glasby 1999).

Biotic Gradients

Consumer pressure is often greatest in the low intertidal zone (Connell 1975; Paine 1974; Menge 1976, 1983; Figure 13.7) contributing to the generalization that biotic variables (predation, competition) primarily determine the lower distributional limits of intertidal plants and attached invertebrates

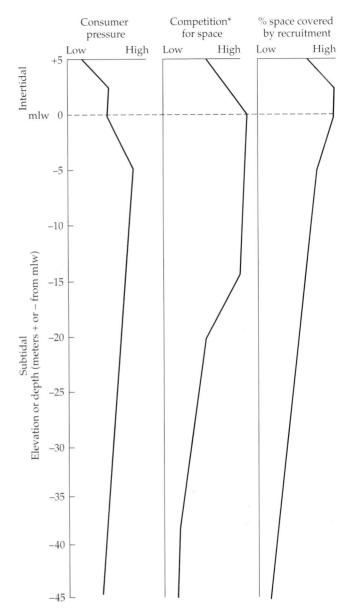

Figure 13.7 Hypothesized changes in the relative levels of biotic processes influencing rocky subtidal communities at typical wave-exposed sites. Competition refers to spatial competition among algae or algal–invertebrate competition.

(Connell 1975; Paine 1974). In contrast, upper distributional limits are thought to be principally regulated by physical factors such as heat and desiccation stress (Paine 1974; Connell 1975; Menge and Sutherland 1976). This conceptual model of community structure underemphasized the role of recruitment (Underwood and Denley 1984; Menge and Sutherland 1987), but it nonetheless provides an important framework for posing hypotheses about the relative importance of different processes shaping local community structure.

Like elevational differences in the intertidal zone, the influence of biotic processes varies with depth in the subtidal zone (Figure 13.7). There have been few direct tests of Connell's (1975) or Menge and Sutherland's (1976, 1987) models for subtidal comminutes. We evaluate the suitability of these models for rocky subtidal communities by examining the evidence for three predictions. These are: *prediction 1*, that predation is reduced in physically harsh environments; *prediction 2*, that biotic factors set lower zonal limits; and *prediction 3*, that physical factors control upper distributional limits in subtidal communities.

CONSUMER PRESSURE.   The lowest consumer pressure apparently occurs at shallow, wave-exposed locations (Figure 13.7) because the survival (Denny et al. 1985) and feeding ability of most mobile consumers is reduced by wave impact and extreme water movement. Support for this statement comes from the literature and comparative data on the distribution of one of the most important subtidal consumers, the sea urchin, at wave-exposed sites in different geographic locales (Figure 13.8). For example, sea urchins are typically absent from the shallowest few meters of the subtidal zone where hydrodynamic forces are highest. This situation occurs on the wave-exposed side of Halfway Rock in the Gulf of Maine, where green sea urchins *Stronglyocentrotus droebachiensis* were absent from shallow depths (1.0 to 4.5 m; Figure 13.8). They became abundant at 6.0 m depth on the wave-exposed side, but less than a hundred meters away on the wave-protected side of the island, they occurred in high densities (average 33 per 0.25m^{-2}) in the shallowest habitat (1.5 m depth, J. Witman

and C. Siddon, unpublished data). Drag forces were high enough to exceed the average attachment strength of 43 newtons and dislodge ~30 % of large urchins at shallow depths (1.5–3.0 m depth) at the exposed site (J. Witman and C. Siddon, unpublished data). The depth distribution of tropical sea urchins, *Diadema savignyi* and *Echinothrix echinothrix*, from a wave-exposed site in the granitic Seychelles also indicated a shallow zone devoid of urchins (Figure 13.8). The same pattern of low urchin abundance at shallow, wave-exposed sites occurs in the Galapagos, where *Tripneustes* were abundant below 4 m depth (Figures 13.3, 13.8). The inverse relation between the distribution of sea urchins and the strength of water motion has also been noted in subtidal habitats in southern California (Lissner 1983) and Iceland (Hjorleifsson et al. 1995). The ability of urchins like *Eucidaris* and *Echinometra* to bore into the substrate and inhabit depressions they create undoubtedly reduces their risk of dislodgment from hydrodynamic forces, enabling boring urchins to persist in shallow, physically stressful subtidal habitats. Another grazer, the snail *Astraea undosa*, has a depth distribution similar to sea urchins in wave-exposed subtidal habitats off southern California (Alfaro 1994). The snails were least abundant at 2–3 m depth where maximum flow speeds were highest. Alfaro (1994) attributed this pattern to a high probability of dislodgment at 2–3 m depth. Although they are dislodged in large numbers during extreme hydrodynamic conditions in exceptional storms (Witman 1996), sea stars seem able to feed

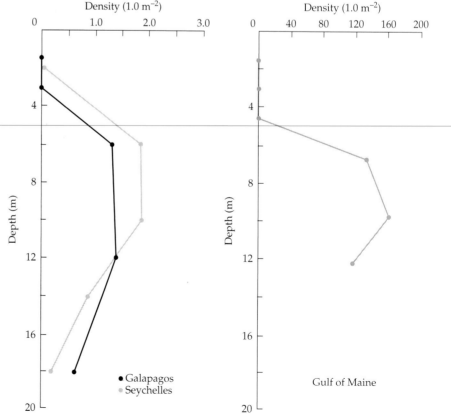

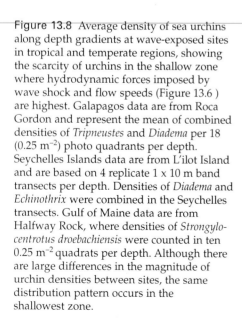

Figure 13.8 Average density of sea urchins along depth gradients at wave-exposed sites in tropical and temperate regions, showing the scarcity of urchins in the shallow zone where hydrodynamic forces imposed by wave shock and flow speeds (Figure 13.6) are highest. Galapagos data are from Roca Gordon and represent the mean of combined densities of *Tripneustes* and *Diadema* per 18 (0.25 m^{-2}) photo quadrants per depth. Seychelles Islands data are from L'ilot Island and are based on 4 replicate 1 x 10 m band transects per depth. Densities of *Diadema* and *Echinothrix* were combined in the Seychelles transects. Gulf of Maine data are from Halfway Rock, where densities of *Strongylocentrotus droebachiensis* were counted in ten 0.25 m^{-2} quadrats per depth. Although there are large differences in the magnitude of urchin densities between sites, the same distribution pattern occurs in the shallowest zone.

more effectively in shallow, wave-exposed habitats than sea urchins (Menge 1979; Hulbert 1980). This may be due to the combination of a low profile drag and high attachment strength of sea stars (Denny 1995). Measurements of attachment strength, hydrodynamic drag, and lift on *Asterias vulgaris* and *Asterias forbesi* taken during nonstormy conditions indicated that hydrodynamic forces in flow speeds up to 3 m · s⁻¹ weren't high enough to exceed average attachment strength of 31 newtons and dislodge the sea stars (J. Witman and C. Siddon, unpublished data). In northern Chile, Vasquez (1993) and Vasquez and Buschmann (1997) concluded that water movement impedes the ability of the sea urchin *Tetrapygus niger* to control the distribution of subtidal kelp *Lessonia trabeculata* at shallow sites.

We hypothesize that the ability of predators to forage in the shallowest subtidal habitats and impact rocky subtidal communities depends on the relationship between predator mobility and the return time of physically stressful conditions such as large hydrodynamic forces, low salinity, and temperature extremes (Figure 13.9). Return time is used here to mean the time required for the stress to recur. That is, return time would be short on a rough day where short period waves repeatedly strike the coast or when the low salinity layer typical of fjord surface waters changes depth rapidly. The dependent variable, per capita prey removal rate, is directly proportional to return time, predator mobility, and consumption rate. Therefore, the prey removal rate should increase with longer return times and faster consumption rates. The shape of the functions for predators varying in mobility shown in Figure 13.9 are approximations, but they should be

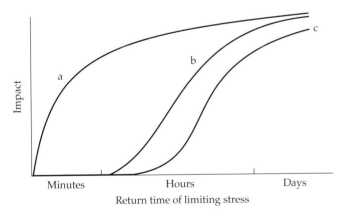

Figure 13.9 Model predicting the magnitude of per capita predator impact on prey populations in the shallow subtidal zone based on predator mobility and the return time of physically stressful conditions such as large hydrodynamic forces, low salinity, and temperature extremes. a = curve for birds, fish, b = crabs and lobsters, c = snails, sea stars, and sea urchins. Highly mobile vertebrates like birds and fish can have a large impact in environments where the return time of physical limiting forces is short because they can extract prey rapidly and, if necessary, transport prey to less-stressful habitats to finish consumption. Comparatively sluggish predatory invertebrates like sea urchins and sea stars are less effective in the most stressful habitats where return times are short.

nonlinear and asymptotic because consumption rate is constrained by satiation as well as by the rate of food processing (Holling 1959).

By virtue of their high mobility, birds and fish can be effective in the shallowest wave-exposed habitats where the period between waves is on the order of seconds to minutes. Gulls are voracious predators on a variety of prey living at the upper fringe of the subtidal zone including whelks, crabs, sea urchins, and sea stars (Irons et al. 1986; Good 1992; Dumas and Witman 1993; Wootton 1997; J. Ellis, unpublished data). The effectiveness and potentially high impact of fish (Ojeda and Dearborn 1991; Loher 1992) and birds in the shallow subtidal community also stems from their ability to extract prey from physically stressful habitats and to bring prey elsewhere to feed on them. The model predicts that their community impact rises steeply up to an asymptote at an hour or so return time, then rises more slowly due to the time required to consume the prey (handling time) in another habitat. Fish and birds are able to feed sporadically at wave-exposed sites by darting down to remove prey organisms from the substrate during brief intervals of low water movement. For example, we have videotaped wrasses, *Tautogolabrus adspersus*, feeding on small mussels at 2 m depth in flow velocities exceeding 1.0 m s⁻¹ in the New England subtidal. Wrasses accomplish feeding in these conditions by darting down to bite mussels as the fish are being carried by surge (J. Witman and B. Pavlin, video data). Parrotfish, surgeon fish, and wrasses commonly bite the substrata in tropical rocky subtidal communities of Palau, Galapagos, and Seychelles Islands subjected to wave surge to feed on algae, barnacles, and corals (J. Witman, unpublished observations).

The most mobile invertebrate consumers, lobsters and crabs, have difficulty foraging in wave surge (Heydorn 1969) where return times of hydrodynamic forces large enough to reduce feeding or to dislodge them occur in minutes, but they can have a high impact over a tidal cycle of a few hours duration (Robles 1987; Barkai and McQuaid 1988). The higher mobility of some species of lobsters and crabs gives them the potential to feed in on shallow prey and retreat to lower flow habitats because they can feed and leave the shallow zone before experiencing the stress or limiting force. The impact of decapod predators is further reduced by handling time (Elner and Hughes 1978).

The predation impact of comparatively sluggish invertebrate consumers such as snails, sea stars, and sea urchins spans a range of return times from hours to weeks (Figure 13.9). Some fast-moving whelks and sea stars are capable of consuming prey in a few hours (Barkai and McQuaid 1988; Witman and Grange 1998); however, sea stars and sea urchins typically require several days to weeks of uninterrupted feeding to have a detectable impact on the distribution of preferred prey such as encrusting epifauna, mussels, and kelp (Ayling 1981; Witman 1985; Briscoe and Sebens 1988; Scheibling et al. 1999). Sea stars can have a major community impact (Paine, 1966; Menge 1979) when the return times of limiting physical stresses are a day or longer. Grazers can increase the mortality of kelp sporophytes in a just a few hours at high flow sites because even a grazed nick or hole in the stipe of an attached plant makes the kelp more vulnerable to dislodgment (Koehl and Wainwright 1977). The whelks *Burnapea* spp. are possibly the most voracious gastropods studied, as large aggregations these snails can subdue and consume a rock lobster in < 1 hr (Barkai and McQuaid 1988). By reducing lobster densities and their impacts on mussels, *Burnapea* apparently plays an important role in maintaining alternate community states in subtidal communities off the west coast of South Africa (Barkai and McQuaid 1988). We suggest that extreme water movement is an especially effective physical factor limiting the impact of subtidal predators, because it may constrain both aspects of a predator's functional response, handling time and encounter rate with their prey. Our individual-based model is largely untested and does not consider emergent or synergistic effects of multiple predators (Sih et al. 1998), which may alter the shape of the curves. Nor does it predict sublethal effects of environmental stress on predators and grazers.

Many invertebrate predators track the abundance of low intertidal prey and concentrate their feeding at or near the intertidal/subtidal ecotone when they aren't prevented from foraging at such shallow depths by physical stress. This was the situation in subtidal communities of New Zealand fjords where the greatest concentrations of predatory invertebrates occurred at 5 m depth, corresponding to the lower limit of a dense mussel zone (*Mytilus galloprovincialis*; Witman and Grange 1998). Harsh physical conditions in a surface low salinity layer excluded sea stars, sea urchins, and lobsters from the shallow zone (< 5 m) dominated by mussels. This is in accord with Menge and Sutherland's (1976) environmental stress model, as predation decreased with increasing environmental harshness. There wasn't an inverse relationship between environmental harshness and snail grazing intensity in a California kelp bed, as Watanabe (1984) found that grazing intensity depended more on the presence of local algal refuges than on harsh physical conditions. Robles (1987) found that spiny lobsters were effective predators on intertidal mussels during high tides on a sheltered rocky shore and asserted that the reduction of predation by environmental stress isn't a general phenomenon. This result may partly reflect the choice of a relatively protected study site, as lobster predation in habitats fully exposed to waves wasn't examined (Robles 1987). In summary, there is some support from the shallow subtidal zone for *prediction 1*, that predation is diminished by environmental harshness. The evidence is mainly descriptive in terms of inverse relations between water movement and depth distributions of urchins and snails, with some support from experiments that show reduced predation intensity in low salinity layers. What is lacking is a manipulative study of the role of consumers across the physically harsh intertidal/subtidal ecotone.

Although it is surely not the only biotic factor controlling the distribution of subtidal species, there is also support for *prediction 2*, that biological factors control lower distributional

limits in the rocky subtidal. This was demonstrated in one of the first sea urchin removal experiments, where Kain and Jones (1967) showed that the lower limit of kelp was regulated by urchin grazing. Similarly, Witman (1987) extended the lower depth limit of the *Laminaria* zone at a site in the Gulf of Maine by removing green sea urchins *Strongylocentrotus droebachiensis,* and Scheibling et al. (1999) documented the same phenomenon off the coast of Nova Scotia. In the Gulf of Maine, the limitation by biotic factors (grazing) occurred above the critical light extinction depth (1% surface irradiance) for *Laminaria*, which was at 20 m (Witman 1984). Dense bands of sea stars crop the subtidal border of intertidal blue mussel beds at 3–6 m depth in the United Kingdom (Sloan and Aldridge 1981), in New Zealand (Witman and Grange 1998), and in the Gulf of Maine (Witman et al., in preparation). Similarly, predation by rock lobsters off Malgas Island, Africa, is high enough to eliminate the subtidal recruitment of black mussels, *Choromytilus meridionalis* (Barkai and McQuaid 1988). These researchers suggested that the intertidal zone of the island represented a refuge from intense lobster predation in the rocky subtidal (Barkai and McQuaid 1988). Predatory sea urchins and sea stars have been observed controlling the lower depth limit of kelp and blue mussel zones, respectively, in the same benthic landscape (Figure 13.10). The highest consumer pressure occurs a few meters below the surface at exposed locations (Figure 13.7). In some cases interspecific competition among kelp limits the lower depth limit of beds, supporting the prediction that biotic interactions set lower distributional limits (Dayton et al. 1992).

The upper distribution of subtidal organisms is ultimately truncated by intolerance to air at the land–sea interface, obviously supporting *prediction 3,* that physical conditions control upper distributional limits. The same hydrodynamic forces that restrict predator foraging in the shallow subtidal may regulate the upper distributional limits of subtidal species as well. For example, a physical force, hydrodynamic drag on horse mussels overgrown by kelp, was sufficient to reduce the shallow distribution of horse mussels without mutualistic sea urchins (Witman 1987). This documentation of a strong positive interaction ameliorating harsh environmental conditions is in accord with Bertness and Callaway's (1994) model of positive interactions. Shallow, wave-exposed habitats may be a good place to look for other examples of positive interactions in the subtidal. An increasing amount of evidence suggests that grazer-based mutualisms facilitate the persistence of sessile invertebrates in subtidal communities by reducing negative effects of competition with algae (Miller and Hay 1997; Stachowitz and Hay 1999).

In apparent contrast to the rocky intertidal, there are many situations where the lower distribution of subtidal species is regulated by physical factors. The most obvious is the case of light limitation in subtidal macroalgae, where the amount of light for photosynthesis determines the depth that algae can penetrate into the subtidal zone. If grazing isn't limiting, the infralittoral zone extends deeper into the subtidal in clear than in turbid water conditions (Moore 1973). This situation

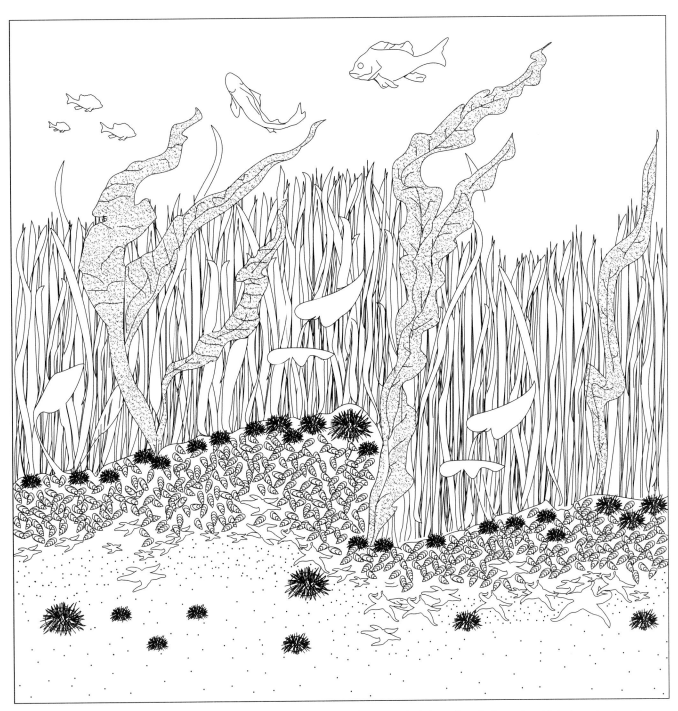

Figure 13.10 Predation regulating the lower limit of a kelp (*Laminaria* and *Alaria*) and blue mussel bed (*Mytilus*) in the shallow subtidal (10 m depth) of the Gulf of Maine. Green sea urchins can be seen consuming the stipes and holdfasts of the kelp at the habitat edge and have created the barren zone in the foreground. A dense band of sea stars (*Asterias vulgaris* and *A. forbesii*) are preying *Mytilus*, effectively stopping the recruitment from covering large areas of substrate at greater depths. (Drawing based on a photograph taken at Anderson Ledge, Gulf of Maine.)

has been documented from the Baltic Sea (Luning and Dring 1979), the west coast of South Africa (Field et al. 1980), the Gulf of Maine (Vadas and Steneck 1988; Witman and Sebens 1988), and the southeastern United States (Miller and Hay 1996). Kelp, in particular, may extend as much as 10 (Vadas and Steneck 1988; Witman and Sebens 1988) to 20 m deeper (Field et al. 1980) into the rocky subtidal zone with increased water clarity. Sedimentation is another physical factor influencing the lower distributional limits of subtidal epifauna. The percent of the rocky substrate covered by sediment usually increases with depth (Witman and Sebens 1988). Although experiments haven't been conducted to separate correlation from causality, the decrease in overall abundance of sponges and other suspension feeders at the 45–60 m depth range in the Gulf of Maine corresponds to a large increase in the percent cover of sediment, suggesting that sedimentation may be limiting sessile invertebrate populations in the deep subtidal (Witman and Sebens 1988). Barnes et al. (1996) attributed the truncated distribution of encrusting bryozoans between 34 and 42 m in the low Antarctic partly to high sedimentation. High sedimentation reduced the growth of an encrusting bryozoan at a deep (> 28 m) coastal site in the Gulf of Maine (Genovese and Witman 1999). Substrate limitation, as a physical factor, occurs in many cases in the rocky subtidal where hard substrate ultimately gives way to soft sediment on the continental shelf, thus limiting the distribution of invertebrates and plants. We suggest that *prediction 3* is often supported in the shallow subtidal, but seldom applies to deeper regions of the subtidal zone, where the opposite situation of lower distributional limits regulated by physical factors is common.

COMPETITION.   Space is frequently a limiting resource in rocky subtidal communities (Jackson 1977; Osman 1977; Russ 1982; Sebens 1986; Figure 13.3). As Sebens (1985) pointed out, space on the rocks enables sessile organisms to acquire other resources such as light and food. Competition for space is influenced by a variety of mechanisms including alleopathy, overgrowth, overtopping, aggression, and algal whiplash (Dayton 1975; reviewed in Branch 1984). Spatial competition, although important, probably shows less variation with depth than other biotic processes, and thus we hypothesize depth-related trends only for competition among algae and for competition between algae and invertebrates (Figure 13.7) in temperate regions. We assigned a high relative importance to algal–algal competition in the shallow subtidal because strong competition for space and light occurs between canopy and understory macroalgae and among different species of kelp (Dayton 1975; Duggins 1980; Johnson and Mann 1988; Dayton et al. 1992). We hypothesize that competition among algae decreases with depth as the density of erect macroalgae thins out in the deep rocky subtidal (Figure 13.7).

Similarly, plant–animal competition is lower in the deep subtidal than in the shallows because the abundance of macroalgae decreases with depth. Subtidal algae negatively impact sessile invertebrates by overgrowth (Dayton 1973; Paine 1976a; Witman 1987; Coyer et al. 1993; Davis et al. 1997; Stachowicz and Hay 1999) and kelp whiplash (Dayton 1975; Velimirov and Griffiths 1979). Kelp–invertebrate competition occurs off western South Africa where the sweeping action of *Laminaria pallida* fronds clears the substrate of dense sea cucumbers, *Pentacta doliolum*, and other invertebrates (Velimirov and Griffiths 1979). The cleared patches around the base of the kelp are colonized by *Laminaria*, allowing the kelp to expand their spatial coverage (Velimirov and Griffiths 1979; Branch and Branch 1981). Kelp whiplash effects have

also been observed impacting sea anemones, *Metridium senile*, and sponges (Figure 13.3; J. Witman, unpublished data). Strong interference competition for attachment space with kelp limits the shallow (8–10 m depth) distribution of horse mussels at wave exposed sites in the Gulf of Maine (Witman 1987). Large numbers of mussels are overgrown by kelp and dislodged during northeast storms. Witman (1984, 1987) asserted that the relationship was a competitive one because overgrown mussels had lower gonad weights than nonovergrown ones, and both species lost fitness when they were cast ashore and died. Kelps dominated the ensuing patch space in this system because they recruited faster than horse mussels.

Kelp–invertebrate interactions are complex and multifaceted because kelp have positive (+) as well as negative (-) effects on invertebrates. For example, South African researchers advanced the idea that kelp detritus can be highly nutritive to intertidal and subtidal consumers (Branch and Branch 1981; Stuart et al. 1982; Seiderer and Newell 1985; Fielding and Davis 1989; Bustamente and Branch 1996). Stable isotope analysis of subtidal consumers in Arctic (Dunton and Schell 1987) and Pacific Northwest kelp beds (Duggins et al. 1989) indicated that kelp detritus increased the supply of particulate food to suspension-feeding invertebrates, enhancing their growth (but see Duggins and Eckman 1997). In a holistic sense, the positive effects of kelp on sessile invertebrates are to increase food resources, whereas the negative effects occur via competitive interactions and increased sedimentation (Eckman and Duggins 1991). We suggest, as have others in various forms (e.g., Hiscock 1983; Witman 1987), that the sign (i.e., +/−) of the interaction between kelp and subtidal suspension feeders depends on the nature and magnitude of water movement. In high-flow regimes typical of wave-exposed sites on the coast or on offshore reefs, flow is characterized by surge, wave shock, and rapid flow accelerations. In these extreme flow conditions, kelp tend to have a negative impact on benthic invertebrates immediately in contact with them by decreasing the fitness of neighboring sessile invertebrates via whiplash or by dislodging species that they attach to. Kelp would also have positive effects on suspension feeders at high-flow sites in terms of contributing detrital food, but these potential benefits are sometimes overridden by negative effects on the local community. For example, enhanced growth is of limited benefit if death is a predictable outcome of the interaction. Kelp detritus may subsidize food webs at sites some distance from the local (source) habitat, as detrital kelp may be transported out of the immediate habitat in high-flow regimes (Duggins and Eckman 1994). In this sense, we speculate that the spatial separation or connectivity of sites contributing kelp detritus should be considered on larger spatial scales to evaluate potential benefits of detrital kelp food resources. The kelp–invertebrate relationship may switch to a predominately positive one (with some negative impacts of sedimentation) at low to intermediate flow velocities or regimes of wave shock not high enough to cause whiplash or dislodgment. Because kelp–invertebrate interactions are modulated by flow, it would be illuminating to investigate them across a broad spectrum of different types of water motion from wave-dominated flow along exposed outer coasts to wave-protected tidal inlets to fully understand their ecological importance.

Many studies of spatial competition among epifaunal invertebrates have been conducted in fouling communities where overgrowth competition is common (Sutherland and Karlson 1977; Sebens 1986). Although spatial competition is pervasive in rocky subtidal communities, it is highly variable over small spatial scales (Bruno and Witman 1996; Figure 13.3) in terms of the mechanisms of interaction, the limiting resource(s) and the type of species involved. Thus, generalizations about competition among epifaunal invertebrates, beyond Jackson's (1977) prediction that colonial invertebrates should outcompete solitary ones, are slow to be forthcoming. In some subtidal communities spatial competition is hierarchical with clear dominant species that overgrow nearly all others (Sebens 1986; Witman 1992; Barnes et al. 1996). In other encrusting invertebrate communities, the relationships are best described as a competitive network with reversals of competitive ability (*sensu* Buss and Jackson 1979) with many species ranked equally (Russ 1982).

EXTENSIVE RECRUITMENT. The ability of settling barnacle and mussel larvae to cover vast areas of rocky intertidal shores was initially described from Europe by Hatton (1938), Kitching et al. (1959), Connell (1961), Lewis (1964), and Seed (1969). These early studies and recent observations of large differences in intertidal community structure in habitats receiving high and low recruitment of barnacles (Underwood et al. 1983; Gaines and Roughgarden 1985) led to the development of "supply-sided" models of community ecology predicting that settlement and recruitment processes have a key influence on the patterns of adult community structure (Gaines and Roughgarden 1985; Roughgarden et al. 1988).

In the rocky subtidal zone, the tendency for larvae to settle in large, dense aggregations that effectively "blanket" the rock surface as in the some intertidal communities appears to be restricted to the shallow subtidal zone (Figure 13.7). In the Northwest Atlantic, the settlement of blue mussels, *Mytilus edulis*, typically covers large areas (tens to hundreds of m^{-2}) down to a depth of 5 m or so during late spring and summer. An unusually large and widespread settlement of *M. edulis* covered 30–95% of the bottom on rocky ledges down to a depth of 15 m in the southern Gulf of Maine during August to September of 1995 (Witman et al., in preparation). This mesoscale recruitment event covered kilometers of bottom at many sites, and it was documented from 76% of 17 sites spanning a 125 km region. The cohort of *Mytilus* persisted for one year before it was eliminated by sea star, crab, and urchin predation (Witman et al., in preparation). On smaller spatial scales, predation by snails drastically reduced the recruitment of ascidians in coastal epifaunal communities (Osman and Whitlatch 1995). Shallow subtidal settlement of *Mytilus* has also been described from southern England (Sloan and

Aldridge 1981). Occasional heavy sets of barnacles occur down to 10 m off the Isles of Shoals, at sites in Massachusetts Bay and off Monhegan Island on the U.S. coast. Based on the distribution patterns of adults and juveniles, barnacle settlement is common down to at least 9 m depth in the Galapagos Islands (Figure 13.2; J. Witman, unpublished data). On the west coast of South Africa, large m^{-2} patches of *Choromytilus* mussel recruitment were only observed down to 12–15 m depth (J. Witman, personal observations).

Kelp recruitment typically covers much smaller areas of the bottom than barnacles and mussels, because the dilution of zoospores from the parent plant reduces the gametophyte density below the threshold of necessary for fertilization (Anderson and North 1966). The effective dispersal range was initially described as only a few meters (Anderson and North 1966). For this reason, the effective spore dispersal of *Macrocystis* is limited; however, drifting plants and fertile drift sporophylls can vastly increase the effective dispersal distance (Dayton 1984). Some species of brown algae such as *Desmerestia* will carpet large areas after major disturbances, and these may inhibit succession for many months (Dayton et al. 1992).

We suggest that the tendency for recruitment to "blanket" the substrate is relatively rare in deep communities and that it represents an important difference between the community ecology of shallow and deep rocky subtidal zones. The observation of the scarcity of heavy recruitment in deeper areas of the subtidal could be due to high predation on recruits in the shallow subtidal zone, to differences in life history and dispersal of shallow versus deep species, or to a combination of all three factors.

TROPHIC CASCADES. Like recruitment, predation is a process shaping community structure on small spatial scales, but can transcend the spatial scale of a single site to unite many sites under similar levels of influence. Trophic cascades are one of the most obvious situations where consumer effects extend to large spatial scales of the ecosystem (Carpenter and Kitchell 1988). Trophic cascades are food webs controlled by strong interactions (Paine 1980) where consumers on one trophic level regulate the abundance of prey on the trophic level immediately below and cause an alternating sequence ("cascade") of predator control and release from predation down through to the basal trophic level of primary producers. One of the best examples of a trophic cascade comes from North Pacific rocky subtidal communities where sea otter, *Enhydra lutris*, predation regulates sea urchin densities, which are well known to strongly influence the distribution of kelp (Simenstad et al. 1978). Sea otters, once widely distributed across the Pacific Rim, were hunted to near extinction in the eighteenth and nineteenth centuries (Estes and Duggins 1995). The initial observations leading to a trophic cascade hypothesis were that dramatically different community states occurred on adjacent islands in the Aleutian Archipelago of Alaska with and without *Enhydra* (Simenstad et al. 1978). In the presence of otters, kelp communities are characterized by a surface layer of *Alaria fistulosa*, a second canopy layer of four species of *Laminaria*, and a prostrate canopy usually composed of *Agarum clathratum* (Dayton 1975). These abundant kelp associations support detritus-based food webs of crustaceans, fish, and suspension-feeding invertebrates (Simenstad et al. 1978; Duggins et al. 1989). In the absence of otters, dense populations of sea urchins, *Strongylocentrotus* sp., along with limpets and chitons, virtually exclude fleshy macroalgae; fishes are considerably less common and usually associated with pelagic food webs.

The role of sea otters in Alaska is clear because modern observers have been able to compare situations with and without otters, as well as the transitions that occurred as these mammals expanded their range. Estes and Duggins (1995) examined the generality of the sea otter trophic cascade "paradigm" by comparing temporal and spatial variability in the Aleutian Islands and southeast Alaska. Despite regional variation in species composition and the abundance of kelps and urchins that affect the trajectories of change between kelp-dominated and urchin-dominated domains, they found the role of sea otter predation to be predictable and widespread in its influence on kelp community structure in Alaska. Estes (1996) reports that the pattern is broadly similar for Vancouver Island (Canada) as well. The situation is more complicated in California and Baja California, however. There are episodes of destructive sea urchin grazing, and otters predictably decimate urchin populations here as well, but giant kelp, *Macrocystis pyrifera*, forests also show considerable persistence in the absence of otters. Foster and Schiel (1988) reviewed 220 surveys outside the otter range in California and found urchin-dominated or deforested habitats to be the exception, < 10% of the sites surveyed. They found a range of community states between the extremes identified in Alaska and that the extremes were uncommon. Storms, interannual variability in ocean climate, and other physical factors affecting the recruitment and growth of kelp, as well as other sea urchin predators, echinoid recruitment events, and diseases are also important to kelp community structure in California (Dayton 1985; Ebeling et al. 1985; Harrold and Reed 1985; Tegner and Dayton 1987).

Mesoscale Processes

As we asserted in the beginning of this chapter, the proper understanding of spatial and temporal scales in marine ecology is extremely challenging and important. The overarching biological order results from a coupling between dispersal and internal community dynamics. The patch structure that characterizes most ecological structure decays in isolation. Dispersal is the main means of interconnection between these components. In this sense, dispersal is a pivotal process integrating ecological organization across all scales. With regard to spatial scales, this includes the ambits of individuals as they relate to foraging and reproductive behavior, population biology (immigration and emigration), and community organization (colonization and flux). With regard to scales in time, dispersal processes are links between generations, bio-

geography, and evolution. Dispersal processes are a common unifying thread (Dayton et al. 1992; Palmer et al. 1996).

Connectivity via Dispersal

Local populations of plants and invertebrates living in rocky subtidal communities are connected by the dispersal of their asexual propagules and larvae. Establishing the spatial scale of their dispersal is a key area of research for conservation biology and basic ecology. A review of larval dispersal is beyond the scope of this chapter, and it has been covered recently in several excellent reviews (Levin and Bridges 1995; Shanks 1995; Young 1995). It is apparent, however, that few generalizations are currently possible about the distance of larval dispersal in the rocky subtidal zone beyond those based on the mode of larval development. On the far end of the scale, maximum dispersal distances of subtidal species with planktotrophic development such as snails, bivalves, polychaetes, barnacles, decapod crustaceans, barnacles, sea urchins, and sea stars range from mesoscale to transoceanic distances (few kilometers to thousands of kilometers (Thorson 1950; Levin and Bridges 1995). Subtidal species that produce large asexual buds or lecithotrophic, brooded or crawl-away larvae tend toward short-distance dispersal, sometimes not exceeding a few meters from the adults that produced them (Strathman 1974). Examples of known short-distance dispersers include ascidians (Olson 1985; Graham and Sebens 1996) soft corals (Sebens 1984), solitary cup corals (Gerrodette 1981), black corals (Miller 1998), sponges (Battershill and Bergquist 1990), bryozoans (Keough and Downes 1982; Keough 1983), and hydroids (Graham and Sebens 1996). Kelp dispersal is apparently intermediate between these two extremes (Anderson and North 1966; Dayton 1984; Leinaas and Christie 1996; Reed et al. 1998).

There is often a large difference between the potential distance of dispersal predicted by the longevity of passively dispersing larvae and the actual dispersal distance achieved due to a number of factors such as variable currents and the location of the larvae in the water column (Young 1995; Palumbi 1995). For example, large numbers of asexual buds of a demosponge, which in general are expected to disperse relatively short distances, were recovered in passive tube traps in high flow regimes at the tops of pinnacles (28–30 m depth) in the Gulf of Maine (Witman and Arnold 1989). We estimated that the sponge propagules had a potential dispersal exceeding 10 km in a tidal cycle, based on the flow regime at this site (Figure 13.6B). The important influence that location of larvae in the water column can have on dispersal distance was illustrated in McShane et al.'s (1988) study of abalone larvae off Tasmania. Larvae were retained close to their natal rocky reef throughout their one-week dispersal period because they remained near the bottom around topographically rough rocky reefs (McShane et al. 1988). The larvae would have dispersed substantially farther (kilometers) if the larvae left the low-flow regime near the bottom. These two examples point to the need for more field work to document the actual location of the larvae in the water column as they are dispersing and to measure the flow regime that the larvae experience, in order to obtain more accurate estimates of larval dispersal distances in the rocky subtidal zone.

It is well known that both the velocity of wave-induced flow and the velocity of wind-driven circulation (e.g., Ekman transport) decrease with depth (Pond and Pickard 1983; Mann and Lazier 1996). We suggest that this general pattern of decreasing flow velocity with depth has important, but largely unrecognized, implications for the scale of larval and propagule transport and for the extent of coupling between sites in the subtidal zone. We propose a working hypothesis of variation in connectivity among rocky subtidal populations along continuous sections of coastline. An underlying premise of the hypothesis is that horizontal velocity (advection) typically exceeds the vertical velocity of moving water is well supported in the oceanographic literature (Okubo 1980; Williams and Elder 1989; Tremblay et al. 1994). It stands to reason that a passively dispersed larva or propagule of a benthic organism of the same longevity will be transported farther in the shallow subtidal than in the deep subtidal zone (e.g., > 25 m) as a result of reduced current transport in the deep subtidal. This implies that there will be greater regional connectivity among populations and communities between sites in the shallow subtidal than in the deep subtidal zone. As a consequence, the dynamics of local populations and communities may be more synchronized in the shallow zone than in the deep subtidal. It follows that deep coastal subtidal populations should have smaller demes, greater small-scale patchiness, and more restricted gene flow than shallow populations that are more highly linked to regional processes by advective transport of propagules and/or larvae. For invertebrates with nonmotile adult stages, the hypothesized decrease in connectivity with depth would create a greater attenuation of gene flow with distance along the shore in deep than in shallow populations. The depth of transition between the hypothesized high connectivity in the shallow zone and low connectivity in the deep subtidal will depend on the local current regime, but we suggest as a first approximation that the bottom of the pycnocline is a likely depth for the transition, because steep pycnoclines can reduce the transfer of wind-generated momentum (current velocity) to water masses below it (Pond and Picard 1983; Williams and Elder 1989). Support for decreased current velocity with depth comes from numerical simulations of current circulation in the Gulf of Maine (Lynch et al. 1996), in southern New England (Tremblay et al. 1994), and off the mid-Atlantic coast of the United States (Gregg and Walsh 1992), all of which show a substantial decrease in the length of current vectors from the surface to > 30 m depth. Deep-dwelling species with swimming, photopositive larvae could increase their maximum dispersal distance by ascending into higher velocity currents in the shallow subtidal.

We predict that the hypothesis of depth variation in connectivity would hold for nonupwelling regions of continuous sections of rocky coastline such as on the eastern sides of continents at mid to high latitudes. The predicted decrease in horizontal connectivity with depth would be interrupted by coastal upwelling, storms, topographically enhanced currents in the deep subtidal, peninsulas, rivers, or other irregularities in the coastline that change the hydrodynamic regime. Nonetheless, the hypothesis offers a framework to test patterns of connectivity across large regions of the rocky subtidal zone. It is also consistent with our observations of a decrease in "blanketing" recruitment with depth in the rocky subtidal.

Disease

In addition to the dispersal of adults or larvae, the dispersal of pathogens by currents can cause synchronous changes in subtidal populations over mesoscales. This has been documented along 130 kilometers of the Nova Scotia coast where mass mortalites of sea urchins (*S. droebachiensis*) are caused by outbreaks of the disease paramoebiasis (Scheibling and Hennigar 1997). Because urchins are key grazers, the disease had the large-scale effect of reducing grazing on kelp, which may have switched the subtidal communities from an urchin barrens to kelp beds. Sponges are also susceptible to diseases; however, they have only been observed impacting local populations (Ayling 1981; Witman 1998). It is not known whether populations of gorgonians and ahermatypic corals in tropical rocky subtidal habitats will be impacted by the recent spread of bacterially based diseases like their counterparts on coral reefs (Harvell et al. 1999).

Productivity

Mesoscale differences in the biomass of phytoplankton are common and predictable at the surface of ocean (Longhurst 1998). Such large-scale variation in food at the surface may create mesoscale patterns in bottom communities via mechanisms of benthic-pelagic coupling, especially for suspension feeders in depositional environments (reviewed in Graf 1992). In hard-substrate habitats, dense populations of benthic suspension feeders occur in phytoplankton-rich upwelling regions like the Benguela ecosystem off south Africa (Field et al. 1980; Branch and Griffiths 1988). The importance of oceanographic processes in creating large-scale variability in nutrient supply and recruitment to subtidal communities was recognized early on by Dayton and Tegner (1984a). A similar oceanographic perspective was applied along the shoreline by Menge (1992) and Bustamente et al. (1996), who proposed that upwelling-driven areas of high productivity have a "bottom-up" influence on adjacent rocky intertidal food webs, potentially explaining some of the high biomass there and variation in community structure over large spatial scales (Menge et al. 1997). Increased research on the influence of productivity regimes on rocky subtidal communities are likely to increase our understanding of the causes of changes in rocky subtidal community structure across large spatial scales. This work is challenging, however, as responses by the subtidal suspension feeders utilizing the production is sometimes not predictable based on concentrations of chlorophyll a at the surface. Surface phenomena are sometimes decoupled from those on the rocky bottom due to (1) local variation in the components of food particle flux (e.g., concentration of food and speed of bottom currents; Wildish and Kristmanson 1997) and (2) the existence of concentrated phytoplankton layers below the ocean surface (Subsurface Chlorophyll Maximum layers, SCM; Witman et al. 1993), both of which strongly influence the actual delivery of food to benthic suspension feeders. For example, mapping of surface chlorophyll a concentration in the Gulf of Maine shows far higher levels of productivity in the coastal than in the offshore Gulf (Yentsch and Garfield 1981). This led to the hypothesis that "bottom-up" (e.g., food supply) forces were more important in the coastal zone than in the offshore region. The flux of food particles to the suspension-feeding community, however, turned out to be higher offshore (Genovese and Witman 1999). This was partly due to the downwelling of the SCM layer by internal waves in the offshore region (Witman et al. 1993), which wasn't visible from surface chlorophyll sensors, and to greater rates of food delivery in topographically enhanced high flow regimes offshore (Genovese 1996; Genovese and Witman 1999).

Thermoclines

The influence of thermoclines on rocky subtidal communities extends far beyond local effects on subtidal zonation, food, and nutrient supply, as the depth of the thermocline often sets the boundary of a species' biogeographic range. For example, species with centers of distribution in warm water regions occur above the thermocline at their northern limit, and the distribution of boreal–subarctic species exhibits the reverse pattern by inhabiting cold waters below the thermocline at their southern biogeographic range (Gosner 1971). This pattern is displayed by the temperate sea star *Asterias forbesi*, which is restricted to shallow depths above the thermocline in the cold Gulf of Maine, but has a wider bathymetric range farther south in the Virginian biogeographic province where it originates (Gosner 1971; Hulbert 1980). A temperate cup coral, *Balanophyllia elegans* (Gerodette 1981) and arctic species of sea stars and basket stars display the opposite pattern of submergence at the southern limit of their biogeographic range (Gosner 1971). Clearly, future studies of the effects of climatic change in marine hard-bottom ecosystems should consider how species ranges are influenced by changes in thermocline depth brought about by warming of the surface of the ocean.

Summary

Our understanding of local community structure in rocky subtidal habitats has progressed to the point where it is possible to make rough predictions about the types of species assemblages that are likely to occur at a given depth range. This is partly because environmental factors such as light, flow, physical disturbance, and sedimentation show directional variation along depth gradients. The strength of some biotic factors structuring communities, particularly consumer pres-

sure and recruitment, also show depth-related trends. For these reasons, depth is an important ecological axis in the rocky subtidal zone, much like tidal elevation in the intertidal. Considerable patchiness of the main habitat-forming species makes it more difficult to predict alongshore variation in community structure. As in other communities, physical and biotic factors interact to influence community structure, and there is still much research to be done to understand the causes of the realized niche of subtidal species. We suggest that this type of work should be focused on foundation species, as they have broad effects on many species. There are likely many important exchanges of food, larvae, and consumers that take place across habitats and across ecosystems (Polis et al. 1997) in the rocky subtidal zone (Witman et al. 2000), such as between intertidal and subtidal habitats. Consequently, we feel that we can learn about subtidal community dynamics by shedding the typical within-habitat perspective to investigate cross-habitat and cross-ecosystem linkages.

Models of intertidal community structure provide a good starting point for testing hypotheses in the subtidal zone. Physical factors such as large hydrodynamic forces at exposed sites or low salinity in fjords can regulate the upper distributional limits of subtidal invertebrates and modulate consumer pressure (top-down forces), supporting environmental stress models of community regulation in some cases. In contrast to intertidal models, there appear to be more situations where physical factors regulate the lower distribution of species in the subtidal than intertidal zone. Consumer pressure is especially intense in the rocky subtidal zone where it can regulate the lower depth limits of species distribution, define edges of habitats, and restrict species to spatial and temporal refuges. Considering that consumer pressure in the rocky subtidal has been substantially reduced from past levels by overfishing of large predatory fish and other human activities (Witman and Sebens 1992; Dayton et al. 1995; Steneck 1997; Dayton et al. 1998), the fact that most subtidal studies from 1970–1989 focused on the effects of predators and grazers nonetheless (Figure 13.1) underscores the key role that consumers have played in shaping community structure in the rocky subtidal zone. More research on subtidal recruitment may reveal that recruitment is more frequently eliminated by predation in subtidal than intertidal communities. Large-scale episodic events are extremely important because they override the more typical physical and biological processes structuring local benthic communities.

One of the major challenges of the millennium for subtidal ecology and community ecology in general, as we see it, is to place these vignettes of local community structure onto a larger screen to view how they are connected at the mesoscale (Dayton 1994).

We have hypothesized that connectivity among rocky subtidal populations decreases with depth, but this needs to be rigorously tested. Meeting this broad challenge will require more work at the interface of oceanography and benthic community ecology, as the rules of exchange between local communities are largely dictated by physical oceanography and biological processes. But the potential payoffs are great, as a better perspective on connectedness in the rocky subtidal zone will aid the choice of management units in marine conservation and lead to better theory predicting the consequences of anthropogenic impacts.

ACKNOWLEDGMENTS

We thank Mark Bertness for the opportunity to contribute to this book. Thanks also to C. H. Peterson, D. O. Duggins, and two anonymous reviewers for providing constructive criticism that improved the chapter. Of course, all errors or omissions are the responsibility of our dogs, Jasper Witman and Ellen B. Scripps. Thanks to Robert Laverdiere for illustrating Figures 13.2 and 13.10. Our research in subtidal ecology has been generously supported by the National Science Foundation (JDW and PKD), California Sea Grant (PKD), and the National Undersea Research Program at Avery Point, CT (JDW).

LITERATURE CITED

Airoldi, L. 1998. Roles of disturbance, sediment stress, and substratum retention on spatial dominance in algal turf. *Ecology* 79: 2759–2770.

Airoldi, L. and F. Cinelli. 1997. Effects of sedimentation on subtidal macroalgal assemblages: An experimental study from a Mediterranean rocky shore. *J. Exp. Mar. Biol. Ecol.* 215: 269–288.

Alfaro, A. 1994. Effects of hydrodynamics, intraspecific competition and seasonality on the zonation patterns of the marine snail *Astrea undosa* at Bird Rock, Santa Catalina Island. Masters Thesis, California State University at Northridge.

Anderson, E. K. and W. J. North. 1966. In situ studies of spore production and dispersal in the giant kelp *Macrocystis*. In *Proceedings of the Fifth International Seaweed Symposium*, pp. 73–86. Pergamon Press, Oxford.

Andrew, N. L. 1993. Spatial heterogeneity, sea urchin grazing, and habitat structure on reefs in temperate Australia. *Ecology* 74: 292—302.

Ayling, A. 1981. The role of biological disturbance in temperate subtidal encrusting communities. *Ecology* 62: 830–847.

Ayling, A. 1983. Growth and regeneration rates in thinly encrusting Demospongiae from temperate waters. *Biol. Bull.* 165: 343—352.

Barkai, A. and C. D. McQuaid. 1988. Predator–prey role reversal in a marine benthic ecosystem. *Science* 242: 62–64.

Barnes, D. K. A., A. Clarke and P. Rothery. 1996. Colonization and development of encrusting communities from the Antarctic intertidal and sublittoral. *J. Exp. Mar. Biol. Ecol.* 196: 251–265.

Battershill, C. N. and P. R. Bergquist. 1990. The influence of storms on asexual reproduction, recruitment and survivorship of sponges. In K. Rutzler (ed.), *New Perspectives in Sponge Biology*, pp. 397–415. Smithsonian Institution Press, Washington, DC.

Baynes, T. W. 1999. Factors structuring a subtidal encrusting community in the southern Gulf of California. *Bull. Mar. Sci.* 64: 419–450.

Bertness, M. D. and R. Callaway. 1994. Positive interactions in communities. *Trends Ecol. Evol.* 9: 191–193.

Bertness, M. D., G. H. Leonard, J. M. Levine, P. R. Schmidt and A. O. Ingraham. 1999. Testing the relative contribution of positive and negative interactions in rocky intertidal communities. *Ecology* 80: 2711–2726.

Bologna, P. A. and R. S. Steneck. 1993. Kelp beds as habitat for American lobster *Homarus americanus. Mar. Ecol. Prog. Ser.* 100: 127–134.

Bosman, A. L., P. A. R. Hockey and W. R. Siegfried. 1987. The influence of coastal upwelling on the functional structure of rocky intertidal communities. *Oecologia* 72: 226–232.

Branch, G. and M. Branch. 1981. *The Living Shores of Southern Africa.* Struik Publishers, Cape Town, South Africa.

Branch, G. M. 1984. Competition between marine organisms: Ecological and evolutionary implications. *Oceanogr. Mar. Biol. Annu. Rev.* 22: 429–523.

Branch, G. M. and C. L. Griffiths. 1988. The Benguela ecosystem. V. The coastal zone. *Oceanogr. Mar. Biol. Annu. Rev.* 26: 395–486.

Briscoe, C. S. and K. P. Sebens. 1988. Omnivory in *Strongylocentrotus droebachiensis* (Muller) (Echinodermata: Echinoidea): Predation on subtidal mussels. *J. Exp. Mar. Biol. Ecol.* 115: 1–24.

Bruno, J. F. and J. D. Witman. 1996. Defensive mechanisms of scleractinian cup corals against overgrowth by colonial invertebrates. *J. Exp. Mar. Biol. Ecol.* 207: 229–241.

Buss, L. W. and J. B. C. Jackson. 1979. Competitive networks: Non-transitive competitive relationships in cryptic coral reef environments. *Amer. Nat.* 113: 223–234.

Bustamente, R. H. and G. M. Branch. 1996. The dependence of intertidal consumers on kelp-derived organic matter on the west coast of South Africa. *J. Exp. Mar. Biol. Ecol.* 196: 1–28.

Bustamente, R. H., G. M. Branch, S. Eekhout, B. Roberston, P. Zoutendyk, M. Schleyer, A. Dye, N. Hanekom, D. Keats, M. Jurd and C. McQuad. 1996. Gradients of intertidal primary productivity around the coast of South Africa and their relationships with consumer biomass. *Oecologia* 102: 189–201.

Bustamente, R. H., G. M. Branch and S. Eekhout. 1997. The influences of physical factors on the distribution and zonation patterns of South African rocky shore communities. *S. African J. Mar. Sci.* 18: 119–136.

Carpenter, S. R. and J. F. Kitchell. 1988. Consumer control of lake productivity. *BioScience* 38: 764–769.

Chapman, A. R. 1986. Population and community ecology of seaweeds. *Adv. Mari. Biol.* 23: 1–161.

Choat, J. H. and D. R. Schiel. 1982. Patterns of distribution and abundance of large brown algae and invertebrates in subtidal regions of northern New Zealand. *J. Exp. Mar. Biol. Ecol.* 60: 129–162.

Conlan, K. E., H. S. Lenihan, R. G. Kvitek and J. S. Oliver. 1998. Ice scour disturbance to benthic communities in the Canadian High Arctic. *Mar. Ecol. Prog. Ser.* 166: 1–16.

Connell, J. H. 1961. The influence of interspecific competition and other factors on the distribution of the barnacle *Chthamalus stellatus. Ecology* 42: 710–723.

Connell, J. H. 1975. Some mechanisms producing structure in natural communities: A model and evidence from field experiments. In M. L. Cody and J. M. Diamond (eds.), *Ecology and Evolution of Communities*, pp. 460–490. Belknap Press, Cambridge, MA.

Connell, J. H. and M. J. Keough. 1985. Disturbance and patch dynamics of subtidal marine animals on hard substrata. In S. T. A. Pickett and P. S. White (eds.), *The Ecology of Natural Disturbance and Patch Dynamics*, pp. 125–147. Academic Press, Orlando, FL.

Coyer, J. A., R. F. Ambrose, J. M. Engle and J. C. Carrol. 1993. Interactions between corals and algae on a temperate zone rocky reef: Mediation by sea urchins. *J. Exp. Mar. Biol. Ecol.* 167: 21–37.

Cullen, J. J. 1982. The deep chlorophyll maximum: Comparing vertical profiles of chlorophyll a. *Canad. J. Fish. Aquat. Sci.* 39: 791–803.

Davis, A. R., D. E. Roberts and S. P. Cummins. 1997. Rapid invasion of a sponge dominated deep-reef by *Caulerpa scalpelliformis* (Chlorophyta) in Botany Bay, New South Wales. *Austral. J. Ecol.* 22: 146–150.

Dayton, P. K. 1971. Competition, predation, and community organization: The provision and subsequent utilization of space in a rocky intertidal community. *Ecol. Monogr.* 41: 351–389.

Dayton, P. K. 1972. Toward an understanding of community resilience and the potential effects of enrichment to the benthos at Mc-Murdo Sound, Antarctica. In B. C. Parker (ed.), *Proceedings of the Colloquium on Conservation Problems in Antarctica*, pp. 81–95. Allen Press, Lawrence, KS.

Dayton, P. K. 1973. Dispersion, dispersal and persistence of the annual intertidal alga, *Postelsia palmaeformis* Ruprecht. *Ecology* 54: 433–438.

Dayton, P. K. 1975. Algal canopy interactions in a sea otter–dominated kelp community at Amchitka Island, Alaska. *Fish. Bull.* 73: 670–684.

Dayton, P. K. 1984. Processes structuring some marine communities: Are they general? In D. R. Strong, D. Simberloff, L. Abele and A. Thistle (eds.), *Ecological Communities: Conceptual Issues and the Evidence*, pp. 181–197. Princeton University Press, Princeton, NJ.

Dayton, P. K. 1985. The structure and regulation of some South American kelp communities. *Ecol. Monogr.* 55: 447–468.

Dayton, P. K. 1985. Ecology of kelp communities. *Annu. Rev. Ecol. Syst.* 16: 215–245.

Dayton, P. K. 1989. Interdecadal variation in an Antarctic sponge and its predators from oceanographic climate shifts. *Science* 245: 1484–1496.

Dayton, P. K. 1992. Community landscape: Scale and stability in hard bottom communities. In P. S. Giller, A. G. Hildrew and D. G. Raffaelli (eds.), *Aquatic Ecology: Scale, Pattern, and Process*, pp. 289–332. Blackwell Scientific Publications, Oxford.

Dayton, P. K. and M. J. Tegner. 1984a. The importance of scale in community ecology. In P. W. Price et al. (eds.), *A New Ecology*, pp. 457–481. John Wiley and Sons, London.

Dayton, P. K. and M. J. Tegner. 1984b. Catastrophic storms, El Niño, and patch stability in a Southern California kelp community. *Science* 224: 283–285.

Dayton, P. K., G. A. Robilliard and A. L. De-Vries. 1969. Anchor ice formation in Mc-Murdo Sound, Antarctica, and its biological effects. *Science* 163: 273–274.

Dayton, P. K., G. A. Robilliard and R. T. Paine. 1970. Benthic faunal zonation as a result of anchor ice at McMurdo Sound, Antarctica. In Martin Holdgate (ed.), *Antarctic Ecology*, pp. 244–257. Academic Press, London.

Dayton, P. K., G. A. Robilliard, R. T. Paine and L. B. Dayton. 1974. Biological accommodation in the benthic community at McMurdo Sound, Antarctica. *Ecol. Monogr.* 44: 105–128.

Dayton, P. K., V. Currie, T. Gerrodette, B. D. Keller, R. Rosenthall and D. Van Tresca. 1984. Patch dynamics and stability of some California kelp communities. *Ecol. Monogr.* 54: 253–289.

Dayton, P. K., R. J. Seymour, P. E. Seymour and M. J. Tegner. 1989. Unusual marine erosion in San Diego County from a single storm. *Estuarine, Coastal and Shelf Sci.* 29: 151–160.

Dayton, P. K., M. J. Tegner and P. B. Parnell Edwards. 1992. Temporal and spatial patterns of disturbance and recovery in a kelp forest community. *Ecol. Monogr.* 62: 421–445.

Dayton, P. K., B. J. Mordida and F. Bacon. 1994. Polar marine communities. *Amer. Zool.* 34: 90–99.

Dayton, P. K., S. F. Thrush, M. Tundi Agardy and R. J. Hoffman. 1995. Environmental effects of marine fishing. *Aquat. Conserv.* 5: 205–232.

Dayton, P. K., M. J. Tegner, P. B. Edwards and K. L. Riser. 1998. Sliding baselines, ghosts, and reduced expectations in kelp forest communities. *Ecol. Appl.* 8: 309–322.

Dayton, P. K., M. J. Tegner, P. B. Edwards and K. L. Riser. 1999. Temporal and spatial scales of kelp demography: The role of oceanographic climate. *Ecol. Monogr.* 69: 219–250.

Denny, M. W. 1982. Forces on intertidal organisms due to breaking ocean waves: Design and application of a telemetry system. *Limnol. Oceanogr.* 27: 178–183.

Denny, M. W. 1988. *Biology and Mechanics of the Wave-Swept Environment.* Princeton University Press, Princeton, NJ.

Denny, M. W. 1995. Predicting physical disturbance: Mechanistic approaches to the study of survivorship on wave-swept shores. *Ecol. Monogr.* 65: 371–418.

Denny, M. W., T. L. Daniel and M. A. R. Koehl. l985. Mechanical limits to size in wave-swept organisms. *Ecol. Monogr.* 55: 69–102.

Drew, E. A. 1974. An ecological study of *Laminaria ochroleuca* growing in the straits of Messina. *J. Exp. Mar. Biol. Ecol.* 15: 11–24.

Drew, E. A. 1983. Light. In R. Earll and D. G. Erwin (eds.), *Sublittoral Ecology*, pp. 10–57. Clarendon Press, Oxford.

Dugan, J. E. and G. E. Davis. 1993. Applications of marine refugia to coastal fisheries management. *Canad. J. Fish. Aquat. Sci.* 50: 2029–2042.

Duggins, D. O. 1980. Kelp beds and sea otters: An experimental approach. *Ecology* 61: 447–453.

Duggins, D. O. 1988. The effects of kelp forests on nearshore environments: Biomass, detritus and altered flow. In G. R. Van Blaricom and J. A. Estes (eds.), *The Community Ecology of Sea Otters.* Springer Verlag, Berlin.

Duggins, D. O. and J. E. Eckman. 1994. The role of kelp detritus in the growth of benthic suspension feeders in an understorey kelp forest. *J. Exp. Mar. Biol. Ecol.* 176: 53–68.

Duggins, D. O. and J. E. Eckman. 1997. Is kelp detritus good food for suspension feeders? Effects of kelp species, age and secondary metabolites. *Mar. Biol.* 128: 489–495.

Duggins, D. O., C. A. Simenstad and J. A. Estes. 1989. Magnification of secondary production by kelp detritus in coastal marine ecosystems. *Science* 245: 170–173.

Duggins, D. O., J. E. Eckman and A. T. Sewell. 1990. Ecology of understory kelp environments. II. Effect of kelps on recruitment of benthic invertebrates. *J. Exp. Mar. Biol. Ecol.* 143: 27–45.

Dumas, J. V. and J. D. Witman. 1993. Predation by gulls on two rocky intertidal crabs, *Cancer irroratus* and *Carcinus maenus. J. Exp. Mar. Biol. Ecol.* 169: 89–101.

Dunton, K. and D. M. Schell. 1987. Dependence of consumers on macroalgal (*Laminaria solidungula*) carbon in an Arctic kelp community: ¹³C evidence. *Mar. Biol.* 93: 615–625.

Earll, R. and D. G. Erwin (eds.). 1983. *Sublittoral Ecology.* Clarendon Press, Oxford.

Ebeling, A. W., D. R. Laur and R. J. Rowley. 1985. Severe storm disturbance and reversal

of community structure in a Southern California kelp forest. *Mar. Biol.* 84: 287–294.

Eckman, J. E. and D. O. Duggins. 1991. Life and death beneath macrophyte canopies: Effects of understory kelps on growth rates and survival of marine benthic suspension feeders. *Oecologia* 87: 473–487.

Eckman, J. E., D. O. Duggins and A. T. Sewell. 1989. Ecology of understorey kelp environments. I. Effects of kelps on flow and particle transport near the bottom. *J. Exp. Mar. Biol. Ecol.* 129: 173–187.

Edgar, G. J. 1984. General features of the ecology and biogeography of Tasmanian rocky reef communities. *Papers Proc. R. Soc. Tasmania* 118: 173–186.

Elner, R. N. and R. N. Hughes. 1978. Energy maximization in the diet of the shore crab *Carcinus maenus. J. Anim. Ecol.* 47: 103–116.

Estes, J. A. 1996. The influence of large, mobile predators in aquatic food webs: Examples from sea otters and kelp forests. In S. P. R. Greenstreet and M. L. Trasker (eds.), *Aquatic Predators and Their Prey*, pp. 65–72. Fishing News Books, Blackwell, Oxford.

Estes, J. A. and D. O. Duggins. 1995. Sea otters and kelp forests in Alaska: Generality and variation in a community ecological paradigm. *Ecol. Monogr.* 75–100.

Etter, R. J. 1988. Physiological stress and color polymorphism in the intertidal snail *Nucella lapillus. Evolution* 42: 660–680.

Field, J. G., C. L. Griffiths, R. J. Griffiths, N. Jarman, P. Zoutendyk, B. Velimirov and A. Bowes. 1980. Variation in structure and biomass of kelp communities along the South West Cape coast. *Trans. R. Soc. S. Africa* 44: 145–203.

Fielding, P. J. and C. L. Davis. 1989. Carbon and nitrogen resources available to kelp bed filter feeders in an upwelling environment. *Mar. Ecol. Prog. Ser.* 55: 181–189.

Fowler, S. and D. Laffoley. 1993. Stability in Mediterranean–Atlantic sessile epifaunal communities at the northern limits of their range. *J. Exp. Mar. Biol. Ecol.* 172: 109–127.

Gaines, S. D. and J. Roughgarden. 1985. Larval settlement rate: A leading determinant of structure in an ecological community of the marine intertidal zone. *Proc. Natl. Acad. Sci. USA* 8: 3707–3711.

Garrity, S. D. and S. C. Levings. 1981. A predator–prey interaction between two physically and biologically constrained tropical rocky shore gastropods: Direct, indirect and community effects. *Ecol. Monogr.* 51: 267–286.

Genin, A., P. K. Dayton, P. F. Lonsdale and F. N. Spiess. 1986. Corals on seamount peaks provide evidence of current acceleration over deep-sea topography. *Nature* 322: 59–61.

Genovese, S. J. 1996. Regional and temporal variation in the ecology of an encrusting bryozoan in the Gulf of Maine. PhD Dissertation, Northeastern University, Boston.

Genovese, S. J. and J. D. Witman. 1999. Interactive effects of flow speed and particle concentration on growth rates of an active suspension feeder. *Limnol. Oceanogr.* 44: 1120–1131.

Gerodette, T. 1981. Dispersal of the solitary coral *Balanophyllia elegans* by demersal planular larvae. *Ecology* 62: 611–619.

Gill, J. M. and R. Coma. 1998. Benthic suspension feeders: Their paramount role in littoral marine food webs. *Trends Ecol. Evol.* 13: 316–321.

Glasby, T. M. 1999 Effect of shading on subtidal epibiotic assemblages. *J. Exp. Mar. Biol. Ecol.* 234: 275–290.

Glynn, P. W. 1988. El-Nino–Southern Oscillation 1982–1983: Nearshore, population, community, and ecosystem responses. *Annu. Rev. Ecol. Syst.* 19: 309–345.

Glynn, P. W. and G. M. Wellington. 1983. *Corals and Coral Reefs of the Galápagos Islands.* University of California Press, Berkeley.

Golikov, A. N. and O. A. Scarlato. 1968. Vertical and horizontal distribution of biocoenoses in the upper zones of Japan and Okhotsk Seas and their dependence on the hydrological system. *Sarsia* 34: 109–116.

Good, T. P. 1992. Experimental assessment of gull predation on the Jonah crab *Cancer borealis* in New England rocky intertidal and shallow subtidal zones. *J. Exp. Mar. Biol. Ecol.* 157: 275–284.

Gosner, K. L. 1971. *Guide to the Identification of Marine and Estuarine Invertebrates.* John Wiley and Sons, New York.

Graf, G. 1992. Benthic–pelagic coupling: A benthic view. *Oceanogr. Mar. Biol. Annu. Rev.* 30: 149–190.

Graham, K. R. and K. P. Sebens. 1996. The distribution of marine invertebrate larvae near vertical surfaces in the rocky subtidal zone. *Ecology* 77: 933–949.

Grange, K. R., R. J. Singleton, J. R. Richardson, P. J. Hill and W. D. L. Main. 1981. Shallow rock-wall biological associations of some southern fiords of New Zealand. *New Zealand J. Zool.* 8: 209–227.

Gregg, W. W. and J. J. Walsh. 1992. Simulation of the 1979 spring bloom in the mid-Atlantic Bight: A coupled physical/biological/optical model. *J. Geophys. Res.* 97: 5723–5743.

Gulliksen, B. 1982. Sedimentation close to a near vertical rocky wall in Balsfjorden, Northern Norway. *Sarsia* 21–27.

Hanski, I. A. and M. E. Gilpin. 1997. *Metapopulation Biology.* Academic Press, London.

Hanski, I. A. and M. Gyllenberg. 1993. Two general metapopulation models and the core-satellite species hypothesis. *Amer. Nat.* 142: 17–41.

Harris, L. G. and K. P. Irons. 1982. Substrate angle and predation as determinants in fouling community succession. In J.Cairns (ed.), *Artificial Substrates*, pp. 131–174. Ann Arbor Scientific Publications, Ann Arbor, MI.

Harris, L. G, A. W. Ebling , D. R. Laur and R. J. Rowley. 1984. Community recovery after storm damage: A case of facilitation in primary succession. *Science* 224: 1336–1338.

Harrold, C. and D. C. Reed. 1985. Food availability, sea urchin grazing and kelp forest community structure. *Ecology* 66: 1160–1169.

Harvell, C. D., K. Kim and 12 others. 1999. Emerging marine diseases: Climate links and anthropogenic factors. *Science* 285: 1505–1510.

Hatton, H. 1938. Essais de Bionomie explicative sur quelques especes intercotidales d'algues et d'animaux. *Ann. Inst. Oceanogr. Monaco* 17: 241–348.

Heine, J. 1989. Effects of ice scour on the structure of sublittoral marine assemblages of St. Lawrence and St. Matthew. Islands, Alaska. *Mar. Ecol. Prog. Ser.* 52: 253–260.

Heydorn, A. E. F. 1969. The rock lobster of southern African west coast, *Jasus lalandii.* 2. Population studies, behavior, reproduction, molting, growth and migration. Republic of South Africa Department of Industries, Division of Fisheries Investigational Report No. 71.

Hill, M., J. D. Witman and H. Caswell. In review. A Markovian model of a rocky subtidal community: Patch dynamics, disturbance and succession. *Ecology.*

Hisock, K. 1976. The influence of water movement on the ecology of sublittoral rocky areas. PhD Thesis, University of Wales.

Hisock, K. 1983. Water movement. In R. Earll and D. G. Erwin (eds.), *Sublittoral Ecology*, pp. 58–96. Clarendon Press, Oxford.

Hisock, K. 1985. Aspects of the ecology of rocky sublittoral areas. In P. G. More and R. Seed (eds.), *The Ecology of Rocky Coasts*, pp. 290–329. Hodder and Stoughton, London.

Hisock, K. and Mitchell, R. 1980. The description and classification of sublittoral epibenthic ecosystems. In J. H. Price, D. E. G. Irvine and W. F. Farnham (eds.), *The Shore Environment*,Vol 2, pp. 323–370. Academic Press, London.

Hjorleifsson, E., O. Kaasa, and K. Gunnarson. 1995. Grazing of kelp by green sea urchin in Eyjafoedur, North Iceland. In H. R. Skjoldal, C. Hopkins, K. E. Erikstad and H. P. Leinaas (eds.), *Ecology of Fjords and Coastal Waters*, pp. 593–597. Elsevier Science, Amsterdam.

Holling, C. S. 1959. The components of predation as revealed by a study of small mammal predation of the European pine sawfly. *Canad. Entomol.* 91: 293–320.

Hughes, R. G. 1975. The distribution of epizooites on the hydroid *Nemertesia antennina* (L.). *J. Mar. Biol. Assoc. U.K.* 55: 275–294.

Hulbert, A. W. 1980. The functional role of *Asterias vulgaris* Verrill (1866) in three subtidal communities. PhD Dissertation, University of New Hampshire, Durham.

Hulbert, A. W., K. Pecci, J. D. Witman, L. G. Harris, J. R. Sears and R. A. Cooper. 1982. Ecosystem definition and community structure of the macrobenthos of the NEMP monitoring station at Pigeon Hill in the Gulf of Maine. NOAA Technical Memorandum NMFS-F/NEC 14.

Irons, D. B, R. G. Anthony and J. A. Estes. 1986. Foraging strategies of glaucous winged gulls in a rocky intertidal community. *Ecology* 67: 1460–1474.

Jackson, G. A. 1984. Internal wave attentuation by coastal kelp stands. *J. Phys. Oceanogr.* 14: 1300–1306.

Jackson, G. A. and C. D. Winant. 1983. Effect of a kelp forest on coastal currents. *Cont. Shelf Res.* 2: 75–80.

Jackson, J. B. C. 1977. Competition on marine hard substrata: The adaptive significance of solitary and colonial strategies. *Amer. Nat.* 111: 743–767.

Jackson, J. B. C. 1991. Adaptation and diversity of reef corals. *BioScience* 41: 475–482.

Jerlov, N. G. 1970. Light: General introduction. In O. Kinne (ed.), *Marine Ecology,* Vol. 1, pp. 95–102. Wiley Interscience, London.

Johnson, C. and K. Mann. 1988. Diversity, patterns of adaptation, and stability of Nova Scotian kelp beds. *Ecol. Monogr.* 58: 129–154.

Kain, J. M. 1971. Continuous recording of underwater light in relation to *Laminaria* distribution. In D. J. Crisp (ed.), *Fourth European Marine Biology Symposium*, pp. 335–346. Cambridge University Press, London.

Kain, J. M. 1979. A view of the genus *Laminaria. Oceanogr. Mar. Biol. Annu. Rev.* 17: 101–161.

Kain, J. M. and N. S. Jones. 1967. Subtidal algal colonization follwing the removal of *Echinus. Helgolander wiss Meersunters* 15: 460–466.

Kay, A. M. and M. J. Keough. 1981. Occupation of patches in the epifaulnal communities on pier pilings and the bivalve *Pinna bicolor* at Edithburgh, South Australia. *Oecologia* 48: 123–130.

Keats, D. W., G. R. South and D. H. Steele. 1985. Algal biomass and diversity in the upper subtidal at a pack-ice-disturbed site in eastern Newfoundland. *Mar. Ecol. Prog. Ser.* 25: 151–158.

Kennely, S. J. 1989. Effects of kelp canopies on understory species due to shade and scour. *J. Exp. Mar. Biol. Ecol.* 50: 215–224.

Keough, M. J. 1983. Patterns of recruitment of sessile invertebrates in two subtidal habitats. *J. Exp. Mar. Biol. Ecol.* 66: 213–245.

Keough, M. J. and B. J. Downes. 1982. Recruitment of marine invertebrates: The role of active larval choices and early mortality. *Oecologia* 54: 348–352.

Kitching, J. A. 1939. Studies on sublittoral ecology. II. Recolonization at the upper margin of the sublittoral region with a note on the denudation of the *Laminaria* forest by storms. *J. Ecol.* 25: 482–491.

Kitching, J. A. 1941. Studies on sublittoral ecology. III. *Laminaria* forest on the west coast of Scotland: A study of zonation in relation to wave action and illumination. *Biol. Bull.* 80: 324–337.

Kitching, J. A. and F. J. Ebling. 1967. Ecological studies at Lough Ine. *Adv. Ecol. Res.* 4: 197–291.

Kitching, J. A., S. J. Lilly, S. M. Lodge, J. F. Sloane, R. Bassinndale and F. J. Ebling. 1952. The ecology of Lough Ine Rapids with special reference to water currents. III. *J. Ecol.* 40: 482–491.

Kitching, J. A., J. F. Sloan and F. J. Ebling. 1959. The ecology of Lough Ine. VIII. Mussels and their predators. *J. Anim. Ecol.* 28: 113–126.

Knaus, J. 1995. *Introduction to Oceanography.* Plenum Press, New York.

Koehl, M. A. R. and S. A. Wainwright. 1977. Mechanical adaptations of a giant kelp. *Limnol. Oceanogr.* 22: 1067–1071.

Konar. B. and C. Roberts. 1996. Large scale landslide effects on two exposed rocky subtidal areas in California. *Botanica Marina* 39: 517–524.

Konnecker, G. 1977. Epibenthic assemblages as indicators of environmental conditions. In B. F. Keegan, P. O. Ceidigh and P. J. S. Boaden (eds.), *Biology of Benthic Organisms*, pp. 391–395. Pergamon Press, Oxford.

Larson, D. W, U. Matthes and P. E. Kelly. 1999a. Cliffs as natural refuges. *Amer. Sci.* 87: 411–417.

Larson, D. W., U. Matthes, J. A. Gerrath, J. M. Gerrath, J. C. Nekola, G. L. Walker, S. Porembski, A. Chartlon and N. W. K. Larson. 1999b. Ancient stunted trees on cliffs. *Nature* 398: 382–383.

Leichter, J. J., and J. D. Witman. 1997. Water flow over subtidal rock walls: effects on distribution and growth of suspension feeders. *J. Exp. Mar. Biol. Ecol.* 209: 293–307.

Leinaas, H. P. Christie, H. 1996. Effects of removing sea urchins (*Strongylocentrotus droebachiensis*): stability of the barren state and succession of kelp forest recovery in the east Atlantic. *Oecologia* 105: 524–536.

Leonard, G. J., M. Levine, P. R. Schmidt and M. D. Bertness. 1998. Flow–driven variation in intertidal community structure in a Maine estuary. *Ecology* 79: 1395–1411.

Lesser, M. P., J. D. Witman and K. P. Sebens. 1994. Effects of flow and seston availability on scope for growth of benthic suspension feeding invertebrates in the Gulf of Maine. *Biol. Bull.* 187: 319–335.

Levin, L. A. and T. S. Bridges. 1995. Pattern and diversity in reproduction and development. Pp 1–48 in L. McEdward ed., *Ecology of Marine Invertebrate Larvae*. CRC Press, Boca Raton, FL.

Lewbell, G. S., A. Wolfson, T. Gerrodette, W. H. Lippincott, J. L. Wilson and M. M. Littler. 1981. Shallow water benthic communities on California's outer continental shelf. *Mar. Ecol. Prog. Ser.* 4: 159–168.

Lewis, J. R. 1964. *The Ecology of Rocky Shores.* English Universities Press, London.

Lissner, A. L. 1983. Relationship of water motion to the shallow water distribution and morphology of two species of sea urchin. *J. Mar. Res.* 41: 691–709.

Loher, T. 1992. Cunner predation in the shallow rocky subtidal: Effects on juvenile barnacles and mussels. Masters Thesis, Northeastern University, Boston.

Longhurst, A. 1998. *Ecological Geography of the Sea.* Academic Press, New York.

Luning, K. and R. Asmus. 1991. Physical characteristics of littoral ecosystems with special reference to marine plants. In A. C. Mathieson and P. H. Nienhuis (eds.), *Intertidal and Littoral Ecosystems*, pp. 7–26. *Ecosystems of the World* Vol. 24. Elsevier, Amsterdam.

Luning, K. and M. J. Dring. 1979. Continuous underwater light measurement near Helgoland (North Sea) and its significance for characteristic light limits in the sublittoral region. *Helgolander wiss Meeresunters* 32: 403–424.

Lundalv, T. 1971. Quantitative studies on rocky-bottom biocoenoses by underwater photogrammetry. *Thallassia Jugoslavica* 7: 201–208.

Lynch, D. R., J. T. C. Ip, C. E. Naimie and F. E. Werner. 1996. Comprehensive coastal circulation model with application to the Gulf of Maine. *Cont. Shelf. Res.* 16: 875–906.

Mann, K. H. and J. R. N. Lazier. 1996. *Dynamics of Marine Ecosystems: Biological–Physical Interactions in the Ocean*, 2nd ed. Blackwell Scientific, Boston.

Mathieson, A. C., C. A. Penniman and L. G. Harris. 1991. Northwest Atlantic rocky shore ecology. In A. C. Mathieson and P. H. Nienhuis (eds.), *Intertidal and Littoral Ecosystems*, pp. 109–191. *Ecosystems of the World* Vol. 24. Elsevier, Amsterdam.

McShane, P. E, K. P. Black and M. G. Smith. 1988. Recruitment processes in *Haliotis rubra* (Mollusca: Gastropoda) and regional hydrodynamics in southeastern Australia imply localized dispersal of larvae. *J. Exp. Mar. Biol. Ecol.* 124: 175–203.

Menge, B. A. 1976. Organization of the New England rocky intertidal community role of predation competition and environmental heterogeneity. *Ecol. Monogr.* 46:355–393.

Menge, B. A. 1978. Predation intensity in a rocky intertidal community: effect of an algal canopy, wave action and desiccation on predator feeding rates. *Oecologia.* 34: 17–35.

Menge, B. A. 1979. Coexistence between the seastars *Asterias vulgaris* and *A. forbesi* in a heterogenous environment: A non-equilibrium explanation. *Oecologia* 41: 245–272.

Menge, B. A. 1983. Components of predation intensity in the low zone of the New England rocky intertidal region. *Oecologia* 58: 141–155.

Menge, B. A. 1992. Community regulation: Under what conditions are bottom-up factors important on rocky shores? *Ecology* 73: 755–765.

Menge, B. A. and T. M. Farrell. 1989. Community structure and interaction webs in shallow marine hard-bottom communities: Tests of an environmental stress model. *Adv. Ecol. Res.* 19: 189–262.

Menge, B. A. and J. P. Sutherland. 1976. Species diversity gradients: synthesis of the roles of predation, competition, and temporal heterogeneity. *Amer. Nat.* 110: 351–369.

Menge, B. A. and J. P. Sutherland. 1987. Community regulation: variation in disturbance, competition, and predation in relation to environmental stress and recruitment. *Amer. Nat.* 130: 730–757.

Menge, B. A., B. A. Daley, P. A. Wheeler, E. Dahlhoff, E. Sanford and T. T. Strub. 1997. Benthic–pelagic links and rocky intertidal communities: Bottom-up effects on top-down control? *Proc. Natl. Ac. Sci. USA* 94: 14530–14535.

Miller, K. J. 1998. Short-distance dispersal of black coral larvae: Inference from spatial analysis of colony genotypes. *Mar. Ecol. Prog. Ser.* 163: 225–233.

Miller, M. W. and M. E. Hay. 1996. Coral–seaweed–grazer nutrient interactions on temperate reefs. *Ecology* 66: 323–344.

Moore, P. G. 1973. The kelp fauna of northeast Britain. II. Multivariate classification: Turbidity as an ecological factor. *J. Exp. Mar. Biol. Ecol.* 13: 127–163.

Neushul, M. 1967. Studies of subtidal marine vegetation in western Washington. *Ecology* 48: 83–94.

Norse, E. 1993. *Global Marine Biological Diversity.* Island Press, Washington, DC.

North, W. J. (ed.). 1971. The biology of giant kelp (*Macrocystis*) in California. *Nova Hedwigia* 32: 1–600.

Ojeda, F. P. and J. H. Dearborn. 1991. Feeding ecology of benthic mobile predators: Experimental analyses of their influence in rocky subtidal habitats of the Gulf of Maine. *J. Exp. Mar. Biol. Ecol.* 149: 13.

Okubo. 1980. *Diffusion and Ecological Problems: Mathematical Models.* Springer Verlag. Berlin.

Olson R. R. 1985. The consequences of short distance larval dispersal in a sessile marine invertebrate. *Ecology* 66: 30–39.

Osman, R. W. 1977. The establishment and development of a marine epifaunal community *Ecol. Monogr.* 47: 37–63.

Osman, R. W and R. B. Whitlatch. 1995. Predation on early ontogenetic life stages and its effect on recruitment into a marine community. *Mar. Ecol. Prog. Ser.* 117: 111–126.

Paine, R. T. 1966. Food web complexity and species diversity. *Amer. Nat.* 100: 65–75.

Paine, R. T. 1974. Intertidal community structure: Experimental studies on the relationship between a dominant competitor and its principal predator. *Oecologia* 15: 93–120.

Paine, R. T. 1976a. Biological observations on a subtidal *Mytilus californianus* bed. *Veliger* 19: 125–130.

Paine, R. T. 1976b. Size-limited predation: An observational and experimental approach with the *Mytilus–Pisaster* interaction. *Ecology* 567: 858–873.

Paine, R. T. 1980. Food webs, linkage, interaction strength, and community infrastructure. *J. Anim. Ecol.* 49: 667–685.

Paine, R. T. and S. A. Levin. 1981. Intertidal landscapes: Disturbance and the dynamics of pattern. *Ecol. Monogr.* 51: 145–178.

Palmer, M. A., J. D. Allan and C. A. Butman. 1996. Dispersal as a regional process affecting the local dynamics of marine and stream benthic invertebrates. *Trends Ecol. Evol.* 11: 322–326.

Palumbi, S. R. 1995. Using genetics as an indirect estimator of larval dispersal. In L. McEdward (ed.), *The Ecology of Marine Invertebrate Larvae*, pp. 323–368. CRC Press, Boca Raton, FL.

Pansini, M. and R. Pronzato. 1990. Observations on the dynamics of a Mediterranean sponge community. In K. Rutzler (ed.), *New Perspectives in Sponge Biology*, pp. 404–415. Smithsonian Institution Press, Washington, DC.

Patterson, M. R. 1984. Patterns of whole-colony prey capture in the octocoral *Alcyonium siderium. Biol. Bull.* 167: 613–629.

Peck, L. S., S. Brockington, S. Van Hove and M. Beghyn. 2000. Community recovery following catastrophic iceberg impacts in a soft-sediment shallow-water site at Signy Island, Antarctica. *Mar. Ecol. Prog. Ser.*

Pequenat, W. E. 1964. The epifauna of a California siltstone reef. *Ecology* 45: 272–282.

Peres, J. M. and R. Molinier. 1957. Compte rendu du colloque tenue a genes par la comite du benthos de la Commission Internationale pour L'Exploration Scientifique de la Mer Mediterranee. *Recl. Trav. Stn., Mar. Endoume* 22: 5–15.

Polis, G. A., W. B. Anderson and R. D. Holt. 1997. Toward an integration of landscape and food web ecology: the dynamics of spatially subsidized food webs. *Annu. Rev. Ecol. Syst.* 28: 289–316.

Pond, S. and G. L. Pickard. 1983. *Introductory Dynamical Oceanography*, 2nd ed. Pergamon Press, Oxford.

Reed, D. D. R. Laur and A. W. Ebling. 1998. Variation in algal dispersal and recruitment: the importance of episodic events. *Ecol. Monogr.* 58: 321–335.

Riedl, R. 1971. Water movement: Animals. In O. Kinne (ed.), *Marine Ecology*, Vol. 1, pp. 1123–1149. Wiley-Interscience, London.

Robles, C. 1987. Predator foraging characteristics and prey population structure on a sheltered shore. *Ecology* 68: 1502–1514.

Roughgarden, J., S. D. Gaines and H. Possingham. 1988. Recruitment dynamics in complex life cycles. *Science* 241: 1460–1466.

Russ, G. R. 1982. Overgrowth in a marine epifaunal community: Competitive hierarcies and competitive networks. *Oecologia* 53: 12–19.

Sanford, E., D. Bermudez, M. D. Bertness and S. D. Gaines. 1994. Flow, food supply, and acorn barnacle population dynamics. *Mar. Ecol. Prog. Ser.* 104: 49–62.

Santelices, B. 1991. Littoral and sublittoral communities of continental Chile. In A. C. Mathieson and P. H. Nienhuis (eds.), *Intertidal and Littoral Ecosystems*, pp. 347–370. *Ecosystems of the World*, Vol. 24. Elsevier, Amsterdam.

Santelices, B. and F. P. Ojeda. 1984. Population dynamics of coastal forests of *Macrocystis pyrifera* in Puerto Toro, Isla Navarino, Southern Chile. *Mar. Ecol. Prog. Ser.* 14: 175–183.

Scheibling, R. E. and A. W. Hennigar. 1997. Recurrent outbreaks in sea urchins *Strongylocentrotus droebachiensis* in Nova Scotia: Evidence for a link with large-scale meteorologic and oceanographic events. *Mar. Ecol. Prog. Ser.* 152: 155–165.

Scheibling, R. E., A. W. Hennigar and T. Balch. 1999. Destructive grazing, epiphytism, and disease: The dynamics of sea urchin–kelp interactions in Nova Scotia. *Canad. J. Fish. Aquat. Sci.* 56: 2300–2314.

Schiel, D. R. and M. Foster. 1986. The structure of subtidal algal stands in temperate waters. *Oceanog. Mar. Biol. Annu. Rev.* 24: 265–307.

Sears, J. R. and R. A. Cooper. 1978. Descriptive ecology of offshore, deep-water benthic algae in the temperate western North Atlantic Ocean. *Mar. Biol.* 44: 309–314.

Sebens, K. P. 1984. Water flow and coral colony size: Interhabitat comparisons of the octocoral *Alyconium siderium. Proc. Natl. Acad. Sci. USA* 81:5473–5477.

Sebens K. P. 1985. Community ecology of vertical walls in the Gulf of Maine USA: Small-scale processes and alternative community states. In P. G. Moore and R. Seed (eds.), *The Ecology of Rocky Coasts*. Hodder and Stoughton, Toronto.

Sebens K. P. 1986. Spatial relationships among encrusting marine organisms in the New England subtidal zone. *Ecol. Monogr.* 56: 73–96.

Sebens, K. P., J. D. Witman, R. Allmon and E. J. Maney. 1988. Early community development experiments in rocky subtidal habitats (Gulf of Maine, 30–80 m). In I. Babb and M. De Luca (eds.), *Benthic Productivity and Marine Resources of the Gulf of Maine*, pp. 45–66. National. Undersea Research Program, Research Report 88-3.

Seed, R. 1969. The ecology of *Mytilus edulis* on exposed rocky shores. I. Breeding and settlement. *Oecologia* 3: 277–316.

Seiderer, L. J. and R. C. Newell. 1985. Relative significance of phytoplankton, bacteria and plant detritus as carbon and nitrogen resources for the kelp bed filter feeder *Choromytilus meridionalis. Mar. Ecol. Prog. Ser.* 22: 127–139.

Shanks, A. L. 1995. Mechanisms of cross-shelf dispersal of larval invertebrates and fish. In L. McEdward (ed.), *Ecology of Marine Invertebrate Larvae*, pp. 323–368. CRC Press, Boca Raton, FL.

Shanks, A. L. and W. G. Wright. 1986 Adding teeth to wave action: the destructive effects of wave borne rocks on intertidal organisms *Oecologia* 69: 420–428.

Sheild, C. J. and J. D. Witman. 1993. The impact of *Henricia sanginolenta* predation on the finger sponges, *Isodictya* spp. *J. Exp. Mar. Biol. Ecol.* 166: 107–133.

Shepard. C., A. Price and C. Roberts. 1992. *Marine Ecology of the Arabian Sea Region*. Academic Press, London.

Shepard, S. A. and H. B. S. Womersley. 1970. The sublittoral ecology of West Island, South Australia. I. Environmental features and algal ecology. *Trans. R. Soc. Austral.* 94: 105–137.

Sih, A., G. Englund and D. Wooster. 1998. Emergent impacts of multiple predators on prey. *Trends Ecol. Evol.* 13: 350–355.

Simenstad, C. A., J. A. Estes and K. W. Kenyon. 1978. Aleuts, sea otters, and alternate stable-state communities. *Science* 200: 403–411.

Sloan, N. A. and T. H. Alldridge. 1981. Observations on an aggregation of the starfish *Asterias rubens* L. in Morecambe Bay, Lancashire, England. *J. Nat. Hist.* 15: 407–418.

Smith, F. 1999. Subtidal landscapes of a New Zealand fjord: Patterns of species diversity, community structure and recruitment processes. PhD Thesis, University of Otago, New Zealand.

Smith, F. and J. D. Witman. 1999. Patterns of species diversity in subtidal landscapes: maintenance by physical processes and larval recruitment. *Ecology* 80: 51–69.

Sousa, W. P. 1985. Disturbance and patch dynamics on rocky intertidal shores. In S. T. A. Pickett and P. S. White (eds.), *Natural Disturbance: The Patch Dynamics Perspective*. Academic Press, New York.

Stachowitz, J. J. and M. E. Hay. 1999. Reducing predation through chemically mediated campuflage.: Indirect effects of plant defenses on herbivores. *Ecology* 80: 495–509.

Stanton, B. R. and G. L. Pickard. 1981. Physical oceanography of the New Zealand fiords. *New Zealand Oceanogr. Mem.* 88: 37.

Steele, J. H. 1978. Some comments on plankton patches. In J. H. Steele (ed.), *Spatial Pattern in Plankton Communities*. Plenum Press, New York.

Steneck, R. S. 1986. The ecology of coralline algal crusts: consequent patterns and adaptive strategies. *Annu. Rev. Ecol. Syst.* 17: 273–303.

Steneck, R. S. 1997. Fisheries induced biolgical changes to the structure and function of the Gulf of Maine ecosystem. In G. T. Wallace and E. F. Braasch (eds.), *Proc. Gulf of Maine Ecosystem Dynamics*, pp. 153–167. RARGOM Report 97–1, Hanover, NH.

Stuart, V., J. G. Field and R. C. Newell. 1982. Evidence for the absorption of kelp detritus by the ribbed mussel *Aulacomya* after using new ^{15}C–labelled microsphere technique. *Mar. Ecol. Prog. Ser.* 49: 57–64.

Strathman, R. R. 1974. The spread of sibling larvae of sedentary marine invertebrates. *Amer. Nat.* 108: 29–44.

Sutherland, J. P and R. H. Karlson. 1977. Development and stability of the fouling community at Beaufort, North Carolina. *Ecol. Monogr.* 47: 425–446.

Svane, I. 1984. Observations on the long-term population dynamics of the perennial ascidian *Ascidia mentula* on the Swedish West Coast. *Biol. Bull.* 167: 630–646.

Svedrup, H. U., M. W. Johnson and R. H. Fleming. 1942. *The Oceans: Their Physics, Chemistry and General Biology*. Prentice Hall, Englewood Cliffs, NJ.

Tegner, M. J. and Dayton, P. K. 1987. El Niño effects on southern California kelp forest communities. *Adv. Ecol. Res.* 17: 243–279.

Thorson, G. 1950. Reproductive and larval ecology of marine bottom invertebrates. *Biol. Rev.* 25: 1–45.

Tremblay, J. M., J. W. Loder, F. E. Werner, C. E. Naime, F. H. Paige and M. M. Sinclair. 1994. Drift of sea scallop larvae *Placopecten magellanicus* on Georges Bank: A model study of the roles of mean advection, larval behavior and larval origin. *Deep Sea Res.* 41: 7–49.

Underwood, A. J. and E. J. Denley. 1984. Paradigms, explanations, and generalizations in models for the structure of intertidal communities on rocky shores. In D. R. Strong, D. Simberloff, L. G Abele and A. B. Thistle (eds.), *Ecological Communities: Conceptual Issues and the Evidence*, pp. 151–180. Princeton University Press, Princeton, NJ.

Underwood, A. J., E. J. Denley and M. J. Moran. 1983. Experimental analyses of the structure and dynamics of mid shore rocky intertidal communities in New South Wales. *Oecologia* 56: 202–219.

Underwood, A. J., M. J. Kingsford and N. L. Andrew. 1991. Patterns in shallow subtidal marine assemblages along the coast of New South Wales. *Austral. J. Ecol.* 16: 231–249.

Uriz, M. J., M. Maldonado, X. Turon and R. Marti. 1998. How do reproductive output, larval behavior, and recruitment contribute to adult spatial patterns in Mediterranean encrusting sponges? *Mar. Ecol. Prog. Ser.* 167: 137–148.

Vadas, R. L. and R. S. Steneck. 1988. Zonation of deep water benthic algae in the Gulf of Maine. *J. Phycol.* 24: 338–346.

Vance, R. R. 1978. A mutualistic interaction between a sessile marine clam and its epibionts. *Ecology* 59: 679–685.

Vance, R. R. 1988. Ecological succession and the climax community on a marine subtidal rock wall. *Mar. Ecol. Prog. Ser.* 48: 125–136.

Vasquez, J. A. 1993. Abundance, distributional patterns and diets of main herbivorous and carnivorous species associated with *Lessonia trabeculata* kelp beds in northern Chile. *Serie Ocasional Universidad Católica del Norte* 2: 212–229.

Vasquez, J. A. and A. H. Buschmann. 1997. Herbivore–kelp interactions in Chilean subtidal communities: A review. *Revista Chileña de Historia Natural* 70: 41–52.

Vasquez, J. A, J. C. Castilla and B. Santelices. 1984. Distributional patterns and diets of four species of sea urchins in a giant kelp forest (*M. pyrifera*) of Puerto Toro, Navarino Island, Chile. *Mar. Ecol. Prog. Ser.* 19: 55–64.

Velimirov, B. and C. L. Griffiths. 1979. Wave induced kelp movement and its importance for community structure. *Botanica Marina* 22: 169–172.

Velimirov, B., J. G. Field, C. L. Griffiths and P. Zoutendyk. 1977. The ecology of kelp bed communities in the Benguela upwelling system. *Helgolander wiss Meeresunters* 30: 495–518.

Waldron, H. N and T. A. Probyn. 1992. Nitrate supply and potential new production in the Benguela upwelling system. In A. I. L. Payne, K. H. Brink, K. H. Mann and R. Hilborn (eds.), *Benguela Trophic Functioning. S. African J. Mar. Sci.* 12: 29–39.

Watanabe, J. M. 1984. The influence of recruitment, competition, and benthic predation on the spatial distributions of three species of kelp forest gastropods. *Ecology* 65: 920–936.

Watling, L., 1998. Benthic fauna of soft substrates in the Gulf of Mexico. In E. M. Dorsey and J. Pederson (eds.), *Effects of Fishing Gear on the Sea Floor of New England*, pp. 20–29. MIT Sea Grant Publication 98-4.

Wethey, D. S. 1984 Thermal effects on the distribution of barnacle populations in New England. *Biol. Bull.* 59: 160–169.

Wiens, J. A. 1989. Spatial scaling in ecology. *Funct. Ecol.* 3: 385–397.

Wildish, D. and D. Kristmanson. 1997. *Benthic Suspension Feeders and Flow*. Cambridge University Press, Cambridge.

Williams, J. and S. A Elder. 1989. *Fluid Physics for Oceanographers and Physicists: An Introduction to Incompressible Flow*. Pergamon Press, Oxford.

Wing, S. R., J. J. Leichter and M. W. Denny. 1993. A dynamic model for wave induced light fluctuations in a kelp forest. *Limnol. Oceanogr.* 38: 396–407.

Witman, J. D. 1984. Ecology of rocky subtidal communities: The role of *Modiolus modiolus* and the influence of disturbance, competition, and mutualism. PhD Dissertation, University of New Hampshire, Durham.

Witman, J. D. 1985. Refuges, biological disturbance, and rocky subtidal community structure in New England. *Ecol. Monogr.* 55: 421–445.

Witman, J. D. 1987. Subtidal coexistence: Storms, grazing, mutualism, and the zonation of kelps and mussels. *Ecol. Monogr.* 57: 167–187.

Witman, J. D. 1992. Physical disturbance and community structure of exposed and protected reefs: A case study from St. John, U.S. Virgin Islands. *Amer. Zool.* 32: 641–634.

Witman, J. D. 1996. Dynamics of Gulf of Maine benthic communities. In D. and E. Braasch (eds.), *The Health of the Gulf of Maine Ecosystem: Cumulative Impacts of Multiple Stressors*. RARGOM Report 96-1. Dartmouth College, Hanover, NH.

Witman, J. D. 1998. Natural disturbance and colonization on subtidal hard substrates in the Gulf of Maine. In E. M. Dorsey and J. Pederson (eds.), *Effects of Fishing Gear on the Sea Floor of New England*, pp. 30–37. MIT Sea Grant Publication 98-4.

Witman, J. D and C. E. Arnold. 1989. Larval supply at two offshore pinnacles: Effect of topography. *Amer. Zool.* 29: 4 42.

Witman, J. D. and R. A. Cooper. 1983. Disturbance and contrasting patterns of population structure in the brachiopod *Terebratulina septentrionalis* from two subtidal habitats. *J. Exp. Mar. Biol. Ecol.* 73: 57–79.

Witman, J. D and K. R. Grange. 1998. Links between rain, salinity, and predation in a rocky subtidal community. *Ecology* 79: 2429–2447.

Witman, J. D. and K. P. Sebens. 1988. Benthic community structure at a subtidal rock pinnacle in the central Gulf of Maine. In I. Babb and M. De Luca (eds.), *Benthic Productivity and Marine Resources of the Gulf of Maine*, pp. 67–104. National Undersea Research Program Research Report 88-3.

Witman, J. D. and K. P. Sebens. 1990. Distribution and ecology of sponges at a subtidal rock ledge in the central Gulf of Maine. In K. Rutzler (ed.), *New Perspectives in Sponge Biology*, pp. 391–396. Smithsonian Institution Press, Washington, DC.

Witman, J. D. and K. P. Sebens. 1992. Regional variation in fish predation intensity: A historical perspective in the Gulf of Maine. *Oecologia* 90: 305–315.

Witman, J. D. and T. H. Suchanek. 1984. Mussels in flow: Drag and dislodgment by epizoans. *Mar. Ecol. Prog. Ser.* 16: 259–268.

Witman, J. D., A. W. Hulbert, L. G. Harris, K. Pecci, K. McCarthy and R. A. Cooper. 1980. Community structure of the macrobenthos of Pigeon Hill in the Gulf of Maine: A baseline report from the Ocean Pulse monitoring program. Ocean Pulse Tech. Report.

Witman, J. D., J. J. Leichter, S. J. Genovese, and D. A. Brooks. 1993. Pulsed phytoplankton supply to the rocky subtidal zone: Influence of internal waves *Proc. Natl. Acad. Sci. USA* 90: 1686–1690.

Witman, J. D., M. R. Patterson and S. J. Genovese. 2000. Benthic–pelagic linkages in rocky subtidal communities: Influence of food subsidy by internal waves. In G. A. Polis and M. Power (eds.), *Food Webs at the Landscape Level*. University of Chicago Press, Chicago.

Witman, J. D., S. J. Genovese, J. Bruno and J. McLaughlin. In review. Community ecology at the mesoscale: Massive recruitment triggers bottom-up effects and population regulation. *Ecology*.

Wolanksi, E. and W. M. Hamner. 1988. Topographically controlled fronts in the ocean and their biological influence. *Science* 241: 177–181.

Woodley, J. D., E. A. Chornesky and 18 others. 1981. Hurricane Allen's impact on Jamaican coral reefs. *Science* 214: 749–755.

Wootton, J. T. 1997. Estimates and tests of per capita interaction strength: diet, abundance and impact of intertidally foraging birds. *Ecol. Monogr.* 67: 45–64.

Yentsch, C. S. and N. Garfield. 1981. Principal areas of vertical mixing in the waters of the Gulf of Maine with reference to the total productivity of the area. In J. F. R. Gower (ed.), *Oceanography from Space*, pp. 303–322. Plenum Press, New York.

Young, C. R. 1995. Behavior and locomotion during the dispersal phase of larval life. In L. McEdward (ed.), *Ecology of Marine Invertebrate Larvae*, pp. 249–321. CRC Press, Boca Raton, FL.

Zenkevitch, L. 1983. *Biology of the Seas of the U.S.S.R.* Allen and Unwin, London.

Zimmerman, R. C. and J. N. Kremer. 1984. Episodic nutrient supply to a kelp forest ecosystem in southern California. *J. Mar. Res.* 42: 591–604.

chapter 14

Deep-Sea Communities

Ron J. Etter and Lauren S. Mullineaux

The deep sea is a vast and complex environment covering nearly two-thirds of the earth's surface. Early views considered the deep sea to be a monotonous ecosystem with a constant physical environment (e.g., temperature, salinity), a featureless bottom with weak currents, a steady drizzle of food from surface production, and an impoverished fauna. Discoveries over the past three decades have radically altered this perception, revealing a dynamic ecosystem in both space and time. The bottom is topographically complex, varying from the gentle rolling hills of the abyss to the rugged terrain of the continental slope (Mellor and Paull 1994) to the largest mountain chain on earth—the mid-ocean ridge system. Currents vary dramatically from weak flows (<1 cm/s) to benthic storms, which can last for days and disturb huge areas of the seafloor (Gage 1997). Far from being a steady rain, the flux of organic matter to the deep sea can be highly pulsed over much of the ocean floor reflecting seasonal blooms in surface production (e.g., Billett et al. 1983; Rice et al. 1986; Smith et al. 1998). Community structure, population dynamics, metabolic rates, activity levels, and reproductive cycles of the benthos can vary in response to the seasonal pulses of surface-derived phytodetritus (e.g., Tyler 1988; Gooday and Turley 1990; Smith et al. 1994; Drazen et al. 1998). Species diversity is now known to be surprisingly high (Hessler and Sanders 1967), with recent quantitative samples suggesting it may rival the richest terrestrial and shallow-water ecosystems (Grassle and Maciolek 1992). Recently discovered hydrothermal vent and cold seep habitats and their chemosynthetically based faunas constitute a unique and completely unsuspected class of ecosystems that play an important role in global biogeochemical cycles. Clearly, the deep sea is not a single environment with a characteristic fauna. It varies across a wide variety of spatial and temporal scales and has a rich array of habitats with often very distinct associated faunas.

In this chapter, we review the ecological processes that appear to structure deep-sea benthic communities on rocky and sediment substrates. The organisms inhabiting these two habitats are distinct, possess many different lifestyles and have often been studied with different approaches. For example, on rocky bottoms, most organisms are epifaunal suspension feeders, whereas those from sediments are primarily infaunal deposit feeders. Boxcores, which have been instrumental in quantifying patterns in sediment-dwelling communities, do not work on hard surfaces. Instead, rocky habitats have been studied using nonquantitative dredges and more recently by quantitative tools such as towed cameras, remotely operated vehicles (ROVs), or submersibles. Consequently, research on rocky substrates tends to be focused on a specific process, testing biological predictions based on hypothesized interactions between the organisms and their environment. Many of these studies have been motivated initially by oceanographic or geological observations. For example, vent communities were discovered after water-column chemical anomalies suggested the presence of undersea hydrothermal activity. Faunas on isolated underwater mountains (seamounts) and abrupt topographic discontinuities on the continental margins (banks) received study after water-column studies indicated that these abrupt topographic features were associated with accelerated flows and elevated phytoplankton productivity. Ecological studies on these hard substrates are typically restricted in range and rarely include comprehensive collection of specimens, which limits the information on diversity and depth- or latitude-related patterns. In contrast, sediment studies are more pattern driven—patterns in community structure are quantified followed by experimental and comparative re-search on putative processes. For example, the remarkably high macrofaunal diversity in deep-sea sediments identified by Hessler and Sanders (1967) led to considerable research on the ecological and evolutionary processes that regulate diversity. Because of these differences, in the following sections we separate rocky and sediment habitats and organize discussion of these communities along the lines of their typical scientific inquiry.

The scope of this chapter is limited by necessity, and many topics of interest are not covered. Those included were chosen because they illustrate broad themes in the community ecology of the deep sea and have received sufficient study to make substantial progress in the field. Gage and Tyler (1991) provide a more detailed and extensive review of the deep sea including the biology and ecology of deep-sea organisms.

PHYSICAL CHARACTERISTICS

The deep sea lies below 200 m in depth and is characterized by cold temperatures, constant salinity, perpetual darkness, and high pressures. It is primarily a soft-substrate habitat with the vast majority of the bottom covered by (1) coarse particles of terriginious origin, (2) biogenic oozes from surface production, and (3) fine clays. The composition of the sediments varies with depth, latitude, hydrodynamic regime, topography, and overlying surface production (Gage and Tyler 1991).

The vast expanses of sediment-covered seafloor are punctuated by islands of hard-bottom habitat consisting of rock, mineral deposits, or biogenic material. The size of these habitats ranges from hundreds of kilometers along seafloor mountain ranges to a few centimeters on an individual manganese nodule (a rocklike mineral concretion). Deep-sea hard bottoms also provide topographic complexity to the habitat and create their own undersea "climates" in terms of flow regime and particulate organic matter (POM) fluxes. Large topographic features such as ridges, seamounts, and escarpments alter deep-ocean circulation and interact with internal waves (e.g., tides) to generate flows that affect food supply and dispersal of planktonic larval stages. Smaller features, such as manganese nodules and biogenic objects (live or dead), may lift inhabitants out of the slowest flows in the benthic boundary layer or elevate them above layers of fine particulates that interfere with filter feeding.

Because the deep sea lies below the photic zone (where there is sufficient sunlight for photosynthesis), there is no primary productivity, except for the unusual circumstances around hydrothermal vents and cold seeps. Organisms rely on POM sinking from surface waters or advected laterally by various mechanisms (e.g., turbidity currents). Vertical POM flux decreases exponentially with depth and parallels surface production over large geographic scales (Turley et al. 1995), creating a food-poor environment where energy constraints become more severe with increasing depth or distance from continental margins.

SEDIMENT COMMUNITIES

The organisms inhabiting deep-sea sediments are phylogenetically similar to those in shallow water and usually are divided into three broadly overlapping major groups based primarily on their size. The "megafauna" are mostly epifaunal and are sufficiently large to be identified in deep-sea photographs. They include highly mobile forms such as the demersal and benthopelagic fishes, echinoderms, cephalopods, and arthropods such as decapods, large scavenging amphipods, and pycnogonids. More sedentary forms include the sponges, a variety of different cnidarians such as soft corals, gorgonians, sea pens, and sea anemones, and enormous protozoans (e.g., foraminifera and xenophyophores). The macrofauna, are much smaller than the megafauna (usually defined as those retained on a 300 µm sieve), live on or within the sediments, include most metazoan phyla, and are the most taxonomically diverse group. Polychaetes are typically the most abundant, often comprising more than half the species, followed by peracarid crustaceans and molluscs. Although the deep-water macrofauna may generally be similar to that in shallow water, there are important differences. Taxa such as aplacophorans, priapulids, sipunculans, tanaids, and isopods are considerably more abundant in typical lower bathyal or abyssal assemblages. Even among the polychaetes, different families dominate in shallow and deep water. The smallest size category, the meiofauna (those retained on a 42 µm sieve), lives interstitially and include both metazoans (e.g., entomostracan crustaceans, nematodes, and other pseudocoelomate phyla) and protozoans (e.g., foraminiferans). The nematodes are by far the most abundant forms, often comprising more than 80% of the metazoan meiofauna. The discussion of the sediment communities that follows will focus primarily on the macrofauna.

The most distinctive feature of the deep-sea macrofauna is their small average body size compared to shallow-water relatives. For example, rissoid gastropods in shallow water may reach 2–3 cm as adults, whereas closely related rissoids in the deep sea may only reach 2–3 mm, an order of magnitude smaller. Similar patterns exist for most other macrofaunal organisms such that a 1 mm mesh sieve used to collect the macrofauna in shallow water would collect virtually no specimens from most deep-sea samples (Hessler and Jumars 1974). At the community level, average organism size also decreases with depth, reflecting an increase in the relative abundance of meiofauna (Thiel 1979) as well as a decrease in the average size of both the macrofaunal and meiofaunal species (Gage 1977; Schwinghamer 1985; Shirayama and Horikoshi 1989). The megafauna, in contrast, tend to show little change in average body size with depth (Haedrich et al. 1980; Lampitt et al. 1986).

The trend toward smaller size for the macrofauna appears to reflect larger species being replaced by smaller species along the depth gradient. This trend does not appear to hold within species; careful measurements of bathymetric variation within macrofaunal species have found size often increases with depth in the deep sea (Wilson 1983; Rex and

Etter 1998). This suggests that intra- and interspecific patterns may be shaped by different forces. Although the ecological and evolutionary mechanisms favoring smaller size are unclear, it is generally attributed to the reduced food supply (i.e., POM flux) in the deep sea.

Another key feature of deep-sea communities is the extremely low standing stock of organisms. Both the biomass and density of macrofauna decline exponentially with depth (Figure 14.1) such that in shallow water there may be 10^2 g/m^2 and 10^4 individuals/m^2, whereas at abyssal depths this drops to less than 1 g/m^2 and 100 individuals/m^2. Similar trends are observed for the meiofauna (Thiel 1979; Shirayama 1983) and megafauna (Rowe and Menzies 1969; Haedrich et al. 1980; Lampitt et al. 1986). The exponential decline in standing crop is widely thought to be caused by the parallel decline in POM flux (Rowe 1983). Support for this hypothesis is provided by the consistently strong correlations between geographic (or bathymetric) variation in standing crop and direct measures of POM flux (Tietjen et al. 1989; C. R. Smith

et al. 1998) as well as various surrogates of POM flux such as sediment organic carbon (Schaff and Levin 1994; Levin and Gage 1998), differences in overlying surface production, distance from shore, width of the continental shelf, and latitude (Rowe 1971; Rowe et al. 1974; Rowe and Pariente 1992). These relationships are sufficiently strong that the standing crop of the benthos is often considered to be the best indication of energy flux to the deep sea (Rowe 1971, 1983; Rex 1976, 1983; C. R. Smith et al. 1998). Sediment community oxygen consumption (SCOC—a measure of metabolic demand for organic carbon) also decreases with depth and distance from land (Smith and Hinga 1983; K. L. Smith 1987), suggesting that energetic demands by the community parallel food supply. Interestingly, microbes often account for the bulk of the respiratory demand of deep-sea soft-sediment communities and megafauna account for most of its biomass. Whatever the causes, deep-water communities are characterized by low density, little biomass, and small organisms, all of which appear to be coupled ultimately to the low food supply.

Species Diversity

One of the most thoroughly studied aspects of community structure in deep-sea soft-substrate habitats is species diversity. Species diversity varies geographically and bathymetrically (Rex et al. 1997), but typically is much greater than in similar coastal soft-sediment communities (Hessler and Sanders 1967; Sanders 1968; Gage 1996). For example, compare diversity between a series of deep-water samples collected off the coast of Massachusetts (the Northern data are part of the Atlantic Continental Slope and Rise study—ACSAR) to a very similar set of samples collected from the nearby shallow waters of Georges Bank (Table 14.1). The shallow and deep samples are geographically adjacent (both just off the coast of Massachusetts), were collected in a similar way, and were sorted over the same size sieves. The taxonomy was consistent (identified by the same individuals), the entire macrofaunal

(A)

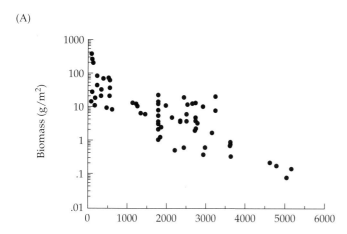

(B)

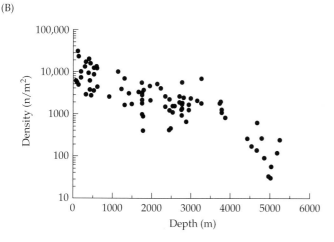

Figure 14.1 Estimates of benthic biomass (g/m² wet weight) and density (numbers/m²) as a function of depth for the western North Atlantic. Samples were collected with an anchor dredge, boxcorer, or a modified Ekman grab. (Data compiled from Maciolek et al. 1987a,b; Rowe et al. 1974; and Sanders et al. 1965.)

TABLE 14.1 Average measures of diversity and density for the Georges Bank and the ACSAR (Deep Sea North) samples.

	Georges Bank	ACSAR North	ACSAR North (130 m)[a]
Samples	1149	191	63
Depth range (m)	38–167	250–2180	1220–1350
Species/m²	165	278	319
E(S1000)[b]	68.80	156	188
Shannon-Weiner	4.09	5.59	6.70

Data are from Maciolek et al. (1987b) and Maciolek-Blake et al. (1985).

[a]ACSAR North (130 m) are averages based only on samples collected between 1220–1350 m from the North.

[b]E(S1000) are Hurlbert's (1971) expected number of species normalized to 1000 individuals.

community was enumerated, and the ACSAR data represent the most extensive quantitative samples collected from the deep sea. As far as we know, no other shallow- and deep-water data are as comparable. The Georges Bank samples were collected with 0.04 m^2 Eckman cores from 38–167m depths. The ACSAR samples were collected with 0.25 m^2 box-cores from 250–2500 m depth, but only the center 0.09 m^2 of the deep-sea boxcores were used for community analysis. For the deep-water samples (those > 200m), on average 278 species coexist in an area of 1 m^2 and the expected number of species was 156 when normalized to 1000 individuals (ES$_{1000}$). In contrast, the shallow-water samples produced an average of only 165 species m^2 and 68.8 species per 1000 individuals (Table 14.1). This comparison of averages is conservative because the deep-sea samples span a 2000 m depth gradient and include relatively shallow depths that are low in diversity. If the deep-sea samples are restricted to a 130 m depth gradient (similar to the Georges Bank samples) centered at 1300 m, the differences are even more pronounced (Table 14.1). Species accumulation curves based on either individuals or area also indicate that diversity is greater in the deep-sea samples (Figure 14.2). Species diversity in this region of the North Atlantic is parabolically related to depth with peak macrofaunal diversity around 1250 m (Figure 14.3).

Relative abundance distributions also differ dramatically between shallow- and deep-water communities. In deep-sea samples, it is rare that any single species comprises more than 10% of the total abundance, and the overwhelming majority of species (> 90%) make up less than 2% each (e.g., Hessler and Jumars 1974; Grassle and Maciolek 1992). In shallow-water communities, the numerically dominant species may account for 10–25% of the total individuals (e.g., Sanders 1968; Gray 1994). For example, the numerically dominant species comprise a much greater fraction of the total abundance within the macrofaunal community in the Georges Bank samples (10–70%) than in the deep-water samples (Figure 14.4). Deep-water samples also appear to have many more rare species (i.e., singletons), although proportionately the number of singletons make up about 30% of the species independent of depth (Figure 14.5; see also Carney 1997).

Processes Maintaining High Deep-Sea Diversity

How can more than 250 species, most of which are feeding on the nutrient poor sediments, coexist within a small patch (1 m^2) of the deep seafloor? This question is especially intriguing because the deep sea lacks the obvious structural complexity that is known to be important in other high-diversity environments (e.g., tropical rain forests, coral reefs) and the vast majority of deep-water species are deposit feeders, relying on the labile components of detritus for nutrition (Sanders and Hessler 1969; Hessler and Jumars 1974; Gage and Tyler 1991). The coexistence of such a large number of species, apparently exploiting the same resource, has intrigued deep-sea biologists for more than 30 years (Sanders 1968; Jumars and Gallagher 1982; Gage 1996).

The initial discovery of high species diversity in the deep-sea benthos (Hessler and Sanders 1967) presented a dilemma

for community ecologists. What was the mechanism of species coexistence in such an apparently uniform environment with limited resources? Theoretical advances during the past 30 years have provided four major classes of solutions to species coexistence: (1) local spatial heterogeneity (MacArthur 1972; Tilman 1982), (2) nonequilibrium dynamics (Caswell 1978; Armstrong and McGehee 1980), (3) interactions among three or more trophic levels (Janzen 1970), and (4) recruitment limitation (Tilman 1994; Hurtt and Pacala 1995). Which of these are most important in explaining the remarkably rich deep-sea fauna?

Early theories spanned the gamut of equilibrial and nonequilibrial thinking in ecology. Sanders (1968) proposed that the high diversity in the deep sea resulted from the unusual physical stability over evolutionary time, which allowed greater competitive niche partitioning. Dayton and Hessler (1972) argued that niche partitioning would be limited in the deep sea because it was spatially and temporally homogeneous. They suggested that predation by the megafauna enhanced diversity by alleviating competition in the macrofauna, much as argued by Paine (1966) in the intertidal zone. Grassle and Sanders (1973) pointed out that the low density and K-type life histories of most deep-sea species were incompatible with the high mortality levels suggested by Dayton and Hessler. Instead, they argued that species may be specialized to exploit a particular stage of succession that resulted after a local disturbance. Because patches will vary in their stage of succession, diversity could be maintained through contemporaneous disequilibrium. Others suggested that greater diversity in the deep sea may simply reflect the larger area relative to shallow water (Osman and Whitlatch 1978; Abele and Walters 1979), but this has subsequently been shown to be unlikely (Rex 1983). These early theories provided the framework, and impetus, for much of the research conducted on community structure in the deep sea over the last 30 years.

SPATIAL HETEROGENEITY. Both spatial heterogeneity and the nonequilibrial dynamics of various types of patches seem to be important, but they appear to operate on much smaller spatial scales and longer temporal scales than in similar shallow-water communities and involve many more biotic and physical structures. The important scales of heterogeneity in the deep sea were identified by analyzing spatial dispersion, within partitioned 0.25 m^2 boxcores and among boxcores placed varying distances apart. These studies revealed some degree of aggregation for different taxa and multispecies assemblages on scales ranging from centimeters and meters to kilometers (Hessler and Jumars 1974; Jumars 1975, 1976, 1978; Hecker and Paul 1979; Jumars and Eckman 1983). However, the most diverse component of the benthos, small sedentary macrofaunal species, tend to show little patchiness (Jumars 1975, 1976; Gage 1977), suggesting that environmental heterogeneity may be experienced by most species on scales smaller than those sampled (< 0.01m^2).

This led Jumars (1975, 1976) to propose that biogenically produced heterogeneity on the scale of an individual may be

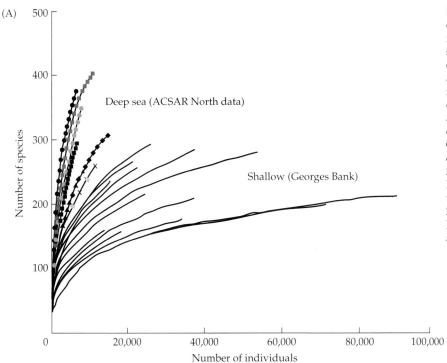

(A)

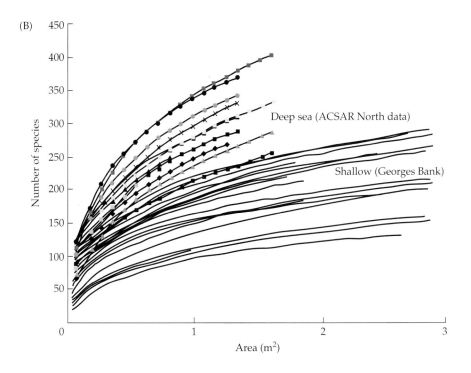

(B)

Figure 14.2 Species accumulation curves computed using EstimateS (Colwell 1997) for numbers of (A) individuals or (B) areas sampled. Each curve represents the average cumulative number of species at one station as samples are pooled. The cumulative number of species are averages from 50 randomizations of pooling replicates 1, 2, 3...R at a time, where R = the number of replicates taken at a particular station. The Georges Bank samples (solid lines) were collected with 0.04 m^2 Eckman cores from 38–167 m depths. The ACSAR (Deep Sea North data; lines with symbols) samples were collected with 0.25 m^2 boxcores from 250–2500 m depth. (Data compiled from Maciolek et al. 1987b and Maciolek-Blake et al. 1985.)

important in maintaining diversity in the deep sea. Biogenic sources of small-scale heterogeneity include polychaete mudballs (Jumars 1975; Thistle and Eckman 1990; Levin and Edesa 1997), protozoan tests (Levin et al. 1986; Levin 1991), sponge spicules (Jumars and Eckman 1983; Bett and Rice 1992), tubes (Gooday et al. 1992; Schaff and Levin 1994), burrows (Aller and Aller 1986), pits (Schaff and Levin 1994; Snelgrove et al. 1994), and mounds (Levin et al. 1991a; Kukert and Smith 1992). The relative stability of deep-sea sediments al-

lows these structures to persist for long periods of time (e.g., years—Jumars 1976; Smith and Hessler 1987; Kukert and Smith 1992), potentially providing distinct microhabitats for specialized macro- and meiofauna (see Figure 14.6). Several studies have provided support for this hypothesis by documenting correlations between community structure and biogenic features or identifying individual species that are associated primarily with specific biogenic structures (e.g., Thistle 1978; Thistle 1979; Jumars and Eckman 1983; Thistle 1983a;

Figure 14.3 Hurlbert's (1971) expected number of species for each sample when normalized to 100 individuals as a function of depth. (Data compiled from Maciolek et al. 1987b and Maciolek-Blake et al. 1985.)

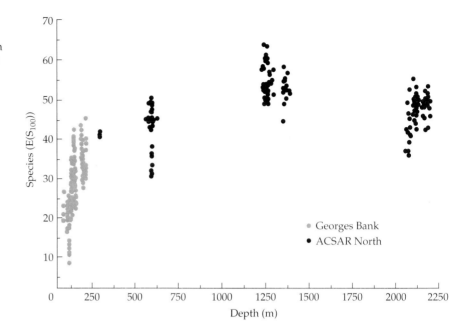

Smith et al. 1986; Eckman and Thistle 1991; Levin 1991; Gooday et al. 1992; Thistle et al. 1993; Schaff and Levin 1994). Because these correlations are generally quite weak and account for only a small proportion of the species within a local community, heterogeneity on these scales cannot alone account for the tremendously high levels of species coexistence.

SEDIMENT CHARACTERISTICS.   On very small scales, heterogeneity in sediment grain size may be important because it provides diverse food resources. It has long been known that the structure and composition of soft-sediment communities are related to sediment characteristics (e.g., Petersen 1913; Sanders 1958; Rhoads 1974; Gray 1981), but the explanations for these relationships are varied and remain controversial (Snelgrove and Butman 1994). The nature of the sediments

may play an especially important role in structuring deep-sea communities because the deposit feeders that comprise the overwhelming majority of species (Sanders and Hessler 1969; Jumars and Gallagher 1982) live on or within the sediments and rely on the sediments for nutrition. Potential foods for deposit feeders include microbes, organic debris, and meiofauna, but the relative importance of these sources in their diet is poorly understood (Levinton 1979; Tenore et al. 1982; Jumars and Wheatcroft 1989; Mayer 1989). Theoretical predictions based on optimal foraging theory suggest that deposit feeders should selectively ingest the smaller particles because of the greater surface area for organics (Taghon et al. 1978), and several studies with shallow- and deep-water organisms support this prediction (Whitlatch 1980; Taghon 1982; Wheatcroft and Jumars 1987; Self and Jumars 1988; Wheatcroft 1992). In addi-

Figure 14.4 The percent of the individuals that are from the single most abundant species as a function of the total number of species recorded from pooled replicate samples at each station. The Georges Bank data are from pooling six 0.04 m^2 Eckman cores (= 0.24 m^2) taken during a single cruise to each station. The ACSAR North data are from pooling three 0.09 m^2 boxcores (= 0.27 m^2) taken during a single cruise to each station. (Data compiled from Maciolek et al. 1987b and Maciolek-Blake et al. 1985.)

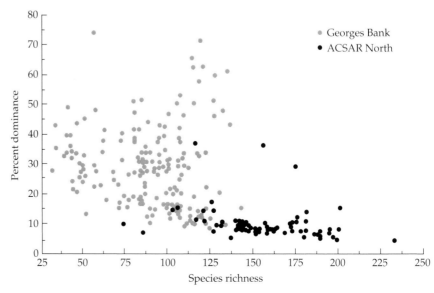

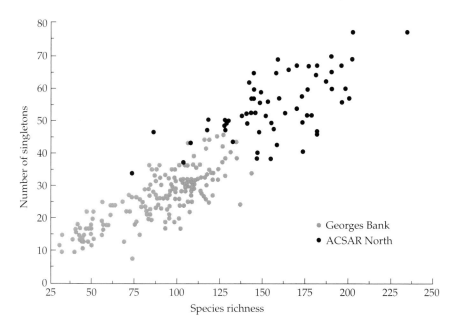

Figure 14.5 The number of species represented by a single individual as a function of the total number of species recorded from pooled replicate samples at each station. The pooled replicates are as described in Figure 14.4. (Data compiled from Maciolek et al. 1987b and Maciolek-Blake et al. 1985.)

tion, several species exhibit interspecific differences in particle size preference (Fenchel et al. 1975; Fenchel and Kofoed 1976; Whitlatch 1980), suggesting that the sediments may be partitioned by size in some shallow-water communities. Partitioning the sediments with respect to size may be even more likely in the deep sea if there is strong selection for macrophagy (consuming one food particle at a time—e.g., one sediment particle), as suggested by Jumars et al. (1990). They argue that the reduced food supply in the deep sea and the digestive constraints imposed by tiny organisms feeding on deposits would select for a shift from microphagy (consuming multiple particles at one time) to macrophagy, allowing species to selectively ingest the more labile components of the sediments. This selection pressure may be most intense on newly settled

larvae of deep-sea macrofauna because they lack energy reserves and have high weight-specific energetic demands.

Etter and Grassle (1992) proposed that if deep-sea organisms partition sediments with respect to size, much of the variability in species diversity may reflect variability in particle-size distributions—a greater range of particle sizes would permit the coexistence of more species. They tested this hypothesis using 558 boxcores collected from bathyal depths (250–3029 m) in the western North Atlantic and found a strong positive relationship between macrofaunal diversity and grain-size diversity of the silt fraction, the particles typically consumed by deposit feeders (Whitlatch 1980; Taghon 1982; Self and Jumars 1988). The relationship accounted for a similar proportion of the variance at inter-regional (> 100 km),

Figure 14.6 The seafloor at 2645 m in the Scotia Sea (60°46′S 49°20′W). Note the heterogeneity from mounds, pits, tubes, and animal tracings. (From Heezen and Hollister 1971; used with permission.)

regional (1–100 km) and local scales (< 1 km), suggesting that gradients in sediment characteristics may explain variation in diversity across a variety of scales. Consistent with this notion, well-known bathymetric patterns of species diversity (Rex 1981, 1983) appeared to be largely attributable to a gradient in sediment heterogeneity. These results suggest that sediment diversity may play an important role in determining the number of species within a community. Because similar findings have been documented in shallow water (Whitlatch 1981), the effects of sediment diversity on species diversity may be a ubiquitous feature of soft-sediment communities. However, the correlations may be spurious or reflect more important proximal factors (e.g., food availability, hydrodynamics, larval supply, etc.). In situ experiments will be necessary to assess the causal nature of this relationship and tease apart the potentially confounding mediating mechanisms.

PATCH DYNAMICS. Patches created by small-scale disturbances may enhance diversity if their dynamics are asynchronous creating a landscape that is a spatiotemporal mosaic of patches in various stages of succession (Grassle and Sanders 1973; Caswell 1978; Connell 1978; Sousa 1979a; Paine and Levin 1981). The dynamics (successional changes) may be driven by species specialized to a specific stage of a patch and/or simple differences in life histories such as colonization ability or longevity. Patch dynamics may be especially important in the deep sea (Grassle and Sanders 1973; Grassle and Morse-Porteous 1987; Grassle 1989) because life-history characteristics are highly diverse (Gage and Tyler 1991; Young and Eckelbarger 1994), and the time scale of the dynamics is considerably longer than in shallow water. Patches in shallow water are rapidly (days to weeks) homogenized by storms, high rates of colonization, and greater bioturbation (Levin and Smith 1984; Smith and Brumsickle 1989; Hall 1994), whereas in many deep-sea settings they can persist for more than 5 years (Smith and Hessler 1987). The slower dynamics will promote coexistence by reducing the rate at which inferior species are excluded, both locally and regionally (Caswell and Cohen 1991a, 1991b; Caswell and Etter 1999). A variety of processes may create small-scale disturbances including bioturbation (Smith et al. 1986; Kukert and Smith 1992) and megafaunal predation. Grassle and colleagues (Grassle and Morse-Porteous 1987; Grassle and Grassle 1992) have argued that localized concentrations of food such as wood, clumps of macroalgae, phytodetritus pulses from surface blooms that collect in depressions, and carcass falls are also important patch structures in the deep sea because they occur on a background of low productivity, temporally alleviate competition, and initiate changes in community structure.

Experimental emplacement of carcasses (Smith 1985, 1986; Grassle and Morse-Porteous 1987), wood (Turner 1973, 1977), and macroalgae (Grassle and Morse-Porteous 1987) demonstrate that deep-sea communities respond to patches of organic matter, but the nature of the response and the time scales involved are highly variable. For example, fish carcasses were consumed so rapidly by the large assemblage of highly mobile scavengers that little organic enrichment of the local community occurs. The primary effect was to mechanically disturb the sediments, which depressed diversity and altered the composition of the local fauna. The dynamics of these patches varied greatly, being considerably faster in the eastern Pacific (Smith 1985, 1986) than in the western Atlantic (Grassle and Morse-Porteous 1987). In contrast, on the "wood islands" an entire community developed within a year (Turner 1973, 1977), and the conversion of the wood to more labile organic material by the wood-boring bivalves enriched the nearby soft-sediment community and altered its structure and composition (Grassle and Morse-Porteous 1987). Whale carcasses impact adjacent sediment communities for many years (10+) causing reduced macrofaunal abundances and increased diversity, although both these changes were attributed primarily to effects on a single paraonid polychaete, which was the numerically dominant species in the assemblage (C. R. Smith et al. 1998). These types of events can initiate changes in community structure that persist for years and potentially enhance diversity, but they are extremely rare over most of the vast deep sea, and thus their relative contribution is probably modest.

Deep-sea populations also may respond to patches created by phytodetritus aggregates from surface blooms (Rice et al. 1986; Smith et al. 1994; Lauerman and Kaufmann 1998), phytodetritus accumulating in individual burrows (Aller and Aller 1986), or other aspects of bottom topography that increase sediment organic content (Billett et al. 1983; Lampitt 1985, Gooday and Turley 1990). Communities of bacteria (Lochte and Turley 1988), meiofauna (Gooday et al. 1996; Drazen et al. 1998), and macrofauna (Pfannkuche 1993) as well as sediment community oxygen consumption (Smith and Baldwin 1984; Graf 1989; Smith et al. 1994), are known to vary temporally in response to seasonal pulses of phytodetritus. Whether this can be extrapolated to spatial variation (patches) in phytodetritus is unclear because no studies have compared communities on the appropriate spatial scales.

Disturbance due to biogenic activity is likely to be more common than the arrival of large parcels of organic matter and may be a more important source of spatiotemporal heterogeneity. Small-scale manipulative experiments involving defaunated sediment trays, nutrient enriched sediment trays (Grassle 1977; Levin and Smith 1984; Desbruyères et al. 1985; Smith 1985, Grassle and Morse-Porteous 1987; Levin and DiBacco 1995; Snelgrove et al. 1992, 1996), and artificial sediment mounds (Smith et al. 1986; Kukert and Smith 1992) have been used extensively to quantify colonization rates and test the importance of disturbance in maintaining high local diversity. The experiments have been conducted in a wide variety of habitats and under diverse physical settings, but several broad conclusions can be made. (1) Patch dynamics are spatially and temporally variable—the species involved in succession can vary as well as the time required to reach background community characteristics. Most importantly, there is some evidence that different species respond to different types of patches suggesting that species may specialize on particular patch types (Snelgrove et al. 1996). In addition, patches can persist for long periods (2 to more than

5 years) providing time for fugitive-type species to colonize new patches. (2) Opportunists often respond to disturbed habitats and coexist with more equilibrium-type species during the early stages of succession. Relatively rapid responses occur in sediments enriched with POM (Grassle and Morse-Porteous 1987; Snelgrove et al. 1996) or when disturbances better mimic natural processes (Smith et al. 1986; Kukert and Smith 1992). (3) Certain species are found exclusively in patches suggesting that disturbance is necessary for their persistence, although this may also reflect the difficulty of detecting locally rare species in a background community that is comprised of a large number of species represented by a single individual. Nevertheless, the increase in relative abundance of typically rare species is consistent with the patch mosaic model. (4) Species diversity increases within patches through time, sometimes exceeding that of ambient sediments during recovery.

These experiments together provide compelling evidence that small-scale disturbances, patch dynamics, and the mosaic nature of deep-sea sediments can contribute to high local diversity in these communities. Although we do not know to what extent organisms are specialized to a particular type or stage of a patch or whether competition drives succession, all that is necessary to maintain diversity is for species to exhibit trade-offs between their ability to colonize a patch and longevity (Hubbell 1979; Tilman 1994). What remains troubling is that the duration of patches or various biogenic structures is probably still much shorter (years) than the life span, and reproductive age of most deep-sea species. If organisms depend on patches for persistence, they must be able to survive within the patch at least to maturity. It is difficult to assess this issue because we know very little about the growth, age of maturity, and longevity of most deep-sea organisms. Some have argued that heterogeneity may only be important at larval and juvenile stages because this is where species will be most vulnerable to competition for food (Snelgrove et al. 1996).

PARTICULATE ORGANIC MATTER FLUX. The amount of energy available to organisms in a particular area is widely thought to be an important mechanism regulating the number of species coexisting within communities (reviewed in Rosenzweig 1995). Exactly how productivity regulates the number of species is unclear, but numerous hypotheses have been formulated (Rosenzweig and Ambrasky 1993). In the deep sea, productivity has frequently been invoked to explain both geographic (e.g., Levin et al. 1991; Rex et al. 1993) and bathymetric (e.g., Rex 1981; Levin et al. 1994) variation in diversity. Except for the unusual conditions around hydrothermal vents and cold seeps, there is no primary productivity in the deep sea, so organisms must rely on POM sinking from surface waters or transported horizontally by various mechanisms.

POM flux has not been widely measured in the deep sea. Most evidence for the importance of productivity depends on correlations between community structure (abundance, composition, and diversity) and gradients in various proxies for POM flux such as depth (Rex 1981), latitude (Rex et al. 1993),

sediment organic carbon (Levin et al. 1994; Levin and Gage 1998), macrophyte detritus (Vetter and Dayton 1998), or combinations of these (Sibuet et al. 1989; Cosson-Sarradin et al. 1998). Where direct quantitative measures of in situ POM flux (derived from sediment traps) have been used, abyssal macrofaunal abundance (C. R. Smith et al. 1998) and diversity (Smith, personal communication) along a latitudinal gradient in the equatorial Pacific and meiofaunal abundance in the Atlantic (Tietjen et al. 1989) correlated positively with flux. The relationship between diversity and various proxies of production is usually unimodal with peak diversity at intermediate productivity (e.g., Rex 1981; Levin and Gage 1998). However, some have found monotonic increasing or decreasing patterns, which may simply imply that they have only measured one side of the unimodal curve. Small-scale experimental enhancements of POM also indicate that energy availability may be important in structuring communities. Short-term experimental enrichment often leads to an increase in abundance, a shift to more opportunistic species, increased dominance, and a decrease in diversity (Grassle and Morse-Porteous 1987; Snelgrove et al. 1996). This is remarkably similar to what is observed under regions of naturally high POM flux (Rex 1983; Rex et al. 1993; Levin et al. 1994; Schaff et al. 1992; Levin and Gage 1998), including enriched sediments adjacent to hydrothermal vents and cold seeps (Grassle et al. 1985; Grassle 1989; Petrecca and Grassle 1990). Similar changes in community structure observed under high-energy current regimes (e.g., HEBBLE, Rockall Trough) have been attributed to enhanced POM enrichment and increased microbial productivity (Gage 1977, 1997; Thistle et al. 1985, 1991; Aller 1997).

As in other environments, the mechanism for how food levels potentially regulate community structure is poorly understood. Most researchers agree that when food availability is low, such as in abyssal environments, few species coexist because there are insufficient resources to support viable populations for diverse assemblages. As food availability increases, more species can maintain viable populations and thus local diversity increases. The perplexing aspect is why diversity eventually declines as food availability (or productivity) continues to increase along a gradient. Rex and colleagues suggested that for both shallow depths (Rex 1983) and high latitudes (Rex et al. 1993), the decline in diversity with increasing POM flux reflects the increased seasonal variability associated with these higher fluxes. They argue the variability increases extinction rates of more specialized species, either through demographic instabilities or accelerating rates of competitive exclusion, precluding the development of diverse upper trophic levels. Levin and Gage (1998) recently suggested that depressed diversity associated with regions of high POM flux may reflect differential numerical responses by species, which would increase dominance and possibly lead to competitive exclusion. Consistent with this hypothesis, samples from regions of high POM flux typically exhibit much higher dominance and a shift to more opportunistic species (Schaff et al. 1992; Blake and Grassle 1994; Levin and Gage 1998). Moreover, when increases in POM flux lead to abiotic stress (e.g., low pore water oxygen), there are clear declines in species richness in deep-water assemblages (Levin et al. 1991b; Levin and Gage 1998; Levin et al. 2000). Increasing POM, either naturally along a gradient or experimentally, eventually leads to an increase in abundance, a shift to more opportunistic species, increased dominance, and a decrease in diversity.

HYDRODYNAMICS. The hydrodynamic regime profoundly affects many of the ecological processes thought to be important in regulating the structure of benthic communities (Jumars and Nowell 1984) and may be fundamental to understanding why diversity is higher in deep water. Sediment characteristics such as grain size, sorting coefficient, organic content, and stability are all intimately related to the boundary-layer flow regime, often in complex and interdependent ways. Pore water chemistry and the depth to which the sediments are oxygenated are also affected by the hydrodynamic regime. Near-bed flow directly influences POM flux to the sediment surface and microbial productivity (Nowell and Jumars 1984) and indirectly affects sediment organic carbon by controlling particle-size distributions. Because larvae of many soft-sediment invertebrates are similar in size to the sediments, possess fall velocities that approximate the sediments (Peterson 1986; Butman et al. 1988; Grassle et al. 1992), and are largely unable to swim against even weak horizontal flows, their distributions and supply rates will mirror the sediments and be equally dependent on hydrodynamics across a variety of scales (Butman 1987). High flows can also act as a disturbance, eliminating patch structure on some scales and creating patches on other scales. In addition to affecting these ecological processes, flow can directly alter the distribution of sediment-dwelling organisms. High currents can initiate sediment transport, which will erode small epifauna, especially meiofauna and recently settled larvae, and potentially preclude species with structures (e.g., tubes, appendages) that extend above the sediment surface. The pervasive effects of the hydrodynamic regime on the benthos and on the ecological mechanisms that control the distribution of organisms suggest that near-bed flow regimes exert a powerful force on the structure of local soft-sediment communities (Snelgrove and Butman 1994).

Evidence for the impact of hydrodynamics on deep-sea communities derives primarily from studies in high energy environments such as the High Energy Benthic Boundary Layer Experiment (HEBBLE) (Thistle et al. 1985, 1991; Aller 1997), the Rockall Trough (Gage 1977; Paterson and Lambshead 1995), and Setubal Canyon (Gage et al. 1995; Gage 1997), where near-bottom flows can intermittently exceed 50 cm s^{-1} due to benthic storms, downward propagated vortices from surface storms, and large-scale topographic features that accelerate tidally driven currents. The high currents initiate sediment transport that can destroy patch structure and erode meiofauna, larvae, and even small macrofauna such as isopods (Thistle et al. 1985, 1991; Thistle and Wilson 1987, 1996; Aller 1997). However, despite erosion during benthic storms at HEBBLE, the meiofauna as a whole were similar in abundance to quiescent areas (Thistle et al. 1985, 1991). In contrast, the larger macrofauna (polychaetes, bivalves, tanaids) had significantly enhanced densities, in some cases an order of magnitude larger than typically found at these depths, although populations were dominated by subadults (Thistle et al. 1985, 1991). The higher macrofaunal densities were attributed to increased POM flux and microbial production resulting from more energetic flow regimes. Gage (1997) recently compared macrofaunal community structure among high-energy environments and quiescent areas at similar depths and found that high-flow sites had enhanced abundance, greater dominance, and depressed macrofaunal diversity. The structure of these communities is remarkably similar to those in shallow water, suggesting that differences in the hydrodynamic regime may play an important role in explaining depth-related differences in diversity. Indeed, Paterson and Lambshead (1995) suggested that bathymetric variation in polychaete community structure in the Rockall Trough reflected disturbance mediated by depth-related changes in the frequency of high-energy current events. In addition to these large-scale comparative studies, Thistle and Levin (1998) showed that experimentally increasing flow on small scales altered the composition of the community, but not its diversity on short time scales (6.5 weeks).

DYNAMIC EQUILIBRIUM. Numerous studies in a wide variety of habitats suggest that species diversity may reflect a dynamic balance between the relative rates of competitive exclusion and the frequency of disturbance (reviewed in Huston 1994). Similar arguments have been invoked to explain the unimodal bathymetric gradient in species diversity in the deep sea (Huston 1979; Rex 1981). According to this model, the rate of competitive exclusion should be a positive function of population growth because it determines how quickly communities approach competitive equilibrium, where competitively superior species begin to exclude inferior species, thereby depressing diversity. Disturbance crops down populations, slowing the approach to competitive equilibrium and should thus reduce exclusion rates and promote coexistence. The balance between these two rates should determine local diversity.

But how do these rates change with depth? Because deep-sea organisms rely on food sinking from surface waters, population growth rates, and thus competitive exclusion rates, should be a function of POM flux, which declines exponentially with depth (Rowe and Pariente 1992; Turley et al. 1995). Disturbance is more difficult to estimate because there is no simple analog that has been measured along a depth gradient, and it is often unclear what constitutes a disturbance. If predation pressure can be inferred from the depth-related patterns of predatory snail diversity, megafaunal diversity, and fish diversity, then biological disturbance varies parabolically with depth (Rex 1983). However, predation pressure is probably much higher in shallow water because of the much larger densities, larger sizes, and greater mobility of predators. Also, predation pressure does not include bioturbation as a source of disturbance (e.g., Smith et al. 1986), which should vary with the density, size, and activity of bioturbators. Physical disturbance is typically thought to decrease linearly with depth, and this is consistent with estimates based on the frequency of high-velocity current events in the Eastern North Atlantic (Patterson and Lambshead 1995). In general, disturbance from both biotic and abiotic forces probably decreases with depth.

Combining estimates of depth-related variation in population growth and disturbance rates in the conceptual context of the dynamic equilibrium hypothesis predicts qualitative patterns in diversity that are consistent with observed bathymetric trends in the western North Atlantic (Huston 1979; Rex 1981, 1983). However, recent large-scale disturbance experiments at abyssal depths in the Southeastern Pacific depressed diversity for more than three years (Borowski and Thiel 1998), which seems inconsistent with the dynamic equilibrium hypothesis. In the abyss, where disturbance would be infrequent, this model predicts communities to be near competitive equilibrium. Disturbance should increase diversity, although the opposite findings may simply reflect the extremely slow recovery of abyssal populations that are unaccustomed to disturbance.

The dynamic equilibrium hypothesis efficiently integrates gradients in POM flux, hydrodynamics, and biological disturbance and underscores the importance of depth-related variation in these processes, but because we have few quantitative estimates of the critical rates of competitive exclusion or disturbance, it will be difficult to test these ideas.

Summary of Sediment Communities

Can we synthesize the hypotheses discussed above and develop a more integrated understanding of why local (1–10 m^2) diversity is often greater in deep-sea communities relative to those in shallow water? Based on our limited knowledge of deep-water ecosystems, it seems likely that multiple processes are involved, and these may interact in complex and subtle ways. Spatiotemporal heterogeneity appears to be more diverse, on smaller spatial scales and longer time scales, than in similar shallow-water environments, suggesting that patch dynamics may be relatively more important in the structure of deep-sea communities. A great variety of small-scale microhabitats are potentially available to deep-sea organisms (e.g., biogenic structures, disturbance patches, food patches) that are either not available in shallow water or are highly ephemeral. The longer duration of patches in the deep sea indicates that successional dynamics are slower, providing more time for ephemeral (or competitively inferior) species to find new patches. This should reduce local, as well as regional, extinction rates (Caswell and Cohen 1991a, b; Caswell and Etter 1999) and increase the importance of metapopulation processes. In a metapopulation, even if a species becomes extinct locally, it will persist regionally as long as colonization of new patches exceeds the average rate at which it is lost from a patch. Both the greater array of microhabitats and the slower successional processes provide more opportunities for partitioning the sediments, and this may contribute to high local diversity. The increase in the relative importance of small-scale spatiotemporal heterogeneity in the deep sea depends on a reduction in POM flux and a less-energetic flow regime.

The exponential decline in POM flux with depth creates a food-poor environment with far-reaching ramifications for understanding diversity. Probably the most significant and consistent feature of life in the deep sea is the small size of most organisms, much smaller than their shallow-water counterparts. Small body size, per se, may be an important part of the explanation for greater diversity simply because smaller organisms tend to be more diverse than larger ones (Dial and Marzluff 1988; May 1988; Blackburn and Gaston 1994; Siemann et al. 1996), presumably because they experience the environment on a smaller scale and in a more coarse-grained way. This is consistent with the hypothesis that small-scale heterogeneity is relatively more important in the deep sea (Jumars 1975, 1976). Small body size also limits fecundity and places constraints on energy assimilation from largely refractory detritus, both of which will preclude the strong numerical responses to seasonal pulses of organic input so typical of shallow-water ecosystems. Indeed, deep-sea macrofauna are much more likely to exhibit facultative (e.g., caching) rather than numerical responses to food pulses (Jumars et al. 1990). The inability to respond numerically to short-term pulses of food may, in part, explain why dominance is so much lower in the deep sea and may reduce competitive exclusion rates fostering coexistence as hypothesized in the dynamic equilibrium model (Huston 1979; Rex 1981).

Low fecundity coupled with low macrofaunal density may lead to recruitment limitation. A species is recruitment limited if it fails to colonize all patches that are favorable for its growth and survival. Both theoretical (Tilman 1994; Dial and Roughgarden 1998) and empirical evidence from other high diversity communities (Tilman, 1997; Hubbel et al. 1999) indicate that recruitment limitation can promote coexistence by reducing the intensity of biotic interactions. For example, under recruitment limitation, patches can be "won" by inferior competitors simply because the superior competitors have failed to colonize. Ultimately, competitive exclusion will occur, but recruitment limitation so slows the process that an essentially unlimited number of species utilizing the same resource can easily coexist (Tilman 1994; Hurtt and Pacala 1995).

The decline in POM flux also may increase the relative importance of heterogeneity by increasing differences among patches. One hypothesis advanced to explain how increasing production can lead to a decline in diversity is that high productivity makes patches more similar in quality, decreasing the importance of heterogeneity (Rosenzweig 1995; Levin et al., in press). This may be especially important in the deep sea because high POM fluxes will quickly overwhelm the ability of organisms to consume or cache labile organic matter.

Boundary-layer flows are typically much lower in the deep sea, and this can also influence diversity in numerous ways. Various types of small-scale patches and biogenic structures can persist for exceptionally long periods because of the reduced flows, and as noted above, these are thought to be critical to the maintenance of diversity. If patches are important, coexistence of any particular suite of species will depend on rates of exclusion, rates of patch creation, and the ability of each species to locate and colonize new patches, all of which will depend to some degree on the hydrodynamic regime. Lower flow will decrease larval supply rates and coupled with the small size and low fecundity of deep-sea macro-fauna, this may limit recruitment. Lower flow may also decrease POM flux and microbial productivity, which should decrease rates of population growth and possibly competitive exclusion (Huston 1979; Rex 1981). Because flow manifests itself in such a wide variety of ways and operates across several spatial and temporal scales, a considerable amount of work is needed to identify specific mechanisms.

Although many of the above hypotheses are highly plausible, not mutually exclusive, and supported by compelling circumstantial evidence, critical tests are lacking. To a large extent this reflects the difficulty of conducting these experiments in the remote deep sea. Future research efforts should strive to design and implement experiments that critically test the mechanisms that potentially underlie these patterns. These experiments will be challenging to design and costly to conduct, but are essential for developing a more complete understanding of the ecological and evolutionary processes that regulate the structure of deep-sea communities. In addition, more samples are needed, both qualitative epibenthic sleds and quantitative boxcores, strategically placed to test whether observed patterns (e.g., unimodal bathymetric diversity gradients) are general or idiosyncratic and to simply explore the vast regions of the deep sea that have yet to be sampled. Most importantly, we need much more information on the natural history of the organisms that inhabit deep-sea sediments.

HARD-BOTTOM COMMUNITIES

The preceding section describing deep-sea communities in soft sediments is centered around intriguing patterns of species diversity and the processes that form them. A discussion of hard-bottom communities, however, does not lend itself to a comparable structure because differences in sampling techniques have resulted in quite different data sets, with much less emphasis on quantitative analysis of diversity. Therefore, the following section will concentrate on three specific processes that have motivated much of the research in hard-bottom habitats: feeding in flow, dispersal between island habitats, and biological interactions within communities. In the future, as studies of hard-bottom habitats move toward including more quantitative sampling of specimens and become broader geographically, and studies of soft-sediment habitats move toward direct analyses of process, we anticipate that the approaches in these two fields will converge.

Hard-Bottom Habitats

MID-OCEAN RIDGES. Ridges of basalt are located throughout the deep seafloor along mid-ocean spreading centers (Figure 14.7). These ridges are the crustal expression of seafloor spreading, where magma rises up from the mantle to create new oceanic crust at the boundaries of the tectonic plates (Fornari and Embley 1995). Ridges are fragmented by trans-

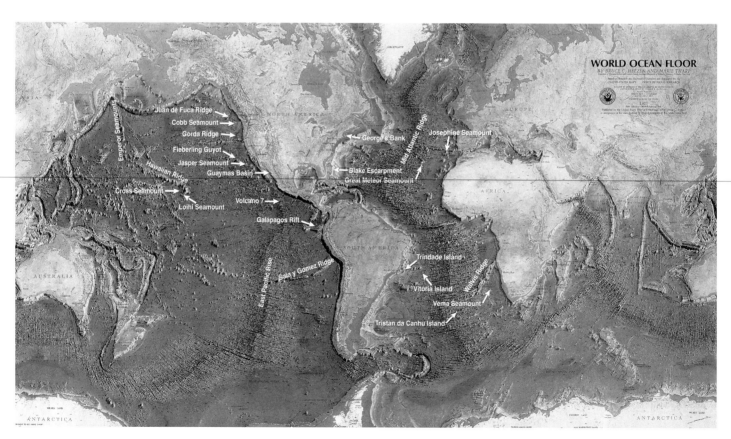

Figure 14.7 Map of seafloor topography showing mid-ocean ridge systems, seamounts, and back-arc basins. Prominent seafloor features and locations mentioned in the text are identified. (Map redrawn from Heezen and Tharp 1977; copyright by M. Tharp.)

form faults into segments, tens to hundreds of kilometers long. The ridge axis typically reveals exposed basalt, often with a ropey or pillowlike morphology and a glassy surface characteristic of recent magmatic flows. The surface gradually becomes more sedimented as it ages and moves away from the axis. In some nearshore locations with heavy sedimentation, such as Guaymas Basin or Gorda Ridge in the Pacific, the ridge axis is covered with a substantial layer of sediment.

Hydrothermal vents occur in volcanically active sections of the ridge where seawater percolates down through the seafloor, becomes heated from below, and re-emerges at the seafloor in the form of high-temperature fluids laden with reduced chemicals. The chemicals, in particular H_2S, provide energy for chemoautotrophic microbial production of organic carbon. The geographic spacing of vents varies among ridges. For instance, vents are numerous and closely spaced (tens of meters to tens of kilometers) on the volcanically very active East Pacific Rise, whereas they are uncommon and widely spaced (hundreds of kilometers) on the less-active Mid-Atlantic Ridge. Vents are ephemeral and may have life spans of only years to decades on active spreading centers (MacDonald et al. 1980; Haymon et al. 1993). On slower spreading ridges, vents may be active (although intermittently) for as long as 100,000 years (Lalou et al. 1993).

Currents near mid-ocean spreading centers are affected by the topography of the ridge. The ridge steers deep-water currents, causing them to flow parallel to the strike of the ridge axis (Thomson et al. 1990; Anderson-Fontana et al. 1992). The ridge also interacts with oceanic tides and longer-period motions to amplify currents at the seafloor (Thomson et al. 1990), and theory suggests that amplification of these motions is a general feature of ridge-associated currents (Anderson-Fontana et al. 1992). Thus, flows near the ridge are sheared, with maximal current velocities at heights of a few hundred meters above the ridge (Thomson et al. 1989; Thomson et al. 1990; Cannon et al. 1991). Horizontal shear also may occur because circulation cells form at the scale of individual ridge segments, causing flows on opposite sides of the ridge to be oriented in opposite directions (Helfrich et al. 1998).

The buoyant plumes emanating from hydrothermal vents exit from sulfide chimneys with vertical velocities reaching 5–10 cm s^{-1} (Converse et al. 1984), and this further complicates flows near the ridge. The vertical motion of the plume induces rotational flows (because the fluid rises away from the center of the rotating earth), and theory suggests these vortices will remain near the vent and then eventually break off and move away (reviewed in Helfrich and Speer 1995). Field evidence for vortices has been demonstrated by measuring currents and density structure of the water column (Helfrich et al. 1998; Joyce et al. 1998). The fluid output at vents increases markedly during episodic events or "megaplumes" (Baker et al. 1998), which are often associated with magmatic eruptions. These event plumes rise higher above the seafloor and have stronger rotational flows (Lupton et al. 1998) than the chronic plumes.

SEAMOUNTS. Underwater mountains, or seamounts, occur on the deep seafloor, most often in chains or associated with mid-ocean ridges, but also as isolated individuals (Craig and Sandwell 1988). Seamounts are numerous: 30,000 are estimated to be in the Pacific Ocean (Smith and Jordan 1988), and they cover as much as 6% of the deep seafloor. Many seamounts are aligned in chains oriented perpendicular to the motion of the tectonic plates on which they reside. These seamounts are a crustal expression of a magma source deep in the earth's mantle, and they are formed sequentially as the plate moves past the "hot spot"(Okal and Batiza 1987). The Hawaiian Islands are an example of a hot-spot chain, with the oldest islands to the northwest and the youngest (the hydrothermally active seamount Loihi) to the south of the big island of Hawaii.

Seamounts can be very large (for example, the moderately sized seamount Fieberling Guyot rises more than 4 km above the seafloor and is roughly the size of Mt. Rainier in the U.S. Pacific Northwest), and like ridges, they have strong effects on currents. Numerical models suggest seamounts interact with currents to produce overlying rotational flows (Chapman and Haidvogel 1992), and these flows have been observed in the field (Freeland 1994; Brink 1995). Eddies in the wake of a seamount have also been predicted (Boyer and Zhang 1990) and then later observed in drifter studies (Bograd et al. 1997). In addition, turbulent mixing is intensified near seamounts (Kunze and Toole 1997; Toole et al. 1997). In some situations, mixing and vertical flows around seamounts appear to bring nutrient-rich waters up into the photic zone (Boehlert and Genin 1987; Dower et al. 1992) and affect local primary production. Benthic environments on seamounts may be either rocky or sedimented, depending on the angle of the slope and the intensity of currents; steep spires tend to be bare rock, whereas calderas and plateaus often are sediment covered.

MANGANESE NODULES AND OTHER SMALL HABITATS. The deep, sedimented seafloor is strewn with a variety of objects that provide solid footing for organisms. In polar seas, dropstones are carried away from land on ice flows and deposited in deep water (Oschmann 1990). On the deep abyssal plains, mineral concretions called manganese nodules occur in extensive fields, covering as much as 70% of the deep seafloor (Bischoff and Piper 1979; Frazer and Fisk 1981). These nodules, which are typically on the order of 5 to 10 cm in diameter, rest at the sediment–water interface (Figure 14.8). Measures of mineral accretion indicate that the nodules grow very slowly, an observation that has generated heated discussion of how they stay at the surface under a constant rain of sediment. Suggestions range from dynamic particle sorting processes (i.e., in sediments with mixed particle sizes, the large ones move to the surface) to episodic jostling and uplifting by mobile benthic organisms (discussed in Jeong et al. 1994).

Many benthic organisms serve as habitat for other deep-sea species. Organisms colonize glass sponges, tube-building foraminifera, and other types of sessile benthos, both live and

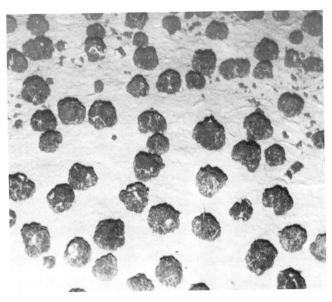

Figure 14.8 Manganese nodule field in the abyssal Pacific at 5145 m depth east of New Zealand (44°59′S 145°20′W). Nodules are roughly 5–10 cm in diameter, and colonists (tube-building polychaetes, foraminifers, and hydroids) are visible. (From Heezen and Hollister 1971; used with permission.)

dead. Sessile organisms provide a habitat that is fundamentally different from ridges, seamounts, and nodules, but analogous to hydrothermal vents in the sense that both are ephemeral and may persist on time scales comparable to the life spans of their colonists.

Hard-Bottom Faunas

The dominant megafauna living on seamounts, ridges, escarpments, and smaller hard surfaces tend to be invertebrates that feed on suspended particles (Figure 14.9). Larger taxa, which can be identified from photographs, include sponges,

hydroids, zoanthids, anenomes, gorgonians, sea pens, corals, crinoids, brisingid asteroids, holothurians, and tunicates (images and descriptions in Heezen and Hollister 1971; Genin et al. 1986; Grigg et al. 1987; Wilson and Kaufmann 1987; Carey et al. 1990; Chave and Jones 1991; Genin et al. 1992; Copley et al. 1996). Other, smaller suspension-feeding taxa, such as xenophyophores, foraminifers, solitary corals, and tube-building polychaetes and crustaceans, are found in collections from hard surfaces (Mullineaux 1987; Mullineaux and Butman 1990; Oschmann 1990, Beaulieu, in press), making the faunal composition very different from the deposit-feeder dominated communities found in sediments. The larger mobile taxa, on the other hand, are similar to other deep-sea communities and include asteroids, ophiuroids, holothuroids, gastropods, crustacea, and fish.

At hydrothermal vents, the community is composed mostly of endemic species (367 of 443 known species, as of last count in Tunnicliffe et al. 1998) with specific adaptations to the extreme and variable physical, chemical, and nutritional environment. The primary food source for these communities comes from chemoautotrophic microbes living either freely in the water column, in symbiotic associations with invertebrates, or in mats on the seafloor (Jannasch 1995). Large cnidarians and colonial taxa are notably rare (Grassle et al. 1985). Instead, the fauna is dominated by three major phyla: molluscs, arthropods, and annelids (Figure 14.10). The vent communities were first discovered along the Galapagos Rift (Corliss et al. 1979), where the faunas are characterized by the striking red-plumed vestimentiferan tubeworms, as well as by extensive beds of bivalves and mobile decapod scavengers. Vents in other locations, however, may have distinctly different faunas; in the northern Atlantic the prominent colonists are mobile shrimp (Van Dover et al. 1996), whereas

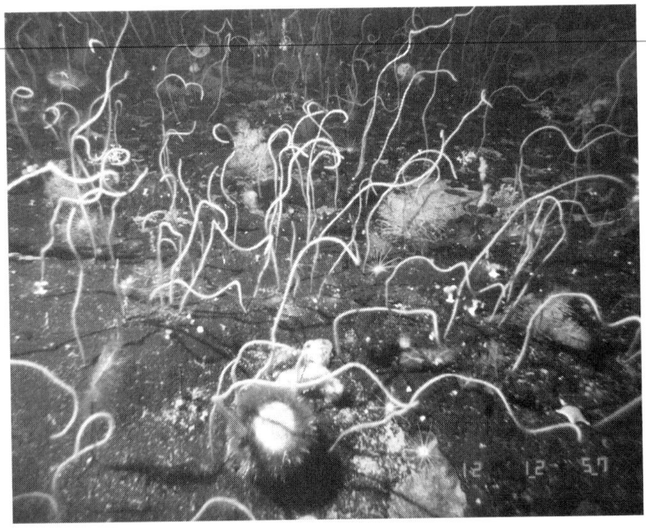

Figure 14.10 Vestimentiferan tubeworms (*Tevnia jerichonana* and *Riftia pachyptila*) at a deep (2515 m) hydrothermal vent near 9°50′N on the East Pacific Rise. On the vestimentiferan tubes and basalt surfaces are archaeogastropod limpets (small dots) and bythograeid and galatheid crabs. (Photo by L. Mullineaux.)

Figure 14.9 Suspension-feeding sponges, octocorals, and other anthozoans near the summit of Fieberling Guyot at 500 m water depth in the Eastern Pacific. (Photo by L. Mullineaux.)

vents in the western Pacific are characterized by their unusual gastropods and barnacles (Desbruyères et al. 1994).

Foraminifera are ubiquitous, but frequently ignored, colonists of all hard-bottom habitats in the deep sea, including seamounts (Mullineaux and Butman 1990; Verlaan 1992; Bertram and Cowen 1994), hydrothermal vents (Van Dover et al. 1988; Mullineaux et al. 1998), manganese nodules (Mullineaux 1987; Thiel et al. 1993), and biogenic material (Gooday and Haynes 1983; Gooday 1984; Beaulieu, in press). Very little is known about the role these organisms play in benthic communities, but it is likely that they are involved in benthic microbial loops that are important in cycling of carbon and energy to the better-known macrofauna and megafauna.

Some faunas inhabiting seamounts and ridges do not live on rocky surfaces. For instance, the axial ridges of mid-ocean spreading centers are sedimented in a few locations, particularly in the eastern North Pacific. Vent habitats at these sites provide a very different environment for colonists and are inhabited by a suite of species (Grassle et al. 1985; Petrecca and Grassle 1990) that have more in common with other sediment-dwelling communities than with hard-bottom faunas. These communities will not, therefore, be discussed in the following sections.

Feeding in Flow on Deep-Sea Topography

Organisms inhabiting hard surfaces in the deep sea typically are exposed to amplified current speeds relative to those living in sedimented habitats. This situation occurs on ridges, seamounts, and escarpments due to interactions between oceanic flows and local topography, and on smaller scale habitat (e.g., nodules, biogenic structures) due to elevation above the slowest flows of the benthic boundary layer. Organisms exposed to faster flows are subject to enhanced horizontal particle fluxes (unless the particulate load decreases substantially with elevation), which effectively increase the supply of organic matter to suspension feeders (only rarely do flow speeds in these environments reach levels thought to inhibit feeding). Note also that some stalked organisms living in sediment, such as sponges, pennatulaceans, and crinoids, are able to elevate their feeding appendages into faster flows.

The feeding mechanisms, growth forms, and spatial distributions of prominent taxa on deep-sea hard surfaces indicate that they take advantage of this enhanced particle flux. As mentioned above, most of the taxa living on ridges, seamounts, and escarpments are suspension feeders (with the exception of the specialized symbiotic associations found at vents). Of these taxa, gorgonian species having upright, fan-shaped, branching forms tend to orient perpendicular to the direction of prevailing currents (Chave and Jones 1991) and presumably maximize the area over which they can intercept particles. The abundance of black coral (*Stichopathes* sp.) on Jasper Seamount in the northeast Pacific is well correlated with topographic highs (knobs and pinnacles), which are inferred to be regions of increased current velocity (Genin et al. 1986). Similar associations of abundant suspension feeders occurring on local topographic highs of seamounts have also

been observed elsewhere. Moskalev and Galkin (1986) found increased abundances of gorgonians, antipatharians, and sponges along the edges of terraces on seamounts of the Magellan Range in the Equatorial Pacific, and Tunnicliffe et al. (1985) noted high abundances of ophiuroids, hexactinellid sponges, ascidians, and hydroids on the vertical walls of the caldera system on top of Axial seamount, a hydrothermally active volcano on the Juan de Fuca Ridge (northeast Pacific) However, in the latter submersible study, the region observed was near active vent sites, and the high abundances (up to 100 individuals m^{-2}) may have been due in part to export of POM from vent communities.

Few quantitative data are available on depth-related abundance patterns in hard-bottom communities. One study on Cross Seamount used camera tows and dredges to show that abundances tended to decrease with depth (Grigg et al. 1987), presumably because POM supply became depleted with increasing distance from its sea-surface source (this pattern also is observed in sediment-dwelling communities). Exceptions to this pattern occur in locations where POM is enhanced by a process unrelated to surface production. For instance, unusually strong currents (100 cm s^{-1} and greater) have been recorded at 3500 m on the Blake Spur on the western Atlantic continental margin and coincide with very high abundances of sponges and gorgonian corals on vertical walls (Genin et al. 1992). This environment has very low particle concentrations, but the high horizontal flux rates appear to supply sufficient energy to support high biomass in these communities.

Enhanced benthic abundances and biomass also have been observed on a seamount (Volcano 7 in the northeastern Pacific) at depths corresponding to the lower boundary of the oxygen minimum zone (Wishner et al. 1990; Levin et al. 1991b). Particle concentrations appear to be increased at this depth, possibly due to the absence of planktonic particle feeders in the overlying low-oxygen layer (Wishner et al. 1990; Levin et al. 1991b). Benthic habitats that intersect the most intense band of the oxygen minimum are inhabited by the few species adapted to low oxygen levels, whereas those at the lower boundary are inhabited by abundant, diverse communities.

Elevated primary production over seamounts, due to mixing of nutrient-rich waters up into the photic zone, has been proposed as a mechanism to support the rich fish stocks observed on seamounts (Uda and Ishino 1958; Hubbs 1959). Evidence for this hypothesized production, however, is sparse. Elevated chlorophyll concentrations were found to be associated with Minami-Kasuga Seamount (Genin and Boehlert 1985), but only for a few days, and a more comprehensive survey of Pacific seamounts revealed little evidence for enhanced primary production (A. Genin, unpublished data). Consistent elevation of chlorophyll levels has been found only in the uncommon situation where the seamount summit intersected the photic zone (Genin and Boehlert 1985; Dower et al. 1992), and that primary production did not appear to enhance zooplankton stocks (Dower and Mackas 1996). Thus, enhanced, in situ, primary production is not a likely cause of the abundant benthic populations (fish or invertebrates) observed on seamounts currently.

Because seamounts originate as volcanoes, some of the younger ones remain hydrothermally active. The chemoautotrophic microbial production at hydrothermal vents may provide an additional source of food supply to suspension feeding organisms outside the vent community (as was suggested for the abundant fauna reported on Axial Seamount by Tunnicliffe et al. 1985). The response to this food supply could potentially result in patterns of suspension-feeder abundance that are independent of depth or flow velocity.

Migration between Deep-Sea Islands

Species living on ridge segments, seamounts, or any of the smaller-scale hard-bottom habitats that constitute islands in a sea of sediments in the deep sea are faced with the potential problem of local extinction. For those species unable to disperse, local catastrophes would result in decreased population size, reduced genetic diversity, and constricted geographic ranges. Because this life-history constraint is a dominant feature of hard-bottom habitats, processes influencing dispersal, colonization, and gene flow have a broad impact on the structure of the communities and their geographic ranges. Species living at vents have the added constraint of being in an ephemeral environment, one that is highly variable in physical and chemical characteristics and may last only decades.

Because most hard-bottom species are sessile or have limited mobility as adults, dispersal occurs predominantly in the larval stage of the life cycle (although some crustacea, such as amphipods, are notable exceptions to this generalization). Larvae are typically small and relatively weak swimmers, but they potentially can be transported long distances in oceanic currents. Thus, the dispersal trajectory is influenced strongly by deep-ocean circulation. This correlation between basin-wide circulation patterns and larval dispersal is well characterized for many coastal species (see Scheltema 1986 for examples), but remains largely untested for deeper dwelling organisms. These values are only just now being investigated for larvae of deep-sea species (Mullineaux and Manahan 1999), but evidence from Antarctic habitats (e.g., Pearse et al. 1991; Shilling and Manahan 1994) indicate that larval metabolic rates are low and life spans quite long in cold waters. The maximum dispersal range depends on larval energy stores and metabolic rates. Successful colonization of habitats away from the source population requires that they be within the dispersal ambit of species as constrained by larval behaviors, life spans, and currents. Gene flow occurs in these situations when the migrants are sufficiently abundant and frequent to counteract speciation in separate habitats.

DISPERSAL BETWEEN SEAMOUNTS. To reproduce successfully, species living on seamounts either must recolonize their source habitat or colonize another seamount. Many of the taxa on deep seamounts reproduce via larvae with expected life spans as long as weeks to months, raising the question of

whether these larvae remain near the seamount or are swept away. The currents generated by interactions between seamounts and tides or larger-scale flows potentially have a strong influence on the retention of larvae near a seamount and their dispersal paths once advected off the seamount.

It has been suggested that rotational flows (termed *Taylor columns* or, more recently, *Taylor caps*) near a seamount should accumulate organisms because water residence times are increased (Shomura and Barkley 1980). Fluid dynamics theory indicates that Taylor caps may retain fluid and particles (like larvae) over time scales of weeks (Goldner and Chapman 1997), which may be long enough to allow them to recolonize their source communities. For this process to work, however, the larvae must be near-neutrally buoyant and produced on the seamount within the flow feature (i.e., no mechanism is known to accumulate larvae from an external source). In a field test of this process (Mullineaux and Mills 1997) abundances of the dominant larval taxa were found to be elevated over Fieberling Guyot (N. Pacific) in a pattern consistent with a scenario of retention in seamount flows. On other locations, however, such as Cobb Seamount off the western coast of North America, water residence times appear to be shorter than larval development times (Parker and Tunnicliffe 1994), and seamount populations may be subsidized by nearby coastal communities. For benthic fish, little direct evidence exists for larval retention, although populations of many species show genetic differentiation on the scale of individual seamounts, indicating that some process is limiting dispersal (reviewed in Rogers 1994; Creasey and Rogers 1999).

Because seamounts often occur in chains and deep circulation is steered by the topography of the chain as a whole (reviewed in Roden 1987), dispersal is likely to occur as a stepping-stone process (Hubbs 1959). For example, drifter studies demonstrate that currents follow the contour of the Walvis Ridge (southeastern Atlantis) and can explain the co-occurrence of a species of rock lobster on the slopes of Vema Seamount and Tristan da Cunha (Lutjeharms and Heydorn 1981). Species distribution patterns on seamount chains also support the idea of current-mediated dispersal. For instance, on the Vitória-Trindade Seamount Chain (off the east coast of Brazil), the species composition of prosobranch gastropods is relatively similar on closely spaced seamounts, but quite dissimilar on the more widely spaced ones (Leal and Bouchet 1991). On a larger scale, some of the most widely distributed species are those with distributions that extend along relatively uninterrupted seamount chains, such as the chain outlining the Pacific rim and the line of guyots (flat-topped seamounts) and ridges connecting the Indo-West Pacific to the southeastern Pacific (Wilson and Kaufmann 1987).

On a global scale, deep seamount faunas tend to be dominated by cosmopolitan species, whereas those on shallower seamounts reflect the species composition of nearby areas on the continental shelves (Wilson and Kaufmann 1987). A substantial number of the species inhabiting seamounts (as high as 28%), however, appear to be endemic to single seamounts or seamount groups. This pattern could be due to larval retention (as described above), isolation of individual seamount populations by geographic distance, or circulation patterns. Some evidence for reproductive isolation is provided by intraspecific morphological and genetic studies. For instance, Grasshoff (1972) found that populations of the gorgonian *Ellisella flagellum* differed in size and coloration between Great Meteor and Josephine seamounts in the eastern Atlantic and concluded that they were genetically distinct (as did Ehrich 1977). At Horizon seamount in the central North Pacific, Bucklin et al. (1987) found marked genetic differentiation between amphipod populations (*Eurythenes gryllus*) at the base of the seamount and at the summit. They postulated that gene flow may have been restricted between the two habitats due to limited vertical excursions by the adults or that the summit population had experienced strong selection.

DISPERSAL BETWEEN HYDROTHERMAL VENTS. The ability of species to disperse successfully from one vent to another depends on their larval dispersal range (as controlled by metabolism and energy stores), the direction and speed of currents, and the geographic alignment and spacing of vent sites. During the early years of vent research, ecologists speculated that larvae of vent species should be planktotrophic (feed in the water column) to disperse successfully (e.g., Lutz et al. 1980). Subsequent studies, however, showed that the larvae of most dominant vent species did not feed in the plankton (Desbruyères and Laubier 1983; Van Dover et al. 1985; Berg and Van Dover 1987; Lutz 1988; McHugh 1989). These species appeared to be constrained in their larval dispersal mode primarily by phylogenetic affinities; that is, planktotrophy was not found in any ancestral or closely related species (Turner et al. 1985). When the life span of vent larvae was inferred from related shallow species, the dispersal range appeared to be restricted to hours or days (Lutz et al. 1984). This result raised the paradox of how vent species could possibly maintain their populations, given the substantial distances between vents along ridges. The most probable answer is that larvae of vent species have much lower metabolic rates, and thus longer dispersal ranges, than closely related shallow species (reviewed in Mullineaux and France 1995; Tyler and Young 1999).

Flows generated by ridge topography and the buoyant hydrothermal plume potentially have a strong influence on larval dispersal between vents. Some of the larvae are entrained into the buoyant hydrothermal plume and brought up several hundreds of meters above the seafloor (Kim et al. 1994; Mullineaux et al. 1995). Larvae at these heights may disperse in very different directions and at different speeds than those remaining near the seafloor, due to vertical shear in currents. This is a process similar to that observed in estuaries, where the vertical position of larvae dispersing in sheared flows determines whether they are exported from, or retained in, a specific estuary (e.g., Epifanio et al. 1988; Forward 1988). An analysis of currents and larval abundances near vents suggests the individuals remaining near the seafloor are likely to disperse successfully among the closely spaced vents along a segment of the quickly spreading East

Pacific Rise, but that the gap between segments may present a barrier to larger-scale dispersal (Kim and Mullineaux 1998). Larvae dispersing in stronger currents up above the ridge might be transported fast enough to cross intersegment gaps, although the number actually locating and colonizing a new vent might be vanishingly low. The observation of postlarval and juvenile vent species in the water column (Mullineaux et al. 1995; Herring and Dixon 1998) indicates that even species with apparent nondispersive larvae may travel substantial distances (discussed in Chevaldonné et al. 1997). The problem of larval dispersal at vents is intriguing because we know the answer but not the mechanism—clearly species must disperse because they maintain their geographic distributions despite the opening and closing of vents, but the processes involved are only just now being discovered.

One obvious question remaining unanswered is how larvae dispersing in the water column are able to locate suitable vents for recolonization. Many researchers have speculated that a chemical cue is used to relocate vents, but no cue has yet been discovered. Larvae colonize new vents quickly (within months to years) when the vents are within tens of kilometers of established communities (Lutz et al. 1994; Tunnicliffe et al. 1997; Mullineaux et al. 2000). However, at more remote habitats, such as the new vents at Loihi seamount (Grigg 1997), many years may pass before invertebrate vent taxa colonize. Recruitment studies on the East Pacific Rise have demonstrated that some invertebrate species, such as the vestimentiferan tubeworm *Tevnia jerichonana*, are early colonists, whereas others are later arrivals (Hessler et al. 1985; Hessler et al. 1988; Shank et al. 1998). These studies suggest that vent species vary in their dispersal capabilities. Furthermore, at least one gastropod species appears to colonize episodically, rather than continuously (Mullineaux et al. 1998), suggesting that reproduction may be noncontinuous, despite the presumed absence of seasonal forcing at these depths. A possible alternative would be periodic or episodic changes in vent fluid flow that could synchronize reproduction directly through a thermal or chemical cue or indirectly by modifying local primary production.

The different possible dispersal pathways and variations in larval life spans among vent species suggest that the gaps between ridge segments should be barriers to gene flow of some species but not others. This interaction among circulation, geography, and life history controls gene flow and speciation in many coastal ecosystems (reviewed in Knowlton 1993; Palumbi 1994). Genetic similarity of populations distributed along ridges has been investigated for many species by characterizing allozymes or gene sequences (reviewed in Vrijenhoek 1997). In one vent species, the brooding amphipod *Ventiella sulfuris*, populations show distinct genetic differentiation across a gap in the ridge system between the East Pacific Rise and Galapagos Rise (France et al. 1992). However, a shrimp from the Mid-Atlantic Ridge, *Rimicaris exoculata*, shows no differentiation between two vents separated by 370 km (Creasey et al. 1996). Populations of one vestimentiferan species, *Riftia pachyptila*, showed evidence of increased genetic differentiation with distance along the East Pacific Rise in one study (Black et al. 1994), but not another (Bucklin 1988). However, sample spacing in these studies was too coarse to determine whether segment gaps or some other factor constituted a barrier. Studies of other vestimentiferan species in the eastern Pacific showed no distance-related pattern (Southward et al. 1996; Black et al. 1998), although sample sizes and ranges may have been too limited to detect an effect. Similarly, vent bivalves and gastropod populations have shown little or no differentiation along ridges in the Pacific (Moraga et al. 1994; Craddock et al. 1995; Karl et al. 1996; Craddock et al. 1997), with the exception of one study on the mussel *Bathymodiolus thermophilus* (Grassle 1985). Populations of alvinellid polychaetes show differentiation among vents, but no clear pattern of divergence across segment gaps (Jollivet et al. 1995). Although vent species do not show much genetic differentiation in populations along individual ridges, Vrijenhoek (1997) notes that rare alleles (those with low frequencies in the population) are uncommon, possibly due to frequent cycles of genetic bottlenecks and founder events. This idea is consistent with a scenario of frequent extinction at senescent vents and recolonization of new vent sites.

Although gaps between ridge segments do not appear to constitute a major barrier to dispersal for most vent species, gaps between ridge systems do. Boundaries of species ranges are well correlated with ridge discontinuities (Tunnicliffe et al. 1996), with both continents and large expanses of ocean appearing to be present-day barriers to dispersal. For instance, vent communities at the mid-Atlantic Ridge share only a single species with those in the Pacific. Within the Pacific, separate ridges (e.g., East Pacific Rise, Juan de Fuca ridge, and the back-arc basins in the western Pacific) share fewer than 10 species. Only the Galapagos Rift and the East Pacific Rise share more than 10 species, but the two ridges are located near each other and join at a triple junction. Although restricted dispersal appears to be maintaining these biogeographic patterns, the species distributions display a strong imprint of the timing and geometry of ancient plate boundaries. For instance, the similarity in species and genera between vent communities on the Juan de Fuca Ridge and the East Pacific Rise may be explained by migration during the mid-Tertiary, when those regions were linked by the unbroken Pacific-Farallon ridge. Furthermore, the low species diversity at the Galapagos vents might be due to the relatively recent (20 Myr ago) start of tectonic spreading in that region.

Biological Interactions in Vent Communities

Hydrothermal vent communities occur on ridges and seamounts because the magmatic processes producing topography on the seafloor also heat the fluids containing reduced chemicals that fuel microbial chemoautotrophy. The main focus of biological research at vents has been on chemoautotrophic production, microbe/invertebrate symbioses, and physiological tolerances and nutritional requirements of dominant vent species. Recent, comprehensive reviews have covered these topics (Childress and Fisher 1992; Fisher 1995; Jan-

nasch 1995), and they will not be discussed further. Instead, some less-studied biological interactions will be explored.

Striking faunal zonation occurs in many vent communities, which corresponds to gradients in hydrothermal fluid flux (and thus thermal and chemical gradients). This zonation has been best characterized in communities on the East Pacific Rise (Hessler and Smithey 1983; Hessler et al. 1985). Four habitats typically exist: (1) high-temperature flows (exceeding 50°C) from sulfide chimneys supporting a community dominated by alvinellid polychaetes; (2) vigorous, but moderate-temperature (less than 30°C) flows, characterized by the presence of vestimentiferans; (3) low-temperature (less than 5°C) flow, characterized by the presence of bivalves; and (4) regions with very low or no detectable vent flow, characterized by the presence of suspension-feeding species (serpulid polychaetes, barnacles, and/or anemones) and the absence of symbiont-containing fauna. The physical/chemical boundaries between contiguous habitats are gradational, but the faunal boundaries are distinct in most areas.

This zonation initially was attributed to physiological responses and nutrient requirements in the strong physicochemical gradients (Childress and Fisher 1992). More recent manipulative experiments indicate that larval settlement, predation, and competition all play a role in setting the zonal boundaries and influencing community structure and dynamics (Micheli et al. 1998; Millineaux, unpublished data). For instance, some species are able to recruit and mature outside their adult zone if other faster-growing species are removed. Furthermore, the exclusion of predators can shift the community from predominantly sessile tube dwellers to mobile grazers. Interestingly, this progression in understanding of vent community structure from a physicochemical to a biological perspective has paralleled advances made in intertidal ecology several decades earlier. Correlations between vertical gradients in physical stress and population distributions in the rocky intertidal habitat had long been interpreted as evidence that vertical biological zonation was largely a consequence of differing adaptations to physiological stressors (e.g., Lewis 1964). Subsequent experimental manipulations, however, demonstrated the significance of biological factors such as competition, predation, and biological disturbance in setting limits to species distributions (e.g., Connell 1961, 1972; Paine 1966; Dayton 1971; Sousa 1979b; Paine and Levin 1981). The lesson learned from these studies is that a significant correlation with physical/chemical factors provides insufficient evidence for inferring causation of zonation along an environmental gradient.

Vent faunas on the East Pacific Rise appear to follow a consistent successional pattern over time (Hessler et al. 1985; Fustec et al. 1987; Hessler et al. 1988; Shank et al. 1998). Microbial production begins immediately when a new vent site opens, and if the site is near other established vent communities, mobile vent fauna migrate in and graze on the microbes. The initial vestimentiferan species to settle is *Tevnia jerichonana*, followed by two other species, the larger *Riftia pachyptila* and the more cryptic *Oasisia alvinae*. Mussels begin to recruit into the community and eventually displace the vestimentiferans, possibly by diverting hydrothermal fluids or inhibiting larval settlement. Two alternative mechanisms have been proposed to explain this successional sequence. One hypothesis (articulated most recently in Shank et al. 1998) proposes that each species has different nutritional requirements and physiological tolerances to the hot, metal-rich hydrothermal fluids. These differences are thought to cause the species to replace each other as the physical/chemical environment evolves over the vent life span. An alternative hypothesis proposes that biological interactions are mediating the sequence. One study suggests that the pioneer vestimentiferan species (*Tevnia*) may facilitate the other (*Riftia*) and later be outcompeted by it (Mullineaux et al. 2000); another speculates that the mussels eventually actively displace the vestimentiferans (Hessler et al. 1988). Additional manipulative experiments are needed to resolve this controversy.

Summary of Hard-Bottom Community Structure

On large scales, the patterns of distribution and abundance of hard-bottom species living in the deep sea are strongly influenced by how these organisms interact with their physical and nutritional environment. Because many of these species are suspension feeders, their abundances relate to POM flux (which is dependent on hydrodynamic conditions) and not necessarily on the standing stock of organic matter. Vertical POM flux is usually inversely correlated with depth and distance from land, but accelerated currents with enhanced horizontal particle fluxes and correspondingly abundant faunas are found in numerous locales, even at great depths. Species distributions typically are associated with the geographic layout of "island" habitats, and abrupt or wide discontinuities in habitat correlate well with boundaries in species ranges.

Patterns of diversity in communities living on hard bottoms are not well documented because the kind of all-inclusive sampling done in sedimented areas (e.g., boxcores) is rarely attempted on bare rock. For instance, hydrothermal vent communities are not considered to be highly diverse, and most collections are dominated by a few abundant species. However, more careful sampling of vent faunas has revealed a highly diverse assemblage of tiny, previously overlooked species (C. Fisher and colleagues, unpublished data), which may compel ecologists to revise their image of vents as being low-diversity communities in highly productive habitat. Similar sampling efforts in both sedimented and hard-bottom habitats will be necessary to develop a comprehensive theory of what controls diversity in the deep sea.

CONCLUSIONS

Over the past century, our knowledge of the deep sea and its inhabitants has changed dramatically, yet it remains quite fragmentary. Most of the vast reaches of the deep ocean, possibly including entire biogeographic provinces, remain unexplored, especially at high latitudes and in remote regions. Gage (1996) recently estimated that no more than 500 m² of

the deep ocean floor had been sampled quantitatively. He notes that even if all the nonquantitative epibenthic sled and trawl samples were included, we still would have sampled an insignificant fraction of the 270 million km² of the deep seafloor. Advances in our understanding of the ecology of deep-sea communities will require well-thought-out sampling programs, extensive observations on the natural history of the inhabitants, and cleverly designed experiments that identify the processes that shape spatiotemporal variation in community structure.

One of the most pressing needs is to compile the existing data from independent research programs. A large number of deep-sea samples have been taken by researchers in North America, Europe, Australia, and Asia, but the data have not been synthesized and often remain unpublished. Although the samples were collected with quite different aims and with a variety of sampling gear, a central database including locality, depth, species abundance, and any environmental data would provide timely, crucial, and unparalleled information for quantifying what we know and for developing more coordinated and systematic sampling efforts. More samples clearly need to be taken, both quantitative and qualitative, from specific locations to quantify the distributions of organisms and better assess how they respond to oceanographic, topographic, and geochemical features. We also need to improve our knowledge of the natural history of the organisms living at great depths. The lack of this fundamental information is one of the greatest impediments to advancing our understanding of deep-sea communities.

The mechanisms that regulate community structure in the deep sea should be examined critically using a variety of approaches, but especially with manipulative experiments that can unequivocally establish causation. Processes such as competition, predation, disturbance, larval supply, nutrient flux, and hydrodynamics have all been shown to be important in structuring shallow-water communities, but their role in regulating deep-sea assemblages remains very inferential. These experiments will be difficult to conduct in such a remote setting, but they are essential for identifying the relative importance of the myriad of processes that potentially influence the structure of deep-sea communities.

During the past 30 years, research in the deep sea has focused primarily on the ecological causes of community structure. Very little is known about how this rich and highly endemic fauna evolved. In terrestrial and shallow-water systems, there is a growing realization that broader scale processes (e.g., dispersal from regional species pools, metapopulation dynamics) and historical events may be important in structuring local assemblages (Ricklefs and Schluter 1993). Thus, knowledge of how the regional species pool builds up and disperses to local habitats will be essential for developing an integrated understanding of the processes structuring communities on different scales. Work on the evolution of the deep-sea fauna is just beginning (e.g., Wilson 1983; Bucklin et al. 1987; Etter and Rex 1990; France et al. 1992; Rogers 1994; Mullineaux and France 1995; France and Kocher 1996; Tunnicliffe et al. 1996; Vrijenhoek 1997; Wilson 1998; Creasey and Rogers 1999; Etter et al. 1999), but should provide valuable insight about the scale and frequency of dispersal, as well as a geographic and bathymetric context for the origins of this remarkable fauna.

Communities in the deep sea are also not immune to human activities, and as in shallow water, the potential consequences of these activities are becoming increasingly apparent. A notable example is the precipitous decline in populations of orange roughy, a benthopelagic fish that has been trawled from seamounts around New Zealand and Australia. The trawling has removed not only the fish but also deep-water corals and other invertebrates, raising concerns over the loss of biodiversity and essential fish habitat. Mining of manganese nodules and hydrothermal deposits in the deep sea is also likely to have broad impact on local communities and regional species pools. Most nodule mining techniques suspend sediments that drift in a plume downstream of the mining activities and are deposited over wide areas of abyssal seafloor that typically receive little sedimentation. Mining of hydrothermal deposits has recently become of economic interest and has the potential for causing local and regional extinctions of vent species endemic to restricted locales. However, commercial activities are not the only ones to impact hydrothermal vent communities; collections by research scientists are now known to have at least a short-term impact. The impacts of waste disposal in the deep sea, including dredge spoil, sewage sludge, industrial waste, radioactive waste, and excess CO_2, are largely unknown but of concern due to disturbance of benthic communities and the potential for contaminants reappearing in coastal food webs. One of the most promising approaches for studying long-term variation in deep-sea communities and potential anthropogenic effects is through the establishment of marine reserves and experimental areas. Such areas have been established at seamounts near New Zealand and the Endeavour hydrothermal vent site off the west coast of Canada, and additional deep-sea locations are being proposed.

Given the tiny fraction of this remote, immense, and complex environment that has been studied, we have made enormous strides in documenting patterns of community structure and identifying the processes that potentially shape this variation. However, much is still to be done. It is entirely possible that new discoveries in the deep sea will provide substantial leaps in our understanding of community structure and evolution. The discovery of hydrothermal vents 20 years ago demonstrated that unique communities with structures fundamentally different than those from terrestrial and shallow marine systems exist in the deep ocean. Continual exploration of the deep sea will undoubtedly reveal other surprising discoveries.

ACKNOWLEDGMENTS

Comments from Lisa Levin, Mike Rex, Craig Smith, Anna Metaxas, Stace Beaulieu, Susan Mills, and two anonymous reviewers improved this manuscript. We'd like to thank Marie Tharp and Charlie Hollister (deceased) for permission to reproduce figures. This review was influenced by several workshops (Deep-Sea Biodiversity: Pattern and Scale) conducted at the National Center for Ecological Analysis and Synthesis, a Center funded by NSF (Grant #DEB-94-21535), the University of California/Santa Barbara, and the State of California. R.E. was supported by NSF grant OCE-9811925; and L.M. was supported by NSF grant OCE-9712233. This is WHOI contribution 10341.

LITERATURE CITED

Abele, L. G. and K. Walters. 1979. Marine benthic diversity: A critique and alternative explanation. *J. Biogeogr.* 6: 115–126.

Aller, J. Y. 1997. Benthic community response to temporal and spatial gradients in physical disturbance within a deep-sea western boundary region. *Deep-Sea Res.* 44: 39–69.

Aller, J. Y., and R. C. Aller. 1986. Evidence for localized enhancement of biological activity associated with tube and burrow structures in deep-sea sediments at the HEBBLE site; western North Atlantic. *Deep-Sea Res.* 33: 755–790.

Anderson-Fontana, S., H. T. Rossby and S. Riser. 1992. RAFOS floats in the southeastern Pacific Ocean 1987–1989. University of Rhode Island, Graduate School of Oceanography Technical Report 92–1: 121.

Armstrong, R. A. and R. McGehee. 1980. Competitive exclusion. *Amer. Nat.* 115: 151–170.

Baker, E. T., G. J. Massoth, R. A. Feely, G. A. Cannon and R. E. Thomson. 1998. The rise and fall of the CoAxial hydrothermal site, 1993–1996. *J. Geophys. Res. - Solid Earth* 103: 9791–9806.

Beaulieu, S., in press. Life on glass houses: Sponge stalk communities in the deep sea. *Mar. Biol.*

Berg, C. J. and C. L. Van Dover. 1987. Benthopelagic macrozooplankton communities at and near deep-sea hydrothermal vents in the eastern Pacific Ocean and the Gulf of California. *Deep-Sea Res.* 43: 379–401.

Bertram, M. and J. Cowen. 1994. Testate rhizopod growth and mineral deposition on experimental substrates from Cross Seamount. *Deep-Sea Res.* 41: 575–601.

Bett, B. J. and A. L. Rice. 1992. The influence of hexactinellid sponge (*Pheronema carpenteri*) spicules on the patchy distribution of macrobenthos in the Porcupine Seabight (bathyal NE Atlantic). *Ophelia* 36: 217–226.

Billett, D. S. M., R. S. Lampitt, A. L. Rice and R. F. C. Mantoura. 1983. Seasonal sedimentation of phytoplankton to the deep-sea benthos. *Nature* 302: 52–522.

Bischoff, J. L. and D. Z. Piper. 1979. *Marine Geology and Oceanography of the Pacific Manganese Nodule Province.* Plenum, New York.

Black, M. B., R. A. Lutz and R. C. Vrijenhoek. 1994. Gene flow among vestimentiferan tube worm (*Riftia pachyptila*) populations from hydrothermal vents of the Eastern Pacific. *Mar. Biol.* 120: 3–39.

Black, M., A. Trivedi, P. Maas, R. Lutz and R. Vrijenhoek. 1998. Population genetics and biogeography of vestimentiferan tube worms. *Deep-Sea Res.* 45: 365–382.

Blackburn, T. M. and K. J. Gaston. 1994. The distribution of body sizes of the world's bird species. *Oikos* 70: 127–130.

Blake, J. A. and J. F. Grassle. 1994. Benthic community structure on the U.S. South Atlantic slope off the Carolinas: Spatial heterogeneity in a current-dominated system. *Deep-Sea Res.* 41: 835–874.

Boehlert, G. W. and A. Genin. 1987. A review of the effects of seamounts on biological processes. In B. H. Keating, P. Fryer, R. Batiza and G. W. Boehlert (eds.), *Seamounts, Islands, and Atolls*, pp. 319–344. Geophysical Monograph Series 43. American Geophysical Union, Washington, DC.

Bograd, S. J., A. B. Rabinovich, P. H. Leblond and J. A. Shore. 1997. Observations of seamount-attached eddies in the North Pacific. *J. Geophys. Res.—Oceans* 102: 12441–12456.

Borowski, C. and H. Thiel. 1998. Deep-sea macrofaunal impacts of a large-scale physical disturbance experiment in the Southeast Pacific. *Deep-Sea Res.* 45: 55–81.

Boyer, D. L. and X. Zhang. 1990. Motion of oscillatory currents past isolated topography. *J. Phys. Oceanogr.* 20: 1425–1448.

Brink, K. H. 1995. Tidal and lower frequency currents above Fieberling Guyot. *J. Geophys. Res.* 100: 10,817–10,832.

Bucklin, A. 1988. Allozymic variability of *Riftia pachyptila* populations from the Galapagos Rift and 21°N hydrothermal vents. *Deep-Sea Res.* 35: 1759–1768.

Bucklin, A., R. Wilson and K. Smith. 1987. Genetic differentiation of seamount and basin populations of the deep-sea amphipod *Eurythenes gryllus. Deep-Sea Res.* 34: 1795–1810.

Butman, C. A. 1987. Larval settlement of soft-sediment invertebrates: The spartial scales of pattern explained by active habitat selection and the emerging role of hydrodynamical processes. *Oceanogr. Mar. Biol. Annu. Rev.* 25: 113–165.

Butman, C. A., J. P. Grassle and C. M. Webb. 1988. Substrate choices made by marine larvae settling in still water and in a flume flow. *Nature* 333: 771–773.

Cannon, G. A., D. J. Pashinski and M. R. Lemon. 1991. Middepth flow near hydrothermal venting sites on the southern Juan de Fuca ridge. *J. Geophys. Res.* 96: 12,815–12,831.

Carey, A. G., D. L. Stein and P. L. Rona. 1990. Benthos of the Gorda Ridge axial valley (NE Pacific Ocean): Taxonomic composition and trends in distribution. *Prog. Oceanogr.* 24: 47–57.

Carney, R. S. 1997. Basing conservation policies for the deep-sea floor on current-diversity concepts: a consideration of rarity. *Biodivers. Cons.* 6: 1463–1485.

Caswell, H. 1978. Predator-mediated coexistence: A nonequilibrium model. *Amer. Nat.* 112: 127–153.

Caswell, H. and J. E. Cohen. 1991a. Communities in patchy environments—a model of disturbance, competition, and heterogeneity. In J. Kolasa and S. T. A. Pickett (eds.), *Ecological Heterogeneity*, pp. 97–122. Springer-Verlag, New York.

Caswell, H. and J. E. Cohen. 1991b. Disturbance, interspecific interaction and diversity in metapopulations. *Biol. J. Linn. Soc.* 42: 193–218.

Caswell, H. and R. J. Etter. 1999. Cellular automaton models for competition in patchy environments: Facilitation, inhibition and tolerance. *Bull. Math. Biol.* 61: 625–649.

Chapman, D. C. and D. B. Haidvogel. 1992. Formation of Taylor caps over a tall isolated seamount in a stratified ocean. *Geophys. Astrophys. Fluid Dyn.* 64: 31–65.

Chave, E. H. and A. T. Jones. 1991. Deep-water megafauna of the Kohala and Haleakala slopes, Alenuihaha Channel, Hawaii. *Deep-Sea Res.* 38: 781–803.

Chevaldonné, P., D. Jollivet, A. Vangriesheim and D. Desbruyères. 1997. Hydrothermal-vent alvinellid polychaete dispersal in the eastern Pacific. 1. Influence of vent site distribution, bottom currents, and biological patterns. *Limn. Oceanogr.* 42: 67–80.

Childress, J. J. and C. R. Fisher. 1992. The biology of hydrothermal vent animals: Physiology, biochemistry, and autotrophic symbioses. *Oceanogr. Mar. Biol. Annu. Rev.* 30: 61–104.

Colwell, R. K. 1997. *EstimateS: Statistical Estimation of Species Richness and Shared Species from Samples.* Version 5. Users Guide and application published at http://viceroy.eeb.uconn.edu/estimates.

Connell, J. H. 1961. Effects of competition, predation by *Thais lapillus*, and other factors on natural populations of the barnacle *Balanus balanoides. Ecol. Monogr.* 31: 61–104.

Connell, J. H. 1972. Community interactions on marine rocky intertidal shores. *Annu. Rev. Ecol. Syst.* 3: 169–172.

Connell, J. H. 1978. Diversity in tropical rain forests and coral reefs. *Science* 199: 1302–1310.

Converse, D. R., H. D. Holland and J. M. Edmond. 1984. Flow rates in the axial hot springs of the East Pacific Rise (21°N): Implications for the heat budget and the formation of massive sulfide deposits. *Earth Plan. Sci. Lett.* 69: 159–175.

Copley, J. T. P., P. A. Tyler, M. Sheader, B. J. Murton and C. R. German. 1996. Megafauna from sublittoral to abyssal depths along the Mid-Atlantic Ridge south of Iceland. *Oceanolog. Acta* 19: 549–559.

Corliss, J. B., J. Dymond, L. I. Gordon, J. M. Edmond, R. P. v. Herzen, R. D. Ballard, K. Green, D. Williams, A. Bainbridge, K. Crane and T. H. v. Andel. 1979. Submarine thermal springs on the Galapagos Rift. *Science* 203: 1073–1083.

Cosson-Sarradin, N., M. Sibuet, G. L. J. Paterson and A. Vangriesheim. 1998. Polychaete diversity at tropical Atlantic deep-sea sites: Environmental effects. *Mar. Ecol. Prog. Ser.* 165: 173–185.

Craddock, C., W. R. Hoeh, R. A. Lutz and R. C. Vrijenhoek. 1995. Extensive gene flow in the deep-sea hydrothermal vent mytilid *Bathymodiolus thermophilus. Mar. Biol.* 124: 137–146.

Craddock, C., R. A. Lutz and R. C. Vrijenhoek. 1997. Patterns of dispersal and larval development of archaeogastropod limpets at hydrothermal vents in the eastern Pacific. *J. Exp. Mar. Biol. Ecol.* 210: 37–51.

Craig, C. H. and D. T. Sandwell. 1988. Global distribution of seamounts from Seasat profiles. *J. Geophys. Res.* 93: 10408–10420.

Creasey, S. S. and A. D. Rogers. 1999. Population genetics of bathyal and abyssal organisms. In A. J. Southward, P. A. Tyler and C. M. Young (eds.), *Advances In Marine Biology, V*, pp. 1–151. Academic Press, London.

Creasey, S., A. D. Rogers and P. A. Tyler. 1996. Genetic comparison of two populations of the deep-sea vent shrimp *Rimicaris exoculata* (Decapoda: Bresiliidae) from the Mid-Atlantic Ridge. *Mar. Biol.* 125: 473–482.

Dayton, P.K. 1971. Competition, disturbance, and community organization: The provision and subsequent utilization of space in a rocky inter-tidal community. *Ecol. Monogr.* 41: 351–389.

Dayton, P. K. and R. R. Hessler. 1972. Role of biological disturbance in maintaining diversity in the deep sea. *Deep-Sea Res.* 19: 199–208.

Desbruyères, D. and L. Laubier. 1983. Primary consumers from hydrothermal vent animal communities. In P. A. Rona, K. Bostrom, L. Laubier and K. L. Smith (eds.), *Hydrothermal Processes at Seafloor Spreading Centers*, pp. 711–734. Plenum Press, New York.

Desbruyères, D., J. Deming, A. Dinet and A. Khirpounoff. 1985. Reactions de l'ecysteme benthique profond aux pertubations: Nouveaux resultats experimentaux. In L. Laubier and C. Monniot (eds.), *Peuplements Profonds du Golfe de Gascogne*, pp.121–142. Institut Francais de Recherche pour l'Exploitation de la Mer, Brest.

Desbruyères, D., A.-M. Alayse-Danet and S. Ohta. 1994. Deep-sea hydrothermal communities in southwestern Pacific back-arc basins (the North Fiji and Lau Basins): Composition, microdistribution and food web. *Mar. Geol.* 116: 227–242.

Dial, K. P. and J. M. Marzluff 1988. Are the smallest organisms the most diverse? *Ecology* 69: 1620–1624.

Dial, R. and J. Roughgarden. 1998. Theory of marine communities: The intermediate disturbance hypothesis. *Ecology* 79: 1412–1424.

Dower, J. F. and D. L. Mackas. 1996. "Seamount effects" in the zooplankton community near Cobb Seamount. *Deep-Sea Res.* 43: 837–858.

Dower, J., H. Freeland and K. Juniper. 1992. A strong biological response to oceanic flow past Cobb Seamount. *Deep-Sea Res.* 39: 1139–1145.

Drazen, J. C., R. J. Baldwin and K. L. Smith. 1998. Sediment community response to a temporally varying food supply at an abyssal station in the NE Pacific. *Deep-Sea Res.* 45: 893–913.

Eckman, J. E. and D. Thistle. 1991. Effects of flow about a biologically produced structure on harpacticoid copepods in San-Diego Trough. *Deep-Sea Res.* 38: 1397–1416.

Ehrich, S. 1977. Die Fischfauna der Grossen Meterbank. *Meteor Forschungsergerbnisse. D* 25: 1–23.

Epifanio, C. 1988. Dispersal strategies of two species of swimming crab on the continental shelf adjacent to Delaware Bay. *Mar. Ecol. Prog. Ser.* 49: 243–248.

Etter, R. J. and J. F. Grassle. 1992. Patterns of species diversity in the deep sea as a function of sediment particle size diversity. *Nature* 360: 576–578.

Etter R. J. and M. A. Rex 1990 Population differentiation decreases with depth in deep-sea gastropods. *Deep-Sea Res.* 37: 1251–1261

Etter, R. J., M. A. Rex, M. Chase and J. Quattro. 1999. A genetic dimension to deep-sea biodiversity. *Deep-Sea Res.* 46: 1095–1099.

Fenchel, T. and L. H. Kofoed. 1976. Evidence of exploitive interspecific competition in mud snails (Hydrobiidae). *Oikos* 27: 19–32.

Fenchel, T., L. H. Kofoed and A. Lappalainen. 1975. Particle size selection of two deposit feeders: The amphipod *Corophium volutator* and the prosobranch *Hydrobia ulvae. Mar. Biol.* 30: 119–128.

Fisher, C. R. 1995. Toward an appreciation of hydrothermal-vent animals: Their environment, physiological ecology, and tissue stable isotope values. In S. E. Humphris, R. A. Zierenberg, L. S. Mullineaux and R. E. Thomson (eds.), *Seafloor Hydrothermal Systems: Physical, Chemical, Biological, and Geological Interactions*, pp. 297–316. Geophysical Monograph 91. American Geophysical Union, Washington, DC.

Fornari, D. J. and R. W. Embley. 1995. Tectonic and volcanic controls on hydrothermal processes at the mid-ocean ridge: An overview based on near-bottom and submersible studies. In S. E. Humphris, R. A. Zierenberg, L. S. Mullineaux and R. E. Thomson (eds.), *Seafloor Hydrothermal Systems: Physical, Chemical, Biological, and Geological Interactions*, pp. 1–46. Geophysical Monograph 91. American Geophysical Union, Washington, DC.

Forward, R. B. 1988. Diel vertical migration: Zooplankton photobiology and behaviour. *Oceanogr. Mar. Biol. Annu. Rev.* 26: 361–393.

France, S. C. and Kocher, T. D. 1996 Geographic and bathymetric patterns of mitochondrial 16S rRNA sequence divergence among deep-sea amphipods, *Eurythenes gryllus. Mar. Biol.* 126: 633–644.

France, S. C., R. R. Hessler and R. C. Vrijenhoek. 1992. Genetic differentiation between spatially-disjunct populations of the deepsea, hydrothermal vent-endemic amphipod *Ventiella sulfuris. Mar. Biol.* 114: 551–559.

Frazer, J. and M. Fisk. 1981. Geological factors related to characteristics of sea-floor manganese nodule deposits. *Deep-Sea Res.* 28: 1533–1551.

Freeland, H. 1994. Ocean circulation at and near Cobb Seamount. *Deep-Sea Res.* 41: 1715–1732.

Fustec, A., D. Desbruyères and S. K. Juniper. 1987. Deep-sea hydrothermal vent communities at 13°N on the East Pacific Rise: Microdistribution and temporal variations. *Biol. Oceanogr.* 4: 121–164.

Gage, J. D. 1977. Structure of the abyssal macrobenthic community in the Rockall Trough. In B. F. Keegan, P. O. Ceidigh and P. J. S. Boaden (eds.), *Biology of Benthic Organisms*, pp. 247–260. Pergamon, Oxford.

Gage, J. D. 1996. Why are there so many species in deep-sea sediments? *J. Exp. Mar. Biol. Ecol.* 200: 257–286.

Gage, J. D. 1997. High benthic species diversity in deep-sea sediments: The importance of hydrodynamics. In R. F. G. Ormond, J. D. Gage and M. V. Angel (eds.), *Marine Biodiversity*, pp. 148–177. Cambridge University Press, Cambridge.

Gage, J. D. and P. A. Tyler. 1991. *Deep-Sea Biology.* Cambridge University Press, Cambridge.

Gage, J. D., P. A. Lamont and P. A. Tyler. 1995. Deep-sea macrobenthic communities at contrasting sites off Portugal—preliminary results: I Introduction and diversity comparisons. *Intl. Rev. Gesamten Hydrobiol.* 80: 235–250.

Genin, A. and G. W. Boehlert. 1985. Dynamics of temperature and chlorophyll structures above a seamount: An oceanic experiment. *J. Mar. Res.* 43: 907–924.

Genin, A., P. Dayton, P. Lonsdale and F. Spiess. 1986. Corals on seamount peaks provide evidence of current acceleration over deep-sea topography. *Nature* 322: 59–61.

Genin, A., C. Paull and W. Dillon. 1992. Anomalous abundances of deep-sea fauna on a rocky bottom exposed to strong currents. *Deep-Sea Res.* 39: 293–302.

Goldner, D. R. and D. C. Chapman. 1997. Flow and particle motion induced above a tall seamount by steady and tidal background currents. *Deep-Sea Res.* 44: 719–744.

Gooday, A. J. 1984. Records of deep-sea rhizopod tests inhabited by metazoans in the North-East Atlantic. *Sarsia* 69: 45–53.

Gooday, A. J. and J. R. Haynes. 1983. Abyssal foraminifers, including two new genera, encrusting the interior of *Bathysiphon rusticus* tubes. *Deep-Sea Res.* 30: 591–614.

Gooday, A. J. and C. M. Turley. 1990. Responses by benthic organisms to inputs of organic material to the ocean floor: A review. *Phil. Trans. Roy. Soc. London A.* 331: 119–138.

Gooday, A. J., L. A. Levin, C. L. Thomas and B. Hecker. 1992. The distribution and ecology of *Bathysiphon filiformis sars* and *B. major de folin* (protista, foraminiferida) on the continental slope off North Carolina. *J. Foraminiferal Res.* 22: 129–146.

Gooday, A. J., O. Pfannkuche and P. J. D. Lambshead. 1996. An apparent lack of response by metazoan meiofauna to phytodetritus deposition in the bathyal north-eastern Atlantic. *J. Mar. Biol. Assn. U.K.* 76: 297–310.

Graf, G. 1989. Benthic pelagic coupling in a deep-sea benthic community. *Nature* 341: 437–439.

Grasshoff, M. 1972. Die Gorgonaria des ostlichen Nordatlantik und des Mittelmeres. I. Die familie Ellisellidae (Cnidaria: Anthozoa). *Meteor Forschungsergerbnisse, D* 10: 73–87.

Grassle, J. F. 1977. Slow recolonization of deep-sea sediment. *Nature* 265: 618–619.

Grassle, J. F. 1989. Species diversity in deep-sea communities. *Trends Ecol. Evol.* 4: 12–15.

Grassle, J. F. and J. P. Grassle. 1992. Notes from the abyss: The effects of a patchy supply of organic material and larvae on soft-sediment benthic communities. In P. Giller, A. Hildrew and D. Rafaelli (eds.), *Aquatic Ecology: Scale, Pattern and Process. The 34th Symposium of the British Ecological Society*, pp. 499–515. Blackwell, Oxford.

Grassle, J. F. and N. J. Maciolek. 1992. Deep-sea species richness: Regional and local diversity estimate from quantitative bottom samples. *Amer. Nat.* 139: 313–341.

Grassle, J. F. and L. S. Morse-Porteous. 1987. Macrofaunal colonization of disturbed deep-sea environments and the structure of deep-sea benthic communities. *Deep-Sea Res.* 34: 1911–1950.

Grassle, J. F. and H. L. Sanders. 1973. Life histories and the role of disturbance. *Deep-Sea Res.* 20: 643–659.

Grassle, J. F., L. S. Brown-Leger, L. Morse-Porteous, R. Petrecca and I. Williams. 1985. Deep-sea fauna in the vicinity of hydrothermal vents. *Bull. Biol. Soc. Washington* 6: 443–452.

Grassle, J. P. 1985. Genetic differentiation in populations of hydrothermal vent mussels (Bathymodiolus thermophilus) from the Galapagos Rift and 13°N on the East Pacific Rise. *Bull. Biol. Soc. Washington* 6: 429–442.

Grassle, J. P., P. V. R. Snelgrove and C. A. Butman. 1992. Larval habitat choice in still water and flume flows by the opportunistic bivalve Mulinia lateralis. *Neth. J. Sea Res.* 30: 33–44.

Gray, J. S. 1981. *The Ecology of Marine Sediments.* Cambridge University Press, Cambridge.

Gray, J. S. 1994. Is deep-sea species diversity really so high? Species diversity of the Norwegian continental shelf. *Mar. Ecol. Prog. Ser.* 112: 205–209.

Grigg, R. 1997. Benthic communities on Lo'ihi submarine volcano reflect high-disturbance environment. *Pacific Sci.* 51: 209–220.

Grigg, R. W., A. Malahoff, E. H. Chave and J. Landahl. 1987. Seamount benthic ecology and potential environmental impact from manganese crust mining in Hawaii. In B. H. Keating, P. Fryer, R. Batiza and G. W. Boehlert (eds.), *Seamounts, Islands, and Atolls*, pp. 355–378. American Geophysical Union, Washington, DC.

Haedrich, R. L., G. T. Rowe and P. T. Polloni. 1980. The megabenthic fauna of the deep sea south of New England, U.S.A. *Mar. Biol.* 57: 165–179.

Hall, S. J. 1994. Physical disturbance and marine benthic communities: Life in unconsolidated sediments. In A. D. Ansell, R. N. Gibson and M. Barnes (eds.), *Oceanography and Marine Biology*, Vol. 32, pp. 179–239. U.C.L. Press, London.

Haymon, R. M., D. J. Fornari, K. L. Von Damm, M. D. Lilley, M. R. Perfit, J. M. Edmond, W. C. Shanks III, R. A. Lutz, J. M. Grebmeier, S. Carbotte, D. Wright, E. McLaughlin, M. Smith, N. Beedle and E. Olson. 1993. Volcanic eruption of the mid-ocean ridge along the East Pacific Rise crest at 9° 45–52'N: Direct submersible observations of sea-floor phenomena associated with an eruption event in April, 1991. *Earth Planet. Sci. Lett.* 119: 85–101.

Hecker, B. and A. Z. Paul. 1979. Abyssal community structure of the benthic infauna of the Eastern Equatorial Pacific: DOMES sites A, B, and C. In J. Bischoff and D. Piper (eds.), *Marine Geology and Oceanography of the Pacific Manganese Nodule Province*, pp. 83–112. Plenum Press, New York.

Heezen, B. C. and C. D. Hollister. 1971. *The Face of the Deep*. Oxford University Press, New York.

Helfrich, K. R. and K. G. Speer. 1995. Oceanic hydrothermal circulation: Mesoscale and basin-scale flow. In S. E. Humphris, R. A. Zierenberg, L. S. Mullineaux and R. E. Thomson (eds.), *Seafloor Hydrothermal Systems: Physical, Chemical, Biological, and Geological Interactions*, pp. 347–356. Geophysical Monograph 91. American Geophysical Union, Washington, DC.

Helfrich, K. R., T. M. Joyce, G. A. Cannon, S. A. Harrington and D. J. Pashinski. 1998. Mean hydrographic and velocity sections near Pipe Organ vent at Juan de Fuca Ridge. *Geophys. Res. Lett.* 25: 1737–1740.

Herring, P. J. and D. R. Dixon. 1998. Extensive deep-sea dispersal of postlarval shrimp from a hydrothermal vent. *Deep-Sea Res.* 45: 2105–2118.

Hessler, R. R. and W. M. Smithey. 1983. The distribution and community structure of megafauna at the Galapagos Rift hydrothermal vents. In P. S. Rona, K. Bostrom, L. Laubier and K. L. Smith (eds.), *Hydrothermal Processes at Seafloor Spreading Centers*, pp. 735–770. NATO Conference Series. Plenum Press, New York.

Hessler, R. R. and P. A. Jumars. 1974. Abyssal community analysis from replicate box cores in the central North Pacific. *Deep-Sea Res.* 21: 185–209.

Hessler, R. R. and H. L. Sanders. 1967. Faunal diversity in the deep sea. *Deep-Sea Res.* 14: 65–78.

Hessler, R. R., W. M. Smithey and C. H. Keller. 1985. Spatial and temporal variation of giant clams, tubeworms and mussels at deep-sea hydrothermal vents. *Bull. Biol. Soc. Washington* 6: 465–474.

Hessler, R. R., W. M. Smithey, M. A. Boudrias, C. H. Keller, R. A. Lutz and J. J. Childress. 1988. Temporal change in megafauna at the Rose Garden hydrothermal vent (Galápagos Rift; eastern tropical Pacific). *Deep-Sea Res.* 35: 1681–1709.

Hubbell, S. 1979. Tree dispersion, abundance, and diversity in a tropical dry forest. *Science* 203: 1299–1309.

Hubbell, S. P., R. B. Foster, K. E. O'Brien, R. Harms, B. Condit, S. J. Wechsler, S. Wright and L. D. Lao. 1999. Light-gap disturbances, recruitment limitation, and tree diversity in a neotropical forest. *Science* 283: 554–557.

Hubbs, C. L. 1959. Initial discoveries of fish faunas on seamounts and offshore banks in the eastern Pacific. *Pacific Sci.* 13: 311–316.

Hurtt, G. C. and S. W. Pacala. 1995. The consequences of recruitment limitation: Reconciling chance, history and competitive differences between plants. *J. Theor. Biol.* 176: 1–16.

Huston, M. 1979. A general hypothesis of species diversity. *Amer. Nat.* 113: 81–101.

Huston, M. 1994. *Biological Diversity*. Cambridge University Press, Cambridge.

Jannasch, H. W. 1995. Microbial interactions with hydrothermal fluids. In S. E. Humphris, R. A. Zierenberg, L. S. Mullineaux and R. E. Thomson (eds.), *Seafloor Hydrothermal Systems: Physical, Chemical, Biological and Geological Interactions*, pp. 273–296. Geophysical Monograph 91. American Geophysical Union, Washington, DC.

Janzen, D. H. 1970. Herbivores and the number of tree species in tropical forests. *Amer. Nat.* 104: 501–528.

Jeong, K., J. Kang and S. Chough. 1994. Sedimentary processes and manganese nodule formation in the Korea deep ocean study (KODOS) area, western part of Clarion-Clipperton fracture zones, Northeast Equatorial Pacific. *Mar. Geol.* 122: 125–150.

Jollivet, D., D. Desbruyères, F. Bonhomme and D. Moraga. 1995. Genetic differentiation of deep-sea hydrothermal vent alvinellid populations (Annelida: Polychaeta) along the East Pacific Rise. *Heredity* 74: 376–391.

Joyce, T. M., G. A. Cannon, D. Pashinski, K. R. Helfrich and S. A. Harrington. 1998. Vertical and temporal vorticity observations at Juan de Fuca Ridge: Hydrothermal signatures. *Geophys. Res. Lett.* 25: 1741–1744.

Jumars, P. A. 1975. Environmental grain and polychaete species' diversity in a bathyal benthic community. *Mar. Biol.* 30: 253–266.

Jumars, P. A. 1976. Deep-sea species diversity. Does it have a characteristic scale? *J. Mar. Res.* 34: 217–246.

Jumars, P. A. 1978. Spatial autocorrelation with RUM (remote underwater manipulator): Vertical and horizontal structure of a bathyal benthic community. *Deep-Sea Res.* 25: 589–604.

Jumars, P. A. and J. E. Ekman. 1983. Spatial structure within deep-sea benthic communities. In G. T. Rowe (ed.), *The Sea*, pp. 399–452. Wiley, New York.

Jumars, P. A. and E. D. Gallagher. 1982. Deep-sea community structure: Three plays on the benthic proscenium. In W. Ernst and J. Morin (eds.), *The Environment of the Deep Sea*, pp. 217–255. Prentice-Hall, Englewood Cliffs, NJ.

Jumars, P. A. and A. R. M. Nowell. 1984. Fluid and sediment dynamic effects on marine benthic community structure. *Amer. Zool.* 24: 45–55.

Jumars, P. A. and R. A. Wheatcroft. 1989. Responses of benthos to changing food quality and quantity, with a focus on deposit feeding and bioturbation. *Productivity Ocean: Present Past* 44: 235–253.

Jumars, P. A., L. L. Mayer, J. W. Deming, J. A. Baross and R. A. Wheatcroft. 1990. Deep-sea deposit-feeding strategies suggested by environmental and feeding constraints. *Phil. Trans. R. Soc. London* A 331: 85–101.

Karl, S., S. Schutz, D. Desbruyeres, R. Lutz and R. Vrijenhoek. 1996. Molecular analysis of gene flow in the hydrothermal vent clam (*Calyptogena magnifica*). *Molec. Mar. Biol. Biotech.* 5: 193–202.

Kim, S. L. and L. S. Mullineaux. 1998. Distribution and near-bottom transport of larvae

and other plankton at hydrothermal vents. *Deep-Sea Res.* 45: 423–440.

Kim, S. L., L. S. Mullineaux and K. R. Helfrich. 1994. Larval dispersal via entrainment into hydrothermal vent plumes. *J. Geophys. Res.* 99: 12,655–12,665.

Knowlton, N. 1993. Sibling species in the sea. *Annu. Rev. Ecol. Syst.* 24: 189–216.

Kukert, H. and C. R. Smith. 1992. Disturbance, colonization and succession in a deep-sea sediment community: artificial mound experiments. *Deep-Sea Res.* 39: 1349–1371.

Kunze, E. and J. M. Toole. 1997. Tidally driven vorticity, diurnal shear, and turbulence atop Fieberling Seamount. *J. Phys. Oceanogr.* 27: 2663–2693.

Lalou, C., J. E. Reyss, E. Brichet, M. Arnold, G. Thompson, Y. Fouquet and P. A. Rona. 1993. Geochronology of TAG and Snake Pit hydrothermal fields, Mid-Atlantic Ridge: Witness to a long and complex hydrothermal history. *Earth Planet. Sci. Lett.* 97: 113–128.

Lampitt, R. S. 1985. Evidence for the seasonal deposition of detritus to the deep-sea floor and its subsequent resuspension. *Deep-Sea Res.* 32: 885–897.

Lampitt, R. S., D. S. M. Billett and A. L. Rice. 1986. Biomass of the invertebrate megabenthos from 500–4100 m in the northeast Atlantic Ocean. *Mar. Biol.* 93: 69–81.

Lauerman, L. M. L. and R. S. Kaufmann. 1998. Deep-sea epibenthic echinoderms and a temporally varying food supply: results from a one year time series in the NE Pacific. *Deep-Sea Res.* 45: 817–842.

Leal, J. H. and P. Bouchet. 1991. Distribution patterns and dispersal of prosobranch gastropods along a seamount chain in the Atlantic ocean. *J. Mar. Biol. Assn. U.K.* 71: 11–25.

Levin, L. A. 1991. Interactions between metazoans and large, agglutinating protozoans: Implications for the community structure of deep-sea benthos. *Amer. Zool.* 31: 886–900.

Levin, L. A. and C. DiBacco. 1995. Influence of sediment transport on short-term recolonization by seamount infauna. *Mar. Ecol. Prog. Ser.* 123: 163–175.

Levin, L. A. and S. Edesa. 1997. The ecology of cirratulid mudballs on the Oman margin, northwest Arabian Sea. *Mar. Biol.* 128: 671–678.

Levin, L. A. and J. D. Gage. 1998. Relationships between oxygen, organic matter and the diversity of bathyal macrofauna. *Deep-Sea Res.* 45: 129–163.

Levin, L. A. and C. R. Smith. 1984. Response of background fauna to disturbance and enrichment in the deep sea: a sediment tray experiment. *Deep-Sea Res.* 31: 1277–1285.

Levin, L. A., D. J. DeMasters, L. D. McCann and C. L. Thomas. 1986. Effects of giant protozoans (class Xenophyophorea) on deep-seamount benthos. *Mar. Ecol. Prog. Ser.* 29: 99–104.

Levin, L. A., S. E. Childers and C. R. Smith. 1991a. Epibenthic, agglutinating foraminiferans in the Santa Catalina basin and their response to disturbance. *Deep-Sea Res.* 38: 465–483.

Levin, L. A., C. L. Huggett, and K. F. Wishner. 1991b. Control of deep-sea benthic community structure by oxygen and organic-matter gradients in the eastern Pacific Ocean. *J. Mar. Res.* 49: 763–800.

Levin, L. A., G. R. Plaia and C. L. Huggett. 1994. The influence of natural organic enhancement on life histories and community structure of bathyal polychaetes. In C. Young and K. Eckelbarger (eds.), *Reproduction, Larval Biology, and Recruitment of the Deep-Sea Benthos*, pp. 261–283. Columbia University Press, New York.

Levin, L. A., J. D. Gage, C. Martin and P. A. Lamont. 2000. Macrobenthic community structure within and beneath the oxygen minimum zone, NW Arabian Sea. Deep-Sea Research Special Volume: Benthic Processes in the Arabian Sea. *Deep-Sea Res.* Part II 47: 189–226.

Levinton, J. S. 1979. Particle feeding by deposit feeders: Models, data and prospectus. In K. Tenore and B. Coull (eds.), *Marine Benthic Dynamics*, pp. 423–439. University of South Carolina Press, Columbia.

Lewis, J. R. 1964. *The Ecology of Rocky Shores.* English Universities Press, London.

Lochte, K. and C. M. Turley. 1988. Bacteria and cyanobacteria associated with phytodetritus in the deep sea. *Nature* 333: 67–69.

Lupton, J. E., E. T. Baker, N. Garfield, G. J. Massoth, R. A. Feely, J. P. Cowen, R. R. Greene and T. A. Rago. 1998. Tracking the evolution of a hydrothermal event plume with a RAFOS neutrally buoyant drifter. *Science* 280: 1052–1055.

Lutjeharms, J. R. E. and A. E. F. Heydorn. 1981. The rock-lobster (*Jasus tristani*) on Vema Seamount: Drifting buoys suggest a possible recruiting mechanism. *Deep-Sea Res.* 28A: 631–636.

Lutz, R. A. 1988. Dispersal of organisms at deep-sea hydrothermal vents: A review. *Oceanol. Acta Sp.*: 23–29.

Lutz, R. A., D. Jablonski, D. C. Rhoads and R. D. Turner. 1980. Larval dispersal of a deep-sea hydrothermal vent bivalve from the Galapagos Rift. *Mar. Biol.* 57: 127–133.

Lutz, R. A., D. Jablonski and R. D. Turner. 1984. Larval development and dispersal at deep-sea hydrothermal vents. *Science* 226: 1451–1454.

Lutz, R. A., T. M. Shank, D. J. Fornari, R. M. Haymon, M. D. Lilley, K. Von Damm and D. Desbruyères. 1994. Rapid growth at deep-sea vents. *Nature* 371: 663–664.

MacArthur, R. H. 1972. *Geographical Ecology.* Harper and Row, New York.

MacDonald, K. C., K. Becker, F. N. Spiess and R. D. Ballard. 1980. Hydrothermal heat flux of the "black smoker" vents on the East Pacific Rise. *Earth Planet. Sci. Lett.* 48: 1–7.

Maciolek, N. J., J. F. Grassle, B. Hecker, P. D. Boehm, B. Brown, B. Dade, W. G. Steinhaur, E. Baptiste, R. E. Ruff and R. Petrecca. 1987a. *Study of Biological Processes on the U.S. Mid-Atlantic Slope and Rise.* Phase 2. Final Report

prepared for U.S. Dept. of Interior, Minerals Management Service, Washington, DC.

Maciolek, N. J., J. F. Grassle, B. Hecker, B. Brown, J. A. Blake, P. D. Boehm, R. Petrecca, S. Duffy, E. Baptiste and R. E. Ruff. 1987b. *Study of Biological Processes on the U.S. North Atlantic Slope and Rise.* Final Report prepared for U.S. Dept. of Interior, Minerals Management Service, Washington, DC.

Maciolek-Blake, N. J., J. F. Grassle, J. A. Blake and J. M. Neff. 1985. *Georges Bank Infauna Monitoring Program: Final Report for the Third Year of Sampling.* Prepared for U.S. Dept. of Interior, Minerals Management Service, Washington, DC.

May, R. M. 1988. How many species are there on earth? *Science* 241: 1441–1449.

Mayer, L. M. 1989. The nature and determination of non-living sedimentary organic matter as a food source for deposit feeders. In G. T. G. Lopez and J. Levinton (eds.), *Ecology of Marine Deposit Feeders*, pp. 98–113. Springer-Verlag, New York.

McHugh, D. 1989. Population structure and reproductive biology of two sympatric hydrothermal vent polychaetes, *Paralvinella pandorae* and *P. palmiformis. Mar. Biol.* 10: 95–106.

Mellor, C. A. and C. K. Paull. 1994. Sea beam bathymetry of the Manteo 467 lease block off Cape Hatteras, North Carolina. *Deep-Sea Res.* 41: 711–718.

Micheli, F., L. Mullineaux, S. Mills, C. Peterson, G. Sancho, C. Fisher and G. Johnson. 1998. Species interactions at hydrothermal vents: How predation structures communities in an extreme environment. *RIDGE Results Symposium: Field studies along the East Pacific Rise 9°–10°N.*

Moraga, D., D. Jollivet and F. Denis. 1994. Genetic differentiation between two *Bathymodiolus* spp. of two western back-arc basins and *Bathymodiolus thermophilus* (13°N: East Pacific Rise). *Deep-Sea Res.* 41: 1551–1567.

Moskalev, L. I. and S. V. Galkin. 1986. Investigations of the fauna of submarine upheavals during the 9th trip of the research vessel "Academic Mstislav Keldysh". *Zoologicheskii Zhurnal* 65: 1716–1720. (Russian with English summary.)

Mullineaux, L. S. 1987. Organisms encrusting manganese nodules and crusts: Distribution and abundance at three North Pacific sites. *Deep-Sea Res.* 34: 165–184.

Mullineaux, L. S. and C. A. Butman. 1990. Recruitment of benthic invertebrates in boundary-layer flows: A deep water experiment on Cross Seamount. *Limn. Oceanogr.* 35: 409–423.

Mullineaux, L. S. and S. C. France. 1995. Dispersal of deep-sea hydrothermal vent fauna. In S. E. Humphris, R. A. Zierenberg, L. S. Mullineaux and R. E. Thomson (eds.), *Seafloor Hydrothermal Systems: Physical, Chemical, Biological, and Geological Interactions*, pp. 408–424. American Geophysical Union, Washington DC.

Mullineaux, L. S. and D. T. Manahan. 1999. Deep-Sea Diaspora: The LARVE project explores how species migrate from vent to vent. *Oceanus* 41: 6–9.

Mullineaux, L. S. and S. W. Mills. 1997. A test of the larval retention hypothesis in seamount-generated flows. *Deep-Sea Res.* 44: 745.

Mullineaux, L. S., P. H. Wiebe and E. T. Baker. 1995. Larvae of benthic invertebrates in hydrothermal vent plumes over Juan de Fuca Ridge. *Mar. Biol.* 122: 585–596.

Mullineaux, L. S., S. W. Mills and E. Goldman. 1998. Recruitment variation during a pilot colonization study of hydrothermal vents (9° 50'N, East Pacific Rise). *Deep-Sea Res.* 45: 441–464.

Mullineaux, L. S., C. R. Fisher, C. H. Peterson and S. W. Schaeffer. 2000. Vestimentiferan tubeworm succession at hydrothermal vents: Use of biogenic cues to reduce habitat selection error? *Oecologia* 123: 275–284.

Nowell, A. R. M. and P. A. Jumars. 1984. Flow environments of aquatic benthos. *Annu. Rev. Ecol. Syst.* 15: 303–328.

Okal, E. A. and R. Batiza. 1987. Hotspots: The first 25 years. In B. H. Keating, P. Fryer, R. Batiza and G. W. Boehlert (eds.), *Seamounts, Islands and Atolls*, pp. 1–12. Geophysical Monograph 43. American Geophysical Union, Washington, DC.

Oschmann, W. 1990. Dropstones—rocky mini-islands in high-latitude pelagic soft substrate environments. *Senckenbergiana marit.* 21: 55–75.

Osman, R. W. and R. B. Whitlatch. 1978. Patterns of species diversity: Fact or artifact? *Paleobiology* 4: 41–54.

Paine, R. T. 1966. Food web complexity and species diversity. *Amer. Nat.* 100: 65–75.

Paine, R. T. and S. A. Levin. 1981. Intertidal landscapes: disturbance and the dynamics of pattern. *Ecol. Monogr.* 51: 145–178.

Palumbi, S. 1994. Genetic divergence, reproductive isolation, and marine speciation. *Annu. Rev. Ecol. Syst.* 25: 547–572.

Parker, T. and V. Tunnicliffe. 1994. Dispersal strategies of the biota on an oceanic seamount: Implications for ecology and biogeography. *Biol. Bull.* 187: 336–345.

Paterson, G. L. J. and P. J. D. Lambshead. 1995. Bathymetric patterns of polychaete diversity in the Rockall Trough, northeast Atlantic. *Deep-Sea Res.* 42: 1199–1214.

Pearse, J., J. McClintock and I. Bosch. 1991. Reproduction of Antarctic benthic marine invertebrates: Tempos, modes, and timing. *Amer. Zool.* 3: 165–180.

Petersen, C. G. J. 1913. Valuation of the sea. II. The animal communities of the sea bottom and their importance for marine zoogeography. *Report of the Danish Biological Station to the Board of Agriculture* 21: 1–44.

Peterson, C. H. 1986. Enhancement of *Mercinaria mercinaria* densities in seagrass beds: Is pattern fixed during settlement season or altered by subsequent differential survival? *Limn. Oceanogr.* 31: 200–205.

Petrecca, R. and J. F. Grassle. 1990. Notes on fauna from several deep-sea hydrothermal vent and cold seep soft-sediment communities. In G. R. McMurray (ed.), *Gorda Ridge: A*

Seafloor Spreading Center in the United States' Exclusive Economic Zone, pp. 278–284. Springer-Verlag, New York.

Pfannkuche, O. 1993. Benthic response to the sedimentation of particulate organic matter at the BIOTRANS station, 47°N 20°W. *Deep-Sea Res.* 40: 135–149.

Rex, M. A. 1976. Biological accommodation in the deep-sea benthos: Comparative evidence on the importance of predation and productivity. *Deep-Sea Res.* 23: 957–987.

Rex, M. A. 1981. Community structure in the deep-sea benthos. *Annu. Rev. Ecol. Syst.* 12: 331.

Rex, M. A. 1983. Geographic patterns of species diversity in the deep-sea benthos. In G. T. Rowe (ed.), *The Sea*, pp. 453–472. Wiley, New York.

Rex, M. A. and R. J. Etter. 1998. Bathymetric patterns of body size: Implications for deep-sea biodiversity. *Deep-Sea Res.* 45: 103–127.

Rex, M. A., C. T. Stuart, R. R. Hessler, J. A. Allen, H. L. Sanders and G. D. F. Wilson. 1993. Global-Scale latitudinal patterns of species diversity in the Deep-Sea benthos. *Nature* 365: 636–639.

Rex, M. A., R. J. Etter and C. T. Stuart. 1997. Large-scale patterns of species diversity in the deep-sea benthos. In R. F. G. Ormond, J. D. Gage and M. V. Angel (eds.), *Marine Biodiversity*, pp. 94–121. Cambridge University Press, Cambridge.

Rhoads, D. C. 1974. Organism-sediment relations on the muddy sea floor. In A. D. Ansell, R. N. Gibson and M. Barnes (eds.), *Oceanography and Marine Biology*, pp. 263–300. U.C.L. Press, London.

Rice, A. L., D. S. M. Billett, J. Fry, A. W. G. John, R. S. Lampitt, R. F. C. Mantoura and R. J. Morris. 1986. Seasonal deposition of phytodetritus to the deep-sea floor. *Proc. Roy. Soc. Edinburgh* 88B: 265–279.

Ricklefs, R. E. and D. Schluter. 1993. Species diversity—regional and historical influences. In R. E. Ricklefs and D. Schluter (eds.), *Species Diversity in Ecological Communities*, pp. 350–363. University of Chicago Press, Chicago.

Roden, G. I. 1987. Effect of seamounts and seamount chains on ocean circulation and thermohaline structure. In B. H. Keating, P. Fryer, R. Batiza and G. W. Boehlert (eds.), *Seamounts, Islands, and Atolls*, pp. 335–354. American Geophysical Union, Washington, DC.

Rogers, A.D. 1994. The biology of seamounts. *Adv. Mar. Biol.* 30: 305–350.

Rosenzweig, M. L. 1995. *Species Diversity in Space and Time*. Cambridge University Press, Cambridge.

Rosenzweig, M. L. and Z. Abramsky. 1993. How are diversity and productivity related. In R. E. Ricklefs and D. Schluter (eds.), *Species Diversity in Ecological Communities*, pp. 52–65. University of Chicago Press, Chicago.

Rowe, G. T. 1971. Benthic biomass and surface productivity. In J. Costlow (ed.), *Fertility of the Sea*, pp. 441–454. Gordon and Breach, New York.

Rowe, G. T. 1983. Biomass and production of the deep-sea macrobenthos. In G. T. Rowe (ed.), *The Sea*, pp. 97–121. Wiley, New York.

Rowe, G. T. and R. J. Menzies. 1969. Zonation of large benthic invertebrates in the deep-sea off the Carolinas. *Deep-Sea Res.* 16: 531–537.

Rowe, G. T. and V. Pariente. 1992. *Deep-Sea Food Chains and the Global Carbon Cycle*. Kluwer Academic Publishers, Dordrecht.

Rowe, G. T., P. T. Polloni and S. G. Horner. 1974. Benthic biomass estimates from the northwestern Atlantic Ocean and northern Gulf of Mexico. *Deep-Sea Res.* 21: 641–650.

Sanders, H. L. 1958. Benthic studies in Buzzards Bay. I: Animal–sediment relationships. *Limn. Oceanogr.* 3: 245–258.

Sanders, H. L. 1968. Marine benthic diversity: A comparative study. *Amer. Nat.* 102: 243–282.

Sanders, H. L. and R. R. Hessler. 1969. Ecology of the deep-sea benthos. *Science* 163: 1419–1423.

Sanders, H. L., R. R. Hessler and G. R. Hampson. 1965. An introduction to the study of deep-sea benthic faunal assemblages along the Gay Head-Bermuda transect. *Deep-Sea Res.* 12: 845–867.

Schaff, T. R. and L. A. Levin. 1994. Spatial heterogeneity of benthos associated with biogenic structures on the North Carolina continental slope. *Deep-Sea Res.* 41: 901.

Schaff, T., L. Levin, N. Blair, D. Demaster, R. Pope and S. Boehme. 1992. Spatial heterogeneity of benthos on the Carolina continental slope—large (100-km)-scale variation. *Mar. Ecol. Prog. Ser.* 88: 143–160.

Scheltema, R. 1986. On dispersal and planktonic larvae of benthic invertebrates: An eclectic overview and summary of problems. *Bull. Mar. Sci.* 39: 290–322.

Schwinghamer, P. 1985. Observations on the size-structure and pelagic coupling of some shelf and abyssal benthic communities. *European Symp. Mar. Biol.* 19: 347–359.

Self, R. F. L. and P. A. Jumars. 1988. Cross-phyletic patterns of particle selection by deposit feeders. *J. Mar. Res.* 46: 119–143.

Shank, T. M., D. J. Fornari, K. L. Vondamm, M. D. Lilley, R. M. Haymon and R. A. Lutz. 1998. Temporal and spatial patterns of biological community development at nascent deep-sea hydrothermal vents (9° 50′N, East Pacific Rise). *Deep-Sea Res.* 45: 465.

Shilling, F. and D. Manahan. 1994. Energy metabolism and amino acid transport during early development of antarctic and temperate echinoderms. *Biol. Bull.* 187: 398–407.

Shirayama, Y. 1983. Size structure of deep-sea meio- and macrobenthos in the western Pacific. *Internationale Revue der gesamten Hydrobiologie* 68: 799–810.

Shirayama, Y. and M. Horikoshi. 1989. Comparison of the benthic size structure between sublittoral, upper-slope and deep-sea areas of the western Pacific. *Internationale Revue der gesampten Hydrobiologie* 74: 1–13.

Shomura, R. S. and R. A. Barkley. 1980. Ecosystem dynamics of seamounts—a working hypothesis. *Fourth Symposium for the Coop-*

ative Study of the Kuroshio and Adjacent Regions, pp. 789–790.

Sibuet, M., C. E. Lambert, R. Chesselet and L. Laubier. 1989. Density of the major size groups of benthic fauna and trophic input in deep basins of the Atlantic Ocean. *J. Mar. Res.* 47: 851–867.

Siemann, E., D. Tilman and J. Haarstad. 1996. Insect species diversity, abundance and body size relationships. *Nature* 380: 704–706.

Smith, C. R. 1985. Food for the deep sea: Utilization dispersal and flux of nekton falls at the Santa Catalina Basin floor. *Deep-Sea Res.* 32: 417–442.

Smith, C. R. 1986. Nekton falls low-intensity disturbance and community structure of infaunal benthos in the deep sea. *J. Mar. Res.* 44: 567–600.

Smith, C. R. and S. J. Brumsickle. 1989. The effects of patch size and substrate isolation on colonization modes and rates in an intertidal sediment. *Limn. Oceanogr.* 34: 1263–1277.

Smith, C. R. and R. R. Hessler. 1987. Colonization and succession in deep-sea ecosystems. *Trends Ecol. Evol.* 2: 359–363.

Smith, C. R., H. L. Maybaum, A. R. Baco, R. H. Pope, S. D. Carpenter, P. L. Yager, S. A. Macko and J. W. Deming. 1998. Sediment community structure around a whale skeleton in the deep Northeast Pacific: Macrofaunal, microbial and bioturbation effects. *Deep-Sea Res.* 45: 335–364.

Smith, C. R., P. A. Jumars and D. J. DeMaster. 1986. In situ studies of megafaunal mounds indicate rapid sediment turnover and community response at the deep-sea floor. *Nature* 323: 251–253.

Smith, K. L. 1987. Food energy supply and demand; a discrepancy between particulate organic carbon flux and sediment community oxygen consumption in the deep sea. *Limn. Oceanogr.* 32: 201–220.

Smith, K. L. and R. J. Baldwin. 1984. Seasonal fluctuations in deep-sea sediment community oxygen consumption: central and eastern North Pacific. *Nature* 307: 624–626.

Smith, K. L. and K. R. Hinga. 1983. Sediment community respiration in the deep sea. In G. T. Rowe (ed.), *The Sea*, pp. 331–370. Wiley, New York.

Smith, K. L., R. S. Kaufmann and R. J. Baldwin. 1994. Coupling of near-bottom pelagic and benthic processes at abyssal depths in the eastern North Pacific Ocean. *Limn. Oceanogr.* 39: 1101–1118.

Smith, K. L., R. J. Baldwin, R. C. Glatts, R. S. Kaufmann and E. C. Fisher. 1998. Detrital aggregates on the sea floor: Chemical composition and aerobic decomposition rates at a time-series station in the abyssal NE Pacific. *Deep-Sea Res.* 45: 843–880.

Smith, W. O. and T. H. Jordan. 1988. Seamount statistics in the Pacific Ocean. *J. Geophys. Res.* 93: 2899–2919.

Snelgrove, P. V. R. and C. A. Butman. 1994. Animal sediment relationships revisited: Cause versus effect. In A. D. Ansell, R. N. Gibson and M. Barnes (eds.), *Oceanography and Marine Biology*, Vol. 32, pp. 111–177. U.C.L. Press, London.

Snelgrove, P. V. R., J. F. Grassle and R. F. Petrecca. 1992. The role of food patches in maintaining high deep-sea diversity—field experiments with hydrodynamically unbiased colonization trays. *Limn. Oceanogr.* 37: 1543–1550.

Snelgrove, P. V. R., J. F. Grassle and R. F. Petrecca. 1994. Macrofaunal response to artificial enrichments and depressions in a Deep-Sea habitat. *J. Mar. Res.* 52: 345–369.

Snelgrove, P. V. R., J. F. Grassle and R. F. Petrecca. 1996. Experimental evidence for aging food patches as a factor contributing to high deep-sea macrofaunal diversity. *Limn. Oceanogr.* 41: 605–614.

Sousa, W. P. 1979a. Disturbance in marine intertidal boulder fields: The nonequilibrium maintenance of species diversity. *Ecology* 60: 1225–1239.

Sousa, W. P. 1979b. Experimental investigations of disturbance and ecological succession in a rocky intertidal algal community. *Ecol. Monogr.* 49: 227–254.

Southward, E. C., V. Tunnicliffe, M. Black, D. R. Dixon and L. R. J. Dixon. 1996. Ocean ridge segmentation and hot vent tubeworms in the northeast Pacific. In C. J. MacLeod, P. A. Tyler and C. L. Walker (eds.), *Geological Society Special Publication*, Vol. 118, pp. 211–224.

Taghon, G. L. 1982. Optimal foraging by deposit-feeding invertebrates: Roles of particle size and organic coating. *Oecologia* 52: 295–304.

Taghon, G. L., R. F. L. Self and P. A. Jumars. 1978. Predicting particle selection by deposit-feeders: A model and predictions. *Limn. Oceanog.* 23: 752–759.

Tenore, K. R., L. Cammen, S. E. G. Findlay and N. Phillips. 1982. Perspectives of research on detritus: Do factors controlling the availability of detritus to macroconsumers depend on its source? *J. Mar. Res.* 40: 473–490.

Thiel, H. 1979. Structural aspect of the deep-sea benthos. *Ambio Special Report* 6: 25–31.

Thiel, H., G. Schriever, C. Bussau and C. Borowski. 1993. Manganese nodule crevice fauna. *Deep-Sea Res.* 40: 419–423.

Thistle, D. 1978. Harpacticoid dispersion patterns: Implications for deep-sea diversity maintenance. *J. Mar. Res.* 36: 377–397.

Thistle, D. 1979. Harpacticoid copepods and biogenic structures: Implications for deep-sea diversity maintenance. In R. J. Livingstone (ed.), *Ecological Processes in Coastal and Marine Systems*, pp. 217–231. Plenum, New York.

Thistle, D. 1983. The role of biologically produced habitat heterogeneity in deep-sea diversity maintenance. *Deep-Sea Res.* 30: 1235–1245.

Thistle, D. 1998. Harpacticoid copepod diversity at two physically reworked sites in the deep sea. *Deep-Sea Res.* 45: 13–24.

Thistle, D. and J. E. Eckman. 1990. The effect of a biologically produced structure on the benthic copepods of a deep-sea site. *Deep-Sea Res.* 37: 541–554.

Thistle, D. and L. A. Levin. 1998. The effect of experimentally increased near-bottom flow

on metazoan meiofauna at a deep-sea site, with comparison data on macrofauna. *Deep-Sea Res.* 45: 625–638.

Thistle, D. and G. D. F. Wilson. 1987. A hydrodynamically modified abyssal isopod fauna. *Deep-Sea Res.* 34A: 73–87.

Thistle, D. and G. D. F. Wilson. 1996. Is the HEBBLE isopod fauna hydrodynamically modified? A second test. *Deep-Sea Res.* 43: 545–554.

Thistle, D., J. Y. Yingst and K. Fauchald. 1985. A deep-sea benthic community exposed to strong near-bottom currents on the Scotion rise (western Atlantic). *Mar. Geol.* 66: 91–112.

Thistle, D., S. C. Ertman and K. Fauchald. 1991. The fauna of the HEBBLE site: Patterns in standing stock and sediment-dynamic effects. *Mar. Geol.* 99: 413–422.

Thistle, D., B. Hilbig and J. E. Eckman. 1993. Are polychaetes sources of habitat heterogeneity for harpacticoid copepods in the deep sea? *Deep-Sea Res.* 40: 151–157.

Thomson, R. E., R. L. Gordon and J. Dymond. 1989. Acoustic doppler current profiler observations of a mid-ocean ridge hydrothermal plume. *J. Geophys. Res.* 94: 4709–4720.

Thomson, R. E., S. E. Roth and J. Dymond. 1990. Near-inertial motions over a mid-ocean ridge: Effects of topography and hydrothermal plumes. *J. Geophys. Res.* 95: 12961–12966.

Tietjen, J. H., J. W. Deming, G. T. Rowe, S. Macko and R. J. Wilke. 1989. Meiobenthos of the Hatteras Abyssal Plain and Puerto Rico Trench: Abundance, biomass and associations with bacteria and particulate fluxes. *Deep-Sea Res.* 36A: 1567–1577.

Tilman, D. 1982. *Resource Competition and Community Structure.* Princeton University Press, Princeton, NJ.

Tilman, D. 1994. Competition and biodiversity in spatially structured habitats. *Ecology* 75: 2–16.

Tilman, D. 1997. Community invasibility, recruitment limitation, and grassland biodiversity. *Ecology* 78: 81–92.

Toole, J. M., R. W. Schmitt, K. L. Polzin and E. Kunze. 1997. Near-boundary mixing above the flanks of a midlatitude seamount. *J. Geophys. Res.—Oceans* 102: 947–959.

Tunnicliffe, V., S. K. Juniper and M. E. de Burgh. 1985. The hydrothermal vent community on Axial Seamount, Juan de Fuca Ridge. *Bull. Biol. Soc. Washington* 6: 453–464.

Tunnicliffe, V., A. McArthur and D. McHugh. 1998. A biogeographical perspective of the deep-sea hydrothermal vent fauna. *Adv. Mar. Biol.* 34: 355–442.

Tunnicliffe, V., C. Fowler and A. G. McArthur. 1996. Plate tectonic history and hot vent biogeography. In C. J. MacLeod, P. A. Tyler and C. L. Walker (eds.), *Tectonic, Magmatic, Hydrothermal and Biological Segmentation of Mid-Ocean Ridges*, pp. 225–238. Geological Society Special Publication.

Tunnicliffe, V., R. W. Embley, J. F. Holden, D. A. Butterfield, G. J. Massoth and S. K. Juniper. 1997. Biological colonization of new hydrothermal vents following an erup-

tion on Juan de Fuca Ridge. *Deep-Sea Res.* 44: 1627.

Turley, C. M., K. Lochte and R. S. Lampitt. 1995. Transformations of biogenic particles during sedimentation in the northeastern Atlantic. *Philos. Trans. Roy. Soc. Lond. Biol.* 348: 179–189.

Turner, R. D. 1973. Wood-boring bivalves, opportunistic species in the deep sea. *Science* 180: 1377–1379.

Turner, R. D. 1977. Wood, mollusks, and deep-sea food chains. *Bull. Amer. Malacol. Union* 1977: 13–19.

Turner, R. D., R. A. Lutz and D. Jablonski. 1985. Modes of molluscan larval development at deep-sea hydrothermal vents. *Bull. Biol. Soc. Washington* 6: 167–184.

Tyler, P. A. 1988. Seasonality in the deep sea. *Oceanogr. Mar. Biol. Annu. Rev.* 26: 227–258.

Tyler, P. A. and C. M. Young. 1999. Reproduction and dispersal at vents and cold seeps. *J. Mar. Biol. Assn. U.K.* 79: 193–208.

Uda, M. and M. Ishino. 1958. Enrichment patterns resulting from eddy systems in relation to fishing grounds. *J. Tokyo Univ. Fish.* 44: 105–119.

Van Dover, C. L., C. J. Berg and R. D. Turner. 1988. Recruitment of marine invertebrates to hard substrates at deep-sea hydrothermal vents on the East Pacific Rise and Galapagos Spreading Center. *Deep-Sea Res.* 35: 1833–1849.

Van Dover, C. L., D. Désbruyeres, M. Segonzac, T. Comtet, T. Saldanha, A. Fiala-Médioni and C. Langmuir. 1996. Biology of the Lucky Strike hydrothermal field. *Deep-Sea Res.* 43: 1509–1529.

Van Dover, C. L., J. R. Factor, A. B. Williams and C. J. Berg. 1985. Reproductive patterns of decapod crustaceans from hydrothermal vents. *Bull. Biol. Soc. Washington* 6: 223–227.

Verlaan, P. 1992. Benthic recruitment and manganese crust formation on seamounts. *Mar. Biol.* 113: 171–174.

Vetter, E. W. and P. K. Dayton. 1998. Macrofaunal communities within and adjacent to a detritus-rich submarine canyon system. *Deep-Sea Res.* 45: 25–54.

Vrijenhoek, R. C. 1997. Gene flow and genetic diversity in naturally fragmented metapopulations of deep-sea hydrothermal vent animals. *J. Hered.* 88: 285–293.

Wheatcroft, R. A. 1992. Experimental tests for particle size-dependent bioturbation in the deep ocean. *Limn. Oceanogr.* 37: 90–104.

Wheatcroft R. A. and P. A. Jumars 1987. Statistical reanalysis for size dependence in deep-sea mixing. *Mar. Geol.* 77: 157–163.

Whitlatch, R. B. 1980. Patterns of resource utilization and coexistence in marine intertidal deposit-feeding communities. *J. Mar. Res.* 38: 743–765.

Whitlatch, R. B. 1981. Animal–sediment relationships in intertidal marine benthic habitats: Some determinants of deposit-feeding species diversity. *J. Exp. Mar. Biol. Ecol.* 53: 31–45.

Wilson, G. D. 1983. Variation in the deep-sea isopod Eurycope iphthima (Asellota, Eurycopidae): Depth related clines in rostral morphology and in population structure. *J. Crust. Biol.* 3: 127–140.

Wilson, G. D. F. 1998. Historical influences on deep-sea isopod diversity in the Atlantic Ocean. *Deep-Sea Res.* 45: 279–301.

Wilson, R. R. and R. S. Kaufmann. 1987. Seamount biota and biogeography. In B. H. Keating, P. Fryer, R. Batiza and G. W. Boehlert (eds.), *Seamounts, Islands, and Atolls*, pp. 355–378. Geophysical Monograph 43. American Geophysical Union, Washington, DC.

Wishner, K., L. Levin, M. Gowing and L. Mullineaux. 1990. Involvement of the oxygen minimum in benthic zonation on a deep seamount. *Nature* 346: 57–59.

Young, C. M. and K. J. Eckelbarger. 1994. *Reproduction, Larval Biology, and Recruitment of the Deep-Sea Benthos*. Columbia University Press, New York.

chapter 15

The Ecology of Coral Reefs

Nancy Knowlton and Jeremy B. C. Jackson

*I*n the simplest sense, coral reefs are wave-resistant piles of limestone and calcareous sediments built by a thin veneer of living organisms (Hubbard 1997). But these piles are of great ecological and resource significance for their massiveness, extremely high biodiversity, and distinct trophic structure and primary production. Reefs grow most prolifically in clear, warm, shallow, and nutrient-poor waters of the western tropical Atlantic and Indo-West Pacific, and more poorly in the eastern Pacific and eastern Atlantic where upwelling and high planktonic productivity inhibit reef development (Achituv and Dubinsky 1990). Scleractinian corals, hydrocorals, and coralline red algae are the primary framework constructors of coral reefs, although a host of other algae and invertebrate phyla also contribute to reef mass.

The scale of reefs is enormous, and they are the largest durable bioconstruction projects on earth. The Panama Canal is still one of the most significant human construction projects, but it is paltry by comparison with the unexceptional coral reefs along the Caribbean coast of Panama. Moreover, modern reefs are only youngsters—less than 10,000 years old—because older reefs were drowned by the rapid Holocene rise in sea level (Hubbard 1997). Over the longer term of millions of years, even small atolls like Enewetak have accumulated 2- to 3-km-thick piles of limestone, just as Darwin (1842) predicted.

There are two aspects of the scale of reef bioconstruction that define the ecological setting for everything else in this chapter. First, reefs determine the physical structure of the coastline and that of adjacent environments and ecosystems (Ogden 1997). Wherever they co-occur, reefs are the protective barrier against the sea for seagrass beds (see Williams and Heck, Chapter 12, this volume) and mangroves (see Ellison and Farnsworth, Chapter 16, this volume), just as man-

groves and seagrasses trap and stabilize runoff from the land and thereby prevent reefs from being drowned in sediments. These linkages can also have negative effects; for example, contaminated sediments continued to kill offshore reef corals for years after a large oil spill killed the mangroves along the central Caribbean shoreline of Panama (Jackson et al. 1989; Guzmán et al. 1994). Thus, in a very real sense the actual habitats as well as all their inhabitants are alive.

The second major point about bioconstruction is that the apparent physical stability of reefs belies an underlying natural turmoil of growth, death, and destruction of calcareous organisms (Glynn 1997; Hallock 1997; Hubbard 1997). Much like a modern city, reefs are constantly being rebuilt and torn down at the same time. Corals are the bricks, broken pieces of plant and animal skeletons the sand, and algal crusts and chemical cements the mortar. The production, accumulation, and cementation of all this calcareous material into solid limestone determine reef growth. Destruction is due to storm damage and even more to pervasive grazing and excavation by organisms. The key point is that even small changes in rates of construction or destruction may cause big increases or decreases in reef mass. For example, eastern Pacific reefs virtually disappeared after the strong El Niño of 1983 due to coral death and intense bioerosion (Glynn and Colgan 1992). This fragility also scales up in geological time; the history of reefs over the past half billion years is punctuated by long episodes of little or very different kinds of reef development that were modulated by shifts in oceanographic regimes (Hallock 1997; Wood 1999).

Coral reefs are the most taxonomically diverse of all marine ecosystems, but the nature and extent of this diversity is known only in the broadest outlines for most groups (Paulay 1997). Coral reefs probably contain at least a million species, but fewer than 100,000 of these have been described (Reaka-Kudla 1997). Our ignorance of the extent of biodiversity on coral reefs is not limited to obscure, poorly studied phyla; taxonomic uncertainty hinders ecological understanding in many corals, sponges, mollusks, and crustaceans (Knowlton and Jackson 1994). The widespread occurrence of sibling species in groups that have been genetically analyzed (Knowlton 1993, 2000) suggests that much diversity remains to be documented.

One can in many cases ignore this cryptic biodiversity by concentrating on "guilds" or functional groups (Jackson 1977, 1979; Steneck and Watling 1982; Steneck and Dethier 1994; Mumby and Harborne 1999). For example, studies of the replacement of corals by macroalgae capture the essence of this ecological phenomenon even if the species compositions of these two groups are ignored. Studies of the reproductive ecology of reef organisms, on the other hand, are seriously compromised by ignoring species boundaries, because individual organisms recognize such distinctions even if scientists currently do not. The importance of subtle ecological differences between morphologically similar forms is largely unknown in most specific cases, although we favor the view that overly conservative taxonomy has obscured the extent to which species are ecologically specialized and biogeographically limited (Knowlton and Jackson 1994).

With that caveat in mind, we organize this chapter from the bottom up, moving from the individual organisms themselves, to the interactions involving competition, consumption, disease, and to the physical disturbances affecting reef organisms. We then consider coral reefs as communities and ecosystems, and the Phanerozoic history of coral reef development. We conclude with a discussion of the future of reefs in the face of massive anthropogenic impacts. We draw most of our examples from the Caribbean and the Great Barrier Reef because of our greater familiarity with these systems.

THE MAJOR PLAYERS ON CORAL REEFS

Coral Animals

Two groups of anthozoans are important reef builders: the true stony corals (Anthozoa, Scleractinia) and stony hydrozoans (especially the Milleporina). Like other cnidarians, members of these groups contain nematocysts, which may be used in the capture of prey (zooplankton), as well as in defense. Many, however, rely nutritionally to varying degrees on their symbiotic dinoflagellates.

Most reef-building corals are clonal, and many form substantial colonies consisting of numerous interconnected polyps. Clonal organisms are defined by their ability to engage in asexual as well as sexual reproduction; growth and asexual reproduction are often equivalent in these groups (Jackson 1977; Jackson and Coates 1985). Asexual reproduction can also result in the establishment of genetically identical individuals at new locations on a reef. Corals have several different modes of asexual propagation (Kramarsky-Winter

and Loya 1996; Kramarsky-Winter et al. 1997; Richmond 1997), but the most common form in corals is fragmentation, particularly in species with branching growth forms (Highsmith 1982; Richmond 1997). Fragments may be produced by predation, bioerosion or waves, and subsequently dispersed by currents or wave action. Many fragments fail to successfully reattach to the bottom, but the probability of survival for asexual fragments is much greater than that of sexual propagules because the former are so much larger (Hughes 1985). Physiologically isolated colonies can also be produced by partial mortality and lost by fusion. Together with the more conventional processes of sexual recruitment and whole-colony death, these various mechanisms of colony creation and disappearance lead to complex life history matrices in which size and age are decoupled (Figure 15.1) (Hughes and Connell 1987).

Most corals also reproduce sexually (Figure 15.2) and, like many other groups of marine invertebrates, have an enormous array of reproductive alternatives (Harrison and Wallace 1990). These include selfing versus outcrossing, hermaphroditism versus separate sexes (gonochorism), brooding versus broadcasting of eggs, short versus long reproductive

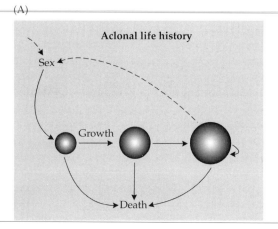

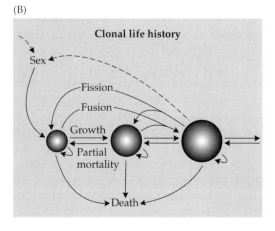

Figure 15.1 (A) Aclonal and (B) clonal life histories represented schematically in terms of individual size, with the arrows indicating all possible transitions among size classes and mortality. (Diagrams courtesy of T. Hughes.)

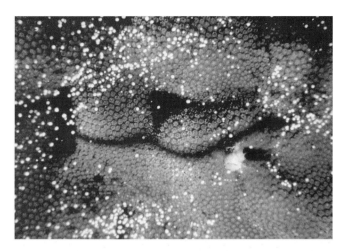

Figure 15.2 Release of egg–sperm bundles by the coral *Montastraea faveolata*. (Photo courtesy G. J. Gast.)

seasons, and limited versus wide dispersal of young. These different options, together with asexual reproduction, have important ecological as well as genetic consequences (Knowlton and Jackson 1993).

Sexual reproduction involves the union of egg and sperm to produce a zygote. Corals release sperm into the water. Eggs may also be released, or they may be retained in the mother until after fertilization. In either case, success in fertilization is strongly influenced by the distance between mates. For example, percentages of fertilization can be close to zero for corals greater than 2 m apart (Morse et al. 1996). These data suggest that coral species may be subject to strong Allee effects and experience nearly complete reproductive failure when they become rare (Levitan 1998).

Sessile forms rely on close synchronization in their reproductive output in order to maximize the probability of fertilization (Oliver and Babcock 1992). However, coral reproduction is often synchronized not only within species but also between them (Harrison et al. 1984; Richmond 1997). On the Great Barrier Reef, where mass spawning was first discovered, over one hundred species reproduce during a single one-week period each year, and slicks of gametes and larvae that extend for hundreds of meters can be seen from the air after spawning occurs (Oliver and Willis 1987). One of the consequences of community-wide mass spawning may be the swamping of potential predators on eggs and larvae, although the phenomenon may simply reflect multispecific use of common cues (Levitan 1998).

Although many coral species release unfertilized eggs or zygotes and engage in mass spawning, others brood fertilized eggs and release them as planula larvae. Most brooders do not participate in annual mass spawning events, but release their larvae on a lunar cycle. Their reproductive season varies in length from a few months to year round. All brooded larvae contain symbiotic algae from their mother, while most eggs and zygotes released in mass spawning species do not (Richmond 1997). Brooding is proportionally much more common in the Caribbean than in the Indo-Pacific and Red

Sea, and seems to be associated with a somewhat weedy lifestyle, small colony size, or specialized environmental conditions (Knowlton and Jackson 1993; Shlesinger et al. 1998). These are also the only corals that appear to self-fertilize at high rates (Carlon 1999).

The potential for dispersal of asexual, brooded, and broadcast propagules varies widely (Jackson 1986). Typically, fragments have the most limited dispersal and small larvae produced by broadcast spawners the greatest. It has been argued that the zooxanthellae of brooded coral larvae allow them to travel long distances. However, brooded offspring of most marine invertebrates typically settle very close to their parents (e.g., Olson 1985), and this is likely for corals as well. Nevertheless, rare long-distance dispersal events could be important in range expansions and recolonization following local extinction. Rafting of recruits attached to floating debris also may lead to very long distance movements (Jokiel 1984). Unfortunately, as with most marine organisms, we know almost nothing about the actual distribution of dispersal distances for coral reef animals and plants. Such information is crucial for determining the extent to which populations on different reefs are interconnected ecologically and genetically by dispersal (Benzie 1999), and their potential, for example, to behave according to the dynamics of metapopulations (Stone et al. 1996; Mumby 1999).

Factors that influence settlement behavior of coral larvae on reefs are poorly understood. However, Morse and colleagues (1996) have shown that distantly related corals, including both broadcast spawners and brooders, all require crustose coralline red algae for successful metamorphosis and settlement. These algae require moderately intense grazing by herbivorous fishes or limpets to clean their surfaces of rapidly growing fleshy algae. Thus coral recruitment must also depend on grazing. Within the coral genus *Agaricia*, different species exhibit different degrees of stringency and specificity in their settlement cues, which could promote niche diversification (Morse et al. 1988).

Algal Symbionts of Corals

All multicellular organisms host communities of microbial symbionts, but these communities are often ignored when discussing the ecology of their hosts. However, one cannot understand the ecology of reef-building corals without understanding the biology of the mutualistic dinoflagellate algae (often referred to as zooxanthellae) that live within them (Trench 1987; Muscatine 1990; Falkowski et al. 1993; Rowan 1998). Zooxanthellae fix inorganic carbon photosynthetically and pass some of this fixed carbon to their hosts (Muscatine 1990). The nutritional benefits received by the corals from their symbiotic algae are responsible for the high rates of calcification that underlie the creation of reefs (Muller-Parker and D'Elia 1997).

For many years, the zooxanthellae in corals and other marine invertebrates were all thought to represent a single species, *Symbiodinium microadriaticum*. Perhaps for this reason, the study of coral–algal symbiosis was typically the province of physiologists and was ignored by ecologists. This perspective has changed with the realization that symbiotic zooxanthellae exhibit substantial genetic and ecological diversity, not only with respect to the hosts with which they associate (Trench 1987; Rowan 1998), but also with respect to other ecological factors such as ambient light levels (Rowan 1998). The discovery that even single coral colonies may host multiple types of symbionts has led to the recognition that the coral host represents a landscape of differing environmental conditions over which members of the symbiotic community interact (Rowan et al. 1997).

The landscape ecology of coral–algal symbiosis has been studied in greatest detail for the Caribbean species complex *Montastraea annularis*. Each generation, these corals acquire their symbionts anew from the environment (eggs and sperm lack zooxanthellae), and they can host all of the known major groups of zooxanthellae (Rowan et al. 1997; Toller et al., in press b). In the shallowest water on offshore reefs, the symbiotic community is dominated by genotypes that are tolerant of high light (types A and B), while in deeper water, shade-loving symbionts (type C) prevail. At intermediate depths, one typically finds light-tolerant symbionts on the tops of colonies and shade-loving symbionts on the sides or in other low-light microenvironments (Rowan et al. 1997). Nearshore reefs also show complex patterns, with a fourth type of zoo-xanthella (E) that is rare on offshore reefs being relatively abundant (Toller et al., in press b). Several lines of evidence indicate that these zonation patterns are maintained dynamically. For example, although the daily and seasonal pattern of incident illumination that a coral receives is generally fairly stable (barring natural toppling or overgrowth by a neighbor), experiments altering the orientation of colonies result in a shift in the communities of symbionts (Rowan et al. 1997). Extreme disruption of these symbioses can lead to dramatic changes in types of zooxanthellae present; the uncharacteristic dominance by type A zooxanthellae in corals recovering from the effects of prolonged experimental darkness suggests that type A is an ecological weed (Toller et al., in press a).

Temperature can have profound effects on coral–algal symbioses, most vividly seen in the phenomenon known as coral bleaching. High water temperature, often in synergy with high light, damages the photosynthetic capabilities of the algae (Warner et al. 1999) and results in their expulsion or death. In a study of bleaching of *Montastraea* in Panama, it was found that only certain genotypes in certain locations (Figure 15.3) were severely affected, in particular, the shade-loving symbionts at the high-light end of their distributions (Rowan et al. 1997). Moreover, another genotype appeared to increase in response to the temperature stress, perhaps as a consequence of the reduction in numbers of one of its competitors. Similar associations of the type of zooxanthellae with vulnerability to bleaching have also been reported across reef corals generally in Belize (McField 1999). Bleaching can occur in response to a variety of other stresses (Brown 1997a). This breakdown in the coral–algal symbiosis reflects the in-

Figure 15.3 The coral *Montastraea faveolata* exhibiting characteristic blotch bleaching due to the presence of more than one type of zooxanthella in the colony. (Photo courtesy of A. Baker.)

trinsic instability of many mutualisms (Herre et al. 1999); such associations have both costs and benefits, so that when one partner is unable to provide the normal level of benefits due to stress, the other partner may be better off in the short-term by terminating the relationship.

We have only begun to explore the ecological complexity of these symbiotic associations. Some patterns seem to be general; for example, in other species of corals capable of hosting multiple types of symbionts, types A or B are typically shallower than type C, although the actual depth at which symbiont type changes varies widely across coral taxa (Rowan 1998). However, not all coral species host multiple symbionts (Rowan 1998), and some corals acquire their symbionts directly from the mother rather than environmentally (Trench 1987; Muller-Parker and D'Elia 1997). There are also important biogeographic differences in the distributions of the major types of symbionts (Baker and Rowan 1997). Thus the ecology of coral–algal symbiosis will continue to be a fruitful topic of experimental research in the future, and also has considerable applied importance in the context of global climate change.

Sessile Organisms

MARINE INVERTEBRATES. Other sessile marine invertebrates that occupy substantial space on reefs include other cnidarians [horny corals (Gorgonacea), soft corals (Alcyonacea), zoanthids

(Zoanthidea), thorny (e.g., "black") corals (Antipatharia), sea anemones (Actinaria) and corallimorphs (Corallimorpharia)], as well as sponges, bryozoans, and ascidians. All of these are filter feeders, suspension feeders or carnivores, but may also host photosynthetic symbionts (Rowan 1998).

Many of these groups, like corals, have a clonal life history and are capable of extensive asexual reproduction, typically by fragmentation (Karlson 1986; Wulff 1991). Their patterns of sexual reproduction are diverse. Large organisms often produce widely dispersing propagules, but most small, encrusting reef animals produce large, nonswimming or weakly swimming larvae that commonly disperse only a few centimeters to meters before settlement (Jackson 1986). All sessile organisms are potentially vulnerable to Allee effects. For example, fertilization success is very low for female gorgonians 4 m from the nearest spawning male (Coma and Lasker 1997). Mass spawning events often involve other taxa besides corals (reviewed in Levitan 1998).

MACROALGAE. Algae on coral reefs fall into several functional groups (Littler and Littler 1984; Steneck and Watling 1982; Steneck and Dethier 1994). Coral reef algae have been comparatively little studied reproductively, although by extrapolation from other algae it seems likely that all but the weedy, ephemeral taxa have fairly limited powers of dispersal (Santelices 1990). Mass spawning in green algae has recently been documented (Clifton and Clifton 1999), but in contrast to mass spawning corals, gametes are negatively buoyant, reproductive thalli die following gamete release, and reproduction occurs over a several month period. Thus despite superficial similarities, these two groups are quite distinct in their reproductive ecologies.

Mobile Organisms

INVERTEBRATES. The most important mobile marine invertebrates on reefs are polychaete worms, gastropods, crustaceans, and echinoderms (including sea urchins, starfish, brittlestars, crinoids, and holothurians). Several species have been well studied because of their critical roles as grazers (e.g., the sea urchin *Diadema*) and as coral predators (e.g., the polychaete *Hermodice*, the snails *Drupella* and *Coralliophila*, and the crown-of-thorns starfish *Acanthaster*), as discussed below. Other groups clearly play important roles as micrograzers, predators, and deposit feeders, but very little is known ecologically about most mobile marine invertebrates on reefs.

The great majority of mobile marine invertebrates on reefs are aclonal, although there are exceptions (e.g., in echinoderms, Mladenov 1996). Direct transfer of sperm into the reproductive tract of females has evolved in some groups, but others spawn eggs and sperm into the water column. Aggregation is important for high success in fertilization in these groups. For example, fertilization of the gregarious urchin *Diadema antillarum* dropped to 7% with only one male per square meter (Levitan 1991). On the other hand, more than 20% of *Acanthaster planci* eggs were fertilized by a single male

60 m upstream (Babcock et al. 1994), although the high fertilization potential of *Acanthaster* appears to be exceptional.

FISHES. Coral reef fish occupy a diverse array of trophic niches on reefs, including herbivores, planktivores, and small and large carnivores (Sale 1991a). Like vertebrates generally, coral reef fish exhibit much less diversity in ecologically important aspects of reproduction than do marine invertebrates. All are outcrossing and most have separate sexes. Reproduction typically occurs daily to monthly, and offspring are usually capable of considerable dispersal, either as the egg and larva, or as a larva following the hatching of benthic eggs (Victor 1991; Warner 1997). Despite this great potential for dispersal, many reef fishes may recruit back to or near their natal reefs (Jones et al. 1999; Swearer et al. 1999; Cowen et al. 2000). Moreover, the behavioral biology of reef fish reproduction differs widely within and among groups. Analysis of this diversity has played a critical role in furthering our understanding of, for example, the evolution of hermaphroditism and the operation of sexual selection (e.g., Warner 1984).

INTERACTIONS AND DISTURBANCE

Competition

Competitive interactions occur frequently on coral reefs. They are especially conspicuous among sessile organisms, because scleractinian corals, other coelenterates, sponges, ascidians, or algae cover much of the available hard substratum. As in other habitats, consumers of these different groups may modulate the outcome of competitive interactions.

COMPETITION AMONG SESSILE ORGANISMS. Competition among sessile reef invertebrates and algae may be for space, light, or food (Jackson 1977; Buss 1979, 1986; Stimson 1985). Modes of competition are often categorized as being either direct (involving physical contact) or indirect (occurring at a distance) (Connell 1973). Because of the enormous diversity of reefs, competition is typically more frequent between members of different species (interspecific) than between members of the same species (intraspecific), and indeed often occurs between members of different phyla or kingdoms (Woodin and Jackson 1979). Studies of reef organisms prompted considerable interest in the extent to which interactions are transitive (hierarchical) or intransitive (nonhierarchical), and the possible implications of such patterns of interaction for maintenance of species diversity (Jackson and Buss 1975, Buss and Jackson 1979, Connell 1978).

Competition among scleractinian corals may involve numerous mechanisms (Lang and Chornesky 1990). Direct competition (Figure 15.4) occurs by digestion of tissues, damage of tissues from contact with tentacles, and even smothering by mucus. Indirect interactions most often involve shading of neighbors, although competition via the release of toxic chemicals has also been documented. The latter may be of particular importance for the inhibition of settlement near

Figure 15.4 Direct competition between two corals. (Photo courtesy of H. Moody.)

adult colonies (Fearon and Cameron 1997). Slowly growing colonies often excel at direct competition, but ultimately, in the absence of other factors, rapidly growing corals that can overtop and shade their neighbors are often competitively dominant (Stimson 1985). These corals also inhibit recruitment by other corals below them, by mechanisms that are probably not limited to reduction of light alone (Fisk and Harriott 1993). Although competitive interactions are typically assumed to have costs in addition to those associated with mortality per se, comprehensive studies of the broader fitness consequences (e.g., reduction in growth and reproduction) for corals engaged in competition are surprisingly limited (Rinkevich and Loya 1985; Tanner 1997).

Other sessile organisms, such as soft corals, sponges, ascidians, bryozoans, and algae, are also abundant on reefs and are often competitively dominant over corals (Rützler and Muzik 1993; Bak et al. 1996; Aerts and van Soest 1997; Griffith 1997; Hill 1998). Many have rich biochemical defense mechanisms and complex allelochemical interactions (Jackson and Buss 1975), although simple overgrowth without chemical mediation may also result in competitive success (Griffith 1997). Competitive dominance between neighbors in cryptic communities depends on sensitivity to allelochemicals, relative rates of growth, interference competition for food, the ability to produce specialized overgrowth and defensive structures, as well as idiosyncratic aspects of the particular interaction, such as angle of attack and colony surface condition (Jackson and Buss 1975; Buss 1979, 1986; Jackson 1979; Palumbi and Jackson 1982; Lidgard and Jackson 1989; McKinney and Jackson 1988). Because species differ in these features and conditions vary, no one species is clearly dominant over all others and patterns of overgrowth are typically intransitive (Jackson and Buss 1975; Buss 1986).

COMPETITION AMONG MOBILE ORGANISMS. Studies of the sea urchin *Diadema antillarum* provide some of the best data for

intra- and interspecific competition in mobile coral reef organisms (Levitan 1989; Robertson 1991; Lessios 1995). Prior to catastrophic mortality in the 1980s, population density and body size tended to be inversely correlated. This relationship suggests substantial intraspecfic competition for food, which has been confirmed experimentally (Levitan 1989). Body size and gonad volume (but not mortality rates) were highly sensitive to crowding in the field and the amount of food provided in the laboratory. Individual urchins achieved this through size regulation – large urchins shrank but small urchins grew until all achieved the size appropriate for the amount of food available. The regional demise of *Diadema* provided further opportunities to explore the roles of intra- and interspecific competition, but the results of this natural experiment have been somewhat contradictory. Not all sites show the expected increase in body size following enormous decreases in density (Lessios 1995). Moreover, although herbivorous surgeonfish increased in abundance (Robertson 1991), the herbivorous sea urchin *Echinometra viridis* did not (Lessios 1995), despite the fact that earlier, small-scale experiments suggested competition between it and *Diadema* (Williams 1981). Furthermore, Lessios (1995) found that recruitment or juvenile survivorship of *Diadema* appeared to be aided by the presence of *E. viridis*, suggesting that the effect of *E. viridis* on *Diadema* is not negative across all life stages of the latter.

Studies of interspecific competition among co-occurring territorial damselfish (*Stegastes planifrons, S. partitus,* and *S. variabilis*) also reveal complex competitive interactions (Robertson 1996). Removal of the larger and more aggressive *S. planifrons* resulted in a doubling of the population sizes of the other two species, although these increases did not result in as high a level of total biomass as *S. planifrons* had before its removal. Removal of *S. partitus*, on the other hand, had no effect on the abundance of the other two species. Competition in these damselfishes is thus highly asymmetric in its effects.

Mutualism

Positive interactions among sessile reef taxa are probably widespread but have received surprisingly little attention by ecologists. Positive interactions help to maintain the physical integrity of salt marshes (Bertness and Hacker 1994) and coral reefs (Wulff and Buss 1979). Positive interactions are especially common among reef sponges, perhaps because of their extreme homogeneity and flexibility of design (Wulff 1997a). Sponges protect corals from competitors and excavating organisms (Goreau and Hartman 1966), reduce harmful effects of predators and physical disturbances (Wulff 1997a), and hold together the physical structure of reef rubble until it becomes cemented by slower-growing calcareous algal cements (Wulff and Buss 1979).

Positive interactions involving mobile reef invertebrates and fishes have received greater attention, but the behaviors associated with these interactions are typically far better known than the ecological consequences. For example, experiments designed to assess the benefits associated with "cleaning" symbioses between fish and other fish or shrimp are surprisingly equivocal (Grutter 1997; Spotte 1998). Similarly, many mobile organisms receive clear protection from predators by sheltering near corals or sea anemones, but the benefit to the latter has only occasionally been documented (Meyer et al. 1983; Liberman et al. 1995).

Predation and Herbivory

Sessile organisms on coral reefs commonly defend themselves against predators or herbivores by a great variety of chemical or physical means (Jackson and Buss 1975; Steneck 1983). Associates of these defended organisms, such as small crustaceans living in distasteful algae or sponges, are often protected from predation as well (Hay 1997; Sotka et al. 1999). As in other ecosystems, however, predators have evolved that can overcome these defenses.

Many reef animals and plants are grazed rather than eaten in their entirety, a phenomenon termed partial predation (Bak et al. 1977; Palumbi and Jackson 1982; Steneck 1983; Jackson and Hughes 1985). Partial predation generally is accompanied by the potential to regenerate. Regeneration varies among species, and also as a function of the size, depth, and location of the injury. Larger wounds generally require longer to repair, and successful establishment of a superior competitor in the area of predation is consequently more likely. Partial predation may occur along the edges of an organism, or it may divide clonal organisms into physiologically separate entities that may remain separate or subsequently be rejoined through fusion.

Figure 15.5 The crown-of-thorns starfish, *Acanthaster planci*, with nearby recently consumed coral (white skeleton). (Photo courtesy of T. Hughes.)

PREDATION. Numerous studies and reviews (Glynn 1990; Carpenter 1997; Hixon 1997) have focused on predators on corals. Starfish (*Acanthaster, Culcita*), sea urchins (*Eucidaris*), snails (*Coralliophila, Drupella, Jenneria*), polychaetes (*Hermodice*), many butterflyfish (Chaetondontidae), some pufferfishes (Tetraodontidae), and some triggerfishes (Balistidae) are the predators that have the greatest impact on corals. Most of these predators prefer rapidly growing species of corals, so they probably contribute in important ways to maintaining diversity on reefs. Predators on other sessile invertebrates are comparatively less studied.

The crown-of-thorns starfish, *Acanthaster planci*, is the most conspicuous and extensively studied predator on coral reefs (Moran 1986; Bradbury 1990; Johnson 1992; Carpenter 1997)(Figure 15.5). The starfish digests away the living tissues of corals by everting its stomach over their surfaces. The large size of the starfish, coupled with a propensity for spectacular population explosions, can result in massive coral mortality. To give but one example, on Green Island in the Great Barrier Reef, nearly 90% of the corals were killed over a several month period in 1979–1980 by aggregations of starfish whose numbers were estimated at between 350,000 and 2,000,000 (Moran 1986). Modeling suggests that the population structure of corals before the outbreak is not consistent with levels of predation to which reefs are currently subject, implying that outbreaks were either less frequent or less intense in the past (Done 1988).

Other invertebrate predators on corals are smaller and often less conspicuous in their effects (Carpenter 1997), and some are functionally parasites rather than conventional predators (Oren et al. 1998). However, outbreaks of snails in the genus *Drupella* can result in substantial coral mortality (Cumming 1999). Predation by fishes on corals may be locally intense, but is generally of minor importance on reefs today, perhaps because of overfishing.

For sponges, in contrast, fishes are now the most important predators on reefs (Wulff 1997b; Pawlik 1998; Hill 1998), although hawksbill turtles, which are obligate sponge feeders, were probably more important in the past (Meylan 1988). Sponges are more conspicuous on Caribbean reefs than in the Indo-West Pacific, and the limited number of fishes that feed on sponges in the Caribbean led to the suggestion that predation was less intense there than in the Pacific (Wulff 1997b). However, several studies suggest that many Caribbean sponges are restricted to mangrove, grass bed, or cryptic reef habitats due to predation by angelfishes, filefishes, boxfishes, and parrotfishes (Wulff 1997b; Pawlik 1998). Moreover, experimental exclusion of fishes can result in increased overgrowth of corals by sponges (Hill 1998).

HERBIVORY. The most important ecological interactions on reefs commonly involve indirect effects of herbivores as mediators of competition between algae and corals (Pennings 1997). Macroalgae grow much more rapidly than corals un-

(A)

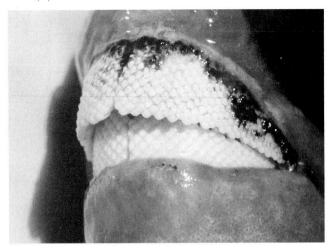

(B)

Figure 15.6 Herbivores on reefs. (A) The massive teeth of a parrot fish. (Photo courtesy of D. Bellwood.) (B) Sea urchin showing teeth of Aristotle's lantern. (Photo courtesy of R. Steneck.)

ga 1998) that were avoided by herbivorous fishes in Morrison's (1988) study. The recent proliferation of these distasteful algae is presumably due to the demise of the less selective *Diadema*. A variety of typically smaller polychaetes, molluscs, and crustaceans also graze on algae, but their ecological effects are not so well known (Carpenter 1997).

"Herbivores" do not eat only plants (Figure 15.7). When urchins become very abundant, their indiscriminant grazing also results in consumption of coral (McClanahan and Shafir 1990). Large "herbivorous" fish, such as the stoplight parrotfish *Sparisoma viride*, may graze heavily on some corals and limit their distributions to primarily non-reef habitats (Miller and Hay 1998). Territorial damselfish also kill coral to provide surfaces on which to grow their algal gardens (Kaufman 1977; Hixon 1997). Many herbivores contribute substantially to bioersion in the course of their feeding (Bellwood 1995).

Disease

Diseases have been documented in a number of tropical marine plants, invertebrates and vertebrates, and their effects can be severe (Peters 1997; Richardson 1998). Reports of diseases on reefs, particularly of corals, seagrasses, sponges, and sea urchins, have increased dramatically since the early 1970s (Richardson 1998; Harvell et al. 1999). Most of these diseases are poorly understood, and in many cases even the causative agent is unknown. The apparent increase in the incidence of diseases over the last 25 years may be a symptom of the general stress on reef ecosystems associated with multiple anthropogenic effects (e.g., global warming, introduction of novel pathogens from terrestrial run-off and ballast water, eutrophication, pollution). However, hard evidence to support this claim is largely lacking.

The ecological importance of disease has been particularly striking in the Caribbean, where major changes in reef community structure have occurred following the drastic declines of elkhorn and staghorn acroporid corals and the sea urchin

der most conditions, so that the existence of reefs as coral-dominated assemblages often depends on the removal of algae by grazers (Hay 1997). Hence, understanding herbivory is critical to understanding the ecology of reefs.

The two most important groups of herbivores on reefs are sea urchins and fish (Figure 15.6). Herbivorous fishes may bite coral reefs at rates of over 150,000 bites/m^2/day, and either fishes or urchins alone may remove nearly 100% of algal production (Hay 1997). Members of these groups are not all equivalent in their effects, however. For example, parrotfish can be classified as either excavators or scrapers; their distinct feeding modes result in very different patterns of algal mortality and rates of bioerosion (Bellwood and Choat 1990). Urchins are generally less selective feeders than fishes, so that these two groups of herbivores are also not ecologically equivalent (Morrison 1988). Caribbean reefs are now often dominated by precisely those groups of algae (*Lobophora, Dictyota*, and *Halimeda*) (Hughes 1994; McClanahan and Muthi-

Figure 15.7 Damselfish garden in colony of staghorn coral (*Acropora cervicornis*). The coral is killed by the fish to provide a substrate for algal growth. (Photo courtesy of L. Kaufman.)

Diadema antillarum. Acropora palmata and *A. cervicornis* were dominant corals at shallow to moderate depths throughout the Caribbean in the mid 1970s, but they are now rare throughout much of their former range, primarily due to mortality from "white band" disease (Gladfelter 1982; Aronson et al. 1998). Even more strikingly, an unknown pathogen reduced the formerly abundant *D. antillarum* to less than 2% of its former numbers over a one-year period in 1983–1984 (Figure 15.8a) (Lessios 1988), and populations have largely failed to recover (Lessios 1995, but see Aronson and Precht 2000). Changes in reef community structure associated with these two diseases have been profound. Moreover, Caribbean reefs in the 1990s appear to be confronting a new suite of emerging diseases (Richardson 1998; Harvell et al. 1999), and prominent among the victims are species of the abundant *Montastraea annularis* complex (e.g., Santavy et al. 1999) (Figure 15.8B). It is thus conceivable that disease will ultimately play a major role in the decline of all the formerly dominant corals of the region.

Physical Disturbance

Wave energy (Rogers 1993; Connell et al. 1997), lowered salinity (Jokiel et al. 1993), extreme temperatures (Porter et al. 1982; Glynn 1993; Fadlallah et al. 1995), excessive sedimentation (Rogers 1990; Riegl 1995), extremely low tides (Fadlallah et al. 1995), uplift or destruction by earthquakes, and changes in flow patterns (Connell et al. 1997) are among the most common natural sources of physical disturbance on reefs. Some of these disturbances have increased or may increase in the future due to human activities. Extreme disturbances, as measured by either their maximum strength or duration, happen rarely, by definition. However, events that are rare during a human lifetime may be routine for many corals and other reef taxa that may live for centuries (Jackson 1991, 1992; Woodley 1992). Although more extreme events typically produce more disturbance, the past history of disturbance can influence the relationship between the intensity of an event and the amount and kind of destruction that results (Paine et al. 1998; Hughes and Connell 1999).

Hurricanes and typhoons are the strongest physical disturbances to which most reefs are subjected (Figure 15.9). Nevertheless, regions with the greatest number of typhoons and hurricanes overlap to a substantial extent with areas of greatest reef development (Scoffin 1993). Damage caused by major storms has been quantified in both the Pacific and the Atlantic (Woodley et al. 1981; Harmelin-Vivien and Laboute 1986; Rogers 1993; Connell et al. 1997). Mortality is typically greatest in shallow water, but "avalanches" on steep deeper slopes can sometimes result in nearly 100% destruction. In

(A)

(B)

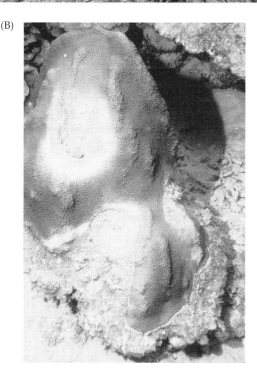

Figure 15.8 Effects of disease on reef organisms. (A) Dying *Diadema antillarum.* (Photo courtesy of T. Hughes.) (B) *Montastraea faveolata* coral showing extensive mortality from disease. (Photo courtesy of W. Toller.) In both cases the pathogens are unknown.

Figure 15.9 Field of coral rubble in the *Acropora palmata* zone of Discovery Bay, Jamaica, caused by waves from Hurricane Allen. (Photo courtesy of L. S. Land.)

general, more rapidly growing branching corals are most vulnerable to storm damage, and more slowly growing massive corals are least vulnerable. For this reason, sporadic major storms often favor species that are competitively subordinate during routine conditions, thus promoting the coexistence of both types (Rogers 1993).

THE STRUCTURE AND ASSEMBLY OF CORAL REEF COMMUNITIES

Community structure is determined by processes that bring species to the community and the population dynamics and species interactions of its members (Roughgarden 1989). Marine species with a planktonic larval phase commonly fluctuate in adult abundance more than species without planktonic larvae, suggesting that processes affecting larval survival, transport, and settlement are important determinants of pattern (Thorson 1950; Roughgarden et al. 1988; Grosberg and Levitan 1992). Renewed attention to this "supply side" of marine ecology is commonly associated with a Gleasonian view of density-independent community structure (Connell 1978; Doherty 1991; Sale 1991b; Williams 1991; Hubbell 1997). On a suitably large scale, however, larval recruitment depends on the abundance, fecundity, and proximity for fertilization or mutual defense of reproductive adults (positive feedback), and the availability of suitable habitat free of competitors or predators (negative feedback). This density dependence brings the biology of species and their niches back into the equation (Chesson 1997). Indeed, as we have seen, corals and other reef organisms may be injured or die from a great variety of causes, and their vulnerability to these processes varies greatly among species (Jackson and Hughes 1985, Knowlton and Jackson 1994).

Many kinds of biological interactions, physical disturbances, and processes affecting dispersal and recruitment have been shown to affect small-scale patterns of community structure and assembly on coral reefs (Doherty 1991; Karlson and Hurd 1993; Carpenter 1997; Connell et al. 1997; Hay 1997; Hixon 1997; Peters 1997). However, we do not know the relative magnitude of the direct and indirect effects of all these different processes, and their synergisms, in more than a handful of cases. Two general problems have impeded progress. First, basic patterns of distribution and abundance, community structure and zonation on coral reefs are poorly documented on all but a few reefs (e.g., Goreau 1959; Loya 1972; Glynn 1976; Done 1982; Liddell and Ohlhurst 1992), so that it is difficult to generalize beyond the simplest patterns (Done 1983, 1992; Jackson 1991; Wilkinson and Cheshire 1988). Thus, in the most basic sense, we often do not know what we are trying to explain.

Second, landscape patterns of interactions, disturbance, and succession on coral reefs comparable to those documented for rocky intertidal communities (Paine and Levin 1981; Roughgarden et al. 1988) and kelp forests (Dayton et al. 1992, 1999) can rarely be observed over appropriate spatial and temporal scales that characteristically extend beyond the resources and lifetimes of ecologists. Extreme hurricanes occur on decadal to century scales, generation times of dominant coral species are commonly measured in decades to centuries, and pivotal successional events are set and reset by fluctuations in sea level measured in tens of thousands of years (Jackson 1991, 1992). Differences among species in competitive abilities, resistance to predation, life histories, and the resulting patterns of community succession on reefs, can be viewed as evolutionary adaptations to characteristic patterns of interaction and disturbance (Jackson and Hughes 1985). But these hypotheses are not directly testable because the longest running study of reef community structure involving observations of individual organisms is only 30 years (Connell et al. 1997). In spite of all these problems, real progress has been made in a few reef systems that have been studied using numerous complementary approaches across a range of spatial and temporal scales.

Recruitment

Local populations of species with weakly dispersing larvae and sessile or sedentary adults are demographically closed; they exhibit potentially high levels of inbreeding (Knowlton and Jackson 1993) and stability in abundance (Jackson and Hughes 1985; Jackson and Kaufmann 1987) compared to species with planktonic larvae or highly vagile adults. Many small incrusting marine invertebrates and macroalgae have larvae that disperse very little. In contrast, virtually all reef fishes and about 85 percent of reef coral species have a planktonic larval stage (Leis 1991; Richmond 1997), so that larval recruits in these groups may be almost entirely or exclusively derived from elsewhere. This implies that their local populations are demographically open and that their populations cannot be regulated by local fecundity (Roughgarden et al. 1988; Caley et al. 1996). However, new evidence suggests that potentially widely dispersed larvae of reef fishes may return to their natal population (Jones et al. 1999; Swearer et al. 1999; Cowen et al. 2000). It is thus especially unfortunate that almost all ecological studies of reef fishes and corals have been made on the small spatial scale of local populations for logistical reasons.

At a larger scale, however, groups of local populations (metapopulations) are effectively closed, with boundaries set by limitations to larval dispersal (Caley et al. 1996). It is only on this larger scale that relations among adult abundance, fecundity, and recruitment of species with planktonic larvae can be examined (Hughes et al. 2000). Moreover, the evolution of life history traits and larval behaviors, such as the selection of specific habitats for recruitment, can only be understood at these larger scales (Paine and Levin 1981; Jackson 1991; Warner 1997).

CRYPTIC REEF COMMUNITIES. Undersurfaces of plating corals and coral rubble, crevices in reef framework, and the walls and roofs of caves are dominated by hundreds of species of small encrusting bryozoans, colonial ascidians, sponges, and calcareous algae (Vasseur 1974; Jackson 1977, 1983; Jackson and Hughes 1985; Kobluk et al. 1988; Hughes and Jackson

1992; Harmelin 2000). Recruitment limitation at early stages of community development is evident in extremely low rates of larval settlement on panels suspended from racks situated more than a few meters from a reef (Jackson 1977; Buss and Jackson 1981; Winston and Jackson 1984). Recruitment also drops off to nearly zero after substrates are entirely encrusted, except when substrate is bared by injury to established colonies (Palumbi and Jackson 1983; Winston and Jackson 1984; Jackson and Kaufmann 1987).

REEF CORALS. Connell et al. (1997) observed changes in coral populations in fourteen 1-m² quadrats at four low intertidal reef sites at Heron Island over 30 years (Figure 15.10). The sites include exposed pools, exposed reef crest, protected reef crest, and inner reef flat environments situated from 300 to 2000 meters apart. Recruitment of corals was measured by the first appearance of juveniles observed in photographs taken 1 to 4 years apart, thereby comprising some unknown but small fraction of the original larval recruits. Recruitment was highly concordant among the 2–5 replicate quadrats at a site but not among sites. Recruitment varied independently from year to year with no obvious temporal pattern over 30 years. However, recruitment was positively correlated with amount of free space for settlement at three of the four sites; the only exception was the protected crest, where free space never fell below 25%. Thus, recruitment of juvenile corals into the sessile population was strongly density dependent.

A similar 16-year photographic study of coral populations in replicate 1-m² quadrats in deeper water in Jamaica (Hughes and Jackson 1985; Hughes 1985, 1990; Hughes and Tanner, 2000) provides a basis for comparison between the Caribbean and Indo-West Pacific. Rates of recruitment of juvenile corals visible in photographs (aged 7–12 months) were similar to those at Heron Island (Connell et al. 1997), even though recruitment rates of very young corals (< 3 months) in the Caribbean are typically about 1% of those on the Great Barrier Reef. Thus survival of juveniles must be much higher in the Caribbean than Australia, a relationship that is in keeping with the higher proportion of brooding coral species in the Caribbean (Richmond 1997). Coral recruitment in Jamaica was also strongly density dependent, as demonstrated by the significant positive correlation of recruitment rate with percent free space. This result was confirmed experimentally by removal of all corals from 6 quadrats and measuring the subsequent severalfold increase in recruitment (Hughes 1985).

(A)

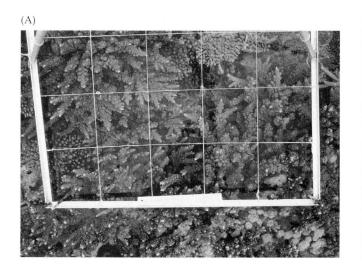

(C)

(B)

Figure 15.10 Time series of reef communities at 1 m depth on Heron Island, showing changes due to death and recruitment. (A) 1988. (B) 1992, just after a typhoon. (C) 1998. (Photos courtesy of J. Connell.)

The most comprehensive analysis of stock-recruitment relations, involving a variety of spatial scales, is the product of a two-year study of coral abundance, fecundity, and larval recruitment along the entire Great Barrier Reef (Hughes et al. 1999, 2000). Rates of recruitment and total coral abundance and cover were measured on the crests of 33 reefs. Sites were chosen in a hierarchical sampling design consisting of sectors (250–500 km), reefs (10–15 km), sites (0.5–3 km), and replicates (1–5 m). Recruitment rates for spawning species varied more than 25-fold among sectors and more than 200-fold among sites and replicates, versus 5–8-fold for brooders among sectors and 100-fold among sites and replicates. In contrast, adult abundance in transects at the same sites did not vary significantly among sectors, so that there was no relationship between adult abundance and recruitment. However, proportions of gravid colonies of common species of *Acropora* varied from 15 to 100% among the same sites 10 days before the predicted mass spawning. When applied to the entire *Acropora* population, coral abundance weighted by these variations in fecundity explains 72% of the variation in recruitment on the sector scale and no other factors were significant (Figure 15.11). This strong stock-recruitment effect was nonlinear, with numbers of recruits increasing exponentially towards higher values of fecundity. This suggests a threshold density for increases in fertilization success or satiation of predators, and thus strong positive feedback in the stock-recruitment relationship.

REEF FISHES. Local populations of coral reef fishes may be open in the extreme because of the very long planktonic phase of larval development that typically lasts from 10 to more than 100 days (Leis 1991). Indeed, many species are panmictic on the scale of the entire Caribbean or Great Barri-

er Reef (Doherty et al. 1995; Shulman and Bermingham 1995). Most work on fish recruitment has been done on artificial or natural patch reefs 1 m² or smaller (Doherty 1991). Large and apparently stochastic variations in recruitment into these miniature habitats comprise the primary basis for the hypothesis that population sizes and assembly of communities of reef fishes are mainly determined by insufficient and unpredictable larval recruitment (Sale 1977, 1991b; Doherty 1991). If recruitment is indeed limiting, then patterns of adult abundance in similar environments should be predictable on the basis of recruitment statistics alone (Doherty and Fowler 1994; Caley et al. 1996). However, if numbers of adults are independent of recruitment then recruitment alone cannot be limiting.

The small, common damselfish *Pomacentrus moluccensis* exhibits highly variable recruitment on the southern Great Barrier Reef (Doherty and Fowler 1994). Rates of recruitment measured over 9 years varied consistently by more than an order of magnitude among patch reefs in seven lagoons across 70 km. The historical average of recruitment explained 84% of the variance in adult abundance in the different lagoons. Moreover, the abundance of fishes in different age classes (determined from numbers of rings in their ear bones) at the end of the experiment clearly reflected the magnitude of recruitment of their year class. Thus the abundance and population structure of this species can be explained almost entirely by its magnitude of recruitment. In contrast, Robertson (1988a,b,c) showed that densities of adults were not correlated with settlement patterns over 6 years in three species of surgeonfishes, a triggerfish and a damselfish in Panama. In addition, many studies have demonstrated positive and negative density-dependent effects (as well as no effects) of the presence of resident adult fishes on the rate of larval recruitment (Sweatman 1983, 1985; Jones 1991); some density-dependent effects on recruitment are expressed primarily at the earliest stages immediately after settlement (Caselle 1999; Schmitt and Holbrook 1999). Remarkably, given the level of controversy, large-scale stock-recruitment relations have not been studied for any coral reef fish species.

Post-Recruitment Processes

CRYPTIC REEF COMMUNITIES. Undersurfaces of platy corals support a highly diverse encrusting community of mostly sponges, bryozoans, colonial ascidians, and coralline algae (Jackson and Buss 1975; Jackson and Winston 1982). Most of the undersurface is occupied, so that growth of one organism almost inevitably involves partial or complete mortality of a neighbor. Grazing by sea urchins and other predators is also common in shallow environments but decreases with depth. Analyses of weekly photographs under corals in Jamaica (Figure 15.12) demonstrate that community composition at any fixed point changes rapidly due to grazing and overgrowth, but other processes appeared unimportant (Jackson and Kaufmann 1987). Grazing killed organisms occupying one-third of the surface per year prior to the demise of *Dia-*

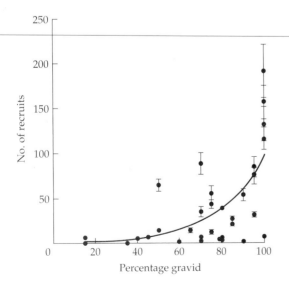

Figure 15.11 Relationship between abundance weighted by fecundity and recruitment for *Acropora* corals on the Great Barrier Reef. (From Hughes et al. 2000.)

(A)

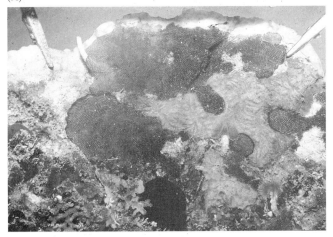

(B)

Figure 15.12 Time series of changes for cryptic community under coral in Jamaica. (A) June 1983. (B) September 1983. (Photos by J. B. C. Jackson.)

dema, and overgrowth killed another third. Nevertheless, community composition was stable across the reef because growth and regeneration by dominant species approximately equaled their losses. Rates of predation decreased greatly after the *Diadema* died, but community composition changed little over two years because *Diadema* had grazed mostly upon competitively inferior organisms. Slow increases in abundance of erect animals previously eaten by *Diadema* suggest that they could eventually grow to dominate the community the way seaweeds overgrew corals (Hughes 1994), but there are no data.

REEF CORALS. Most mortality of reef corals measured in long-term studies in Australia and before the demise of *Diadema* in Jamaica was due to routine processes of competition, predation, and sedimentation rather than catastrophic storms or outbreaks of predators or disease (Hughes and Jackson 1985; Bythell et al. 1993; Connell et al. 1997; Hughes and Connell

1999). However, we have little idea of the relative importance of different routine causes of mortality, nor their magnitude compared with recent outbreaks of disease, crown-of-thorns starfish, coral bleaching, and overgrowth of corals by seaweeds in the Caribbean in the 1980s (Hughes 1994; Connell et al. 1997; Done 1997, 1999; Richardson 1998). For example, various species of *Acropora* form dense, nearly monospecific stands at the expense of other species. Rapid growth, clonal propagation, resistance to breakage by all but the most severe storms, and tall, arborescent colony form allow *Acropora* to overtop and shade out slow growing corals (Kaufman 1977; Porter et al. 1981; Stimson 1985; Jackson 1991; Fisk and Harriott 1993). However, we cannot scale these competitive effects relative to those of predators, disease, or routine physical disturbances. The same problem affects all other forms of competition involving corals, such as digestive dominance, although the strong inverse correlation between aggressive rank and growth rates suggest that these factors were once highly important (Lang 1973; Lang and Chornesky 1990).

Many studies of effects of predation on corals concern small invertebrates and fishes (Kaufman 1977; Knowlton et al. 1990). Rates of partial predation may be as high as in cryptic reef communities, but have not been followed closely. Effects of predators may change radically with prey density, as in the case of the continued decline of staghorn coral *Acropora cervicornis* due to predation after the coral's mass mortality following a severe hurricane (Knowlton et al. 1981, 1990). Concentrations of predators on survivors of a strong El Niño event in the eastern Pacific similarly contributed to the continued decline of corals after normal temperatures returned (Glynn and Colgan 1992). In contrast, recruitment of benthic macroalgae after the mass mortality of *Diadema* exceeded the abilities of other resident herbivores to consume them, resulting in the massive buildup of seaweed populations that have overgrown corals throughout the Caribbean (Lessios 1988; Hughes 1994). These threshold effects of relative predator and prey densities, and other nonlinear interactive effects of competition and predation, modulate variations in community structure and may lead to the existence of alternate stable or quasi-stable states (Knowlton 1992; Done 1992, 1997).

There has been a major effort in Australia to model the dynamics of outbreaks and dispersal of the crown-of-thorns starfish *Acanthaster planci* along the Great Barrier Reef using a variety of approaches (Bradbury 1990; Johnson 1992; Bradbury and Seymour 1997). The frequency and movement of starfish outbreaks, and the patterns of outbreaks relative to prevailing hydrodynamic conditions are reasonably well understood; less clear are the key issues of shifts between low- and high-density populations and stock-recruitment relationships (McCallum 1992). The dynamics of outbreaks are also changing because the proportion of reefs available to host major outbreaks is declining (Figure 15.13) (Bradbury and Seymour 1997).

There has also been considerable progress in modeling responses to devastation by *Acanthaster* and subsequent successional dynamics of the sessile reef community, compara-

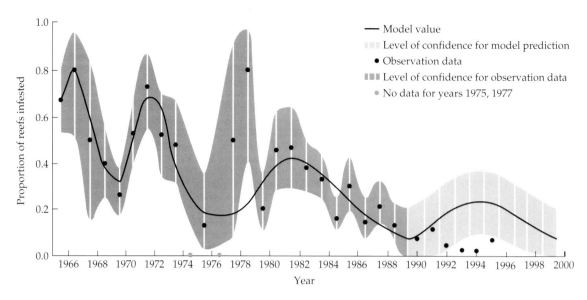

Figure 15.13 Changes in the frequency of outbreaks in crown-of-thorns starfish over the last two decades. (After Bradbury and Seymour 1997.)

ble to Paine and Levin's (1981) analyses of the landscape dynamics of temperate rocky intertidal mussel beds. The main difficulty is to obtain data on changes in benthic community composition on appropriately large spatial and temporal scales. Transition-matrix models have been used to project periods of recovery of coral populations (Done 1992, 1997, 1999). Recognition of deliberately simplified alternative sessile communities (algal, colonizing coral, recovering coral, old coral, and other) permits observations of the persistence of different states and rates of shifts between them. However, a century or more of data may be required to test alternative predictions because the relevant time scales are so long (Jackson 1991).

REEF FISHES. The importance of post-settlement processes in the assembly and structure of reef fish communities has been obscured by the rhetoric of recruitment limitation (Jones 1991; Williams 1991). Larval habitat selection has also been treated as an evolutionary black box (Doherty 1991; Doherty and Fowler 1994) without consideration of the natural selection (i.e., ecology) necessary to maintain such otherwise costly behavior (e.g., Morse and Morse 1996 for corals). However, recent work is reviving interest in post-recruitment processes. Detailed surveys of 75 reefs around two adjacent islands on the southern Great Barrier Reef demonstrate much greater predictability in fish distributions among habitats on large, contiguous reefs than among small, isolated patch reefs (Ault and Johnson 1998). This is important because, as we have seen, most of the support for recruitment limitation comes from studies of very small patches. In addition, Robertson (1996) has demonstrated intense, asymmetric interspecific competition among adult damselfish based on removals of two common species over many years. The experiments are highly unusual in their duration, which exceeds the average generation times of the species involved, and in the consider-

able number of years required to begin to see persistent effects (Yodzis 1988).

ECOSYSTEM STRUCTURE AND FUNCTION

Reef Ecosystems Today

Ecosystem ecology concerns the processes that link the physical and chemical environment to the resident, interacting assemblage of organisms, and the boundary conditions, physical scales, and rate constants that affect the action of these processes (Hatcher 1997). The most important ecosystem processes on coral reefs are trophic and bioconstructional (Done et al. 1997). The outstanding trophic characteristics are the (1) overwhelming contribution of endosymbiotic zooxanthellae and benthic algae to primary production, and the correspondingly minor role of phytoplankton (Hatcher 1988, 1990; Kinsey 1991); (2) sensitivity of benthic production to nutrient inputs and sedimentation (Hallock and Schlager 1986; Birkeland 1987); and (3) large number and high diversity of trophic levels in food webs (Figure 15.14, Grigg et al. 1984). The outstanding bioconstructional features are the enormous biogenic production of limestone and calcareous sediment, and the conflicting balance of processes that bind these materials together into reef framework versus processes of physical and biological destruction and erosion that break down framework into sediment (Figure 15.15) (Buddemeier and Hopley 1988; Hubbard 1988, 1997; Glynn and Colgan 1992).

In essence, what makes a reef a reef is determined by the relative amounts of carbon invested in trophic pathways versus bioconstruction, and this in turn depends upon the relative abundance and production of calcifying versus noncalcifying primary producers. There is an enormous literature on the mechanisms and controlling factors of the productive and calcifying pathways on coral reefs (Hatcher 1988, 1990, 1997;

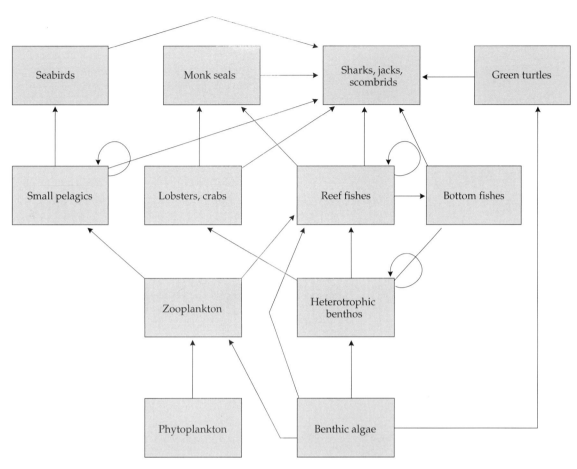

Figure 15.14 Food web for French Frigate Shoals. (After Grigg et al. 1984.)

Kinsey 1991; Done et al. 1997; Muller-Parker and D'Elia 1997), the details of which are beyond the scope of this review. Here we concentrate on two basic kinds of interactions among population and ecosystem processes that are of particular relevance to the recent degradation of coral reef communities.

The first concerns the balance between calcifying organisms, noncalcifying organisms, and bioeroders that deter-

Figure 15.15 Massive bioerosion caused by sea urchins on Caribbean reefs. (Photo from Jackson 1983.)

mines whether or not reef mass increases or decreases. This balance can be shifted by catastrophic mortality of the first group, particularly corals, due to hurricanes (Knowlton et al. 1981, 1990; Woodley et al. 1981), coral bleaching (Glynn and Colgan 1992), and outbreaks of predators (Done 1992, 1997) or disease (Richardson 1998). In all these cases, continued predation on surviving corals further tips the balance in favor of uncalcified benthic animals and fleshy algae that cover the substratum and inhibit coral and coralline algal settlement and recovery (Knowlton 1992; Done 1992, 1999). Patterns of carbon flux and structure of food webs change dramatically (Kinsey 1988; Johnson et al. 1995). The mass mortality of the sea urchin *Diadema antillarum* also permitted an explosion in growth of fleshy algae that overgrew and killed their coral and coralline algal neighbors (Figure 15.16) (Lessios 1988; Hughes 1994). This shift from dominance by corals to fleshy algae also greatly reduces rates of calcification and increases rates of erosion by grazing animals (Glynn 1997). Reef accretion stops and reef mass decreases in size, further decreasing chances of the reestablishment of corals (Buddemeier and Hopley 1988; Hubbard 1997).

Increased nutrient inputs also have deleterious effects on coral abundance and reef growth for many reasons (Hallock and Schlager 1986; Done et al. 1997). Increased nutrients fertilize phytoplankton whose increased growth reduces water transparency and thus the light available to zooxanthellae at

Figure 15.16 Effects of mortality of *Diadema antillarum*; note the lush growth of algae on the bottom. (Photo courtesy of T. Hughes.)

the bottom. Increased phytoplankton also favors recruitment and growth of benthic suspension-feeding animals that overgrow or bioerode coral skeletons (Highsmith 1980; Hallock and Schlager 1986; Birkeland 1987; Hallock 1988). Finally, increased nutrients favor growth of benthic fleshy algae that overgrow corals. All of these different effects of increased nutrients and the catastrophic disturbances discussed above act synergistically to suppress the growth of Caribbean corals and coral reefs (although the loss of herbivores appears to have had a greater effect than increases in nutrients; Hughes et al. 1999; Miller et al. 1999).

Half a Billion Years of Reef Ecosystems

Geologists agonize about what and what not to call a reef (James 1984; Fagerstrom 1987; Hallock 1997). Their most important criteria for "true" coral reef development include (1) presence of framework built by colonial metazoans containing endosymbionts or by crustose coralline algae, (2) topographical relief of the living reef surface above the surrounding sea floor, and (3) resistance of the framework to wave action and storms. By this definition, large-scale development of true reefs occurred during just three episodes of geologic time that altogether lasted about one-quarter of the Phanerozoic or roughly 125 million years (Wood 1999). Principally tabulate corals and stromatoporoid sponges constructed extensive Silurian and Devonian reef tracts as large as the Great Barrier Reef. Highly integrated growth across the colony surface over which small polyps were arrayed strongly suggests that tabulates possessed endosymbionts that contributed to their extensive calcification (Coates and Jackson 1987), but there is no definitive evidence that stromatoporoids contained endosymbionts. The second and third major phases of extensive and geographically widespread framework development occurred in the Jurassic and in the mid to late Cenozoic to recent. These reefs were built largely by colonial scleractinian corals with varying contributions by larger foraminifera, and calcareous

or coralline algae. Both stable isotopic and morphological analyses indicate that scleractinians possessed endosymbionts in the Late Triassic or Early Jurassic (Coates and Jackson 1987; Swart and Stanley 1989). In all three episodes, the surface area of cryptic reef environments within the reef framework greatly exceeded that of open reef surface, and was inhabited by a highly characteristic assemblage of calcareous sponges and other encrusting animals.

Regional changes in nutrient levels also have been implicated as the controlling factor for turning on or off major episodes of reef development over geological time (Hallock and Schlager 1986; Edinger and Risk 1994). Patterns of extinction selectivity and distribution of endolithic organisms in coral skeletons across the Oligocene-Miocene boundary 25 million years ago suggest that collapse of extensive Oligocene reef tracts and coral diversity in the Caribbean was associated with eutrophication. Species diversity of reef corals slowly recovered until the end of the Pliocene about 2 million years ago, when there was another mass extinction of reef corals (Budd and Johnson 1997) associated with oceanographic changes and intensifying sea level fluctuations (Jackson 1994b). Throughout this period of increasing diversity, large-scale reef buildups were absent, and sedimentological evidence suggests that water-column productivity remained high. Then, after the second mass extinction, reef development increased dramatically with declining productivity (Collins et al. 1996), even though coral diversity never recovered.

In contrast, "reef" development during the remaining three-quarters of the Phanerozoic was limited to low-lying buildups, or bioherms, of carbonate skeletal debris in a mud matrix without any obvious structural framework (Wood 1999). However, uncalcified sponges may have helped hold such structures together just as they hold corals together today (Wulff and Buss 1979). The two major groups responsible for such buildups were (1) cyanobacteria, calcareous algae, and weakly calcified or hexactinellid sponges and (2) heterotrophic, mostly solitary animals including corals, bivalve mollusks, brachiopods, bryozoans, and archeocyathids. Only one or the other of the two groups was generally abundant at any time. The most abundant and geologically spectacular heterotrophs are early Cambrian archeocyath sponges (Wood et al. 1993), middle Paleozoic solitary and simple colonial rugose corals (Fagerstrom 1987), Permian calcified sponges, bryozoans and brachiopods (Wood et al. 1995), and Cretaceous rudist bivalves (Ross and Skelton 1993). Animals with endosymbionts were apparently rare or absent, and cryptic environments were much less developed than in reefs with true framework.

Much of this variation in mode and extent of Phanerozoic reef development and taxonomic composition can be explained by (1) relations between variations in nutrient availability and modes of growth and life histories of dominant reef builders, as well as (2) types and abundance of predators (Figure 15.17) (Wood 1999). However, the record of nutrient levels and productivity in Phanerozoic seas is still preliminary, and their role in reef development is largely inferred

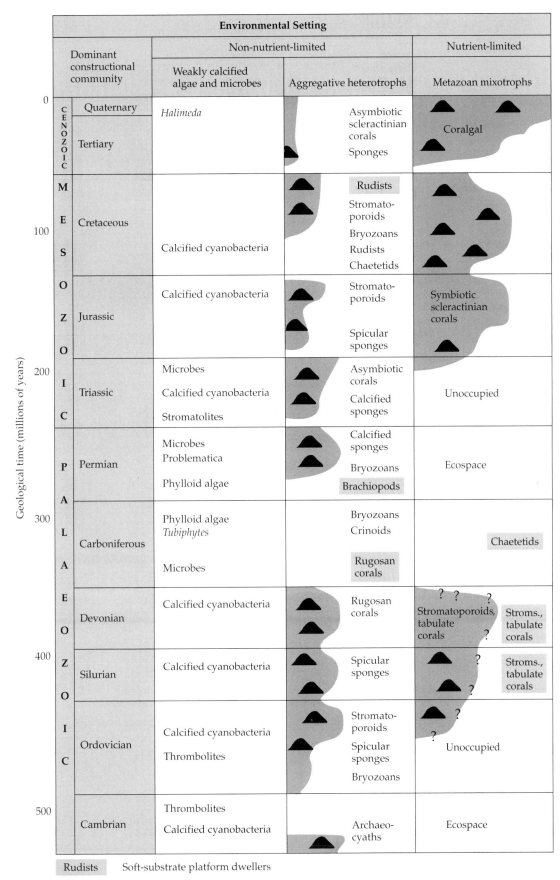

Figure 15.17 Geological record of reef development, showing relationships between abundance of major reef builders and physical conditions. (From Wood 1995.)

from what is known about variations in growth and life histories of reef dwellers in relation to nutrients in recent seas.

Factors leading to episodes of reef building by solitary heterotrophs can be understood in terms of factors that regulate the relative abundance of solitary and colonial animals today (Jackson 1977, 1983; Jackson and Coates 1985). Dense aggregations of benthic organisms can form by aggregative larval recruitment or by indeterminate growth and clonal propagation across the substrate. Larval aggregation is most common among aclonal, solitary animals like oysters, mussels, and tube worms that are poor overgrowth competitors for space except in very high densities, when they may dominate the entire community. Clonal propagation is characteristic of many algae, sponges, and colonial animals like corals that are excellent overgrowth competitors.

Levels of nutrients and primary production in the plankton modulate the balance of power between aclonal and clonal groups (Littler and Littler 1984; Birkeland 1988; Hallock 1988). Eutrophic conditions with very high levels of nutrients and planktonic productivity favor solitary animals. This is because increased food supplies allow enormous production of larvae and suppress growth of photoautotrophs and mixotrophs like algae and corals. Low productivity favors clonal organisms that do not require constantly high recruitment to maintain high population densities. Significantly, fossil reefs built by heterotrophs predominate in mudstones that almost certainly reflect high turbidity, nutrients, and planktonic productivity (Wood 1999; Ross and Skelton 1993), the same conditions that favor aggregations of solitary animals like oysters today.

In contrast, dominance by fleshy algae over corals and coralline algae in recent seas is favored by (1) moderate levels of nutrients that promote algal growth and (2) low abundance of grazers that otherwise maintain hard substrates clean of fleshy algae (Littler and Littler 1984; Birkeland 1988; Hallock 1988). Significantly, the geological first appearance of many of the most important grazers immediately precedes or follows closely upon the beginning of each of the three major episodes of framework reef building (Steneck 1983; Signor and Brett 1984; Vermeij 1987). The relative importance of reef building by algae in the absence of heterotrophs also falls off throughout the Phanerozoic as grazers with more and more effective dentition evolved.

THE LAST TWO MILLION YEARS, THE LAST FIVE HUNDRED YEARS, AND THE FORESEEABLE FUTURE

Pleistocene Perspectives on the Structure and Assembly of Reef Communities

The fossil record is the only source of long-term ecological data on time scales that encompass the natural variability of coral reef ecosystems (Hubbard 1988; Jackson 1991, 1992; Pandolfi 1999). Individual coral skeletons provide a wealth of paleoenvironmental data (Dodge and Vaisnys 1977; Fair-

banks et al. 1997) that can be used to determine time series of major climatic perturbations and their ecological consequences (Glynn and Colgan 1992), as well as recording past biological interactions and physical disturbance (Jackson 1983). Corals are commonly preserved in life position or with minimal transport. Thus, line transects or quadrats laid across outcrops of uplifted reefs can be used to record paleocommunity composition and diversity just as on a living reef (Figure 15.18A) (Stemann and Johnson 1992; Pandolfi 1996; Pandolfi and Jackson, in press). This method is commonly used on Late Pleistocene or Holocene reefs that have been uplifted above sea level. Alternatively, cores can be obtained or trenches dug into subtidal reef framework to obtain a record of more recent events leading up to present-day communities (Macintyre and Glynn 1976; Fairbanks 1989; Aronson and Precht 1997; Aronson et al. 1998). This approach is most useful for the Holocene record of sea level rise over the past 10,000–15,000 years. Environments of deposition and

(A)

(B)

Figure 15.18 Fossil reefs of New Guinea. (A) Corals in growth position. (B) Reef terraces created by uplift and sea level changes. (Photos courtesy of J. Pandolfi.)

water depths can be determined independently of the corals themselves to avoid circularity in interpretation (Pandolfi et al., in press). Moreover, comparisons of distributions and abundance of live coral and dead coral on recent reefs with similar fossil data demonstrate that fossil coral communities faithfully record the original living coral community (Greenstein et al. 1998a).

Pandolfi (1996, 1999) examined coral community composition on nine Late Pleistocene reef terraces on the Huon Peninsula of Papua New Guinea that were formed by the interaction of local tectonic uplift and glacial sea level fluctuations over 95,000 years (Figure 15.18B). Each uplift event comprised a separate ecological experiment in coral community assembly following a major disturbance. Reef crest and reef slope assemblages were recognized and sampled separately at three sites along 35 km of coast. There were no significant differences in community composition or species richness in each environment over time (among the nine terraces) but there were consistent differences among sites along the shore.

Community membership over 95,000 years was much more stable than expected from a random sample of the habitat-specific species pools (i.e., only those species known to occur in each specific environment rather than all species known from the geographic region). Restriction of the analysis to the habitat-specific species pool is essential because far fewer species occur in any local habitat than occur in the regional species pool. Indeed, this is a basic problem (Westoby 1998) with the analysis of so-called local versus regional effects on coral community structure and diversity (Karlson and Cornell 1998). For example, only 18 species of *Acropora* occur along the coast of the Huon Peninsula today, out of the roughly 125 species of *Acropora* from the broader West Pacific region, and only four of these 18 species are common. These same four *Acropora* species dominate Pandolfi's Pleistocene communities and, in general, both the reef crest and reef slope communities were dominated consistently by fewer than 25% of the 66–92 species encountered in each environment in the Pleistocene and the recent. Moreover, dominant species are no more widely distributed than rarer species in the same environments. Thus, consistent dominance does not appear to result only from superior dispersal ability as predicted by Hubbell (1997).

The New Guinea study was criticized (Aronson and Precht 1997) for using only presence or absence of corals. However, similar community stability was observed using the same methods of analysis with relative abundance data from three different reef environments on the 125,000-year-old terrace in Curaçao (Pandolfi and Jackson 1997, in press). Community composition was different among environments but not over distances of as much as 40 km within the same environments. As in New Guinea, coral communities were dominated by only a small percentage of the roughly 30 species recorded from each paleocommunity, which is similar to recent species richness along the same coasts. Dominant species were no more widely distributed than rarer species in the same habitats.

Curaçao is rarely subjected to hurricanes (Pandolfi and Jackson, in press). Woodley (1992) suggested that the extreme dominance of shallow water Jamaican reefs by *Acropora palmata* and *Acropora cervicornis* was an artifact of infrequent damage by hurricanes during the early studies of reef zonation in Jamaica (Goreau 1959; Kinzie 1973). However, paleoecological studies in areas strongly affected by hurricanes demonstrate apparently uninterrupted dominance by one or the other of these *Acropora* species for thousands of years during individual high stands of sea level (Jackson 1992; Aronson and Precht 1997; Aronson et al. 1998; Greenstein et al. 1998b). In general, growth rates of acroporid corals are so high that competitive dominance occurs over intervals shorter than the average period between major hurricanes at any particular site.

The paleontological data provide an ecological baseline of predictable patterns of coral community assembly and membership over large spatial and temporal scales before intense modern human disturbance (Jackson 1992; Pandolfi and Jackson 1997, in press; Pandolfi 1999). The probability approaches certainty that the community at any particular reef site will be devastated by some form of disturbance over decades to millennia (Connell 1978; Jackson 1991; Woodley 1992; Connell et al. 1997; Hughes and Connell 1999). Recovery will be varyingly affected by recruitment limitation, interactions among established organisms and further disturbance (Done 1992, 1997, 1999; Connell et al. 1997; Hughes and Tanner 2000); and diversity commonly, although not always, peaks at intermediate levels of disturbance (Tanner et al. 1994) as hypothesized by Connell (1978). Nevertheless, the fossil data require that these disturbances are (or were) sufficiently predictable over large scales of the reefscape for the development of predictable coral community composition, just as on rocky intertidal shores (Paine and Levin 1981).

With this perspective, distinctions break down between equilibrium and nonequilibrium communities, open versus closed populations, and Gleasonian versus Eltonian community assembly (Chesson 1997). On the scale of the regional landscape, interspecific differences in life histories and niches produce predictable patterns of community development (Jackson and Hughes 1985; Jackson 1991; Knowlton and Jackson 1994; Tanner et al. 1994; Hughes 1996; Hughes et al. 2000). However, none of these conclusions require or imply tightly integrated mechanisms of community structure (Jackson 1994a) as has sometimes been assumed by paleoecologists (Aronson and Precht 1995; Jablonski and Sepkoski 1996).

What Was Natural on Coral Reefs?

Until the 1980s, most coral reef ecologists assumed that reefs they were studying were "natural" (Sheppard 1995), despite evidence to the contrary from fisheries (Munro 1983; Hatcher et al. 1989) and absence of baseline data before industrialization and the modern, exponential rise in human populations (Jackson 1995, 1997). Opinions changed, however, with increasing reports of catastrophic mortality of corals due to outbreaks of disease, predators, bleaching, overgrowth by fleshy algae, over-fishing, eutrophication, oil spills, and a host of other factors (Hay 1984; Tomascik and Sander 1987; Jackson et al. 1989; Ginsburg 1993; Hughes 1994; Brown 1997a, b; Done 1997, 1999; Peters 1997; Richardson 1998; but see Grigg 1992). Coral cover declined precipitously and relative abundance of surviving species changed at sites around the world over the last two decades (Wilkinson 1992; Hughes 1994). Effects of repeated disturbances appear increasingly severe, suggesting that reefs do not entirely recover before new perturbations (Done 1988; Paine et al. 1998; Hughes and Connell 1999). This negative synergism is equally apparent for natural disturbances such as hurricanes and anthropogenic impacts such as oil spills.

In spite of widespread basis for concern, we cannot quantify using standard ecological methods how much of this decline is within the range of natural variability of coral reef ecosystems, and how much is due to anthropogenic change (Jackson 1992; Sapp 1999). This is not a trivial problem. Well-documented, natural variations in other marine ecosystems may be extremely large. For example, the order of magnitude, boom–bust cycles in abundance of anchovies and sardines in the eastern Pacific are driven by climatic fluctuations with a periodicity longer than the longest environmental time series from the region (Baumgartner et al. 1992; MacCall 1996; McGowan et al. 1998). There are no comparable observational records from any coral reef environment.

Paleoecological, archeological, and historical data (hereafter collectively referred to as paleo data) are therefore the only means for obtaining the necessary long-term perspective (Jackson 1992, in press). Paleo data are necessarily descriptive rather than experimental, but they uniquely encompass the time scales necessary to distinguish natural from anthropogenic variation. Moreover, most long-term ecological studies of living reefs are also entirely descriptive (Connell et al. 1997; Hughes and Tanner 2000), and that fact has not hindered their application to similar ecological problems (Hughes 1994; Connell et al. 1997). The application of paleo data to coral reef ecology is still in its infancy, but there are already clear examples of the power of the approach for both corals and mobile consumers such as sea urchins, fish, and turtles.

We have seen how detailed surveys of Pleistocene and Holocene reef corals can provide an ecological baseline for the apparently low natural variability in coral community composition (Pandolfi 1996, 1999; Aronson and Precht 1997; Aronson et al. 1998; Greenstein et al. 1998a; Pandolfi and Jackson, in press). The same studies demonstrate that recent dominance of Caribbean shallow-water reefs on exposed coasts by comparatively opportunistic, brooding species of *Agaricia* and *Porites* instead of *Acropora* are unprecedented on fossil reefs so far examined extending back for 125,000 years. Prehistoric shifts to dominance of reefs by soft-bodied organisms like fleshy algae (Lessios 1988; Hughes 1994) should be detectable by detailed analyses of horizons of extensive bioerosion on fossil reefs, but this has not been attempted. Nevertheless, there is clearly no paleontological evidence for anything like the modern situation on Caribbean reefs.

There also are good historical data showing that the decline of shallow-water *Acropora* in the Caribbean began in Barbados as early as the nineteenth century (Lewis 1984). Extensive tracts of *Acropora palmata* persisted around much of the island until the 1920s but had disappeared before the first modern ecological surveys in the 1950s (Lewis 1960), apparently due to increased eutrophication and runoff that began with the deforestation of the island for sugarcane in the seventeenth century. This historical discovery helps to explain the apparently anomalous difference between the persistence of dense stands of *Acropora* spp. throughout the past half-million years on Barbados and its earlier reported absence in the recent in Barbados (Jackson 1992).

Paleontological data for mobile reef animals have produced less consistent results because of greater problems of sampling and reworking of sediments that mix skeletal remains. For example, the vast amounts of skeletal debris formed by the mass mortality of *Diadema antillarum* in the Caribbean were soon mixed unrecognizably into older sediments (Greenstein 1989). On the other hand, preservation of fossil *Diadema* is sufficient to determine that it was the most abundant sea urchin on Caribbean reefs 125,000 years ago (Gordon and Donovan 1992), long before overfishing began. Likewise, we still do not know if outbreaks of crown-of-thorns starfish happened in the past, because abundant skeletal remains of the starfish sampled at depth in cores of reef sediments may have been reworked (Keesing et al. 1992; Pandolfi 1992). However, this problem could be easily resolved by analysis of Holocene reefs in New Guinea or elsewhere that were uplifted before observed outbreaks of starfish began. Similar constraints and possibilities apply to fossil otoliths of reef fishes that could be used to determine the taxonomic composition and body size of reef fish populations and communities before intensive human exploitation.

Historical data clearly demonstrate the great magnitude of ecological effects of human exploitation on reefs. Large predatory fishes and sharks were extremely abundant in the Caribbean in the sixteenth and seventeenth centuries (Oviedo 1526; Dampier 1729). These were fished down to levels so low that inhabitants shifted their efforts to smaller and smaller carnivores and herbivorous fishes (Munro 1983; Jackson 1997). The net effect on reef environments was to fish down the trophic level of reef fish communities, just as has been documented for larger commercial fisheries worldwide (Pauly et al. 1998).

The best historical data are for green turtles in the Caribbean because of the enormous importance of these animals in the colonial economy of the Caribbean, where populations of human slaves were fed on turtles for more than a century (Jackson 1997). Historical reports of voyagers describe populations so huge that ships could navigate in the fog by the noises of migrating animals, that could also impede the progress of ships that sailed directly into the vast aggregations! Green turtles used to crop "turtlegrass" (*Thalassia testudinum*) at hundreds of sites around the Caribbean whose names (e.g., Dry Tortugas) refer to the once abundant turtles that are now very rarely, if ever, seen. Estimates of adult abundances based on hunting data produce astonishing numbers ranging from approximately 16- to 35-million 100-kg adult turtles for the entire tropical western Atlantic (Jackson 1997; Bjorndal et al. 2000). Estimates based on experimental data for the carrying capacity of turtle grass beds yield numbers up to 10–20 times higher. Even the smallest, conservative estimates exceed the biomass of large vertebrates in east Africa today; and there is every reason to believe that abundances of other large vertebrates including other sea turtles, manatees, and sharks were of comparable size.

Clearly, studying grazing and predation on reefs today is like trying to understand the ecology of the Serengeti by studying the termites and the locusts while ignoring the wildebeest and the elephants. The remaining small fishes and invertebrate predators and grazers feed very differently from their larger precursors (Figure 15.19) because they nibble at rather than break apart their prey and (unlike turtles and manatees) cannot digest cellulose. Loss of megavertebrates drastically reduced and qualitatively changed grazing and excavation of seagrasses, predation on sponges, export of pro-

(A)

(B)

Figure 15.19 (A) A dugong feeding. (B) Aerial photo illustrating massive disturbance to seagrass beds associated with grazing by these large vertebrates. (Photos courtesy of H. Marsh.)

duction to adjacent ecosystems, and the structure of food chains. Likewise, patterns of carbon flux were changed on the Great Barrier Reef after devastation by crown-of-thorns starfish (Johnson et al. 1995). It is no accident that the only published food web for coral reef environments that includes large vertebrates is for the French Frigate Shoals (Figure 15.14) (Grigg et al. 1984), thousands of kilometers from any human populations. No large vertebrates are even mentioned in Sale's (1991a) compendium on the ecology of coral reef fishes.

Whither Coral Reefs?

Coral reefs were already greatly altered by human activities long before the first coral reef ecologists began to study them. Nevertheless, we are beginning to understand the magnitude of these changes and their consequences (Done 1992, 1997, 1999; Bradbury 1990; Hughes 1994; Bradbury and Seymour 1997; Jackson 1997, in press). These insights can be summarized in two elementary models of the causes and consequences of outbreaks of crown-of-thorns starfish *Acanthaster planci* on the Great Barrier Reef and the demise of the sea urchin *Diadema antillarum* in the Caribbean (Figure 15.20). Both models ignore for simplicity important spatial questions of hydrodynamics and larval dispersal that are essential to the metapopulation dynamics of these systems.

On Caribbean and East African reefs, abundant predatory and herbivorous fish once suppressed sea urchin and macroalgal abundance, and coral cover was high (Figure 15.20A, plane A) (Hughes 1994; McClanahan et al. 1996). Fishing initially decreased predatory fish populations, resulting in increases in sea urchins and small herbivorous fishes that grazed on algae, and coral abundance remained high (plane B). Eventually, intense subsistence over-fishing also greatly reduced herbivorous fish abundance which, after the mass mortality of *Diadema antillarum* in the Caribbean, permitted enormous increases in unpalatable macroalgae that are progressively overgrowing corals throughout the region (plane C). Increased nutrient levels due to agriculture and human waste, decreased coral abundance due to hurricanes, increased sedimentation due to deforestation, and outbreaks of disease or coral bleaching have further lowered thresholds for macroalgal dominance over corals in all cases (Harvell et al. 1999; Jackson, in press).

More hypothetically on the Great Barrier Reef, high densities of fish (and other predators) probably suppressed *Acanthaster* population growth, so that outbreaks did not occur or were very rare (Bradbury and Seymour 1997). Coral cover greatly exceeded that of macroalgae, soft corals, or other potentially dominant sessile taxa (Figure 15.20B, plane A). Reduction of predatory fish populations below some unknown threshold density due to moderate fishing contributed to the increased frequency of starfish outbreaks, that decimated coral cover (plane B) and resulted in presumably unstable limit cycles of starfish-coral-macroalgal abundance. Finally, we can speculate that increased fishing will further reduce abundance of less preferred herbivorous species. Then, the sudden growth of macroalgae following coral mortality due to starfish outbreaks would greatly exceed consumption by

Figure 15.20 Models of changes in relative abundance of predators, corals and algae as a response to fishing and other human interference. (A) Caribbean and East Africa: plane A, pristine situation prior to fishing, with grazing of algae shared among diverse fish and invertebrates, especially sea urchins; plane B, increased abundance of *Diadema* and other invertebrate grazers due to overfishing compensates for loss of grazing fishes so that the ratio of corals to algae remains high; plane C, mass mortality of *Diadema* permits explosive growth of algae that overgrow corals. (B) Great Barrier Reef: plane A, pristine situation prior to fishing, with populations of crown-of-thorns starfish held in check by predatory fishes and corals dominant across the reef; plane B, overfishing permits outbreaks of crown-of-thorns starfish, with corals reduced and replaced by algae and other uncalcified sessile organisms on many reefs; plane C, hypothesized response to further overfishing, with chronically high crown-of-thorns populations reducing corals to very low levels and dominance of the reefscape by algae.

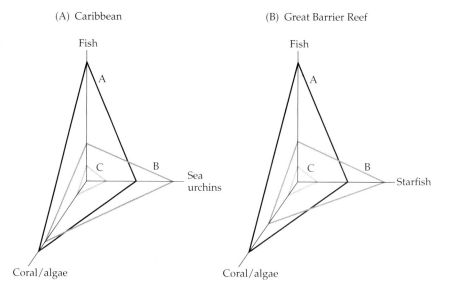

herbivores. This would in turn result in a shift in dominance from palatable to unpalatable macroalgal species (plane C) that might persist even if herbivore populations subsequently increased. This has not occurred in economically prosperous Australia, but is to be expected in areas of intensive subsistence overfishing around the Philippines or Indonesia. As in the Caribbean, increased nutrients or decreased coral abundance due to cyclones, sedimentation, disease or bleaching should lower thresholds for shifts from dominance by corals to macroalgae.

The value of such simplified models is that they summarize current knowledge and help focus on processes and hypotheses to falsify. They also overwhelmingly demonstrate that almost everything we have learned about coral reef ecology has been based on ecosystems greatly altered by humanity (Bradbury 1990; Hughes 1994; Bradbury and Seymour 1997; Knowlton 1997; Jackson 1995, in press). They also help to understand the time lag between the historically much earlier fishing down of consumers (such as manatees, turtles, large fishes) and increasing inputs from the land, and the much later collapse of the sessile, habitat-structuring corals and seagrasses that define the character of these ecosystems (Figure 15.21). The initial great decline in large, mobile consumers and inputs from the land began in the seventeenth century in the Caribbean and in the nineteenth century in the Indo-West Pacific. Corals and seagrasses were apparently unaffected by these initial events, although this could be tested by analyses of growth rings and incidence of injuries preserved in ancient corals. These altered reef communities are what passed as baseline until the widespread collapse of coral and seagrass communities in the 1980s associated with extreme subsistence overfishing, increased inputs from the land due to exponential human population growth, and disease (Jackson 1997, in press; Harvell et al. 1999).

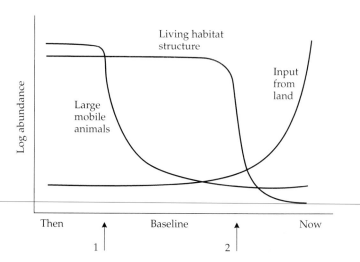

Figure 15.21 General model of coral reef community collapse due to human disturbance. The *y*-axis is logarithmic to capture the orders of magnitude changes in the abundances of large mobile animals and living habitat structure such as corals and seagrasses. The time axis is deliberately general because onset of major changes depends more on the timing of the onset of intensive harvesting or land-based activities than on chronological age. Near-elimination of most megaherbivores and megapredators defines the first major transition (arrow 1), which corresponds to the shift from plane A to plane B in Figure 15.20. The loss of these large animals preceded ecological investigations so that their absence has been uncritically accepted as the natural "baseline" condition. The second major transition (arrow 2) reflects sudden collapse of living habitat structure due to indirect effects of overfishing down the food chain and the concurrent exponential increase in inputs of sediments and nutrients from the land due to human population increase. This transition corresponds to the shift from plane B to plane C in Figure 15.20.

LITERATURE CITED

Achituv, Y. and Z. Dubinsky. 1990. Evolution and zoogeography of coral reefs. In Z. Dubinsky (ed.), *Coral Reefs*, pp. 1–9. *Ecosystems of the World* Vol. 25. Elsevier, Amsterdam.

Aerts, L. A. M. and R. W. M. van Soest. 1997. Quantification of sponge/coral interactions in a physically stressed reef community, NE Colombia. *Mar. Ecol. Prog. Ser.* 148: 125–134.

Aronson, R. B. and W. F. Precht. 1995. Landscape patterns of reef coral diversity: A test of the intermediate disturbance hypothesis. *J. Exp. Mar. Biol. Ecol.* 192: 1–14.

Aronson, R. B. and W. F. Precht. 1997. Stasis, biological disturbance, and community structure of a Holocene coral reef. *Paleobiology* 23: 326–346.

Aronson, R. B. and W. F. Precht. 2000. Herbivory and algal dynamics on the coral reef at Discovery Bay, Jamaica. *Limnol. Oceanogr.* 45: 251–255.

Aronson, R. B., W. F. Precht and I. G. Macintyre. 1998. Extrinsic control of species replacement on a Holocene reef in Belize: The role of coral disease. *Coral Reefs* 17: 223–230.

Ault, T. R. and C. R. Johnson. 1998. Spatially and temporally predictable fish communities on coral reefs. *Ecol. Monogr.* 68: 25–50.

Babcock, R. C., C. N. Mundy and D. Whitehead. 1994. Sperm diffusion models and in situ confirmation of long-distance fertilization in the free-spawning asteroid *Acanthaster planci. Biol. Bull.* 186: 17–28.

Bak, R. P. M., J. Brouns and F. Heys. 1977. Regeneration and aspects of spatial competition in the scleractinian corals *Agaricia agaricites* and *Montastrea annularis. Proc. 3rd Int. Coral Reef Symp.* 1: 143–148.

Bak, R. P. M., D. Y. M. Lambrechts, M. Joenje, G. Nieuwland and M. L. J. van Veghel. 1996. Long-term changes on coral reefs in booming populations of a competitive colonial ascidian. *Mar. Ecol. Prog. Ser.* 133: 303–306.

Baker, A. C. and R. Rowan. 1997. Diversity of symbiotic dinoflagellates (zooxanthellae) in scleractinian corals of the Caribbean and eastern Pacific. *Proc. 8th Int. Coral Reef Symp.* 2: 1301–1306.

Baumgartner, T., A. Soutar and V. Ferreira-Bartrina. 1992. Reconstruction of the history of Pacific sardine and northern anchovy populations over the past two millennia from sediments of the Santa Barbara Basin, California. *California Coop. Oceanic Fish Invest. Rep.* 33: 24–40.

Bellwood, D. R. 1995. Direct estimate of bioerosion by two parrotfish species, *Chlorurus gibbus* and *C. sordidus*, on the Great Barrier Reef, Australia. *Mar. Biol.* 121: 419–429.

Bellwood, D. R. and J. H. Choat. 1990. A functional analysis of grazing in parrotfishes (family Scaridae): The ecological implications. *Environ. Biol. Fish* 28: 189–214.

Bertness, M. D. and S. D. Hacker. 1994. Physical stress and positive associations among marsh plants. *Amer. Nat.* 144: 363–372.

Benzie, J. A. H. 1999. Genetic structure of coral reef organisms: Ghosts of dispersal past. *Amer. Zool.* 39: 131–145.

Birkeland, C. 1987. Nutrient availability as a major determinant of differences among coastal hard-substratum communities in different regions of the tropics. *UNESCO Reps. Mar. Sci.* 46: 45–97.

Birkeland, C. 1988. Geographic comparisons of coral-reef community processes. *Proc. 6th Int. Coral Reef Symp.* 1: 211–220.

Bjorndahl, K. A., A. B. Bolten and M. Y. Chaloupka. 2000. Green turtle somatic growth model: Evidence for density dependence. *Ecol. Appl.* 10: 269–282.

Bradbury, R. H. (ed.). 1990. *Acanthaster and the Coral Reef: A Theoretical Perspective*. Lecture Notes in Biomathematics 88. Springer-Verlag, Berlin.

Bradbury, R. and R. Seymour. 1997. Waiting for COTS. *Proc. 8th Int. Coral Reef Symp.* 2: 1357–1362.

Brown, B. E. 1997a. Coral bleaching: Causes and consequences. *Coral Reefs* 16 (Suppl.): S129–S138.

Brown, B. E. 1997b. Disturbances to reefs in recent times. In C. Birkeland (ed.), *Life and Death of Coral Reefs*, pp. 354–379. Chapman & Hall, New York.

Budd, A. F. and K. G. Johnson. 1997. Coral reef community dynamics over 8 million years of evolutionary time. *Proc. 8th Int. Coral Reef Symp.* 1: 423–428.

Buddemeier, R. W. and D. Hopley. 1988. Turn-ons and turn-offs: Causes and mechanisms of initiation and termination of coral reef growth. *Proc. 6th Int. Coral Reef Symp.* 1: 253–261.

Buss, L. W. 1979. Bryozoan overgrowth interactions: The interdependence of competition for space and food. *Nature* 281: 475–477.

Buss, L. W. 1986. Competition and community organization on hard surfaces in the sea. In T. Case and J. Diamond (eds.). *Community Ecology*, pp. 517–536. Harper and Row, New York.

Buss, L. W. and J. B. C. Jackson. 1979. Competitive networks: Nontransitive competitive relationships in cryptic coral reef environments. *Amer. Nat.* 113: 223–234.

Buss, L. W. and J. B. C. Jackson. 1981. Planktonic food availability and suspension-feeder abundance: Evidence of in situ depletion. *J. Exp. Mar. Biol. Ecol.* 49:151–161.

Bythell, J. C., E. H. Gladfelter and M. Bythell. 1993. Chronic and catastrophic mortality of three common Caribbean reef corals. *Coral Reefs* 12: 143–152.

Caley, M. J., M. H. Carr, M. A. Hixon, T. P. Hughes, G. P. Jones and B. A. Menge. 1996. Recruitment and the local dynamics of open marine populations. *Annu. Rev. Ecol. Syst.* 27: 477–500.

Carlon, D. B. 1999. The evolution of mating systems in tropical reef corals. *Trends Ecol. Evol.* 14: 491–495.

Carpenter, R. D. 1997. Invertebrate predators and grazers. In C. Birkeland (ed.), *Life and Death of Coral Reefs*, pp. 198–229. Chapman & Hall, New York.

Casselle, J. E. 1999. Early post-settlement mortality in a coral reef fish and its effect on local population size. *Ecol. Monogr.* 69: 177–194.

Chesson, P. 1997. Diversity maintenance by integration of mechanisms over various scales. *Proc. 8th Int. Coral Reef Symp.* 1: 405–410.

Clifton, K. E. and L. M. Clifton. 1999. The phenology of sexual reproduction by green algae (Bryopsidales) on Caribbean coral reefs. *J. Phycol.* 35: 24–34.

Coates, A. G. and J. B. C. Jackson. 1987. Clonal growth, algal symbiosis and reef formation in corals. *Paleobiology* 13: 363–378.

Collins L. S., A. F. Budd and A. G. Coates. 1996. Earliest evolution associated with closure of the tropical American seaway. *Proc. Natl. Acad. Sci. USA* 93: 6069–6072.

Coma, R. and H. R. Lasker. 1997. Small-scale heterogeneity of fertilization success in a broadcast spawning octocoral. *J. Exp. Mar. Biol. Ecol.* 214: 107–120.

Connell, J. H. 1973. Population ecology of reef-building corals. In O. A. Jones and R. Endean (eds.), *Biology and Geology of Coral Reefs.* Vol. II: *Biology I*, pp. 205–245. Academic Press, New York.

Connell, J. H. 1978. Diversity in tropical rain forests and coral reefs. *Science* 199: 1302–1310.

Connell, J. H., T. P. Hughes and C. C. Wallace. 1997. A 30-year study of coral abundance, recruitment, and disturbance at several scales in space and time. *Ecol. Monogr.* 67: 461–488.

Cowen, R. K., K. M. M. Lwiza, S. Sponaugle, C. B. Paris and D. B. Olson. 2000. Connectivity of marine populations: Open or closed? *Science* 287: 857–859.

Cumming, R. L. 1999. Predation on reef-building corals: Multiscale variation in the density of three corallivorous gastropods. *Coral Reefs* 18: 147–170.

Dampier, W. 1729. *A New Voyage Around the World.* Reprinted 1968, Dover, New York.

Darwin, C. 1842. *The Structure and Distribution of Coral Reefs.* University of Arizona Press, Tucson.

Dayton, P. K., M. J. Tegner, P. E. Parnell and P. B. Edwards. 1992. Temporal and spatial patterns of disturbance and recovery in a kelp forest community. *Ecol. Monogr.* 62: 421–445.

Dayton, P. K., M. J. Tegner, P. B. Edwards and K. L. Riser. 1999. Temporal and spatial scales of kelp demography: The role of oceanographic climate. *Ecol. Monogr.* 69: 219–250.

Dodge, R. E. and J. R.Vaisnys. 1977. Coral populations and growth patterns: Responses to sedimentation and turbidity associated with dredging. *J. Mar. Res.* 35: 715–730.

Doherty, P. J. 1991. Spatial and temporal patterns in recruitment. In P. F. Sale (ed.), *The Ecology of Fishes on Coral Reefs*, pp. 261–293. Academic Press, San Diego.

Doherty, P. and T. Fowler. 1994. An empirical test of recruitment limitation in a coral reef fish. *Science* 263: 935–939.

Doherty, P. J., S. Planes and P. Mather. 1995. Gene flow and larval duration in seven species of fish from the Great Barrier Reef. *Ecology* 76: 2373–2391.

Done, T. J. 1982. Patterns in the distribution of coral communities across the central Great Barrier Reef. *Coral Reefs* 1: 95–107.

Done, T. J. 1983. Coral zonation: Its nature and significance. In D. J. Barnes (ed.), *Perspectives on Coral Reefs*, pp. 107–147. Australian Institute of Marine Science and Brian Clooston, Manuka, ACT, Australia.

Done, T. J. 1988. Simulation of recovery of pre-disturbance size structure in populations of *Porites* spp. damaged by the crown of thorns starfish *Acanthaster planci*. *Mar. Biol.* 100: 51–61.

Done, T. 1992. Constancy and change in some Great Barrier Reef coral communities: 1980–1990. *Amer. Zool.* 32: 655–662.

Done, T. J. 1997. Decadal changes in reef-building communities: Implications for reef growth and monitoring programs. *Proc. 8th Int. Coral Reef Symp.* 1:411–416.

Done, T. J. 1999. Coral community adaptability to environmental change at the scales of regions, reefs and reef zones. *Amer. Zool.* 39: 66–79.

Done, T. J., J. C. Ogden, W. J. Weibe and B. R. Rosen. 1997. Biodiversity and ecosystem function of coral reefs. In H. A. Mooney, J. H. Cushman, E. Medina, O. E. Sala and E.-D. Schulze (eds.), *Functional Roles of Biodiversity: A Global Perspective*, pp. 393–429. John Wiley, Chichester, U.K.

Edinger, E. N. and M. J. Risk. 1994. Oligocene–Miocene extinction and geographic restriction of Caribbean corals: Roles of turbidity, temperature, and nutrients. *Palaios* 9: 576–598.

Fadlallah, Y. H., K. W. Allen and R. A. Estudillo. 1995. Mortality of shallow reef corals in the western Arabian Gulf following aerial exposure in winter. *Coral Reefs* 14: 99–107.

Fagerstrom, J. A. 1987. *The Evolution of Reef Communities*. Wiley, New York.

Fairbanks, R. G. 1989. A 17,000-year glacio-eustatic sea level record: Influence of glacial melting rates on the Younger Dryas event and deep ocean circulation. *Nature* 342: 637–642.

Fairbanks , R. G., M. N. Evans, J. L. Rubenstone, R. A. Mortlock, K. Broad, M. D. Moore and C. D. Charles. 1997. Evaluating climate indices and their geochemical proxies measured in corals. *Coral Reefs* 16 (Suppl.): S93–S100.

Falkowski, P. G., Z. Dubinsky, L. Muscatine and L. McCloskey. 1993. Population control in symbiotic corals. *Bioscience* 43: 606–611.

Fearon, R. J. and A. M. Cameron. 1997. Preliminary evidence supporting the ability of hermatypic corals to affect adversely larvae and early settlement stages of hard coral competitors. *J. Chem. Ecol.* 23: 1769–1780.

Fiske, D. A. and V. J. Harriott. 1993. Are understorey coral communities recruitment limited? *Proc. 7th Intl. Coral Reef Symp. Guam* 1: 517–520.

Ginsburg, R. N. (compiler). 1993. *Proceedings of the Colloquium and Forum on Global Aspects of Coral Reefs: Health, Hazards and History*. Rosenstiel School of Marine and Atmospheric Sciences, University of Miami, Coral Gables, FL.

Gladfelter, W. B. 1982. White band disease in *Acropora palmata*: Implications for the structure and growth of shallow reefs. *Bull. Mar. Sci.* 32: 639–643.

Glynn, P. W. 1976. Some physical and biological determinants of coral community structure in the eastern Pacific. *Ecol. Monogr.* 46: 431–456.

Glynn, P. W. 1990. Feeding ecology of selected coral-reef macroconsumers: Patterns and effects on coral community structure. In Z. Dubinsky (ed.), *Coral Reefs*, pp. 365–400. *Ecosystems of the World* Vol. 25. Elsevier, Amsterdam.

Glynn, P. W. 1993. Coral reef bleaching: Ecological perspectives. *Coral Reefs* 12: 1–17.

Glynn, P. W. 1997. Bioerosion and coral-reef growth. In C. Birkeland (ed.), *Life and Death of Coral Reefs*, pp. 68–95. Chapman & Hall, New York.

Glynn, P. W. and M. W. Colgan. 1992. Sporadic disturbances in fluctuating coral reef environments: El Niño and coral reef development in the eastern Pacific. *Amer. Zool.* 32: 707–718.

Gordon, C. M. and S. K. Donovan. 1992. Disarticulated echinoid ossicles in paleoecology and taphonomy: The last interglacial Falmouth Formation of Jamaica. *Palaios* 7: 157–166.

Goreau, T. F. 1959. The zonation of Jamaican coral reefs. I. Species composition and zonation. *Ecology* 40: 67–90.

Goreau, T. F. and W. D. Hartman. 1966. Sponge: Effect on the form of reef corals. *Nature* 151: 343–344.

Greenstein, B. J. 1989. Mass mortality of the West-Indian echinoid *Diadema antillarum* (Echinodermata: Echinoidea): A natural experiment in taphonomy. *Palaios* 4: 487–492.

Greenstein, B. J., H. A. Curran and J. M. Pandolfi. 1998a. Shifting ecological baselines and the demise of *Acropora cervicornis* in the western North Atlantic and Caribbean Province: A Pleistocene perspective. *Coral Reefs* 17: 249–261.

Greenstein, B. J., J. M. Pandolfi and H. A. Curran. 1998b. The completeness of the Pleistocene fossil record: Implications for stratigraphic adequacy. In S. K. Donovan (ed.), *The Adequacy of the Fossil Record*, pp. 75–109. John Wiley and Sons, London.

Griffith, J. K. 1997. Occurrence of aggressive mechanisms during interactions between soft corals (Octocorallia: Alcyoniidae) and other corals on the Great Barrier Reef, Australia. *Mar. Freshwater Res.* 48: 129–135.

Grigg, R. W. 1992. Coral reef environmental science: Truth versus the Cassandra syndrome. *Coral Reefs* 11: 183–186.

Grigg, R. W., J. J. Polovina and M. J. Atkinson. 1984. Model of a coral reef ecosystem. III. Resource limitation, community regulation, fisheries yield and resource management. *Coral Reefs* 3: 23–27.

Grosberg, R. K. and D. R. Levitan. 1992. For adults only? Supply-side ecology and the history of larval biology. *Trends Ecol. Evol.* 7: 130–133.

Grutter, A. S. 1997. Effect of the removal of cleaner fish on the abundance and species composition of reef fish. *Oecologia* 111: 137–143.

Guzmán, H. M., K. A. Burns and J. B. C. Jackson. 1994. Injury, regeneration and growth of Caribbean reef corals after a major oil spill in Panama. *J. Exp. Mar. Biol. Ecol.* 105: 231–241.

Hallock, P. 1988. The role of nutrient availability in bioerosion: Consequences to carbonate buildups. *Palaeogogr. Palaeoclim. Palaeoecol.* 63: 275–291.

Hallock, P. 1997. Reefs and reef limestones in earth history. In C. Birkeland (ed.), *Life and Death of Coral Reefs*, pp. 13–42. Chapman & Hall, New York.

Hallock, P. and W. Schlager. 1986. Nutrient excess and the demise of coral reefs and carbonate platforms. *Palaios* 1: 389–398.

Harmelin, J.-G. 2000. Ecology of cave and cavity dwelling bryozoans. In A. Herrera and J. B. C. Jackson (eds.), *Proceedings of the 11th International Bryozoology Association Conference*, pp. 38–53. Smithsonian Tropical Research Institute, Panama.

Harmelin-Vivien, M. L. and P. Laboute. 1986. Catastrophic impact of hurricanes on atoll outer reef slopes in the Tuamotu (French Polynesia). *Coral Reefs* 5: 55–62.

Harrison, P. L. and C. C. Wallace. 1990. Reproduction, dispersal and recruitment of scleractinian corals. In Z. Dubinsky (ed.), *Coral Reefs*, pp. 133–207. *Ecosystems of the World* Vol. 25. Elsevier, Amsterdam.

Harrison, P. L., R. C. Babcock, G. D. Bull, J. K. Oliver, C. C. Wallace and B. L. Willis. 1984. Mass spawning in tropical reef corals. *Science* 223: 1186–1189.

Harvell, C. D. and 12 others. 1999. Emerging marine diseases: Climate links and anthropogenic factors. *Science* 285: 1505–1510.

Hatcher, B. G. 1988. The primary productivity of coral reefs: A beggar's banquet. *Trends Ecol. Evol.* 3: 106–111.

Hatcher, B. G. 1990. The primary productivity of coral reefs: A hierarchy of pattern and process. *Trends Ecol. Evol.* 5: 149–155.

Hatcher, B. G. 1997. Coral reef ecosystems: How much greater is the whole than the sum of the parts. *Coral Reefs* 16 (Suppl.): S77–S91.

Hatcher, B. G., R. E. Johannes and A. I. Robertson. 1989. Review of research relevant to the conservation of shallow tropical marine ecosystems. *Oceanogr. Mar. Biol. Annu. Rev.* 27: 337–414.

Hay, M. E. 1984. Patterns of fish and urchin grazing on Caribbean reefs: Are previous results typical? *Ecology* 65: 446–454.

Hay, M. E. 1997. The ecology and evolution of seaweed–herbivore interactions on coral reefs. *Coral Reefs* 16 (Suppl.): S67–S76.

Herre, E. A., N. Knowlton, U. G. Mueller and S. A. Rehner. 1999. The evolution of mutualisms: Exploring the paths between conflict and cooperation. *Trends Ecol. Evol.* 14: 49–53.

Highsmith, R. C. 1980. Geographic patterns of coral bioerosion: A productivity hypothesis. *J. Exp. Mar. Biol. Ecol.* 46: 177–196.

Highsmith, R. C. 1982. Reproduction by fragmentation in corals. *Mar. Ecol. Prog. Ser.* 7: 207–226.

Hill, M. S. 1998. Spongivory on Caribbean reefs releases corals from competition with sponges. *Oecologia* 117: 143–150.

Hixon, M. A. 1997. Effects of reef fishes on corals and algae. In C. Birkeland (ed.), *Life and Death of Coral Reefs*, pp. 230–248. Chapman & Hall, New York.

Hubbard, D. K. 1988. Controls of fossil and modern reef development: Common ground for biological and geological research. *Proc. 6th Int. Coral Reef Symp.* 1: 243–252.

Hubbard, D. K. 1997. Reefs as dynamic systems. In C. Birkeland (ed.), *Life and Death of Coral Reefs*, pp. 43–67. Chapman & Hall, New York.

Hubbell, S. P. 1997. A unified theory of biogeography and relative species abundance and its application to tropical rain forests and coral reefs. *Coral Reefs* 16 (Suppl.): S9–S22.

Hughes, D. J. and J. B. C. Jackson. 1992. Distribution and abundance of cheilostome bryozoans on the Caribbean reefs of central Panama. *Bull. Mar. Sci.* 51: 443–465.

Hughes, T. P. 1985. Life histories and population dynamics of early successional corals. *Proc. 5th Int. Coral Reef Symp.* 5:101–106.

Hughes, T. P. 1990. Recruitment limitation, mortality and population regulation in open systems: A case study. *Ecology* 71: 12–20.

Hughes, T. P. 1994. Catastrophes, phase shifts, and large-scale degradation of a Caribbean coral reef. *Science* 265: 1547–1551.

Hughes, T. P. 1996. Demographic approaches to community dynamics: A coral reef example. *Ecology* 77: 2256–2260.

Hughes, T. P. and J. H. Connell. 1987. Population dynamics based on size or age? A reef-coral analysis. *Amer. Nat.* 129: 818–829.

Hughes, T. P. and J. H. Connell. 1999. Multiple stressors on coral reefs: A long-term perspective. *Limnol. Oceanogr.* 44: 932–940.

Hughes, T. P. and J. B. C. Jackson. 1985. Population dynamics and life histories of foliaceous corals. *Ecol. Monogr.* 55:141–166.

Hughes, T. P. and J. E. Tanner. 2000. Recruitment failure, life histories, and long-term decline of Caribbean corals. *Ecology* 81: 2250–2263.

Hughes, T. P., A. H. Baird, E. A. Dinsdale, N. A. Moltschaniwskyj, M. S. Pratchett, J. E. Tanner and B. L. Willis. 1999. Patterns of recruitment and abundance of corals along the Great Barrier Reef. *Nature* 397: 59–63.

Hughes, T. P., A. H. Baird, E. A. Dinsdale, N. A. Moltschaniwskyj, M. S. Pratchett, J. E. Tanner and B. L. Willis. 2000. Supply-side ecology works both ways: The link between benthic adults, fecundity and larval recruits. *Ecology* 81: 2241–2249.

Hughes, T. P., A. M. Szmant, R. Steneck, R. Carpenter and S. Miller. 1999. Algal blooms on coral reefs: What are the causes? *Limnol. Oceanogr.* 44: 1583–1586.

Jablonski, D. and J. J. Sepkoski Jr. 1996. Paleobiology, community ecology and scales of ecological pattern. *Ecology* 77: 1367–1378.

Jackson, J. B. C. 1977. Competition on marine hard substrata: The adaptive significance of solitary and colonial strategies. *Amer. Natur.* 111: 743–767.

Jackson, J. B. C. 1979. Overgrowth competition between encrusting cheilostome ectoprocts in a Jamaican cryptic reef environment. *J. Anim. Ecol.* 48: 805–823.

Jackson, J. B. C. 1983. Biological determinants of present and past sessile animal distributions. In M. Tevesz and P. W. McCall (eds.), *Biotic Interactions in Recent and Fossil Benthic Communities*, pp. 39–120. Plenum Press, New York.

Jackson, J. B. C. 1986. Modes of dispersal of clonal benthic invertebrates: Consequences for species' distributions and genetic structure of local populations. *Bull. Mar. Sci.* 39: 588–606.

Jackson, J. B. C. 1991. Adaptation and diversity of reef corals. *BioScience* 41: 475–482.

Jackson, J. B. C. 1992. Pleistocene perspectives on coral reef community structure. *Amer. Zool.* 32: 719–731.

Jackson, J. B. C. 1994a. Community unity? *Science* 264: 1412–1413.

Jackson, J. B. C. 1994b. Constancy and change of life in the sea. *Philos. Trans. R. Soc. B* 344: 55–60.

Jackson, J. B. C. 1995. The role of science in coral reef conservation and management. In *Partnership Building and Framework Development: Report of the ICRI Workshop*, pp. 5–9. Dumaguete City, Philippines.

Jackson, J. B. C. 1997. Reefs since Columbus. *Coral Reefs* 16 (Suppl.): S23–S32.

Jackson, J. B. C. In press. What was natural in the oceans? *Proc. Natl. Acad. Sci. USA.*

Jackson, J. B. C. and L. W. Buss. 1975. Allelopathy and spatial competition among coral reef invertebrates. *Proc. Natl. Acad. Sci.* 72: 5160–5163.

Jackson, J. B. C. and A. G. Coates. 1985. Life cycles and evolution of clonal (modular) animals. *Philos. Trans. R. Soc. Lond. B* 313: 7–22.

Jackson, J. B. C. and T. P. Hughes. 1985. Adaptive strategies of coral-reef invertebrates. *Amer. Sci.* 73: 265–274.

Jackson, J. B. C. and K. W. Kaufmann. 1987. *Diadema antillarum* was not a keystone predator in cryptic reef environments. *Science* 235: 687–689.

Jackson, J. B. C. and J. E. Winston. 1982. Ecology of cryptic coral reef communities. I. Distribution and abundance of major groups of encrusting organisms. *J. Exp. Mar. Biol. Ecol.* 57: 135–147.

Jackson, J. B. C. and 17 others. 1989. Ecological effects of a major oil spill on Panamanian coastal marine communities. *Science* 243: 37–44.

James, N. P. 1984. Reefs. In P. A. Scholle et al. (eds.), *Carbonate Depositional Environments*, pp. 345–440. American Association of Petroleum Geologists Memoir 33.

Johnson, C. (ed.). 1992. *Crown-of-Thorns Starfish on the Great Barrier Reef: Reproduction, Recruitment and Hydrodynamics*. CSIRO, Australia.

Johnson, C., D. Klumpp, J. Field and R. Bradbury. 1995. Carbon flux on coral reefs: Effects of large shifts in community structure. *Mar. Ecol. Prog. Ser.* 126: 123–143.

Jokiel, P. L. 1984. Long distance dispersal of reef corals by rafting. *Coral Reefs* 3: 113–116.

Jokiel, P. L., C. L. Hunter, S. Taguchi and L. Watarai. 1993. Ecological impact of a freshwater "reef kill" in Kaneohe Bay, Oahu, Hawaii. *Coral Reefs* 12: 177–184.

Jones, G. P. 1991. Postrecruitment processes in the ecology of coral reef fish populations: A multifactorial perspective. In P. F. Sale (ed.), *The Ecology of Fishes on Coral Reefs*, pp. 294–328. Academic Press, San Diego.

Jones, G. P., M. J. Milicich, M. J. Emslie and C. Lunow. 1999. Self-recruitment in a coral reef fish population. *Nature* 402: 802–804.

Karlson, R. H. 1986. Disturbance, colonial fragmentation, and size-dependent life history variation in two coral reef cnidarians. *Mar. Ecol. Prog. Ser.* 28: 245–249.

Karlson, R. H. and L. E. Hurd. 1993. Disturbance, coral reef communities, and changing ecological paradigms. *Coral Reefs* 12: 117–125.

Karlson, R. H. and H. V. Cornell. 1998. Scale-dependent variation in local vs. regional effects on coral species richness. *Ecol. Monogr.* 68: 259–274.

Kaufman, L. 1977. The threespot damselfish: Effects on benthic biota of Caribbean coral reefs. *Proc. 3rd Int. Coral Reef Symp.* 1: 559–564.

Keesing, J. K., R. H. Bradbury, L. M. DeVantier, M. J. Riddle and G. De'ath. 1992. Geological evidence for recurring outbreaks of the crown-of-thorns starfish: A reassessment from an ecological perspective. *Coral Reefs* 11: 79–85.

Kinsey, D. W. 1988. Coral reef system response to some natural and anthropogenic stresses. *Galaxea* 7: 113–128.

Kinsey, D. W. 1991. The coral reef: An owner-built, high-density, fully-serviced, self-sufficient housing estate in the desert—or is it? *Symbiosis* 10: 1–22.

Kinzie, R. A., III. 1973. The zonation of West Indian gorgonians. *Bull. Mar. Sci.* 23: 93–155.

Knowlton, N. 1992. Thresholds and multiple stable states in coral reef community dynamics. *Amer. Zool.* 32: 674–682.

Knowlton, N. 1993. Sibling species in the sea. *Annu. Rev. Ecol. Syst.* 24: 189–216.

Knowlton, N. 1997. Hard decisions and hard science: Research needs for coral reef management. In M. E. Hatziolos, A. J. Hooten and M. Fodor (eds.), *Coral Reefs: Challenges and Opportunities for Sustainable Management*, pp. 183–187. World Bank, Washington, DC.

Knowlton, N. 2000. Molecular genetic analyses of species boundaries in the sea. *Hydrobiologia* 420: 73–90.

Knowlton, N. and J. B. C. Jackson. 1993. Inbreeding and outbreeding in marine invertebrates. In N. W. Thornhill (ed.), *The Natural History of Inbreeding and Outbreeding: Theoretical and Empirical Perspectives*, pp. 200–249. University of Chicago Press, Chicago.

Knowlton, N. and J. B. C. Jackson. 1994. New taxonomy and niche partitioning on coral reefs: Jack of all trades or master of some? *Trends Ecol. Evol.* 9: 7–9.

Knowlton, N., J. C. Lang, M. C. Rooney and P. Clifford. 1981. Evidence for delayed mortality in hurricane-damaged Jamaican staghorn corals. *Nature* 294: 251–252.

Knowlton, N., J. C. Lang and B. D. Keller. 1990. Case study of natural population collapse: Post-hurricane predation on Jamaican staghorn corals. *Smithson. Contr. Mar. Sci.* 31: 1–25.

Kobluk, D. R., R. J. Cuffey, S. S. Fonda and M. A. Lysenko. 1988. Cryptic Bryozoa, leeward fringing reef of Bonaire, Netherlands Antilles, and their paleoecological significance. *J. Paleontol.* 62: 427–439.

Kramarsky-Winter, E. and Y. Loya. 1996. Regeneration versus budding in fungiid corals: A trade-off. *Mar. Ecol. Prog. Ser.* 134: 179–185.

Kramarsky-Winter, E., M. Fine and Y. Loya. 1997. Coral polyp expulsion. *Nature* 387: 137.

Lang, J. C. 1973. Interspecific aggression by scleractinian corals. II. Why the race is not always to the swift. *Bull. Mar. Sci.* 23: 260–279.

Lang, J. C. and E. A. Chornesky. 1990. Competition between scleractinian reef corals: A review of mechanisms and effects. In Z. Dubinsky (ed.), *Coral Reefs*, pp. 209–252. *Ecosystems of the World* Vol. 25. Elsevier, Amsterdam.

Leis, J. M. 1991. The pelagic stage of reef fishes: The larval biology of coral reef fishes. In P. F. Sale (ed.), *The Ecology of Fishes on Coral Reefs*, pp. 183–230. Academic Press, San Diego.

Lessios, H. A. 1988. Mass mortality of *Diadema antillarum* in the Caribbean: What have we learned? *Annu. Rev. Ecol. Syst.* 19: 371–393.

Lessios, H. A. 1995. *Diadema antillarum* 10 years after mass mortality: Still rare, despite help from a competitor. *Proc. R. Soc. Lond.* B 259: 331–337.

Levitan, D. R. 1989. Density-dependent size regulation in *Diadema antillarum*: Effects on fecundity and survivorship. *Ecology* 70: 1414–1424.

Levitan, D. R. 1991. Influence of body size and population density on fertilization success and reproductive output in a free-spawning invertebrate. *Biol. Bull.* 181: 261–268.

Levitan, D. R. 1998. Sperm limitation, gamete competition, and sexual selection in external fertilizers. In T. R. Birkehead and A. P. Moller (eds.), *Sperm Competition and Sexual Selection*, pp. 175–217. Academic Press, San Diego.

Lewis, J. B. 1960. The coral reefs and coral communities of Barbados, W.I. *Canad. J. Zool.* 38: 1133–1145.

Lewis, J. B. 1984. The *Acropora* inheritance: A reinterpretation of the development of fringing reefs in Barbados, West Indies. *Coral Reefs* 3: 117–122.

Liberman, T., A. Genin and Y. Loya. 1995. Effects of growth and reproduction of the coral *Stylophora pistillata* by the mutualistic damselfish *Dascyllus marginatus*. *Mar. Biol.* 121: 741–746.

Liddell, W. D. and S. L. Ohlhurst. 1992. Ten years of disturbance and change on a Jamaican fringing reef. *Proc. 7th Int. Coral Reef Symp.* 1: 144–150.

Lidgard, S. and J. B. C. Jackson. 1989. Growth in encrusting cheilostome bryozoans. I. Evolutionary trends. *Paleobiology* 15: 255–282.

Littler, M. M. and D. S. Littler. 1984. Models of tropical reef biogenesis: The contribution of algae. *Prog. Phycol. Res.* 3: 323–364.

Loya, Y. 1972. Community structure and species diversity of hermatypic corals at Eilat, Red Sea. *Mar. Biol.* 13: 100–123.

MacCall, A. D. 1996. Patterns of low-frequency variability in fish populations of the California Current. *Cal. Coop. Oceanic Fish. Invest. Rep.* 37: 100–110.

Macintyre, I. G. and P. W. Glynn. 1976. Evolution of modern Caribbean fringing reef, Galeta Point, Panama. *Amer. Assoc. Petrol. Geol. Bull.* 60: 1054–1071.

McCallum, H. 1992. Completing the circle: Stock–recruitment relationships and *Acanthaster*. In C. Johnson (ed.), *Crown-of-Thorns Starfish on the Great Barrier Reef: Reproduction, Recruitment, and Hydrodynamics*, pp. 653–662. CSIRO, Australia.

McClanahan, T. R. and N. A. Muthiga. 1998. An ecological shift in a remote coral atoll of Belize over 25 years. *Environ. Conserv.* 25: 122–130.

McClanahan, T. R., A. T. Kamukuru, N. A. Muthiga, M. Gilagabher Yebio and D. Obura. 1996. Effect of sea urchin reductions on algae, coral and fish populations. *Conserv. Biol.* 10: 136–154.

McClanahan, T. R. and S. H. Shafir. 1990. Causes and consequences of sea urchin abundance and diversity in Kenyan coral reef lagoons. *Oecologia* 83: 362–370.

McField, M. D. 1999. Coral response during and after mass bleaching in Belize. *Bull. Mar. Sci.* 64: 155–172.

McGowan, J. A., D. R. Cayan and L. M. Dorman. 1998. Climate-ocean variability and ecosystem response in the northeast Pacific. *Science* 281: 210–217.

McKinney, F. K. and J. B. C. Jackson. 1988. *Bryozoan Evolution*. Unwin Hyman, Boston.

Meyer, J. L., E. T. Schultz and G. S. Helfman. 1983. Fish schools: An asset to corals. *Science* 220: 1047–1049.

Meylan, A. 1988. Spongivory in hawksbill turtles: A diet of glass. *Science* 239: 393–395.

Miller, M. W. and M. E. Hay. 1998. Effects of fish predation and seaweed competition on the survival and growth of corals. *Oecologia* 113: 231–238.

Miller, M. W., M. E. Hay, S. L. Miller, D. Malone, E. E. Sotka, and A. M. Szmant. 1999. Effects of nutrients versus herbivory on reef algae: A new method for manipulating nutrients on coral reefs. *Limnol Oceanogr.* 44: 1847–1861.

Mladenov, P. V. 1996. Environmental factors influencing asexual reproductive processes in echinoderms. *Oceanol. Acta* 19: 227–235.

Moran, P. J. 1986. The *Acanthaster* phenomenon. *Oceanogr. Mar. Biol. Ann. Rev.* 24: 379–480.

Morrison, D. 1988. Comparing fish and urchin grazing in shallow and deeper coral reef algal communities. *Ecology* 69: 1367–1382.

Morse, A. N. C. and D. E. Morse. 1996. Flypapers for coral and other planktonic larvae. *BioScience* 46: 254–262.

Morse, A. N. C., K. Iwao, M. Baba, K. Shimoike, T. Hayashibara and M. Omori. 1996. An ancient chemosensory mechanism brings new life to coral reefs. *Biol. Bull.* 191: 149–154.

Morse, D. E., N. Hooker, A. N. C. Morse and R. A. Jensen. 1988. Control of larval metamorphosis and recruitment in sympatric agariciid corals. *J. Exp. Mar. Biol. Ecol.* 116: 193–217.

Muller-Parker, G. and C. F. D'Elia. 1997. Interactions between corals and their symbiotic algae. In C. Birkeland (ed.), *Life and Death of Coral Reefs*, pp. 96–113. Chapman & Hall, New York.

Mumby, P. J. 1999. Can Caribbean coral populations be modelled at metapopulation scales? *Mar. Ecol. Prog. Ser.* 180: 275–288.

Mumby, P. J. and A. R. Harborne. 1999. Development of a systematic classification scheme of mapping habitats to facilitate regional management and mapping of Caribbean coral reefs. *Biol. Conserv.* 88: 155–163.

Munro, J. L. (ed.). 1983. *Caribbean Coral Reef Fisheries*, 2nd ed. ICLARM Stud. Rev. 7: 1–276.

Muscatine, L. 1990. The role of symbiotic algae in carbon and energy flux in reef corals. In Z. Dubinsky (ed.), *Coral Reefs*, pp. 75–87. *Ecosystems of the World* Vol. 25. Elsevier, Amsterdam.

Ogden, J. C. 1997. Ecosystem interactions in the tropical coastal seascape. In C. Birkeland (ed.), *Life and Death of Coral Reefs*, pp. 288–297. Chapman & Hall, New York.

Oliver, J. and R. Babcock. 1992. Aspects of the fertilization ecology of broadcast spawning corals: Sperm dilution effects and in situ measurements of fertilization. *Biol. Bull.* 183: 409–417.

Oliver, J. K. and B. L. Willis. 1987. Coral-spawn slicks in the Great Barrier Reef (Australia): Preliminary observations. *Mar. Biol.* 94: 521–530.

Olson, R. R. 1985. The consequences of short-distance larval dispersal in a sessile marine invertebrate. *Ecology* 66: 30–39.

Oren, U., I. Brickner and Y. Loya. 1998. Prudent sessile feeding by the corallivore snail *Coralliophila violacea* on coral energy sinks. *Proc. R. Soc. Lond.* B 265: 2043–2050.

Oviedo, G. F. de. 1526. *Sumario de la Historia Natural de las Indias*. Reprinted 1950, Biblioteca Americana, Fondo de Cultura Economica, Mexico.

Paine, R. T. and S. Levin. 1981. Intertidal landscapes: Disturbance and the dynamics of pattern. *Ecol. Monogr.* 51: 145–178.

Paine, R. T., M. J. Tegner and E. A. Johnson. 1998. Compounded perturbations yield ecological surprises. *Ecosystems* 1: 535–545.

Palumbi, S. R. and J. B. C. Jackson. 1982. Ecology of cryptic coral reef communities. II. Recovery from small disturbance events by encrusting Bryozoa: The influence of "host" species and lesion size. *J. Exp. Mar. Biol. Ecol.* 64: 103–115.

Palumbi, S. R. and J. B. C. Jackson. 1983. Aging in modular organisms: Ecology of zooid senescence in *Steginoporella* sp. (Bryozoa: Cheilostomata). *Biol. Bull.* 164: 267–278.

Pandolfi, J. M. 1992. A palaeobiological examination of the geological evidence for recurring outbreaks of the crown-of-thorns starfish, *Acanthaster planci*. *Coral Reefs* 11: 87–93.

Pandolfi, J. M. 1996. Limited membership in Pleistocene reef coral assemblages from the Huon Peninsula, Papua, New Guinea: Constancy during global change. *Paleobiology* 22: 152–176.

Pandolfi, J. M. 1999. Response of Pleistocene coral reefs to environmental change over long temporal scales. *Amer. Zool.* 39: 113–130.

Pandolfi, J. M. and J. B. C. Jackson. 1997. The maintenance of diversity on coral reefs: Examples from the fossil record. *Proc. 8th Int. Coral Reef Symp.* 1: 397–404.

Pandolfi, J. M. and J. B. C. Jackson. In press. Community structure of Pleistocene coral reefs of Curaçao, Netherlands Antilles. *Ecol. Monogr.*

Pandolfi, J. M., G. Llewellyn and J. B. C. Jackson. In press. Interpretation of ancient reef environments in paleoecological studies of community structure. *Coral Reefs.*

Paulay, G. 1997. Diversity and distribution of reef organisms. In C. Birkeland (ed.), *Life and Death of Coral Reefs*, pp. 298–353. Chapman & Hall, New York.

Pauly, C., V. Christensen, J. Dalsgaard, R. Froese and F. Torres Jr. 1998. Fishing down marine food webs. *Science* 279: 860–863.

Pawlik, J. R. 1998. Coral reef sponges: Do predatory fishes affect their distribution? *Limnol. Oceanogr.* 43: 1396–1399.

Pennings, S. C. 1997. Indirect interactions on coral reefs. In C. Birkeland (ed.), *Life and Death of Coral Reefs*, pp. 249–272. Chapman & Hall, New York.

Peters, E. C. 1997. Diseases of coral-reef organisms. In C. Birkeland (ed.), *Life and Death of Coral Reefs*, pp. 114–139. Chapman & Hall, New York.

Porter, J. W., J. D. Woodley, G. J. Smith, J. E. Neigel, J. F. Battey and D. G. Dallmeyer. 1981. Population trends among Jamaican reef corals. *Nature* 294: 249–250.

Porter, J. W., J. F. Battey and G. Jason Smith. 1982. Perturbation and change in coral reef communities. *Proc. Natl. Acad. Sci. USA* 79: 1678–1681.

Reaka-Kudla, M. L. 1997. The global biodiversity of coral reefs: A comparison with rain forests. In M. L. Reaka-Kudla, D. E. Wilson, and E. O. Wilson (eds.), *Biodiversity II*, pp.83–108. Joseph Henry Press, Washington, DC.

Richardson, L. L. 1998. Coral diseases: What is really known? *Trends Ecol. Evol.* 13: 438–443.

Richmond, R. H. 1997. Reproduction and recruitment in corals: Critical links in the persistence of reefs. In C. Birkeland (ed.), *Life and Death of Coral Reefs*, pp. 175–197. Chapman & Hall, New York.

Riegl, B. 1995. Effects of sand deposition on scleractinian and alcyonacean corals. *Mar. Biol.* 121: 517–526.

Rinkevich, B. and Y. Loya. 1985. Intraspecific competition in a reef coral: Effects on growth and reproduction. *Oecologia* 66: 100–105.

Robertson, D. R. 1988a. Abundances of surgeonfishes on patch-reefs in Caribbean Panama: Due to settlement, or post-settlement events? *Mar. Biol.* 97: 495–501.

Robertson, D. R. 1988b. Extreme variation in settlement of the Caribbean triggerfish *Balistes vetula* in Panama. *Copeia* 1988: 698–703.

Robertson, D. R. 1988c. Settlement and population dynamics of *Abudefduf saxatilis* on patch reefs in Caribbean Panama. *Proc. 6th Int. Coral Reef Symp.* 2: 839–843.

Robertson, D. R. 1991. Increases in surgeon fish populations after mass mortality of the sea urchin *Diadema antillarum* in Panama indicate food limitation. *Mar. Biol.* 111: 437–444.

Robertson, D. R. 1996. Interspecific competition controls abundance and habitat use of territorial Caribbean damselfishes. *Ecology* 77: 885–899.

Rogers, C. S. 1990. Responses of coral reefs and reef organisms to sedimentation. *Mar. Ecol. Prog. Ser.* 62: 185–202.

Rogers, C. S. 1993. Hurricanes and coral reefs: The intermediate disturbance hypothesis revisited. *Coral Reefs* 12: 127–137.

Ross, D. J. and P. W. Skelton. 1993. Rudist formations of the Cretaceous: A paleoecological, sedimentological and stratigraphical review. In V. P. Wright (ed.), *Sedimentology Review 1*, pp. 73–91. Blackwell Scientific Publications, Oxford.

Roughgarden, J. 1989. The structure and assembly of communities. In J. Roughgarden, R. M. May and S. A. Levin (eds.), *Perspectives in Ecological Theory*, pp. 203–226. Princeton University Press, Princeton, NJ.

Roughgarden, J., S. Gaines and H. Possingham. 1988. Recruitment dynamics in complex life cycles. *Science* 241:1460–1466.

Rowan, R. 1998. Diversity and ecology of zooxanthellae on coral reefs. *J. Phycol.* 34: 407–417.

Rowan, R., N. Knowlton, A. Baker and J. Jara. 1997. Landscape ecology of algal symbionts creates variation in episodes of coral bleaching. *Nature* 388: 265–269.

Rützler, K. and K. Muzik. 1993. *Terpios hoshinota*, a new cyanobacteriosponge threatening Pacific reefs. *Scientia Marina* 57: 395–403.

Sale, P. F. 1977. Maintenance of high diversity in coral reef fish communities. *Amer. Nat.* 111: 337–359.

Sale, P. F. (ed.). 1991a. *The Ecology of Fishes on Coral Reefs.* Academic Press, San Diego.

Sale, P. F. 1991b. Reef fish communities: Open nonequilibrium systems. In P. F. Sale (ed.), *The Ecology of Fishes on Coral Reefs*, pp. 564–598. Academic Press, San Diego.

Santavy, D. L., E. C. Peters, C. Quirolo, J. W. Porter and C. N. Bianchi. 1999. Yellow-blotch disease outbreak on reefs of the San Blas Islands, Panama. *Coral Reefs* 18: 97.

Santelices, B. 1990. Patterns of reproduction, dispersal and recruitment in seaweeds. *Oceanogr. Mar. Biol. Annu. Rev.* 28: 177–276.

Sapp, J. 1999. *What is Natural? Coral Reef Crisis.* Oxford University Press, Oxford.

Schmitt, R. J. and S. J. Holbrook. 1999. Mortality of juvenile damselfish: Implications for assessing processes that determine abundance. *Ecology* 80: 35–50.

Scoffin, T. P. 1993. The geological effects of hurricanes on coral reefs and the interpretation of storm deposits. *Coral Reefs* 12: 203–221.

Sheppard, C. 1995. The shifting baseline syndrome. *Mar. Poll. Bull.* 30: 766–767.

Shlesinger, Y., T. L. Goulet and Y. Loya. 1998. Reproductive patterns of scleractinian corals in the northern Red Sea. *Mar. Biol.* 132: 691–701.

Shulman, M. J. and E. Bermingham. 1995. Early life histories, ocean currents, and population genetics of Caribbean reef fishes. *Evolution* 49: 897–910.

Signor. P. W. and C. W. Brett. 1984. The mid-Paleozoic precursor to the Mesozoic marine revolution. *Paleobiology* 10: 229–245.

Sotka, E. E., M. E. Hay and J. D. Thomas. 1999. Host-plant specialization by a non-herbivorous amphipod: Advantages for the amphipod and costs for the seaweed. *Oecologia* 118: 471–482.

Spotte, S. 1998. "Cleaner" shrimps? *Helgolander wiss Meersunters* 52: 59–64.

Stemann, T. A. and K. G. Johnson. 1992. Coral assemblages, biofacies, and ecological zones in the mid-Holocene reef deposits of the Enriquillo valley, Dominican Republic. *Lethaia* 25: 231–241.

Steneck, R. S. 1983. Escalating herbivory and resulting adaptive trends in calcareous algal crusts. *Paleobiology* 9: 44–61.

Steneck, R. S. and M. N. Dethier. 1994. A functional group approach to the structure of algal-dominated communities. *Oikos* 69: 476–498.

Steneck, R. S. and Watling, L. 1982. Feeding capabilities and limitation of herbivorous molluscs: A functional group approach. *Mar. Biol.* 68: 299–319.

Stimson, J. 1985. The effect of shading by the table coral *Acropora hyacinthus* on understory corals. *Ecology* 66: 40–53.

Stone, L., E. Eilam, A. Abelson and M. Ilan. 1996. Modelling coral reef biodiversity and habitat destruction. *Mar. Ecol. Prog. Ser.* 134: 299–302.

Swart, P. K. and G. D. Stanley. 1989. Intraskeletal variations in the carbon and oxygen isotopic composition of a late Triassic coral *Toechastraea major*: Implications for the development of symbiotic associations in scleractinian corals. *Geol. Soc. Amer. Abstr. Prog.* 12: A111.

Swearer, S. E., J. E. Caselle, D. W. Lea and R. R. Warner. 1999. Larval retention and recruitment in an island population of a coral-reef fish. *Nature* 402: 799–802.

Sweatman, H. P. A. 1983. Influence of conspecifics on choice of settlement sites by larvae of two pomacentrid fishes (*Dascyllus aruanus* and *D. reticulatus*) on coral reefs. *Mar. Biol.* 75: 225–229.

Sweatman, H. P. A. 1985. The influence of adults of some coral reef fishes on larval recruitment. *Ecol. Monogr.* 55: 469–485.

Tanner, J. E. 1997. Interspecific competition reduces fitness in scleractinian corals. *J. Exp. Mar. Biol. Ecol.* 214: 19–34.

Tanner, J. E., T. P. Hughes and J. H. Connell. 1994. Species coexistence, keystone species, and succession: A sensitivity analysis. *Ecology* 75: 2204–2219.

Thorson, G. 1950. Reproduction and larval ecology of marine bottom invertebrates. *Biol. Rev.* 25: 1–45.

Toller, W. W., R. Rowan and N. Knowlton. In press a. Repopulation of zooxanthellae in the Caribbean corals *Montastraea annularis* and *M. faveolata* following experimental and disease-associated bleaching. *Biol. Bull.*

Toller, W. W., R. Rowan and N. Knowlton. In press b. Zooxanthellae of the *Montastraea annularis* species complex: Patterns of distribution of four taxa of *Symbiodinium* on different reefs and across depths. *Biol. Bull.*

Tomascik, T. and F. Sander. 1987. Effects of eutrophication on reef-building corals. II. Structure of scleractinian coral communities on fringing reefs, Barbados, West Indies. *Mar. Biol.* 94: 3–75.

Trench, R. K. 1987. Dinoflagellates in non-parasitic symbioses. In F. R. J. Taylor (ed.), *The Biology of Dinoflagellates*, pp. 530–570. Blackwell Scientific, Oxford.

Vasseur, P. 1974. The overhangs, tunnels and dark reef galleries of Tuléar (Madagascar) and their sessile invertebrate communities. *Proc. 2nd Int. Coral Reef Symp.* 2: 143–159.

Vermeij, G. J. 1987. *Evolution and Escalation, an Ecological History of Life.* Princeton University Press, Princeton, NJ.

Victor, B. C. 1991. Settlement strategies and biogeography of reef fishes. In P. F. Sale (ed.), *The Ecology of Fishes on Coral Reefs*, pp. 231–260. Academic Press, San Diego.

Warner, M. E., W. K. Fitt and G. W. Schmidt. 1999. Damage to photosystem II in symbiotic dinoflagellates: A determinant of coral bleaching. *Proc. Natl. Acad. Sci. USA* 96: 8007–8012.

Warner, R. R. 1984. Mating systems and hermaphroditism in coral reef fish. *Amer. Sci.* 72: 128–136.

Warner, R. R. 1997. Evolutionary ecology: How to reconcile pelagic dispersal with local adaptation. *Coral Reefs* 16 (Suppl.): S115–S120.

Westoby, M. 1998. The relationship between local and regional diversity: Comment. *Ecology* 79: 1825–1827.

Wilkinson, C. R. 1992. Coral reefs of the world are facing widespread devastation: Can we prevent this through sustainable management practices? *Proc. 7th Int. Coral Reef Symp.* 1: 11–21.

Wilkinson, C. R. and A. C. Cheshire. 1988. Cross-shelf variations in coral reef structure and function: Influences of land and ocean. *Proc. 6th Int. Coral Reef Symp.* 1: 227–233.

Williams, A. H. 1981. An analysis of competitive interactions in a patchy back-reef environment. *Ecology* 62: 1107–1120.

Williams, D. McB. 1991. Patterns and processes in the distribution of coral reef fishes. In P. F. Sale (ed.), *The Ecology of Fishes on Coral Reefs* pp. 437–474. Academic Press, San Diego.

Winston, J. E. and J. B. C. Jackson. 1984. Ecology of cryptic coral reef communities. IV. Community development and life histories of encrusting cheilostome Bryozoa. *J. Exp. Mar. Biol. Ecol.* 76: 1–21.

Wood, R. 1993. Nutrients, predation, and the history of reef-building. *Palaios* 8: 526–543.

Wood, R. 1995. The changing biology of reef-building. *Palaios* 10: 517–529.

Wood, R. 1999. *Reef Evolution.* Oxford University Press, Oxford.

Woodin, S. A. and J. B. C. Jackson. 1979. Interphyletic competition among marine benthos. *Amer. Zool.* 19: 1029–1043.

Woodley, J. D. 1992. The incidence of hurricanes on the north coast of Jamaica since 1870: Are the classic reef descriptions atypical? *Hydrobiologia* 247: 133–138.

Woodley, J. D. and 19 others. 1981. Hurricane Allen's impact on Jamaican coral reefs. *Science* 214: 749–755.

Wulff, J. L. 1991. Asexual fragmentation, genotype success, and population dynamics of erect branching sponges. *J. Exper. Mar. Biol. Ecol.* 149:227–247.

Wulff, J. L. 1997a. Mutualisms among species of coral reef sponges. *Ecology* 78: 146–159.

Wulff, J. L. 1997b. Parrotfish predation on cryptic sponges of Caribbean coral reefs. *Mar. Biol.* 129: 41–52.

Wulff, J. L. and L. W. Buss. 1979. Do sponges help hold coral reefs together? *Nature* 281: 474–475.

Yodzis, P. 1988. The indeterminacy of ecological interactions as perceived through perturbation experiments. *Ecology* 69: 508–515.

chapter *16*

Mangrove Communities

Aaron M. Ellison and Elizabeth J. Farnsworth

Mangrove forests are excellent systems in which to study ecological processes at the community and the ecosystem level. Coastal environments uniquely shape plant physiology, ecological interactions, and patterns of biological diversity, all of which in turn strongly affect dynamics of ecological communities. Occurring at the interface of land and sea, mangroves encompass elements of both terrestrial and marine environments—providing double the fun for the inquiring ecologist. Although mangroves have fascinated natural historians since the days of Theophrastus (Rollet 1981), much remains to be learned about how mangrove communities form, cycle, and exchange materials and energy and withstand and recover from disturbance. Ignored by ecotourists and maligned in literature (Steinbeck, for example, vilified them as "salt-water-eating bushes" full of "quiet, stalking murder" [1941: 123]), their relative inaccessibility has discouraged both extensive resource exploitation and intensive ecological experimentation until quite recently. A comprehensive understanding of community-level processes in mangrove forests becomes all the more critical as the need to conserve, manage, and restore these systems intensifies throughout the world. This chapter reviews facets of the ecology of mangrove communities, with particular attention to their biogeography and physiological ecology; interactions among their plant and animal associates; community-wide responses to disturbance; and the maintenance and regeneration of mangrove ecosystems in the face of anthropogenic stresses. Despite 600 years of research, our understanding of these ecosystems is still far from complete, and new phenomena remain to be discovered.

WHAT ARE MANGROVES?

Authors have used the word *mangrove* to denote both a type of plant and a type of ecosystem. For clarity here, we distin-guish the individual "mangrove" species from the wetland community ("mangal") of which it is the defining feature. Simply put, the term *mangrove* refers to any woody, tropical halophyte that is an obligate inhabitant of mangal (Tomlinson 1986). Around the globe, some 54–70 species (including hybrids) in 20–27 genera and 16–19 families fit comfortably into this broad category (the lower values according to Tomlinson [1986]; upper values according to Cronquist [1981] and Duke [1992]). Some generalist species are more challenging to classify using this definition—the Neotropical tree *Conocarpus erectus* (Combretaceae) or some of the rattan palms (*Calamus* spp.; Arecaceae), for example. These species frequently occur in mangal, but do not appear to be *restricted* to saline areas and may penetrate into freshwater swamps. Certain true mangrove species also may opportunistically occur in freshwater swamps, but this is a rare phenomenon. Mangroves vary both in their salinity tolerance and the degree to which salinity may be necessary to maintain their growth and competitive dominance—an important focus of research that we discuss later in this chapter.

BIOGEOGRAPHY OF MANGROVES

Global Distribution and Diversity

Mangroves grow throughout the tropics wherever the average monthly minimum air temperature is 20°C (Chapman 1976). The winter 20°C seawater isotherm generally limits the poleward extension of mangroves, although prevailing warm currents and a broader tolerance of environmental extremes allow the extension of *Avicennia marina* (Avicenniaceae) southward to the north island of New Zealand (Duke et al. 1998a), whereas its congener *A. germinans* ranges northward to the southern coast of Louisiana (U.S.). Overall species rich-

423

ness of mangroves declines from a peak of about 30 species (per 15° longitude) in Southeast Asia to < 5 species in the Caribbean (Figure 16.1). Explaining this anomalous (sensu Ricklefs and Latham 1993) biogeographic pattern has preoccupied biogeographers since the turn of the century (see Ellison et al. 1999 for a review).

Early researchers hypothesized that all mangrove taxa originated in the Indo-West Pacific (e.g., Schimper 1903; Aubréville 1964; Ricklefs and Latham 1993), but more recent studies have emphasized the role of continental drift and vicariant events in determining global patterns of mangrove species diversity (McCoy and Heck 1976; Duke 1995; Duke et al. 1998a; Saenger 1998; Ellison et al. 1999). These latter studies hypothesize a Cretaceous-Tertiary origin of most mangrove genera (and some modern species) on the shores of the Tethys Sea. Modern distributions are then thought to result from: in situ diversification following dispersal across the proto-Atlantic and Pacific; continental drift; the closure of the Tethys Sea and global cooling (in the late Miocene ~18 Mya); and finally, the uplift of the Panamanian Isthmus (~3 Mya), which isolated the Pacific mangrove flora from the Atlantic flora. The mangrove fossil record (reviewed in Ellison et al. 1999), biogeographic comparisons of associated fauna (McCoy and Heck 1976; Saenger 1998; Ellison et al. 1999), biochemical studies (Dodd et al. 1995; Rafii et al. 1996), and genetic analyses (Duke et al. 1998b) all support the vicariance model. Current debates focus on the direction(s) of dispersal of mangroves from the Tethys into the proto-Atlantic and Pacific regions (e.g., van Steenis 1962; Specht 1981; Mepham 1983; Duke 1995; Plaziat 1995; Saenger 1998; Ellison et al. 1999). Similar analyses have been applied to global biogeographic patterns of coral diversity (McCoy and Heck 1976; Veron 1995) and seagrass diversity (Heck and McCoy 1979; Specht 1981) with parallel results. These methods can be used to analyze global biogeographic patterns of most species assemblages.

Continental and Regional Diversity

The global patterns illustrated above (Figure 16.1) belie substantial continental and regional variation in mangrove species richness. For example, the Indo-West Pacific as a whole has 40–50 species of mangroves, of which 39 are found in Australia. Within Australia, however, species richness ranges from 25 species in northernmost Queensland to only 5–10 species in Western Australia (Duke 1992). On the western coasts of Africa and Australia, aridity (< 30 mm rainfall per month) dramatically reduces mangrove occurrences (Duke 1992; Saenger 1998), but species richness of mangroves does not vary with rainfall patterns in Central and South America (Ellison, in press). In the Neotropics, species richness is highest on the Pacific coasts of Columbia, Panama, and Costa Rica and declines with latitude (Duke et al. 1998a). Limits to waterborne dispersal of mangrove propagules likely constrain mangrove distribution within regions, but data addressing this hypothesis are sparse (Rabinowitz 1978a; Steinke 1986; Ellison 1996; Sun et al. 1998). Overall, when compared with studies of patterns of both global species richness (above) and local species distributions (below), there is a surprising lack of analysis of continental and regional-scale patterns of mangrove diversity (Duke et al. 1998a).

Local Diversity and Zonation

Within a site, individual mangrove species appear on first glance to occupy distinct and discrete zones of tree species along a presumed tidal gradient (MacNae 1968; Chapman 1976; Smith 1992). Certain species are noted to occupy the seaward fringes of swamps, whereas others occur more commonly in the upland reaches, albeit with considerable overlap (Watson 1928; Smith 1992). Such zonation has been variously attributed to: interspecific differences in tolerance of edaphic factors that co-vary with tidal elevation (Watson 1928; MacNae 1968; Ellison and Farnsworth 1993; McKee 1993, 1995); sorting of dispersed propagules during stranding (Rabinowitz 1978b); interspecific competition (Ball 1980); and frequency-dependent preferences of seed predators (Smith 1987; Smith et al. 1989; but see Sousa and Mitchell 1999). However, the identity and taxonomic affiliation of these species shifts between locales in the Neo- and Paleotropics (e.g., different *Avicennia* species occur low in the intertidal in Australasian mangal, but high in the intertidal of Caribbean mangal). In a critical review of available data bearing on hypotheses controlling mangrove zonation, Smith (1992) says that "there appear to be many papers which give specific examples of mangrove zonation and few papers which provide rigorous experimental tests of the hypotheses which attempt to explain why mangrove zonation occurs." Recent experimental work (cited above) provides conflicting results and

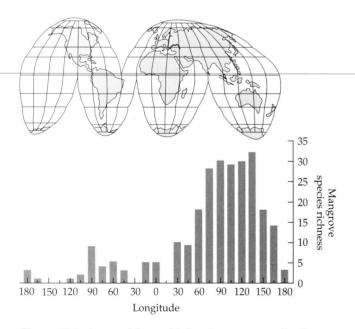

Figure 16.1 A map of the world showing mangrove distribution, adapted from Tomlinson 1986, as well as gradients of species richness illustrating the biodiversity anomaly.

does not yet allow for generalizations about the existence of zonation and the ecological mechanisms maintaining such zonation.

Other intertidal communities have provided fertile ground for testing hypotheses of species zonation (e.g., Connell 1961; Bertness and Ellison 1987) and developing statistical tests for zonation (Pielou 1977; Underwood 1978; Dale 1988), but species zonation in mangal rarely has been quantified. Recent statistical analyses have failed to detect significant, repeatable patterns of discrete zonation in Australian riverine mangal (Bunt 1996) or the Sundarbans of India (Ellison et al. 2000). Because different mangrove species vary in their tolerances to underlying edaphic gradients, considerable overlap among species occurs, and discrete zones are difficult to identify. Rather than focusing on the description of discrete vegetation zones in mangal, investigators should focus on the variation of patterns of species co-occurrence across tidal gradients (Ball 1998). Experimental work demonstrates that, as in other coastal communities, multiple physiological (Ball 1998) and biotic factors (McKee 1995) *in combination* influence recruitment of mangrove seedlings into the adult canopy and their patterns of occurrence within mangal. Patterns of and processes controlling mangrove distributions at local scales warrant careful and critical re-appraisal (Duke et al. 1998a), especially as we begin to characterize mangal at ever-larger scales using remote-sensing and other technologies for spatial analysis and community classification (Blasco et al. 1998). Furthermore, the role of human land-use history (e.g., selective harvesting and alteration of substrate) in determining mangrove profiles has been all but ignored in the majority of studies that take place in apparently pristine or protected mangrove swamps; realistic ecological paradigms must incorporate this ubiquitous force on communities.

CONVERGENT PROPERTIES OF MANGROVES AND MANGAL

When we think of "mangroves," we typically envision peculiar trees with tangled prop roots that spend much of their time inundated by tides. However, mangroves assume a variety of life forms reflecting the diversity of their origins: palms, shrubs, and ferns are all represented in mangal. Likewise, mangals exhibit a range of physiognomies that reflect the dynamic geomorphology, storm frequency, and nutrient status of the substrate that they inhabit: from squat, scrubby stands on exposed, hypersaline carbonate flats to 40-meter-tall gallery forests lining the rich alluvium of river mouths (Figure 16.2; Lugo and Snedaker 1974; Twilley 1995; Feller 1996; Lugo 1997). Even single mangrove species can display an impressive range of appearances depending on the edaphic and biotic conditions in which they are found.

Across this diversity in phenotypes and species, mangroves share certain notable commonalities in physiology, architecture, and life history that appear to reflect convergent "solutions" to evolutionary "challenges." Such characters have important implications for mangrove community inter-

actions and may lead to convergences in ecosystem-level properties. For example, physiological traits can affect local, regional, and global patterns of distribution; plant-plant and plant-animal interactions may be mediated by architecture; and plant life-histories can determine the timing and effectiveness of responses to disturbance. Mangroves afford such a species-rich model system in which to identify and study convergent (pleisiomorphic) traits. It is tempting to interpret many shared mangrove characters as "adaptive." However, as others have admonished in the evolutionary literature (Gould and Lewontin 1979; Harvey and Pagel 1991), we caution that such traits must be evaluated critically with respect to their benefits and costs to fitness, their pleiotropic interactions with other traits, and the phylogenetic constraints under which they may have evolved.

Physiological Convergence

Within and among mangrove species, subtle physiological adjustments regulate responses to salinity, bright tropical sun, variable and often low nutrient availability, flooding, soil anoxia, and tidal action. All of these responses further influence community- and ecosystem-level processes in mangal.

RESPONSES TO SALINITY. Despite living in a saline environment, mangroves require fresh water. In order to obtain the fresh water required for growth, mangroves must maintain a tissue water potential below the osmotic potential of the very salty substrate (Naidoo 1985; Sperry et al. 1988; Sternberg et al. 1991). Ball (1996) provides a comprehensive recent review of many of the mechanisms by which mangroves achieve such a balance. All mangrove species exclude most of the sodium chloride and other dissolved salts in sea and soil interstitial water at the roots via a poorly understood ultrafiltration process (Scholander et al. 1962; Scholander 1968), even as transpiration rates increase (Ball 1988). Typical of other halophytes, mangroves accumulate what sodium and chloride ions do enter the transpiration stream in leaf vacuoles (where they are sequestered away from sensitive metabolic centers in the cell) and also may synthesize compatible solutes in other cellular compartments to maintain osmotic equilibrium (Popp et al. 1993). Some mangrove species possess salt glands in the leaves from which they excrete excess sodium (Dschida et al. 1992; Fitzgerald et al. 1992). Those without glands can accommodate rising sodium concentrations by exchange with potassium ions (Werner and Stelzer 1990), cell expansion (leaf growth), and increased leaf succulence (Camilleri and Ribi 1983; Ball 1996; see also Feller 1996 on leaf schleromorphy as an adjustment to nutrient availability). Anatomical differences in leaves may also be accompanied by differences in xylem anatomy—especially shorter and thicker vessels—that resist cavitation and embolism under very negative water potentials (Sperry et al. 1988). The solute content of leaves, together with other water-conserving foliar characteristics like succulence, pubescence, and the presence of a thick cuticle, may in part select for specializations on the part of insect folivores that result in niche-parti-

Figure 16.2 Mangrove communities throughout the world. Clockwise from top left: *Ceriops* mangal in a semi-arid environment (Australian Institute of Marine Sciences, Townsville, Australia); *Xylocarpus* stand in the very wet forests of Kosrae, Federated States of Micronesia; *Rhizophora* thicket on bare lava (Galápagos Islands, Ecuador); Managed stand of *Rhizophora apiculata* (Matang, Malasyia); Boardwalk through the *Sonneratia* fringe of Bako National Park (Sarawak); *Rhizophora* fringe with the endemic *Heritiera fomes* emerging from the canopy (Sundarbans Biosphere Reserve, India). The crab in the center is *Scylla serrata*. All photographs by the authors.

tioning among mangrove species (Murphy 1990; Farnsworth and Ellison 1991; Veenakumari et al. 1997).

PHOTOSYNTHESIS AND WATER-USE EFFICIENCY. Studies across six genera (*Aegiceras, Avicennia, Bruguiera, Ceriops, Rhizophora,* and *Sonneratia*) illustrate that mangroves also tend to exhibit high water-use efficiency, as stomatal conductance remains low even as moderate photosynthetic rates are achieved (Ball 1988; Clough and Sim 1989; Cheeseman 1994). High water-use efficiency enables mangroves to transpire, to withdraw water very slowly from the soil, and hence to slow a buildup of salt around the roots (Ball and Passioura 1993). Mangroves also can flexibly increase water-use efficiency when exposed to increased soil salinities (Ball 1996) and elevated atmospheric carbon dioxide (Ball et al. 1997; Farnsworth et al. 1996). The conservative photosynthetic rates exhibited by mangroves tend to saturate at relatively low light levels (< 1000 μmol m^{-2} s^{-1}), given the high irradiance characteristic of exposed, tropical coasts (> 2000 μmol m^{-2} s^{-1}). Mangrove leaves must therefore accommodate an excessive light load whose excitation energy can readily damage photosystems. Mangroves may dissipate this energy and avoid photoinhibition by producing protective xanthophyll pigments in sun leaves (Lovelock and Clough 1992) and UV-absorbing phenolics (Lovelock et al. 1992) at the cost of reduced efficiency of quantum yield at low irradiance (Björkmann et al. 1988; Farnsworth and Ellison 1996b). Allocation to pigments and other secondary compounds may entail a nitrogen cost and alter the palatability of leaves to consumers and detritivores—an idea that has not yet been explored.

Mangroves can also adjust leaf display angle, leaf size, specific leaf area, leaf turnover rates, and whole-plant deployment of leaves to evade high light and elevated leaf temperatures (Ball 1996; Farnsworth and Ellison 1996b). Thus, light, salinity, and high temperatures act synergistically on foliar architecture, chemistry, and physiology—characters that themselves change as both leaves and whole mangrove plants age (Farnsworth and Ellison 1996b). Although mangrove leaves may look superficially homogeneous, there is considerable heterogeneity within and among individuals and species that have implications for carbon gain, evapotranspiration, and leaf processing by consumers at the system level.

PHYTOHORMONES AND VIVIPARY. Although some aspects of mangrove physiology have been well studied, little is yet known about how plant hormones regulate mangrove responses to stresses such as salinity. Changes in phytohormone action may figure importantly in the evolution of mangrove traits such as viviparous reproduction (Farnsworth and Farrant 1998) and prolonged floating of propagules during dispersal (Smith et al. 1996). Precocious seed germination (in which the embryo never enters physiological dormancy) and its extreme variant, viviparous reproduction (in which there is translocation of maternal resources to a constantly growing embryo) are unusual traits among angiosperms in general, but have arisen in nine genera of six families of mangroves.

Comparisons with other nondormant wetland plants and with viviparous mutants suggests a common physiological basis for this phenomenon, namely reduced production of abscisic acid and stress proteins that are involved both in the enforcement of dormancy in the developing embryo and the adjustment of the maternal plant to osmotic stress (Farrant et al. 1996; Farnsworth and Farrant 1998). The physiology of vivipary remains a fruitful area for further study, and mangroves constitute an excellent model system for comparative study of seed ontogeny in general. The fitness advantages of this apparent convergence have been articulated in the literature since the early 1900s (reviewed by Farnsworth 1997), but there are attendant maternal costs with investing energy in producing numerous propagules that are highly apparent to herbivores and that can remain on the parent tree for up to a year (Pannier 1962; Farnsworth and Ellison 1997a).

ROOTS. In the underlying peats and mucks, mangrove roots encounter saturated, anoxic, and saline soils, making nutrient and water extraction difficult for the plant. Many mangroves possess wildly elaborated root systems, including knees, pneumatophores, stilt roots and plank roots that are studded with lenticels (air pores) and consist largely of aerenchyma. These systems permit passive diffusion of oxygen from the atmosphere and boundary layer into root tissues during low tides (Curran 1985). Simultaneously, however, roots leaking oxygen oxidize the soil surrounding them (Thibodeau and Nickerson 1986). The impact of localized soil oxidation on microbial ecology and nutrient availability for different mangrove species deserves further study (Sherman et al. 1998). Mangrove roots also afford habitat for burrowing intertidal organisms, especially crabs, which in turn oxygenate and nutrify soils (Smith et al. 1991), and for fouling epibenthic species that may have important impacts on the host plants (Farnsworth and Ellison 1996b; see "Animal-Plant Interactions in Mangal," following).

Architectural and Physiognomic Convergence

The virtually impenetrable thicket of aerial roots may be one of the most distinctive features of mangroves, but they share other architectural attributes as well. Tomlinson (1986) observed that many mangrove species seem to converge on Attim's or Petit's architectural models of plant form (sensu Hallé et al. 1995), in which a single monopodial trunk gives rise to equivalent branches initiated at fixed angles. Many mangroves loosely resemble a candelabra, in which clusters of leaves are held far from each other at the tips of twigs. Hence, even in dense forest stands some dappled light reaches the understory (by our measurements ~10% of full sun on average), and a mangrove forest is rarely "dark" compared to other tropical forests (cf. Chazdon and Fetcher 1984). The mangrove light environment is made more complex by water reflectivity and diffraction, which complicate unidimensional models of light capture.

Despite their adherence to a few, relatively simple baüplans, mangroves can be quite plastic in form. Hypersaline or drought-stressed areas tend to support sparse assemblages of scrubby trees that are short, brittle, and exceedingly slow-growing relative to trees growing in riverine or basin mangals (Figure 16.2). Lugo and Snedaker (1974) recognized no less than six mangal typologies in the Neotropics alone, which arise at least in part from the geomorphological milieu in which the trees occur and from differential limitation of nutrients, especially phosphorus (Feller 1995). Primary productivity, hydrology, litter turnover, responses to stress, and the species composition of faunal associates all vary among these contrasting physiognomic types (Lugo and Snedaker 1974; Lin and Sternberg 1992; Twilley 1995), factors that must be accounted for when modeling ecosystem properties at a landscape scale. Geomorphological processes such as erosion and sedimentation regimes can significantly influence growth rates and productivity of mangroves, even where species composition and physiognomy appear superficially similar (Ellison and Farnsworth 1996b).

Community-Level Similarities among Mangals

THE MANGROVE UNDERSTORY. The apparent lack of a layer of understory plants in mangal has stimulated considerable discussion (Janzen 1985; Corlett 1986; Lugo 1986; Snedaker and Lahmann 1988). With the exception of transient carpets of mangrove seedlings produced in seasonal reproductive flushes (Ellison and Farnsworth 1993), the understory generally lacks the shrubs, vines, and other mid-size plants that typically stratify more diverse upland tropical forests. Janzen (1985), working in the Neotropics, suggested that the filtered light of the understory is insufficient to support growth of many non-mangrove species that are simultaneously contending with edaphic stress—a hypothesis elaborated on by Lugo (1986) and Snedaker and Lahmann (1988) that remains largely untested in the field. Observations of paleotropical mangal, however, reveal a richer collection of understory species (Corlett 1986), although Snedaker and Lahmann (1988) considered these data to reflect high levels of disturbance within the studied mangal. Additionally, the pantropical fern *Achrostichum aureum* can monopolize the ground level in mangal, dramatically altering patterns of mangrove seedling recruitment (Srivastava et al. 1987). Finally, in many parts of the world, grapsid crabs rapidly consume seeds and fallen propagules of mangroves (Smith et al. 1989), and these crabs likely would consume the occasional non-mangrove recruit as well (Snedaker and Lahmann 1988). Crabs, disturbance regimes, light environments, and other factors differ significantly around the world, and no single explanation for the lack of a mangrove understory is likely to have universal applicability. These observations highlight the importance of comparing mangrove structure and function across a broad array of sites. Of current concern is the potential for invasive plant species to colonize this underused spatial resource, especially where human or natural disturbances have altered canopy density and ecotone boundaries (Smith et al. 1994). Lugo (1998) hypothesizes that most invasive species will

have difficulty penetrating mangroves unless given the opportunity by large disturbance events.

ECOSYSTEM DYNAMICS. For many years, mangrove forests worldwide were viewed as identical, essentially detritus-based ecosystems that exported significant amounts of carbon and nutrients to adjacent seagrass meadows, coral reefs, and the open ocean (Odum and Heald 1975). Although research in the intervening two decades has shown this model to be overly simplistic (reviewed by Alongi el al. 1992; Robertson et al. 1992; Alongi 1998), ecosystem-level processes in mangals throughout the world do share many characteristics. In most mangrove forests, 30–80% of fallen leaves, branches, flowers, and fruits are consumed rapidly and directly by sesarmid crabs (Robertson et al. 1992), whereas < 50% of the litter is decomposed microbially. Carbon export to adjacent systems varies among mangals by as much as two orders of magnitude (Twilley et al. 1992) and is controlled principally by local hydrodynamics (Wolanski et al. 1992). Most adjacent pelagic food webs are based on epiphytic algae and phytoplankton, rather than on mangrove detritus itself (Newell et al. 1995). Nutrient retention in mangal is surprisingly high (Alongi et al. 1992; Alongi 1998), and fewer nutrients appear to be exported to adjacent ecosystems than thought previously. Complete ecosystem models are available only for two mangals—Hitchinbrook Island, Australia (Alongi et al. 1992; Roberston et al. 1992), and Rookery Bay, Florida (Twilley 1985; Twilley and Chen 1998)—so global generalizations regarding ecosystem functioning in mangal will require additional research in other geomorphological and climatic settings. Given the paucity of data, it is probably premature to assign ecosystem "functions" to the many taxonomically diverse components of the mangal ecosystem.

COMMUNITY ECOLOGY OF MANGROVES

Plant-Plant Interactions in Mangal

INTERACTIONS AMONG MANGROVES. Because mangals are relatively simple systems in terms of tree species composition, the probability that conspecifics will co-occur, and presumably interact in ecologically meaningful ways, is high. Thus, it is somewhat surprising that intraspecific interactions—and in fact, interspecific interactions—among mangroves have received very little attention in the literature to date. The few studies that have addressed this issue have examined how seedlings are influenced by adult trees. McKee (1995) and Clarke (1993) provided evidence from field surveys that seedling densities of *Rhizophora mangle* and *Avicennia marina* (in Belize and Australia, respectively) are correlated with proximity to reproductive conspecifics; by contrast, establishment rates of *Rhizophora racemosa* and *Avicennia bicolor* seedlings in western Costa Rica show no such correlations (Jiménez and Sauter 1991). These differences may reflect differential consumption of propagules by grapsid crags in different parts of the world (Smith et al. 1989). All of these processes are mediated by dispersal dynamics and subsequent establishment of mangrove propagules, of which little is known (Steinke 1986; McGuinness 1997). Reflecting this uncertainty, the numerous hypotheses that purport to explain how viviparous reproduction and differential dispersability confer selective advantages on buoyant mangrove propagules (Elmqvist and Cox 1996) remain to be tested.

In any case, both pre- and post-dispersal seed and seedling herbivores can seriously alter the availability of viable propagules establishing in an area (Rabinowitz 1977; Smith et al. 1989; Robertson et al. 1990; Dadouh-Guebas et al. 1997; Farnsworth and Ellison 1997a). Mature plants also can act as local sources for other types of herbivores on seedlings (Onuf et al. 1977). Ellison and Farnsworth (1993), for example, observed that rates of folivory were significantly lower on *Rhizophora mangle* seedlings growing in an area where the canopy of adult conspecifics had been removed. The canopy removal experiment described in Ellison and Farnsworth (1993) also demonstrated that seedlings in gaps grew significantly faster than those suppressed under a canopy, a result that was later supported with observations comparing naturally occurring sun and shade populations (Farnsworth and Ellison 1996). Other studies of mangrove gap dynamics following storms or other disturbances are beginning to yield data on the successional regeneration of mangal (Roth 1992; Smith et al. 1994). However, almost nothing is known about potential below-ground interactions among mangroves or about the roles of plant competition and facilitation in shaping mangal. Ball (1988) speculated that mechanisms of competitive exclusion may contribute to species richness patterns along salinity gradients; the experiments have yet to be done to test this interesting hypothesis. In addition to transplant studies (Smith 1987; Ellison and Farnsworth 1993; McKee 1995; Osunkoya and Creese 1997), well-controlled, experimental field manipulations of plant densities, canopy structure, and edaphic factors are needed in order to make strong inferences about the importance of plant-plant interactions in mangrove community ecology. We also need to understand regeneration following canopy removal in large stands managed for forestry (see "Management, Restoration and Conservation of Mangal," following).

MANGROVES AND THEIR EPIPHYTES. Although understory plants are uncommon in mangal, vascular plants do inhabit the mangrove canopy, which itself does not suffer from the same edaphic constraints of the peat surface. Epiphytes are still subject to salinity stress from salt spray, and the species diversity of ephiphytic orchids, bromeliads, mistletoes, and ferns in mangal (Rico-Gray et al. 1989; Goldstein et al. 1990; Gomez and Winkler 1991; Murren and Ellison 1996) is substantially lower than that found in upland tropical forests. Although most of these epiphytes exhibit few direct interactions with mangroves, mistletoes do affect water, carbon, and nitrogen balances of their mangrove hosts (Orozco et al. 1990). One of the common orchids in Neotropical mangal, *Schomburgkia*

tibicinis, hosts ants in its enlarged pseudobulbs (Rico-Gray et al. 1989), but the mealy-bugs tended by the ants reduce the fitness of the orchid (Rico-Gray and Thien 1989).

Algae and cyanobacteria grow epiphytically on roots, stems, and leaves of mangrove trees (Lambert et al. 1987; Littler et al. 1989; Steinke and Naidoo 1990; Sheridan 1991; King and Puttock 1994; Farnsworth and Ellison 1995; Pedroche et al. 1995; Saifullah et al. 1997). Because their growth is usually limited by both light and nutrients, these epiphytes account for a variable but generally small fraction of the total primary productivity in mangal (Lapointe et al. 1987; Alongi 1994, 1998; Dawes 1996). In some mangrove forests, however, nitrogen fixation by epiphytic cyanobacteria may contribute substantially to the total nitrogen budget of the ecosystem (Alongi et al. 1992; Sheridan 1992). Algal and bacterial epiphytes on fallen leaves also are the dominant contribution of mangroves to offshore food webs (Newell et al. 1995).

Animal-Plant Interactions in Mangal

REPRODUCTION AND POLLINATION. The flowers of some mangrove species support a diverse—and in some areas economically important—fauna of native pollinators. The honey derived from *Avicennia* flowers and the nectar from *Nypa fruticans*, for example, are important food sources for humans and other consumers in both Caribbean (Padrón et al. 1993) and Indo-Pacific (Tomlinson 1986) mangal. The exuberant, pollen-rich flowers of *Sonneratia* support the same populations of bats that fertilize the coveted *Durio* fruit trees of Southeast Asia (Marshall 1983). Other mangrove species appear to be wind-pollinated (Tomlinson 1986) or cleistogamous (Klekowski et al. 1994), but the breeding systems and plant-pollinator interactions of mangroves worldwide have not been documented systematically. Rates of outcrossing will influence the heterozygosity, genetic diversification, and fitness of mangroves. Conservation of mangroves and their pollinators should be informed by a more comprehensive understanding of their population genetics, mutation loads, and viability (Klekowski and Godfrey 1989; Lowenfeld and Klekowski 1992), as well as morphometric (Dominguez et al. 1998) and biochemical variability (Dodd et al. 1998).

HERBIVORY. In addition to their roles in establishment described above, herbivores can clearly influence whole-plant growth of mangroves throughout the world. Neotropical mangals host a diverse insect fauna, including generalist, species-specific, and organ-specific herbivores (Onuf et al. 1977; Farnsworth and Ellison 1991, 1993; Feller 1995; Feller and Mathis 1997). These insects can remove 10–25% of primary production (Farnsworth and Ellison 1991), potentially slow growth rates of understory seedlings (Ellison and Farnsworth 1993), influence leaf form and secondary chemistry (Lacerda et al. 1986; Schoener 1987), and alter the branch architecture of mature trees (Feller and Mathis 1997), and forests (Feller and McKee 1999). The insect fauna of paleotropical mangal is at least an order of magnitude more diverse than that of the Neotropics (Murphy 1990), paralleling the global pattern of mangrove species richness. Although insect herbivory in paleotropical mangal has not been studied extensively (Murphy 1990; Lee 1991), there are several reports of insects defoliating entire stands of trees (Newberry 1980; Piyakarnchana 1981; Whitten and Damanik 1986; Anderson and Lee 1995; McKillup and McKillup 1997).

Marine invertebrates consume mangrove leaves and roots as well. Grapsid crabs not only consume fallen leaf litter and propagules, but also eat leaves, flower buds, flowers, and fruits directly off the tree (Warner 1967; Beever et al. 1979; Farnsworth and Ellison 1991). Isopod crustaceans burrow into developing mangrove roots, reducing root growth rate by up to 50% (Rehm and Humm 1973; Perry 1988; Ellison and Farnsworth 1990). Major mammalian herbivores occur in paleotropical mangal. Proboscis monkeys eat mangrove leaves in Borneo, deer forage on shoots in the mangals of the Indian Sundarbans and the Andaman Islands, and hippopotami frequent the mangals of South Africa. Interactions between these large mammals and mangrove plants or forests have not been studied. These interactions may become increasingly important as mangals provide refugia for mammals driven out of their primary, upland habitats because of large-scale anthropogenic disturbance (Ellison, in press).

INTERACTIONS WITH NON-CONSUMER MARINE INVERTEBRATES. Mangrove forests share characteristics of both hard-substrate and soft-sediment benthic communities. The peaty mucks in which mangroves grow have a high silt content and are inhospitable to most suspension- and filter-feeding invertebrates. In contrast, mangrove roots and trunks represent islands of hard substrate surrounded by soft sediments. Depending on local tidal amplitude and geomorphological setting, roots and trunks can constitute either subtidal or intertidal habitats. All community-level studies to date have focused on one or the other of these two habitats within mangal. However, this dual physical setting presents unique opportunities for comparative studies of the relative importance of ecological processes shared by soft-sediment and hard-substrate communities.

Mud-dwelling sesarmid, portunid, and ocypodid crabs, predominantly in the genera *Cardisoma, Scylla, Sesarma, Uca,* and *Ucides,* are ubiquitous in mangal (Jones 1984; Tan and Ng 1994; Keenan et al. 1998; Figure 16.2). As described earlier in this chapter, these crabs may directly process the bulk of the leaf litter produced in a given season and can directly alter plant reproductive effort and success. Further, the burrowing activity of these crabs oxygenates the peat substrate, alters the distribution of toxins within the peat, and changes local microtopography (Smith et al. 1991; reviewed by Lee 1998). These activities also significantly affect distribution and abundance patterns of sediment epifauna and meiofauna (Dye and Lasiak 1986; Olafsson 1996). These results are directly analogous to those derived from similar studies conducted in temperate salt-marshes (Hoffman et al. 1984; Bertness 1985). Because mangrove crabs are a prized food source,

they are harvested in large quantities in many parts of the world (Hudson and Lester 1994; Fouda and Almuharrami 1995; Blakensteyn et al. 1997). Although this practical interest in mangrove crabs has led to much research on the autecology of these species, the impact of harvesting crabs on community and ecosystem dynamics within mangal has been considered only rarely (Fouda and Almuharrami 1995).

As one moves out of the soft sediment and onto the hard mangrove roots, the species composition of the invertebrate communities changes dramatically. Where tidal amplitude is relatively low (generally < 1 m) and peat banks are undercut by tidal action, roots are continuously submerged and host a luxuriant community of sessile filter- and suspension-feeders dominated by ascidians and sponges (Rützler 1969; Ellison and Farnsworth 1992; Goodbody 1993, 1994; Farnsworth and Ellison 1996a; Bingham and Young 1996). As with many other subtidal fouling communities, the patterns of distribution and abundance of mangrove-root epibionts is controlled at local scales by larval recruitment dynamics and at larger scales by physical factors, current regimes, and stochastic events (Farnsworth and Ellison 1996a; Bingham and Young 1996).

Whereas most of these epibionts do not interact directly with the plants, the dominant group within this fouling community, massive sponges, have both direct and indirect effects on plant growth. The presence of sponges precludes colonization of, and subsequent damage to, roots by isopod crustaceans (Ellison and Farnsworth 1990); this indirect positive effect of sponges on root growth appears to be mediated principally by the physical structure of the sponges themselves. Massive sponges also are a significant nitrogen source for mangroves (Ellison et al. 1996). When present on roots, massive sponges can induce fine rootlet formation by mangroves. These rootlets absorb nitrogenous wastes (principally ammonium) produced by the sponges and also leak significant amounts of carbon compounds that are incorporated into the sponge tissue (Ellison et al. 1996). Based on these data, we estimate that in fringing mangroves in Belize, Central America, 5–10% of the plant's nitrogen uptake may be derived from massive sponges. Sponge-dominated assemblages on mangrove roots are found most commonly and have been studied only in the Caribbean basin. We also have encountered them on mangrove roots on the Pacific Islands of Hawai'i, Pohnpei, and Palau, in the Indian Ocean on the Andaman and Nicobar Islands, and the Kenyan coast, but the relationships between root fauna and their host plants in these areas are as yet unknown.

Intertidal mangrove-root communities are dominated by barnacles and oysters (Mattox 1949; Bacon 1971; Pinto and Wignarajah 1980; Ross and Underwood 1997). Barnacle cover can reduce root growth rates significantly (Perry 1988), but consumption of barnacles by predatory snails ameliorates this negative effect (Ellison and Farnsworth 1992). Casual observations suggest that heavy colonization by oysters on roots could lead to their mechanical damage or breakage, but this has not been studied. Like mangrove crabs, mangrove oysters, especially those in the genus *Crassostrea,* are consumed worldwide by humans and other primates (Mattox 1949; Pinto and Wignarajah 1980; Fernandes 1991). In contrast with crabs, however, most mangrove oysters destined for human use are cultivated (e.g., Quesada et al. 1985; Vélez 1991), and there may be little direct impact to mangal resulting from oyster harvests.

Fungi and Pathogens

There is a very high diversity of fungal species in mangal, and dozens of new species are described annually (see reviews by Kohlmeyer 1969; Hyde and Jones 1988; Steinke and Gareth-Jones 1993; Hyde et al. 1998). These marine fungi are the dominant agents of decomposition of mangrove wood and leaves (Swift and Cragg 1982; Newell 1992; Tan and Leong 1992; Kohlmeyer et al. 1995; Hyde et al. 1998) and are hypothesized to play a significant role in nutrient cycling within mangal (Hyde and Lee 1995). Fungi that grow on living leaves are the primary food source for the mangrove periwinkle *Littoraria angulifera* (Kohlmeyer and Bebout 1986), whereas others decompose fallen leaf litter (Newell 1992; Hyde and Lee 1995; Hyde et al. 1998). In a recent review, Hyde et al. (1998) hypothesized that the high diversity of mangrove fungi likely includes many "redundant" species, in terms of their functional roles in mangrove ecosystem dynamics. This hypothesis merits additional research, given the apparent importance of fungi in mangal.

Pathogens, by contrast, have been poorly studied in mangal. Recently, Weir et al. (2000) identified the fungal pathogen *Cytospora rhizophorae* as the causative agent of mass die-back of *Rhizophora mangle* in Puerto Rico (see also Tattar et al. 1994). These pathogens may become more frequent in mangals that are heavily impacted by pollution (Ellison and Farnsworth 1996a).

DISTURBANCE AND MANGROVE COMMUNITY DYNAMICS

The importance of disturbance in population and community dynamics is widely recognized and extensively studied. Curiously, although major syntheses of the role of disturbance in ecological communities have emerged from studies in the marine intertidal (e.g., Paine and Levin 1981) and in upland tropical forests (e.g., Denslow 1987), there has been little application of these theories to either the animal or plant communities in mangal (also see Ellison and Farnsworth 1993; Smith et al. 1994). We suspect that the lack of attention paid to disturbance in mangal reflects the perception that the comparatively low (plant) species composition and diversity of mangal will be unaffected by disturbance and the currently dominant paradigm that these systems are in "steady-state" (Lugo 1980).

We classify disturbances to mangrove ecosystems along three axes defined by the duration, intensity, and frequency of occurrence (Figure 16.3). Although "natural" disturbances such as tree falls, lightning strikes, and cyclonic storms are relatively infrequent, anthropogenic disturbances such as se-

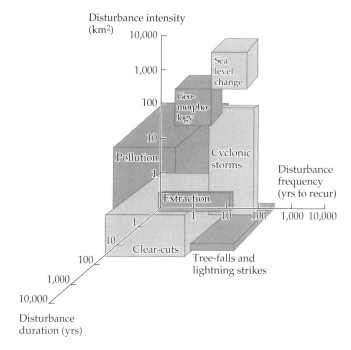

Figure 16.3 Typology of disturbances to mangal.

lective extraction, forest clear-cuts, and pollution events (oil spills, garbage disposal, etc.) occur more frequently in mangal. Anthropogenic disturbances also tend to have both large intensities and durations, whereas natural disturbance processes are either large in intensity or of long duration, but rarely both. Geomorphological processes and changes in local sea level can also be placed in the disturbance "space" illustrated in Figure 16.3; they are uniquely of large intensity, duration, and return time. Anthropogenic impacts on climate, however, may substantially decrease the return time of these two large-scale types of disturbance.

Tree-Falls, Lightning Strikes, and Cyclones

Compared to the attention they have received in upland tropical forests, tree-fall gaps have been little studied in mangal. Lightning strikes are a regular source of canopy disturbance in mangals of Australia, Florida, the Dominican Republic, and Panama (Smith et al. 1994). We found that suppressed seedlings growing in the understory responded rapidly to experimental removal of the mangrove canopy (Ellison and Farnsworth 1993). Soil characteristics and infaunal composition are likely to change following gap creation; the former has been studied only correlatively (Ewel et al. 1998; Feller and McKee 1999), and the latter not at all.

The effects of tropical cyclonic storms (hurricanes, typhoons, and cyclones) on mangals have been widely documented (e.g., Wadsworth and Englerth 1959; Steinke and Ward 1989; Roth 1992; Smith et al. 1994; Imbert et al. 1996; Swiadek 1997; Alleng 1998). Although mangals afford significant protection from cyclonic storms to upland habitats (UNESCO 1979), mangroves themselves can be killed by wind damage, lightning strikes, and surges accompanying severe storms (Roth 1992; Doyle et al. 1995; McCoy et al. 1996; Imbert et al. 1996; Swiadek 1997). Only a handful of mangrove species resprout following damage to the main trunk (Tomlinson 1986; Roth 1992), and regeneration of mangrove forests following hurricanes results almost entirely from seedlings. This regeneration can lead to a rearrangement of species sequences along intertidal gradients. For example, in Florida, the normally high-intertidal species *Laguncularia racemosa* now dominates the lower intertidal in regenerating stands in mangal of southern Florida destroyed by Hurricane Andrew in 1995 (Baldwin et al. 1995; A. M. Ellison, pers. obs.). The aforementioned studies on mangals' responses to cyclonic storms illustrate that these communities have recovery times on the order of decades, but that the trajectories of recovery are system specific and rarely predictable. The 50–100 year return time of cyclonic storms also necessitates a reevaluation of the concept of old-growth forests as applied to mangal (Lugo 1997). Much additional research is needed to integrate mangal into current syntheses concerning community- and ecosystem-level responses to "natural" disturbance regimes.

Anthropogenic Disturbances to Mangal

Because of their occurrence on coastlines where the majority of the world's population lives, there is much more information on the responses of mangal to anthropogenic disturbances (reviewed recently by Saenger et al. 1983; JIAM/ISME 1993; Ellison and Farnsworth 1996a; Farnsworth and Ellison 1997b; Farnsworth 1998). Mangrove forests once occupied ~75% of sheltered tropical coasts worldwide, but people are displacing mangroves at alarming rates throughout the world. A recent global survey identified reclamation for village expansion, agriculture, tourism, and aquacultural impoundments as the primary global threats to mangal (Farnsworth and Ellison 1997b). Oil spills have impacted mangal dramatically in the Caribbean (Ellison and Farnsworth 1996a), but because of less tanker traffic are less of a threat elsewhere in the world. Activities that occur outside mangal boundaries *sensu stricto*, such as upland farming and road construction, can also exert indirect pressures on these systems by diverting freshwater or releasing pollutants (e.g., Twilley et al. 1998). Ecologists must team with economists and sociologists to examine the factors that promote mangrove exploitation in certain areas, to model the reciprocal effects that human economic pressures and mangrove decline exert on one another, and to develop biologically tenable measures of success for a range of conservation strategies (see Ruitenbeek 1994; Gilbert and Janssen 1998; Twilley et al. 1998 for useful examples).

Although it is becoming easier to detect and quantify losses of mangal using remote-sensing technology (where military or political impediments to such data gathering do not exist), less is understood about how the loss of mangrove tree species affects the diversity and ecology of other members of mangal and adjacent communities such as seagrass beds and coral reefs. It is also imperative to assess the ecological im-

pacts of potential "solutions" for mangrove conservation "problems." For example, ecotourism has long been regarded as a means of encouraging public appreciation for, and hence conservation of, mangrove systems (e.g., Barzetti 1993). However, accommodating tourists often entails conversion of these same habitats for visitors' facilities (e.g., Hudson 1983), installation of boardwalks that themselves alter benthic community structure (Figure 16.2; Kelaher et al. 1998a,b), and increased boat traffic with attendant wakes and noise (the ecological ramifications of which have received little attention). Ecological studies can greatly augment the reliability of cost-benefit analyses of these projects. Much of the scientific information is in place to comprehend the functional consequences of our actions on mangroves and to predict the outcome of various conservation scenarios (e.g., Ruitenbeek 1994; Gilbert and Janssen 1998). However, education of local users and policy makers is essential to ensure that mangroves are protected and restored properly, and ecologists are in arguably the best position to disseminate accurately data on mangrove ecology and their values to ecosystem function.

Mangal Responses to Sea Level Rise

It is now widely accepted that global climate has been and is likely to continue changing due to accelerating anthropogenic releases of carbon (IPCC 1997). A measurable rise in sea level on many coasts is a probable outcome of the oceanic thermal expansion and subsidence of ice sheets that will accompany such "global warming," and mangal, like other coastal systems, will be among the first ecosystems to experience this change. How will mangrove communities respond to increased sea level and possible changes in tidal amplitude? We can glean predictions from three sources of information: (1) paleoecological studies that reconstruct mangal's responses to sea level increases in the past; (2) long-term field studies characterizing how the shape and structure of mangal is changing in response to contemporary changes in tidal regime; and (3) laboratory and field experiments that elucidate individual responses to manipulated tidal conditions.

Analyses of stratigraphic sequences from peat cores indicate that mangals gradually moved upland and their seaward fringes died back as sea level rose during periods of Holocene transgression (Woodroffe 1982; Ellison and Stoddart 1991; Ellison 1993; but see Alleng 1998). Today, such inland migration can occur only where mangal can colonize amenable wetland habitat along an elevational gradient, and where such habitats are not constrained or fragmented by road development, urbanization, or water diversion.

Local sedimentation regimes can offset (Pernetta 1993) or exacerbate (Ellison and Farnsworth 1996b) negative effects of sea level rise on mangrove growth. Mangals on shallow, flat, carbonate platforms throughout tropical reef areas may eventually be submerged altogether if sediment accretion cannot keep pace with erosion and inundation (Parkinson et al. 1994).

Bacon (1994) reviewed methods for evaluating the risks of sea level rise to different types of mangal in the Caribbean.

This type of assessment must be applied to other regions, and restoration and mitigation measures developed, particularly in areas where the consequences of sea level rise and inappropriate coastal zone management measures are already being felt (Mimura and Nunn 1998). Mangals themselves are potentially excellent tools for monitoring the changes currently underway (Blasco et al. 1996; Ellison and Farnsworth 1996a; Michener et al. 1997). Species responses will reflect differential tolerances to salinity and flooding and the influence of these features on interspecific interactions. Several mangrove species exhibit depressed growth when grown under flooded treatments that mimic field conditions (Naidoo 1985; Hovendon et al. 1995; McKee 1996; Ellison and Farnsworth 1997), yielding pessimistic prognoses for mangals that are restricted in area. Multi-species trials are required to determine how rising sea level will influence mangrove species richness, composition of floral and faunal components of the community, and indicators of ecosystem function.

Mangrove Community Responses to Other Facets of Climate Change

As the climate changes, rising sea level will be accompanied by increases in atmospheric concentrations of carbon dioxide and probable increases in mean annual temperatures of both air and ocean surface waters. Studies to date of mangrove responses to climate change have not yet considered all these factors together, and multi-species factorial experiments must be performed before issuing prognoses of mangrove performance (Field 1995). Reports of mangrove responses to elevated CO_2 alone suggest that water use efficiency and growth of individual trees will be enhanced, but that the magnitude of these effects will differ among species and photosynthetic acclimation may inhibit long-term responsiveness (Ball and Munns 1992; Farnsworth et al. 1996; Ball et al. 1997; Snedaker and Araújo 1998). Age at first reproduction, as well as patterns of reproductive phenology, may be altered in some species (Farnsworth et al. 1996), with implications for plant-pollinator syndromes, seed predation, and seedling establishment. As soil, air, and water temperatures increase, species composition and activities of microbial and benthic associates of mangroves will likely change. At larger scales, it is necessary to predict whether mangroves will shift their ranges as some regions grow arid and others grow lush under modified rainfall regimes. Currently limited at their northern (Florida/Bermuda) and southern (New Zealand) boundaries by their sensitivity to cold (MacMillan 1975), mangroves could expand their foothold as temperatures moderate.

MANAGEMENT, RESTORATION, AND CONSERVATION OF MANGAL

For centuries, mangrove forests have provided a wide range of products that people use, including (but not limited to) timber and fuelwood, finfish and edible crustaceans, and bioactive compounds for tanning and medicine (reviewed by Walsh 1977; Bandaranayake 1998). Only in the last hundred years or so, however, have these forests been managed actively, first for timber, fuelwood, and pulpwood production (reviews in Hamilton and Snedaker 1984; JIAM/ISME 1993; Chowdhury and Ahmed 1994; FAO 1994), and more recently for cultivation of fish, shrimp, and especially the tiger prawn, *Penaeus monodon* (e.g., Hamilton and Snedaker 1984; Hong and San 1993; Chaudhuri and Choudhury 1994; Primavera 1995; de Graaf and Xuan 1998; Semesi 1998; Twilley et al. 1998) or eco-tourism (Bacon 1987; Barzetti 1993; Government of West Bangal, n.d.). Despite repeated claims that mangrove forests can be managed sustainably (e.g., Hamilton and Snedaker 1984; FAO 1994; Chowdhury and Ahmed 1994), managed (and unmanaged) mangals continue to degrade (e.g., Gong and Ong 1995; Farnsworth and Ellison 1997b). As a result, much current attention is focused on restoration of degraded mangal (Field 1996, 1998; Kalay and Jones 1998) and conservation of the remaining less-impacted mangal throughout the world (e.g., Clough 1993; Diop 1993; Lacerda 1993; Suman 1994).

Mangrove Forestry

Many mangrove species, especially in Southeast Asia, India and Bangladesh, and East Africa, grow large enough to be used extensively as construction and boat-building timbers (JIAM/ISME 1993; FAO 1994). The ± 10,000 km^2 of mangrove forests that cover the Sundarbans region of India and Bangladesh have the longest history of management for timber and provide an illustrative example of how even deliberate, well-intentioned management has resulted in the decline and degradation of the world's largest mangal. The earliest forest inventory for this mangal dates to 1769, and the first detailed working (harvest) plan was prepared in 1893–1894 (Chowdhury and Ahmed 1994). The focus of this and subsequent working plans was on two species, the Sundarbans endemic *Heritiera fomes* and *Excoecaria agallocha*. Other harvested species included *Avicennia officinalis*, *Xylocarpus granatum*, *Sonneratia apetala*, *Bruguiera gymnorhiza*, and *Amoora cucullata*.

Prior to 1930, the management plans set the minimum harvestable size of *H. fomes* at 90–100 cm diameter at breast height (dbh), and the other species at ~ 60 cm dbh (Chaffey et al. 1985; Chowdhury and Ahmed 1994). Prompted by increasing demand and a perception that "overmature" trees were not being exploited, Curtis (1933) developed a new 20-year working plan for these forests that reduced the minimum harvestable diameter of *H. fomes* to 7–30 cm dbh (depending on quality), and that of *E. agallocha* to 10–30 cm dbh. Other species were similarly reduced. These diameters corresponded to tress ranging in age from 100–125 years old. A subsequent inventory and management plan further reduced the minimum cuttable diameter to 16–26 cm for *H. fomes*, 11–15 cm for *E. agallocha*, and comparable reductions for the other species (Choudhury 1968). By 1983, the total saleable volume of timber of these two species had been reduced by 40–50%, and the forest was considered seriously over-exploited (Hussain and Ahmed 1994). Commercial harvesting of *H. fomes* has been banned in Bangladesh since 1994.

This last period of intensive harvesting of mangroves coincided with dramatic increases in the numbers of human inhabitants in the Sundarbans of Bangladesh (approximately 10 million in 1995) and concomitant increases in human mortality during annual cyclones. Recognition of the relationship between deforestation of mangroves and increased damage and mortality from cyclones led to the initiation of mangrove reforestation projects beginning in the mid-1960s (Siddiqi and Khan 1996). Through 1995, nearly 140,000 ha had been replanted, primarily with *Sonneratia apetala* and *Avicennia officinalis*, both of which grow rapidly and are transplanted more easily and successfully than the other native species (Siddiqi and Khan 1996). Overall, reforestation success has varied dramatically among sites, although causes of local failure are hard to pinpoint (Siddiqi and Khan 1996).

A parallel example is provided by the ~ 40,000 ha mangrove forest of Matang, Malaysia. Most (~85 %, or 35,000 ha) of this forest has been managed for fuelwood production since 1902. The managed forest is now a virtual monoculture of *Rhizophora apiculata*, which provides charcoal that has very high caloric value, burns very slowly, and produces virtually no smoke (Bandaranayake 1998). Clear-cutting of stands occurs on a 30-year rotation. Despite assertions that the managed mangrove forest of Matang is "one of the best managed [mangrove forests] in the world" (Chan 1996: 75), yields have declined dramatically: from 296 t/ha in the virgin stands of the early 1900s, to 158 t/ha in the late 1960s and 136 t/ha in the 1970s (Gong and Ong 1995; Chan 1996). Continued exploitation of this forest requires intensive use of herbicides to remove the mangrove ferns *Acrostichum aureum* and *A. speciosum* (which inhibit *Rhizophora* seedling growth) and direct planting of seedlings and saplings (Chan 1996). Economic costs of these activities can exceed $800/ha, while the realized income from the forest rarely tops $1,000/ha (Chan 1996).

Elsewhere in the world, existing regulations concerning the extraction of wood products from mangroves are generally unenforced (Ellison and Farnsworth 1996a; Farnsworth and Ellison 1997b), and reforestation efforts are sporadically applied and only now being assessed for their long-term efficacy (Field 1996; Kaly and Jones 1998). Despite the known relationships between mangrove plant productivity and animal (especially finfish and edible crustacean) productivity, management and reforestation plans focus almost exclusively on the trees (Kaly and Jones 1998). This results in the creation of forests that may be biological deserts: for example, mangrove crabs are uncommon in managed stands of *Rhizophora apiculata* in Matang (A. M. Ellison and E. J. Farnsworth, pers. obs.)

Fisheries, Aquaculture, and Mariculture

The relationship between mangrove forest cover and yields of finfish and crustaceans is well known and well documented (e.g., D'Croz and Kwiecinski 1980; Jeyaseelan and Krishnamurthy 1980; Ong 1982; Krishnamurthy et al. 1984; Mepham and Petr. 1986; Richards and Bohnsack 1990; Twil-

ley et al. 1991, 1998; Ruitenbeek 1994; Fouda and Almuharrami 1995; Vance et al. 1996; de Graaf and Xuan 1998; Primavera 1998). It is routine to hear that fish and prawn catches decline where mangroves are removed, following selective extraction of high-grade trees or clear-cuts for fuelwood or pulpwood destined for rayon mills. Similar losses are asserted where mangroves are cleared for aquaculture (finfish) or mariculture (shrimp and prawn) ponds, but quantification of these losses is scarce.

In the Philippines and Ecuador, > 50% of the mangrove forests have been converted to shrimp ponds in the last 30 years (Twilley et al. 1993; Primavera 1995), and shrimp pond production increased 30-fold (from 3,000 ha to 100,000 ha) in Vietnam from 1980–1992 (de Graaf and Xuan 1998). In their initial phases, these mariculture operations rely on locally caught wild larvae to seed the shrimp ponds. Rapid depletion of wild larval supplies (which rely on mangal for food and protection from predators) leads to an increasing emphasis on lab-reared larvae (e.g., de Graaf and Xuan 1998). In the early 1990s, viral infections decimated shrimp ponds worldwide, and they remain persistent in coastal waters around the world (Primavera 1995; Corea et al. 1998; de Graaf and Xuan 1998). At the same time, coastal fisheries have shown parallel declines (Richards and Bohnsack 1990; Ellison and Farnsworth 1996a). Data from Vietnam illustrate that the catch per unit effort peaked in 1982, but declined precipitously with the construction of shrimp ponds and is now at its lowest recorded level ever (de Graaf and Xuan 1998). Because construction of shrimp ponds results in the exposure of strongly reducing, acid-sulphate soils, replanting of mangroves in abandoned ponds is difficult to impossible (Corea et al. 1998; de Graaf and Xuan 1998).

More integrated management of mangrove forestry and fisheries is clearly required. A recent simulation study by Twilley et al. (1998) suggested that maintenance of mangrove forest stands in and around shrimp ponds in Ecuador could ameliorate the increased eutrophication and decreased water quality in estuaries cleared of mangroves for shrimp pond construction. Binh et al. (1997) demonstrated 30–50% higher economic returns from management schemes in Vietnam that integrated mangrove forestry with shrimp farming relative to either one by itself. In areas where aquaculture and mariculture operations in mangroves are just beginning (notably, East Africa [Semesi 1998]), there are real opportunities to develop joint aquaculture-forestry operations within mangal that may be truly sustainable.

Conservation and Ecotourism

Most elements of the mangrove flora and fauna are unique to this ecosystem, and this observation has led to a marked increase in attempts to inventory, protect, and conserve the remaining, relatively undisturbed, mangals throughout the world. Most countries in Latin America, Southeast Asia, and the Indian subcontinent have developed conservation plans for, broad educational programs about, and strict legislation concerning uses of mangal (reviews in Clough 1993; Lacerda

1993; Suman 1994), while development of similar national strategies in Africa lags by several decades (compare reviews in Diop 1993). Ecotourism is being developed increasingly as an opportunity for apparently low-impact use of mangal (but see our previous discussion of disturbance) that simultaneously can provide high economic returns and has the potential to educate visitors about the social, economic, and intrinsic values of mangal (Bacon 1987; Barzetti 1993). For example, because of the concentration of waterbirds in mangal, these ecosystems are high on the list of places for bird-watchers to visit (e.g., Bacon 1987; Klein et al. 1995; Ellison and Farnsworth 1996a). We note, however, that even ecotourism can have significant negative impacts on mangal. These impacts include: habitat destruction attendant to hotel construction (Hudson 1983; Bildstein 1990; Conde and Alarcón 1993); coastal pollution that leads to eutrophication and species loss (Aguilera et al. 1992; Tattar et al. 1994; Klekoswki et al. 1999); changes in substrate structure, seedling distribution, faunal diversity, and species composition following boardwalk construction (Skilleter 1996; Kelaher et al. 1998a, 1998b; Skilleter and Warren 2000); and erosion of peat banks when high-speed motorboats cruise through mangrove-lined channels (Farnsworth and Ellison 1997b).

In virtually all countries where mangal occurs, governments, corporations, and individuals recognize the economic, social, and intrinsic values provided by these ecosystems. Increased understanding of the ecology of mangal makes it truly feasible to develop strategies for the long-term sustainable use and conservation of these systems (reviewed by Farnsworth 1998). Site management and conservation plans can be developed that incorporate forestry, aquaculture, tourism, and areas with restricted access (Figure 16.4). Development of these plans requires a fundamental appreciation for the intrinsic value of mangal and a comprehensive understanding of the links between mangal, adjacent ecosystems, and human inhabitants. In this chapter, we have documented the existence of the basic information necessary for a better understanding of mangal in the service of such a plan. Although many open questions remain regarding the ecology of mangal, we are optimistic that this unique ecosystem will be protected and maintained far into the future if existing (and future) data are widely shared and disseminated, if mangal is recognized as a genuine conservation and management priority, and if all parties affected by land-use decisions are involved in the development of site conservation and management plans.

RECOMMENDATIONS FOR FUTURE RESEARCH

Our review has illustrated that substantial data are available to address the ecology of mangroves and mangal, but there are also ample lacunae in our understanding of these plants and the communities that they define. Biogeographic patterns are clearly documented, but the roles of propagule dispersal and seedling establishment in determining these patterns at local, regional, continental, and global scales remains

poorly understood. Species-specific ecophysiological processes—including regulation of salt uptake, oxygen levels, and microbial activity at the soil-root interface; water transport; tolerance of salinity during growth and reproduction; and nutrient-use efficiency—have been studied in only a few mangrove species, but are major drivers of population-, community-, and ecosystem-level dynamics. Similarly, investigations of trade-offs between osmotic physiology, carbon balance, nutrient-use efficiency, nutrient limitation, and production of plant secondary compounds are needed to develop a better understanding of specialization of herbivores and pathogens and the patterns of insect and fungal outbreaks in mangal.

Ecosystem models are well developed for only two mangals, and there is a real need for expanding the scope of these models to incorporate mangrove forests that grow in different geomorphological situations (from estuaries to carbonate platforms); that occur in a wide range of tidal amplitudes; and that fully account for past land-use history and cross the spectrum from "pristine" sites to degraded and restored sites. These models need to fully incorporate physiological-, population- and community-level interactions that mediate and control system-wide nutrient and energy fluxes.

The impacts of human activities on mangal increase daily, and data are sorely needed that can be applied directly to conservation, management, and restoration of these communities. Fragmentation of these communities worldwide could disrupt plant-pollinator interactions and lead to isolation of small populations. A more detailed understanding of mangrove population genetics is needed to assess the importance of inbreeding depression in isolated stands. Dispersal and establishment properties of mangrove propagules can limit or enhance such isolation. A better understanding of establishment dynamics is also needed to aid in management of mangal. Because population-level studies of mangroves have emphasized controls by edaphic factors on plant population dynamics and mutualisms between mangroves and faunal associates, we know little about how intra- and interspecific interactions could change in fragmented or managed stands. Such data could also be used to devise sound strategies for sustainable forestry, afforestation programs, and restoration of degraded mangal. These data would allow for the assessment of the effects, both positive and negative, of conservation "solutions" on mangrove populations and communities. Because mangals are coastal communities, there is a pressing need to develop experimentally testable, quantitative models for the responses of these communities and their constituent species to changes in sea level. Additional studies on the responses of individual species and whole communities to other facets of global change, including carbon and nitrogen enrichment, are also needed to more reliably predict the effects of such global-scale anthropogenic disturbances on mangal.

It appears to us to be especially important to view these research topics through four broad, conceptual lenses. First, general ecological theories deriving from decades of research in physiology and physiological ecology, marine biology,

Figure 16.4 Hypothetical site conservation plan for sustained use and conservation of a mangal ecosystem. Modified from Farnsworth (1998).

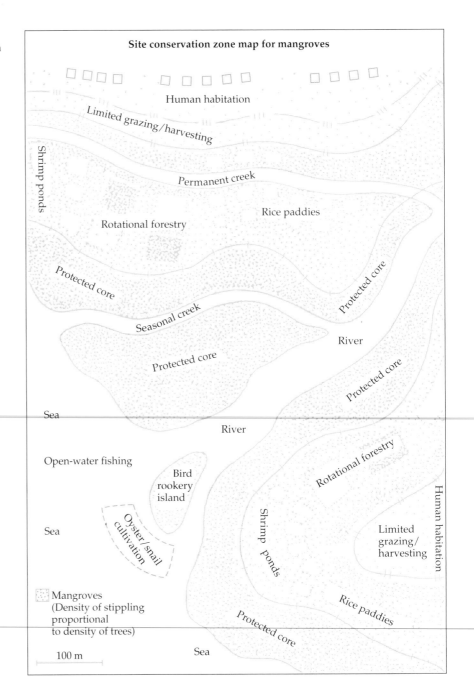

Site conservation zone map for mangroves

Human habitation

Limited grazing/harvesting

Shrimp ponds

Permanent creek

Rice paddies

Rotational forestry

Protected core

Seasonal creek

Protected core

Protected core

River

Protected core

Sea

River

Open-water fishing

Bird rookery island

Rotational forestry

Sea

Oyster/snail cultivation

Shrimp ponds

Human habitation

Limited grazing/ harvesting

Mangroves
(Density of stippling proportional to density of trees)

Rice paddies

Protected core

100 m

Sea

community ecology, and evolutionary biology should be applied to studies of mangrove ecology; in the past such theories have been applied only rarely. Second, these studies should take advantage of the fact that mangal is simultaneously a hard-substrate and a soft-sediment system. This fact can be used to develop new general theories that unite data from studies in other benthic communities that occur in only one of these habitat types. Third, such studies should cross levels of biological organization, from individual physiology through ecosystems. The comparatively small number of species in mangal (relative to other tropical communities) should make it possible to clearly link physiological processes to population dynamics and population processes to com-

munity and ecosystem-level phenomena. Lastly, the existence of global, taxonomically-independent convergences in structure and function of individual mangrove species and whole mangrove communities make it feasible to undertake experimentally-based comparative studies of ecological processes. Mangrove ecology remains a rich area for intellectual exploration, and mangrove forests themselves are compelling places in which to work.

Acknowledgments

Our studies of mangroves since 1987 have been supported by the Arnold Arboretum, Earthwatch (The Center for Field Research), the Exploration Fund of the Explorer's Club, Harvard University, Mount Holyoke College, the National Geographic Society, Smithsonian Institution (CCRE Program), Swarthmore College, and the U.S. National Science Foundation. We have had the privilege of visiting and studying mangroves on five continents and are grateful to the individuals—taxi drivers, pilots, boatmen, private landowners, farmers, undergraduate field assistants, research scientists, foresters, and reserve managers—who have shared their knowledge, who enabled us to access remote sites, and who have worked with us in the field.

LITERATURE CITED

Aguilera, A., J. E. Corredor and J. M. Morrell. 1992. Oxido nitroso en el Mar Caribe nororiental. *Carib. J. Sci.* 28: 70–80.

Alleng, G. P. 1998. Historical development of the Port Royal mangrove wetland, Jamaica. *J. Coast. Res.* 14: 951–959.

Alongi, D. M. 1994. Zonation and seasonality of benthic primary production and community respiration in tropical mangrove forests. *Oecologia* 98: 320–327.

Alongi, D. M. 1998. *Coastal Ecosystem Processes.* CRC Press, Boca Raton, FL.

Alongi, D. M., K. G. Boto and A. I. Robertson. 1992. Nitrogen and phosphorus cycles. In A. I. Robertson and D. M. Alongi (eds.), *Tropical Mangrove Ecosystems*, pp. 251–292. American Geophysical Union, Washington, DC.

Anderson, C. and Lee, S. Y. 1995. Defoliation of the mangrove *Avicennia marina* in Hong Kong: Causes and consequences. *Biotropica* 27: 218–226.

Aubréville, A. 1964. Problémes de la mangrove d'hier det d'aujourd'hui. *Adansonia, n.s.* 4: 19–23.

Bacon, P. R. 1971. The maintenance of a resident population of *Balanus eburneus* (Gould) in relation to salinity fluctuations in a Trinidad mangrove swamp. *J. Exp. Mar. Biol. Ecol.* 6: 187–198.

Bacon, P. R. 1987. Use of wetlands for tourism in the insular Caribbean. *Ann. Tour. Res.* 14: 104–117.

Bacon, P. R. 1994. Template for evaluation of impacts of sea level rise on Caribbean coastal wetlands. *Ecol. Engin.* 3: 171–186.

Baldwin, A. H., W. J. Platt, K. L. Gathen, J. M. Lessmann, and T. J. Rauch. 1995. Hurricane damage and regeneration in fringe mangrove forests of southeast Florida, USA. *J. Coast. Res.* 21:169–183.

Ball, M. C. 1980. Patterns of secondary succession in a mangrove forest of southern Florida. *Oecologia* 44: 226–235.

Ball, M. C. 1988. Salinity tolerance in the mangroves *Aegiceras corniculatum* and *Avicennia marina*. I. Water use in relation to growth, carbon partitioning, and salt balance. *Aust. J. Plant. Phys.* 15: 447–464.

Ball, M. C. 1996. Comparative ecophysiology of mangrove forest and tropical lowland moist forest. In S. S. Mulkey, R. L. Chazdon and A. P. Smith (eds.). *Tropical Forest Plant Ecophysiology*, pp. 461–496. Chapman & Hall, New York.

Ball, M. C. 1998. Mangrove species richness in relation to salinity and waterlogging: A case study along the Adelaide River floodplain, northern Australia. *Global Ecol. Biogeogr. Letts.* 7: 73–82.

Ball, M. C. and R. Munns. 1992. Plant responses to salinity under elevated atmospheric concentrations of CO_2. *Aust. J. Bot.* 40: 515–525.

Ball, M. C. and J. B. Passioura. 1993. Carbon gain in relation to water use: Photosynthesis in mangroves. In E.-D. Schulze and M. M. Caldwell (eds.), *Ecophysiology of Photosynthesis*, pp. 247–259. Springer-Verlag, Berlin.

Ball, M. C., M. J. Cochrane and H. M Rawson. 1997. Growth and water use of the mangroves Rhizophora apiculata and R. stylosa in response to salinity and humidity under ambient and elevated concentrations of atmospheric CO_2. *Plant, Cell, and Environment* 20: 1158–1166.

Bandaranayake, W. M. 1998. Traditional and medicinal uses of mangroves. *Mangroves and Salt Marshes* 2: 133–148.

Barzetti, V. (ed.). 1993. *Parks and Progress: Protected Areas and Economic Development in Latin America and the Caribbean.* IUCN, Cambridge, UK.

Beever, J. W. III, D. Simberloff, and L. L. King. 1979. Herbivory and predation by the mangrove tree crab *Aratus pisonii. Oecologia* 43: 317–328.

Bertness. M. D. 1985. Fiddler crab regulation of *Spartina alterniflora* production on a New England salt marsh. *Ecology* 66: 1042–1055.

Bertness, M. D. and A. M. Ellison. 1987. Determinants of pattern in a New England salt marsh plant community. *Ecol. Monogr.* 57: 129–147.

Bildstein, K. L. 1990. Status, conservation and management of the scarlet ibis *Eudocimus ruber* in the Caroni Swamp, Trinidad, West Indies. *Biol. Cons.* 54: 61–78.

Bingham, B. L. and C. M. Young. 1996. Stochastic events and dynamics of a mangrove root epifaunal community. *Mar. Ecol.* 16: 145–163.

Binh, C. T., M. J. Phillips and H. Demaine. 1997. Integrated shrimp-mangrove farming systems in the Mekong delta of Vietnam. *Aquaculture Res.* 28: 599–610.

Björkmann, O., B. Demmig and T. J. Andrews. 1988. Mangrove photosynthesis: Response to high irradiance stress. *Aust. J. Plant Phys.* 15: 43–61.

Blankensteyn, A., D. Cunha and A. S. Freire. 1997. Distribution, fisheries and proteic content of the mangrove crab *Ucides cordatus* (L. 1763) (Brachyura: Ocypodidae) in the Laranjetras Bay and adjacent areas, Parana, Brazil. *Arq. Biol. Tecn.* 40: 331–349.

Blasco, F., P. Saenger and E. Janodet. 1996. Mangroves as indicators of coastal change. *Catena* 27: 167–178.

Blasco, F., T. Gauquelin, M. Rasolofoharinoro, J. Denis, M. Aizpuru and V. Caldairou. 1998. Recent advances in mangrove studies using remote sensing data. *Mar. Freshwater Res.* 49: 287–296.

Bunt, J. S. 1996. Mangrove zonation: An examination of data from 17 riverine estuaries in tropical Australia. *Ann. Bot.* 78: 333–341.

Camilleri, J. C. and G. Ribi. 1983. Leaf thickness of mangroves (*Rhizophora mangle*) growing in different salinities. *Biotropica* 15: 139–141.

Chaffey, D. R., F. R. Miller, and J. H. Sandom. 1985. A forest inventory of the Sundarbans, Bangladesh, Main Report. Overseas Development Administration, Land Resources Development Centre, United Kingdom.

Chan, H. T. 1996. Mangrove reforestation in peninsular Malasyia: A case study of Matang. In C. Field (ed.), *Restoration of Mangrove Ecosystems*, pp. 65–76. International Tropical Timber Organization and International Society for Mangrove Ecosystems, Okinawa, Japan.

Chapman, V. J. 1976. *Mangrove Vegetation.* J. Cramer, Vaduz.

Chaudhuri, A. B. and A. Choudhury. 1994. *Mangroves of the Sundarbans.* Vol 1: *India.* IUCN Wetlands Programme, Gland, Switzerland.

Chazdon, R. L. and N. Fetcher. 1984. Light environments of tropical forests. In E. Medina, H. A. Mooney and C. Vázquez-Yánes (eds.), *Physiological Ecology of Plants of the Wet Tropics*, pp. 27–36. Dr. W. Junk, Boston.

Cheeseman, J. M. 1994. Depressions of photosynthesis in mangrove canopies. In N. R. Baker (ed.). *Photoinhibition of Photosynthesis: From Molecular Mechanisms to the Field*, pp. 377–389. BIOS Scientific Publishers, Oxford.

Choudhury, A. M. 1968. *Working Plan of the Sundarbans Forest Division for the Period 1960–61 to 1979–80.* East Pakistan Government Press, Dacca.

Chowdhury, R. A. and I. Ahmed. 1994. History of forest management. In Z. Hussain and G. Acharya (eds.), *Mangroves of the Sundarbans, Vol. 2: Bangladesh*, pp. 155–180. IUCN Wetlands Programme, Gland, Switzerland.

Clarke, P. J. 1993. Dispersal of grey mangrove (*Avicennia marina* var. *australasica*) propagules in south-eastern Australia. *Aquat. Bot.* 45: 195–204.

Clough, B. F. (ed.). 1993. *The Economic and Environmental Values of Mangrove Forests and their Present State of Conservation in the South-East Asia/Pacific Region.* Mangrove Ecosystems Technical Reports 1, International Society for Mangrove Ecosystems, Okinawa, Japan.

Clough, B. F. and R. G. Sim. 1989. Changes in gas exchange characteristics and water use efficiency of mangroves in response to salinity and vapour pressure deficit. *Oecologia* 79: 38–44.

Conde, J. E. and C. Alarcón. 1993. Mangroves of Venezuela. In L. D. Lacerda (ed.), *Conservation and Sustainable Utilization of Mangrove Forests in Latin America and Africa Regions*, Part I: *Latin America*, pp. 211–244. International Society for Mangrove Ecosystems, Okinawa, Japan.

Corea, A., R. Johnstone, J. Jayasinghe, S. Ekaratne and K. Jayawardene. 1998. Self-pollution: A major threat to the prawn farming industry in Sri Lanka. *Ambio* 27: 662–668.

Corlett, R. T. 1986. The mangrove understory: Some additional observations. *J. Trop. Ecol.* 2: 93–94.

Connell, J. H. 1961. Effects of competition, predation by *Thais lapillus* and other factors on natural populations of the barnacle *Balanus balanoides*. *Ecol. Monogr.* 31: 61–104.

Cronquist, S. 1981. *An Integrated System of Classification of Flowering Plants*. Columbia University Press, New York.

Curran, M. 1985. Gas movements in the roots of *Avicennia marina* (Forsk.) Vierh. *Aust. J. Plant Phys.* 12: 97–108.

Curtis, S. J. 1933. *Working Plans for the Forests of the Sundarbans Division for the Period from 1st April 1930 to 31st March 1951*. Bengal Government Press, Calcutta, India.

Dahdouh-Guebas, F., M. Verneirt, J. F. Tack, and N. Koedam. 1997. Food preferences of *Neosarmatium meinerti* de Man (Decapoda: Sesarminae) and its possible effect on the regeneration of mangroves. *Hydrobiologia* 347: 83–89.

Dale, M. R. T. 1988. The spacing and intermingling of species boundaries on an environmental gradient. *Oikos* 53: 351–356.

Dawes, C. 1996. Macroalga diversity, standing stock and productivity in a northern mangal on the west coast of Florida. *Nova Hedw.* 112: 525–535.

D'Croz, L. and B. Kwiecinski. 1980. Contribución de los manglares a las pesquerías de la Bahía de Panamá. *Rev. Biol. Trop.* 28: 13–29.

de Graaf, G. J. and T. T. Xuan. 1998. Extensive shrimp farming, mangrove clearance and marine fisheries in the southern provinces of Vietnam. *Mangroves and Salt Marshes* 2: 159–166.

Denslow, J. S. 1987. Tropical rainforest gaps and tree species diversity. *Annu. Rev. Ecol. Syst* 18:431–452.

Diop, E. S. (ed.). 1993. *Conservation and Sustainable Utilization of Mangrove Forests in Latin America and Africa*. Part II: *Africa*. Mangrove Ecosystems Technical Reports 3. International Society for Mangrove Ecosystems, Okinawa, Japan.

Dodd, R. S., F. Fromard, Z. A. Rafii and F. Blasco. 1995. Biodiversity among West African *Rhizophora*: Foliar wax chemistry. *Biochem. Syst. Ecol.* 23: 859–868.

Dodd, R. S., Z. A. Rafii, F. Fromard and F. Blasco. 1998. Evolutionary diversity among Atlantic coast mangroves. *Acta Oecolog.* 19: 323–330.

Dominguez, C. A., L. E. Eguiarte, J. Nuñez-Farfán and R. Dirzo. 1998. Flower morphometry of *Rhizophora mangle* (Rhizophoraceae): Geographical variation in Mexican populations. *Amer. J. Bot.* 85: 637–648.

Doyle, T. W., T. J. Smith, III and M. B. Robblee. 1995. Wind damage effects of hurricane Andrew on mangrove communities along the southwest coast of Florida. *J. Coast. Res.* 21: 159–168.

Dschida, W., K. Platt-Aloia and W. Thomson. 1992. Epidermal peels of *Avicennia germinans* (L.) Stern: A useful system to study the function of salt glands. *Ann. Bot.* 70: 501–509.

Dye, A. and T. Lasiak. 1986. Microbenthos, meiobenthos and fiddler crabs: Trophic interactions in a tropical mangrove sediment. *Mar. Ecol. Prog. Ser.* 32: 259–264.

Duke, N. C. 1992. Mangrove floristics and biogeography. In A. I. Robertson and D. M. Alongi (eds.), *Tropical Mangrove Ecosystems*, pp. 63–100. American Geophysical Union, Washington, DC.

Duke, N. C. 1995. Genetic diversity, distributional barriers and rafting continents—more thoughts on the evolution of mangroves. *Hydrobiologia* 295: 167–181.

Duke, N. C., M. C. Ball and J. C. Ellison. 1998a. Factors influencing biodiversity and distributional gradients in mangroves. *Global Ecol. Biogeogr. Letts.* 7: 27–47.

Duke, N. C., J. A. H. Benzie, J. A. Goodall and E. R. Ballment. 1998b. Genetic structure and evolution of species in the mangrove genus *Avicennia* (Avicenniaceae) in the Indo-West Pacific. *Evolution* 52: 1612–1626.

Ellison, A. M. In press. Wetlands of Central America. *Wetlands Ecol. Mgmt.*

Ellison, A. M. and E. J. Farnsworth. 1990. The ecology of Belizean mangrove-root fouling communities. I. Epibenthic fauna are barriers to isopod attack of red mangrove roots. *J. Exp. Mar. Biol. Ecol.* 142: 91–104.

Ellison, A. M. and E. J. Farnsworth. 1992. The ecology of Belizean mangrove-root fouling communities: Patterns of distribution and abundance and effects on root growth. *Hydrobiologia* 247: 87–98.

Ellison, A. M. and E. J. Farnsworth. 1993. Seedling survivorship, growth, and response to disturbance in Belizean mangal. *Amer. J. Bot.* 80: 1137–1145.

Ellison, A. M. and E. J. Farnsworth. 1996a. Anthropogenic disturbance of Caribbean mangrove ecosystems: Past impacts, present trends, and future predictions. *Biotropica* 28:549–565.

Ellison, A. M. and E. J. Farnsworth. 1996b. Spatial and temporal variability in growth of *Rhizophora mangle* saplings: Links with insolation, herbivory, and local sedimentation regimes on Belizean coral cays. *J. Ecol.* 80: 717–731.

Ellison, A. M. and E. J. Farnsworth. 1997. Simulated sea level change alters anatomy, physiology, growth, and reproduction of red mangrove (*Rhizophora mangle* L.). *Oecologia* 112: 435–446.

Ellison, A. M., E. J. Farnsworth, and R. R. Twilley. 1996. Facultative mutualism between red mangroves and root-fouling sponges in Belizean mangal. *Ecology* 77: 2431–2444.

Ellison, A. M., E. J. Farnsworth and R. E. Merkt. 1999. Origins of mangrove ecosystems and the mangrove biodiversity anomaly. *Global Ecol. Biogeogr. Letts.* 8: 95–115.

Ellison, A. M., B. B. Mukherjee and A. Karim. 2000. Scale-dependent vegetation-environment relationships of mangroves in the Sundarbans of Bangladesh, with special attention to the endemic species, *Heritiera fomes* (Sterculiaceae). *J. Ecol.* 88: 813–824.

Ellison, J. C. 1993. Mangrove retreat with rising sea-level, Bermuda. *Estuarine Coastal and Shelf Sci.* 37: 75–87.

Ellison, J. C. 1996. Pollen evidence of Late Holocene mangrove development in Bermuda. *Global Ecol. Biogeogr. Letts.* 5: 315–326.

Ellison, J. C. and D. R. Stoddart. 1991. Mangrove ecosystem collapse during predicted sea-level rise: Holocene analogues and implications. *J. Coastal Res.* 7: 151–165.

Elmqvist, T. and P. A. Cox. 1996. The evolution of vivipary in flowering plants. *Oikos* 77: 3–9.

Ewel, K. C., S. Zheng, A. S. Pinzón and J. A. Bourgeois. 1998. Environmental effects of canopy gap formation in high-rainfall mangrove forests. *Biotropica* 30: 502–509.

FAO. 1994. *Mangrove Forest Management Guidelines*. FAO Forestry Paper 117, Food and Agriculture Organization of the United Nations, Rome.

Farnsworth, E. J. 1998. Values, uses and conservation of mangroves in India: Lessons for mangroves of the world. *Env. Aware.* 21: 11–19.

Farnsworth, E. J. 2000. The ecology and physiology of viviparous and recalcitrant seeds. *Annu. Rev. Ecol. Syst.* 31: 107–138.

Farnsworth, E. J. and A. M. Ellison. 1991. Patterns of herbivory in Belizean mangrove swamps. *Biotropica* 23: 555–567.

Farnsworth, E. J. and A. M. Ellison. 1993. Dynamics of herbivory in Belizean mangal. *J. Trop. Ecol.* 9: 435–453.

Farnsworth, E. J. and A. M. Ellison. 1996a. Scale-dependent spatial and temporal variability in biogeography of mangrove-root epibiont communities. *Ecol. Monogr.* 66: 45–66.

Farnsworth, E. J. and A. M. Ellison. 1996b. Sun-shade adaptability of the red mangrove, *Rhizophora mangle* (Rhizophoraceae): Changes through ontogeny at several levels of biological organization. *Amer. J. Bot.* 83: 1131–1143.

Farnsworth, E. J. and A. M. Ellison. 1997a. Global patterns of pre-dispersal propagule predation in mangrove forests. *Biotropica* 29: 316–330.

Farnsworth, E. J. and A. M. Ellison. 1997b. The global conservation status of mangroves. *Ambio* 26: 328–334.

Farnsworth, E. J. and J. M. Farrant. 1998. Reductions in abscisic acid are linked with viviparous reproduction in mangroves. *Amer. J. Bot.* 85: 760–769.

Farnsworth, E. J., A. M. Ellison and W. K. Gong. 1996. Elevated CO_2 alters anatomy, physiology, growth, and reproduction of red mangrove (*Rhizophora mangle* L.). *Oecologia* 108: 599–609.

Farrant, J. M., N. W. Pammenter, P. Berjak, E. J. Farnsworth and C. W. Vertucci. 1996. Presence of dehydrin-like proteins and levels of abscisic acid in recalcitrant (desiccation-sensitive) seeds may be related to habitat. *Seed Sci. Res.* 3: 1–13.

Feller, I. C. 1995. Effects of nutrient enrichment on growth and herbivory of dwarf red mangrove (*Rhizophora mangle*). *Ecol. Monogr.* 65: 477–505.

Feller, I. C. 1996. Effects of nutrient enrichment on leaf anatomy of dwarf *Rhizophora mangle* L. (red mangrove). *Biotropica* 28: 13–22.

Feller, I. C. and K. L. McKee. 1999. Light-gap creation in a Belizean mangrove forest by a wood-boring insect. *Biotropica* 31: 607–616.

Feller, I. C. and W. N. Mathis. 1997. Primary herbivory by wood-boring insects along an architectural gradient of *Rhizophora mangle*. *Biotropica* 29: 440–451.

Fernandes. M. 1991. Tool use and predation of oysters (*Crassostrea rhizophorae*) by the tufted Capuchin, *Cebus apella apella*, in brackish water mangrove swamp. *Primates* 34: 529–531.

Field, C. (ed.). 1996. *Restoration of Mangrove Ecosystems*. International Tropical Timber Organization and International Society for Mangrove Ecosystems, Okinawa, Japan.

Field, C. 1998. Rationales and practices of mangrove afforestation. *Mar. Freshwater Res.* 49: 353–358.

Field, C. D. 1995. Impact of expected climate change on mangroves. *Hydrobiologia* 295: 75–81.

Fitzgerald, M. A., D. A. Orlovich and W. G. Allaway. 1992. Evidence that abaxial leaf glands are the sites of salt secretion in leaves of the mangrove *Avicennia marina* (Forsk.) Vierh. *New Phytol.* 120: 1–7.

Fouda, M. M. and M. Almuharrami. 1995. An initial assessment of mangrove resources and human activities at Mahout Island, Arabian Sea, Oman. *Hydrobiologia* 295: 353–362.

Gilbert, A. J. and R. Janssen. 1998. Use of environmental functions to communicate the values of a mangrove ecosystem under different management regimes. *Ecol. Econ.* 25: 323–346.

Goldstein, G., F. Rada, L. Sternberg, J. L. Burguera, M. Burguera, A. Orozco, M. Montilla, O. Zabala, A. Azocar, M. J. Canales and A. Celis. 1989. Gas exchange and water balance of a mistletoe species and its mangrove hosts. *Oecologia* 78: 176–183.

Gomez, M. and S. Winkler. 1991. Bromelias en manglares del Pacifico de Guatemala. *Rev. Biol. Trop.* 39: 207–214.

Gong, W. K. and J. E. Ong. 1995. The use of demographic studies in mangrove silviculture. *Hydrobiologia* 295:255–261.

Goodbody, I. 1993. The ascidian fauna of a Jamaican lagoon: Thirty years of change. *Rev. Biol. Trop., Suppl.* 41: 35–38.

Goodbody, I. 1994. The tropical Western Atlantic Perophoridae (Ascidiaceae). I. The genus *Perophora*. *Bull. Mar. Sci* 55: 176–192.

Gould, S. J. and R. C. Lewontin, 1979. The spandrels of San Marco and the Panglossian paradigm: A critique of the adaptationist program. *Proc. R. Soc. Lond. B* 205: 581–598.

Government of West Bengal. no date. *Project Sundarbans: Harmony between Development and Conservation is Essential for your own Existence and Sustenance*. Department of Forests, Sundarbans Biosphere Reserve, West Bengal, India.

Hallé, F., R. A. A. Oldeman and P. B. Tomlinson. 1978. *Tropical Trees and Forests: An Architectural Analysis*. Springer-Verlag, Berlin.

Hamilton, L. S. and S. C. Snedaker (eds.). 1984. *Handbook for Mangrove Area Management*. United Nations Environment Programme and East-West Center, Honolulu, HI.

Harvey, P. H. and M. D. Pagel. 1991. *The Comparative Method in Evolutionary Biology*. Oxford University Press, Oxford.

Heck, K. L., Jr. and E. D. McCoy. 1979. Biogeography of seagrasses: Evidence from associated organisms. *N. Z. DSIR Info. Ser.* 137: 109–128.

Hoffman, J. A., J. Katz, and M. D. Bertness. 1984. Fiddler crab deposit-feeding and meiofaunal abundance in salt marsh habitats. *J. Exp. Mar. Biol. Ecol* 82: 161–174.

Hong, P. N. and H. T. San. 1993. *Mangroves of Vietnam*. IUCN Wetlands Programme, Gland, Switzerland.

Hovendon, M. J., M. Curran, M. A. Cole, P. F. E. Goulter, N. J. Skelton and W. G. Allaway. 1995. Ventilation and respiration in roots of one-year-old seedlings of grey mangrove *Avicennia marina* (Forsk.) Vierh. *Hydrobiologia* 295: 23–29.

Hudson, B. J. 1983. Wetland reclamation in Jamaica. *Carib. Geog.* 1: 75–88.

Hudson, D. A. and R. J. G. Lester. 1994. Parasites and symbionts of wild mud crabs *Scylla serrata* (Forskal) of potential significance in aquaculture. *Aquaculture* 120: 183–199.

Hussain, Z. and I. Ahmed. 1994. Management of forest resources. In Z. Hussain and G. Acharya (eds.), *Mangroves of the Sundarbans*, Vol. 2: *Bangladesh*, pp. 181–202. IUCN Wetlands Programme, Gland, Switzerland.

Hyde, K. D. and E. B. G. Jones. 1988. Marine mangrove fungi. *Mar. Ecol.* 9: 15–33.

Hyde, K. D. and S. Y. Lee. 1995. Ecology of mangrove fungi and their role in nutrient cycling: What gaps occur in our knowledge? *Hydrobiologia* 295: 107–118.

Hyde, K. D., E. B. G. Jones, E. Leano, S. B. Pointing, A. D. Poonyth and L. L. P. Vrijmued. 1998. Role of fungi in marine ecosystems. *Biodiv. Conserv.* 7: 1147–1161.

Imbert, D., P. Labbé and A. Rousteau. 1996. Hurricane damage and forest structure in Guadeloupe, French West Indies. *J. Trop. Ecol.* 12: 663–680.

Intergovernmental Panel on Climate Change (IPCC). 1997. *Special Report on Regional Impacts of Climate Change*. Cambridge University Press, Cambridge.

Janzen, D. H. 1985. Mangroves: Where's the understory? *J. Trop. Ecol.* 1: 84–92.

Japan International Association for Mangroves (JIAM) and International Society for Mangrove Ecosystems (ISME). 1993. *The Economic and Environment Value of Mangrove Forests and their Present State of Conservation*. Report PCF(XII)/14 of the International Tropical Timber Organization, Kuala Lumpur, Malaysia.

Jeyaseelan, M. J. P. and K. Krishnamurthy. 1980. Role of mangrove forests of Pichavaram as fish nurseries. *Proc. Indian Nat. Sci. Acad*. B46: 48–53.

Jiménez, J. A. and K. A. Sauter. 1991. Structure and dynamics of mangrove forests along a flooding gradient. *Estuaries* 14: 49–56.

Jones, D. A. 1984. Crabs of the mangal ecosystem. In F. D. Por and I. Dor (eds.), *Hydrobiology of the Mangal*, pp. 89–110. Dr. W. Junk, The Hague.

Kalay, U. L. and G. P. Jones. 1998. Mangrove restoration: A potential tool for coastal management in tropical developing countries. *Ambio* 27: 656–661.

Keenan, C. P., P. J. F. Davie and D. L. Mann. 1998. A revision of the genus *Scylla* de Haan, 1833 (Crustacea: Decapoda: Brachyura: Portunidae). *Raffles Bull. Zool.* 46: 217–245.

Kelaher, B. P., M. G. Chapman and A. J. Underwood. 1998a. Changes in benthic assemblages near boardwalks in temperate urban mangrove forests. *J. Exp. Mar. Biol. Ecol.* 228: 291–307.

Kelaher, B. P., A. J. Underwood, and M. G. Chapman. 1998b. Effect of boardwalks on the semaphore crab *Heloecius cordiformis* in temperate urban mangrove forests. *J. Exp. Mar. Biol. Ecol.* 227:281–300.

King, R. J. and C. F. Puttock. 1994. Macroalgae Associated with Mangroves in Australia: Rhodophyta. *Bot. Mar.* 37: 181–191.

Klein, M. L., S. R. Humphrey and H. F. Percival. 1995. Effects of ecotourism on distribution of waterbirds in a wildlife refuge. *Cons. Biol.* 9: 1454–1465.

Klekowski, E. J. Jr. and P. J. Godfrey. 1989. Ageing and mutation in plants. *Nature* 340: 389–391.

Klekowski, E. J. Jr., R. Lowenfeld and P. K. Hepler. 1994. Mangrove genetics. 2. Outcrossing and lower spontaneous mutation rates in Puerto Rican *Rhizophora*. *Intl. J. Plant Sci.* 155: 373–381.

Klekowski, E. J. Jr., S. A. Temple, A. M. Siung-Chang, and K. Kumarsingh. 1999. An association of mangrove mutation, scarlet ibis, and mercury contamination in Trinidad, West Indies. *Env. Pollut.* 100: 1–5.

Kohlmeyer, J. 1969. Ecological notes on fungi in mangrove forests. *Trans. Brit. Mycol. Soc.* 53: 237–250.

Kohlmeyer, J. and B. Bebout. 1986. On the occurrence of marine fungi in the diet of *Littorina angulifera* and observations on the behavior of the periwinkle. *Mar. Ecol.* 7: 333–343.

Kohlmeyer, J., B. Bebout and B. Volkmann-Kohlmeyer. 1995. Decomposition of mangrove wood by marine fungi and teredinids in Belize. *Mar. Ecol.* 16: 27–39.

Krishnamurthy, K., M. J. P. Jeyaseelan and M. A. S. Ali. 1984. The distribution of fishes in the global mangroves. *Curr. Sci.* 53: 901–906.

Lacerda, L. D. (ed.). 1993. *Conservation and Sustainable Utilization of Mangrove Forests in Latin America and Africa, Part I - Latin America.* Mangrove Ecosystems Technical Reports 2. International Society for Mangrove Ecosystems, Okinawa, Japan.

Lacerda, L. D., D. V. José, C. E. de Rezende, M. C. F. Francisco, J. C. Wasserman and J. C. Martins. 1986. Leaf chemical characteristics affecting herbivory in a new world mangrove forest. *Biotropica* 18: 350–355.

Lambert, G., T. D. Steinke and Y. Naidoo. 1987. Algae associated with mangroves in southern African estuaries. I. Rhodophyceae. *S. Afr. J. Bot.* 53: 349–361.

Lapointe, B., M. Littler and D. Littler. 1987. A comparison of nutrient-limited productivity in microalgae from a Caribbean barrier reef and from a mangrove ecosystem. *Aquatic Bot.* 28: 243–255.

Lee, S. Y. 1991. Herbivory as an ecological process in a *Kandelia candel* (Rhizophoraceae) mangal in Hong Kong. *J. Trop. Ecol.* 7: 337–348.

Lee. S. Y. 1998. Ecological role of grapsid crabs in mangrove ecosystems: A review. *Mar. Freshwater Res.* 49: 335–343.

Lin, G. and L. Sternberg. 1992. Comparative study of water uptake and photosynthetic gas exchange between scrub and fringe red mangroves, *Rhizophora mangle* L. *Oecologia* 90:399–403.

Littler, D. S., M. M. Littler, K. E. Bucher and J. E. Norris. 1989. *Marine Plants of the Caribbean: A Field Guide from Florida to Brazil.* Smithsonian Institution Press, Washington, DC.

Lowenfeld, R. and E. J. Klekowski Jr. 1992. Mangrove genetics. I. Mating systems and mutation rates of *Rhizophora mangle* in Florida and San Salvador Island, Bahamas. *Int. J. Plant Sci.* 153: 394–399.

Lovelock, C. E. and B. F. Clough. 1992. Influence of solar radiation and lead angle on xanthophyll concentrations in mangroves. *Oecologia* 91: 518–525.

Lovelock, C. E., B. F. Clough and I. E. Woodrow. 1992. Distribution and accumulation of ultraviolet radiation-absorbing compounds in leaves of tropical mangroves. *Planta* 188: 143–154.

Lugo, A. E. 1980. Mangrove ecosystems: Successional or steady state? *Biotropica* 12 (suppl.): 65–72.

Lugo, A. E. 1986. The mangrove understory: An expensive luxury? *J. Trop. Ecol.* 2: 287–288.

Lugo, A. E. 1997. Old-growth mangrove forests in the United States. *Conserv. Biol.* 11: 11–20.

Lugo, A. E. 1998. Mangrove forests: A tough system to invade but an easy one to rehabilitate. *Mar. Pollut. Bull.* 37.

Lugo, A. E. and S. C. Snedaker. 1974. The ecology of mangroves. *Annu. Rev. Ecol. Syst.* 5: 39–64.

MacMillan, C. 1975. Adaptive differentiation to chilling in mangrove populations. In G. E. Walsh, S. C. Snedaker and H. J. Teas (eds.), *Proceedings of the International Symposium on Biology and Management of Mangroves,* pp.

62–68. Institute of Food and Agricultural Sciences, Gainesville, FL.

MacNae, W. 1968. A general account of the fauna and flora of mangrove swamps and forests in the Indo-West Pacific region. *Adv. Mar. Biol.* 6: 73–270.

Marshall, A. G. 1983. Bats, flowers and fruit: Evolutionary relations in the Old World. *Biol. J. Linn. Soc.* 20: 155–235.

Mattox, N. T. 1949. Studies on the biology of the edible oyster, *Ostrea rhizophorae* Guilding in Puerto Rico. *Ecol. Monogr.* 19: 339–356.

McCoy, E. D. and K. L. Heck. 1976. Biogeography of corals, seagrasses, and mangroves: An alternative to the center of origin concept. *Sys. Zool.* 25: 201–210.

McCoy, E. D., H. R. Mushinsky, D. Johnson and W. E. Meshaka. 1996. Mangrove damage caused by hurricane Andrew on the southwestern coast of Florida. *Bull. Mar. Sci.* 59: 1–8.

McGuinness, K. A. 1997. Dispersal, establishment and survival of *Ceriops tagal* propagules in a north Australian mangrove forest. *Oecologia* 109: 80–87.

McKee, K. L. 1993. Soil physicochemical patterns and mangrove species distribution: Reciprocal effects? *J. Ecol.* 81:477–488.

McKee, K. L. 1995. Seedling recruitment patterns in a Belizean mangrove forest: Effects of establishment ability and physico-chemical factors. *Oecologia* 101: 448–460.

McKee, K. L. 1996. Growth and physiological responses of neotropical mangrove seedlings to root zone hypoxia. *Tree Physiol.* 15: 883–998.

McKillup, S. C. and McKillup, R. V. 1997. An outbreak of the moth *Achaea serva* (Fabr.) on the mangrove *Excoecaria agallocha* (L.). *Pan-Pacific Entomol.* 73: 184–185.

Mepham, R. H. 1983. Mangrove floras of the southern continents. I. The geographical origin of Indo-Pacific mangrove genera and the development and present status of the Australian mangroves. *S. African J. Bot.* 2: 1–8.

Mepham, R. and T. Petr (eds.). 1986. *Papers Contributed to the Workshop on Strategies for the Management of Fisheries and Aquaculture in Mangrove Ecosystems.* FAO Fisheries Report No. 370 Supplement, Bangkok, Thailand.

Michener, W. K, E. R. Blood, K. L. Bildstein, M. M. Brinson and L. R. Gardner. 1997. Climate change, hurricanes and tropical storms and rising sea level in coastal wetlands. *Ecol. Appl.* 7: 770–801.

Mimura, N. and P. D. Nunn. 1998. Trends of beach erosion and shoreline protection in rural Fiji. *J. Coastal Res.* 14: 37–46.

Murphy, D. H. 1990. The natural history of insect herbivory of mangrove trees in and near Singapore. *Raffles Bull. Zool.* 38: 119–203.

Murren, C. J. and A. M. Ellison. 1996. Effects of habitat, plant size, and floral display on male and female reproductive success of the neotropical orchid *Brassavola nodosa. Biotropica* 28: 30–41.

Naidoo, G. 1985. Effects of waterlogging and salinity on plant water relations and on the

accumulation of solutes in three mangrove species. *Aquat. Bot.* 22: 133–143.

Newberry, D. McC. 1980. Infestation of the coccid, *Icerya seychellarum* (Westw.), on the mangrove *Avicennia marina* (Forsk.) Vierh. on Aldabra Atoll, with special reference to tree age. *Oecologia* 45: 325–330.

Newell, R. I. E., N. Marshall, A. Sasekumar and V. C. Chong. 1995. Relative importance of benthic microalgae, phytoplankton, and mangroves as sources of nutrition for penaeid prawns and other coastal invertebrates from Malaysia. *Mar. Biol.* 123: 595–606.

Newell, S. 1992. Estimating fungal biomass and productivity in decomposing litter. In G. Carroll and D. Wicklow (eds.), *The Fungal Community: Its Organization and Role in the Ecosystem,* pp. 521–561. Marcel Dekker, New York.

Odum, W. E. and E. J. Heald. 1975. The detritus food web of an estuarine mangrove community. In L. Cronin (ed.), *Estuarine Research,* pp. 265–286. Academic Press, New York.

Olafsson., E. 1996. Meiobenthos in mangrove areas in eastern Africa with emphasis on assemblage structure of free-living marine nematodes. *Hydrobiologia.* 312: 47–57.

Ong, J. E. 1982. Mangroves and aquaculture in Malaysia. *Ambio* 11: 252–257.

Onuf, C. P., J. M. Teal, and I. Valiela. 1977. Interactions of nutrients, plant growth, and herbivory in a mangrove ecosystem. *Ecology* 58: 514–526.

Orozco, A., F. Rada, A. Azocar and G. Goldstein. 1990. How does a mistletoe affect the water, nitrogen and carbon balance of two mangrove ecosystem species. *Plant, Cell Env.* 13: 941–947.

Osunkoya, O. O. and R. G. Creese. 1997. Population structure, spatial pattern and seedling establishment of the grey mangrove, *Avicennia marina* var. *australasica,* in New Zealand. *Aust. J. Bot.* 45: 707–725.

Padrón, C. M., S. O. Llorente and L. Menéndez. 1993. Mangroves of Cuba. In L. D. Lacerda (ed.), *Conservation and Sustainable Utilization of Mangrove Forests in Latin America and Africa Regions,* Part I: *Latin America,* pp. 147–154. International Society for Mangrove Ecosystems, Okinawa, Japan.

Paine, R. T. and S. A. Levin. 1981. Intertidal landscapes: Disturbance and the dynamics of pattern. *Ecol. Monogr.* 51: 145–178.

Pannier, F. 1962. Estudio fisiológico sobre la vivparia de *Rhizophora mangle* L. *Acta Cien. Venez.* 13: 184–197.

Parkinson, R. W., R. D. DeLaune and J. R. White. 1994. Holocene sea-level rise and the fate of mangrove forests within the wider Caribbean region. *J. Coastal Res.* 10: 1077–1086.

Pernetta, J. C. 1993. *Mangrove Forests, Climate Change and Sea Level Rise: Hydrological Influences on Community Structure and Survival, with Examples from the Indo-West Pacific.* IUCN, Gland.

Perry, D. M. 1988. Effects of associated fauna on growth and productivity in the red mangrove. *Ecology* 69: 1064–1075.

Pedroche, F. F., J. A. West, G. C. Zuccarello, A. Senties and U. Karsten. 1995. Marine red algae of the mangroves in southern Pacific México and Pacific Guatemala. *Bot. Mar.* 38: 111–119.

Piyakarnchana, T. 1981. Severe defoliation of *Avicennia alba* Bl. by larvae of *Cleroa injectaria* Walker. *J. Sci. Soc. Thailand* 7: 33–36.

Pielou, E. C. 1977. The latitudinal spans of seaweed species and their patterns of overlap. *J. Biogeog.* 4: 299–311.

Pinto, L. and S. Wignarajah. 1980. Some ecological aspects of the edible oyster *Crassostrea cucullata* (Born) occurring in association with mangroves in Negombo lagoon, Sri Lanka. *Hydrobiologia* 69: 11–19.

Plaziat, J.-C. 1995. Modern and fossil mangroves and mangals: Their climatic and biogeographic variability. *Geol. Soc. Special Pub.* 83: 73–96.

Popp, M., J. Polania and M. Weiper. 1993. Physiological adaptations to different salinity levels in mangrove. In H. Lieth and A. Al Masoom (eds.), *Towards the Rational Use of High Salinity Tolerant Plants,* Vol. 1, pp. 217–224. Kluwer Academic Publishers, Amsterdam.

Primavera, J. H. 1995. Mangroves and brackishwater pond culture in the Philippines. *Hydrobiologia* 295: 303–309.

Primavera, J. H. 1998. Mangroves as nurseries: Shrimp populations in mangrove and nonmangrove habitats. *Est. Coastal Shelf Sci.* 46: 457–464.

Quesada, R., E. Madrigal, J. Alfaro, O. Pacheco and E. Zamora. 1985. Crecimiento y supervivencia del ostión de manglar (*Crassostrea rhizophorae* Guilding, 1828), traslado de Estero Vizcaya, Costa del Caribe a estanques de cultivo de camarones en Chomes, Costa Pacífica de Costa Rica. *Rev. Biol. Trop.* 33: 7–12.

Rabinowitz, D. 1977. Effects of a mangrove borer *Poecilips rhizophorae* on propagules of *Rhizophora harrisonii* in Panama. *Fl. Entomol.* 60: 129–134.

Rabinowitz, D. 1978a. Dispersal properties of mangrove propagules. *Biotropica* 10: 47–57.

Rabinowitz, D. 1978b. Early growth of mangrove seedlings in Panama, and an hypothesis concerning the relationship of dispersal and zonation. *J. Biogeogr.* 5: 113–133.

Rafii, Z. A., R. S. Dodd and F. Fromard. 1996. Biogeographic variation in foliar waxes of mangrove species. *Biochem. Syst. Ecol.* 24: 341–345.

Rehm, A. and H. J. Humm. 1973. *Sphaeroma terebrans:* A threat to the mangroves of southwestern Florida. *Science* 182: 173–174.

Richards, W. J.and J. A. Bohnsack. 1990. The Caribbean Sea: A large marine ecosystem in crisis. In K. Sherman, L. M. Alexander and B. D. Gold (eds.), *Large Marine Ecosystems: Patterns, Processes, and Yields,* pp. 44–53. American Association for the Advancement of Science, Washington, DC.

Ricklefs, R. E. and R. E. Latham. 1993. Global patterns of species diversity in mangrove floras. In R. E. Ricklefs and D. Schluter (eds.), *Species Diversity in Ecological Communities: Historical and Geographical Perspectives,* pp. 213–233. University of Chicago Press, Chicago.

Rico-Gray, V. and L. B. Thien. 1989. Ant-mealybug interaction decreases reproductive fitness of *Schomburgkia tibicinis* (Orchidaceae) in Mexico. *J. Trop. Ecol.* 5: 109–112.

Rico-Gray, V., J. T. Barber, L. B. Thien, E. G. Ellgaard and J. J. Toney. 1989. An unusual animal-plant interaction: Feeding of *Schomburgkia tibicinis* (Orchidaceae) by ants. *Amer. J. Bot.* 76: 603–608.

Robertson, A. I., D. M. Alongi and K. G. Boto. 1992. Food chains and carbon fluxes. In A. I. Robertson and D. M. Alongi (eds.). *Tropical Mangrove Ecosystems,* pp. 293–326. American Geophysical Union, Washington, DC.

Robertson, A. I., R. Giddens, and T. J. Smith, III. 1990. Seed predation by insects in tropical mangrove forests: Extent and effects on seed viability and the growth of seedlings. *Oecologia* 83: 213–219.

Rollet, B. 1981. *Bibliography on Mangrove Research, 1600–1975.* UNESCO, Paris.

Ross, P. M. and Underwood, A. J. 1997. The distribution and abundance of barnacles in a mangrove forest. *Austral. J. Ecol.* 22: 37–47.

Roth, L. C. 1992. Hurricanes and mangrove regeneration: Effects of Hurricane Joan, October 1988, on the vegetation of Isla del Venado, Bluefields, Nicaragua. *Biotropica* 24: 375–384.

Ruitenbeek, H. J. 1994. Modelling economyecology linkages in mangroves: Economic evidence for promoting conservation in Bintuni Bay, Indonesia. *Ecol. Econ.* 10: 233–247.

Rützler, K. 1969. The mangrove community, aspects of its structure, faunistics and ecology. In *Lagunas Costeras: Un Simposio,* pp. 515–525. Universidad Nacional Autonoma de México, UNESCO, Mexico.

Saenger, P. 1998. Mangrove vegetation: An evolutionary perspective. *Mar. Freshwater Res.* 49: 277–286.

Saenger, P., E. J. Hegerl and J. D. S. Davie. 1983. Global status of mangrove ecosystems. *The Environmentalist* 3 (Suppl. 3): 1–88.

Saifullah, S. M., K. Aisha and F. Rasool. 1997. Algal epiphytes on mangroves of Balbochistan, Pakistan. *Pakistan. J. Bot.* 29: 191–197.

Schimper, A. F. W. 1903. *Plant Geography* (translated by W. R. Fisher). Clarendon Press, Oxford.

Schoener., T. W. 1987. Leaf pubescence in buttonwood: Community variation in a putative defense against defoliation. *Proc. Natl. Acad. Sci. USA* 84: 7992–7995.

Scholander, P. F. 1968. How mangroves desalinate sea water. *Phys. Plant.* 21: 251–261.

Scholander, P. F., H. T. Hammel, E. A. Hemmingsen and W. Garey. 1962. Salt balance in mangroves. *Plant Phys.* 37: 722–729.

Semesi, A. K. 1998. Mangrove management and utilization in eastern Africa. *Ambio* 27: 620–626.

Sheridan, R. P. 1991. Epicaulous, nitrogen-fixing microepiphytes in a tropical mangal community, Guadeloupe, French West Indies. *Biotropica* 23: 530–541.

Sheridan, R. P. 1992. Nitrogen fixation by epicaulous cyanobacteria in the Pointe de la Saline Mangrove community, Guadeloupe, French West Indies. *Biotropica* 24: 571–574.

Sherman, R. E., T. J. Fahey and R. W. Howarth. 1998. Soil–plant interactions in a neotropical mangrove forest: Iron, phosphorus and sulfur dynamics. *Oecologia* 115: 553–563.

Skilleter, G. A. 1996. Validation of rapid assessment of damage in urban mangrove forests and relationships with molluscan assemblages. *J. Mar. Biol. Assn. U.K.* 76: 701–716.

Skilleter, G. A. and X. X. Warren. 2000. Effects of habitat modification in mangroves on the structure of mollusc and crab assemblages. *J. Exp. Mar. Biol. Ecol.* 244: 107–129.

Siddiqi, N. A. and M. A. S. Khan. 1996. Planting techniques for mangroves on new accretions in the coastal areas of Bangladesh. In C. Field (ed.), *Restoration of Mangrove Ecosystems,* pp. 143–159. International Tropical Timber Organization and International Society for Mangrove Ecosystems, Okinawa, Japan.

Smith, S. M., Y. Y. Yang, Y. Kamiya and S. C. Snedaker. 1996. Effect of environment and gibberellins on the early growth and development of the red mangrove, *Rhizophora mangle* L. *Plant Growth Reg.* 20: 215–223.

Smith, T. J. III. 1987. Effects of light and intertidal position on seedling survival and growth in tropical, tidal forests. *J. Exp. Mar. Biol. Ecol.* 110: 133–146.

Smith, T. J. III. 1992. Forest structure. In A. I. Robertson and D. M. Alongi (eds.), *Tropical Mangrove Ecosystems,* pp. 101–136. American Geophysical Union, Washington, DC.

Smith, T. J. III, K. G. Boto, S. D. Frusher and R. L. Giddins. 1991. Keystone species and mangrove forest dynamics: The influence of burrowing by crabs on soil nutrient status and forest productivity. *Est., Coast. Shelf. Sci.* 33: 419–432.

Smith, T. J. III, H. T. Chan, C. C. McIvor and M. B. Robblee. 1989. Comparisons of seed predation in tropical tidal forests from three continents. *Ecology* 70: 146–151.

Smith, T. J. III, M. B. Robblee, H. R. Wanless and T. W. Doyle. 1994. Mangroves, hurricanes, and lightning strikes. *BioScience* 44: 256–262.

Snedaker, S. C. and R. J. Araújo. 1998. Stomatal conductance and gas exchange in four species of Caribbean mangroves exposed to ambient and increased CO_2. *Mar. Freshwater Res.* 49: 325–327.

Snedaker, S. C. and E. J. Lahmann. 1988. Mangrove understorey absence: A consequence of evolution. *J. Trop. Ecol.* 4: 311–314.

Sousa, W. P., and B. J. Mitchell. 1999. The effect of seed predators on plant distributions: Is there a general pattern in mangroves? *Oikos* 86: 55–66.

Specht, R. L. 1981. Biogeography of halophytic angiosperms (salt-marsh, mangrove and seagrass). In A. Keast (ed.), *Ecological Biogeography of Australia,* pp. 577–589. Dr. W. Junk, The Hague.

Sperry, J. S., M. T. Tyree and J. R. Donnelly. 1988. Vulnerability of xylem to embolism in a mangrove vs. an inland species of Rhizophoraceae. *Phys. Plant.* 74: 276–283.

Srivastava, P. B. L., G. B. Keong and A. Muktar. 1987. Role of *Achrostichum* species in natural regeneration of *Rhizophora* species in Malaysia. *Trop. Ecol.* 28: 274–288.

Steinbeck, J. 1941. *The Log from the Sea of Cortez.* Penguin Books, New York.

Steinke, T. D. 1986. A preliminary study of buoyancy behaviour in *Avicennia marina* propagules. *S. Afr. J. Bot.* 52: 559–565.

Steinke, T. D. and E. B. Gareth-Jones. 1993. Marine and mangrove fungi from the Indian Ocean coast of South Africa. *S. Afr. J. Bot.* 59: 385–390.

Steinke, T. D. and Y. Naidoo. 1990. Biomass of algae epiphytic on pneumatophores of the mangrove, *Avicennia marina*, in the St Lucia estuary. *S. Afr. J. Bot.* 56: 226–232.

Steinke, T. D. and C. J. Ward. 1989. Some effects of the cyclones Domoina and Imboa on mangrove communites in the St. Lucia estuary. *S. Afr. J. Bot.* 55: 340–348.

Sternberg, L. da. S. L., N. Ish-Shalom, M. Ross and J. Obrien. 1991. Water relations of coastal plant communities near the ocean/freshwater boundary. *Oecologia* 88: 305–310.

Suman, D. O. (ed.). 1994. *El Ecosistema de Manglar en America Latina y La Cuenca del Caribe: Su Manejo y Conservación.* Rosensteil School of Marine and Atmospheric Sciences, University of Miami, Coral Gables, FL.

Sun, M., K. C. Wong, and J. S. Y. Lee. 1998. Reproductive biology and population genetic structure of *Kandelia candel* (Rhizophoraceae), a viviparous mangrove species. *Amer. J. Bot* 85: 1631–1637.

Swiadek, J. W. 1997. The impacts of Hurricane Andrew on mangrove coasts in southern Florida: A review. *J. Coast. Res.* 13: 242–245.

Swift, M. and S. Cragg. 1982. The role of fungi in wood decomposition in Papuan mangroves. *Bull. Brit. Mycol. Soc.* 16: 10.

Tan, C. G. S. and P. K. L. Ng. 1994. An annotated checklist of mangrove brachyuran crabs from Malaysia and Singapore. *Hydrobiologia* 285: 75–84.

Tan, T. K. and W. F. Leong. 1992. Lignicolous fungi of tropical mangrove wood. *Mycol. Res.* 96: 413–414.

Tattar, T. A., E. J. Klekowski Jr. and A. I. Stern. 1994. Dieback and mortality in red mangrove, *Rhizophora mangle* L., in southwest Puerto Rico. *Arbor. J.* 18:419–429.

Thibodeau, F. R. and N. H. Nickerson 1986. Differential oxidation of mangrove substrate by *Avicennia germinans* and *Rhizophora mangle*. *Amer. J. Bot.* 73: 512–516.

Tomlinson, P. B. 1986. *The Botany of Mangroves.* Cambridge University Press, Cambridge, UK.

Twilley, R. R. 1985. The exchange of organic carbon in basin manrove forests in a southwest Florida estuary. *Est. Coast. Shelf Sci.* 20: 543–557.

Twilley, R. R. 1995. Properties of mangrove ecosystems and their relation to the energy signature of coastal environments. In C. A. S. Hall (ed.), *Maximum Power*, pp. 43–62. University of Colorado Press, Boulder.

Twilley, R. R. and R. H. Chen. 1998. A water budget and hydrology model of a basin mangrove forest in Rookery Bay, Florida. *Mar. Freshwater Res.* 49: 309–323.

Twilley, R. R., A. Bodero and D. Robadue. 1993. Mangrove ecosystem biodiversity and conservation in Ecuador. In C. S. Potter, J. I. Cohen and D. Janczewski (eds.), *Perspectives on Biodiversity: Case Studies of Genetic Resource Conservation and Development*, pp. 105–127. AAAS Press, Washington, DC.

Twilley, R. R., R. H. Chen and T. Hargis. 1992. Carbon sinks in mangroves and their implications to carbon budget of tropical coastal ecosystems. *Water, Air, Soil Pollut.* 64: 265–288.

Twilley, R. R., R. R. Gottfried, V. H. Rivera-Monroy, W. Zhang, M. M. Armijos and A. Bodero. 1998. An approach and preliminary model of integrating ecological and economic constraints of environmental quality in the Guayas River estuary, Ecuador. *Environmental Science and Policy* 1: 271–288.

Twilley, R. R., L. Solórzano and R. Zimmerman. 1991. *The Importance of Mangroves in Sustaining Fisheries and Controlling Water Quality in Coastal Ecosystems.* U.S. Agency for International Development (USAID), Project 8.333.

Underwood, A. J. 1978. The detection of non-random patterns of distribution of species along a gradient. *Oecologia* 36: 317–326.

UNESCO. 1979. The mangrove ecosystem: Scientific aspects and human impact. *UNESCO Rep. Mar. Sci.* 9.

Vance, D. J., M. D. E. Haywood, D. S. Heales, R. A. Kenyon, N. R. Loneragan and R. C. Pendrey. 1996. How far do prawns and fish move into mangroves? Distribution of juvenile banana prawns *Penaeus merguiensis* and fish in a tropical mangrove forest in northern Australia. *Mar. Ecol. Prog. Ser.* 131: 115–124.

van Steenis, C. G. G. J. 1962. The distribution of mangrove plant genera and its significance for palaeogeography. *Proc. Konink. Nederland. Akad. Wetenschap. Ser. C* 65: 164–169.

Veenakumari, K., P. Mohanraj and A. K. Bandyopadhyay. 1997. Insect herbivores and their natural enemies in the mangals of the Andaman and Nicobar Islands. *J. Nat. Hist.* 31: 1105–1126.

Vélez, A. 1991. Reproduction and cultivation of the mangrove oyster *Crassostrea rhizophorae* in Venezuela. In G. F. Newkirk and B. A. Field (eds.), *Oyster Culture in the Caribbean*, pp. 35–50. Mollusc Culture Network, Dalhousie University, Halifax, Nova Scotia.

Veron, J. E. N. 1995. *Corals in Space and Time: The Biogeography and Evolution of the Scleractinia.* Cornell University Press, Ithaca, NY.

Walsh, G. E. 1977. Exploitation of mangal. In V. J. Chapman (ed.), *Wet Coastal Ecosystems*, pp. 347–355. Elsevier, New York.

Warner, G. F. 1967. The life history of the mangrove tree crab, *Aratus pisonii*. *J. Zool.* 153: 321–335.

Wadsworth, F. H. and G. H. Englerth. 1959. Effects of the 1956 hurricane on the forests in Puerto Rico. *Carib. For.* 20: 38–51.

Watson, J. G. 1928. Mangrove forests of the Malay Peninsula. *Malay Forest Rec.* No. 6.

Weir, A. M., T. A. Tattar and E. J. Klekowski Jr. 2000. Disease of red mangrove, *Rhizophora mangle*, in southwest Puerto Rico caused by *Cytospora rhizophorae*. *Biotropica* 32: 299–306.

Werner, A. and R. Stelzer. 1990. Physiological responses of the mangrove *Rhizophora mangle* grown in the absence and presence of NaCl. *Plant Cell Env.* 13: 243–255.

Whitten, A. J. and Damanik, S. J. 1986. Mass defoliation of mangroves in Sumatra, Indonesia. *Biotropica* 18: 176.

Wolanski, E., Y. Mazda and P. Ridd. 1992. Mangrove hydrodynamics. In A. I. Robertson and D. M. Alongi (eds.), *Tropical Mangrove Ecosystems*, pp. 43–62. American Geophysical Union, Washington, DC.

Woodroffe, C. D. 1982. Geomorphology and development of mangrove swamps, Grand Cayman Island, West Indies. *Bull. Mar. Sci.* 32: 381–398.

part *III*

Conservation Issues

chapter 17

Human Alterations of Marine Communities
Students Beware!

Robert S. Steneck and James T. Carlton

*A*s students of marine communities we are often impressed with the number of intimate associations and assemblages we see. We observe and determine why patterns of zonation exist, we learn what organism eats what, which species dominate competitively over which others. We are often lulled into thinking that the wonderfully complex and apparently stable marine community we see has always been this way. We may even be tempted to speculate, as many have in publications, how this "natural" system evolved. Only in the past decade have we come to realize that most marine communities are profoundly altered from the system that had evolved prior to human influences. Our *"Students beware!"* is a warning to all of us that what was natural over evolutionary time in most cases is not what we view as natural today.
Human activity has profoundly changed marine communities—from marshes, rocky shores, and coral reefs to midocean surface waters and the deepest seas—in five major ways (Norse 1993; National Research Council 1995):

- Overextraction of marine organisms
- Invasions of nonindigenous (exotic) species
- Chemical pollution, eutrophication, and related consequences such as toxic phytoplankton blooms
- Alteration of physical habitats
- Global climate change

Within this broad suite of important and long-term anthropogenic changes to the ocean, we focus on aspects of the first two phenomena—the deletion of species (via extinction or functionally through overextraction) and the addition of species (through human-mediated invasions). By concentrating on these two phenomena, we do not imply that the remaining impacts are less important. In fact, there are likely to be significant interactions among all of these factors. However, the topic of human alterations of marine communities is simply too large to be covered in one chapter, so we will limit our scope to these two human influences. Aspects of the other impacts are mentioned in other chapters and in the published literature (e.g., eutrophication, Cooper and Brush 1993; Grigg 1994; Burkholder 1999; habitat alteration, Watling and Norse 1998; global climate change, Atwood et al. 1992; Klypas et al. 1999).

What evidence exists that the subtraction or addition of species to a "natural" marine community fundamentally alters its structure and function? Is it possible that marine communities or ecosystems are no longer functioning in ways that resemble their aboriginal state? If so, what consequences are there to how we view the system and what does this mean to the field of marine community ecology?

To address these questions, we examine a well-known region of the western North Atlantic Ocean, the Gulf of Maine. It is representative of the changes that have occurred in many coastal marine systems around the world. We will focus on the trophic structure and dominant organisms of this system, how they have changed due to human activities, and the consequences of some of those changes. However, it is impossible to describe the massive restructuring of marine communities in historical times at a global scale in one chapter. The scope of the problem is evident in vignettes of human alterations found in several other chapters of this volume (e.g., Menge and Branch; Witman and Dayton; Knowlton and Jackson; Peterson and Estes; and Palumbi). The scope is easy to find in numerous scientific and popular articles that list species that were once abundant but are now rare or extinct and species that have been introduced to natural marine systems. However, it is much more difficult to answer the question, So what? In the context of *marine community ecology*, it is necessary to consider what happens to the entire community when major players have been recently removed or introduced. To illustrate this idea, we offer the Gulf of Maine as a case study in which we focus on a few groups that fundamentally control the structure and function of the system. Following this discussion, we briefly review selected examples from other marine ecosystems around the world to demonstrate the global nature of these phenomena and their impacts.

OVEREXTRACTION BY FISHERIES CHANGES COASTAL MARINE COMMUNITIES

Fisheries exploitation can change natural marine ecosystems more rapidly and at a spatial scale larger than most other human-induced effects. This has been demonstrated for many areas of the world (Aronson 1994; Hughes 1994; Pauly et al. 1998) and is particularly evident in the Gulf of Maine, where centuries of escalating fishing pressure have taken a toll on targeted populations. We will focus on evidence of changes in this marine ecosystem's structure by documenting changes in the distribution, abundance, and body size of its dominant species. We will discuss changes in diversity, structure, and function of the food web that are likely to cause other components of the ecosystems to change. Some changes in exploited populations alter ecosystem function because exploited species are predators, and changes in their abundance have cascading influences on their prey populations. To consider change in the Gulf of Maine ecosystem due to human activities requires examining coastal zones where, due to proximity to population centers, potential impacts are likely to be greatest.

Globally, fisheries often target higher-order, apex predators because they have high food and economic value (see Peterson and Estes, Chapter 18, this volume). Such predators also have a disproportionately large impact on the rest of the ecosystem because of their role as predators (see Menge and Branch, Chapter 9, this volume). Examples of single top predators or "keystone species" are well known for many marine ecosystems (Paine 1969; Simenstad et al. 1978), but more recently the focus has shifted to consider the result of a functional loss of an entire trophic level (e.g., Hughes 1994; Steneck 1994). Therefore, we will first focus our attention on human impacts that control apex predators, the trophic structure of food webs, and the cascading effects related to those changes in coastal communities of the Gulf of Maine.

Stability and Change of Large Predatory Fish over the Past 5000 Years

Large, coastal groundfish such as Atlantic cod have dominated shallow north-temperate to subarctic marine communities in the western North Atlantic for a long time. We know this because for an equally long time people relied on them for food and left clues about their distribution, abundance, and body size. The first clear evidence of human exploitation of marine resources of the Gulf of Maine is found in middens of people

from the Late Archaic period dating to about 5000 years ago (Bourque 1996). These people carved large fish hooks from deer bones to catch the Atlantic cod (*Gadus morhua*). This large, predatory, bottom-feeding fish was well represented in middens from several coastal sites in Maine (Bourque 1996). Cod were predominantly 1 to 1.5 m in length in middens from at least five discrete occupations spanning from 5000 to 400 years ago (Bourque 1996). In another series of middens dated from 2500 to 500 years ago, over 80% of the excavated bone mass was identified as cod (Figures 17.1, 17.2) (Carlson 1986). Evidently, large cod, the extinct sea mink (*Mustela macrodon*), and swordfish have been exploited for literally thousands of years in coastal regions of the Gulf of Maine.

When the first Europeans explored the Gulf of Maine, it was the abundance of large fish that impressed them (Rosier 1605). The northern half of Vespucci's 1526 map of the New World was identified as *Bacallaos*—which is Portuguese for "land of the codfish." In 1602, Bartholemew Gosnold named Cape Cod for the myriad fish that "vexed" his ship. Captain John Smith reported three important facts in 1616: (1) that cod were abundant along the coast, (2) that native Americans already knew this, and (3) that the cod in Maine were two to three times larger than those found elsewhere in the new world (Smith 1616). Fishing villages and colonies sprung up at many locations along the shore (Churchill 1979; Caldwell 1981). In the early 1600s, seafood from the Gulf of Maine had a larger share of the market in Europe than it does today (Caldwell 1981). At that time, 10,000 men were employed fishing for cod in New England (Caldwell 1981). By the 1880s, three times that number were employed in Nova Scotia alone (Barnard 1986). At this time, advances in ships and fishing practices greatly increased harvesting effectiveness. The late nineteenth century may have been the zenith of the codfish industry. Up to that time, humans living along the shore had fished this species for at least 5000 years. By any measure of stability (see Connell and Sousa 1983), large predatory fish such as Atlantic cod appear to have been a stable component of the Gulf of Maine ecosystem.

Recent and Rapid Extirpation of Large Predators

Since the 1800s, cod, haddock and other large-bodied predatory fish targeted by fishermen have declined in abundance and size until they have been virtually eliminated from coastal habitats. This decline is evident in charts of coastal fishing grounds published over the past century. Nearshore fishing grounds first identified and mapped in the 1830s (Collins and Rathbun 1887; Watson 1996) shrank little over the next century when they were remapped in the 1920s (Rich 1929; Steneck 1997). However, from the 1930s to the 1960s the old grounds were significantly reduced as new inshore grounds and up-estuary locations were being exploited (Steneck 1997). This inshore exploitation, however, was short lived and today there is no significant inshore fishery (Conkling and Ames 1996).

Coincident with the rapid decline in fishable stocks along the coast was a change in fishing methods. Hook and line fishing, beginning with deer-bone hooks thousands of years ago (Bourque 1996), continued as the predominant means of

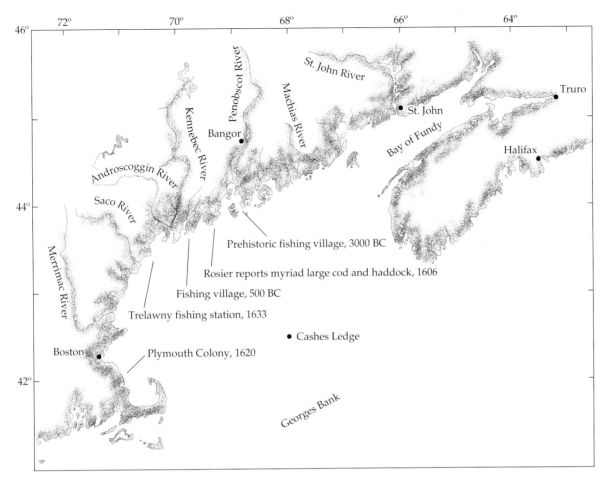

Figure 17.1 The Gulf of Maine and the locations of early records of observers and exploiters of large, bottom-feeding fishes in the Gulf of Maine.

harvest through the 1920s (Collins and Rathbun 1887; Rich 1929; Watson 1996; Steneck 1997). In the 1930s, vessels capable of trawling and refrigerating the otherwise difficult to preserve fish represented a radical departure in the way fish were harvested (Steneck 1997).

Estimating the abundance of fishes based on fisheries data is difficult, especially as fishing technology, methods, and effort change. However, the hook and line harvest may be comparable over time. Since it is likely to be effective only where dense aggregations of feeding fishes occur, abundance estimates over the same general areas with the same fishing techniques over a long period of time should provide evidence of temporal change. Charts of prime fishing grounds made in the 1880s and 1920s show where such concentrations existed (Collins and Rathbun 1887; Rich 1929). Until the advent of vessels capable of refrigeration and dragging otter trawls,

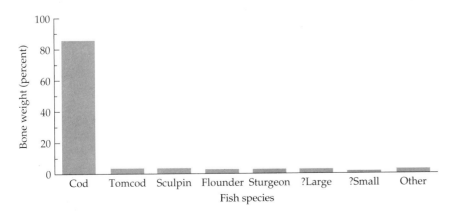

Figure 17.2 Abundance of fish bones discarded by humans 500 to 2500 years ago and preserved in their middens from the Boothbay Harbor region of Maine. "?" indicates unidentifiable species from bone fragments of large and small fish. (After Carlson 1986.)

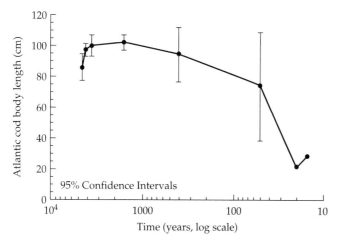

Figure 17.3 Decreasing average size of cod in coastal regions of Maine over the past 5000 years. Data from Bigelow and Schroeder 1953; Hacunda 1981; Ojeda and Dearborn 1989; Bourque 1996; and unpublished data from B. Bourque, Maine State Museum.

breeding aggregations were avoided because of their poor market value and difficulties in bringing those fish to market. However, once those technological hurdles were cleared, massive landings of spawning groundfish in near-shore coastal zones occurred (Conkling and Ames 1996). This change in fishing method and the targeting of spawning individuals was coincident with the extirpation of coastal groundfish stocks. The annual assessment of coastal groundfish stocks by Maine's commissioner of Sea and Shore Fisheries documented this rapid decline. In 1918 stocks were said to be "flourishing," in 1934 the commissioner stated, "Most species of groundfish are growing scarcer," in 1949 the commissioner concluded that "groundfish stocks have been depleted" (Conkling and Ames 1996).

In addition to declining abundances, average fish body size also steadily dropped. In 1895 a 96 kg (= 211.25 lb.) cod was caught on a long-line off the Massachusetts coast (Bigelow and Schroeder 1953) and many ranging in size from 45–73 kg (100–160 lb.) were caught in the 1800s (Goode 1884). However, since the turn of the century, fish greater than 45 kg have become exceedingly rare (Bigelow and Schroeder 1953). The decline in average body size of cod in coastal zones is particularly dramatic over the past 40 years, especially compared to the large cod harvested for thousands of years earlier by native Americans (Figure 17.3).

Shifts in Dominance: Replacement of Large Predatory Fish by Commercially Less Valuable Species

Large predatory fish were ubiquitous in coastal zones through at least the 1920s but are rare or absent today. In the 1920s a compilation of 147 coastal fishing grounds found over 90% of them yielded Atlantic cod, which was the most ubiquitous harvested species at that time (Rich 1929). Cod

along with haddock and hake comprised over 65% of the landings in Maine and five of the six most commonly harvested fish (Figure 17.4), and they are among the six largest species of benthic fishes found in the Gulf of Maine (Figure 17.5). With the virtual extirpation of large-bodied groundfish from coastal zones, the dominant fish predators today are all relatively small and mostly unmarketable species (Figure 17.6). Small species such as sculpins (grubbies, short-horned and long-horned sculpins), rock gunnel, shanny, and cunner are the dominant fish predators in coastal zones of Maine (Malpass 1992; Witman and Sebens 1992). In hundreds of hours of videos at five coastal locations (from Boston to nearly the Canadian border), no cod or other large-bodied gadids were observed (Malpass 1992; Steneck et al. 1995; Vadas and Steneck 1995). Today the predominant fisheries species for the coastal areas reported for the 1920s (Figure 17.4A) are nonpredatory fish such as herring or invertebrates species such as lobsters, sea urchins, shrimp, or sea cucumbers (Figure 17.4B), many of which were prey of the large predators of the past.

The fisheries-induced declines in groundfish such as Atlantic cod continued throughout the Gulf of Maine, but stock collapse occurred much later in the offshore areas of Georges Bank. It is widely believed that the population declines in finfish abundance resulted from fishing (e.g., Brown et al. 1978; Mayo et al. 1992) rather than from an oceanographic event. For one thing, the offshore collapse (Figure 17.7) occurred much later than the coastal decline. This temporal pattern conforms with the nearshore to offshore gradient in the timing of fishing intense pressure (Witman and Sebens 1992). Also, large-scale and regulatory changes that reduced fishing pressure resulted in clear increases in harvested stocks (Hennemuth and Rockwell 1987). For example, cod abundance on Georges Bank and the outer continental shelf declined from 1970 until 1977, when the Magnuson Act extended the jurisdiction of the exclusive economic zone around the United States (Figure 17.7). That halted non-U.S. fishing vessels from fishing there, and stocks recovered (e.g., 1978–1982) until the U.S. fleet responded to the recently vacated fishing grounds. Fishing pressure increased, causing a rapid decline in cod abundance from 1989 to 1992. In the 1990s large areas of Georges Bank were placed under protective closure to stem further losses of groundfish. Thus, the Magnuson Act effectively became an experiment that reduced fishing effort enough to observe a population response. This example is widely cited as evidence of human impacts on cod populations (e.g., Mayo et al. 1992; Sinclair and Page 1995).

With the decline in groundfish on Georges Bank, there was a change in the species composition of other fish. As discussed above for coastal zones, Georges Bank saw large commercially important fish replaced by smaller, less commercially important species. For example, whereas gadids such as cod and haddock dominated fish stocks in the 1960s, skates and dogfish dominated by the late 1980s (Figure 17.8) (Sherman 1991; Mayo et al. 1992).

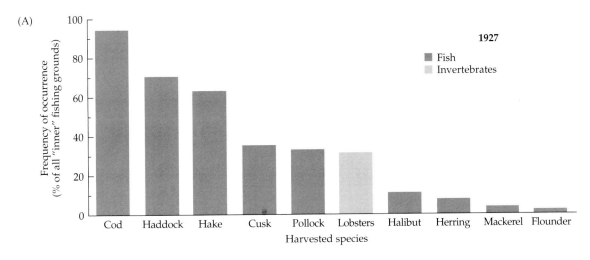

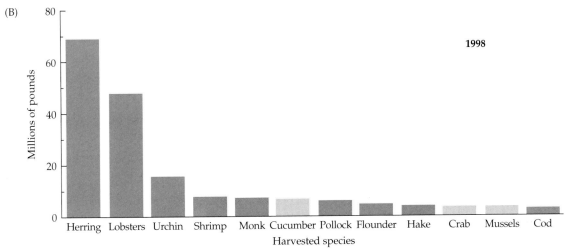

Figure 17.4 Predominant coastal fisheries species identified (A) in 147 coastal ("inner") fishing grounds during the 1920s (Rich 1929), and (B) in state waters of Maine in 1998 (Maine Department of Marine Resources). Note the rise in prominence of invertebrates (black bars) in Maine's coastal fisheries over the 70-year interval.

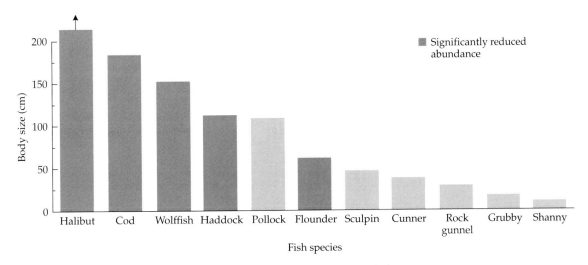

Figure 17.5 Maximum body sizes of dominant fish predators in the Gulf of Maine. Data from Bigelow and Schroeder (1953) and Scott and Scott (1988).

Figure 17.6 Frequency of occurrence of fish predators in coastal benthic surveys taken in 1989 (Malpass 1991). The five study regions were located near Jonesport, Maine; in Mt. Desert and Pemaquid, New Hampshire; and in Nahant, Massachusetts. The sites are all more than 50 km apart, and within each region, study sites were at least 1 km apart. Surveys were conducted by scuba diving 10 m belt transects at a depth of 10 m.

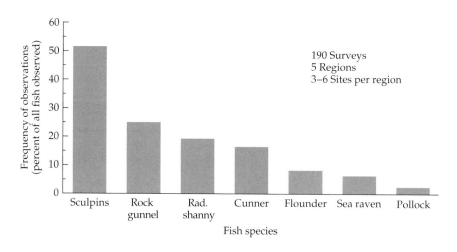

Food-Web Responses to Loss of Large Predators

EXTANT REFUGIA FOR LARGE PREDATORY FISH: A LABORATORY TO STUDY THEIR IMPACT.   The relative absence of large predatory finfish in coastal zones today makes studying their impact difficult. However, there are a few populations of large predatory groundfish located in relatively shallow-water refugia where their impact can be studied. One such refuge is Cashes Ledge, a submarine pinnacle island 130 km offshore that shallows to 15 m of the surface (see Figure 17.1). It has kelp and other coastal community characteristics (Vadas and Steneck 1988), but during the late 1980s and early 1990s it still had significant populations of large predatory fish such as cod, pollock, and wolffish (Figure 17.9A) (Witman and Sebens 1992). Fortuitously, the area was ignored as a fishing grounds for centuries. Collins and Rathbun (1887) reported, "Cashes Ledge.—This is not now a very important fishing-ground . . ." By the 1920s, Rich (1929) reported it was "fur-

nishing . . . its quota [of groundfish] . . . in increasing volume . . . The principal fishing on these grounds is for cod, haddock hake and cusk . . ." However, the abrupt vertical rise of this pinnacle probably made it exceedingly difficult to fish since anchoring was difficult and trawling was impossible without recently available rock-hopping trawling gear. Thus, this small pinnacle was a refuge for large predatory fishes and it became a research laboratory to examine their impact as predators.

Large predatory fish (cod and pollock) were abundant at three offshore sites and rare at three others (Figure 17.9A; Steneck 1997). In situ quadrat surveys quantifying dominant benthic organisms were conducted at each site, and data were pooled according to sites where large predatory fish were rare or abundant.

Lobsters and sea urchins were rare at sites dominated by large predatory fish (Figure 17.9B). Further, algal abundance, particularly kelp, were significantly greater at sites devoid of urchins. This was undoubtedly due to the controlling influence of herbivorous sea urchins on kelp abundance. Fish at-

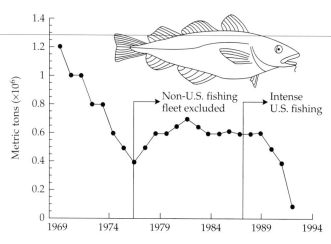

Figure 17.7 Landings of Atlantic cod from 1970 to 1992. (After Sinclair and Page 1995.) The decline from 1970 to 1977 was temporarily reversed when jurisdictional economic zone boundaries were extended in 1977, thus excluding all non-US fishing vessels. The decline continued in the late 1980s after the U.S. offshore fishing fleet developed and targeted cod.

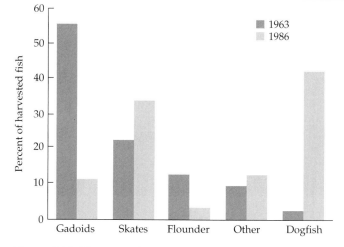

Figure 17.8 Changes in the proportion of harvested fishes on Georges Bank from 1963 to 1986. (After Sherman 1991.) Note that gadoids primarily include cod and haddock.

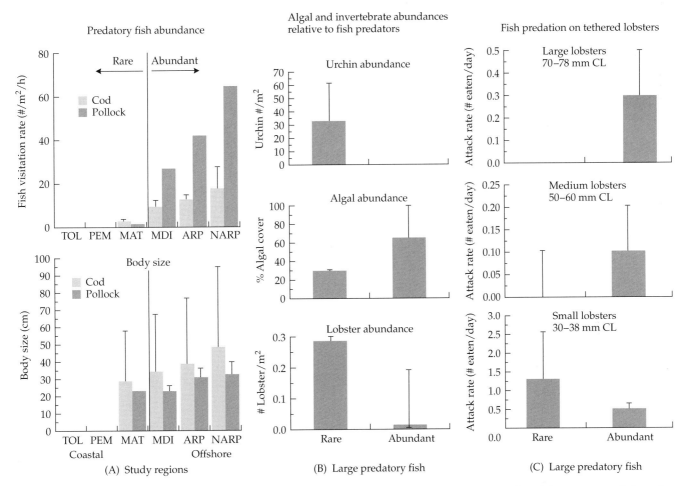

Figure 17.9 Geographic patterns of large predatory fishes at the Cashes Ledge region (ARP, NARP), islands of Matinicus (MAT) and Mt. Desert Rock (MDI) and coastal sites (TOL and PEM). Fish abundance and body size was determined with in situ videos (A). Sea urchin, algal and lobster abundances (B) were quantified with quadrat sampling. (Three sites where fish were rare and three sites where fish were abundant, respectively, were pooled.) Fish predation was determined using tethering techniques for lobsters of small, medium and large size classes (C). Error bars represent one standard deviation in all cases. (From Steneck 1997.)

tacks on tethered lobsters (Figure 17.9 C), and sea urchins were confined to sites where large predatory fish were abundant. In particular, large lobsters (> 60 mm CL, Figure 17.9C), and large urchins (70–80 mm test diameter; Vadas and Steneck 1995) suffered heavy mortality from fish at the offshore, predator-abundant sites. The tethering results indicate that large predatory finfish, when sufficiently abundant, can be "strong interacters" (sensu Paine 1980) capable of feeding on large mobile invertebrates such as lobster, sea urchins (Steneck 1997), and crabs (Witman and Sebens 1992).

CASCADING CONSEQUENCES OF FISHING DOWN FOOD WEBS. Coastal marine food webs have changed as a result of the loss of the large predatory finfish (Figure 17.10). Today, mobile benthic invertebrates (e.g., Menge and Sutherland 1987) and small, commercially unimportant finfish (see Figure 17.6; Wahle and Steneck 1992; Malpass 1992) are abundant and appear to be the most important fish predators in coastal zones of the Gulf of Maine. Evidence for altered abundances due to direct harvesting losses and population release from predatory control were evident at several levels in coastal food webs (Figure 17.10). Redirected fishing effort to formerly prey species at lower trophic levels is known as "fishing down food webs" (sensu Pauly et al. 1998).

Body size is a prime determinant of the outcome of predator–prey interactions. Therefore, as predator size declines, prey vulnerability decreases. Today, lobsters and crabs are vulnerable to predation only very early in life from small, commercially unimportant predatory fishes (Wahle and Steneck 1992). Larger lobsters were vulnerable to predation only where large predatory fish were still present (Figure 17.9C; Witman and Sebens 1992; Steneck 1997). Tethering experiments indicate that adult crab, lobsters, and sea urchins live today in coastal habitats without significant threats from predators (Figure 17.9C; Witman and Sebens 1992; Wahle and Steneck 1992; Steneck et al. 1995; Vadas and Steneck 1995; Steneck 1997). The absence of predators allows more lobsters to live in shelter-poor habitats than was possible

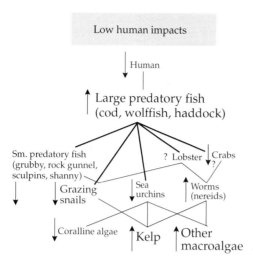
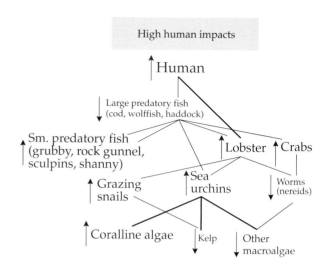

Figure 17.10 Food web changes in coastal zones of the Gulf of Maine resulting from human impacts (Steneck 1997). Strong interactions (sensu Paine 1980) are indicated by heavy lines. Arrows indicate abundance and/or importance to the system. Font size is proportional to abundance.

when predators were abundant (Steneck 1997). This expansion of habitable area for lobsters may have contributed to the currently thriving lobster industry which, in recent years, repeatedly exceeded its previous record harvest set in the 1880s (Figure 17.11).

Long-term increases in lobster landings over the past century may also reflect decreases in large predatory finfish in coastal zones (Steneck 1997). Lobster landings were high in the late 1800s but declined as lobstering expanded. Early in the lobster fishery the average harvested size of lobsters was large. One report from the 1860s indicates that "lobsters weighing twenty to twenty-five pounds were often taken . . . [F]our or five pound lobsters . . . were so common that two pound lobsters were taken and thrown overboard" (Martin

and Lipfert 1985). Large lobsters were probably immune from predation even when large cod were patrolling coastal zones. As lobstering intensified, average body sizes decreased. Rathbun (1887) reported: "Why do we not get larger lobsters? Must be, we catch them faster than they can grow; the smaller the lobsters we retain, the smaller will they become in the future." As lobster populations shifted to smaller size, a larger percentage of the remaining lobster population may have fallen prey to the large predatory fish. This would not only account for the steady decline in lobster abundance from 1890 to 1920 but also the sharp increase in the 1940s after finfish stocks had "been depleted" (Figure 17.11).

Large fish predators may also have limited sea urchin populations. With the decline of coastal predators, urchin populations may have expanded their populations denuding kelp from vast coastal areas (Figure 17.12) thereby reducing coastal productivity and habitat structure for other organisms (e.g., Bologna and Steneck 1993). However, in the late 1980s sea urchins became a targeted fisheries species for their

Figure 17.11 Lobster landings and coastal groundfish abundance in Maine. Coastal groundfish abundances were assessed in annual reports by Maine's Commissioner of Sea and Shore Fisheries.

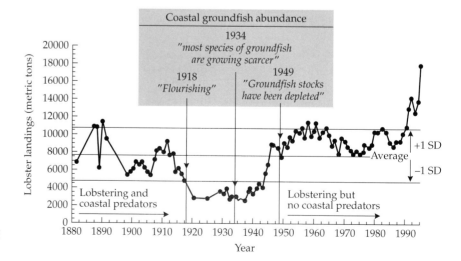

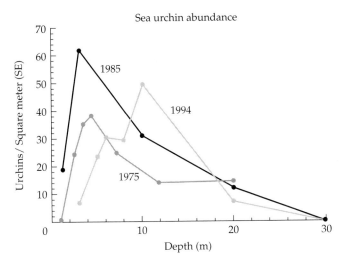

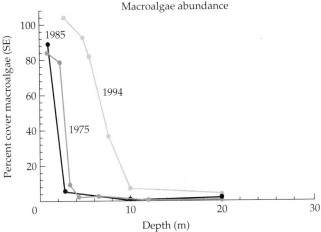

Figure 17.12 Depth and abundance trends in sea urchins (left) and macroalgae (i.e., kelp, bottom) at Pemaquid Point, Maine. (From Steneck et al. 1995.) Note the rapid decline in urchin abundance and increase in kelp abundance in shallow zones as urchin harvesting escalated in the 1990s (see also Figure 17.13).

human exploitation, top predators were removed, allowing for an expansion of middle predator and herbivore species such as lobsters crabs and sea urchins (Figure 17.13). While the fishery targeting lobsters has not yet reduced their abundance (Figure 17.11), the same cannot be said for sea urchins (Figure 17.13). Since the green sea urchin is the principal member of the herbivore trophic level, reductions in its abundance causes dramatic and immediate change to kelp populations and to coastal food webs in general (Figure 17.15 right).

The dramatic phase-shift resulting in large-scale kelp domination (Figures 17.12, 17.14) immediately followed the localized extirpations of sea urchins. This shift also has caused numerous other changes to coastal systems. The increase of kelp, the largest benthic producer in the western North Atlantic, may increase coastal productivity. Recently, large increases in macroalgal detritus have been observed. Kelp reduces wave action and is the host for numerous epiphytic and epizootic organisms (Duggins et al. 1990). Organisms such as crustose coralline algae that can be overgrown and thus out-competed by macroalgae (Steneck 1986) are the preferred food for the limpet *Tectura testudinalis* (Steneck 1982). With the expansion of macroalgae, coralline algae and this dependent limpet have declined in abundance (R. S. Steneck, unpub. data). Lobster habitat use has also changed. At a site where lobsters predominantly occupied rock shelters during the 1980s, a clear shift to the use of kelp shelter was observed (Figure 17.16). Expanded kelp beds may present a significant increase lobster habitat in coastal zones (Bologna and Steneck 1993).

Kelp and other macroalgae are nursery grounds for some large predatory finfish (Levin 1991, 1994; Carr 1994; Levin and Hay 1996). This has been demonstrated with experiments conducted in the Gulf of Maine (Levin 1994). Pollock have been seen for the first time in 20 years at sites formerly devoid of erect macroalgae (R. S. Steneck, pers. obs.). Numerous invertebrate species also recruit to kelp habitats (Duggins

highly valued roe, which is marketed in Japan. This created a "gold rush" and resulted in a classic boom–bust fishery (Figure 17.13).

Under intense fishing pressure, urchin population densities dropped and kelp beds expanded throughout the Gulf of Maine (Steneck et al. 1995, Figure 17.12). This ocurred because urchins are the dominant herbivore in those coastal zones. As their densities declined, rates of herbivory decreased (Figure 17.14, top) and kelp abundance increased markedly (Figure 17.14, bottom). The inverse relationship between urchin and kelp abundance (Figures 17.12, 17.14) demonstrates the controlling influence this species has on the herbivore trophic level (Figure 17.15).

All of this suggests that food webs are changing due to the cascading effects of fishing down food webs. Food webs prior to intense fishing activity (Figure 17.15) were probably dominated by large predatory fish and an abundance of kelp (Davison et al. 1988; Vadas and Steneck 1995). With increased

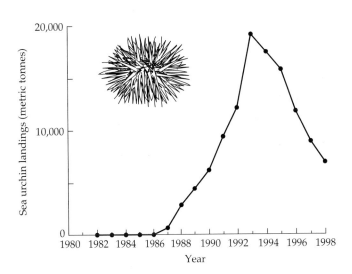

Figure 17.13 Trend in Maine sea urchin harvest (Maine DMR).

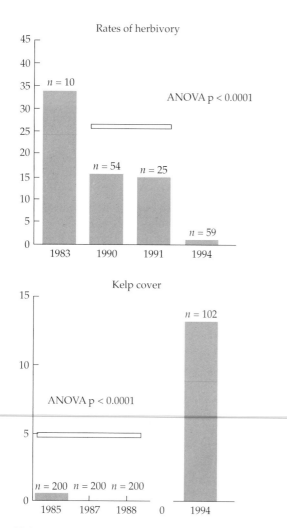

Rates of herbivory

ANOVA p < 0.0001

n = 10

n = 54   n = 25

n = 59

1983   1990   1991   1994

Kelp cover

n = 102

ANOVA p < 0.0001

n = 200 n = 200 n = 200

1985   1987   1988   0   1994

Figure 17.14 Temporal trends in rates of herbivory (top) determined using the kelp strip herbivory bioassay (methods in Steneck et al. 1995) and in percent cover (using quadrat sampling). Urchin harvesting began in 1987 and escalated rapidly in the early 1990s (Figure 17.13). All work was conducted near Crow Island Maine (near TOL site in Figure 17.9; Steneck et al. 1995). *n* = number of kelp strips; horizontal bars indicate samples among which no significant differences were found using analysis of variance.

et al. 1990). Recently, juvenile crabs and amphipods living within macroalgal canopies were found to prey on virtually all of the newly settled sea urchins so that few, if any, survive to their first year (McNaught 1999). This suggests that a change in abundance at a lower trophic level, resulting in an increase in kelp abundance, may control the recruitment potential and resilience of both micropredatory crabs and top predators such as groundfish.

The loss of higher tropic levels often results in increases in fishing pressures on abundant prey species at lower levels. In the Gulf of Maine, as finfish stocks declined, more effort focused on lobsters and then on sea urchins. In 1999, lobsters and sea urchins were the two most valuable species harvested in the Gulf of Maine. Many other species, lower on the food web are currently being harvested. A variety of intertidal and subtidal seaweeds are now harvested for food and fertilizer. In the mid-1980s, fishing began on snails, including the common periwinkle (an herbivore) (Chenoweth and McGowan 1994) and the whelk (a predator). In the late 1990s, harvesting of sea cucumbers began, and in just a few years its landings were sixth in the state of Maine (Figure 17.4). The resulting harvest pressure has risen to levels that some fear cannot be sustained. When biodiversity is high, one species fished down can be compensated by another in that trophic level. What exists now in the Gulf of Maine is different. Entire trophic levels have been functionally eliminated—entire marine communities have been altered. Whereas prehistoric indigenous Americans may have had thousands of years of sustainable harvests (e.g., Figure 17.3), our current concerns of sustainability are on the scale of decades or even just a few years. The evidence is strong that marine communities throughout the Gulf of Maine have changed profoundly as a result of human-mediated resource exploitation.

Overextraction: Some Perspectives

The evidence is strong that changes similar to those described for the Gulf of Maine have occurred and are occurring globally. Large predators in most marine systems are

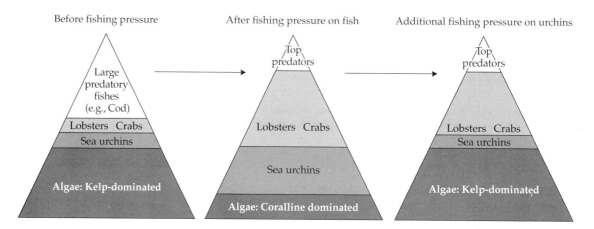

Figure 17.15 Changes in trophic-level abundance for coastal food webs of the Gulf of Maine as fishing pressures escalated. Vertical scale qualitatively represents biomass.

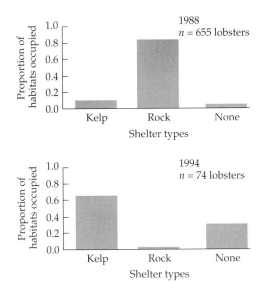

Figure 17.16 Changes in lobster habitat use concurrent with changes in kelp abundance, resulting from reduced rates of herbivory (see Figure 17.14) following harvesting of sea urchins (1987). Data are for precisely the same benthic survey sites at Crow Island, Maine (see Figure 17.15).

first targeted. Because these organisms are relatively long-lived and reach reproductive maturity late and compared to lower trophic levels are relatively few in number, they are easily extirpated. Fishing effort is then displaced to the next trophic level as food webs are serially fished down (Pauly et al. 1998). By the late 1990s 18 percent (by weight) of the 50 major marine species caught globally "are the small and abundant animals that are low on the trophic pyramid, eating phytoplankton (40 percent), zooplankton (38 percent), and algae (3 percent)" (NRC 1999). It is hard to visualize these changes to trophic structure at a global scale, so we will offer a few illustrations from around the world.

The kelp forest ecosystem of Alaska has undergone phase-shifts between kelp and coralline dominance, depending on the abundance of sea urchins. Those urchin populations are controlled by abundant predatory sea otters (Estes and Duggins 1995), which were extirpated in the 1700s by fur trappers. This top predator almost went extinct. However, a treaty banning the trade of its fur was enacted, and sea otter abundances have increased by natural population expansion and by human relocation (Breen et al. 1982). Wherever sea otter populations have increased, urchin abundances have declined and macroalgae (especially kelp) has increased (Estes and Duggins 1995). Overextraction of sea otters was essentially an apex predator exclusion experiment on an ecosystem scale. Its role as a "keystone predator" (sensu Paine 1969) is well known and accepted (Power et al. 1996).

Kelp forest ecosystems in the Aleutian Islands began another phase-shift in the early 1990s, as killer whales invaded the coastal zone and rapidly decimated sea otter populations at some locations, removing their controlling influence on sea urchin and other prey populations (Estes et al. 1998). The

killer whale diet shift from pinnipeds to sea otters may have been due to overfishing and decreased productivity associated with ocean warming that reduced pinniped prey fish stocks. Thus, starving harbor seals and Steller sea lion populations declined sharply, causing killer whales to feed on sea otters (Estes et al. 1998). Regardless of the cause, disruption of a trophic level caused a killer whale to become the new keystone predator in regions of Alaska's coastal zone.

Although overfishing can significantly reduce a species' abundance, extinctions are relatively rare (Carlton et al. 1999). Confirmed species extinctions during historical times in the marine realm include three mammals, five birds, and four snails (Carlton et al. 1999). There easily could have been rare or inconspicuous species that have gone extinct in recent times, but these are not likely to have a large impact on the structure or functioning of marine communities. However, there are examples of potentially important consumers that were hunted to extinction. In the subarctic North Pacific the Steller sea cow (*Hydrodamalis gigas*), which grazed exclusively on kelp and attained 10 m in length, was last seen alive in 1768 (Estes et al. 1989; Carlton et al. 1999). Similarly, in the subarctic North Atlantic the sea mink (*Mustela macrodon*), which had characteristics similar to that of the sea otter of the North Pacific, went extinct in the late 1800s (Bourque 1996; Carlton et al. 1999). The Caribbean monk seal went extinct in the 1900s (Carlton et al. 1999). All of these extinct species were hunted by indigenous people for hundreds or thousands of years prior to their extinction (J. A. Estes, pers. comm.; Bourque 1996; Jackson 1994).

The threat of extinction remains high for some harvested species. The white abalone, *Haliotis sorenseni*, was once extraordinarily abundant in California but has been overfished to the brink of extinction (Tegner et al. 1996). As few as 500 to 600 individuals of that species may exist today (Carlton et al. 1999). In the western North Atlantic, the large, long-lived barndoor skate (*Raja laevis*) has suffered such high rates of mortality from fishing activities directed toward other species that it is now thought to be near extinction (Casey and Myers 1998). Some species are more susceptible to extinction because they have a relatively small gene pool, they grow slowly, reach reproductive maturity late, and are long-lived. As fishing activity increases both directly by targeting species to harvest and indirectly by altering their habitat (Watling and Norse 1998), marine communities will continue to change. It is likely that slow-growing, long-lived species that require a long time to reach reproductive maturity will decline relative to more "weedy" species.

While it's difficult to gauge the impacts of these extinctions, the more common trophic-level dysfunction resulting from population declines of extant species is well documented and striking. Trophic-level dysfunction occurs when all the members of a trophic level are reduced to the point of ecological extinction or where their functional role in the ecosystem is no longer evident. Caribbean coastal ecosystems have been degraded for centuries by the functional loss of large vertebrates such as the green turtle, hawksbill turtle, and manatee

(Jackson 1997). However, the collapse of coral reef systems since the 1980s may have been catalyzed by fisheries-induced trophic-level dysfunction of herbivory (Hughes 1994).

Chronic overfishing has decimated reef fish populations throughout the Caribbean (Hay 1984). On overfished reefs, herbivory was predominately from the sea urchin *Diadema antillarum* (Hay 1984), whereas on reefs with low fishing pressure, a number of species of grazing parrotfish and tangs maintained low algal biomass (Steneck 1988) and high rates of coral recruitment (Birkeland 1977). As human populations swelled throughout the Caribbean, *Diadema* abundance and importance increased (Levitan 1992; but see Jackson 1997). By the early 1980s high population densities of *D. antillarum* performed most of the grazing on reefs (Carpenter 1986). Then a disease swept throughout the Caribbean in 1984, killing over 90% of the *Diadema* populations (Lessios et al. 1984). On reefs lacking herbivorous fish due to overfishing, the loss of *Diadema* caused complete herbivore trophic-level dysfunction and a rapid phase shift to abundant macroalgae (Hughes 1994). On less overfished reefs macroalgal abundance increased less (Steneck 1997). Reduced herbivory invariably resulted in increases in macroalgae on reefs. This in turn resulted in elevated mortality in reef corals (Hughes 1994). Thus, the fisheries-induced loss of diversity among herbivores in Caribbean reefs put those ecosystems at risk of collapse when the last important herbivore species declined.

Overfishing alters the organization and structure of entire marine communities via cascading trophic chain reactions. For example, fishing in coastal zones of the northwest Mediterranean depleted predators, causing the dominant herbivore, the urchin *Paracentrotus liviidus,* to increase; its grazing denuded erect macroalgae, shifting the system to crustose coralline dominance (Sala et al. 1998). When a no-fishing reserve was established, predator abundance increased, herbivore abundance decreased, and the system returned to one dominated by macroalgae. A similar trophic cascade was found along the Kenyan coast in the Indian Ocean where a series of no-fishing protected areas and adjacent control areas showed that attack rates by predators regulated urchin populations (McClanahan and Muthiga 1989). Again, macroalgal abundance varied inversely with the abundance of sea urchins.

The strong interactions evident between sea urchin and macroalgae communities provide excellent examples of the direct and indirect ways in which fishing pressure alters marine communities worldwide. Ironically, in the Caribbean example, the largest change to occur in the urchin population was not the result of fishing; it was the result of a disease. Because this disease was first observed in Panama (Lessios 1988), it's possible that it resulted from a pathogen introduced from the eastern Pacific via the Panama Canal. Although this possible introduced species is not known, myriad species are known to have been introduced to marine communities. In many cases, community change has been as dramatic from introductions of nonnative species as we have just described for examples of overextraction.

BIOLOGICAL INVASIONS IN THE OCEAN

Biological invasions occur when a novel species enters a community for the first time or reenters after having been absent for a long time (the latter usually measured in geological, rather than ecological, time). Species may enter a community *mechanistically* in two ways—by natural movements or by human-mediated movements.

Natural movements generally include two dispersal mechanisms. The first involves marine organisms drifting into a community on water currents. This occurs either as a planktonic stage (eggs, larvae, or postlarvae) or as juveniles or adults on a floating substrate. Floating substrates can consist of algae, wood, pumice, and feathers and human-created materials such as paper (e.g., milk cartons) or plastic, the latter category having become increasingly abundant over time and thus creating more dispersal opportunities (Winston 1982; Minchin 1996). The second mechanism involves marine organisms entering communities by moving along new corridors such as may be created by tectonic events or climatic conditions, opening passageways between ocean basins.

These natural movements (anthropogenic debris aside), referred to as *range expansions,* have been occurring for hundreds of millions of years and serve to explain many ancient and modern geographic patterns of marine life. Such movements are also predictable, in terms of (1) the behavior, direction, and speed of ocean currents (whether either operating on a "normal" base or with periodic changes, such as those that occur in the Pacific Ocean during El Niño/Southern Oscillation [ENSO] events), and (2) the geological history of ocean basins and continents and the concomitant creation or dissolution of dispersal corridors. Thus the natural flow of organisms (marine, fresh-water, and terrestrial) to newly created oceanic islands (e.g., Grigg 1988) follows from predictable dispersal vectors and along predictable pathways. Also predictable would be the colonization of one ocean by biota from another should corridors appear. Such corridors across the Arctic caused the colonization of the North Atlantic Ocean by organisms of the North Pacific during the late Cenozoic era (Vermeij 1991).

In striking contrast to range expansions are the opportunities provided by human transport. Human-mediated invasions are referred to as *introductions.* Five important categories of introduction vectors are (a) vessels (ships and boats), (b) the aquaculture, bait, and aquarium industries, (c) a wide variety of other commercial, government, and private endeavors, (d) scientists, and (e) canals (Table 17.1; Carlton 1985, 1987, 1992a; Carlton and Geller 1993; Cohen and Carlton 1998). Major historical pathways include the movement of marine organisms attached to the outside of or boring into ships, the movements of incalculable masses of commercial oysters, and sea-level canals. These latter three mechanisms taken together have led to the movement of tens of thousands of species. Major modern pathways include the movement of organisms in the ballast water and sediments of ships. Carlton (1999) has calculated that over 15,000 species

TABLE 17.1   Primary human-mediated dispersal mechanisms of marine organisms.

Habitats and Organisms

SIE = SUBLITTORAL INFAUNAL AND EPIBENTHIC SPECIES[a]

Infaunal and epibenthic sublittoral organisms and parasitic, symbiotic, commensal, or epibiota associated with such species; boring organisms such as shipworms (bivalve mollusks) and gribbles (isopods) and associated biota.

PSD= PLANKTONIC, SUSPENDED, OR DRIFTING SPECIES[a]

Planktonic organisms (including holoplankton and meroplankton) and suspended or drifting organisms on floating substrates.

SIM= SUPRALITTORAL (MARITIME), INTERTIDAL, DUNE OR MARSH SPECIES[a]

Shore-dwelling organisms.

Vectors	Organism and Habitat Diversity		
	SIE	PSD	SIM
I. VESSELS (SHIPS, BOATS)	X	X	X
Organisms on or in the hull, sea chests, seawater pipes, anchors, and anchor chains; ballast water or "live well" water (used for fish, shellfish, or bait) in fishing boats; species in ballast sediments, entangled organisms in nets, traps, and trawls, organisms used as fresh food aboard ship or carried in shipboard aquaria; organisms in dry ballast (such as rocks, sand, soil, debris) and in the packing (dunnage) in cargo holds.			
II. AQUACULTURE, BAIT AND OTHER FISHERIES, AND AQUARIUM INDUSTRIES	X	X	X
Transportation and potential release of marine and aquatic organisms for human food, as forage for other organisms, as bait, or for aquaria), including organisms attached to target species, and in transport media.			
III. OTHER COMMERCIAL, GOVERNMENT, AND PRIVATE ACTIVITIES			
Intentional releases:			
(a) Biocontrol releases for pest control	X	X	X
(b) Sea-, marsh-, and dune-grass transplantation			X
(c) Movement of threatened/endangered species	X		X
Intentional or accidental releases:			
(a) Ornamental plants and fish	X	X	X
Organisms associated with the movement of:			
(a) Semisubmersible exploratory drilling platforms	X	X	X
(b) Amphibious and sea planes	X	X	X
(c) Navigation buoys	X	X	X
(d) Log booms	X	X	X
IV. SCIENTIFIC RESEARCH	X	X	X
The movement of experimental organisms and scientific equipment; escapes from laboratories	X	X	X
V. CANALS			
Sealevel, lock (interoceanic and intracontinental), and irrigation canals	X	X	X

[a]Taxa involved potentially include protists, nematodes, sponges, hydroids, jellyfish, sea anemones, flatworms, gnathostomulids, mesozoans, rotifers, kinorhynchs, loriciferans, gastrotrichs, tardigrades, nemerteans, leeches, oligochaetes, polychaetes, sipunculans, echiurans, priapulans, barnacles, amphipods, isopods, tanaids, mysids, copepods, ostracods, crabs, shrimp, insects, sea spiders, snails including sea slugs, clams, mussels, oysters, chitons, scaphopods, cephalopods, bryozoans, entoprocts, phoronids, brachiopods, hemichordates, chaetognaths, echinoderms, sea squirts, algae, sea grasses, marsh and dune plants, fish, bacteria, viruses, and fungi.

could be moved around the world *every week* in ballast water. Fortunately, only a fraction of those species survive. We will focus the remainder of this chapter on the fraction of alien species that have successfully become established in and important to marine communities.

No type of marine organism or habitat is immune to introductions. Human-mediated transport vectors are capable of moving almost any supralittoral, littoral (intertidal), or sublittoral infaunal or epibenthic species and almost any planktonic, suspended, or drifting species (Table 17.1). The result has been that every major marine habitat has received introduced species, including shallow-water communities (estuaries and mangroves, rocky intertidal shores, sandy beaches of all exposure gradients, kelp forests, coral reefs, and seagrass meadows) and deep water communities (continental shelves and the deeper sea).

In distinct contrast to nonhuman-mediated dispersal, introductions are largely unpredictable in both time and space. With the advent of ships and airplanes, natural barriers to dispersal have disappeared. In a matter of days or hours organisms can be transported between oceans and across continents in directions and over distances unrelated to water flow or other natural corridors. The result is that human-mediated dispersal is not simply "speeding up" dispersal that could or would happen anyway; it is creating new marine communities. Species do not naturally disperse in ecological time between the mudflats of California and Brazil, nor between the rocky shores of France and Japan. However, such movements occur regularly and quickly every day by means of human vectors.

Hundreds or thousands of species have been introduced to marine communities in only the past few hundred years. Since these introductions are recent, occurring in ecological time rather than in geological time, they provide insight into how complex marine communities are structured and perhaps how they evolve. They may help us consider fundamental questions such as: "Are ecological communities exclusive associations of closely interdependent and coevolved species, or just a haphazard sample of species inhabiting a region that happen to jointly tolerate the environment of the moment?" (Jackson 1994). If abundant and structurally important species whose histories we do not know have been inserted by means of human introduction into natural assemblages, the potential exists for making fundamental misinterpretations of the natural evolutionary patterns and geography of life.

Our best scientific records of the biogeography and diversity of marine life begin largely after 1800. It will thus require extensive detective work to carefully dissect the modern history of intertidal and shallow-water marine communities in order to determine which species may have naturally occurred and evolved in the places that we now see them, and which species may have been imported recently and instantaneously and thus have no evolutionary history in such systems. In viewing communities today we recognize three categories of species from an evolutionary point of view: species that are native, species that are introduced, and species that are cryptogenic (Carlton 1996). Cryptogenic means hidden origins. Thus, cryptogenic species are those whose biogeographic history in the community is not known.

Despite our lack of knowledge of pre-1800 invasions, recognized introductions are common and ubiquitous. The marine intertidal and sublittoral communities of North America, for example, are known to have been invaded by hundreds of species during and since the nineteenth century. To illustrate

marine bioinvasions and their myriad, complex ecological consequences we will return to the Gulf of Maine.

Invasions in the Gulf of Maine

A visit to the rocky shore, marshes, or estuaries along the cold-water coast of the Gulf of Maine reveals an immediate suite of recognizable, and often abundant, nonnative species that have arrived by means of human intervention in the last 200 years. Fourteen examples of introduced species in the Gulf of Maine are listed in Table 17.2. These represent a broad phyletic range (coelenterates, crustaceans, mollusks, bryozoans, tunicates, and seaweeds) and a broad range of discovery dates on the Gulf of Maine shore (from the 1820s to the 1980s). Some of these species arrived first south of Cape Cod and arrived later in the Gulf of Maine. The total number of introduced and cryptogenic species in the Gulf of Maine is not known, but it may exceed more than 50 species.

These invasions vary in the breadth of their distribution and abundance. Invasions to the Gulf of Maine by the European green crab *Carcinus maenas*, the common periwinkle snail *Littorina littorea*, and the Asian green alga *Codium fragile tomentosoides* are most conspicuous. From southern to central Gulf of Maine shores, European and Asian sea squirts such as *Styela clava, Botrylloides* sp., *Botryllus schlosseri, Diplosoma listerianum*, and *Ascidiella aspersa*, may be common to abundant on hard bottoms from estuarine fouling communities to nearshore open coast sublittoral depths (R. S. Steneck and J. T. Carlton, pers. obs.; L. Harris, pers. comm.). The European or North Pacific kelp bryozoan *Membranipora membranacea* has only became an abundant element throughout Gulf of Maine kelp systems since the 1980s (R. S. Steneck, pers. obs.).

Several of the species that have invaded the Gulf of Maine are now abundant, but are they also important? Too often little or no experimental work is available to advance our understanding beyond general correlations such as species A arrives and species B and C become less abundant. Nevertheless, the probable functional roles of many invasions, even those as yet lacking experimental studies, are compelling and worth noting (Table 17.3).

The Asian seaweed *Codium fragile tomentosoides* is now the dominant plant in many sublittoral regions. Dense stands of this species doubtless influence the abundance and diversity of co-occurring plant and animal species, whether through direct (whiplash abrasion) or indirect competition (by shading understory species). For example, a floristic study conducted in the early 1970s in southern Cape Cod found 142 species of attached benthic macroalgae (Sears and Wilce 1975), but after *Codium* invaded the region, diversity declined to a "virtual monoculture" (J. R. Sears, pers. comm.). Unfortunately, little if any quantitative or experimental data are available after nearly 50 years of *Codium*'s occupation on the Atlantic coast. *Codium* also impacts commercial shellfish such as scallops, upon whose shells it attaches (Carlton and Scanlon 1985).

The invasion of the European green crab (*Carcinus maenas*) has altered the abundance and diversity of many animals

TABLE 17.2   Examples of marine bioinvasions in the Gulf of Maine, arranged in order of decreasing habitat breadth.

Habitats

HIS = Intertidal hard substrate (rocks, jetties, fouling on pilings)
SHS = Sublittoral hard substrate (rocks, jetties; fouling on pilings, wrecks)
ISS = Intertidal soft substrate (mudflats, sandflats, marshes)
SSS = Sublittoral soft substrate (mud, sand)

	Habitat			
	IHS	SHS	ISS	SSS
SPECIES[a]				
Biogeographical origin[b] (Vectors/Date)[c]				
Carcinus maenas Shore crab; Europe (I, 1820s)	x	x	x	x
Diadumene lineata Sea anemone; Asia (I, 1890s)	x	x	x	
Littorina littorea Periwinkle; Europe (I, II, 1840s)	x	x	x	
Hemigrapsus sanguineus Shore crab; Asia (I 1980s)	x	x		
Botryllus schlosseri Seasquirt; Europe (I, 1830s)	x	x		
Botrylloides sp. Seasquirt; origin uncertain (1970s)	x	x		
Codium fragile tomentosoides Green alga; Asia (I 1950s)	x	x		
Styela clava Seasquirt; Asia (I 1970s)	x	x		
Ascidiella aspersa Seasquirt; Europe (I 1980s)	x	x		
Praunus flexuosus Opossum shrimp; Europe (I 1960s)				x
Ostrea edulis Flat oyster; Europe (II 1940s)		x		
Membranipora membranacea Bryozoan; Europe or northwest Pacific Ocean (I 1970s)			x (kelp blades)	
Diplosoma listerianum Seasquirt; Origin uncertain (I 1980s)		x		
Balanus subalbidus Barnacle; Southern U.S. Atlantic (I 1970s)		x		

[a]Systematic position:
Cnidaria: Anthozoa, *Diadumene lineata*
Crustacea: Mysidacea, *Praunus flexuosus*
Crustacea: Cirripedia, *Balanus subalbidus*
Crustacea: Decapoda: Brachyura: *Carcinus maenas, Hemigrapsus sanguineus*
Mollusca: Gastropoda, *Littorina littorea*
Mollusca: Bivalvia, *Ostrea edulis*
Bryozoa: Cheilostomata, *Membranipora membranacea*
Urochordata: Ascidiacea, *Botryllus schlosseri, Botrylloides sp., Styela clava, Ascidiella aspersa, Diplosoma listerianum*
Chlorophyta: *Codium fragile tomentosoides*
[b]The biogeographic origin of the species is not necessarily the origin of the population(s) that colonized the Atlantic American coast.
[c]Mechanism number refers to mechanisms I to V shown in Table 17.1. The date shown is the decade when the species was first detected on the Atlantic North American coast.

TABLE 17.3   Functional roles of marine bioinvasions in the Gulf of Maine.

Species	Functional Roles
CRABS	
Carcinus maenas	Omnivorous mobile intertidal and sublittoral crab feeding upon a vast variety of infaunal and epibenthic prey; when abundant, appears to influence the abundance and diversity of many other species.
Hemigrapsus sanguineus	Same as *Carcinus*.
SNAILS	
Littorina littorea	Omnivorous mobile intertidal snail; can occur in astronomical numbers and can influence the abundance and diversity of many other species (see text).
SEA SQUIRTS: COMPOUND	
Botryllus schlosseri	
Botrylloides sp.	
Diplosoma listerianum	Sheet-forming gelatinous ascidians; may be important space dominant species and major suspension feeders.
SEA SQUIRTS: SOLITARY	
Styela clava	Solitary ascidians; when abundant, may be important space dominant species and major suspension feeders.
Ascidiella aspersa	Same as *Styela*.
BRYOZOANS	
Membranipora membranacea	A kelp-blade living bryozoan; when abundant, may become space dominant, and may also add enough weight to the plant to influence the probability of the kelp being torn away by wave action.
ALGAE	
Codium fragile tomentosoides	Impacts scallop fisheries by forming dense algal forest attached to and over shellfish; a space-dominant species that may outshade the eelgrass *Zostera marina* and lower local algal diversity.

and plants in the Gulf of Maine. It is a voracious omnivore (Cohen et al. 1995) with a fondness for molluscs. After its arrival north of Cape Cod in the nineteenth century, its predation on the native carnivorous whelk *Nucella lapillus* resulted in changes in the snail's spire height and shell thickness (Vermeij 1982). Simultaneously, similar phenotypic changes occurred in *Littorina obtusata*, a small, native, macroalgal-feeding gastropod throughout the Gulf of Maine (Seeley 1986; Trussell 2000). Precipitous declines in the abundance of the native soft-shell clam *Mya arenaria* occurred after this crab (a ravenous *Mya* predator) became abundant in Maine in the 1950s (Glude 1955; Welch 1968).

Perhaps the most conspicuous and important invader to the Gulf of Maine was the common periwinkle *Littorina littorea*. Since its arrival to the Gulf of Maine in the late 1800s (Figure 17.17), no invasion has been better studied. The history and subsequent ecological impacts of this snail can also serve as a general model through which one can view the extent to which a marine bioinvasion can modify community structure. It's worth noting that of the ecological studies summarized below, most of the authors were either unaware, or

chose not to acknowledge, that their study organism, *L. littorea*, was not native to their study region.

The Invasion of the Common Periwinkle Snail, Littorina littorea

NATIVE RANGE AND INTRODUCTION TO THE GULF OF MAINE.   The common periwinkle snail, *Littorina littorea*, occurs naturally in Europe from the White Sea to Portugal (Reid 1996). Despite the existence of earlier populations in North America prior to 1500 in the Gulf of St. Lawrence (based on radiocarbon-dating of shells that may have been naturally occurring in America or brought over by Viking colonists), no records of modern *L. littorea* populations in North America exist prior 1840 and no shells were in hand prior to 1857 (Carlton 1982; Reid 1996). When *L. littorea* first arrived to North America is not known. However, its absence from the Gulf of Maine is very well documented. No *L. littorea* shells have been found in Indian middens excavated throughout the region dating back 5000 years before present (Bourque 1996). Early naturalists and taxonomists certainly would have collected this con-

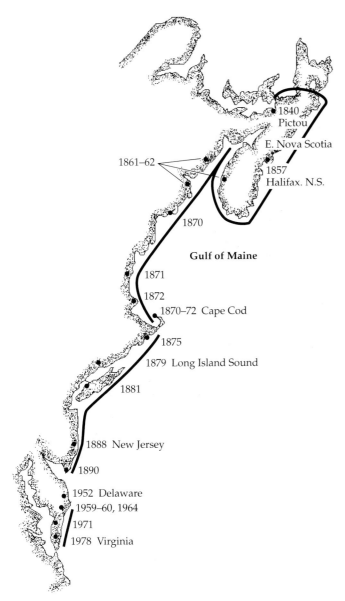

Figure 17.17 The chronology of the southwestern movement of *Littorina littorea* from Nova Scotia (1840) to Virginia (1978). Locations are as follows: 1840 (Pictou), 1857 (Halifax), 1861–1862 (three sites: Digby, Nova Scotia; St. John, New Brunswick, and Eastport, Maine); 1870 (Portland, Maine), 1871 (Hampton Beach, New Hampshire), 1872 (Salem, Massachusetts [MA]), 1870–1872 (Provincetown MA), 1875 (Woods Hole MA), 1879 (New Haven, Connecticut), 1881 (Lloyd's Neck NY), 1888 (Atlantic City, New Jersey [NJ]), 1890 (Cape May, NJ), 1952 (Indian River, Delaware, being the southernmost predictable populations) 1959–1960, 1964 (Ocean City, Maryland), 1971 (Chincoteague, Virginia [VA]), and 1978 (Wachapreague, VA). Dark line indicates area invaded by *Littorina littorea*.

spicuous species had it been present on the shores of the Gulf of Maine by the mid-nineteenth century. The preponderance of evidence indicates that *L. littorea* was introduced to the Gulf of Maine, either accidentally with ballast rocks, or, more

likely, intentionally as a food resource, sometime during the late eighteenth century. Its distributional chronology for the eastern seaboard is well known. Between at least 1857 and 1890 it spread from Halifax, Nova Scotia, to Cape May, New Jersey, a distance of 1500 km in 37 years, or about 41 km per year (Figure 17.17). It is now abundant from the southern Gulf of St. Lawrence to New Jersey, with occasional records to the north in Labrador and to the south in Virginia.

THE ECOLOGICAL CONSEQUENCES OF INSERTING AN ABUNDANT, LARGE ROVING OMNIVORE INTO INTERTIDAL COMMUNITIES. In 1859 Edward Forbes, writing not about the periwinkle invasion of the Gulf of Maine but about the more routine workings of the European seashore, remarked:

> The student of history follows with intense interest the march of a conqueror, or the migrations of a nation . . . Yet, absurd as it may seem . . . there is deeper interest in the march of a periwinkle, and the progress of a limpet. (Forbes 1859.)

Clearly, the march and progress of an introduced periwinkle on the shores of the Gulf of Maine is of interest to marine ecologists and evolutionary biologists. Today, *L. littorea* is one of the largest, most abundant per area biomass (Figure 17.18; Steneck and Dethier 1994) and one of the most important consumers in the intertidal zone of the Gulf of Maine. *Littorina littorea* is most abundant on low to moderate energy-emergent rocky shores (Lubchenco and Menge 1978). However, its abundance and impact is seasonal. In the winter, it is rare, and ephemeral algae form extensive mats and turfs across the tops of boulders and other rock surfaces (Vadas 1992). These filamentous and leafy green and red algae are reduced to zero percent cover by the upwardly mobile grazing snails as they return in spring from the lower shore and subtidal zone (Figure 17.18C; Vadas and Elner 1992). The elimination of ephemeral algae tends to leave vast monocultures of the large, robust brown alga *Ascophyllum nodosum* (Figure 17.18B) as the dominant plant of the shore, and lesser amounts of another large brown alga *Fucus vesiculosus* (Figure 17.18A) along with considerable bare substrate. These large fucoid seaweeds are themselves susceptible to elimination by *L. littorea*, in their zygote, sporeling, germling, and juvenile developmental stages (Steneck and Watling 1982; Lubchenco 1983), but at larger size they are relatively invulnerable. This is because they are "leathery" tough and difficult to ingest and because they sequester polyphenolic compounds that render them unpalatable (Geiselman and McConnell 1981). Microscale refugia in cracks, crevices, and among barnacles may be necessary for the recruitment and establishment of fucoid algae where *Littorina littorea* is seasonally abundant. This is further complicated by *L. littorea*'s ability to ingest and bulldoze away newly settled barnacles, thereby controlling their abundance as well.

The impact of intensive grazing by *L. littorea* on recruitment of *Ascophyllum* lead Vadas and Elner (1992) to suggest

Figure 17.18 The periwinkle snail *Littorina littorea*: (A) Dense aggregations of *Littorina* on a rocky shore (York, Maine); (B) *Littorina* keeps many rock surfaces apparently "bare," often leaving only the algae *Fucus* and *Ascophyllum* (Manomet Point, Plymouth, Mass.); (C) *Littorina* on the lower edge of a *Spartina alterniflora* marsh (Cape Cod, MA.). Photos by J. T. Carlton.

that more free space may be available in the intertidal zone of New England than before *Littorina*'s introduction. They based this conclusion on experiments indicating that the plant's longevity and its naturally low rates of successful settlement may reduce recruitment frequencies to only once every 30 years or more. The abundance and grazing impacts of *L. littorea*, they conclude, could mean that there are fewer opportunities for successful *Ascophyllum* recruitment than there were before the snail arrived to the Gulf of Maine 150 years ago.

It is impossible to know how the two native littorinid species, *Littorina obtusata*, and *L. saxatilis* were affected by the arrival of *L. littorea*. The strongest interaction was likely between *L. littorea* and *L. saxatilis* (Yamada and Mansour 1987) since both occupy rock substrates, graze on microalgae, and have similar dentition in their feeding apparatuses (i.e., their radulas; Steneck and Watling 1982). However, given that *L. littorea* grows to 43 mm in length whereas *L. saxatilis* grows only to 12 mm (Pollock 1997), it is likely that *L. littorea* displaced its ecologically similar relative. Today, *L. saxatilis* is found in the high intertidal zone. *L. obtusata* lives and feeds on fucoid algae and even takes on cryptic coloration pattern of the algae (Wilbur and Steneck 1999). There is little direct interaction between this species and *L. littorea,* but there could be an indirect effect if *L. littorea* altered the abundance of *Ascophyllum,* as suggested by Vadas and Elner (1992).

Littorina littorea controls algal species composition and diversity in rocky-shore tidepools (Figure 17.19; Lubchenco 1978). Under high *L. littorea* population density, almost all species are grazed except for the slower-growing algal crusts and largely inedible red alga (Irish moss) *Chondrus crispus.* At low grazing pressure, the weedy, fast-growing, and highly edible green alga *Enteromorpha* sp. dominates the system to the exclusion of most other species. Both extremes result in low species diversity compared to high diversity that developed under intermediate grazing pressures. This peak in diversity at intermediate levels of disturbance is widely cited as evidence supporting the general ecological theory called the "intermediate disturbance hypothesis" (Huston 1994). It is interesting that this general ecological theory was based on a community response to an introduced species. Similar results have been seen in marine communities composed entirely of native species in tidepools in the eastern North Pacific (Paine and Vadas 1969) and coral reefs in Australia (Connell 1978). This suggests that at least this rule of community assembly applies predictably at a process-level regardless of whether the interacting species have had a long evolutionary (or coevolutionary) association (see Jackson quotation on page 458).

In soft-sediment habitats, such as the seaward sides of *Spartina* salt marshes and open mud flats, *Littorina littorea* func-

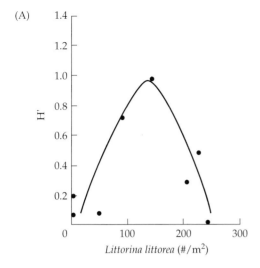

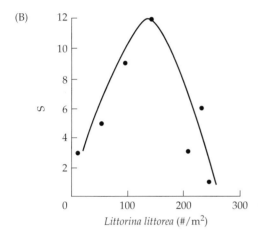

Figure 17.19 Effect of *Littorina littorea* on the diversity of algae in high tide pools (A, B) at Nahant, Massachusetts, and Gulf of Maine. *S* = number of species, H′ = index of diversity based on percentage cover of each species. Each point in A and B represents a different pool. (After Lubchenco 1978.)

tions as habitat modifier. In southern New England, *L. littorea* prevents marsh growth by nibbling outward-growing *Spartina* rhizomes. It also facilitates the erosion of the soft-sediment habitat seaward of the marsh's edge by grazing the sediment-retaining root-mat. As a result, *Spartina* loses substrate to colonize and the shore becomes progressively rockier (Figure 17.20; Bertness 1984).

Littorina littorea and two other invaders have also altered the ecology of the native mudsnail *Ilyanassa obsoleta*. *L. littorea* interacts directly for habitat sites and reproductive success with *Ilyanassa* in intertidal marshes. Brenchley and Carlton (1983) found that when *Littorina* was present in higher intertidal marsh areas, *Ilyanassa* did not enter (Figure 17.21). When *Littorina* was removed, *Ilyanassa* adults invaded. Bertness (1984) also noted that *Ilyanassa* rapidly migrated into sites where *Littorina* had been removed. *L. littorea* also now sets both the upper and lower limit of mudsnail distribution by reducing the substrate available for their egg deposition

and by directly consuming their eggs (Brenchley and Carlton 1983). The introduced green crab can also be an important *Ilyanassa* egg predator as can the native hermit crab *Pagurus longicarpus* that may now be more abundant because of the greater availability of *L. littorea* shells, which it uses as domiciles (Blackstone 1984; Blackstone and Joslyn 1984). The loss in reproductive success of *Ilyanassa* may be offset by the introduced green alga, *Codium fragile tomentosoides*, which arrived in 1975 in this area of New England and is a favored substrate for egg laying. Clearly, the functional role of *Ilyanassa*, a species which can exert considerable control on the fauna and flora of mudflats and marshes, has been influenced by several introduced species. What then might this mean for the rest of the mudflat community?

Taken together, we see a rapid coastal revolution due to species introduced to the Gulf of Maine. Some introductions have profoundly changed the structure and functioning of these coastal marine communities. Intertidal rocky shores, soft bottoms, eelgrass beds, mudflats, and the seaward edges of marshes have all been fundamentally altered by introduced species.

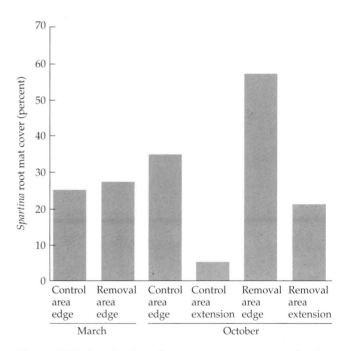

Figure 17.20 *Spartina alterniflora* root-mat cover in control and experimental snail removal areas, Bristol, Rhode Island. Each mean and confidence interval is for 10 quadrats (on the marsh edge) or the area below each quadrat (extension). No *Spartina* root mat was present in extension quadrats in March. In March there is no difference between control and removal sites. In October, the snail removal quadrat has nearly twice as much root mat as the control. In the removal-area extension, which represents extension of the marsh mat below its initial tidal level, the difference is even more striking. Snail-removal quadrats have more than four times as much root mat as quadrats in the control area. (After Bertness 1984.)

Figure 17.21 Movement of the mudsnail *Ilyanassa* into a marsh in *Littorina* experimental removal plots (A, C, E) and control plots (B, D) in Barnstable Harbor, Cape Cod, Massachusetts. Position of plots in upper-right corner. The number of mud snails per quarter square meter are shown for two 0.5-m-wide bands: open area, marsh edge (lower-0.5-m band); shaded area, marsh (upper-0.5-m band). Values are means of 4 (removals) or 5 (control) counts per day per area. Maximum densities of *Ilyanassa* are found 4 days (E), 5 days (A), and 6 days (C) after initial removal of *Littorina* (indicated by arrow). (After Brenchley and Carlton 1983.)

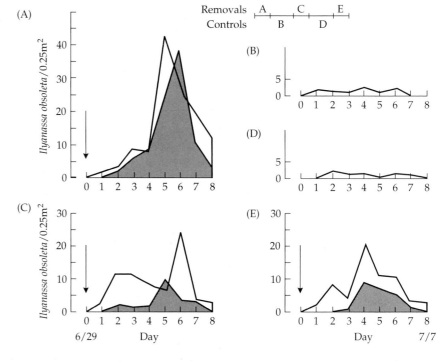

Biological Invasions: Some Perspectives

We focused on a single marine system to illustrate how profoundly marine communities can be altered by introduced species and how natural the system appears when studied post-introduction. However the problem is global in scale. Tens of thousands of marine species have been transported around the world, and hundreds or thousands of these have established new populations, often far from where they evolved (Carlton 1999; Ruiz et al. 1997, 1999).

Some regions have a long history of species introductions. For example, San Francisco Bay has suffered repeated and an accelerating rate of introductions over the past century (Cohen and Carlton 1998). Currently there are at least 164 introduced species in the bay and associated marine and brackish habitats. The dominant groups include arthropods (51 species), mollusks (27 species), cnidarians (16 species), and vascular plants (12 species) (Cohen and Carlton 1998). Another example is the Hawaiian coral reef systems that have had over two dozen nonnative species introduced both accidentally on ship hulls and intentionally by aquaculture scientists and fishermen. The impacts to Hawaiian reefs have been significant. Tropical algae from Florida (*Hypnea musiformis*) and the Philippines (*Eucheuma* sp. and *Kappaphycus* sp.) now overgrow Hawaiian coral and lagoons. The barnacle, *Chthalamus porteus*, an accidental introduction, has become the dominant organism in the upper intertidal zone on O'ahu, Maui, and Kaua'i islands. Several predatory fish (*Lutjanus kasmira*, *L. fulvus*, and *Cephalophalus argus*) were intentionally introduced from French Polynesia, and some have become the apex predators in reef systems. This is a particular problem because over 25% of Hawaiian reef animals are endemic species found only in the Hawaiian Islands (Grigg 1997).

Other regions were overgrown by a single species. For example, the tropical green alga from the Caribbean, *Caulerpa taxifolia*, has overrun benthic communities of the Mediterranean Sea (Strong and Pemberton 2000).

Some strongly interacting species are highly invasive. Examples of species that came to dominate the systems they invaded include the filter-feeding Asian clam *Potamocorbula amurensis* in San Francisco Bay (Carlton et al. 1990), the suspension-feeding American combjelly (ctenophore) *Mnemiopsis leidyi* in the Azov, Black, and Mediterranean Seas (Malyshev and Arkhipov 1992), the Japanese seastar *Asterias amurensis* in Australia (Buttermore et al. 1994), and the European green crab *Carcinus maenas* in South Africa and on the Pacific coast of North America (Griffiths et al. 1992; Cohen et al. 1995). Like *Littorina littorea*, each of these species is now playing a multifaceted role in each respective ecosystem, fundamentally and immediately altering energy flow and the structure of the food web, as well as the longer-term evolutionary pathways that these systems will take. Some introduced species may affect an ecosystem much more than they do in the system in which they evolved. For example, Caribbean algae, *Hypnea musiformis* and *Caulerpa taxifolia* are both common but not abundant algae where they are native but have come to carpet the regions they invaded (Hawaii and Mediterranean, respectively). There is no sign that species introductions are slowing in diversity or in impact. On Atlantic shores, a late-twentieth-century arrival is the omnivorous Asian shore crab *Hemigrapsus sanguineus*, which since its discovery in 1988 in New Jersey has expanded its range from the Gulf of Maine to North Carolina (Lohrer and Whitlatch 1997; Epifanio et al. 1998; McDermott 1998a,b, 1999; Gerard et al. 1999). Along the Rhode Island and Connecticut coasts *Hemi*-

grapsus in 2000 occurred by the tens of thousands on protected rocky shores in regions where *Carcinus* was formerly abundant but now forms less than 1 % of the crab population (J. T. Carlton, pers. obs.). *Hemigrapsus* eats algae, littorinid snails, and barnacles. Its arrival portends another series of dramatic changes to the New England shore.

Biological invasions are unpredictable. Given the number of species traversing the world on a regular basis, it's surprising there are not more invasions. Many species arrive to new biogeographic regions accidentally but perish. Although some intentionally introduced species have taken hold, several such attempts have failed. For example, around the turn of the century there was a concerted, but ultimately unsuccessful, attempt to introduce the American lobster, *Homarus americanus*, to the eastern North Pacific (Herrick 1909). Often the oceanographic conditions such as minimum and maximum temperatures cannot support the potential invader. Some species undoubtedly succumb to local predators or diseases to which they have no defense. Marine systems having high species and functional group diversity may be more resistant to invasions than species-depauperate systems (Stachowicz et al. 1999). Thus, fisheries-induced loss of predators or herbivores could make marine ecosystems more susceptible to colonization by introduced species.

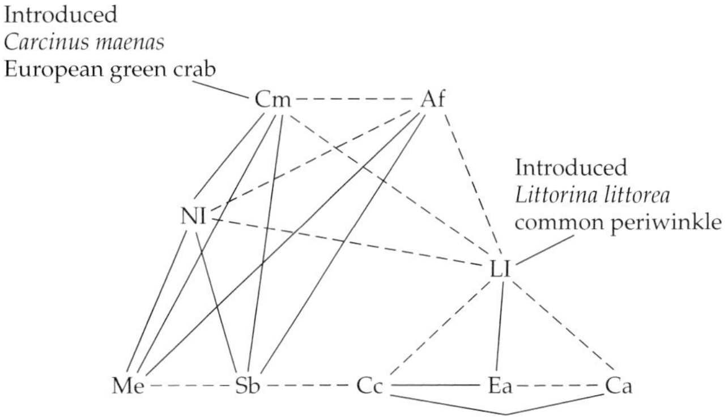

CONCLUSIONS: WHAT'S NATURAL?

Humans have altered most marine communities through both overextractions and species introductions. However, there is a very good chance workers may not recognize these changes because they are not obvious even to trained observers. In a classic study on the regulation of marine communities, Menge and Sutherland (1987) identified the "strong interactions" (sensu Paine 1980) in the rocky intertidal zone of New England as those having a controlling effect on community structure (Figure 17.22). They reported that the green crab was functionally an apex predator and the periwinkle, the dominant herbivore. These species comprised half of the consumers in their interaction web, but they are not native to that community. Equally important is what's missing from their interaction web. There were no large vertebrate predators. Even though it's known that if fish were present they would feed at high tide in the intertidal zone (Edwards et al. 1982), their absence in this interaction web indicates that this group was functionally absent from this system, probably as the result of overfishing. The natural structure of marine communities in New England before human impacts is unknown.

There is nothing wrong with considering the ecology of a marine community based on what is currently there. However, students, researchers, and policy makers must recognize that these communities have been profoundly altered and there are no longer pristine baselines against which human impacts can be measured (Dayton et al. 1998). We have shown that, in the Gulf of Maine, baselines have been changing for centuries, and there are many other examples from around

Figure 17.22 Food web from the low, rocky intertidal region of the Gulf of Maine (modified from Menge and Sutherland 1987). Lines between species in the food web indicate consumer–prey linkages. The thick lines indicate strong interactions (i.e., one species has an ecologically significant, controlling effect on another), and dashed lines indicate weak or insignificant interactions. Species abbreviations: Af, *Asterias forbesi*, NI, *Nucella lapillus*, Me, *Mytilus edulis*, Sb, *Semibalanus balanoides*, Cc, *Chondrus crispus*, Ea, ephemeral algae, Ca, crustose algae.

the world. That so many studies described intricate interactions within marine communities without knowing, or at least not acknowledging, that they had been seriously altered (e.g., Menge and Sutherland 1987), reinforces our warning, *Students beware!* It is probably safer to assume that all marine communities are changing as a result of human influences than to assume they are stable and relatively pristine.

Large-scale changes in species abundance and the functioning of entire trophic levels are often caused by human alterations of marine communities. That these recently altered systems were often treated as natural (e.g., Figure 17.22) suggests that their structure and function does not require stable or tightly coevolved species associations. While some human alterations may be difficult to detect, others cause rapid and conspicuous increases or decreases in populations. We have described some recent and remarkable fisheries-induced declines of consumers that caused dramatic increases in their prey, as well as population explosions resulting from the introduction of novel consumers or producers. These changes, along with human alterations of climate, toxins, and habitat have probably transformed marine communities more than we realize. Many of these marine communities are able to assimilate these alterations and still *appear* natural. Thus, while marine communities have always been changing, the unprecedented scale and rate change of human alterations are anything but natural.

ACKNOWLEDGMENTS

Many of these ideas evolved from discussions with Jim Acheson, Peter Auster, Ted Ames, Mark Bertness, Bruce Bourque, Phil Conkling, Paul Dayton, Jim Estes, Jeremy Jackson, Rich Langton, Wendy Malpass, Doug McNaught, Bob Paine, Alvaro Palma, Ken Sebens, Bob Vadas, Rick Wahle, Steph Watson, Carl Wilson, Jim Wilson, Jon Witman, Steff Zimsen and many others to whom we apologize for not naming individually. We also thank Bob Vadas, Jon Witman, and Ken Sebens for the many years of stimulating collaborative research on Cashes Ledge's Ammen Rock Pinnacle as we all explored the wonders of a large predatory fish-dominated system. We received comments on early drafts from Mark Bertness, Mark Hay, Elizabeth Horan, Mark Hixon, Amanda Leland, Eric Annis, John Vavrinec, and four anonymous reviewers. However, all errors of interpretation and emphasis are solely attributable to us. Funding for the research described here was from NOAA's National Undersea Research Program's National Research Center at the University of Connecticut at Avery Point (Grant No. NA46RU0146 and UCAZP 94–121), the Pew Fellowship for Marine Conservation, the University of Maine's Sea Grant program, Maine's Department of Marine Resources for funding RSS's lobster and sea urchin research, and fellowships to RSS and JTC from the Pew Fellows Program in Maine Conservation. To all, we are grateful.

LITERATURE CITED

Aronson, R. B. 1994. Scale-independent biological processes in the marine environment. *Ocean. Mar. Biol. Annu. Rev.* 32: 435-460.

Atwood, D. K., J. C. Hendee and A. Mendez. 1992. An assessment of global warming stress on Caribbean coral reef ecosystems. *Bull. Mar. Sci.* 51: 118–130.

Barnard, M. 1986. *Sea, Salt and Sweat: A Story of Nova Scotia and the Vast Atlantic Fishery.* Four East Publications and the Nova Scotia Department of Fisheries. Halifax, N.S.

Bertness, M. D. 1984. Habitat and community modification by an introduced herbivorous snail. *Ecology.* 65: 370-381.

Bigelow, H. B. and W. C. Schroeder. 1953. Fishes of the Gulf of Maine. *Fish Wildl. Serv. Fish. Bull.* 53.

Birkeland, C. 1977. The importance of rate of biomass accumulation in early successional stages of benthic communities to the survival of coral recruits. *Proc. 3rd Internatl. Coral Reef Symp.* 1: 15-22.

Blackstone, N. W. 1984. The effects of history on the shell preference of the hermit crab *Pagurus longicarpus* (Say). *J. Exp. Mar. Ecol. Biol.* 81: 225-234.

Blackstone, N. W. and A. R. Joslyn. 1984. Utilization and preference for the introduced gastropod *Littorina littorea* (L.) by the hermit crab *Pagurus longicarpus* (Say) at Guilford, Connecticut. *J. Exp. Mar. Ecol. Biol.* 80: 1-9.

Bologna, P. and R. Steneck. 1993. Kelp beds as habitat for the American lobster, *Homarus americanus. Mar. Ecol. Prog. Ser.* 100: 127-134.

Bourque, B. J. 1996. *Diversity and Complexity in Prehistoric Maritime Societies: A Gulf of Maine Perspective.* Plenum Press, New York.

Breen, P. A., T. A. Carson, J. B. Foster and E. A. Stewart. 1982. Changes in subtidal community structure associated with British Columbia sea otter transplants. *Mar. Ecol. Prog. Ser.* 7: 13-20.

Brenchley, G. A. and J. T. Carlton. 1983. Competitive displacement of native mud snails by introduced periwinkles in the New England intertidal zone. *Biol. Bull.* 165: 543-558.

Brown, B. E., G. A. Brennan, M. D. Grosslein, E. G. Heyerdahl and R. C. Hennemuth. 1978. The effect of fishing on the marine finfish biomass in the northeast Atlantic from the Gulf of Maine to Cape Hatteras. *ICNAF Res. Bull.* 12: 49-69.

Burkholder, J. M. 1999. Lurking perils of *Pfiesteria. Sci. Amer.* 281: 28-35.

Buttermore, R. E., E. Turner and M. G. Morrice. 1994. The introduced northern Pacific seastar *Asterias amurensis* in Tasmania. *Mem. Queensland Museum* 36: 21-25.

Caldwell, B. 1981. *Islands of Maine: Where America Really Began.* Guy Gannett, Portland, ME.

Carlson, C. C. 1986. Maritime catchment areas: An analysis of prehistoric fishing strategies in the Boothbay region of Maine. MS Thesis, University of Maine, Orono.

Carlton, J. T. 1982. The historical biogeography of *Littorina littorea* on the Atlantic coast of North America, and implications for the interpretation of the structure of New England intertidal communities. *Malacol. Rev.* 15: 146.

Carlton, J. T. 1985. Transoceanic and interoceanic dispersal of coastal marine organisms: the biology of ballast water. *Oceanogr.. Mar. Biol. Annu. Rev.* 23: 313-371.

Carlton, J. T. 1987. Patterns of transoceanic marine biological invasions in the Pacific Ocean. *Bull. Mar. Sci.* 41: 452-465.

Carlton, J. T. 1992a. Dispersal of living organisms into aquatic ecosystems as mediated by aquaculture and fisheries activities. In A. Rosenfield and R. Mann (eds.), *Dispersal of Living Organisms into Aquatic Ecosystems,* pp. 13-45. Maryland Sea Grant Publication, College Park, MD.

Carlton, J. T. 1992b. Introduced marine and estuarine mollusks of North America: An end-of-the-20th-century perspective. *J. Shellfish Res.* 11: 489-505.

Carlton, J. T. 1996. Biological invasions and cryptogenic species. *Ecology* 77: 1653-1655.

Carlton, J. T. 1999. The scale and ecological consequences of biological invasions in the world's oceans. In O. Sandlund, P. Schei and Å. Viken (eds.), *Invasive Species and Biodiversity Management,* pp. 195-212. Kluwer, Dordrecht.

Carlton, J. T. and J. B . Geller. 1993. Ecological roulette: The global transport of nonindigenous marine organisms. *Science* 261: 78-82.

Carlton, J. T. and J. A. Scanlon. 1985. Progression and dispersal of an introduced alga: *Codium fragile* sp. *tomentosoides* (Chlorophyta) on the Atlantic coast of North America. *Bot. Mar.* 28: 155-165.

Carlton, J. T., J. K. Thompson, L. E. Schemel and F. H. Nichols. 1990. Remarkable invasion of San Francisco Bay (California, USA) by the Asian clam *Potamocorbula amurensis.* I. Introduction and dispersal. *Mar. Ecol. Prog. Ser.* 66: 81-94.

Carlton, J. T., J. B. Geller, M. L. Reaka-Kudla and E. A. Norse. 1999. Historical extinctions in the sea. *Annu. Rev. Ecol. Syst.* 30: 515-538.

Carpenter, R. C. 1986. Partitioning herbivory and its effects on coral reef algal communities. *Ecology.* 56: 345-363.

Carr, M. H. 1994. Effects of macroalgal dynamics on recruitment of a temperate reef fish. *Ecology.* 75: 1320-1333.

Casey, J. M. and R. A. Myers. 1998. Near extinction of a large, widely distributed fish. *Science.* 281: 690-692.

Chenoweth, S. and J. McGowan 1994. *Periwinkles in Maine: Fishery and Biology.* Maine Department of Marine Resources, Portland.

Churchill, E. A. 1979. Too great the challenge: The birth and death of Falmouth, Maine, 1624-1676. PhD Dissertation, University of Maine, Orono.

Cohen, A. N. and J. T. Carlton. 1998. Accelerating invasion rate in a highly invaded estuary. *Science* 279: 555-558.

Cohen, A. N., J. T. Carlton and M. C. Fountain. 1995. Introduction, dispersal, and potential impacts of the green crab *Carcinus maenas* in San Francisco Bay, California. *Mar. Biol.* 122: 225-237.

Collins, J. W. and R. Rathbun. 1887. Fishing grounds of the eastern coast of North America. In G. B. Goode (ed), *The Fisheries and Fishing Industries of the U. S. Section III.* Printing Office, Washington, DC.

Conkling, P. W. and T. Ames. 1996. Penobscot fisheries in the 20th century. In D. D. Platt (ed.), *Penobscot: The Forest River and Bay,* pp. 46-65. Island Institute, Rockland, ME.

Connell, J. H. 1978. Diversity in tropical rain forests and coral reefs. *Science.* 199: 1302-1310.

Connell, J. H. and W. P. Sousa. 1983. On the evidence needed to judge ecological stability or persistence. *Amer. Nat.* 121: 789-824.

Cooper, S. R. and G. S. Brush. 1993. A 2500-year history of anoxia and eutrophication in Chesapeake Bay. *Estuaries*. 16: 617-626.

Davison, I. R., J. E. Kuebler, R. L. Vadas and R. S. Steneck. 1988. Comparative photosynthetic physiology of shallow and deep water populations of *Laminaria* in the Gulf of Maine. *NOAA Symp. Ser. for Undersea Res.* 6.

Dayton, P. K., M. J. Tegner, P. B. Edwards and K. L. Riser. 1998. Sliding baselines, ghosts, and reduced expectations in kelp forest communities. *Ecol. Appl.* 8: 309-322.

Duggins, D.O., J. E. Eckman and A. T. Sewell. 1990. Ecology of understory kelp environments. II. Effects of kelp on recruitment of benthic invertebrates. *J. Exp. Mar. Biol. Ecol.* 143: 27-45.

Edwards, D. C., D. O. Conover and F. Sutter, III. 1982. Mobile predators and the structure of intertidal communities. *Ecology* 63: 1175-1180.

Epifanio, C. E., A. I. Dittel, S. Park, S. Schwalm and A. Fouts. 1998. Early life history of *Hemigrapsus sanguineus*, a nonindigenous crab in the Middle Atlantic Bight (USA). *Mar. Ecol. Prog. Ser.* 170: 231-238.

Estes, J. A. and D. O. Duggins. 1995. Sea otters and kelp forests in Alaska: Generality and variation in a community ecological paradigm. *Ecol. Monogr.* 65: 75-100.

Estes, J. A., D. O. Duggins and G. B. Rathbun. 1989. The ecology of extinctions in kelp forest communities. *Conserv. Biol.* 3: 252-264.

Estes, J. A., M. T. Tinker, T. M. Williams and D. F. Doak. 1998. Killer whale predation on sea otters linking oceanic and nearshore ecosystems. *Science* 282: 473-476.

Forbes, E. 1859. *The Natural History of the European Seas.* John van Voorst, London.

Geiselman, J. A. and O. J. McConnell. 1981. Polyphenols in brown algae, *Fucus vesiculosus* and *Ascophyllum nodosum*: Chemical defenses against the marine herbivorous snail, *Littorina litorea*. *J. Chem. Ecol.* 7: 1115-1133.

Gerard, V. A., R. M. Cerrato and A. A. Larson. 1999. Potential impacts of a western Pacific grapsid crab on intertidal communities of the northwestern Atlantic Ocean. *Biol. Invas.* 1: 353–361.

Glude, J. B. 1955. The effects of temperature and predators on the abundance of the soft-shell clam, *Mya arenaria*, in New England. *Trans. Amer. Fish. Soc.* 84: 13-26.

Goode, G. B. 1884. *Fishing Industries of the U. S. Section I.* Printing Office, Washington, DC.

Griffiths, C. L., P.A.R. Hockey, C. Van Erkom Schurink and P. J. Le Roux. 1992. Marine invasive aliens on South African shores: Implications for community structure and trophic functioning. *S. African J. Mar. Sci.* 12: 713-722.

Grigg, R. W. 1988. Paleoceanography of coral reefs in the Hawaiian-Emperor chain. *Science*. 240: 1737-1743.

Grigg, R. W. 1994. Effects of sewage discharge, fishing pressure, and habitat complexity on coral ecosystems and reef fishes in Hawaii. *Mar. Ecol. Prog. Ser.* 103: 25-34.

Grigg, R. W. 1997. Hawaii's coral reefs: Status and health in 1997, the International Year of the Reef. In R. W. Grigg, and C. Birkeland (eds.), *Status of Coral Reefs in the Pacific*, pp. 59-72. University of Hawaii Sea Grant College Program, Honolulu.

Hacunda, J. S. 1981. Trophic relationships among demersal fishes in a coastal area of the Gulf of Maine. *Fish. Bull.* 79:775-788.

Hay, M. E. 1984. Patterns of fish and urchin grazing on Caribbean coral reefs: Are previous results typical? *Ecology* 65: 446-454.

Hennemuth, R. C. and S. Rockwell. 1987. History of fisheries conservation and management. In R. H. Backus (ed.), *Georges Bank*, pp. 430–446. MIT Press, Cambridge, MA.

Herrick, F. H. 1909. Natural history of the American lobster. *Bull. Bur. Fish.* 20: 153-408.

Hughes, T. P. 1994. Catastrophes, phase shifts, and large-scale degradation of a Caribbean coral reef. *Science* 265: 1547-1551.

Huston, M. A. 1994. *Biological Diversity. The Coexistence of Species on Changing Landscapes.* Cambridge University Press, Cambridge.

Jackson, J. B. C. 1994. Community unity? *Science* 264: 1412-1413.

Jackson, J. B. C. 1997. Reefs since Columbus. *Coral Reefs* 16: S23-S32.

Kleypas, J. A., R. W. Buddemeier, D. Archer, J. P. Gattuso, C. Langdon and B. N. Opdyke. 1999. Geochemical consequences of increased atmospheric carbon dioxide on coral reefs. *Science* 284: 118-120.

Lessios, H. A. 1988. Mass mortality of *Diadema antillarum* in the Caribbean: What have we learned? *Annu. Rev. Ecol. Syst.* 19: 371-393.

Lessios, H. A., D. R Robertson and J. D. Cubit. 1984. Spread of *Diadema* mass mortality through the Caribbean. *Science* 226: 335-337.

Levin, P. S. 1991. Effects of microhabitat on recruitment variation in a Gulf of Maine reef fish. *Mar. Ecol. Prog. Ser.* 75: 183-189.

Levin, P. S. 1994. Small-scale recruitment variation in a temperate fish: The roles of macrophytes and food supply. *Environ. Biol. Fish.* 40: 271-281.

Levin, P. S. and M. E. Hay. 1996. Responses of temperate reef fishes to alterations in algal structure and species composition. *Mar. Ecol. Prog. Ser.* 134: 37-47.

Levitan, D. R. 1992. Community structure in times past: Influence of human fishing pressure on algal-urchin interactions. *Ecology* 73: 1597-1605.

Lohrer, A. M. and R. W. Whitlatch. 1997. Ecological studies on the recently introduced Japanese shore crab (*Hemigrapsus sanguineus*) in Eastern Long Island Sound. In N. Balcom (ed.), *Proceedings of the Second Northeast Conference on Nonindigenous Aquatic Nuisance Species*, pp. 49–60. Publication Number CTSG-95–02, University of Connecticut Sea Grant College Program, Avery Point.

Lubchenco, J. 1978. Plant species diversity in a marine intertidal community: Importance of herbivore food preference and algal competitive abilities. *Amer. Nat.* 112: 23-39.

Lubchenco, J. 1983. *Littorina* and *Fucus*: Effects of herbivores, substratum heterogeneity, and plant escapes during succession. *Ecology* 64: 1116-1123.

Lubchenco, J. and B. A. Menge. 1978. Community development and persistence in a low rocky intertidal zone. *Ecol. Monogr.* 48: 67-94.

Maine's Commissioner of Sea and Shore Fisheries Annual Report 1949. In P. W. Conkling and T. Ames, Penobscot fisheries in the 20th century. In D. D. Platt, *Penobscot: The Forest River and Bay*, pp. 46-65. Island Institute, Rockland, ME.

Malpass, W. J. 1992. The ecology and resource use patterns of small, benthic, predatory fishes in rocky, nearshore habitats of the Gulf of Maine, U.S.A. MS Thesis, University of Maine, Orono.

Malyshev, V. I. and A. G. Arkhipov. 1992. The ctenophore *Mnemiopsis leidyi* in the western Black Sea. *Hydrobiol. J.* 28: 33-39.

Martin, K. R. and N. R. Lipfert. 1985. *Lobstering and the Maine Coast.* Maine Maritime Museum, Bath.

Mayo, R. K., M. J. Fogarty and F. M. Serchuk. 1992. Aggregate fish biomass and yield on Georges Bank 1960-87. *J. Northwest Atlantic Fish. Sci.* 14: 59-78.

McClanahan, T. and N. Muthiga. 1989. Patterns of predation on a sea urchin *Echinometra mathaei* (de Blainville) on Kenyan coral reef. *J. Exp. Mar. Biol. Ecol.* 126: 77-94.

McDermott, J. J. 1998a. The Western Pacific brachyuran *Hemigrapsus sanguineus* (Grapsidae) in its new habitat along the Atlantic coast of the United States: Reproduction. *J. Crustacean Biol.* 18: 308-316.

McDermott, J. J. 1998b. The Western Pacific brachyuran *Hemigrapsus sanguineus* (Grapsidae) in its new habitat along the Atlantic coast of the United States: Geographic distribution and ecology. *ICES J. Mar. Sci.* 55: 289-298.

McDermott, J. J. 1999. The Western Pacific brachyuran *Hemigrapsus sanguineus* (Grapsidae) in its new habitat along the Atlantic coast of the United States: Feeding, cheliped morphology and growth. In *Crustaceans and the Biodiversity Crisis*, pp. 425-444. *Proc. 4th Internatl.. Crustac. Cong.* Koninklijke Brill NV, Leiden.

McNaught, D. C. 1999. The indirect effects of macroalgae and micropredation on post-settlement success of the green sea urchin in Maine. PhD Dissertation, University of Maine, Orono.

Menge, B. A. and J. P. Sutherland 1987. Community regulation: Variations in disturbance competition, and predation in relation to environmental stress and recruitment. *Amer. Nat.* 130: 730-757.

Minchin, D. 1996. Tar pellets and plastics as attachment surfaces for *lepadid cirripedes* in the North Atlantic Ocean. *Mar. Poll. Bull.* 32: 855-859.

National Research Council (NCR). 1995. *Understanding Marine Biodiversity. A Research Agenda for the Nation.* National Academy Press, Washington, DC.

National Research Council (NCR). 1999. *Sustaining Marine Fisheries.* National Academy Press, Washington, DC.

Norse, E. A. (ed.). 1993. *Global Marine Biological Diversity Strategy: Building Conservation into Decision Making.* Center for Marine Conservation, Washington, DC.

Ojeda, F. P. and J. H. Dearborn. 1989. Diversity, abundance, and spatial distribution of fishes and crustaceans in the rocky subtidal zone of the Gulf of Maine. *Fish. Bull.* 88: 403-410.

Paine, R. T. 1969. A note on trophic complexity and community stability. *Amer. Nat.* 103: 91-93.

Paine, R. T. 1980. Food webs: Linkage, interaction strength and community infrastructure. *J. Anim. Ecol.* 49: 667-685.

Paine, R. T. and R. L. Vadas. 1969. The effect of grazing by sea urchins, *Strongylocentrotus* sp., on benthic algal populations. *Limn. Oceanogr.* 15: 710-719.

Pauly, D., V. Christensen, J. Dalsgaard, R. Froese and F. Torres, Jr., 1998. Fishing down marine food webs. *Science* 279: 860-863.

Pollock, L. W. 1997. *A Practical Guide to the Marine Animals of Northeastern North America.* Rutgers University Press, New Brunswick, NJ.

Power, M. E., D. Tilman, J. A. Estes, B. A. Menge, W. J. Bond, L. S. Mills, G. Daily, J. Castilla, J. Lubchenco and R. T. Paine. 1996. Challenges in the quest for keystones. *BioScience* 46: 609-620.

Rathbun, 1887. The lobster fishery. In Goode, G. R., *The Fisheries and Fishery Industry of the United States. Section V: History and Methods of the Fisheries.* U.S. Government Printing Office, Washington, DC.

Reid, D. G. 1996. *Systematics and Evolution of Littorina.* The Ray Society, Andover, Hampshire, UK.

Rich, W. H. 1929. Fishing grounds of the Gulf of Maine. *Bur. Fish. Doc.* 1959: 51-117.

Rosier, J. 1605. *True Relations of Capt. George Weymouth's Voyage.* George Bishop, London.

Ruiz, G. M., J. T. Carlton, E. D. Grosholz and A. H. Hines. 1997. Global invasions of marine and estuarine habitats by non-indigenous species: Mechanisms, extent, and consequences. *Amer. Zool.* 37: 621-632.

Ruiz, G. M., P. Fofonoff and A. H. Hines. 1999. Non-indigenous species as stressors in estuarine and marine communities: Assessing invasion impacts and interactions. *Limn. Oceanogr.* 44: 950-972.

Sala, E., C. F. Boudouresque and M. Harmelin-Vivien. 1998. Fishing, trophic cascades, and the structure of algal assemblages: Evaluation of an old but untested paradigm. *Oikos.* 83: 15.

Sears, J. R. and R. T. Wilce. 1975. Sublittoeral benthic marine algae of southern Cape Cod and adjacent islands: Seasonal periodicity, associations, diversity, and floristic composition. *Ecol. Monogr.* 45: 337-365.

Seeley, R. H. 1986. Intense natural selection caused a rapid morphological transition in a living marine snail. *Proc. Natl. Acad. Sci.* 83: 6897-6901.

Sherman, K. 1991. The large marine ecosystem concept: Research and management strategy for living marine resources. *Ecol. Appl.* 1: 349-360.

Simenstad, C. A., J. A. Estes and K. W. Kenyon. 1978. Aleuts, sea otters, and alternate stable-state communities. *Science* 200: 403-410.

Sinclair, M. and F. Page. 1995. Cod fishery collapses and North Atlantic GLOBEC. *U.S. GLOBEC News* 8: 1-20.

Smith, J. 1616. *The Description of New England.* H. Lownes, London.

Stachowicz, J. J., R. B. Whitlatch and R. W. Osman. 1999. Species diversity and invasion resistance in a marine ecosystem. *Science* 286: 1577-1579.

Steneck, R. S. 1982. A limpet-coralline algal association: Adaptations and defenses between a selective herbivore and its prey. *Ecology* 63: 507-522.

Steneck, R. S. 1986. The ecology of coralline algal crusts: Convergent patterns and adaptive strategies. *Annu. Rev. Ecol. Syst.* 7: 273-303.

Steneck, R. S. 1988. Herbivory on coral reefs: A synthesis. *Proc. 6th Internatl. Coral Reef Symp.* 1: 37-49.

Steneck, R. S. 1994. Is herbivore loss more damaging to reefs than hurricanes? Case studies from two Caribbean reef systems (1978-1988). In *Proceedings of the Colloquium on Global Aspects of Coral Reefs: Health, Hazards and History 1993*, pp. 220-226. University of Miami, Miami, FL.

Steneck, R. S. 1997. Fisheries-induced biological changes to the structure and function of the Gulf of Maine ecosystem. Plenary paper. In G. T. Wallace and E. F. Braasch (eds), *Proceedings of the Gulf of Maine Ecosystem Dynamics Scientific Symposium and Workshop*, pp. 151-165. RARGOM Report 91-1. Regional Association for Research on the Gulf of Maine, Hanover, NH.

Steneck, R. S. and M. N. Dethier. 1994. A functional approach to the structure of algal-dominated communities. *Oikos* 69: 476-498.

Steneck, R. S. and L. Watling. 1982. Feeding capabilities and limitation of herbivorous molluscs: A functional group approach. *Mar. Biol.* 68: 299-319.

Steneck, R. S., D. McNaught and S. Zimsen. 1995. Spatial and temporal patterns in sea urchin populations, herbivory and algal community structure in the Gulf of Maine. In *1994 Workshop on the Management and Biology of the Green Sea Urchin* (Strongylocentrotus droebachiensis), pp. 34-73. Massachusetts Department of Natural Resources, Boston.

Strong, D. R. and R. W. Pemberton. 2000. Biological control of invading species—risk and reform. *Science.* 288: 1969-1970.

Tegner, M. J., L. V. Basch and P. K. Dayton. 1996. Near extinction of an exploited marine invertebrate. *Trends Ecol. Evol.* 11: 278-280.

Trussell, G. C. 2000. Phenotypic clines, plasticity, and morphological trade-offs in an intertidal snail. *Evolution* 54: 151-166.

Vadas, R. L. 1992. Littorinid grazing and algal patch dynamics. In J. Grahame, P. J. Mill and D. G. Reid (eds.), *Proc. 3rd Internatl. Symp. Littorinid Biol.*, pp. 197–209.

Vadas, R. L. and R. W. Elner. 1992. Plant-animal interactions in the north-west Atlantic. D. M. John, S. J. Hawkins and J. H. Price (eds.), *Plant-Animal Interactions in the Marine Benthos*, pp. 33–60. Clarendon Press, Oxford.

Vadas, R. L. and R. S. Steneck. 1988. Zonation of deep water benthic algae in the Gulf of Maine. *J. Phycol.* 24: 338-346.

Vadas, R. L. and R. S. Steneck. 1995. Overfishing and inferences in kelp-sea urchin interactions. H. R. Skjoldal, C. Hopkins, K. E. Erikstad and H. P. Leinaas (eds.), *Ecology of Fjords and Coastal Waters*, pp. 509-524. Elsevier Science, London.

Vermeij, G. J. 1982. Phenotypic evolution in a poorly dispersing snail after arrival of a predator. *Nature.* 299: 349-350.

Vermeij, G. J. 1991. When biotas meet: Understanding biotic interchange. *Science* 253: 1099-1103.

Wahle, R. A. and R. S. Steneck. 1992. Habitat restrictions in early benthic life: Experiments on habitat selection and in situ predation with the American lobster. *J. Exp. Mar. Biol. Ecol.* 157: 91-114.

Watling, L. and E. A. Norse. 1998. Disturbance of the seabed by mobile fishing gear: A comparison to forest clearcutting. *Conserv. Biol.* 12: 1180-1197.

Watson, S. M. 1996. Overfishing from a multiple scale perspective: Implication for the efficient organization of fisheries management institutions. MS Thesis, University of Maine, Orono.

Welch, W. R. 1968. Changes in abundance of the green crab, *Carcinus maenas* (L.), in relation to recent temperature changes. *Fish. Bull.* 67: 337-345.

Wilbur, A. J. and R. S. Steneck. 1999. Polychromatic patterns of *Littorina obtusata* on *Ascophyllum nodosum*: Are snails hiding in intertidal seaweed? *Northeastern Nat.* 6: 189-198.

Winston, J. E. 1982. Drift plastic-an expanding niche for a marine invertebrate? *Mar. Poll. Bull.* 10: 348-351.

Witman, J. D. and K. P. Sebens. 1992. Regional variation in fish predation intensity: A historical perspective in the Gulf of Maine. *Oecologia* 909: 305-315.

Yamada S. and R. A. Mansour. 1987. Growth inhibition of native *Littorina saxatilis* (olivi) by introduced *Littorina littorea* (L.). *J. Exp. Mar. Biol. Ecol*

chapter *18*

Conservation and Management of Marine Communities

Charles H. Peterson and James A. Estes

After decades of denial, academic ecologists now acknowledge the tremendous modifications that human activities have made to marine ecological systems (e.g., Lubchenco et al. 1991; Botsford et al. 1997; Vitousek et al. 1997a). The extent and magnitude of human-induced changes have raised concerns over the sustainability of the ecological goods and services provided by the natural ecosystems upon which human welfare and survival are based (Daily 1997). Never before in the history of life on earth has the influence of a single species so threatened the sustainability of renewable natural resources (Costanza et al. 1997; Vitousek et al. 1997a). This dire state of affairs is an inevitable consequence of growing human numbers and the per capita increase in natural resource utilization (Murdoch 1980). Yet, the science of ecology can offer some measure of understanding of consequences and guide environmental and natural resource managers towards strategies that may at least limit the damage or at best sustain critical natural ecosystem functions.

While most attention to the problem of human dominance of natural ecosystems has focused on the terrestrial realm, we now realize that a similar situation applies in the sea (Botsford et al. 1997). This not withstanding, terrestrial and marine ecosystems differ in many important ways, so that conservation and management strategies developed for terrestrial systems may not apply to the oceans (Steele 1985). What are these purported differences? Perhaps the most fundamental is that, except for earthquakes and other tectonic events, land is spatially static whereas the ocean is spatially labile. Upwelling and downwelling result in vertical mixing, and ocean currents move water masses vast distances over short time periods. Second, the geographical ranges of both populations and individuals tend to be much larger for marine than terrestrial species (Roughgarden et al. 1988; Botsford et al. 1997).

Third, most people live on land, not in the sea, the result being that numerous terrestrial species are prevented from occupying portions of their natural range by human developments of one kind or another. The amount of suitable habitat for terrestrial species has been greatly reduced and remaining habitat is extensively fragmented, both of which modifications compromise the demographic and genetic viability of populations (Soulé 1987). A fourth major difference between land and sea is the nature of exploited species. Nearly all land-based food production comes from domesticated plants and animals, whereas most marine foods are obtained from wild and genetically unmanipulated stocks. In addition, the trophic status of exploited species differs greatly between land and sea. On land we exploit mostly plants and herbivores, while at sea we have always targeted species near the top of the food web (Pauly et al. 1998a). For these and other reasons, the oceans present unique problems for natural resource managers. Differences between terrestrial and marine ecosystems, and the application of primarily land-based management practices, may help explain why the management record for marine resources is so poor. Failures in management of living marine resources provide a clear signal that new approaches are needed for the conservation and management of marine ecosystems.

In this chapter, we identify the more important anthropogenic stressors on marine ecosystems, explain how and why these stressors exert their impacts, and discuss the implications for management and conservation of life in the sea. Specifically, we discuss global climate change, eutrophication, chemical pollution, habitat modification, and living resource exploitation. We exclude effects of species introductions from our presentation only because they are covered in this volume by Steneck and Carlton (Chapter 17). Human impacts to marine communities are so pervasive that they can hardly be ignored in any review, which necessarily creates some overlaps between our chapter and other contributions in this book. In addition, our views may occasionally conflict with those of other authors. Such disagreement among scientists is not unusual and actually serves to underscore one of the major challenges faced by managers who wish to embrace up-to-date scientific understanding in their rules, regulations, and legislation. Our broad goal in this contribution is to convey an appreciation for the complexity of indirect effects of human activities on marine ecosystems such that management may be induced to adopt a more holistic ecosystem-based view of how to manage human activities to preserve valuable and even critical aspects of marine communities.

MARINE ECOLOGICAL CONSEQUENCES OF GLOBAL CLIMATE CHANGE

The evidence for human-induced global warming is now very strong (Peters and Lovejoy 1994; Hansen et al. 1998). Before discussing the known or suspected impacts of warming on marine systems, it is useful to consider the history of global climate change. Over the past billion or so years, a time-window that includes much of the history of life on earth, the earth's climate has undergone extensive and repeated change between warm and cold (Imbrie and Imbrie 1979; Pielou 1991). Global climate during more than 95 percent of this period was substantially warmer than at present. Extended cool periods (termed glacial ages), each about 10–15 million years in duration, occurred about 800 to 900 million years ago and again about 200 to 300 million years ago. We are presently in the early stages of a third glacial age. Climate variation on this scale is thought to result from tectonic movement of continental land masses. Cold conditions prevailed when land masses drifted into positions that impeded the polar flow of tropical water: warm conditions prevailed during the more common periods when polar flow of tropical water was unimpeded. Although the long intervening warm periods were continuously warm, glacial ages were not continuously cold, instead regularly oscillating between glaciations (each with a duration of 60 to 90 thousand years) and relatively mild interglacial periods (each with a duration 10 to 40 thousand years) on a 100,000 year cycle. The glacial/interglacial oscillation probably is driven by the composite effect of regular change in shape of Earth's orbit around the sun, change in Earth's axis of rotation relative to the orbital plane, and the timing of these two events. We are presently near the end of an interglacial period. Thus, in the context of climatic history, we live in an unusual time.

Ecological Consequences of Changing Ice Dynamics in High Latitudes

Climate changes have particularly large ecological consequences at high latitudes. A 50-year warming trend of 2–3° C has been documented in the Antarctic Peninsula (King 1984;

Stark 1994) and further warming at a more rapid rate is likely operating through the effects of increasing concentrations of greenhouse gases (Conway et al. 1999). Such increases in temperature can drive large changes in seasonal cover of ice, ice edge dynamics, and extent of glaciers and polar ice caps (Weatherly et al. 1991; Murphy et al. 1995). Because the ecology of marine communities in high latitudes is closely tied to sea ice dynamics (e.g., Alexander 1980; Laws 1984; Fraser and Ainley 1986), global warming can be expected to affect ecosystems in the arctic and antarctic indirectly through modifications of ice cover and dynamics. Because changes in atmospheric emissions of greenhouse gases (such as carbon dioxide and methane) are a consequence of human activities (such as clearing of terrestrial forests and burning of fossil fuels), the ecology of high-latitude communities in the sea represents an issue for marine conservationists and environmental managers on a global scale. Despite the international cooperation that has characterized research and management of Antarctica, there is little reason for optimism about that partnership extending to meaningful international agreements to control greenhouse gas emissions.

The earth's climate has experienced dramatic natural cycles, with periods of extensive glaciations and periods characterized by higher temperatures than what prevails today. However, overall temperatures were not necessarily colder during the glaciations. Cool summers and warm winters promoted glacial expansion, whereas warmer summers and colder winters caused glacial recessions (Imbrie and Imbrie 1980). This is because the rate of glacial expansion or retraction is dictated by two factors—starvation and melting. Starvation depends on the rate of snowfall, which varies inversely with winter temperature at high latitudes. Cold winters promote starvation by reducing the atmosphere's capacity to hold water, and by creating large expanses of winter sea ice, which block evaporative water transport from the ocean to the atmosphere. In contrast, melting occurs solely during summer, thus depending entirely on summer temperatures. This is why cool summers and warm winters promoted growth of the continental ice sheets, while warm summers and cold winters promoted their recession.

The ecology of high-latitude communities is strongly affected by sea ice edges because of effects at both the bottom and the top of the food web. For example, phytoplankton blooms at the base of the food web are closely associated with the retreating ice edge in spring and summer (Smith and Nelson 1986). The retreating ice margin during spring and summer in the Bering Sea is responsible for the massive "green belt" of productivity that moves across the entire ocean basin (A. Springer in NRC 1996). There are several reasons for this movement. Melt waters enhance water column stability and thereby decrease the wind-driven turbulent mixing that inhibits bloom induction. Ice edges also can interact with the atmosphere and ocean to produce local upwelling of nutrients (Alexander and Niebauer 1981). The presence of sea ice further reduces wind stress locally, thereby influencing surface water mixing and phytoplankton production (Nelson et al. 1981). Wind-induced turbulence in the surface layer also affects rates of encounter between phytoplankton and zooplankton, which affects the food chain transfers. Finally, the release of algae from ice can inoculate a bloom. Recent studies in the Southern Ocean (Smetacek et al. 1997) have reported phytoplankton blooms to be associated with the polar front rather than with the ice edge, but the polar front physics are related in part to buoyancy forcing from ice melt. Therefore, phytoplankton blooms may be associated with ice edge dynamics in both direct and indirect ways.

Species at the top of the food web are directly as well as indirectly affected by the ice edge. The ice provides nesting grounds for species like the emperor penguin, and haul-out, resting, and pupping sites for various marine mammals. Adelie penguins do not forage in the open sea, so the location of pack ice dictates where they can feed (Croxall 1984). Crabeater seals are likewise tied to the pack ice for foraging grounds, and leopard seals hunt adelie penguins at ice edges (Laws 1984). In the arctic, polar bears influence marine communities by hunting seals and small whales but only where ice cover provides habitat. Indirectly, the ice edge strongly affects the higher trophic levels by inducing prey production. This production may not only influence krill and copepod concentrations near the ice, where they feed on dense phytoplankton, but also induce the more distant zones of production where various seabird species concentrate to forage. For example, Fraser and Ainley (1986) describe two sets of seabirds associated with ice edges: one like the emporer penguin that forages near the ice edge and others like the southern fulmar and Wilson's storm petrel that forage in a zone of production at some distance from the ice, probably taking advantage of the primary production of the polar front and other physical features that concentrate prey.

The ecological consequences of changing polar ice distribution, cover, and dynamics would clearly include impacts on the geographic location of the productive zones. However, whether the species abundances and community compositions would change is less apparent. Moline and Prezelin (1996) suggest that a temporal decline in diatoms and increase in phytoflagellates is already occurring in the Southern Ocean and may already be impacting the zooplankton community. The melting of sea ice may be expected ultimately to reduce the area of pack ice and the linear extent of the sea ice margin. This would probably have large effects on the abundances of top predators in the system. For example, van Franeker et al. (1997) demonstrated that the western zone of the Weddell Sea contained densities of seabirds and marine mammals 5 to 10 times those of the eastern Weddell Sea, where ice cover was substantially lower. Although some calculations (Huntley et al. 1991) have suggested that the top predators respire up to 22% of the carbon fixed by photosynthesis in the high latitudes, more recent estimates (van Franeker et al. 1997) are less than 1%. Consequently, any changes in abundance of top predators in high latitudes as a consequence of global warming may not have large feedbacks on atmospheric carbon dioxide concentrations.

Ecological Consequences of Sea-Level Rise and Human Responses to Shoreline Erosion

Sea level changes accompany the growth and recession of continental ice mass, but for two different reasons (Ruddiman and McIntyre 1981; Clague et al. 1982). Eustatic sea-level changes are the direct consequence of change in ocean volume, which depends largely on how much of Earth's water is held in glacial ice. Isostatic changes result from the immense weight of ice on continental land masses. Growing glaciers force the underlying land downward and, as the glaciers melt, the land rebounds. In contrast with eustatic sea level changes, which are immediate and predictable, isostatic changes are spatially complex and may follow long time delays. While sea level has increased some 85–130 m since the last glacial maximum, further changes in sea level from global warming are difficult to predict. Warmer summers will surely increase the rate of glacial melting; however, warmer winters may also reduce the rate of glacial starvation. Whether the response is a rise or fall in eustatic sea level depends on the relative magnitude of these counteracting processes. This uncertainty is exacerbated by ongoing isostatic sea-level change from the most recent glacial retreat. The local impacts of global warming on sea-level change will depend in part on whether eustatic and isostatic changes occur in the same or opposite directions.

Global warming leads to sea-level rise because of the expansion of water (decreasing its density) at higher temperatures (above 4°C) and melting in high-elevation glaciers and polar ice fields and caps. Increasing concentrations of greenhouse gases in the earth's atmosphere are widely expected to increase the rate of eustatic sea-level rise (NRC 1987). Although the rate of sea-level rise cannot be accurately predicted, the NRC (1987) provided a range of estimates between a low of 0.5 m and a high of 1.5 m by year 2100. More recent estimates of the degree of sea-level rise in the next century fall at the low end of this range (Houghton et al. 1996). Rising sea level through geological time has had dramatic effects on the positions and geometry of shorelines, especially along sedimentary coastlines and coral atolls. For example, the east coast of North America has advanced and retreated during just the past 12,000 years over distances of 2–60 km across the inner continental shelf. The relationship between sea-level rise and shoreline retreat is complex, depending on many factors such as slope, geomorphic variables, and sediment supply. Trend analysis, empirically based, and the Bruun (1962) rule, based on assumed equilibrium geometry, represent two common alternatives for estimating the rate of shoreline retreat as a function of sea-level rise. By a modified Bruun rule, a rise of 1 m in sea level would translate into a shoreline recession of on average 150 m on many sand beach barriers (Leatherman et al. 2000).

If sea level rises fast enough, reef-building organisms can fail to maintain pace, leading to the formation of drowned atolls or sea mounts lacking emergent land. If sea-level rise is not much greater than 1 m in the next century, current coral growth rates may be sufficient to keep up and prevent much loss of atoll and reef habitat. However, coral growth rates could decline because of changes in carbon cycles and carbon pools resulting from carbon dioxide emissions. For instance, the calcification process, which is influenced by the carbon dioxide–bicarbonate equilibrium in the ocean, may be inhibited as atmospheric carbon dioxide levels rise (Kleypas et al. 1999; Gattuso et al. 1998), further compromising corals stressed by high temperatures. Additionally, inorganic carbon has recently been shown to limit terrestrial producers (Wayne et al. 1998; Thomas et al. 1999; Catovsky and Bazzaz 2000), and while the effect of carbon dioxide levels on marine production has not been explored, some reef algae may be carbon-limited (Larkum and Koop 1997).

In the absence of human development on land, sedimentary shorelines retreat toward land under conditions of rising sea level (Leatherman et al. 2000). Depending upon the rate of shoreline recession relative to the generation times of shoreline organisms, this retreat of undeveloped coasts may result in an orderly landward march of shoreline communities (Figure 18.1). Other communities whose dominant organisms have long generation times may suffer reductions. For instance, the projected rates of sea-level rise and thus shoreline retreat may overwhelm the ability of mangroves to keep pace, given the longevity of some of these trees. The extensive salt marshes of the Mississippi delta have failed to keep up with shoreline recession and have been drowning under rising waters, in part because of the combination of eustatic sea-level rise, land subsidence from mining extractions of subsurface oil and gas, and sediment starvation after extensive damming and diversion of the Mississippi River. However, wherever land development has occurred along sedimentary shorelines, there is growing demand for the protection of the investment in coastal buildings and infrastructure. This demand for protection against erosion will be intensified by any realization in the expected increase in rate of sea-level rise and in frequency and severity of hurricanes and other extreme weather events as a consequence of a warmer planet (Houghton et al. 1996). The most ecologically damaging response to attempt to counteract shoreline erosion is the installation of hardened structures (Pilkey and Wright 1989). Seawalls can actually promote the loss of intertidal beach habitat because the force of waves striking the wall is directed downward, resulting in erosion of sediments in front of the wall and lowering of the elevation of the beach (Figure 18.1). Where seawalls or bulkheads are used along estuarine shorelines, the lowering of elevation of intertidal sediments implies spectacular loss of valuable salt marsh habitat. Groins and jetties act to intercept sands during longshore transport. This has the effect of trapping sand on the up-current side, but starving the beach down current. Not only is there no net gain in sediments to counteract sea-level rise and erosion, but, in addition, the imposition of hard substrate and the modification of sediment dynamics are likely to alter the ecology of sand beach communities (NRC 1987, 1988). Offshore breakwaters may be effective in lowering the energy in the waves that ultimately strike the shore and thereby in reducing erosion of sands, but they come with ecological impacts from introduction of hard substrate and from interfering with movement of large animals like sea turtles and coastal fishes (NRC 1988).

There are nonstructural means of combating shoreline erosion, but these also do not come free of ecological impacts (Figure 18.1). Beach nourishment is the process of placing dredged sands onto the beach to rebuild eroded dunes. Because the high-energy beach environment is naturally subjected to substantial sediment transport, including erosion and deposition, one might hypothesize that beach nourishment could be done with minimal ecological impact. This expectation is made especially attractive when one realizes that the fauna of temperate high-energy beaches is often highly seasonal, such that in winter few organisms occupy the exposed beach. Nevertheless, beach nourishment continues to be conducted in ways that fail to minimize its ecological impact (Nelson 1993; Peterson et al. 2000a). Sand dredging to mine sands for transport to beaches is not adequately restricted to the biologically inactive winter season, in part because of the cost of leaving dredge boats inactive for long periods of the year. Despite regulations that restrict the size of particles used in beach nourishment, the application of unnaturally fine sediments continues. These silts and clays cause turbidity that can interfere with visually orienting predators (like many fishes) and cause mortality of suspension-feeding invertebrates like mole crabs (*Emerita* spp) and bean clams (*Donax* spp). Often beach nourishment includes deposition of substantial amounts of shell hash, which can inhibit burrowing of the mobile benthic invertebrates, thereby increasing risk of transport off the beach and risk of predation. Density reduction of sandy-beach macro-invertebrates has implications for the entire beach ecosystem because the crustaceans and bivalve molluscs characteristic of the intertidal beach represent the prey base for migratory shorebirds and surf fishes. Beach nourishment typically has the effect of hardening the surface of the beach, which can reduce the ability of sea turtles to dig nesting holes. Few studies have examined the impact of the removal of sands from the subtidal sea floor that provide the materials for augmenting the intertidal beach, but this process doubtless has at least short-term effects.

In many places beach bulldozing is practiced as a means of pushing sand from lower on the beach to augment the dunes at the back of the beach (Wells and McNinch 1991). This process may not provide any long-term protection for development because it does not actually alter the quantity of sand in the beach profile. Bulldozing does have ecological impacts, including major reductions in numbers of burrowing ghost crabs (*Ocypode*), presumably because changes in the character of the back beach sediments reduce the success of burrowing (Peterson et al. 2000a). Few studies have evaluated the ecological impacts of beach bulldozing, so there may be additional effects on the biological communities. Clearly, the ecological consequences of sea-level rise are not restricted to the direct effects of erosion and shoreline retreat, but also

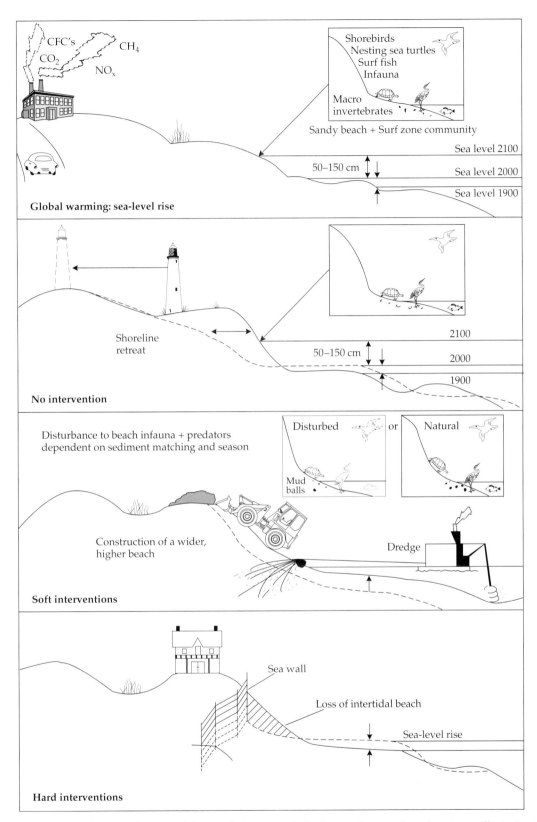

Figure 18.1 Schematic drawing of the coupled geomorphological and ecological impacts of rising sea level and human responses to combat shoreline retreat on sedimentary beaches. The top panel illustrates the growing rate of sea-level rise driven by growing emissions of greenhouse gases. The second panel illustrates the orderly recession of the beach habitats under conditions of no intervention, showing as illustration the moving of a lighthouse back from the ocean as the shoreline moves landward. The third panel illustrates the consequences of "soft responses" to shoreline erosion, beach bulldozing and beach nourishment. The lowest panel illustrates the more dire ecological consequences of "hard" intervention, construction of a sea wall.

include indirect effects caused by subsequent human responses to protect shoreline development.

Latitudinal Range Shifts

When challenged to predict impacts of global warming on ocean ecology, most marine ecologists think first of the direct effects of temperature and thus mention latitudinal range shifts (e.g., Barry et al. 1995). As the surface of the ocean warms, one would predict poleward expansion of biogeographic ranges for species with tropical affinities, perhaps a latitudinal translation of position of the temperate-zone flora and fauna, and a likely shrinking of the boreal biogeographic provinces. Coupled physical-biological models and global circulation models (GCMs) predict increasing rates of ocean warming with growing carbon dioxide and other greenhouse gas concentrations in the atmosphere. The increase in mean surface temperature of the ocean over the next one to two decades is expected to exceed 1.5°C between the latitudes of 10 to 80 degrees N (Manabe et al. 1994). Because biological responses of changing latitudinal distribution integrate temperature experience over large areas and long time periods, the biogeographic changes of organisms are in many ways more sensitive and more representative indicators of pervasive global temperature change than the largely haphazardly located thermometers scattered around the globe.

Studies of changing biogeographic distributions indeed follow a pattern of expansion of tropical species into higher latitudes. For example, Parker and Dixon (1998) showed that from 1980 to 1997 in coastal North Carolina, the 22 species of fishes that increased in abundance were all tropical while the 23 that declined were all cold-water species. Barry et al. (1995) reported similar findings for rocky intertidal invertebrates in California. Average sea surface temperature in this area increased by 0.75°C from the early 1930s to the mid 1990s. During this same period, 8 of 9 southern species increased in abundance while 5 of 8 northern species declined (Figure 18.2).

Changes in ranges of species distributions may not pose huge ecological problems in the ocean. Nevertheless, there are possible consequences of the likely recombinations of species that could extensively alter some communities. We know from analyses of long-term temporal changes in terrestrial trees that different species in a community respond to climate changes by modifying their geographic distributions at different rates (e.g., Davis and Botkin 1985). This creates new associations of species, which can strongly affect interactions that organize and structure the systems. For example, competitive or predatory pressures may change if important competitors or predators move at different rates across the seascape than the other species with which they normally co-occur. Furthermore, changing biogeographic distributions could have large effects on marine species that depend upon geographically fixed aspects of the coast or seafloor for habitat. The coastline and the landmasses will not migrate with changing ocean temperature. Consequently, species on shallow banks like the Grand Banks may be replaced by other species with warmer-water affinities and subsequently them-

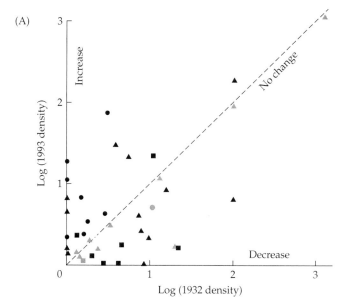

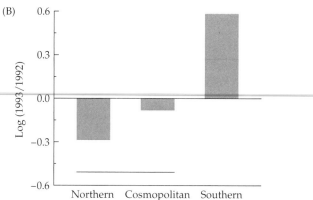

Figure 18.2 Changes in the abundances of intertidal invertebrates between the early 1930s and mid 1990s in southern Monterey Bay, California. (A) Mean abundance of individual species in 1990s [log(abundance + 1)—*y*-axis] plotted against similar values from 1930s (*x*-axis). Circles represent southern species; squares represent northern species; triangles represent cosmopolitan species. Black symbols represent statistically significant changes; gray symbols indicate nonsignificant values. (B) These data indicate that, with ocean warming over the 60-year interval, southern species have become more abundant, northern species have become more rare, and cosmopolitan species have undergone little change in abundance. (After Barry et al. 1995.)

selves find little appropriate habitat in the higher latitudes to which they have moved. Such changes may result in declines in traditional fisheries and expansions of novel ones. Temperature changes can also influence the strength of species interactions, thus altering the nature of an ecosystem without any direct effect on distribution or abundance. For example, periods of ocean cooling associated with upwelling pulses along the coast of Oregon greatly reduce the effect of predation by sea stars on mussel beds in the rocky intertidal community (Sanford 1999). The implications for biodiversity, based on Paine's (1966) classic model, are profound.

Altering Productivity by Changing Global Rainfall Patterns and Seawater Temperature

Direct effects of ocean warming are generally trivial in comparison to the broader oceanographic impacts of indirect effects of global warming on ocean ecosystems. For example, in eastern boundary-current ecosystems, the Bakun (1990) effect of increased upwelling-favorable winds, driven by intensification of the terrestrial low-pressure system, will greatly inhibit recruitment of anchovies and sardines. This reduction in zooplanktivorous fishes induces a redirection of energy flow, shunting biological production through fundamentally different food webs involving euphausiids, red crabs, bonito, mackerel, and to the benthos and demersal fishes (Peterson et al. 1993). More generally, the productivity of the open "blue-water" ocean depends on processes that bring nutrients, especially inorganic nitrogen, close to the sea surface where light levels are sufficient to drive photosynthesis. This process of supplying nutrients to the upper mixed layer of the sea is achieved by several physical mechanisms. Convective transport occurs when surface waters cool to the point where they sink and break up the density stratification of the water column, which is the prime physical feature that inhibits vertical mixing. Advective transport occurs when surface wind stress moves water masses away from continents, creating upwellings of deeper waters along shore to take their place. Diffusive mixing of deeper nutrients occurs when eddies or other mesoscale features develop off of fronts or strong currents and drive a portion of the water mass toward the surface.

Each of these processes of injecting nutrients from deeper ocean waters into the surface layer of the open ocean is inhibited by density stratification of the water column. All the models of global warming predict increased temperatures in the surface ocean and increased rainfall. Each of these changes will have the effect of intensifying the density stratification and thereby increasing the physical energy required to achieve mixing of deep nutrient-rich waters into the surface zone. Fresh water in rainfall is lighter than salt water. Warmer water at the ocean surface likewise is less dense than deeper cold waters and thus inhibits mixing. Thus, both major changes in the open ocean will act to reduce inputs of inorganic nutrients to the surface mixed layer and thereby lower ocean productivity. Long-term data series, such as the measurements from 1956 to present at Station P in the subarctic Northeast Pacific, already show clear evidence of warming surface waters, reductions in surface salinity, and declining nitrate supply to the surface mixed layer (Mackas et al. 1998). The global circulation models (GCMs) predict even more rapid rates of warming in the ocean surface and even more enhancement of global rainfall in colder regions, which are presently the regions of highest productivity.

Food chains of the ocean basins have two radically different structures (Barber 2001). The food chain that has dominated scientific study is one that begins with diatoms, which are eaten by large copepods that themselves serve as prey for fish. A second, less well appreciated food chain that is also ubiquitous in the world's oceans involves microbial loops.

Small phytoplankters are eaten by protozoans like ciliates and rotifers, which have few predators, so that their carbon tends to enter decomposer food chains and be recycled into the atmosphere. The carbon in diatom-copepod-fish food chains is in large measure deposited onto the ocean floor as diatom frustules and copepod feces. The traditional diatom-copepod-fish food chain is differentially stimulated by high nutrients, whereas the microbial loop is benefited under low nutrient concentrations (Barber 2001). Reduced nutrient availability in the surface layer of the open ocean will favor the microbial-loop food chains, in turn resulting in lowered fish production and a consequent reduction in important goods produced by ocean ecosystems. Even more ominous, however, is the positive feedback to climate embedded in this biological response of the open ocean to global warming. Under global warming, a less productive open ocean will utilize less carbon dioxide from seawater, thus removing less carbon dioxide from the atmosphere per unit phytoplankton production because of a shift towards the microbial loop, which does not transport and deposit organic carbon to the seafloor. On the other hand, reduced upwelling in a warmer ocean will simultaneously reduce transport of carbon dioxide from subsurface waters to the atmosphere, in turn helping to compensate for the reduced carbon sedimentation. Consequently, for physical reasons including reduced mixing of atmospheric carbon dioxide into ocean waters and for biological reasons of favoring microbial-loop food chains, the oceans under global warming will actually do a far poorer job of extracting carbon dioxide from the atmosphere. This positive feedback will enhance the rate of increase of atmospheric carbon dioxide and increase the greenhouse effect of global warming (Barber 2001). The ocean is not a buffer for the anthropogenic enhancements of greenhouse gasses, but instead will add to the problem as warming progresses.

Although the specter of global change has inspired enhanced understanding of the relationships between atmosphere, ocean, land, and global climate, the factors that over geological time have caused the reversals in global warming and cooling are less well understood, especially those that occur in intermediate time scales. This limited scientific understanding is a serious impediment to implementing appropriate management actions worldwide to halt the increases in emissions of greenhouse gases. If we cannot explain why long-term trends in global warming and global cooling were ultimately reversed, then there remains the suspicion that our present GCMs lack some important regulatory feedback mechanism or mechanisms that could upset their predictions. Those with eternal optimism or with short-term perspectives can and do appeal to this *deus ex machina* for rescue of the earth's ecosystems.

Coral Bleaching

Coral bleaching is a term that describes the loss of zooxanthellae (symbiotic dinoflagellates) from the tissues of the host corals or the gross reduction in pigmentation of the zooxanthellae. While episodes of coral bleaching have been known for over a century (Glynn 1993), there is growing evidence that coral bleaching events are becoming more frequent, more severe, and more widespread (Glynn 1993; Brown 1997; Winter et al. 1998). While most coral ecologists concur that bleaching is a response to environmental stress, there have been several stresses hypothesized to be involved (Hoegh-Guldberg 1999). These include exposure to low salinity (Goreau 1964), still winds and calm weather (Jaap 1979), high seawater temperature (Hoegh-Guldberg and Smith 1989; Gates et al. 1992), and intense irradiance (Lesser et al. 1990; Gleason and Wellington 1993). The extent of bleaching, meaning the proportion of corals affected and the number of polyps or surface area affected on any given coral, can vary greatly. In the Indo-Pacific, bleaching is usually highly selective against *Acropora* and *Pocillopora* corals (Baird and Marshall 1998). The consequences of coral bleaching range from full recovery of the corals within a few months to almost 100% mortality (Glynn 1984, 1990; Harriott 1985; Fitt et al. 1993). When corals die following a bleaching event, the calcium carbonate reef structure remains and continues to provide structural habitat for a multitude of diverse reef organisms, but bioerosion of the calcium carbonate is rapid enough to result in ultimate loss of the three-dimensional structure (Glynn 1993; Sebens 1994). Such a loss of reef structure may result in declines of reef-associated species and further degradation of the reef ecosystem.

Debate over the causes of coral bleaching has been partially resolved by the recent observations of mass bleaching of corals around the world in response to the 1997–1998 El Niño event (Hoegh-Guldberg 1999; Bruno et al. 2001), which elevated sea surface temperatures by 1–4°C above normal summer highs along many tropical coasts (McPhaden 1999). While multiple stressors may be involved in the induction of coral bleaching, it now seems quite clear that elevated seawater temperature is a direct correlate (Baird and Marshall 1998; Berkelmans and Oliver 1999). Because warmer water temperatures on tropical coasts and calm winds are often associated, the effects of temperature and enhanced UV light penetration are confounded. Thus, the details of the physiological mechanisms of how a warmer ocean acts to induce coral bleaching are not yet fully established. Although the 1997–1998 mass bleachings are not related to global warming but instead to the southern oscillation cycle, which is a redistribution of warm water, the El Niño provides a window into the future under a generally warmer ocean. The sea surface warming, already observed over the past 30 years and predicted to intensify under global warming, represents a very real threat to the health of corals and coral reef communities. On the other hand, it is reasonable to imagine that bleaching represents a challenge to which some corals, especially the branching forms with shorter generation times, might respond by individual adaptation and natural selection for resistance. Optimism generated by recognition of the potential provided by such physiological and genetic responses is probably the only well-substantiated hope for relief from effects of coral bleaching. Management actions to control emissions of greenhouse gases are possible but unlikely, in part because of the high economic costs in the short term and the political difficulty in achieving global international cooperation.

EUTROPHICATION OF ESTUARINE AND COASTAL WATERS

Enhanced Blooms of Nuisance Algae

A variety of nutrients can be limiting to primary producers. The most important of these in many marine systems (especially coastal regions) is nitrogen, although phosphorus may be limiting in tropical systems where calcite sands scavenge the available phosphorus (Lapointe et al. 1992) and micronutrients, such as iron, can limit open ocean productivity (e.g., Barber 2001). Nitrogen occurs in nature in three main forms—ammonium (NH_4), nitrate–nitrite (NO_3–NO_2), and elemental nitrogen (N_2). The limiting nature of available nitrogen on land is evidenced by the billions of dollars spent each year in fertilizer production (Vitousek et al. 1997b; Matson et al. 1999). Nitrogen is the most plentiful element in our biosphere, but most of the global pool occurs as atmospheric nitrogen, which must be "fixed" by adding hydrogen or oxygen radicals before it can be used by most plant species. During the past century, human activities have increased to the point where they fix an amount of nitrogen about equal to that fixed naturally (Vitousek et al. 1997b). In turn, this is changing the chemistry of the atmosphere, enhancing the loss of other soil nutrients, acidifying lakes and streams, and increasing nitrogen nutrients in estuaries and coastal marine systems. Here we focus on the effects of increased nitrogen on estuaries and coastal marine systems. A more comprehensive overview of increased nitrification is provided by Vitousek et al. (1997b).

Cultural eutrophication is the term given to the process of creating excessive loading of inorganic nutrients into water bodies through human activities (Nixon 1995). The activities that contribute most to cultural eutrophication are discharge of human and animal waste, runoff of fertilizers applied to agricultural field crops, atmospheric deposition of nitrogen from industrial releases, car exhaust, and volatilization of animal wastes, and industrial discharges directly into water bodies. In developed countries, nutrient loading into streams, rivers, and lakes has only been partially regulated. The discharge of municipal sewage wastewater and of industrial wastewater has been under control of permits and regulated in the United States for several decades. However, these controls of point-source wastes have had two serious limitations. First, a strong and often exclusive focus has been placed in controlling phosphorus, not nitrogen. Phosphorus is typically the limiting nutrient in fresh waters, but in most estuaries and coastal oceans nitrogen becomes limiting (Paerl 1985). The focus of water quality management agencies has tended to be local near the point of discharge, thereby emphasizing phosphorus. Second, discharge permits have traditionally been written to control the concentration of the nutrients in effluent not their total mass loading. Thus, as flows of wastewater have increased so has the mass loading of nutrients. In addition to these limitations of point-source control programs, there has been virtually no control of nonpoint-source nutrient loading. In many regions, the nonpoint-source loading of nitrogen is estimated to be substantially in excess of the point-source loading.

Agriculture, which has remained free of many regulatory programs, represents a major source of nonpoint-source loading of nitrogen. The tendency of managers has been to encourage the use of best management practices (BMPs) to control agricultural nutrient runoff. This incentive has worked best with phosphorus because phosphorus attaches to sediment particles and every farmer works hard to prevent soil erosion. Inorganic nitrogen is readily dissolved and thus moves in both surface water and groundwater. Consequently, soil erosion protection does little to prevent the escape of nitrogen from farm fields, so nitrogen loading has increased. Worldwide, the green revolution has been achieved through intensive application of fertilizers to stimulate crop growth (Vitousek et al. 1997b). This fertilization necessarily leads to increased nutrient loading of estuaries and coastal oceans because of intrinsic limits to the efficiency of nutrient uptake by row crops. That is to say, under the best of farming practices, there is substantial loss of nutrients from the fields and into nature.

Stormwater that runs off from impervious surfaces such as roads, parking lots, roofs, and other developed structures also contributes significantly to increases in nonpoint-source loading of nutrients into estuaries and coastal oceans. In natural watersheds, much of the rainwater is able to move into the soil where it recharges groundwater resources or serves to feed the needs of trees and other rooted plants, reentering the atmosphere through evapotranspiration. The destruction of riparian forests and wetlands during land development contributes in particular to the problem of nutrient loading in stormwater runoff. Riparian buffers, especially wetlands, intercept some groundwater transport of inorganic nitrogen, depending upon the depth of penetration of the roots of trees and other plants. Nitrogen utilization by those deeply rooted trees thereby reduces the loading of the streams and rivers leading to the sea. Perhaps the major function of trees in a riparian buffer is to induce high rates of denitrification. By providing a nitrogen-rich organic litter on the forest floor in an anoxic environment, microbial denitrification is promoted. This process returns nitrogen compounds to the atmosphere as elemental nitrogen gas, a form that does not stimulate plant production and eutrophication.

Atmospheric deposition of fixed nitrogen represents an additional and growing path of nutrient loading of estuaries and coastal oceans (Paerl 1985). Fixed nitrogen is released into the atmosphere by industrial smokestacks, by mobile sources such as cars and trucks, and by volatilization of ammonia from animal wastes (Nixon 1995; Paerl et al. 1998). The first two sources produce various nitrogen oxides from burning of fossil fuels. Because these forms of fixed nitrogen react with light to form ozone and cause serious human health ef-

fects, there is some enhanced incentive for increasing controls on these emissions. The ammonia released from animal-waste lagoons and spray applications to agricultural fields is a more challenging regulatory problem because of limitations of alternative technologies for handling animal wastes on farms. Atmospheric deposition of fixed nitrogen to coastal estuaries can account for as much as half the total loading of new nitrogen to the system (Paerl et al. 1998).

The consequences of increased loading of nitrogen, phosphorus, and micronutrients to estuaries and coastal oceans has been to enhance the frequency and intensity of nuisance algal and other microbe blooms in these systems (Hallegraef 1993; Anderson and Garrison 1997). Such blooms have significant effects on the entire ecosystem because they often include toxic forms that can kill consumer species in the food chain. For example, blooms of the dinoflagellate *Pfiesteria piscicida* and its relatives are involved in fish kills in several estuaries (Burkholder et al. 1995). The brown tide phytoplankter *Aureococcus anophagefferens* is responsible for severe mortality of benthic suspension-feeding bivalves including the bay scallop and blue mussel in Great South Bay, New York (Bricelj and Lonsdale 1997). The most widespread consequence of enhancing coastal eutrophication worldwide is a dramatic increase in the occurrence of hypoxia/anoxia in bottom waters (Diaz and Rosenberg 1995). The anoxia creates zones of the sea floor in the estuary or coastal ocean where sessile benthic animals are killed and where fish cannot live. The "dead zone" in the Gulf of Mexico created by eutrophication driven by runoff from Mississippi River basin farming covers an area larger than some states (Turner and Rabalais 1994). Regulatory remedies to restore ecosystem goods and services in the northern Gulf of Mexico are possible but involve sufficiently high costs to farmers that suggest political battles for the indefinite future. A recent meta-analysis of all available data sets on consequences of enhanced nutrient loading to pelagic systems has revealed that eutrophication does not strongly couple to increased zooplankton and pelagic fish production because the enhanced phytoplankton production occurs largely among toxic or inedible groups (Micheli 1999).

Promotion of Oxygen Depletion

The high production of microalgae driven by eutrophication of estuarine and coastal ocean waters typically exceeds what can be consumed by pelagic and benthic herbivores. The uneaten fraction of the microalgae is especially high when inedible algae are preferentially enhanced. Consequently, a large fraction of this production sinks to the sea floor, where it is decomposed by microbes. The biological oxygen demand (BOD) of decomposers on the sea floor is further enhanced by direct organic loading from discharge of human and animal sewage into streams, rivers, estuaries, and coastal oceans. The microbial decomposition is an oxygen-consuming process. Consequently, mixing of oxygen-rich surface waters with deeper bottom waters is required to replenish dissolved oxygen (DO) near the sea floor. Density stratification of the water column inhibits that necessary mixing, and if stratification lasts long enough, this combination of high organic loading and water column stability can result in hypoxia (DO < 4 mg/l) or anoxia (DO of 0 mg/l) (Paerl et al. 1998). Microbial decomposition rates are higher at higher temperatures, so the risk of hypoxia and anoxia is greater in summer. Eutrophication of coastal waters has increased the frequency, duration, and intensity of these low-oxygen events in many regions around the world, including the Chesapeake Bay (Cooper and Brush 1993), the Baltic Sea (Elmgren 1989), and the Gulf Coast of North America (Turner and Rabalais 1994; Turner et al. 1998).

Extended periods of severe hypoxia (DO < 2 mg/l) and anoxia (DO = 0 mg/l) have serious repercussions for the entire estuarine or coastal marine ecosystem. Immobile seafloor invertebrates die if deprived of oxygen for sustained periods of time, with sensitivities varying greatly across taxa (Diaz and Rosenberg 1995). The mortality of seafloor invertebrates removes the prey for demersal fish, crabs, and prawns, thereby degrading the foraging habitat and reducing fisheries production (Pihl et al. 1992; Peterson et al. 2000b). Following the death of the benthos from the stress of sustained low oxygen, secondary succession presumably begins (Figure 18.3). This process starts with small surface-dwelling invertebrates, because even after return of oxygen in the water column, only the sediment surface is oxygenated. The activity of mobile benthic invertebrates is necessary to mix oxygen to depth in the sediments and thereby allow development of a later successional stage comprised of the larger polychaetes and bivalves (Rhoads et al. 1978). Only through time does the benthic invertebrate community become reestablished and serve those demersal predators that use it for foraging. It is possible that the early successional stages provide better foraging op-

portunities for prawns that are limited to consuming small surface-dwelling invertebrates (Pihl et al. 1992), such that prawns may actually benefit from occasional hypoxia/anoxia (Figure 18.3). However, during the period of low DO, the benthic habitat is inaccessible and many prawns are killed outright (Lenihan and Peterson 1998). Larger demersal crabs and fishes that prey on bivalves and large polychaetes presumably experience a period of reduced food resources until succession proceeds to replace the dead invertebrates.

Mobile species like swimming crabs and fishes are forced into shallow-water refuges during periods of anoxia/hypoxia (Lenihan et al. 2001). This has the effect of putting abnormally intense feeding pressure on the benthic prey in those refuges and can result in food depletion (Lenihan et al. 2000). In addition, the concentrations of mobile crustaceans and fishes in these refuges can intensify predator–prey interactions among them, thereby altering the normal composition of the system. Even pelagic fishes can suffer mortality during low DO events if bottom waters are upwelled by wind forcing in such a way as to trap them with no escape route (Renaud 1986; Breitburg 1992). The health and productivity of estuaries and coastal oceans are tied to management of water quality.

Reduction of Light Penetration

Blooms of microalgae in the upper water column limit the depth of penetration of light energy. Consequently, eutrophication leads to increased microalgal production but reduced production, abundance, biomass, and bottom cover of seagrasses and other large benthic plants in shallow waters (Valiela et al. 1997). Light levels are a limiting resource for submerged aquatic vegetation, determining, for example, the

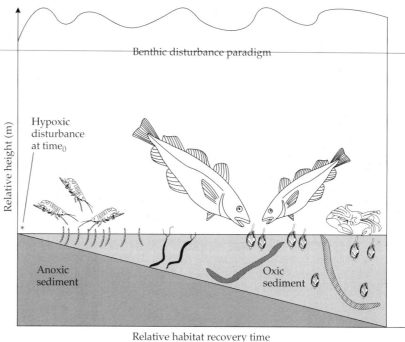

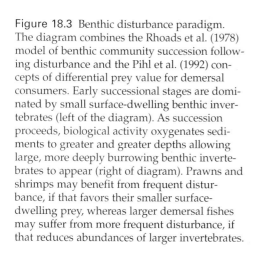

Figure 18.3 Benthic disturbance paradigm. The diagram combines the Rhoads et al. (1978) model of benthic community succession following disturbance and the Pihl et al. (1992) concepts of differential prey value for demersal consumers. Early successional stages are dominated by small surface-dwelling benthic invertebrates (left of the diagram). As succession proceeds, biological activity oxygenates sediments to greater and greater depths allowing large, more deeply burrowing benthic invertebrates to appear (right of diagram). Prawns and shrimps may benefit from frequent disturbance, if that favors their smaller surface-dwelling prey, whereas larger demersal fishes may suffer from more frequent disturbance, if that reduces abundances of larger invertebrates.

lower depth limit to which algal and seagrass beds can extend (Dennison and Alberte 1982; Foster and Schiel 1985). In the extreme case, sufficiently high turbidity can eliminate submerged aquatic vegetation entirely. Because the increased loading of nutrients to estuaries and the coastal ocean is often simultaneously accompanied by sediment erosion because of land development that fails to control sedimentation, the cumulative effect of these two human-caused perturbations has even greater potential to affect submerged aquatic vegetation. Loss of submerged aquatic vegetation reduces the energy that enters detrital food chains (Duggins et al. 1989) and diminishes valuable nursery habitats for juvenile fishes and crustaceans (Thayer et al. 1975). This indirect effect of eutrophication of estuaries and shallow margins of the sea is itself enhanced by the loss of oysters in the estuaries of the East Coast of North America because the tremendous reduction in water filtration by oysters (Newell 1988) also contributes to enhanced turbidity of estuarine waters. The joint effects of shifting food webs towards exclusively plankton-based food chains may be extreme (Baird and Ulanowicz 1989). Better controls of nutrient loading within watersheds and airsheds and better programs to prevent erosion are land-based management activities that could mitigate these problems.

Induction of Macroalgal Growth on Coral Reefs

Eutrophication may contribute at least locally to striking patterns (phase shifts) of increases in macroalgae and corresponding reductions in live coral cover on coral reefs, although reduction in herbivory is a much better supported explanation (McCook 1999; Miller et al. 1999). Some researchers have suggested that nutrient loading is a major cause of extraordinary trends of increasing cover of macroalgae on coral reefs, especially in the Caribbean over the past 30 years (e.g., Lapointe 1997). Many of these effects of enhanced nutrient loading, however, are localized in the vicinity of point-source discharges or developed areas with uncontrolled storm water runoff of nutrients. A more widespread cause of seaweed dominance on coral reefs in the Caribbean appears to be the decline in abundance, size, and effectiveness of herbivorous fishes on coral reefs (Hay 1984). Hughes (1994, 1996) used long-term monitoring data from Jamaican reefs to help distinguish between effects of eutrophication and overfishing in causing these changes in algal cover. He showed that over a period of more than two decades, while coral cover declined and macroalgal cover increased, sponge cover remained constant. He argued that if eutrophication were the primary factor, the sponges, which feed on plankton, would benefit along with the macroalgae because phytoplankton production would also be enhanced. The failure of sponges to respond implies that reduction in herbivory is the more important general factor.

The full explanation for the growing dominance of macroalgae and the decline in coral cover on reefs is much more complex, involving contributions and interactions among various factors (Done 1992; McCook 1999). The degree of degradation of coral reef communities varies greatly geo-graphically. Caribbean coral reefs are badly degraded (Hughes 1996), whereas those of the Great Barrier Reef in Australia have experienced only modest change (Baird and Marshall 1998; Hughes et al. 1999). Such geographic variability in reef health implies a large measure of local causation. Where changes in community composition are large, the following scenario represents a viable explanation of the sequence of events. Overfishing (Hay 1984) reduces the grazing pressure on macroalgae to such a degree that they can grow, overtopping some corals and expanding into available space on the horizontally oriented calcium carbonate surfaces (Lewis 1986). Eutrophication from poor nutrient management, wastewater treatment, and development practices on land further enhances algal growth rates in some areas. The bleaching of corals removes some live coral cover and after bioerosion may lead to subsequent loss of habitat for reef fish, which further reduces grazing intensity. In the Caribbean, the rapid decline of the dominant herbivorous sea urchin *Diadema antillarum* from a disease outbreak (Lessios 1995) removed the last line of defense against seaweed take-over and accelerated the loss of corals and transition to an algal-dominated community. Under conditions of low herbivory, corals and macroalgae also interact directly through at least two types of competition for limited attachment space. First, by overgrowing hermatypic corals, seaweeds can shade their zooxanthellae, reducing coral growth and even causing the death of polyps and whole colonies (Potts 1979; Lewis 1986). Second, the presence of high seaweed cover can preempt coral settlement, thereby preventing recovery of the corals (Hughes 1994).

The ecological understanding of the processes that lead to change and degradation of coral reef communities is not complete, but local management strategies to preserve coral reef communities and ecosystems can still be justified, even under conditions of uncertainty. Because of the economic value of healthy coral reefs, serving both international tourism and local fisheries, there is great need for more enlightened management of coral reefs. To the degree that causes of coral reef community degradation remain local, locally based management can be effective. Unfortunately, reef degradation is not all local. It has occurred in remote reefs, where local human impacts are not readily evident (McClanahan and Muthinga 1998). Coral disease has been advanced as an explanation for regional patterns in the shift from coral to algal domination in the Caribbean (Aronson and Prect 2000). Global warming has also been implicated in widespread declines in coral health (Hoegh-Guldberg 1999). Nevertheless, management measures taken to alleviate effects of overfishing and eutrophication should not be postponed because they will have positive effects locally, but such measures might not reverse the phase shift in the Caribbean and might not prevent it elsewhere. Perhaps the most enlightened management scheme for coral reefs is that adopted by the Great Barrier Reef Parks Authority in Queensland, Australia. The Great Barrier Reef is zoned, with various levels of protection applied to each zone, thereby serving multiple uses (Kelleher et al. 1995). For many island nations, human population increases, growing levels of reef degradation, and poverty amplify the need for both conservation and restoration. This represents a challenge not only to scientists for technological tools but also to the international aid community.

Examples of Cascading Effects of Eutrophication

While many excellent studies have been conducted in recent years to help understand the responses of phytoplankton to eutrophication (Malone 1992; Valiela et al. 1997; Cottingham and Carpenter 1998; McClelland and Valiela 1998; Paerl et al. 1998; Turner et al. 1998), there has been little effort committed to exploring how changes in phytoplankton transit through the food web to alter production at higher trophic levels. Probably the best understanding of these bottom-up effects comes from lakes, where experimental manipulation with replication is possible (Carpenter and Kitchell 1993). In estuaries, recent work has begun to separate phytoplankton into algal groups, based on photopigment contents (Pinckney et al. 1996), which can allow examination of how phytoplankton communities change with nutrient loading. Higher trophic levels can conceivably be affected both by changes in phytoplankton composition and by total phytoplankton production. For example, eutrophication seems to promote blooms of toxic algae and dinoflagellates. Changing toxicity of the microalgae could readily select for zooplankton and benthic herbivorous invertebrates that are less susceptible to the toxins. This could lead to subsequent modifications in higher trophic levels. Simply changing the taxonomic composition of the microalgal community without induction of toxic forms may lead to modifications of how energy flows through the food web because one group like flagellates may be differentially grazed by certain types of herbivores, while another group like diatoms may be preferentially consumed by another type of herbivore. Furthermore, enhancing total production of phytoplankton may affect the proportion of the production that is consumed within the water column and thus the amount that sediments out onto the seafloor because planktonic herbivores may be overwhelmed by more cells than they can handle. These hypotheses have not been tested, but available data suggest that increased phytoplankton production is not strongly linked upwards to zooplankton and fishes in the water column because of the disproportionate enhancement of inedible algae (Micheli 1999). We do know that continuing fertilization of estuaries and coastal oceans causes a state change in these ecosystems as anoxia and severe hypoxia develop (Elmgren 1989; Paerl et al. 1998; Turner and Rabalais 1994; Turner et al. 1998). The consequences of the resulting stress of low oxygen are discussed above. Even for that scenario, the broader linkages to higher trophic levels are largely unexplored but are likely important.

CHEMICAL POLLUTION OF MARINE ENVIRONMENTS

Nearly all chemical contamination in the sea comes from direct discharge, terrestrial point sources, and atmospheric deposition. Marine pollution in nearshore marine environments is especially worrisome because terrestrial runoff gathers materials from large areas and concentrates them within estuaries and around the mouths of streams and rivers at the land–sea interface. The local impacts of hot spots of various marine pollutants have been well documented, but the assessment of effects over larger scales is much more complex. While vast amounts of information exist on contaminant levels in marine systems, little evidence exists for their effects on marine organisms outside of highly impacted areas. Furthermore, most prior studies, including a large bioassay literature, have tended to consider the effects of contaminants in isolation of other factors. The most important impacts of chemical pollutants may well be those that result from interactions with other stressors, such as elevated temperature, reduced productivity, competition, predation, or synergistic effects with different kinds of chemical pollutants. Once chemical pollutants have entered the sea, they have an unusually high potential for redistribution via ocean currents and the long-range movements of organisms that carry them as high body burdens. The role of planktonic organisms in the transport of contaminants that have been absorbed into their bodies or adsorbed onto their body surfaces can also be important. Such dispersal forces may reduce local impacts while making containment and mitigation of point-source pollution more difficult.

Chemical pollutants in the sea are of five general classes—halogenated organic compounds (e.g., DDT, PCBs, dioxins and related compounds), nutrients, organic loading, heavy metals, and petroleum. Each presents unique problems to marine organisms in terms of source identification, dispersal, persistence, ecological impacts, and mitigation. We have already treated two of these types of pollution, nutrient loading from fertilizers and organic loading by sewage discharge, combined under a separate heading as eutrophication.

Halogenated Organic Compounds

The most common halogenated organic compounds with known toxic effects are PCBs, DDT and DDE, chlordane, and dieldrin (Sarokin and Schulkin 1992). DDT was recognized as an insecticide in 1939 (Ware 1989) and was subsequently used worldwide for insect pest control (Carson 1962). PCBs (which include 209 congeners, depending on the number and position of chlorine atoms) were developed in the 1940s and have since been used for numerous industrial purposes, most notably as thermal insulators in electrical transformers. Since the time of their development and widespread use, both PCBs and DDT have attained harmful levels in a number of marine organisms. Because of the tendency to biomagnify at higher trophic levels, the strongest known impacts have been on apex predators (Herman et al. 1969; Muir et al. 1988). Detrimental effects of DDT are most commonly seen in birds, whereas those of PCBs are most common in mammals. Immune suppression and increased susceptibility to infection are the principal known means by which halogenated organics affect organisms. Reproductive inhibition or failure is the most common manifestation of organochlorine toxicity in marine birds and mammals.

Recent findings show that DDT and PCBs mimic the biochemical influence of estrogen in vertebrates, thus causing endocrine dysfunction (Colborn and Clement 1992; Menditto and Turrio-Baldassarri 1999; Younes 1999).

DDT is known or suspected to have severely impacted a number of marine bird species. Some of the better-known examples are reproductive failure in brown pelicans (Blus et al. 1971), peregrine falcons (Jarman et al. 1993), and bald eagles (Stickle et al. 1966). Egg-shell thinning, which increases their breakage rates, is the main reason for reduced reproductive success (Ratcliffe 1970; Anderson and Hickey 1972). Complete reproductive failure from the effects of DDT has been well documented.

Similar effects are suspected for marine mammals, although the evidence here is not as strong as it is for birds (Addison 1989). Premature births in California sea lions were associated with high organochlorine concentrations (Le Boeuf and Bonnell 1971; DeLong et al. 1973). For killer whales, striking differences in both organochlorine concentrations and reproductive success exist between so-called "resident" and "transient" groups (Matkin et al. 1999). This is because the residents feed on fishes, whereas transients feed on other marine mammals (Hoetzel et al. 1998). Stable nitrogen isotope analysis can be used to measure trophic status (Hobson and Welch 1992) because as protein is broken down and reconstituted at each new trophic level, the lighter isotope of nitrogen is differentially retained. Based on dietary and stable nitrogen isotope analysis, the estimated average trophic status of resident and transient whales is about 4.5 and greater than 6, respectively (Matkin et al. 1999; Pauly et al. 1998b). Because organochlorines biomagnify with increased trophic level, their average respective concentrations in Prince William Sound, Alaska, were 16–25 times greater in transients than residents (Matkin et al. 1999). Killer whales have a strongly matrilineal social structure, in which most males and all females remain in the same pod throughout life (Whitehead 1998). Reproductive success (defined as the per capita rate of young whales added to known pods) is much higher for resident than transient groups, a pattern that could be related to reproductive impairment by the organic chemicals contaminating the transient killer whales.

Although organochlorines are stable, levels of these compounds have declined in the California current ecosystem after their use was banned in the late 1960s. These declines are reflected in increased reproductive success in brown pelicans (Anderson et al. 1975) and decreased DDT concentrations in California sea lions (Table 18.1; Lieberg-Clark et al. 1995). While these findings suggest that problems associated with organochlorine contamination are on the wane, concern now is over problems associated with the globalization of resource-based economies—the increased use of organochlorines by developing nations and their long-distance dispersal. Both PCBs and DDT can disperse great distances from their source (Simonich and Hites 1995). This is especially problematic in the sea because of ocean currents and the tendency of many species to move long distances (Barrie et al. 1992; Muir et al. 1992; Iwata et al. 1993, Tanabe et al. 1994). Recent reports have documented harmful levels of PCBs and DDT thousands of miles from any known or suspected source. For instance, while the use of PCBs and DDT has been banned in Canada and the United States for more than three decades, high levels of these contaminants from current use elsewhere in the world have been reported in the Canadian arctic (Norstrom et al. 1988; Barrie et al. 1992; Greegor et al. 1996) and the Aleutian archipelago (Anthony et al. 1999). Penguin eggs in the Antarctic are contaminated by synthetic organochlorines (Rizebrough et al. 1976). Effective mitigation of these problems requires that management of production and use of persistent organic compounds be undertaken on a global scale.

Heavy Metals

In contrast to organochlorines, heavy metals (lead, mercury, cadium, arsenic, copper, tin, and selenium) occur naturally in the sea, but often at very low levels. In fact, only recently did it become apparent that the natural levels of many contaminant metals in the marine environment were much lower than current levels typically measured in the oceans. Nonetheless, distinguishing anthropogenic from natural components is an added difficulty in the assessment of heavy-metal contamination. Most heavy metals are toxic at high concentrations (Chang 1996). Lead and mercury are important neurotoxins

---

TABLE 18.1   Changes in DDE and DDT levels in blubber of male California sea lions from 1970 to 1988–92.

1970[a]			1988–1992		
DDE	DDT	DDT/DDE	DDE	DDT	DDT/DDE
740	17	0.023	5.0	0.16	0.032
(370–1500)	(8.8–34)		(2.5–10)	(0.07–0.35)	
$n = 12$			$n = 7$		

Source: After Lieberg-Clark et al. 1995.
Note: Geometric mean levels of DDE, DDT, and the ratio of DDT/DDE(x 100) in male California sea-lion blubber, with a range of one SD in parentheses. Residue values are expressed as mg kg^{-1} wet wt.
[a]1970 data were originally reported as arithmetic means (Le Boeuf and Bonnell 1971).

(Finklestein et al. 1998; Cranmer et al. 1996), while cadmium causes renal dysfunction (Fowler 1996; Fels 1999). Lead in particular has proven to be a pernicious contaminant owing largely to its significant effects on the central nervous system, even at very low exposures (Finklestein et al. 1998). Copper and tin are toxicants for marine invertebrates, especially crustaceans, because they prevent growth of the exoskeleton and interfere with nerve function.

Environmental lead levels increased greatly with the industrial revolution. Large quantities of lead have been used in refined petroleum products, including gasoline. Throughout much of this century, gasoline combustion released up to 2 grams of lead per gallon of combusted gasoline. Most of this contaminant lead was deposited onto adjacent terrestrial surfaces and thereby available for surface runoff into fresh or marine surface waters, while the remainder was entrained into the atmosphere and redistributed via winds over large distances and eventually deposited in the sea (Flegal et al. 1989). These processes have led to an increase in global ocean lead concentrations by somewhere between 10- and 50-fold (Smith and Flegal 1995; Flegal et al. 1993). Lead differs from most other chemical pollutants in its tendency to biodeplete at higher trophic levels. Biodepletion occurs because lead competes with the more abundant marine calcium in the formation of calcified tissues. For this reason, lead concentrations in apex predators are not good indicators of environmental contamination at lower trophic levels. Smith et al. (1990, 1992) demonstrated this point by contrasting lead concentrations and isotopic compositions in the teeth of modern and prehistoric sea otters. In the case of Amchitka Island (Alaska), overall lead concentrations were similar, even though marine lead concentrations were known to be more than an order of magnitude greater during the latter period. The isotopic analyses showed, however, that prehistoric lead was of local origin, whereas modern lead was primarily of Asian and Canadian origins, in keeping with known lead sources in refined petroleum products from either side of the North Pacific Ocean. In contrast, similar analyses from Monterey Bay (California) otters indicated that increases in body lead burdens had occurred in some contemporary animals, consistent with identified point sources of elevated lead exposures (Smith et al. 1992).

Mercury also occurs in high enough levels in the sea to constitute an environmental health hazard. High mercury levels occur naturally in areas of active volcanism, and from anthropogenesis in estuarine and nearshore sediments at the mouths of streams and rivers where it was used to extract gold (Mason 1996; Fitzgerald 1997). Because mercury can be methylated via microbial activity (Mason et al. 1995), it is a heavy metal that can bioaccumulate to a substantial degree (Rolfhus and Fitzgerald 1995). Thus, high levels of mercury occur in various marine fishes, particularly those at higher trophic levels. In some cases, however, these high levels of mercury may not be the result of point-source discharges but rather of diffuse atmospheric inputs from both natural and anthropogenic sources (Minerals Management Service 1989). For instance, some tuna species may contain such high levels

of mercury that humans must consume them in moderation. Since these animals are apex predators that live exclusively in the oceanic realm, elevated mercury levels are probably a result of their high trophic status and the tendency for mercury to bioaccumulate.

Oil Spills

With increases in submarine petroleum extraction from the continental shelves, petroleum shipment by tanker vessels, and large-vessel traffic, marine oil spills are occurring more frequently and have become a significant concern for marine conservation. From 1993 to 1999, there have been 25 major tanker spills in which roughly 5 million barrels of diesel fuel, crude oil, and other petroleum products were discharged into the sea.

Petroleum spills differ from other forms of chemical pollution in several important ways. For one, they are largely but not exclusively (see Peterson 2001) acute events, usually unforeseeable and nearly always relatively limited in geographical extent. However, local impacts can be devastating. More than any other form of marine pollution, oil spills draw close public attention and elicit strong public emotions. Large sums of money have been spent on environmental assessments in response to the potential financial gains and losses from litigation and compensation for injured wildlife and natural resources. The most comprehensive marine ecological research project ever done followed the *Exxon Valdez* spill in Prince William Sound, Alaska, where industry and government have spent hundreds of millions of dollars on environmental research, environmental clean-up, and litigation.

Effects of spilled oil occur at the levels of individuals, populations, communities, and ecosystems. The effects of spilled oil on contaminated individuals are of two general kinds—internal (toxic) and external (fouling). The toxicity of spilled oil usually is greatest near the time of the spill, before the most volatile compounds are lost to the atmosphere, but chronic toxicity and delayed impacts on ecosystems can persist in sediments buffered from exposure to oxygen (Peterson 2001). Toxic effects usually occur in the respiratory, hepatic, and digestive systems (Williams and Davis 1995). In contrast, fouling effects often become more serious with time as spilled oil emulsifies and congeals. Petroleum fouling can be especially problematic for ciliated filter-feeding organisms and for homeothermic vertebrates that rely on fur or feathers for insulation against the cold sea. Species with a blubber layer are generally less vulnerable to fouling than those lacking blubber (Loughlin 1994).

While the impacts of spilled oil on individuals are usually obvious, effects on populations and communities have proven more difficult to document (Paine et al. 1996; Day et al. 1997). This is because large oil spills are rare events, impossible to predict in space and time. Consequently, pre-spill data from which to assess post-spill effects are seldom available. Inferences about population- and ecosystem-level effects therefore must be based on patterns of recovery or contrasts with areas outside the spill zone. Both approaches are problematic, the first because post-spill changes do not necessarily indicate spill-induced effects, and the second because of the intrinsic spatial and temporal variability in natural systems. Nevertheless, the intensive efforts in assessing impact and recovery of coastal marine communities following the *Torrey Canyon* and *Exxon Valdez* oil spills have lead to several demonstrations of population and community impacts and documentation of recovery times of a decade for shoreline resources, not only from direct acute effects of oiling toxicity and fouling but also from indirect and chronic effects (Southward and Southward 1978; Peterson 2001).

Some large oil spills are followed by monumental efforts to rehabilitate oiled wildlife. These efforts have been criticized because of the unknown survivability of rehabilitated animals after their return to the wild, and the fact that most oiled individuals cannot be obtained and treated in a timely manner (Estes 1991, 1998; Anderson et al. 1996; Sharp 1996). In contrast, the proponents of rehabilitation argue that (1) the survivability of rehabilitated animals can be improved; (2) costs can be reduced; and (3) a concerned public will always demand that every effort be made to save individuals (Jessup 1998).

MODIFICATION OF BOTTOM HABITAT BY FISHING GEAR AND OTHER PHYSICAL DISRUPTIONS

Dynamiting of Tropical Coral Reefs and Other Human-Induced Damages to Coral Reef Habitat

Coral reefs and the diverse communities of plants, invertebrates, and vertebrates that they support (Talbot 1994; Birkeland 1997) are rapidly being degraded by human activities that directly and indirectly damage the reef habitat itself (e.g., Maragos et al. 1996). Failure to conserve coral reef habitats by properly managing human activities is especially disturbing for two fundamentally different reasons. First, the coral reef ecosystem is the most species-diverse ecosystem in the marine environment and one from which ecologists still have much to learn about evolutionary and ecological processes that promote and maintain biodiversity. Second, in most of the coasts of the earth where coral reefs exist, human welfare is largely dependent upon the ecosystem goods and services provided by the reef ecosystem. These services such as providing fishery products, tourism opportunities, and useful natural products, cannot be sustained if management fails to protect the coral reef habitat upon which the ecosystem is founded. Thus mismanagement of potentially disruptive human activities on and around coral reefs carries a large cost to future generations.

Some of the destructive human activities that most threaten sustainability of coral reefs occur by very poor peoples in less developed societies, where management of natural resources is often an unattainable luxury but where reef-produced goods and services are the very essence of human culture, welfare, and subsistence. Nevertheless, the demand for reef goods that are harvested by these nonsustainable practices is largely provided by people in the developed world.

Dynamiting of reefs to extract fishery products is probably the most destructive practice, growing in use through the tropical Pacific (McManus 1996). Recovery of the reef habitat from this fishing practice may take decades. Use of cyanide to harvest fish also removes fish communities but does not necessarily destroy the reef habitat.

Reef habitat is also affected indirectly by all other human activities that threaten the corals, which are the "engineers" of reef habitat structure in the tropics (Jones et al. 1994). The indirect effects of eutrophication, depletion of herbivorous fishes, and global warming have been discussed earlier. Other local human activities also degrade coral reef communities. Sedimentation from urban growth and land development practices that fail to control erosion is a major indirect cause of coral mortality and reef habitat degradation worldwide (Maragos et al. 1996). Many reef-building corals are sensitive to turbidity, so when turbidity and sedimentation are greatly enhanced in waters bathing a reef, living corals are seriously degraded or eliminated. Other types of pollution from human development and industrialization also are degrading coral reef ecosystems, including especially the discharge of sewage and industrial wastewater, agricultural runoff of nutrients and chemicals, mining, dredging for channel construction, chronic oil spills, anchor and ship grounding damage, and construction (Maragos et al. 1996). The damage to coral reef habitat from these human activities is compounded by the direct effects of fishing gear and overfishing. These local and thus far more manageable impacts on coral reef ecosystems could be controlled by proper management.

Dredging of Temperate-Zone Oyster and Polychaete Reefs

In temperate latitudes, the invertebrates that construct biogenic habitat in sedimentary environments are not corals (as in the tropics) but oysters, certain polychaetes, and vermetid gastropods. Polychaete shoals like those made by *Petaloproctus socialis* (Wilson 1979) and *Sabellaria* (Reise 1982) modify the seafloor environment by stabilizing soft sediments, providing emergent hard substratum, and offering niches (literally) and habitat complexity. The interwoven tubes of vermetid gastropods can play a similar role (Safriel 1975). Oysters recruit to the shells of other oysters and gradually build reefs that under natural conditions rise several meters above the estuarine sea floor (Wharton 1957). These temperate-zone habitat engineers are responsible for augmenting biodiversity of co-occurring invertebrates (Wells 1961; Wilson 1979). For example, Wells (1961) compiled a list of over 300 marine invertebrates that occupy oyster reef habitat in a North Carolina estuary. These species are virtually all restricted to hard bottoms and thus would be absent from the sea floor were the oyster reef not available.

In addition to providing stable hard substratum in a habitat of mobile sediments and thereby promoting colonization of epibiotic invertebrates that require hard surface for attachment, oyster reefs also serve as important foraging habitat for mobile crustaceans and fishes (Bahr and Lanier 1981). Fishes are attracted to bottom structure, a behavioral response that is reflected in the success of artificial reefs. Lenihan et al. (2001) recorded 18 species of commercially and recreationally valuable fishes that used oyster reefs in the Pamlico Sound, North Carolina. A review by Coen et al. (1999) confirms that over the geographic range of studies, from Maryland to Texas, oyster reefs are utilized as habitat by numerous species of fishes and mobile crustaceans.

As an abundant suspension-feeding bivalve with a high filtration rate, oysters serve an important role in the ecosystem. By filtering estuarine waters, oysters reduce concentrations of suspended particles, thereby enhancing light penetration and allowing submerged aquatic vegetation to grow to deeper depths, and also channeling energy flow away from the pelagic food chains and into the benthic food chains (Dame 1996). Newell (1988) calculated that at the turn of the century before oyster resources were depleted, the oysters in Chesapeake Bay filtered a volume of seawater equal to that of the entire bay every 3 days. He hypothesized that the century-long decline in oysters in the bay to a level of about 1–2 % of historical abundance is responsible for the explosion in sea nettles (jellyfish), which are pelagic consumers of zooplankton and larval fishes and invertebrates. Elsewhere, changes in abundance of suspension-feeding bivalves have fundamentally altered ecosystem structure by their filtration process. Examples include the Great Lakes after the invasion of the zebra mussel and San Francisco Bay after the invasion of the Asian clam *Potamocorbula amurensis* (Nichols et al. 1990). Consequently, suspension-feeding bivalve molluscs including oysters can represent a strong interactor in aquatic ecosystems through their filtration activity in the water column. Recent evidence suggests that processing of water by oysters also stimulates denitrification by depositing nitrogen-rich feces and pseudofeces on the estuarine sea floor where anoxic conditions promote the microbial production of nitrogen gas (R. I. E. Newell, pers. comm.).

Despite the important role that reef-building oysters play in structuring estuarine ecosystems, there has been no protection of oyster reefs as a habitat of value. Instead oysters have been managed as a fishery resource, which has led to gross degradation of the reef habitat (Rothschild et al. 1994; Lenihan and Peterson 1998). Oyster fishermen are allowed to use dredges that remove not only the living oysters but also the shell matrix of the reef. This damaging gear has reduced the area of oyster reef habitat by at least 50% in the Chesapeake Bay over the past century (Rothschild et al. 1994) and has flattened once tall and species-rich reefs in North Carolina (Lenihan and Peterson 1998). In colonial times, the oyster reefs of the James River in Virginia were described as navigation hazards because of their extent and elevation, reaching nearly to the water surface (Wharton 1957). Now many of these reefs are little more than shell piles on the estuarine sea floor.

Reef height affects the function of oyster reefs in profound ways. Lenihan and Peterson (1998) report results of a set of experiments designed to explore the potential for restoration of oyster reef habitat, in which reef height was manipulated ex-

perimentally. Reefs of two heights (1 m and 2 m) were constructed at three different water depths by depositing and shaping shell mounds, which then received naturally recruiting larval oysters in September. These oysters grew successfully into the following summer, thereby establishing functional oyster reefs. During summer an extended period of bottom water hypoxia and anoxia developed in the Neuse River estuary, driven in part by eutrophication. Exposed to two to three weeks of severe hypoxia, all oysters in waters deeper than 3 m died, while all in the mixed layer above survived (Figure 18.4). Consequently, one function that reef height plays is to elevate the oysters up off the bottom where oxygen depletion can develop in estuaries in which organic loading is high. Failure of fisheries management to preserve the natural elevation of oyster reefs thus contributes to the decline of the oyster and of the ecosystem services it provides. Because excess loading of inorganic nitrogen by human activities in the watershed and airshed induce more frequent, more extensive, and more intense episodes of oxygen depletion in estuaries, oyster declines represent an interaction between two types of management inadequacy—water quality regulations that fail to control nitrogen loading and fisheries regulations that fail to maintain reef height (Lenihan and Peterson 1998).

The height of an oyster reef also has a substantial influence on biogenic habitat function. In terrestrial systems, habitat value has often been related to height or geometric complexity of biogenic structural habitat. The usual explanations for why habitat function follows habitat structure in terrestrial ecosystems involve aspects of how the habitat is used by the organisms that respond to it. For example, bird species diversity is thought to increase with foliage height diversity because of the greater potential for habitat partitioning among species and thereby achieving coexistence (MacArthur and MacArthur 1961). Lenihan (1999) has shown that increased height of oyster reef habitat functions in large part indirectly through the interaction between habitat structure and current flow. Oysters further elevated off the estuarine seafloor are exposed to faster currents, grow faster, have higher physiological condition, suffer less from parasitic oyster diseases, and live longer (Lenihan 1999; Lenihan et al. 1999).

Knowledge of how habitat structure affects the functioning of oyster reefs is important not only to conserving reefs but also to restoring reef habitat. In addition, however, concerns about the spatial arrangement of reefs come into play in managing reef systems. Because oyster reefs are discrete patches of habitat, their spatial configuration is likely to affect their utilization and value to mobile organisms that use the reef. Indeed, Lenihan et al. (2001) demonstrated that by establishing reefs over a range of water depths, fish had a refuge in shallow water to which to retreat if ever bottom water hypoxia degraded deeper reefs (Figure 18.4). Interestingly, the concentration of fishes on the shallow-water reefs during the hypoxia event had the consequence of depleting crustacean prey resources on those shallow reefs. Thus, if the intent of management were to maintain reef sanctuaries in a natural state, the spillover of mobile predators from the degraded

(A)

During periods without density stratification and hypoxia/anoxia

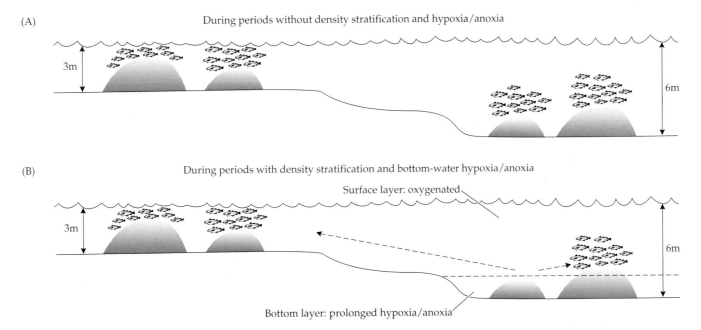

(B)

During periods with density stratification and bottom-water hypoxia/anoxia

Surface layer: oxygenated

Bottom layer: prolonged hypoxia/anoxia

Figure 18.4 Illustration of the effects of prolonged hypoxia/anoxia on oyster reefs and associated fishes, based on Lenihan and Peterson (1998) and Lenihan et al. (2001). When persistent density stratification combines with high organic loading of eutrophication, bottom water hypoxia/anoxia develops in deeper regions of estuaries below about 4-5 m depth. If severe hypoxia/anoxia persists for about 10 days, any oysters or other immobile marine invertebrate below the surface mixed layer are killed. Mobile fishes have a refuge on the tops of tall reefs and on shallow-water reefs, to which they migrate. However, unnaturally high concentrations of these consumers on those reefs rapidly deplete the principal crustacean prey. Oyster dredging is responsible for reducing reef height and thereby depleting oysters and oyster reef habitat in combination with eutrophication.

system would cause shifts in community structure on the sanctuary reefs, thereby diminishing their future value as foraging grounds.

Trawling Effects on Soft-Sediment Communities

Several fisheries targeting prawns, shrimps, crabs, scallops, oysters, and a wide range of demersal fishes utilize gear that disturbs the bottom (e.g., Jennings and Kaiser 1998; Watling and Norse 1998; Hall 1999). Virtually all of these fisheries operate over soft sediments or gravel because rocks and reefs inhibit use of and damage the gear. The one exception to this involves use of dredges specifically targeting reef organisms, such as oysters on temperate oyster reefs. There is controversy over the magnitude of the impact of such bottom disturbance on the ecology of estuarine and nearshore soft-sediment habitats in which bottom-disturbing fishing practices occur. Watling and Norse (1998) have likened the practices of dredge and bottom-trawl fishing to tropical deforestation in that dredges and trawls have been shown to damage emergent biogenic habitat on the soft-sediment seafloor and thus remove and destroy structural habitat (Jones 1992; Dayton et al. 1995). Yet fisheries managers have responded by claiming that there is little structural habitat in soft sediments and that these communities experience high natural rates of physical disturbance, thereby rendering them capable of recovering rapidly from fishing-induced disturbance.

Collie et al. (2000) completed a review and several meta-analyses of all available studies on the effects of bottom-disturbing fishing gears on estuarine and marine soft-bottom communities. This set of analyses separated dredge effects from trawl effects and evaluated both the impacts of bottom-disturbing fishing gears and also the rates of recovery in several different types of soft-bottom habitats, gravel, sands, muds, and biogenic habitat (like seagrass beds and polychaete or oyster reefs). The effects of dredges are generally much greater than the impacts of trawls on the abundance and diversity of benthic invertebrates as well as on biogenic habitat itself. Intertidal dredging is especially damaging to the benthic community. This is not surprising since most dredges are designed to be heavy enough to cut into the bottom to excavate partially or fully buried target species. Bottom trawls may include some device like a chain to induce fish or prawns to swim up off the bottom, but otherwise they sweep across the seafloor with only shallow penetration into the sediments. As a consequence, there is some disruption of the benthic invertebrate community by bottom trawls, but it is small compared to the effects of dredges. The smallest effects are associated with beam trawling in mobile sandy substrates of the North Sea, whereas the most serious effects documented come from dredging the biogenic sponge and coral habitat of eastern Australia. Because trawling is so intense in many areas of the world's shallow oceans and has been conducted for so long without any sanctuaries, concern arises about underestimating the impacts because the soft-bottom seafloor has long been modified (e.g., Jackson 1997). In other words, we have inadequate controls, no pristine ecosystems in which to measure the normal abundance of biogenic habitat in soft sediments. By implementing marine reserves closed to bottom-disturbing gear and maintaining those reserves over some period of years, data could be gathered to resolve this issue.

Collie et al. (2000) also demonstrated that the type of bottom habitat determines recovery rate after disturbance by dredges or trawls. Biogenic habitat is the slowest to recover, with recovery time frames well in excess of 5 years, so that this system never has opportunity to recover before the next fishing season commences. On the other hand, sandy-bottom communities exhibit relatively rapid rates of recolonization and recovery, somewhat faster than invertebrate communities in muddier sediments. This set of distinctions among bottom types in recovery rates makes sense based on first principles of benthic ecology. The species that construct biogenic habitat that emerges up off the seafloor tend to be relatively large organisms with relatively long life spans. Their extension off the bottom increases risk of damage by fishing gear and their size and longevity imply a relatively long time for recolonization and recovery. Likewise, sandy sediments experience more bottom shear stress from currents than do stable mud sediments and thus probably represent an environment in which bottom disturbance is frequent. This selects for opportunistic species preadapted to surviving the disruption of bottom trawling and capable of rapid recolonization and growth after disturbance. But even in sands, recovery takes from 100 days to over a year, such that frequent trawling would maintain the resident benthic communities in a permanently disturbed state. Muddier sediments are found in physically less dynamic depositional environments, where gross disruption of the bottom is rare and thus trawling presents more of a challenge to the survival and recovery abilities of resident organisms.

These differences in response to trawling by the various types of bottom communities should be useful to managers interested in preserving natural functions of the soft-sediment communities. Retention of a more natural ecosystem structure may render fisheries more sustainable and maximize the value or delivery rate of ecosystem goods and services. On the other hand, the disturbance of trawls to the seafloor community of benthic invertebrates may maintain that community in an earlier successional stage, thus providing more prey for certain demersal predators that prefer or specialize on early successional species (Pihl et al. 1992; Peterson et al. 2000b). This process resembles recovery after anoxia, as illustrated in Figure 18.3.

Habitat Fragmentation

Although the consequences of habitat fragmentation by land development activities have been considered important to management of terrestrial communities for many years (see Soulé and Terborgh 1999), marine ecologists have tended to think that the high dispersal rates of coastal marine organisms, dominated by species with pelagic larval life histories, renders habitat fragmentation unimportant to the sea. There

is a long history of evaluating the implications of alternative spatial designs in parks and reserves on land, typically using the theory of island biogeography and more recent models of spatially explicit meta-population dynamics (Hanski 1999). Only recently have marine ecologists, conservationists, and fisheries managers begun to consider the need for and potential value of marine reserves, and the implications of spatial arrangements of habitats in the nearshore marine systems.

Whereas pelagic larval stages of coastal marine fish and invertebrates promote a process that can transport recruits on spatial scales far larger than necessary to provide connections between patches of marine habitat, older life stages of the same species may be unwilling or unable to make the journey across degraded bottom between patches. For example, Micheli (1997) has shown that blue crabs, perhaps the keystone predator in estuarine invertebrate communities on the East Coast of the United States below Cape Cod (Woodin 1976; Virnstein 1977), are sensitive to risk of predation by birds. In the presence of gulls, blue crabs remain and forage in salt marshes even when higher prey abundance on nearby unvegetated sand flats would make foraging there more productive. Furthermore, corridors of vegetated seagrass habitat promote the movement of blue crabs among habitat patches (Micheli and Peterson 1999). Consequently, predation rates on bivalve molluscs preferred by blue crabs are higher on patches of oyster reef that are connected to seagrass habitat than on isolated patches of oyster reef. Isolated patches of oyster reef maintain higher densities and greater species richness of benthic invertebrates than reefs adjacent to salt marsh, which is a habitat offering structural interference to visually orienting avian predators. Consequently, the landscape context of habitat positions plays a role in dictating function and structure in estuarine ecosystems (Irlandi and Crawford 1997). The landscape role can often be understood by examining individual-based behavioral responses to different types of habitat. Thus, for different reasons, habitat fragmentation and landscape scale patterns of spatial interconnections have important functional implications for both marine and terrestrial communities. Perhaps the study of behaviorally based decisions by terrestrial predators will also reveal an effect of habitat position that is driven not by absolute isolation of habitat patches but by perception of risks and rewards that determine behavioral choices like the process at work in marine coastal systems.

An understanding of the role of spatial context of habitat patches in estuarine and coastal marine ecosystems is important to management because many human activities in these systems can and do destroy and degrade habitat in ways that produce fragmentation and patch isolation. Some fishing practices that disturb the bottom endanger and fragment seagrass habitat (Peterson et al. 1987). The dredging of boat channels creates patchworks of remaining shallow habitats. When boats run aground or simply are driven through shallows, they can create habitat damage that fragments the remaining habitat. Once such boat scars are created in seagrass habitat, the high current energy in the scar can make it difficult for the grass to return. In some cases strong current flows along the length of the scar erode additional habitat and widen the separation between patches. Shoreline development is often allowed to break the continuity of intertidal habitats like mangrove forests or salt marshes even in developed countries, while in less developed countries, widespread destruction and fragmentation of intertidal mangrove forests and marshes are routinely practiced. Clearly, management practices should be improved to reduce habitat fragmentation in marine coastal systems.

EFFECTS OF OVERHARVEST BY DIRECTED TAKE AND BY-CATCH MORTALITY

Great Whales

Humans have exploited large cetaceans since aboriginal peoples developed maritime hunting technologies. However, it was not until the eighteenth century that a growing whaling industry began to significantly deplete wild stocks of large cetaceans. The whaling industry developed in part from a growing market for baleen and whale oil, and in part from the creation of fast, long-range vessels. Right whales were the initial targets of this industry, so named because their slow swimming made them the "right" ones to pursue. Once these sluggish animals had been depleted, the industry turned to humpback, sperm, and rorqual (blue, fin, sei, minke, and Breede's) whales.

All the great whales are apex predators and all but the sperm whale feed on schooling or swarming small crustaceans and fishes. One species, the gray whale, feeds on infauna and epifauna in shallow, unconsolidated sediments of the Bering and Chukchi seas. Given the extremely large body sizes and historically high densities of these predators, it stands to reason that depletion of their populations had important ecological consequences to benthic and oceanic ecosystems, although there is little empirical evidence for such roles (Bowen 1997). The best of this evidence is for gray whales in the western arctic. By combining the results of manipulative experiments, direct observations, and side-scan sonar, Oliver and Slattery (1985) determined that the largely recovered gray whale population influenced the shelf ecosystem by resuspending sediments and consuming large numbers of ampeliscid amphipods. The furrows and troughs formed by feeding whales were rapidly colonized by scavenging lysianassid amphipods, and they also served to accumulate detritus, thus impacting populations of infaunal detritivores. Walruses, which co-occur with gray whales in the Bering, further impact the benthic communities by consuming clams and other large infauna, which in turn attract asteroid and ophiuroid sea stars.

The impacts of whales on water column assemblages are less clear. Perhaps the best evidence comes from Antarctica, where the decimation to near extinction of blue, fin, sei, and minke whales is thought to have released krill populations from limitation by predation (Laws 1977; May et al. 1979). Resulting increases in krill may have reset environmental car-

rying capacity for Antarctic pinnipeds, penguins, and perhaps other consumers. There is some evidence for this hypothesis in the increased growth rates and reduced age of first reproduction of seals and whales after the reduction of great whales in Antarctica (Gambell 1973). If this scenario is true, then the indirect consequences on Antarctic marine food webs are probably far more extensive than currently realized. This further suggests that the marine ecology of modern-day Antarctica differs substantially from what it was in the recent past, and that recovery of the great whales will bring considerable change to this system (May et al. 1979). Similar examples have been proposed, but with little supporting empirical evidence. One such case links the overexploitation of great whales with the decline of Steller sea lions (*Eumatopias jubata*) and harbor seals (*Phoca vitulina*) in the North Pacific Ocean (NRC 1996). The proposed scenario goes as follows. Once abundant baleen whales fed on and limited the density of various large zooplankters. As the whale population was diminished, zooplankton increased and thus so did walleye pollock, a gadid fish that also feeds on zooplankton. Pollock, which are voracious predators, may have grown to such numbers that they reduced the abundance of other species of co-occurring fishes, thus creating an abundant but nearly monotypic prey base for pinnipeds and other piscivores. Lipid levels in pollock are unusually low. Many marine birds and mammals are thought to need prey with high lipid content to maintain body mass during winter and to feed dependent young in summer, and captive studies have shown that sea lions and several seabird species cannot maintain their body mass on a diet entirely of pollock (Rosen and Trites 1999).

Harvest of Other Marine Mammals

At one time or another, nearly every species of marine mammal has been depleted by human exploitation. In several instances these reductions have been so extreme as to have caused the extinction or near extinction of species. Steller's sea cow is the one certain example of a human-caused extinction of a marine mammal. These animals were broadly distributed across the rim of the North Pacific Ocean through the late Pleistocene/Recent. Because of their sluggish nature and apparent inability to dive (Domning 1978), they were vulnerable to aboriginal marine mammal hunters. By 1742, the year Vitus Bering discovered Alaska and the beginning of a modern historical record from the North Pacific region, Steller's sea cow apparently had been extirpated by aboriginal peoples throughout nearly all of its natural range. However, sea cows remained abundant at a single location—the Commander Islands at the western end of the Aleutian archipelago. This geographical pattern of extinction and survival is matched by the distribution of aboriginal peoples across the sea cow's range, thus providing a reasonably clear example of late Pleistocene overkill of the New World megafauna (Martin 1973).

Other probable examples of marine mammal overkill by aboriginal hunters include sea otters (Simenstad et al. 1978),

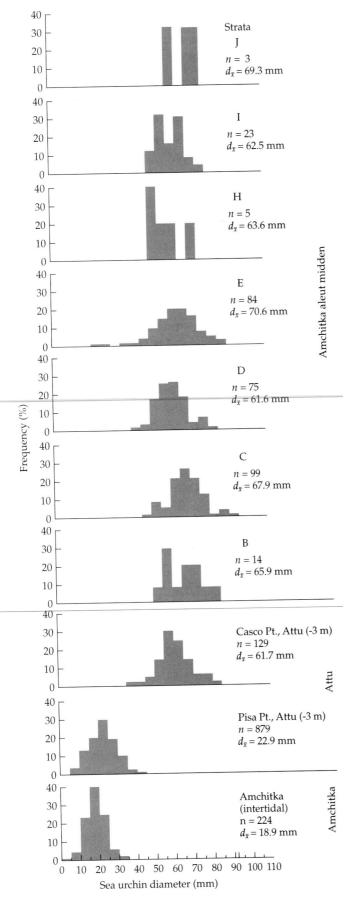

Frequency (%)

Sea urchin diameter (mm)

Figure 18.5 Sea urchin size-frequency distributions from Attu (otters absent) and Amchitka (otters abundant) islands, and from Aleut kitchen middens at Amchitka Island. Stratum J is the oldest and B is the most recent. These data show that otters must have been rare or absent around Aleut village sites during most of their historical occupancy. (After Simenstad et al. 1978.)

northern elephant seals, and northern fur seals. The evidence for sea otters comes from the western Aleutian Islands, where midden sites contain remains that are diagnostic of ecosystems lacking sea otters. This inference was made because sea otters are keystone predators (sensu Power et al. 1996) and kelp forest ecosystems with and without otters contain distinctly different size distributions of sea urchins. Sea urchin remains in midden sites throughout most of human prehistory in the western Aleutian Islands (about 2500 years ago to European contact in 1742) are characteristic of kelp forests lacking sea otters (Figure 18.5). In contrast with the sea cows, aboriginal people probably limited sea otter populations only in localized areas around village sites, as otters were abundant when Russian explorers and fur hunters first arrived in this region.

The evidence for impacts by aboriginal people on northern elephant seals and northern fur seals comes from both behavior and distributional records for these pinnipeds. Northern fur seals, like Steller's sea cow, ranged widely along the West Coast of North America. However, by the time of European contact, their breeding distribution was restricted mostly to the Commander and Pribilof Islands, both places that were not occupied by aboriginal people until very recently. Northern fur seals are unusual among pinnipeds in that they do not flee from humans, thus being vulnerable to limitless slaughter. Northern elephant seals are similar to northern fur seals in their reaction to people. Geographical limits to the southern elephant seal's breeding range in the southern hemisphere (areas that were largely uninhabited by aboriginal people) range from the warm temperate/subtropical convergence to the edge of the Antarctic ice cap. In contrast, shore rookeries of northern elephant seals are absent along the western coast of North America from the southern edge of the Arctic ice cap to central California, a region where maritime hunting cultures were strongly developed.

Despite these diverse indications of marine mammal depletion by aboriginal hunters, it was probably the regionalized scale of exploitation by modern people that drove marine mammals to low levels worldwide. For example, while aboriginal Aleuts depleted sea otters locally, the Pacific maritime fur trade reduced the species to the brink of extinction. The same is almost certainly true for northern fur seals, and probably northern elephant seals as well. And it was the Russian fur hunters who destroyed the last Steller's sea cow. Human exploitation or persecution has depleted many other species of pinnipeds. These animals were exploited mostly for blubber or fur, and persecuted because of perceived conflicts with fisheries. In some cases (e.g., northern elephant seal), they were hunted to the brink of extinction. Ice-dwelling species in the Arctic and Antarctica have been less vulnerable to the effects of human exploitation.

Overfishing

The oceans provide an estimated 19% of the animal protein consumed by humans worldwide and thereby produce goods of tremendous importance to human welfare (FAO 1993). Because of the importance of sustaining the yields of these goods, the management of marine fisheries has been a concern of developed nations for decades. Unfortunately, fisheries management has proved to be a general failure, with overexploitation the rule rather than the exception. Recent estimates suggest that almost half of the world's fish stocks are fully exploited and another 22% overexploited (Garcia and Newton 1998). The underlying cause of the lack of a conservation bias to fisheries management can be traced to the way in which fisheries have been managed within the institutional structures of developed nations. The fishing industry continues to argue for higher catches and can readily show the short-term economic consequences of any reduction in take. On the other hand, biologists charged with predicting the consequences on future yield can provide those estimates only with great uncertainty. The outcome of weighing known losses in the short term against uncertain losses in the long term is almost uniformly a decision that is biased in favor of allowing too much take (Ludwig et al. 1993). The solution to this dilemma must come either from changing our management institutions, so as to allow more ownership of fish stocks by the users through purchase of rights to a fraction of the take, or by enhancing our scientific understanding of the factors that cause variability in fish stocks so as to reduce the uncertainty in predictions (Botsford et al. 1997). Improved understanding almost certainly requires better appreciation of the complex influences of various components of the ecosystem, including physics, climate, and biological interactions that all affect individual populations of fish.

Worldwide, most exploited fish species are carnivores. Some of these occur near the top of the food web and more than a few are apex predators (e.g., sharks, billfishes, tunas, large groupers, to name a few). By examining global fishery statistics compiled by the Food and Agricultural Organization for the second half of the twentieth century, Pauly et al. (1998a) found that the average trophic level of exploited fish species declined significantly, as the larger, longer-lived species were progressively depleted. The shift to species of lower trophic status resulted not only from reduced availability of these more desirable target species, but perhaps also from the consequent enhancement of the next lower trophic level because of reduced control by predation. Pauly et al. (1998a) referred to this progressive trophic depletion as "fishing down food webs." The fishing down of marine food webs is a recurrent pattern of open ocean and reef fisheries from arctic to tropical regions throughout the world.

In some cases, the removal of fishes and other apex predators results in effects on the entire food web. Sea otters and

kelp forests provide a well-known example of complex food web interactions in the coastal ocean (see Witman and Dayton, Chapter 13, this volume). These interactions were discovered because of the overexploitation and subsequent recovery of the otter, which in turn created a fragmented species distribution. The important direct effect of sea otter predation is to limit populations of herbivorous sea urchins, which in turn allows an abundant assemblage of macroalgae to develop (Figure 18.6; Estes and Palmisano 1974). Top-down interactions of this sort are called "trophic cascades" (Carpenter and Kitchell 1993). In many cases, trophic cascades affect the abundance and species composition of autotrophs, depending on the degree to which herbivores are limited by carnivores. In concept, the strength of plant–herbivore interactions should oscillate with trophic complexity, being strong when the number of trophic levels is even and weak when it is odd. This may be one of the more robust features of trophic cascades (Hairston et al. 1960; Fretwell 1987).

Important top-down interactions from apex predators and resulting trophic cascades are now known in many ecosystems (Pace et al. 1999), including several coastal benthic systems and a few in the open sea (Botsford et al. 1997). As examples, several additional cases are worth noting. On rocky shores at temperate latitudes throughout the world, populations of herbivorous limpets are capable of eliminating fleshy macroalgae. Black oystercatchers (*Haematopus* spp.) are important limpet predators. Where oystercatchers are abundant, limpets are typically rare and fleshy macroalgae dominate the substrate's surface. Where oystercatchers are rare, these systems are characterized by abundant limpets and relatively few macroalgae (Frank 1982; Hockey and Branch 1984; Hahn and Denny 1989; Wootton 1995; Lindberg et al. 1998). Black oystercatchers are sensitive to human presence and tend to abandon areas that are frequented by shoregoers. Lindberg et al. (1998) showed that rocky shores in central and southern California were dominated by an abundant limpet fauna, except in those few remaining areas that are inaccessible to people. A second example involves predatory reef fishes from tropical to warm temperate latitudes, many of which feed on benthic invertebrates (Palmer 1979). Throughout the world, reef fish populations have been systematically decimated by human exploitation. This, in turn, has caused sea urchin populations to increase and macroalgae to decline. Pristine coral reef systems also lacked fleshy macroalgae because many of the fish species are herbivores. However, fisheries have indiscriminately reduced the carnivores and the herbivores, thus leaving only sea urchins to control the algae in these impoverished systems (Hay 1984). In the late 1980s, when urchin populations were decimated across the Caribbean by a wasting disease, fleshy algae came to dominate these systems (Lessios 1995). Evidence for the limiting effect of predatory fishes on herbivorous sea urchins comes both from experimental studies in which the removal of fishes caused urchins to increase (Cowen 1983) and marine reserves in which the recovery of predatory reef fishes has caused urchins to decline (Babcock et al. 1999; McClanahan et al.

Figure 18.6 The cascading effects of apex predators in kelp forest communities in the northwest Pacific Ocean. Prior to the early 1990s, these systems were characterized by abundant sea otter populations. Sea otter predation limited sea urchin populations, in turn promoting lush kelp forests. Predation by killer whales has since greatly reduced sea otter numbers, thus causing sea urchins numbers to grow and kelp forests to decline. (After Estes et al. 1998.)

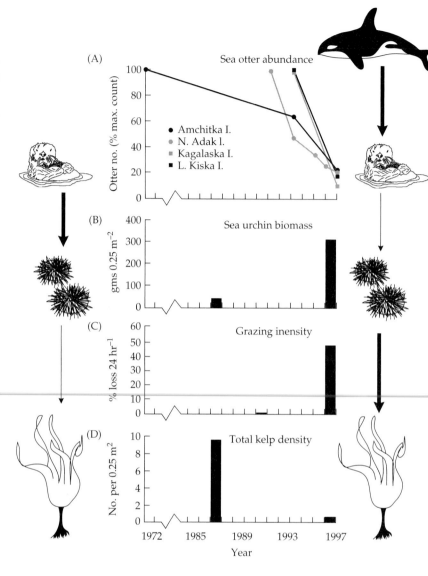

(A) Sea otter abundance

- Amchitka I.
- N. Adak I.
- Kagalaska I.
- L. Kiska I.

(B) Sea urchin biomass

(C) Grazing inensity

(D) Total kelp density

1999). Similar evidence for cascading effects of consumer removal exists for reef systems throughout the world (Hay 1984; Witman and Sebens 1992; Dayton et al. 1998). Hay's (1984) analysis of data gathered across the Caribbean indicates that even the herbivorous fishes have been functionally absent through much of this region for 20 or more years. In some areas, coastal reef systems have been fished down to a single trophic level. This is true for kelp forest systems in parts of southern California (Dayton et al. 1998) and the Gulf of Maine (Steneck 1998).

Two open sea examples of trophic cascades are worth noting. One is the great whales in Antarctica (see earlier section of this chapter). There is some evidence that the great whales limited krill abundance, but influences lower in the food web are unknown. The other example involves pink salmon, zooplankton, and phytoplankton in the North Pacific (Verity and Smetacek 1996). Pink salmon populations undergo predictable interannual fluctuations. Measurements of oceanic phytoplankton and zooplankton abundance over a 10-year

period demonstrate that during years when pink salmon are abundant, zooplankton are depressed and phytoplankton are abundant, whereas during years when pink salmon are rare, zooplankton are abundant and phytoplankton are relatively rare (Figure 18.7). These are but two illustrations of the importance of top-down trophic cascades in the sea and thus the need to consider important multispecies aspects of community organization instead of single-species models in managing marine living resources.

The key to recognizing and more fully understanding the loss of apex predators often lies in the historical record, which in some cases indicates significant anthropogenic influences for centuries or millennia. Jackson's (1997) historical analysis of Caribbean coral reefs makes the general point that many of the large consumers are either extinct or so severely depleted as to be of little or no ecological significance at present, and that these processes have been underway for hundreds of years. Simenstad et al. (1978) provide evidence from kitchen midden excavations indicating that aboriginal Aleuts overex-

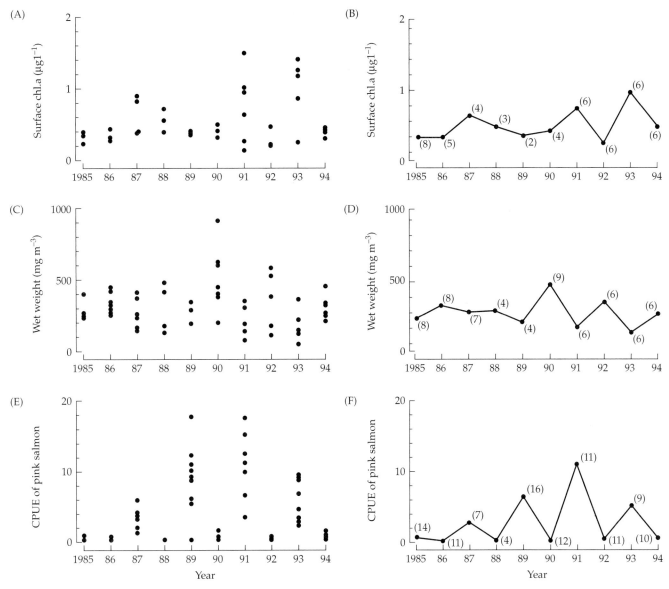

Figure 18.7 Evidence for top-down control of pink salmon, zooplankton, and phytoplankton abundance in the North Pacific Ocean. Pink salmon abundance fluctuates intrinsically on a two-year cycle, in turn driving populations of their major prey (zooplankton) down and releasing phytoplankton from limitation by zooplankton predation during peak pink salmon years. If the system were under bottom-up control, these three trophic levels would be expected to fluctuate synchronously. (Numbers of samples are shown in parentheses.) (After Shiomoto et al. 1997.)

ploited sea otters for at least several thousand years prior to European contact. Additional examples are certain to arise as marine ecologists come to more fully realize the power of historical data in making longer time-scale ecological inferences.

By-catch of Seabirds, Sea Turtles, and Marine Mammals

For most of commercial fishing's long history, the methods of exploitation were limited to hook and line, fish traps, and various sorts of small nets and seines. Technological developments, including powerful ships, precise means of navigation, weather forecasting, and above all, gear improvements

have provided modern fishermen with a means of locating and extracting large quantities of fin- and shellfish very quickly. The four main kinds of harvesting gear that have led to this situation are long-lines, trawls, gill nets, and pots. Although the concept behind each was not new, their sheer size was revolutionary. The effects of modern trawling on the sea-floor have been likened to clear-cutting forests (Watling and Norse 1998); long-lines and gill nets, often miles in length, are presently in use throughout the world's oceans (Richards 1994); and modern pot fishing techniques have depleted many shellfish populations to the point of requiring fishery closures. Together with this greatly increased rate and efficiency of exploitation has come the catch of unwanted species, or by-catch. Populations of invertebrates, fishes, turtles, birds, and mammals have all been impacted by losses to by-catch. The following examples point out the breadth and nature of the problem.

Various species of marine mammals and birds become entangled and killed in a variety of fishing gear, especially long lines and gill nets. Although observer programs have documented large numbers of deaths in some cases, estimating the impacts on populations is difficult. Nonetheless, entanglement and entrapment is commonly a concern. For instance, in the western Atlantic region, some fishing-related mortality was known in 1998 for 23 of 29 species (Waring et al. 1998), and in several cases these losses threaten continued survival of species.

Incidental loss of spotted and spinner dolphins in the purse-seine fishery for yellowfin tuna is perhaps the most well known example of losses to by-catch. The tuna fishery was exclusively hook and line prior to the 1960s. With the development of larger and faster vessels, fishing technology switched to purse-seining, thus allowing enormous quantities of tuna to be taken in brief periods. The success of the fishery resulted in yet more and larger vessels. The seine sets are made around schooling tuna, which often are associated with large schools of dolphins. By the 1970s, tens of thousands of dolphins per year were being killed as by-catch (National Marine Fisheries Service 1999). As a result, the Northeast Pacific offshore spotted and spinner dolphins are depleted, with both estimated to be at 20% or less of original (1959 = start of fishery) size. By the time this problem was recognized, the tuna seine fishery had become so heavily capitalized that to cease fishing would have caused severe economic hardship. Nonetheless, dolphin quotas were set and tuna import regulations were established as U.S. law in an effort to reverse population declines. Overall dolphin mortality was reduced dramatically—from an estimated 66,499 in 1975 to 1,112 in 1997. However, the dolphin populations are not recovering, despite mortality reported to be below replacement level since 1991. Whether that lack of recovery is due to indirect effects of the fishery ("stress" due to chase and encirclement), underreporting of kill, environmental changes, or some other factor or a combination of all of these factors remains unknown (T. Gerrodette, pers. comm.).

Black-browed and gray-headed albatrosses range widely across the southern ocean to feed at the Antarctic convergence. A long-line fishery for bluefin tuna has recently developed in this area. The albatrosses have learned to follow the tuna boats while their lines are being set, and these birds often become hooked before the baits can sink beyond their diving range. This problem was identified by instrumenting albatrosses with satellite radio transmitters, thus allowing researchers to determine the movements and fate of individuals (Prince et al. 1994). Population declines are probably driven by losses to fishing gear. New long-line setting techniques that more quickly submerge the baited hooks beyond the depth that albatrosses can reach by plunge diving are

hoped to reduce this source of mortality. Similar problems are thought to occur for wandering and Amsterdam albatrosses in the Indian Ocean (Weimerskirch et al. 1997).

The shrimp trawl fishery in the Gulf of Mexico has one of the highest known by-catch rates. An estimated 90 percent of the organisms captured in trawls is discarded. A resulting conservation problem is the incidental capture and mortality of Kemp's ridley sea turtles. This species is endangered and declining because of reduced breeding habitat, historical directed harvest of adults and eggs in Mexico, and losses as by-catch in the shrimp trawl fishery. Turtle exclusion devices (TEDs) have been developed to prevent turtles from entering the cod end of shrimp trawls. Many fishermen have been reluctant to use these, despite the threat of prosecution by the National Marine Fishery Service.

The by-catch of unwanted fish species is a problem for numerous specific fisheries. In the northwest Atlantic, barndoor skate are on the verge of extinction solely because of their low reproductive capacity (typical of most elasmobranchs) and high rates of incidental loss to ground fisheries (Casey and Myers 1998). Long-term records of catch in trawl fisheries show that this species occurred in up to 10% of the tow hauls and were common in all fisheries throughout the species' range (Figure 18.8). The catch rate of skates had dropped to zero in 1980. This case is especially interesting because barndoor skates have no commercial value.

By-catch of Marine Invertebrates

The by-catch of invertebrates occurs mainly in association with bottom trawling. Trawls are designed to capture fish, shrimp, and crabs that are found just above the bottom or buried just beneath the surface sediments. Consequently, trawls are designed to fish at the sediment–water interface. This is the habitat also occupied by epibiotic benthic invertebrates and surface-dwelling infaunal invertebrates. Not surprisingly, these are the two types of invertebrates most impacted by trawling worldwide (Dayton et al. 1995). The reductions of epibiota such as sponges, tunicates, gorgonians, and many other species attached to mollusc shells or other suitable hard substrata within the soft-bottom habitats can approach denudation, depending on the frequency and intensity of bottom trawling (Engel and Kvitek 1995; Watling and Norse 1998). Seagrass cover and biomass can be greatly reduced by bottom-disturbing fishing gear, and recovery times even in the absence of subsequent fishing can require years (Peterson et al. 1987).

Because seagrasses and epifaunal invertebrates provide structural habitat that projects above the sediment surface, and such vertical structure typically provides critical habitat for a variety of recruiting fishes and invertebrates, the loss of epibiota to trawl by-catch and seafloor disturbance can be expected to create cascades of impacts on the estuarine and shallow marine ecosystems through reduction of abundances of those fishes and invertebrates dependent on emergent structural habitat. Furthermore, the reductions in abundance of shallow-dwelling infauna represents a perturbation of the

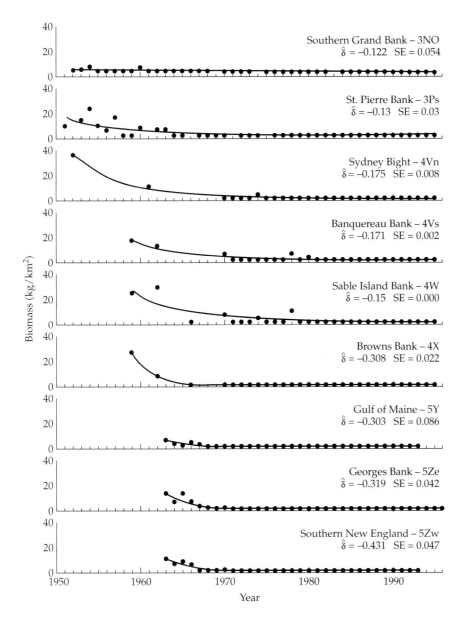

Figure 18.8 Estimates of absolute biomass for barndoor skate. This species is taken incidentally in the ground fishery from the southern Grand Banks to southern New England, which includes most of the species' natural range. The time series indicates that the species is nearly extinct. (After Casey and Myers 1998.)

benthic community that is more selective than sustained hypoxia/anoxia but still can lead to modification of the successional state of the benthic community and thus to changes in its value as forage for demersal fishes, crabs, and shrimps (Pihl et al. 1992). As stated previously, however, scientific assessments of such effects are wrought with difficulty. Because bottom trawling is typically so intensive in fished areas and has been repeatedly conducted for so many years, it may even be difficult to determine these impacts for want of appropriate control areas that have not been trawled. Those areas not fished typically differ from the fished areas in some important ways, including naturally low abundance of the targeted species, and thus they rarely qualify as control areas. It is possible that our characterization of soft-sediment habitats as almost exclusively occupied by infauna as opposed to epifauna (Peterson 1991) is a gross misrepresentation of the natural system.

By-catch of Fishes and Cascading Effects of Discards

Trawling for shrimp, crabs or targeted demersal fishes produces a by-catch of unwanted fish. The by-catch can be huge, with recent estimates of poundage in some fisheries exceeding that of the targeted species by 20 to 1. Such wasteful exploitation is driven by the high value of the targeted species, often shrimp. This by-catch is typically dominated by juveniles of species with commercial or recreational value as adults. The by-catch also includes species of value as forage fish for various piscivores, including fish, seabirds, and marine mammals. Consequently, the fate of the by-catch can have significant effects on other species.

Fish discarded in the by-catch can suffer a variety of fates. Depending on the duration of time on deck, the air temperature and solar insolation on deck, the duration of the trawl, and the physiological hardiness of the species, some fish discarded as by-catch may survive. Others are returned to the water dead, moribund, or injured. The dead and moribund fishes as well as many of the living fishes are subsequently consumed by opportunistic scavengers. The scavengers tend to be dominated by seabirds, especially larger gulls, which converge on trawlers in large numbers. Sharks commonly follow trawlers and consume discards. Some discards are also consumed by demersal scavengers, especially swimming portunid crabs. Consequently, the discarded fishes run the complete gauntlet of air, water, and bottom consumers, in that order.

The most important consequences of capturing, discarding, and killing so many fishes in the by-catch from trawling can be divided into two categories. First, the added mortality of juvenile fishes may reduce the subsequent production and fisheries yield of those species that as adults represent targets of fisheries. The subsequent impact on yield depends on the life history of the species. Those species with naturally low juvenile survivorship may show little demographic effects of imposing further mortality on the juveniles. This is especially true if some sort of compensatory mortality process exists to limit the numbers of adults ultimately produced. Under those circumstances, trawl mortality simply replaces mortality of a different sort. Compensatory growth is a more likely density-dependent process to affect fish. For those species with compensatory growth, ultimate production of adult biomass may be unaltered by trawl mortality of juveniles because the survivors then grow faster and larger in response to lower density. Nevertheless, fishes without strong compensatory mortality or growth processes in their life history will experience reduced yields because of their capture as juveniles in trawls. This is the process apparently limiting recovery of red snapper in the Gulf of Mexico.

A second major consequence of discarding fish as by-catch from trawls is the indirect effects on the ecosystem. The seabirds most likely to benefit from the opportunity to subsidize their diets with discarded fishes are the largest, most aggressive species (e.g., Garthe et al. 1996). If this food subsidy then results in greater productivity of young of these aggressive scavengers, the consequence will be to enhance populations of those species. This has important potential impacts on the entire guild of seabirds because the most aggressive species are often significant egg and chick predators and often practice kleptoparastism, or stealing the catch from other seabirds. Thus, subsidy of large, aggressive seabirds has the potential to cause significant indirect declines and even conservation crises in smaller seabirds. This very scenario has been implicated in seabird dynamics in the North Sea, where bottom trawling is so intense (Furness et al. 1992). There may also be some beneficial effects of such subsidies of scavengers. For example, it is possible that provision of discarded fishes enhances the production of blue crabs in the southeastern United States, thereby elevating and sustaining yield in a valuable fishery. Furthermore, shark populations are severely depleted, so any food subsidy from discards may contribute

to their recovery, should the mortality pressure from overfishing ever be relaxed.

CHALLENGES FOR CONSERVATION AND MANAGEMENT OF MARINE RESOURCES

Scales of Management vs. Scales of Ecological Processes

Perhaps the most pervasive problem with the management of living resources in the sea is the mismatch between scales of management and scales of the ecological processes that affect the managed resource (Levin 1992; Peterson et al. 2000b). This is an issue relative to spatial, and therefore political, scale, as well as a more generic problem of matching management institutions to the complexity of interactions that dictate dynamics of populations and communities. Human societies and human institutions fragment the ecosystem both spatially and functionally. For example, large marine ecosystems (Sherman et al. 1990) are not constrained to match national boundaries and global changes in climate affect even locally endemic populations. Management authorities partition responsibilities for different components of the ecosystem, such as water quality, atmospheric emissions, and fisheries management, despite the recognition by ecologists that multiple aspects of the physical and biological environment contribute to species dynamics and sustainability of ecosystem services.

Perhaps the only management problems that avoid this intrinsic mismatch of scales are those where the threat to the resource is both local in scale—falling within the scope of an effective political boundary—and specific in nature, such that management of a single aspect of the system suffices to address the problem. The best example worldwide of such a rare match of scales comes from work on management of the Chilean fishery for the muricid gastropod *Concholepus concholepus*, or "loco." Significant threats to this fishery—overharvest by fishers— are all local in scale and specific in nature. Consequently, successful management schemes have been developed based upon local ownership and management of the loco resource by communities of fishermen (Castilla and Fernandez 1998). Such management by artisanal fishermen allows conservation and future long-term sustainability to drive management. The match of important ecological scales and management scales makes a solution feasible. Similar issues face abalone fisheries along the west coast of North America, although in this case pollution is an added concern and disease clearly has decimated populations of at least one abalone species (black abalone, *Haliotis cracherodii*) in southern California. Predation by sea otters also severely impacted this fishery in parts of central California. Abundant abalone populations have persisted north of San Francisco Bay, probably in large measure because both commercial harvest and sport take by divers using scuba are prohibited. In southeast Alaska, British Columbia, and southern California, where commercial and recreational exploitation of abalones are regulated on regional scales, local fisheries have collapsed and several species face biological extinction. In contrast, abalone fisheries have persisted along much of the west coast of Baja California, Mexico. These latter fisheries are closely monitored and managed by local cooperatives.

For most living marine resources, conservation challenges come from more than one source. This is especially true in estuaries and coastal oceans, where human influences are so prevalent and multifaceted. For example, within the state of North Carolina, the processes that affect a vital fisheries habitat, seagrass beds, are partitioned among multiple state management agencies. The Coastal Resources Commission is responsible for defining what represents seagrass habitat and therefore what needs protection. This authority also has the responsibility for permitting dredging of navigation channels and boat harbors, both of which can affect seagrass beds by lowering the seafloor below the depth of sufficient light penetration to support growth and survival. The Environmental Management Commission has responsibility for permitting and regulating wastewater loading to rivers and atmospheric emissions, including $NO(x)$ that can harm seagrass through their contributions to eutrophication. The Sedimentation Control Commission regulates land activities that may enhance erosion and sedimentation, which increase turbidity and thereby reduce the area of well-lit estuarine seafloor that can support seagrass. Finally, the Marine Fisheries Commission regulates fishing practices such as scallop and crab dredging that can harm seagrass habitat by uprooting plants. Consequently, four management authorities exist within a single state that have separate jurisdiction over processes of significance to conserving an important coastal habitat. This example is not atypical. Proper management thus requires coordinated planning that is difficult to achieve under the system of fragmented management authorities. The problem is made even worse by overlapping responsibilities of federal agencies, such as the National Marine Fisheries Service, whose efforts require coordination with the state programs.

New initiatives have been announced to try to integrate some of these now separate responsibilities so as to create a more ecosystem-based management approach for some marine resources. The Magnuson–Stevens Fisheries Management Act of 1996 specifies need for creating plans for managing essential fish habitat. These plans will necessarily cross boundaries between multiple federal and state agencies, if they are to be effective efforts at habitat conservation. Nevertheless, problems on a global scale, such as growing greenhouse gas emissions and their effects on global climate, cannot be addressed by a single country and the international cooperation required seems unlikely. So mismatches of scales between management and ecological processes are likely to plague management and conservation of marine resources into the foreseeable future.

Even where a clear legislative framework is in place for the conservation and management of living marine resources, conflicting mandates and jurisdictional problems exist within and among the responsible agencies. For instance, the U.S. National Marine Fisheries Service is responsible for managing fisheries and conserving marine mammals. Often the goals and needs of these mandated activities are in direct conflict. Levels of exploitation within the range of fishery sustainability may be detrimental to the marine mammals that also depend on these fishes. Alternatively, population levels of marine mammals sufficient to satisfy the "optimum sustainable population" mandate of the U.S. Marine Mammal Protection Act may severely impact fisheries. Jurisdictional conflicts and differing management goals of various state and federal agencies also occur. Several U.S. National Parks are adjacent to or include marine habitats. In most cases, the associated state fish and game department manages the fishery resources within these marine habitats. Policies of the Park Service (protection) and state agencies (exploitation for sustained yield) call for fundamentally different management programs. Similar difficulties have arisen with the U.S. National Marine Sanctuary Program, which typically provides no additional protection to fish stocks beyond that afforded by state management agencies. Interagency conflicts may arise for other reasons as well. In central California, the sea otter is managed by the federal Fish and Wildlife Service, while the sea otter's invertebrate prey are managed by the California Department of Fish and Game. Because viable shell fisheries and sea otters cannot coexist (Estes and VanBlaricom 1985), the management goals of these two agencies have been in direct conflict for years.

POVERTY OF PAST PARADIGMS FOR MANAGEMENT

Recent ecological research has focused attention on the scientific basis for current paradigms of management of marine resources. Three widespread paradigms have come under substantial criticism. First, our traditional approach to managing fisheries has been based upon use of single-species models of population dynamics. This conceptualization overlooks a broad suite of interactions among fish species and between the targeted species and other components, both biological and physical, of the ecosystem. The inadequacy of single-species models stems in large part from a growing realization that interactions across trophic levels are important in population regulation. The second traditional paradigm of natural resource management in the sea is that forcing functions across trophic levels are largely bottom-up in nature. The third traditional paradigm that has come under fire after closer scrutiny is the separation of land and sea into two essentially independent systems for the purpose of management. Increasingly, ecologists are finding strong linkages between habitats and communities in the sea and on land. The general prescription for replacing these intellectually impoverished paradigms is to develop and apply a more holistic approach to management, embodied in the concept of ecosystem management (Christensen et al. 1996). However promising, the actual application of this philosophy to marine systems entails solving some fundamental problems in our knowledge of the state of marine ecosystems and in our understanding of their dynamics.

Fishery resources are still managed largely by single-species approaches (Ludwig et al. 1993) despite abundant evidence that food webs are often organized around strong and complex interactions among species. Marine ecologists tend to view these interactions in quite different ways depending upon whether their interest is in oceanic or coastal systems. Ocean ecologists often take a strong "bottom-up" view of the food web, which is to say that trophic status and the production of lower trophic levels dictate the distribution and abundance of populations. Coastal and reef ecologists, in contrast, take more of a "top-down" view, which is to say that the distribution and abundance of populations is governed by the degree to which they are limited by their consumers (Hunter and Price 1992). As illustrated earlier, both processes can have wide-ranging effects on marine communities and ecosystems. However, recent meta-analyses suggest that in the open pelagic ocean, neither top-down nor bottom-up linkages are predictably strong across entire food chains (Micheli 1999).

Managers of living resources, and especially fishery biologists, have long recognized the vulnerability of populations to overexploitation. This realization led to the concept of maximum sustainable yield (MSY). The idea of MSY is based on density-dependent population growth. In the simplest case, where the instantaneous rate of population change linearly declines as population size (N) increases from near zero to equilibrium (K), the yield curve (dN/dt vs. N) is hump-shaped with a maximum at $K/2$. Such estimates of MSY are the default metric for managing many fisheries. The details by which this is done have become vastly more complex. Nonetheless, the basic concept remains as both the typical goal of fishery management and the engine of management models. Fundamental problems with MSY as a fishery management paradigm have been recognized for decades (Larkin 1977). The fact that so very few of the world's fisheries have been sustainable (Botsford et al. 1997; Pauly et al. 1998a) is poignant testimony to the legitimacy of these concerns.

Exactly what are the problems with MSY? There are several. For one, the necessary data on stock size and productivity are difficult to obtain. Most fisheries develop and grow so rapidly that the problem of overexploitation is upon us before scientists and managers can formulate scientifically based management plans. A second problem with MSY is that it assumes spatial and temporal uniformity of populations. We now have abundant evidence for spatial variation in demography. Some populations are "sources" while others are "sinks" in the sense of providing recruits to future generations (Pulliam 1988). Similarly, the yield curve may vary among spatial units of a population. If MSY is computed as the average of this variation (a de facto reality), then the less productive segments of the population will be overexploited to the point of inevitable decline. Temporal variation creates an analogous situation. All species go through good times and bad, and we know that causal conditions vary or cycle on various time scales. Consistently exploiting a population at some empirically derived level of MSY will necessarily drive the population downward during bad times, even to the point of extinction if they last long enough. A third problem with MSY is that most fishery models do not take interspecies interactions into account (Botsford et al. 1997). Fishery biologists have tended to view the behavior of fish populations as being driven largely by internal dynamics, presumably dictated to a large degree by variation in the physical environment. While physical influences on reproduction and survival are clearly important, we now know that complex interactions strongly influence population levels of many species. A fourth problem with the concept of MSY is that density dependence does not account for the Allee effect, negative density dependence at small population size (Courchamp et al. 1999). This can result from such factors as demographic stocasticity, inbreeding, failure to locate mates, and nonlinear interactions between interacting species. The Allee effect probably explains why so many populations of marine organisms that have been exploited to low numbers have failed to recover.

The fragmentation of ecosystems is one of conservation biology's most fundamental concerns (Scott et al. 1999). This is because few natural systems are self-sustaining on small spatial scales, instead requiring some degree of connectivity with other areas. In the sea, the potential for such spatial connectivity is great because of ocean currents and the long distance movements of individuals. Many sedentary marine invertebrates and fishes have complex life cycles with pelagic larvae that can move long distances before settlement, thus creating open populations (Caley et al. 1996). Little is known about larval movements, although there is strong evidence that larval availability often controls the structure and abundance of adult populations. The first unequivocal evidence for such "supply side" control came from studies of intertidal barnacles (Roughgarden et al. 1988). Despite a subsequent proliferation of research on marine plants, invertebrates and fishes from tropical to subarctic ecosystems, the degree to which localized populations of marine organisms are self-replenishing remains largely unknown.

Connectivity in the sea involves a variety of processes besides larval redistribution. Food and nutrient subsidies are one of these (Polis et al. 1997). Macroalgal detritus produced by subtidal kelp beds is transported by wave action into the rocky intertidal zone where it maintains limpet densities far in excess of what would be possible from in situ production alone (Bustamante et al. 1995). Similarly, marine detritus deposited on the beaches of islands in the Gulf of California fuels populations of littoral zone and terrestrial organisms, elevating population levels of primary and secondary consumers and initiating complex interactions in recipient food webs (Polis et al. 1997; Anderson and Polis 1998). Spawning migrations of anadramous salmon may also supply essential marine nutrients to boreal forests (Willson et al. 1998; Bilby et al. 1996, 1998). Episodic inshore spawning migrations of smooth lumpsuckers (an otherwise oceanic fish) during late winter/spring in the Aleutian archipelago release sea otter populations from food limitation, thus altering the otter's dietary composition and perhaps even influencing its role as a keystone predator in coastal ecosystems (Watt et al. 2000).

Nutrient transport from sea to land can also have strong impacts on otherwise impoverished terrestrial ecosystems. Seabirds, which feed in nutrient-rich marine habitats but roost and breed on land, may be a common biological vector for nutrient transport. In the Gulf of California, Anderson and Polis (1999) showed that marine-derived nitrogen predominated in terrestrial plants on islands with seabirds, but not on nearby islands where seabirds were rare or absent. Plant species diversity, and rates of primary and secondary production also were enhanced on the nutrient-enriched islands, especially during wet years when water was less limiting.

Coastal and oceanic ecosystems may also be linked by predators that move between the two. For example, transient killer whales (those that appear to feed largely on other marine mammals) in western Alaska feed on seals and sea lions. The oceanic system in which these pinnipeds feed is supported by a food chain beginning with phytoplankton, in turn leading from zooplankton, to fish, to marine birds and mammals. From the 1970s through the late 1980s, pinniped populations declined by an order of magnitude in the western Gulf of Alaska and Aleutian archipelago (York et al. 1996). Killer whales apparently responded to change in the normal prey base by redirecting their diet to sea otters in the coastal zone. Otter populations were quickly driven downward by killer whale predation, in turn releasing sea urchins from control by sea otter predation. In a matter of only several years, sea urchin populations increased to the point of overgrazing coastal kelp forests (Figure 18.6).

At the extreme opposite end of the food web, regulation of primary production by rare elements such as iron can have strong effects on ocean food webs. Iron deficiency appears to be a key limiting factor in the production of tropical seas (Martin et al. 1994), not nitrogen- and phosphorous-based macronutrients as previously thought. At temperate latitudes, iron enters the ocean from streams and rivers where it is deposited on the continental shelf, later to be absorbed in upwelled water moving from the deep sea across the shelf margin to help fuel coastal production (Flegal et al. 1993; Hutchins et al. 1998). Impoundments may block sediment transport from land to sea, thus inhibiting this important rate-limiting process to coastal production.

Finally, marine contaminants are often transported across ecosystem boundaries by atmospheric convection, ocean currents, and the movements of animals with high body burdens, thereby potentially connecting otherwise uncontaminated systems with problem areas elsewhere. Such long distance movements of contaminants are well known (see earlier section), although impacts on recipient systems are much less clear.

Despite our growing awareness of large-scale connectivity, far too little is known about its importance to the functioning of marine systems. Additional examples undoubtedly will be discovered now that marine ecologists are aware of the issue of connectivity and have begun to think more about it.

This is an important frontier because linkage and connectivity defines the necessary spatial scales of conservation and management.

TOWARDS DEVELOPMENT OF ECOSYSTEM-BASED MANAGEMENT OF MARINE RESOURCES

The challenge now for marine ecologists is to meet, or even approach, the ideal of developing true ecosystem-based management for marine living resources (Christensen et al. 1996). This term does not imply that management be based on traditional ecosystems ecology, the study of material and energy fluxes through food webs. Instead, ecosystem-based management is an approach that incorporates understanding of the complex of interactions among species and between abiotic and biotic components of the system in pursuit of any specific management goal, even that of maximizing sustained harvest of an individual species (Christensen et al. 1996). Ecosystem-based management is far more advanced for terrestrial resources than it is for marine resources (NRC 1994; Botsford et al. 1997). There are several reasons for this disparity. First, the population status of species in the oceans is far less well known than on the land because the land is essentially two-dimensional and we occupy it continuously, as opposed to a three-dimensional sea where human occupation is sporadic and only scratches the surface. Most of our information about the status of marine populations comes from the catch records of industries that exploit them. Other species are rarely monitored, even central players like phytoplankton and zooplankton, which fuel fishery production. Second, there has been a longer tradition of land management than ocean management in the sense that managers of terrestrial resources have more fully incorporated a systems approach that includes the abiotic and biotic portions of the habitat. Management of marine resources has been dominated by fisheries concerns and thus driven by the single-species paradigm. Characterizing the state of marine ecosystems remains one of the fundamental challenges to development of ecosystem-based management in the sea. Ultimately, we must rely on technology to observe and monitor what is often impossible for human eyes to observe.

Food-Web Models

The construction of food webs represents a first step in developing functional relationships among the complex of ocean species. Food webs describe the linkages between consumers and their prey, and thus much of the potential for species interactions within biological communities. Such information is available from gut contents for many important marine species and can be obtained for others. A rich literature of conceptual and theoretical ecology is based on analysis and interpretation of food webs (Cohen 1978; Yodzis 1981; Pimm 1982). Unfortunately, little of what can be confidently inferred from the structure of those food webs described in the literature can be applied successfully to developing ecosystem-based management. All presently described food webs are idiosyncratic in that they never represent the complete system and are taxonomically biased (Paine 1988). They span space and time scales in ways that distort our appreciation of which species actually co-occur and thus may interact. They do not provide any indication of strength of interactions that can be documented by the presence of one species in the diet of another. Food webs are best used by managers as a road map of the structure of trophic interactions that deserve subsequent testing (Paine 1988; Menge 1995).

Energy Flow Webs

One means of moving beyond the simple description of trophic relationships embodied in a food web is to quantify the flow of energy or carbon through its various links. Such energy flow webs provide a static description of the energetics of species in a particular geographic area at a particular period of time. From this information, we know for that time and place which prey contributed most to the diets of each consumer. This information has been used together with information or informed guesses about the biomass abundance of groups of trophically similar species, production to biomass ratios, energetic efficiencies, and primary production to create energetically balanced flow webs for fisheries-relevant ecosystems. A model called ECOPATH (Cristensen and Pauly 1993) with appropriately generic software has been developed and applied to well over 60 marine and estuarine food webs worldwide. Because this modeling exercise is based on a static description of energy flow, it is risky to use it to make projections of future dynamics. For example, a consumer could readily switch to an alternative prey and such nonlinearities would be missed in any use of an energy flow web to project future changes in abundance of one or more components of the web. Furthermore, consumer–prey interactions in which the consumer has limited prey populations to very low levels will necessarily be veiled. Nevertheless, this approach probably represents the only tool currently available to fisheries managers for even beginning to contemplate the consequences of harvest on the rest of the ecosystem. Recent extensions of the static ECOPATH approach have been developed to include a dynamic model that projects the consequences of various alternative scenarios (Walters et al. 1997), but this too has a limited ability to depict the important nonlinearities in species interactions. A further elaboration on the energetic modeling approach called ECOSPACE allows different habitat or patch types to be depicted with migratory interchange among them. This approach may be useful in analyzing the utility of marine protected areas or fisheries reserves, which can be visualized as patches of different assemblages within a region otherwise modified by fishing effects.

Dynamic Models

An alternative approach to modeling the importance of interspecific interactions in marine communities comes from development of explicitly dynamic models that relate population growth rates to abundances of other species (Pimm 1993; Schoener 1993). This approach overcomes the problem of using a static description of energy flow to make dynamic predictions of population trajectories. It also could more readily incorporate interactions that are not based on consumption, such as biogenic habitat dependencies or interference competition, although the approach has not yet been extended to do so. Dynamic modeling can also involve many sorts of nonlinearities that are omitted in energetics-based models. Nevertheless, this approach has limited utility to managers because it requires rather specialized, complex modeling and its outcomes are often quite sensitive to choices made in the structure of the model and values assigned to its parameters (Pimm 1993). To resolve which of these choices more accurately depicts the natural community being modeled makes a set of data demands that go well beyond what is available or likely to become available, given the costs of characterizing marine ecosystems. Nonetheless, the dynamic modeling approach has real potential for future utility, especially in the context of sensitivity analyses that might direct field researchers to evaluate key processes that may influence future change.

Interaction Webs

The ideal understanding of how interactions affect the dynamics of marine food webs would come from assembling, quantifying, and analyzing the entire web of interactions among component species. Most biological communities contain numerous species, thus creating a vast number of potential interactions. This complexity makes the chore of understanding how complex systems work daunting in the extreme. Even the number of direct interactions (i.e., between consumer and prey, or interference between competitors) usually far exceeds the abilities of scientists to evaluate them individually (Polis and Strong 1996; Wootton 1994). This raises two important questions: Are all interactions equally important, and if not, how do we focus on those that are most important? Ecologists still struggle with the question of ecological parity. In one of the few rigorous analyses of this problem, Paine (1992) measured the interaction strengths for each of a number of co-occurring limpet species in the rocky intertidal zone at Tatoosh Island, Washington. He found that strong competitive interactions occurred in this guild, but only among some of the species, and these were not predictable *a priori* from population abundance. Wootton (1994) has proposed the use of path analysis to select those interactions that are most worthy of study.

This task of depicting important interactions is made even more complex when indirect interactions are considered. Yet several case studies show just how wide-ranging the effects of strong interactors can be (Menge et al. 1994). As described previously, the presence or absence of sea otters in coastal marine systems of the North Pacific Ocean acts through a trophic cascade to influence the abundance of kelp and other fleshy macroalgae. This three-trophic-level interaction, in turn, has wide ranging and complex effects throughout the coastal ecosystem, in large part because kelps provide food and habitat for many other species (Figure 18.9). Kelps and other large

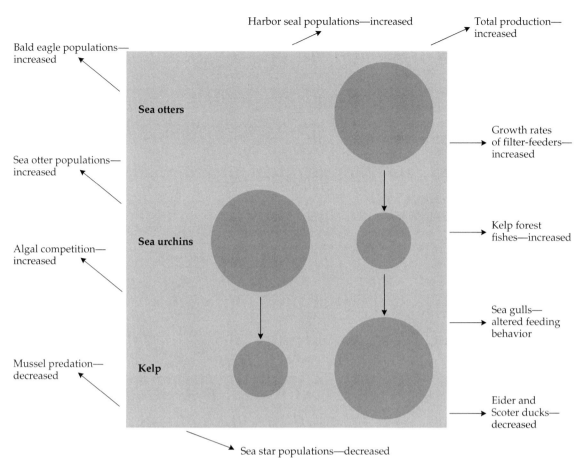

Figure 18.9 Some known or suspected indirect effects of the trophic cascade leading from sea otter to kelp forests

brown algae grow at very high rates, and thus the kelp beds fuel a productive coastal ecosystem. The importance of this process was shown by contrasting growth rates of filter-feeding mussels and barnacles between islands with and without sea otters (and thus with and without well-developed kelp beds). These growth rates were 3 to 4 times greater on islands with sea otters than on nearby islands without them (Duggins et al. 1989). Further work on this system has shown or suggested indirect effects of sea otter predation on the population biology and behavior of fishes, sea ducks, gulls, sea stars, harbor seals, and birds of prey (Estes 1996). There is also evidence that sea otter predation has shaped the character of plant–herbivore interactions in kelp forest communities (Steinberg et al. 1995), specifically the levels of chemical defenses in marine plants and the degree to which herbivorous invertebrates are able to resist those defenses.

While few other marine systems have been evaluated in similar detail, long chains of interaction may be the rule rather than the exception for coastal benthic systems. There is growing evidence that apex predators have important top-down effects in many different systems (Soulé and Terborgh 1999; Pace et al. 1999). Strong plant–herbivore interactions exist in many different reef and rocky intertidal systems throughout the world. Marine plants are also known to influence their

communities and ecosystems in a diversity of ways, such as by altering currents and wave forces, by providing habitat for other species, and by fueling production. Together, these widely recurring patterns suggest that many marine food webs are strongly interconnected. The conservation and management implications are obvious. Focused human activities thus can strongly influence marine ecosystems in unexpected ways.

Coupled Physical–Biological Models

Although our discussion of the problem of predicting community dynamics in marine ecosystems has focussed on interspecific interactions of various sorts, there exists another issue of great significance in marine systems, the role of physical processes. An entire discipline of fisheries oceanography has evolved over the past 20 years or so to better evaluate the linkages between ocean physics and fish population dynamics (e.g., Rothschild 1986; Sinclair 1988; Cushing 1996). Most of this research has been directed towards effects of physical processes such as advective transport and turbulence on recruitment dynamics of fishes. Changing transport regimes can prevent larval fishes from successfully returning to suitable habitat, thereby causing tremendous interannual variability in year class strength (Bakun and Parrish 1982). For some long-lived species, significant recruitment events may occur at decade-long intervals (Pearse and Hines 1987). Changing turbulence in the upper water column can modify biological processes and affect the feeding success of zooplankton and larval fishes by altering the encounter rates of consumers and their prey (Lasker 1975; Rothschild and Osborn 1988). This, in turn, can affect survival both directly (through starvation) and indirectly (through size-dependent predation). Consequently, the problem of modeling community dynamics in marine ecosystems includes added complexity induced by the direct and indirect effects of varying abiotic conditions. Since some of these abiotic forcings may be seriously modified by human-induced change, understanding the relationships has important implications for managers. For example, through increased global warming, winds favorable to upwelling are increasingly strong and persistent along western continental boundaries (Bakun 1990), thereby depriving important forage and commercial fishes like sardines and anchovies of the periods of wind relaxation necessary for larval retention nearshore and thus reducing recruitment (Bakun and Parrish 1982). If global warming were to produce conditions similar to El Niños in which nutrient limitation and intense storm activity destroy kelp beds along the Pacific coast of North America, then recruitment of barnacles and presumably other nearshore species will be greatly enhanced (Gaines and Roughgarden 1985). Such a release from recruitment limitation in the intertidal zone would have important repercussions for community dynamics.

The daunting complexity and practical impossibility of incorporating all the biological processes and abiotic variables into a realistic and tractable model of community dynamics for any marine ecosystem have led ecologists to promote an approach called adaptive management. Adaptive management is the process of learning from responses to regulations and adjusting the regulations accordingly (Walters 1986). The application of this approach to marine systems is based upon the realization that fishing represents such a huge influence on the system that management of the activity can be treated as an experiment from which implications of those fishing activities can be inferred and then applied subsequently to improving sustainability of the ecosystem yields of goods and services. This approach is not limited to fisheries management but can also be applied to water quality management and other environmental arenas. Adaptive management is most effectively achieved when regulations are constructed in anticipation of learning, so that they more closely approach an experimental design with controls and replication. The regulations are also best designed using hypotheses about direct and indirect effects of the managed activity based on the best available scientific understanding, presumably derived from knowledge of the food web structure, energy flows, or the results of dynamic models. This approach of adaptive management is a fundamental part of ecosystem-based management (Christensen et al. 1996) and can be practiced with much greater frequency and much more sophistication that it has in the past (Walters 1986).

Marine Reserves

Establishment of marine reserves or protected areas is envisioned by many scientists, managers, and policy makers as a primary means of managing fisheries, conserving marine resources, and providing for a sustainable ocean (Murray et al. 1999). There are several reasons for this emerging mindset. Perhaps the most important of these is that the approach is simple in concept. No matter what the nature and magnitude of anthropogenic problems, a complete hands-off policy ought to fix it. This mentality is to some degree a carryover from terrestrial conservation biology, where a system of parks and other protected areas has long been in place, and where it has become increasing evident that human activities of many different sorts are incompatible with the long-term survival of certain species. Marine reserves can address, at least in part, the challenge of ecosystem-based management by preserving entire suites of species together with their habitats. Finally, none of the other approaches (sustained yields, quotas, limited entry) taken in fishery management and marine conservation has worked very well.

While marine reserves are typically both small and recent compared with their terrestrial analogues, we have some evidence that they work, at least to a degree (Russ and Alcala 1996; Murray et al. 1999; Paddack and Estes 2000; Halpern, in press). Increased sizes and densities of exploited stocks are seen within marine reserves, and in at least two cases (Babcock et al. 1999; McClanahan et al. 1999) indirect effects on plant–herbivore interactions have been documented. At the present time, however, less that 0.5 percent of the world's oceans are in reserve status (Carr et al. in press). Properly designed and implemented, marine reserves almost certainly will have a sustaining influence on marine resources. Important questions remain on just how to do this. How much area must be protected? How large or small should the reserves be? And where should they be located? The truth is that these questions cannot be answered at present. Nonetheless, if marine reserves are to serve as effective tools in the conservation and management of marine resources, they must either be large enough to include the important linkages or be arrayed in an interconnected network (Carr et al. in press). For instance, a protected area sufficient to protect a population of adult fish will not succeed if the larval source for this population is not also protected, or if the larvae pass through unsuitable habitat because that habitat is not protected. Likewise, a protected area might fail to function if it serves as a sink for predators whose food supply or habitat has been degraded elsewhere (Lenihan et al. 2001). At this time we have very little information from which to determine the scale of connectivity in the sea, although we know that it is sometimes very large. This information void hampers conservation planning and design of networks of effective marine reserves despite the promise that this approach holds. Compelling science must also play a large role in the public education required to build the public and political support required for implementation of any comprehensive plan for establishing and maintaining protected areas in the sea.

Marine ecology cannot offer any politically feasible single cure for the conservation crisis of species and communities in the sea. Nevertheless, the attention now being given by academic ecologists, occasionally in partnership with government agencies, to developing the basic understanding needed to improve management of marine communities is encouraging. Many of the flaws in our present management paradigms and approaches have been exposed, and active research is progressing to develop more sustainable uses of the sea. We are sadly pessimistic, however, about the ability of human institutions to manage global threats to marine ecosystems, such as the indirect effects of global warming. The paralysis of nations to deal with the dual problem of increasing human population and increasing per capita exploitation of natural resources leaves little room for long-term optimism on a global scale. For processes that originate and operate on a local scale, science can probably be advanced to produce schemes to sustain the important goods and services from marine communities. But how long will it be before global-scale events overwhelm those successes?

ACKNOWLEDGMENTS

We appreciate input from R. T. Barber, W. H. Berger, D. R. Croll, T. Gerrodette, M. E. Hay, M. Hixon, T. P. Hughes, W. M. Jarman, H. S. Lenihan, S. P. Powers, D. Smith, and two anonymous reviewers. Funding from the National Science Foundation Biological Oceanography Program and Polar Programs (C.H.P), the U.S. Geological Survey (J.A.E), and the Pew Charitable Trusts (for both authors) is gratefully acknowledged. The development of this review was facilitated by the Marine Records Working Group of NCEAS, the National Center for Ecological Analysis and Synthesis.

LITERATURE CITED

Addison, R. F. 1989. Organochlorines and marine mammal reproduction. *Can. J. Fish. Aquat. Sci.* 46: 360–368.

Alexander, V. 1980. Interrelationships between seasonal sea ice and biological regimes. *Cold Regions Sci. Technol.* 2: 157–178.

Alexander, V. and H. J. Niebauer. 1981. Oceanography of the Eastern Bering Sea ice zone in spring. *Limn. Oceanogr.* 26: 1111–1125.

Anderson, D. M. and D. J. Garrison (eds.). 1997. The ecology and oceanography of harmful algal blooms. *Limn. Oceanogr.* Vol. 42, No. 5, part 2: 1009–1305.

Anderson, D. W. and J. J. Hickey. 1972. Eggshell changes in certain North American birds. *Proc. Internatl. Ornithol. Congr.* 15: 514–540.

Anderson, D. W., J. R. Jehl, R. W. Risebrough, L. A. Woods, Jr., L. R. Deweese and W. G. Edgecomb. 1975. Brown pelicans: Improved reproduction off the southern California coast. *Science* 21: 806–808.

Anderson, D. W., F. Gress and D. M. Fry. 1996. Survival and dispersal of oiled brown pelicans after rehabilitation and release. *Mar. Poll. Bull.* 32: 711–718.

Anderson, W. B. and G. A. Polis. 1999. Marine subsidies of island communities in the Gulf of California: Evidence from stable carbon and nitrogen isotopes. *Oikos* 81: 75–80.

Anderson, W. B. and G. A. Polis. 1999. Nutrient fluxes from water to land: Seabirds affect plant nutrient status on Gulf of California islands. *Oecologia* 118: 324–332.

Anthony, R. G., A. K. Miles, J. A. Estes and F. B. Isaacs. 1999. Productivity, diets, and environmental contaminants in nesting bald eagles from the Aleutian archipelago. *Environ. Toxicol. Chem.* 18: 2054–2062.

Aronson, R. B. and W. F. Prect. 2000. Evolutionary paleoecology of Caribbean coral reefs. In W. Allmon and D. J. Bottjer (eds.), *Evolutionary Paleoecology: The Ecological Context of Macroevolutionary Change.* Columbia University Press, New York.

Babcock, R., S. Kelly, N. T. Shears, J. W. Walker and T. J. Willis. 1999. Changes in community structure in temperate marine reserves. *Mar. Ecol. Prog. Ser.* 189: 125–134.

Bahr, L. M. and W. P. Lanier. 1981. *TheEcology of Intertidal Oyster Reefs of the South Atlantic Coast: A Community Profile.* FWS/OBS/81.15, U.S. Fish and Wildlife Service, Washington, DC.

Baird, A. H. and P. A. Marshall. 1998. Mass bleaching of corals on the Great Barrier Reef. *Coral Reefs* 17: 376.

Baird, D. and R. E. Ulanowicz. 1989. The seasonal dynamics of the Chesapeake Bay ecosystem. *Ecol. Monogr.* 59: 325–364.

Bakun, A. 1990. Global climate change and intensification of coastal upwelling. *Science* 247: 198–201.

Bakun, A. and R. H. Parrish. 1982. Turbulence, transport and pelagic fish in the California and Peru current systems. *Calif. Coop. Oceanic Fish Invest. Rep.* 23: 99–112.

Barber, R. T. 2001. *The Response of Oceanic Ecosystems to the Climate of the 21st Century.* Excellence in Ecology 13, Ecology Institute, Oldendorfe/Luhe, Germany.

Barrie, L. A., D. Gregor, B. Hargrave, B. Lake, D. Muir, R. Shearer, B. Tracey and T. Bideman. 1992. Arctic contaminants: Sources, occurrence and pathways. *Sci. Total Environ.* 122: 1–74.

Barry, J. P., C. H. Baxter, R. D. Sagarin and S. E. Gilman 1995. Climate-related, long-term faunal changes in a California rocky intertidal community. *Science* 267: 672–675.

Berkelmans, R. and J. K. Oliver. 1999. Large-scale bleaching of corals on the Great Barrier Reef. *Coral Reefs* 18: 55–60.

Bilby, R. E., B. R. Fransen and P. A. Bisson. 1996. Incorporation of nitrogen and carbon from spawning coho salmon into the trophic system of small streams: Evidence from stable isotopes. *Can. J. Fish. Aquat. Sci.* 53: 164–173.

Bilby, R. E., B. R. Fransen, P. A. Bisson and J. K. Walter. 1998. Response of juvenile coho

salmon (*Oncorhynchus kisutch*) and steelhead (*Oncorhynchus mykiss*) to the addition of salmon carcasses to two streams in southwestern Washington, USA. *Can. J. Fish. Aquat. Sci.* 55: 1909–1918.

Birkeland, C. 1997. *Life and death of coral reefs.* Chapman and Hall, New York.

Blus, L. J., R. G. Heath, C. D. Gish, A. A. Belisle and R. M. Prouty. 1971. Eggshell thinning in the brown pelican: Implication of DDE. *BioScience* 21: 1213–1215.

Botsford, L. W., J. C. Castilla and C. H. Peterson. 1997. The management of fisheries and marine ecosystems. *Science* 277: 509–515.

Bowen, W. D. 1997. Role of marine mammals in aquatic ecosystems. *Mar. Ecol. Prog. Ser.* 158: 267–274.

Breitburg, D. L. 1992. Episodic hypoxia in Chesapeake Bay: Interacting effects of recruitment, behavior, and physical disturbance. *Ecol. Monogr.* 62: 525–546.

Bricelj, V. M. and D. J. Lonsdale. 1997. *Aureococcus anophagefferens*: Causes and ecological consequences of brown tides in U.S. mid-Atlantic waters. *Limn. Oceanogr.* 42: 1023–1038.

Brown, B. E. 1997. Coral bleaching: Causes and consequences. *Coral Reefs* 16: S129–S138.

Bruno, J. F., C. E. Siddon, J. D. Witman and P. L. Colin. 2001. El Niño-related coral bleaching in Palau, Western Caroline Islands. *Coral Reefs*: in press.

Bruun, P. 1962. Sea-level rise as a cause of shore erosion. *J. Waterways Harbor Div. ASCE* 88: 117–130.

Burkholder, J. M., H. B. Glasgow, Jr. and C. W. Hobbs. 1995. Fish kills linked to a toxic ambush-predator dinoflagellate: Distribution and environmental conditions. *Mar. Ecol. Prog. Ser.* 124: 43–61.

Bustamante, R. H., G. M. Branch and S. Eekhout. 1995. Maintenance of an exceptional intertidal grazer biomass in South Africa: Subsidy by subtidal kelps. *Ecology* 76: 2314–2329.

Caley, M. J., M. H. Carr, M. A. Hixon, T. P. Hughes, G. P. Jones and B. A. Menge. 1996. Recruitment and the local dynamics of open marine populations. *Annu. Rev. Ecol. Syst.* 27: 477–500.

Carpenter, S. R. and J. F. Kitchell (eds.). 1993. *The trophic cascade in lakes.* Cambridge University Press, New York.

Carr, M. H., J. Neigel, S. Andelman, J. Largier, J. Estes, J. Lubchenco and R. Warner. In press. Comparing marine and terrestrial ecosystems: Implications for the objectives and design of marine protected areas. *Ecol. Applic.*

Carson, R. 1962. *Silent spring.* Houghton Mifflin, Boston, MA.

Casey, J. A. and R. A. Myers. 1998. Near extinction of a large, widely distributed fish. *Science* 281: 690–692.

Castilla, J. C. and M. Fernandez. 1998. Small-scale benthic fisheries in Chile: Co-management and sustainable use of benthic invertebrates. *Ecol. Applic.* 8: S124–S132.

Catovsky, S. and F. A. Bazzaz. 2000. Contributions of coniferous and broad-leaved species to temperate forest carbon uptake: A bottom-up approach. *Can. J. Forest Res.* 30: 100–111.

Chang, L. (ed.). 1996. *Toxicology of Metals.* CRC Press, Boca Raton, FL.

Christensen, N. L., A. M. Bartuska, J. H. Brown, S. R. Carpenter, C. D'Antonio, R. Francis, J. F. Franklin, J. A. MacMahon, R. F. Noss, D. J. Parsons, C. H. Peterson, M. G. Turner and R. G. Woodmansee. 1996. The report of the Ecological Society of America Committee on the Scientific Basis for Ecosystem Management. *Ecol. Applic.* 6: 665–691.

Christensen, V. and D. Pauly (eds.). 1993. *Trophic Models of Aquatic Ecosystems.* ICLARM Conf. Proc. 26, Manila, Phillipines.

Clague, J., J. R. Harper, R. J. Hebda and D. E. Howes. 1982. Late Quaternary sea level and crustal movements, coastal British Columbia. *Can. J. Earth Sci.* 19: 597–618.

Coen, L. D., M. W. Luckenbach and D. L. Breitburg. 1999. The role of oyster reefs as essential fish habitat: A review of current knowledge and some new perspectives. In L. R. Benaka (ed.), *Fish Habitat: Essential Fish Habitat and Rehabilitation*, pp. 434–454. American Fisheries Society Symposium 22, Annapolis, MD.

Cohen, J. E. 1978. *Food Webs and Niche Space.* Princeton University Press, Princeton, NJ.

Colborn, T.,and C. Clement. 1992. *Advances in Modern Environmental Toxicology, Vol. 21. Chemical Alterations in Sexual and Functional Development: The Wildlife/Human Connection,* Princeton Sci. Publ. Co., Princeton, NJ.

Collie, J. S., S. J. Hall, M. J. Kaiser and I. R. Poiner. 2000. A quantitative analysis of fishing impacts on shelf-sea benthos. *J. Anim. Ecol.* 69: 785–798.

Conway, H., B. L. Hall, G. H. Denton, A. M. Gades and E. D. Waddington. 1999. Past and future grounding-line retreat of the west Antarctic ice sheet. *Science* 286: 280–283.

Cooper, S. R. and G. S. Brush. 1993. A 2,500-year history of anoxia and eutrophication in Chesapeake Bay. *Estuaries* 16: 617–626.

Costanza, R. and R. d'Arge et al. 1997. The value of the world's ecosystem services and natural capital. *Nature* 387: 253–260.

Cottingham, K. and S. R. Carpenter. 1998. Population, community, and ecosystem variates as ecological indicators: Phytoplankton responses to whole-lake enrichment. *Ecol. Applic.* 8: 508–530.

Courchamp, F., T. Clutton-Brock and B. Grenfell. 1999. Inverse density dependence and the Allee effect. *Trends Ecol. Evol.* 14: 405–410.

Cowen, R. K. 1983. The effect of sheephead (*Semicossyphus pulcher*) predation on red sea urchins (*Strongylocentrotus franciscanus*) populations: An experimental analysis. *Oecologia* 58: 249–255.

Cranmer, M., S. Gilbert and J. Cranmer. 1996. Neurotoxicity of mercury—indicators and effects of low-level exposure: Overview. *Neurotox.* 17: 9–14.

Croxall, J. P. 1984. Seabirds. In R. M. Laws (ed.), *Antarctic Ecology,* pp. 53–616. Academic Press, London.

Cushing, D. H. 1996. *Towards a Science of Recruitment in Fish Populations.* Excellence in Ecology 7, Ecology Institute, Oldendorfe/Luhe, Germany.

Daily, G. C. (ed.). 1997. *Nature's Services.* Island Press, Washington, DC.

Dame, R. F. 1996. *Ecology of Bivalves: An Ecosystem Approach.* CRC Press, Boca Raton, FL.

Davis, M. B. and D. B. Botkin. 1985. Sensitivity of cool-temperate forests and their fossil pollen record to rapid temperature change. *Quart. Res.* 23: 327–340.

Day, R. H., S. M. Murphy, L. N. Smith, J. A. Wiens, G. D. Hayward and E. J. Harner. 1997. Effects of the *Exxon Valdez* oil spill on habitat use by birds in Prince William Sound, Alaska. *Ecol. Applic.* 7: 593–613.

Dayton, P. K., S. F. Thrush, M. T. Agardy and R. J. Hoffman. 1995. Environmental effects of marine fishing. *Aquat. Cons. Mar. Freshw. Ecosyst.* 5: 205–232.

Dayton, P. K., M. J. Tegner, P. B. Edwards and K. L. Riser. 1998. Sliding baselines, ghosts, and reduced expectations in kelp forest communities. *Ecol. Applic.* 8: 309–322.

DeLong, R. I., W. G. Gilmartin and J. G. Simpson. 1973. Premature births in California sea lions: Association with high organochlorine pollutants level. *Science* 181: 1168–1170.

Dennison, W. C. and R. S. Alberte. 1982. Photosynthetic responses of *Zostera marina* L. (eelgrass) to *in situ* manipulations of light intensity. *Oecologia* 55: 137–144.

Diaz, R. J. and R. Rosenberg. 1995. Marine benthic hypoxia: A review of its ecological effects and the behavioural responses of benthic macrofauna. *Oceanogr. Mar. Biol. Ann. Rev.* 33: 245–303.

Domning, D. P. 1978. Sirenian evolution in the North Pacific Ocean. *Univ. Calif. Publ. Geol. Sci.* 118: 1–176.

Done, T. J. 1992. Phase shifts in coral reef communities and their ecological significance. *Hydrobiologia* 247: 121–132.

Duggins, D. O., C. A. Simenstad and J. A. Estes. 1989. Magnification of secondary production by kelp detritus in coastal marine ecosystems. *Science* 245: 170–173.

Elmgren, R. 1989. Man's impact on the ecosystem of the Baltic Sea: Energy flows today and at the turn of the century. *Ambio* 18: 326–332.

Engel, J. and R. G. Kvitek. 1995. Effects of trawling on a benthic community in Monterey Bay Marine Sanctuary. *Cons. Biol.* 12: 1204–1214.

Estes, J. A. 1991. Catastrophes and conservation: Lessons from sea otters and the *Exxon Valdez. Science* 254: 1596.

Estes, J. A. 1996. The influence of large, mobile predators in aquatic food webs: Examples from sea otters and kelp forests. In S. P. R. Greenstreet and M. L. Tasker (eds.), *Aquatic Predators and their Prey,* pp.65–72. Fishing News Books, Oxford.

Estes, J. A. 1998. Concerns about the rehabilitation of oiled wildlife. *Cons. Biol.* 12: 1156–1157.

Estes, J. A. and J. F. Palmisano. 1974. Sea otters: Their role in structuring nearshore communities. *Science* 185: 1058–1060.

Estes, J. A. and G. R. VanBlaricom. 1985. Sea otters and shellfisheries. In R. H. Beverton, D. Lavigne and J. Beddington (eds.), *Conflicts Between Marine Mammals and Fisheries,* pp. 187–235. Allen and Unwin, London.

Estes, J. A., M. T. Tinker, T. M. Williams and D. F. Doak. 1998. Killer whale predation on sea otters linking coastal with oceanic ecosystems. *Science* 282: 473–476.

FAO. 1993. *Fisheries Series No. 40,* Fisheries Statistics Series No. 111, FAO, Rome.

Fels, L. M. 1999. Risk assessment of nephrotoxicity of cadmium. *Renal Failure* 21: 275–81.

Finkelstein, Y., M. E. Markowitz and J. F. Rosen. 1998. Low-level lead-induced neurotoxicity in children: An update on central nervous system effects. *Brain Res. Rev.* 27: 168–176.

Fitt, W. K., H. J. Spero, J. Halas, M. W. White and J. W. Porter. 1993. Recovery of the coral *Montastrea annularis* in the Florida Keys after the 1987 Caribbean "bleaching event." *Coral Reefs* 12: 57–64.

Fitzgerald, W. F. 1997. Biogeochemical cycling of mercury in the marine environment. In A. Sigel and H. Sigel (eds.), *Metal Ions in Biological Systems: Mercury and Its Effects on Environment and Biology.* Marcel Dekker, Inc., New York.

Flegal, A. R. and C. C. Patterson. 1983. Vertical concentration profiles of lead in the central Pacific at 15N and 20S. *Earth Planet. Sci. Letters* 64: 19–2.

Flegal, A. R., T. F. Duda and S. Niemeyer. 1989. High gradients of lead isotopic composition in northeast Pacific upwelling filaments. *Nature* 339: 458–460.

Flegal, A. R., D. L. Garrison and S. Niemeyer. 1993. Lead isotope disequilibria between plankton assemblages and surface waters reflect life cycle strategies of coastal populations within a northeast Pacific upwelling regime. *Limn. Oceanogr.* 38: 670–678.

Foster, M. S. and D. R. Schiel. 1985. *The Ecology of Giant Kelp Forests in California: A Community Profile*. U.S. Fish and Wildlife Service, Biological Report 85(7.2).

Fowler, B. 1996. The nephropathology of metals. In L. Chang (ed.), *Toxicology of Metals*, pp. 721–729. CRC Press, Boca Raton, FL.

Frank, P. W. 1982. Effects of winter feeding on limpets by black oystercatchers, *Haematopus bachmani*. *Ecology* 46: 831–844.

Fraser, W. R. and D. G. Ainley. 1986. Ice edges and seabird occurrence in Antarctica. *Bioscience* 36: 258–263.

Fretwell, S. D. 1987. Food chain dynamics: The central theory of ecology? *Oikos* 20: 169–185.

Furness, R. W., K. Ensor and A. V. Hudson. 1992. The use of fishery waste by gull populations around the British Isles. *Ardea* 80: 105–113.

Gaines, S. and J. Roughgarden. 1985. Larval settlement rate: A leading determinant of variation in an ecological community of the marine intertidal zone. *Proc. Natl. Acad. Sci. U.S.* 82: 3707–3711.

Gambell, R. 1973. Some effects of exploitation in reproduction of whales. *J. Reprod. Fert., Suppl.* 19: 533–553.

Garcia, S. and C. Newton. 1998. Global trends in fisheries management. *Amer. Fish. Soc. Monogr.*

Garthe, S., K. (S. J.) Camphuysen and R. W. Furness. 1996. Amounts of discards by commercial fisheries and their significance as food for seabirds in the North Sea. *Mar. Ecol. Prog. Ser.* 136: 1–11.

Gates, R. D., G. Baghdasarian and L. Muscatine. 1992. Temperature stress causes host cell detachment in symbiotic cnidarians: Implications for coral bleaching. *Biol. Bull.* 182: 324–332.

Gattuso, J.-P., M. Frankignoulle, I. Bourge, S. Romaine and R. W. Buddemeier. 1998. Effect of calcium carbonate saturation of seawater on coral calcification. *Global and Planetary Change* 18: 37–46.

Gleason, D. F. and G. M. Wellington. 1993. Ultraviolet radiation and coral bleaching. *Nature* 365: 836–838.

Glynn, P. W. 1983. Extensive "bleaching" and death of reef corals on the Pacific coast of Panama. *Environ. Conserv.* 10: 149–154.

Glynn, P. W. 1984. Widespread coral mortality and the 1982–83 El Niño warming event. *Environ. Conserv.* 11: 133–146.

Glynn, P. W. 1990. Coral mortality and disturbances to coral reefs in the tropical Eastern Pacific. In P. W. Glynn (ed.), *Global Ecological Consequences of the 1982–83 El Niño-Southern Oscillation*. Elsevier, Amsterdam.

Glynn, P. W. 1991. Coral reef bleaching in the 1980s and possible connections with global warming. *Trends Ecol. Evol.* 6: 175–179.

Glynn, P. W. 1993. Coral reef bleaching: Ecological perspectives. *Coral Reefs* 12: 1–17.

Goreau, T. F. 1964. Mass expulsion of zooxanthellae from Jamaican reef communities after Hurricane Flora. *Science* 145: 383–386.

Gregor, D., C. Teixeira and C. Rowsell. 1996. Deposition of atmospherically transported polychlorinated biphenyls in the Canadian arctic. *Chemosphere* 33: 227–244.

Hahn, T. and M. Denny. 1989. Tenacity-mediated selective predation by oystercatchers on intertidal limpets and its role in maintaining habitat partitioning by '*Collisella*' *scabra* and *Lottia digitalis*. *Mar. Ecol. Prog. Ser.* 53: 1–10.

Hairston, N. G., F. E. Smith and L. B. Slobodkin. 1960. Community structure, population control, and competition. *Amer. Nat.* 94: 421–425.

Hall, S. J. 1999. *The Effects of Fishing on Ecosystems and Communities*. Blackwell, Oxford.

Hallegraef, P. J. 1993. A review of harmful algae blooms and their apparent global increase. *Phycologia* 32: 79–99.

Halpern, B. In press. Marine reserves: Do they work? *Ecol. Applic.*

Hansen, J., M. Sato, J. Glascoe and R. Ruedy. 1998. A common-sense climate index: Is climate changing noticeably? *Proc. Natl. Acad. Sci. U.S.* 95: 4113–4120.

Hanski, I. 1999. *Metapopulation Ecology*. Oxford University Press, Oxford.

Harriott, V. J. 1985. Mortality rates of scleractinian corals before and during a mass bleaching event. *Mar. Ecol. Prog. Ser.* 21: 81–88.

Hay, M. E. 1984. Patterns of fish and urchin grazing on Caribbean coral reefs: Are previous results typical? *Ecology* 65: 446–454.

Herman, S. G., R. L. Garrett and R. L. Judd. 1969. Pesticides and the western grebe. A study of pesticide survival and trophic concentration at Clear Lake, Lake County, California. In M. W. Miller and G. C. Berg (eds.), *Chemical Fallout. Current Research on Persistent Pesticides*. Charles C. Thomas, Springfield, IL.

Hobson, K. A. and H. E. Welch. 1992. Determination of trophic relationships within a high arctic marine food web using δC^{13} and δN^{15} analysis. *Mar. Ecol. Prog. Ser.* 84: 9–18.

Hockey, P. A. R. and G. M. Branch. 1984. Oystercatchers and limpets: Impact and implications. A preliminary assessment. *Ardea* 72: 199–206.

Hoegh-Guldberg, O. 1999. Climate change, coral bleaching, and the future of the world's coral reefs. *Mar. Freshw. Res.* 50: 839–866.

Hoegh-Guldberg, O. and G. J. Smith. 1989. The effects of sudden changes in temperature, light and salinity on the population density and export of zooxanthellae from the reef corals *Stylophora pistillata* Esper and *Seriatopora hystrix* Dana. *J. Exp. Mar. Biol. Ecol.* 129: 279–303.

Hoetzel A. R., M. Dahlheim and S. J. Stern. 1998. Low genetic variation among killer whales (*Orcinus orca*) in the Eastern North Pacific, and genetic differentiation between foraging specialists. *J. Hered.* 89: 121–128.

Houghton, J. T., L. G. Meira Filho, B. A. Callender, N. Harris, A. Kattenberg and K. Maskell (eds.). 1996. *Climate Change 1995—The Science of Climate Change: Contributions of Working Group 1 to the Second Assessment Report of the Inter Governmental Panel on Climate Change*. Cambridge University Press, New York.

Hughes, T. P. 1994. Catastrophes, phase shifts and large-scale degradation of a Caribbean coral reef. *Science* 265: 1547–1551.

Hughes, T. P. 1996. Demographic approaches to community dynamics: A coral reef example. *Ecology* 77: 2256–2260.

Hughes, T. P., A. H. Baird, E. A. Dinsdale, N. A. Moltschaniwsky, M. S. Pratchett, J. E. Tanner and B. L. Lewis. 1999. Patterns of recruitment and abundance of corals along the Great Barrier Reef. *Nature* 397: 59–63.

Hunter, M. D. and P. W. Price. 1992. Playing chutes and ladders: Heterogeneity and the relative roles of bottom-up and top-down forces in natural communities. *Ecology* 73: 724–732.

Huntley, M. E., M. D. G. Lopez and D. M. Karl. 1991. Top predators in the Southern Ocean: A major leak in the biological carbon pump. *Science* 253: 64–66.

Hutchins, D. A., G. R. Ditullio, Y. Zhang and K. W. Bruland. 1998. An iron limitation mosaic in the California upwelling regime. *Limn. Oceanogr.* 43: 1037–1054.

Imbrie, J. and K. P. Imbrie. 1979. *Ice Ages: Solving the Mystery*. Enslow Publishers, Short Hills, NJ.

Imbrie, J. and J. Z. Imbrie. 1980. Modeling the climatic response to orbital variations. *Science* 207: 943–953.

Irlandi, E. A. and M. K. Crawford. 1997. Habitat linkages: The effect of subtidal saltmarshes and adjacent subtidal habitats on abundance, movement, and growth of an estuarine fish. *Oecologia* 110: 231–236.

Iwata, H. S., S. Tanabe, N. Sakai and R. Tatsukawa. 1993. Distribution of persistent organochlorines in the oceanic air and surface seawater and the role of ocean on their global transport and fate. *Environ. Sci. Technol.* 27: 1080–1098.

Jaap, W. 1979. Observations on zooxanthellae expulsion at Middle Sambo Reef, Florida Keys. *Bull. Mar. Sci.* 29: 414–422.

Jackson, J. B. C. 1997. Reefs since Columbus. *Coral Reefs* 16 (SUPPL): S23–S32.

Jarman, W. M., S. A. Burns, R. R. Chang, R. D. Stephens, R. J. Norstrom, M. Simon and J. Linthicum. 1993. Determination of PCDDs, PCDFs, and PCBs in California peregrine falcons (*Falco peregrinus*) and their eggs. *Environ. Toxicol. Chem.* 12: 105–114.

Jennings, S. and M. J. Kaiser. 1998. The effects of fishing on marine ecosystems. *Adv. Mar. Biol.* 34: 201–352.

Jessup, D. A. 1998. Rehabilitation of oiled wildlife. *Cons. Biol.* 12: 1153–1155.

Jones, C. G., J. H. Lawton and M. Shachak. 1994. Organisms as ecosystem engineers. *Oikos* 69: 373–386.

Jones, J. B. 1992. Environmental impact of trawling on the seabed: A review. *New Zealand J. Mar. Freshw. Res.* 26: 59–67.

Kelleher, G., C. Bleakley and S. Wells. 1995. *A Global System of Marine Protected Areas, Vol 1*. World Bank, Washington, DC.

King, J. C. 1984. Recent climate variability in the vicinity of the Antarctic Peninsula. *Internatl. J. Climatol.* 14: 357–369.

Kleypas J. A., R. W. Buddemeier, D. Archer, J. P. Gattuso, C. Langdon and B. N. Opdyke.

1999. Geochemical consequences of increased atmospheric carbon dioxide on coral reefs. *Science* 284: 118–20.

Lapointe, B. E. 1997. Nutrient thresholds for bottom-up control of macroalgal blooms on coral reefs in Jamaica and southeast Florida. *Limn. Oceanogr.* 42: 1119–1131.

Lapointe, B. E., M. M. Littler and D. E. Littler. 1992. Nutrient availability to marine macrophytes in siliciclastic versus carbonate-rich coastal waters. *Estuaries* 15: 75–82.

Larkin, P. A. 1977. An epitaph for the concept of maximum sustained yield. *Trans. Amer. Fish. Soc.* 106: 1–11.

Larkum, A. W. D. and K. Koop. 1997. ENCORE, algal productivity, and possible paradigm shifts. *Proc. 8th Internatl. Coral Reef Symp.* 1: 881–884.

Lasker, R. 1975. Field criteria for survival of anchovy larvae: The relation between inshore chlorophyll maximum layers and successful first feeding. *Fish. Bull.* 73: 453–462.

Laws, R. M. 1977. Seals and whales in the Southern Ocean. *Philos. Trans. Roy. Soc. Lond., B.* 279:81–96.

Laws, R. M. (ed.). 1984. *Antarctic Ecology*, Vol. 2. Academic Press, London.

Leatherman, S. P., K. Khang and B. C. Douglas. 2000. Sea level rise shown to drive coastal erosion. *EOS Trans.* 27: 55–58.

Le Boeuf, B. J. and M. Bonnel. 1971. DDT in California sea lions. *Nature* 234: 108–110.

Lenihan, H. S. 1999. Physical-biological coupling on oyster reefs: How habitat structure influences individual performance. *Ecol. Monogr.* 69: 251–275.

Lenihan, H. S. and C. H. Peterson. 1998. How habitat degradation through fishery disturbance enhances impacts of hypoxia on oyster reefs. *Ecol. Applic.* 8: 128–140.

Lenihan, H. S., F. Micheli, S. W. Shelton and C. H. Peterson. 1999. The influence of multiple environmental stressors on susceptibility to parasites: An experimental determination with oysters. *Limn. Oceanogr.* 44: 910–924.

Lenihan, H. S., C. H. Peterson, J. E. Byers, J. H. Grabowski, G. W. Thayer and D. Colby. 2001. Cascading of habitat degradation: Oyster reefs invaded by refugee fishes escaping stress. *Ecol. Applic.*: in press.

Lesser, M. P., W. R. Stochaj, D. W. Tapley and J. M. Schick. 1990. Bleaching in coral reef anthozoans: Effects of irradiance, ultraviolet radiation, and temperature on the activities of protective enzymes against active oxygen. *Coral Reefs* 8: 225–232.

Lessios, H. A. 1995. *Diadema antillarum* 10 years after mass mortality: Still rare despite help from a competitor. *Proc. Roy. Soc. Lond. B* 259: 331–337.

Levin, S. A. 1992. The problem of pattern and scale in ecology. *Ecology* 73: 1943–1967.

Lewis, S. M. 1986. The role of herbivorous fishes in the organization of a Caribbean reef community. *Ecol. Monogr.* 56: 183–200.

Lieberg-Clark, P., C. E. Bacon, S. A. Burns, W. M. Jarman and B. J. Le Boeuf. 1995. DDT in California sea-lions: A follow-up study after twenty years. *Mar. Poll. Bull.* 30: 744–745.

Lindberg, D. R., J. A. Estes and K. I. Warheit. 1998. Human influences on trophic cascades along rocky shores. *Ecol. Applic.* 8: 880–890.

Loughlin, T. R. 1994. *Marine mammals and the Exxon Valdez.* Academic Press, San Diego.

Lubchenco, J., A. M. Olson, L. B. Brubaker, S. R. Carpenter, M. M. Holland, S. P. Hubbell, S. A. Levin, J. A. MacMahon, P. A. Matson, J. M. Melillo, H. A. Mooney, C. H. Peterson, H. R. Pulliam, L. A. Real, P. J. Regal and P. G. Risser. 1991. The sustainable biosphere initiative: An ecological research agenda. *Ecology* 72: 371–412.

Ludwig, D., R. Hilborn and C. Walters. 1993. Uncertainty, resource exploitation, and conservation: Lessons from history. *Science* 260: 17–18.

MacArthur, R. H. and J. W. MacArthur. 1961. On bird species diversity. *Ecology* 42: 594–598.

Mackas, D. L., R. Goldblatt and A. G. Lewis. 1998. Interdecadal variation in developmental timing of *Neocalanus plumchrus* populations at Ocean Station P in the subarctic North Pacific. *Can. J. Fish. Aquat. Sci.* 55: 1878–1893.

Malone, T. C. 1992. Effects of water column processes on dissolved oxygen, nutrients, phtyoplankton, and zooplankton. In D. E. Smith, M. Leffler and G. Mackiernam (eds.), *Oxygen Dynamics in the Chesapeake Bay, a Synthesis of Recent Research*, pp. 61–112. Maryland Sea Grant, College Park, MD.

Manabe, S., R. J. Stouffer and M. J. Spelman. 1994. Response of a coupled ocean-atmosphere model to increasing atmospheric carbon dioxide. *Ambio* 23: 44–49.

Maragos, J. E., M. P. Crosby and J. W. McManus. 1996. Coral reefs and biodiversity: A critical and threatened relationship. *Oceanography* 9: 83–99.

Martin, J. H. K. H. Coale, K. S. Johnson, S. E. Fitzwater, R. M. Gordon, S. J. Tanner, C. N. Hunter, V. A. Elrod, J. L. Nowicki, T. L. Coley, R. T. Barber, S. Lindley, A. J. Watson, K. Van Scoy, C. S. Law, M. I. Liddicoat, R. Ling, T. Stanton et al. 1994. Testing the iron hypothesis in ecosystems of the equatorial Pacific Ocean. *Nature* 371: 123–129.

Martin, P. S. 1973. The discovery of America. *Science* 179: 969–974.

Mason, R. P. 1996. Sources, sinks and biogeochemical cycling of mercury in the ocean. In W. Baeyens, R. Ebinghaus and O. Vasiliev (eds.), *NATO ASI Series, Series 2, Environment; Global and Regional Mercury Cycles: Sources, Fluxes and Mass Balances.* Kluwer Academic Publishers, Dordrecht, Netherlands.

Mason, R. P., K. R. Rolfhus and W. F. Fitzgerald. 1995. Methylated and elemental mercury cycling in surface and deep ocean waters of the North Atlantic. *Water Air Soil Poll.* 80: 665–677.

Matkin, C. O., D. Scheel, G. Ellis, L. Barrett-Lennard, H. Jurk and E. Saulitis. 1999. *Comprehensive killer whale investigation, Exxon Valdez Oil Spill Restoration Project Final Report (Restoration Project 98012)*, North Gulf Oceanic Society, Homer, Alaska.

Matson, P. A., W. H. McDowell, A. R. Townsend and P. M. Vitousek. 1999. The globalization of N deposition: Ecosystem consequences in tropical environments. *Biogeochem.* 46: 67–83.

May, R. M., J. R. Beddington, C. W. Clarke, S. J. Holt and R. M. Laws. 1979. Management of multi-species fisheries. *Science* 205: 267–277.

McClanahan, T. R. and N. A. Muthinga. 1998. An ecological shift in a remote coral atoll of Belize over 25 years. *Environ. Conserv.* 25: 122–130.

McClanahan, T. R., N. A. Muthiga, A. T. Kamukuru, H. Machano and R. W. Kiambo. 1999. The effects of marine parks and fishing on coral reefs of northern Tanzania. *Biol. Cons.* 89: 161–182.

McClelland, J. W. and I. Valiela. 1998. Changes in food web structure under the influence of increased anthropogenic nitrogen inputs to estuaries. *Mar. Ecol. Prog. Ser.* 168: 259–271.

McCook, L. J. 1999. Macroalgae, nutrients and phase shifts on coral reefs: Scientific issues and management consequences for the Great Barrier Reef. *Coral Reefs* 18: 357–367.

McManus, J. W. 1996. Social and economic aspects of reef fisheries and their management. In N. Polunin and C. Roberts (eds.), *Coral Reef Fisheries.* Chapman and Hall, New York.

McPhaden, M. J. 1999. Genesis and evolution of the 1997–98 El Niño. *Science* 283: 950–954.

Menditto, A. and L. Turrio-Baldassarri. 1999. Environmental and biological monitoring of endocrine disrupting chemicals. *Chemosphere* 39: 1301–1307.

Menge, B. A. 1995. Indirect effects in marine rocky intertidal interaction webs: Patterns and importance. *Ecol. Monogr.* 65: 21–74.

Menge, B. A., E. L. Berlow, C. A. Blanchette, S. A. Navarrete, and S. B. Yamada. 1994. The keystone species concept: Variation in interaction strength in a rocky intertidal habitat. *Ecol. Monogr.* 64: 249–286.

Micheli, F. 1997. Effects of predator foraging behavior on patterns of prey mortality in marine soft bottoms. *Ecol. Monogr.* 67: 203–224.

Micheli, F. 1999. Eutrophication, fisheries, and consumer-resource dynamics in marine pelagic ecosystems. *Science* 285: 1396–1398.

Micheli, F. and C. H. Peterson. 1999. Estuarine vegetated habitats as corridors for predator movements. *Cons. Biol.* 13: 869–881.

Miller, M. W., M. E. Hay, S. L. Miller, D. Malone, E. E. Sotka and A. M. Szmant. 1999. Effects of nutrients vs herbivores on reef algae: A new method for manipulating nutrients on coral reefs. *Limn. Oceanogr.* 44: 1748–1861.

Minerals Management Service. 1989. *Mercury in the Marine Environment: Workshop Proceedings, 29 November to 1 December 1988*, Sheraton Anchorage Hotel, Anchorage, Alaska. U.S. Dept. of the Interior, Minerals Management Service, Alaska OCS Regional Office, Anchorage, Alaska.

Moline, M. A. and B. B. Prezelin. 1996. Long-term monitoring and analyses of physical factors regulating variability in coastal

Antarctic phytoplankton biomass, in situ productivity and taxonomic composition over subseasonal, seasonal and interannual time scales. *Mar. Ecol. Prog. Ser.* 145: 143–160.

Muir, D. C. G., R. J. Norstrom and M. Simon. 1988. Organochlorine contaminants in Arctic marine food chains: Accumulation of specific polychlorinated biphenyls and chlordane-related compounds. *Environ. Sci. Technol.* 22: 1071–1079.

Muir, D. C. G., B. T. Wagemann, B. T. Hargrave, D. J. Thomas, D. B. Peakall and R. J. Norstrom. 1992. Arctic marine ecosystem contamination. *Sci. Total Environ.* 122: 75–134.

Murdoch, W. W. 1980. *The Poverty of Nations: The Political Economy of Hunger and Population.* John's Hopkins University Press, Baltimore, MD.

Murphy, E. J., A. Clarke, C. Symon and J. Priddle. 1995. Temporal variation in Antarctic sea ice: Analysis of a long-term fast-ice record from the South Orkney Islands. *Deep Sea Res.* 42: 1045–1062.

Murray, S. N., R. F. Ambrose, J. A. Bohnsack, L. W. Botsford, M. H. Carr, G. E. Davis, P. K. Dayton, D. Gotshall, D. R. Gunderson, M. A. Hixon, J. Lubchenco, M. Mangel, A. MacCall, D. A. McArdle, J. C. Ogden, J. Roughgarden, R. M. Starr, M. J. Tegner and M. M. Yoklavich. 1999. No-take reserve networks: Protection for fishery populations and marine ecosystems. *Fish. Manage.* 24: 11–21.

National Marine Fisheries Service. 1999. *Report to Congress.* International Dolphin Conservation Program Act, 25 March 1999. http://swfsc.ucsd.edu/mmd/congress/congress.htm

Nelson, D. M., J. J. Goering and D. Boisseau. 1981. Consumption and regeneration of silicic acid in three coastal upwelling systems. In F. A. Richards (ed.), *Coastal Upwelling,* pp. 242–256. American Geophysical Union, Washington, DC.

Nelson, W. G. 1993. Beach restoration in the southeastern US: Environmental effects and biological monitoring. *Ocean Coast. Manage.* 19: 157–182.

Newell, R. I. E. 1988. Ecological changes in Chesapeake Bay: Are they the result of overharvesting the American oyster? In M. P. Lynch and E. C. Krome (eds.), *Understanding the Estuary: Advances in Chesapeake Bay Research,* pp. 536–546. Publ. 129, Chesapeake Bay Research Consortium, Baltimore, MD.

Nichols, F. H., J. K. Thompson and L. E. Schemel. 1990. Remarkable invasion of San Francisco Bay (California, USA) by the Asian clam *Potamocorbula amurensis.* 2. Displacement of a former community. *Mar. Ecol. Prog. Ser.* 66: 95–101.

Nixon, S. W. 1995. Coastal marine eutrophication: A definition, social causes, and future concerns. *Ophelia* 41: 199–219.

Norstrom, R. J., M. Simon, D. C. G. Muir and R. E. Schweinsburg. 1988. Organochlorine contaminants in Arctic marine food chains: Identification, geographical distribution, and temporal trends in polar bears. *Environ. Sci. Technol.* 22: 1063–1071.

NRC (National Research Council). 1987. *Responding to Changes in Sea Level.* National Academy Press, Washington, DC.

NRC (National Research Council). 1988. *Saving Cape Hatteras Lighthouse from the sea: Options and Policy Implications.* National Academy Press, Washington, DC.

NRC (National Research Council). 1994. *Improving the Management of U.S. Marine Fisheries.* National Academy Press, Washington, DC.

NRC (National Research Council). 1996. *The Bering Sea Ecosystem.* National Academy Press, Washington, DC.

Oliver, J. S. and P. N. Slattery. 1985. Destruction and opportunity on the sea floor: Effects of gray whale feeding. *Ecology* 66: 1965–1975.

Oliver, J. S., R. G. Kvitek and P. N. Slattery. 1985. Walrus feeding disturbance: Scavenging habitats and recolonization of the Bering Sea benthos. *J. Exp. Mar. Biol. Ecol.* 91: 233–246.

Pace, M. L., J. J. Cole, S. R. Carpenter and J. F. Kitchell. 1999. Trophic cascades revealed in diverse ecosystems. *Trends Ecol. Evol.* 14: 483–488.

Paddack, M. J. and J. A. Estes. 2000. Kelp forest fish populations in marine reserves and adjacent exploited areas of central California. *Ecol. Applic.* (in press).

Paerl, H. W. 1985. Enhancement of marine primary productivity by acid rain. *Nature* 316: 747–749.

Paerl, H. W., J. L. Pinckney, J. M. Fear and B. L. Peierls. 1998. Ecosystem responses to internal and watershed organic matter loading: Consequences for hypoxia in the eutrophying Neuse River Estuary, North Carolina, USA. *Mar. Ecol. Prog. Ser.* 166: 17–25.

Paine, R. T. 1966. Food web complexity and species diversity. *Amer. Nat.* 100: 65–75.

Paine, R. T. 1988. Food webs: Road maps of interactions or grist for theoretical development. *Ecology* 69: 1648–1654.

Paine, R. T. 1992. Food-web analysis through field measurement of per-capita interaction strength. *Nature* 355: 73–75.

Paine R. T., J. L. Ruesink, A. Sun, E. L. Soulanille, M. J. Wonham, C. D. G. Harley, D. R. Brumbaugh and D. L. Secord. 1996. Trouble on oiled waters: Lessons from the *Exxon Valdez* oil spill. *Ann. Rev. Ecol. Syst.* 27: 197–235.

Palmer, A. R. 1979. Fish predation and the evolution of gastropod shell structure: Experimental and geographic evidence. *Evol.* 33: 697–713.

Parker, R. O.,and R. L. Dixon. 1998. Changes in a North Carolina reef fish community after 15 years of intense fishing—Global warming implications. *Trans. Amer. Fish. Soc.* 127: 908–920.

Pauly, D., V. Christensen, J. Dalsgaard, R. Froese and F. Torres, Jr. 1998a. Fishing down marine food webs. *Science* 279: 860–863.

Pauly, D., A. W. Trites, E. Capuli and V. Christensen. 1998b. Diet composition and trophic levels of marine mammals. *ICES J. Mar. Sci.* 55: 467–481.

Pearse, J. S. and A. H. Hines. 1987. Long term population dynamics of sea urchins in central California kelp forest: Rare recruitment and rapid decline. *Mar. Ecol. Prog. Ser.* 39: 279–283.

Peters, R. L., and T. E. Lovejoy. 1994. *Global Warming and Biological Diversity.* Yale University Press, New Haven, CT.

Peterson, C. H. 1991. Intertidal zonation of marine invertebrates in sand and mud. *Amer. Sci.* 79: 236–249.

Peterson, C. H. 2001. The *Exxon Valdez* oil spill in Alaska: Acute, indirect and chronic effects on the ecosystem. *Adv. Mar. Biol.* 39: 1–103.

Peterson, C. H., H. C. Summerson and S. R. Fegley. 1987. Ecological consequences of mechanical harvesting of clams. *Fish. Bull.* 85: 281–298.

Peterson, C. H., R. B. Barber and G. A. Skilleter. 1993. Global warming and coastal ecosystem response: How northern and southern hemispheres may differ in the eastern Pacific Ocean. In H. A. Mooney, E. R. Fuentes and B. I. Kronberg (eds.), *Earth System Responses to Global Change: Contrasts Between North and South America,* pp. 17–34. Academic Press, New York.

Peterson, C. H., D. H. M. Hickerson and G. Grissom Johnson. 2000a. Short-term consequences of nourishment and bulldozing on the dominant large invertebrates of a sandy beach. *J. Coast. Res.* 16: 368–378.

Peterson, C. H., H. C. Summerson, E. Thomson, H. S. Lenihan, J. Grabowski, L. Manning, F. Micheli and G. Johnson. 2000b. Synthesis of linkages between benthos and fish as a key to protecting essential fish habitat. *Bull. Mar. Sci.:* in press.

Pielou, E. C. 1991. *After the Ice Age.* University of Chicago Press, Chicago, IL.

Pihl, L., S. P. Baden, R. J. Diaz and L. C. Schaffner. 1992. Hypoxia-induced structural changes in the diet of bottom-feeding fish and Crustacea. *Mar. Biol.* 112: 349–361.

Pilkey, O. H., and H. L. Wright. 1989. Seawalls versus beaches. In N. C. Krauss and O. H. Pilkey (eds.), The Effects of Seawalls on Beaches. *J. Coast. Res.,* Special Issue 112: 349–361.

Pimm, S. L. 1982. *Food webs.* Chapman and Hall, New York.

Pimm, S. L. 1993. Discussion: Understanding indirect effects: Is it possible? In J. E. Cohen, and K. Iwasaki (eds.), *Mutualism and Community Organization: Behavioural, Theoretical and Food Web Approaches,* pp. 199–210. H. Kawanabe, Oxford University Press, Oxford.

Pinckney, J. L., D. F. Millie, K. E. Howe, H. W. Paerl and J. P. Hurley. 1996. Flow scintillation counting of ^{14}C-labeled microalgal photosynthetic pigments. *J. Plankton Res.* 18: 1867–1880.

Polis G. A. and D. R. Strong. 1996. Food web complexity and community dynamics. *Amer. Nat.* 147: 813–846.

Polis, G., W. B. Anderson and R. D. Holt. 1997. Towards an integration of landscape and food web ecology: The dynamics of spatially subsidized food webs. *Ann. Rev. Ecol. Syst.* 29: 289–316.

Potts, D. C. 1977. Suppression of coral populations by filamentous algae within damselfish territories. *J. Exp. Mar. Biol. Ecol.* 28: 207–216.

Power, M. E., D. Tilman, J. A. Estes, B. A. Menge, W. J. Bond, L. S. Mills, G. Daily, J. C. Castilla, J. Lubchenco and R. T. Paine. 1996. Challenges in the quest for keystones. *Bioscience* 46: 609–620.

Prince, P. A., P. Rothery, J. P. Croxall and A. G. Wood. 1994. Population dynamics of black-browed and grey-headed albatrosses *Diomedea melanophris* and *D. chrysostoma* at Bird Island, South Georgia. *Ibis* 36: 50–71.

Pulliam, H. R. 1988. Sources, sinks and population regulation. *Amer. Nat.* 132: 652–661.

Ratcliffe, D. A. 1970. Changes attributable to pesticides in egg breakage frequency and eggshell thickness in some British birds. *J. Appl. Ecol.* 7: 67–115.

Reise, K. 1982. Long-term changes in the macrobenthic invertebrate fauna of the Wadden Sea: Are polychaetes about to take over? *Neth. J. Sea Res.* 16: 29–36.

Renaud, M. L. 1986. Hypoxia in Louisiana coastal waters during 1983: implications for the fisheries. *Fish. Bull.* 84: 19–26.

Rhoads, D. C., P. L. McCall and J. Y. Yingst. 1978. Disturbance and production on the estuarine seafloor. *Amer. Sci.* 66: 577–586.

Richards, A. H. 1994. Problems of drift-net fisheries in the South-Pacific. *Mar. Poll. Bull.* 29: 106–111.

Rizebrough, R. W., W. Walker II, T. T. Schmidt, B. W. de Lappe and C. W. Connors. 1976. Transfer of chlorinated biphenyls to Antarctica. *Nature* 264: 738–739.

Rolfhus, K. R. and W. F. Fitzgerald. 1995. Linkages between atmospheric mercury deposition and the methylmercury content of marine fish. *Water Air Soil Poll.* 80: 291–297.

Rosen, D. A. S. and A. W. Trites, 1999. The bioenergetic interactions of thermoregulation, activity, and digestion in Steller sea lions, *Eumetopias jubatus*. *Comp. Biochem. Phys.* Part A 124: S101.

Rothschild, B. J. 1986. *Dynamics of marine fish populations*, Harvard University Press, Cambridge, MA.

Rothschild, B. J. and T. R. Osborn. 1988. Small-scale turbulence and plankton encounter rates. *J. Plankton Res.* 10: 465–474.

Rothschild, B. J., J. S. Ault, P. Goulletquer and M. Héral. 1994. Decline of the Chesapeake Bay oyster population: A century of habitat destruction and overfishing. *Mar. Ecol. Prog. Ser.* 111: 29–39.

Roughgarden, J., S. D. Gaines and H. P. Possingham. 1988. Recruitment dynamics in complex life cycles. *Science* 241: 1460–1466.

Ruddiman, W. F. and A. McIntyre. 1981. Oceanic mechanisms for amplification of the 23,000 year ice-volume cycle. *Science* 212: 617–627.

Russ, G. and A. C. Alcala. 1996. Marine reserves: Rates and patterns of recovery and decline of large predatory fish. *Ecol. Applic.* 6: 947–961.

Safriel, U. N. 1975. The role of vermetid gastropods in the formation of Mediterranean and Atlantic reefs. *Oecologia* 20: 85–101.

Sanford, E. 1999. Regulation of keystone predation by small changes in ocean temperature. *Science* 283: 2095–2097.

Sarokin, D. and J. Schulkin. 1992. The role of pollution in large-scale population disturbances. Part 1: aquatic populations. *Environ. Sci. Technol.* 26: 1476–1484.

Schoener, T. W. 1993. On the relative importance of direct versus indirect effects in ecological communities. In H. Kawanabe, J. E. Cohen, and K. Iwasaki (eds.), *Mutualism and Community Organization: Behavioural, Theoretical and Food Web Approaches*, pp. 365–411. Oxford University Press, Oxford.

Scott., J. M., E. A. Norse, H. Arita., A. Dobson, J. A. Estes, M. Foster, B. Gilbert, D. B. Jensen, R. L. Knight, D. Mattson and M. E. Soulé. 1999. The issue of scale in selecting and designing biological reserves. In M. E. Soulé and J. Terborgh (eds.), *Continental Conservation*, pp. 19–38. Island Press, Washington, DC.

Sebens, K. P. 1994. Biodiversity of coral reefs: What are we losing and why? *Amer. Zool.* 34: 115–133.

Sharp, B. E. 1996. Post-release survival of oiled, cleaned seabirds in North America. *Ibis* 138: 222–228.

Sherman, K., L. M. Alexander and B. D. Gold (eds.). 1990. *Large Marine Ecosystems*, Am. Assoc. Adv. Sci., Washington, DC.

Shiomoto, A., K. Tadokoro, K. Nagasawa and Y. Ishida. 1997. Trophic relations in the subarctic North Pacific ecosystem: Possible feeding effects from pink salmon. *Mar. Ecol. Prog. Ser.* 150: 75–85.

Simenstad, C. A., J. A. Estes and K. W. Kenyon. 1978. Aleuts, sea otters, and alternate stable state communities. *Science* 200: 403–411.

Simonich, S. L. and R. A. Hites. 1995. Global distribution of persistent organochlorine compounds. *Science* 269: 1851–1854.

Sinclair, M. 1988. *Marine Populations. An Essay on Population Regulation and Speciation.* Washington Sea Grant Program, Univ. Washington Press, Seattle, WA.

Smetacek, V., H. J. W. De Baar, U. V. Bathmann, K. Lochte and M. M. Rutgers Van Der Loeff. 1997. Ecology and biogeochemistry of the Antarctic Circumpolar Current during austral spring: A summary of Southern Ocean JGOFS cruise ANT X/6 of R. V. Polarstern. *Deep-Sea Res.* II 44: 1–21.

Smith, D. R. and A. R. Flegal, 1995. Lead in the biosphere: Recent trends. *Ambio* 24: 21–23.

Smith, D. R., S. Niemeyer and A. R. Flegal. 1992. Lead sources to California sea otters: Industrial inputs circumvent natural lead biodepletion mechanisms. *Environ. Res.* 57: 163–174.

Smith, D. R., S. Niemeyer, J. A. Estes and A. R. Flegal. 1990. Stable lead isototopes evidence anthropogenic contamination in Alaskan sea otters. *Environ. Sci. Technol.* 24: 1521–1527.

Smith, W. O. and D. M. Nelson. 1986. Importance of ice edge phytoplankton production in the Southern Ocean. *Bioscience* 36: 251–257.

Soulé, M. E. (ed.) 1987. *Viable Populations for Conservation.* Cambridge University Press, Cambridge, UK.

Soulé, M. E. and J. Terborgh (eds.). 1999. *Continental Conservation.* Island Press, Washington, DC.

Southward, A. J. and E. C. Southward. 1978. Recolonization of rocky shores in Cornwall after the use of toxic dispersants to clean up the Torrey Canyon spill. *J. Fish. Res. Bd. Can.* 35: 682–706.

Stark, P. 1994. Climate warming in the central Antarctic Peninsula area. *Weather* 49: 215–220.

Steele, J. H. 1985. A comparison of terrestrial and marine ecological systems. *Nature* 313: 355–358.

Steinberg, P. D., J. A. Estes and F. C. Winter. 1995. Evolutionary consequences of food chain length in kelp forest communities. *Proc. Natl. Acad. Sci. U.S.* 92: 8145–8148.

Steneck, R S. 1998. Human influences on coastal ecosystems: Does overfishing create trophic cascades? *Trends Ecol. Evol.* 13: 429–430.

Stickle, L. F., N. J. Chura, P. A. Stewart, C. M. Menzie, R. M. Prouty and W. L. Reichel. 1966. Bald eagle pesticides relations. *Trans. North Amer. Wildl. Nat. Resour. Conf.* 31: 190–200.

Talbot, F. H. 1994. Coral reef protected areas: What are they worth? In D. J. Brunkhorst (ed.), *Marine Protected Areas and Biosphere Reserves: Towards a New Paradigm*, pp. 40–44. Australian Nature Conservation Agency, Canberra.

Tanabe, S., H. Iwata and R. Tatsukawa. 1994. Global contamination by persistent organochlorines and their ecological impact on marine mammals. *Sci. Total Environ.* 154: 163–178.

Thayer, G. W., D. A. Wolfe and R. B. Williams. 1975. The impact of man on seagrass systems. *Amer. Sci.* 63: 288–296.

Thomas, S. C., M. Jasienski and F. A. Bazzaz. 1999. Early vs. asymptotic growth responses of herbaceous plants to elevated CO_2. *Ecology* 80: 1552–1567.

Turner, R. E. and N. N. Rabalais. 1994. Coastal eutrophication near the Mississippi River delta. *Nature* 368: 619–621.

Turner R. E., N. Qureshi, N. N. Rabalais, Q. Dortch, J. Dubravko. R. F. Shaw and J. Cope. 1998. Fluctuating silicate:nitrate ratios and coastal plankton food webs. *Proc. Natl. Acad. Sci. U.S.* 95: 13048–13051.

Valiela, I., J. Mclelland, J. Hauxwell, P. J. Behr, D. Hersh and K. Foreman. 1997. Macroalgal blooms in shallow estuaries: Controls and ecophysiological and ecosystem consequences. *Limn. Oceanogr.* 42: 1105–1118.

van Franeker, J. A., U. V. Bathmann and S. Mathot. 1997. Carbon fluxes to Antarctic top predators. *Deep-Sea Res.* II 44: 435–455.

Verity, P. G. and V. Smetacek. 1996. Organism life cycles, predation, and the structure of marine pelagic ecosystems. *Mar. Ecol. Prog. Ser.* 130: 277–293.

Virnstein, R. W. 1977. The importance of predation by crabs and fishes on benthic infauna in Chesapeake Bay. *Ecology* 58: 1199–1217.

Vitousek, P. M., H. A. Mooney, J. Lubchenco and J. M. Melillo. 1997a. Human domination of Earth's ecosystems. *Science* 277: 494–499.

Vitousek, P. M., J. D. Aber, R. H. Howarth, G. E. Likens, P. A. Matson, D. W. Schindler, W. H. Schlesinger and D. G. Tilman. 1997b. Human alteration of the global nitrogen cycle: Source and consequences. *Ecol. Applic.* 7: 737–750.

Walters, C. J. 1986. *Adaptive Management of Renewable Resources.* MacMillan Press, New York.

Walters, C. J., V. Christensen and D. Pauly. 1997. Structuring dynamic models of exploited ecosystems from trophic mass-balance assessments. *Rev. Fish Biol. Fish.* 7: 139–172.

Ware, G. W. 1989. *The Pesticide Book.* 3rd edition. Thomas Publications, Fresno, CA.

Waring, G. T., D. L. Palka, P. J. Clapham, S. Swartz, M. Rossman, T. Cole, K. B. Bisack and L. J. Hansen. 1998. *U.S. Atlantic Marine Mammal Stock Assessments—1998.* NOAA Technical Memorandum, Northeast Fisheries Science Center, Woods Hole, MA.

Watling L. and E. A. Norse. 1998. Disturbance of the seabed by mobile fishing gear: A comparison to forest clearcutting. *Cons. Biol.* 12: 1180–1197.

Watt, J., D. B. Siniff and J. A. Estes. 2000. Interdecadal patterns of population and dietary change in sea otters at Amchitka Island, Alaska. *Oecologia* 124: 289–298.

Wayne, P. M., E. G. Reekie and F. A. Bazzaz. 1998. Elevated CO_2 ameliorates birch response to high temperature and frost stress: Implications for modeling climate-induced geographic range shifts. *Oecologia* 114: 335–342.

Weatherly, J. W., J. E. Walsh and H. J. Zwally. 1991. Antarctic sea ice variations and seasonal air temperature. *J. Geophys. Res.* 96: 15119–15130.

Weimerskirch H., N. Brothers and P. Jouventin. 1997. Population dynamics of wandering albatross *Diomedea exulans* and Amsterdam albatross *D. amsterdamensis* in the Indian Ocean and their relationships with long-line fisheries: Conservation implications. *Biol. Conserv.* 79: 257–270.

Wells, H. W. 1961. The fauna of oyster reefs with special reference to the salinity factor. *Ecol. Monogr.* 31: 239–266.

Wells, J. T. and J. McNinch. 1991. Beach scraping in North Carolina with special reference to its effectiveness during Hurricane Hugo. *J. Coast. Res.,* Special Issue 8: 249–261.

Wharton, J. 1957. *The bounty of the Chesapeake Bay. Fishing in colonial Virginia.* Univ. Virginia Press, Charlottesville, VA.

Whitehead, H. 1998. Cultural selection and genetic diversity in matrilineal whales. *Science* 282: 1708–1711.

Williams, T. M. and R. W. Davis (eds.). 1995. *Emergency Care and Rehabilitation of Oiled Sea Otters: A Guide for Oil Spills Involving Fur-Bearing Marine Mammals.* University of Alaska Press, Fairbanks, AK.

Willson, M. F., S. M. Gende and B. H. Marston. 1998. Fishes and the forest: Expanding perspectives on fish-wildlife interactions. *Bioscience* 48: 455–462.

Wilson, W. H., Jr. 1979. Community structure and species diversity of the sediment reefs constructed by *Petaloproctus socialis* (Polychaeta: Maldanidae). *J. Mar. Res.* 37: 623–641.

Winter, A., R. S. Appeldoorn, A. Bruckner, E. H. Williams, Jr. and C. Goenaga. 1998. Sea surface temperatures and coral reef bleaching off La Parguera, Puerto Rico (northeastern Caribbean Sea). *Coral Reefs* 17: 377–382.

Witman, J. D. and K. P. Sebens. 1992. Regional variation in fish predation intensity: A historical perspective in the Gulf of Maine. *Oecologia* 90: 305–315.

Woodin, S. A. 1976. Refuges, disturbance and community structure: A marine soft-bottom example. *Ecology* 59: 274–284.

Wootton, J. T. 1994. Predicting direct and indirect effects: An integrated approach using experiments and path analysis. *Ecology* 75: 151–165.

Wootton, J. T. 1995. Effects of birds on sea urchins and algae: A lower-intertidal trophic cascade. *Ecoscience* 2: 321–328.

Yodzis, P. 1981. The structure of assembled communities. *J. Theor. Biol.* 92: 103–117.

York, A. E., R. Merrick and T. Loughlin. 1996. An analysis of the Steller sea lion metapopulation in Alaska. In D. R. McCullough (ed.), *Metapopulations and Wildlife Conservation.* Island Press, Washington, DC.

Younes, M. 1999. Specific issues in health risk assessment of endocrine disrupting chemicals and international activities. *Chemosphere* 39: 1253–1257.

chapter 19

The Ecology of Marine Protected Areas

Stephen R. Palumbi

Marine ecology has long since ceased being a spectator sport. The advent of experimental manipulations as a paradigm for ecological investigations on rocky shores established an approach that was much more interactive than the prior mapping surveys of distribution and abundance (Paine 1984). This approach allowed complex interactions to be understood through the sometimes intricate experiments on community composition. Recently, an additional type of involvement has become more common, in which information from ecological studies is used to provide insight to managers of coastal zone areas. The involvement of ecology with environmental policy has come on the heels of increasing revelations that coastal and open ocean habitats are in biological decline and are faced with unprecedented threats (Lubchenco 1998).

In particular, marine fisheries have collapsed all over the world, and at least half of the world's fisheries stocks are now listed as either overfished or fished at capacity (Botsford et al. 1997). The collapse of cod stocks in Atlantic Canada (Hutchings 1995; Walters and Maguire 1996; Myers et al. 1997) and then New England (Ruth and Lindholm 1996), the reduction of multispecies reef fisheries in the Caribbean to nonsubsistence levels (Roberts 1995), the rapid decline in California abalone (Tegner 1993) and sea urchin populations (Tegner 1989), and the serial overfishing of fish communities around the world (Pauly et al. 1998) highlight the serious nature of fisheries problems. In addition, coastal pollution (Paine et al. 1996), overcollecting by people (Castilla 1999), loss of habitat from development (Ruckelshaus and Hayes 1998), invasion of weedy, alien species (Carlton and Geller 1993), and introduction of new marine diseases (Harvell et al. 1999) have combined to threaten the growth or even maintenance of many of the world's coral reefs, wetlands, estuaries, mangroves, seagrass beds, and rocky shores (see Ruckelshaus and Hayes 1998 for review).

These threats have changed the economic and political landscape in which marine ecology is done, and they have demanded crucial shifts in the focus of basic ecological research (Lubchenco 1998). Major developments in marine ecology in the past decade have included a focus on marine invasions (Carlton and Geller 1993) and the realization that the synergy between environmental stress, physiological stress, and genetic variation can determine patterns of mass marine mortality (Rowan et al. 1997). In addition, the realization that weak interactions in trophic webs can play a major community structuring role (Paine 1992) and debates about the importance of biological diversity in ecosystem function (Tilman and Downing 1994) have galvanized attention to many of the "minor" species in marine communities previously overlooked in experimental studies.

These two themes, the panic caused by fishery collapse, and the focus on whole communities as ecological units come together in a debate about the utility of one particular method of marine coastal management—the creation of marine protected areas (MPAs). MPAs have been used effectively for decades, but the acceleration of the decline of marine coastal zones has highlighted their potential to address both the problems of fisheries enhancement and the maintenance of marine biological diversity. Few developments in marine ecology have excited as much hope or generated as much furor as have MPAs. The proposal to establish MPAs has resulted in fisheries officials being hung in effigy by their friends, the firing of scientists from local Fisheries Management Commissions, and the patrolling of reserve boundaries by armed guards. MPAs have also been the source of deep-seated community involvement and considerable local and regional success.

The scientific basis for MPA implementation and monitoring has received a great deal of recent attention, as coastal management officials struggle to understand the potential of MPAs to reduce or reverse the decline of marine communities. The study of MPAs as a management tool has allowed some of the best lessons about marine ecology to be applied to great effect, but has also highlighted some of the crucial areas of marine ecological research that remain weakly understood. This chapter will review definitions of MPAs and discuss what is currently known about how well they function. Connectivity between MPAs and the rest of marine ecosystems emerges from this exercise as a crucial yet poorly understood aspect of MPA (or ecosystem) function. Another critical need is to understand ecological interactions within MPAs so that the impact of reducing human intervention in natural marine communities can be better predicted.

If the huge attention to basic marine research has an applied and practical benefit, one of the primary outlets for that benefit has been in understanding the implications and function of marine reserves in ecosystem maintenance, biodiversity enhancement, and fisheries production. This is not ecology as spectator sport, but as mud wrestling in which the outcome matters a great deal.

DIFFERENT TYPES OF MPAS

Some of the first summaries of marine protected areas as management tools emphasized that different MPAs might be very different from one another, and that the management goals of a particular MPA were intrinsic to their implementation and their success (Agardy 1994). Some MPAs are based on the principle that no extraction of natural resources is allowed within their boundaries. Other, still more restricted definitions, allow no access to the MPA by the general public, but restrict entry to managers and monitors. Other definitions allow MPA designation for any area in which some kind of marine resource use is restricted. For example, no-trawl zones in which bottom dredging is excluded might allow other kinds of commercial or recreational fishing (Armstrong et al. 1993), but still be considered MPAs.

Among the many different "species" of MPAs, there are three broad kinds whose underlying objectives are quite different: (1) fisheries enhancement MPAs focus on protecting local populations as a management tool to augment or stabilize regional fisheries yields; (2) ecosystem diversity MPAs focus on the preservation and maintenance of broad-scale marine biological diversity; and 3) special-feature MPAs focus on preservation of a particular locality because of its cultural importance or its value to a particularly vulnerable life history stage.

Fisheries reserves tend to focus on single-species restrictions or no-take zones in a small area in order to enhance fisheries yields over a much larger area. By contrast, MPAs designed to preserve or augment ecosystem diversity generally require no-take regulations that prohibit any extractive use of the natural resources in the area. These MPAs frequently benefit a wide range of pelagic and benthic species. In some cases, however, no-take reserves appear misnamed because they may be open to particular exploitation. No-take MPAs in the Florida Keys Marine Sanctuary, for example, are open for throw net fishing for baitfish (Florida Keys National Marine Sanctuary Final Management Plan: An overview, p. 16, NOAA, Washington, DC, 1998).

The broad definition of a MPA, adopted by the International Union of Concerned Scientists states that an MPA is "any area of intertidal or subtidal terrain, together with its overlying waters and associated flora, fauna, historical and cultural features, which has been preserved by legislation or other effective means to protect all or part of the enclosed environment" (Kelleher and Recchia 1998). Although this definition may seem too broad, the IUCN also established six categories of MPAs that begin to reflect the diversity of practical uses and ecological settings that MPAs include (Table 19.1).

Biodiversity reserves—those designed primarily to enhance coastal ecosystem stability and multispecies interactions—are most stringently defined in categories I and II. Categories III, V, and VI also have ecosystem protection as a major goal. They differ largely in access to the general public and the degree of extraction allowed. Fishery reserves are largely described in Category IV, whose major objective is to provide an additional management tool for enhancement of a particular target species.

Frequently, an MPA might play more than one role. In particular, fisheries enhancement, the preservation of ecosystem diversity, and nursery ground protection often can go hand in hand. But such coordination of goals is not always possible unless this coordination occurs during the design and implementation of the reserve. For example, a management goal to enhance a single species stock—like New England cod—may require an MPA closed only to cod fishing. In 1994, several areas of Georges Bank off Cape Cod were closed to cod trawling. By 1998, cod had not yet recovered in this area, but the MPAs were densely populated by ocean scallops (Murawski 1999), whose harvest was vociferously requested by local fishers. The success of the cod closure is not yet known, but in this case single-species protection had a secondary effect of protecting the seafloor from trawling damage (Dayton et al. 1995; Watling and Norse 1998), and this physical protection had a wider ecosystem effect. Should these newly protected seafloors be saved from exploitation until cod begin to recover? Or should the scallop resources be snapped up by local fishers who are suffering under the economic collapse of the overfished cod? In the Philippines, local fishers eventually overwhelmed and destroyed local no-take zones in which fish production had increased dramatically (Russ and Alcala 1989). In New England, harvest of the scallops began on June 15, 1999.

These examples point out that MPAs are generally instituted to solve particular, local problems. Because each local

TABLE 19.1 Categories of Marine Protected Areas Established by the IUCN (Kelleher and Recchia 1998)

CATEGORY I.	**Strict Nature Reserve/Wilderness Area: protected area managed mainly for science or wilderness protection**
CATEGORY Ia.	**Strict Nature Reserve: protected area managed mainly for science—definition**: Area of land and/or sea possessing some outstanding or representative ecosystems, geological or physiological features, and/or species, available primarily for scientific research and/or environmental monitoring.
CATEGORY Ib.	**Wilderness Area: protected area managed mainly for wilderness protection—definition:** Large area of unmodified or slightly modified land, and/or sea, retaining its natural character and influence, without permanent or significant habitation, protected and managed so as to preserve its natural condition.
CATEGORY II.	**National Park: protected area managed mainly for ecosystem protection and recreation—definition:** Natural area of land and/or sea, designated to (a) protect the ecological integrity of one or more ecosystems for present and future generations, (b) exclude exploitation or occupation inimical to the purposes of designation of the area, and (c) provide a foundation for spiritual, scientific, educational, recreational, and visitor opportunities, all of which must be environmentally and culturally compatible.
CATEGORY III.	**Natural Monument: protected area managed mainly for conservation of specific natural features—definition:** Area containing one, or more, specific natural or natural/cultural features which is of outstanding or unique value because of its inherent rarity, representative. or aesthetic qualities or cultural significance.
CATEGORY IV.	**Habitat/Species Management Area: protected area managed mainly for conservation through management intervention—definition:** Area of land and/or sea subject to active intervention for management purposes so as to ensure the maintenance of habitats and/or meet the requirements of specific species.
CATEGORY V.	**Protected Landscape/Seascape: protected area managed mainly for landscape/seascape conservation and recreation—definition:** Area of land, with coast and sea as appropriate, where the interaction of people and nature over time has produced an area of distinct character with significant aesthetic, ecological, and/or cultural value, and often with high biological diversity. Safeguarding the integrity of this traditional interaction is vital to the protection, maintenance, and evolution of such an area.
CATEGORY VI.	**Managed Resource Protected Area: protected area managed mainly for the sustainable use of natural ecosystems—definition:** Area containing predominantly unmodified natural systems, managed to ensure long-term protection and maintenance of biological diversity, while providing at the same time a sustainable flow of natural products and services to meet community needs.

problem is unique and because the design of MPAs is linked tightly to their objectives, there are so many different types of MPAs that their categorization is often complex. Sometimes this complexity is reflected in a mosaic of different use patterns, as in the Great Barrier Reef Marine Park, a large protected area with different types of protection in different areas. Some areas in the Park are no-take reserves designed to enhance ecosystem diversity, and these are found scattered inside the larger park, where extractive uses are allowed. The major lesson from these complex zoning mosaics is that the terminology of MPAs should not be allowed to interfere with understanding of the goals and utility of any particular MPA example.

SIMPLIFIED TAXONOMY OF MPAS

There are many different goals for MPAs, and as a consequence, MPAs are implemented in many different ways. Un-

less these differences can be categorized, there is a danger that every new MPA will seem like a unique case that cannot benefit from understanding gained from prior experiences. Broadly speaking, MPAs fall into the same three goal categories as discussed above—those that focus on fisheries, those that focus on ecosystem diversity, and those designed around a particular, crucial geographic area. Within these three broad goals, it is possible to identify two other major criteria by which many reserves differ. These criteria are whether the MPA is expected to have only a local effect within its boundaries, or a wider impact on the ecosystem in which it is found (Figure 19.1). These goals are fundamentally different in that the first requires local effects to be visible within the boundaries of the reserve, whereas the second requires export of a reserve effect from the boundaries of the MPA to the adjoining region. In practice, many fisheries reserves are designed to have regional effects, whereas many biodiversity reserves focus on protecting species in a defined area.

Reserve type	Scale of desired effect
Ecosystem diversity	Local ⟶ Regional
Fisheries management	Local ⟶ Regional
Special feature	Local ⟶ Regional

Figure 19.1 A simplified taxonomy of marine protected areas. Major goals of MPAs are divided into enhancing ecosystem diversity, fisheries enhancement of a single species or a few target taxa, or protection of special areas important to particular life history stages. Each of these types of reserves might be designed to augment an ecosystem at only a local scale (as in a marine park designed for local tourism) or on a regional scale (as in a fishing reserve meant to export products). Other, more comprehensive, taxonomies exist (see text), but the above categories capture most of the biological differences inherent in designing, monitoring, and evaluating MPAs.

DO MARINE RESERVES WORK?

Understanding if marine reserves work requires two levels of analysis. The first requires that particular reserves be evaluated in the context of the goals inherent in their establishment. The second level of analysis should be a broad comparison across reserves in different ecosystems to understand if reserves in general have a local or regional effect. Each reserve is a unique area, often established because of its topographic, biodiversity, or cultural attributes. It is thus difficult to directly assess the effectiveness of reserve status in the strict sense, because each reserve is an unreplicated area. In addition, comparison of reserve to nonreserve areas is often done without the spatial and temporal controls that have become the chief analytical tool of experimental ecology (Paine 1984; Osenberg et al. 1994). These failures of the real world to correspond to experimental niceties are serious cause for caution in interpreting the effect of any single reserve. However, replication across oceans, habitat types, taxa of interest, latitude, investigator, and experimental design may allow broad patterns to emerge despite uncertainty about any particular MPA.

Fisheries Reserves with Local Effects

Many MPAs in which fishing has been eliminated or dramatically curtailed have been reported to have local effects on species diversity or abundance. In particular, reduction of fishing pressure tends to have a dramatic effect on the numbers and size of exploited fish (Roberts 1995). Recruitment of these fish is thought to be derived from larvae imported from elsewhere in the ecosystem. When such recruitment is strong, fish stocks can increase within only a few years of the creation of the reserve. Such patterns have been observed frequently in temperate and tropical reef habitats (Table 19.2), where fish tend to be fairly sedentary as adults, and populations can be defined on a local scale.

In several small Caribbean preserves Polunin and Roberts (1993), recorded increases in abundance or biomass of about one-third of the species of demersal fish on protected reefs. Although most species did not increase in abundance, many

of these were initially rare. Summed across the data sets, there were 18 recorded increases of abundance compared to nonreserve areas, and only one decrease in abundance. There were 20 increases in biomass or length and no instances of declines inside versus outside the reserve (Figure 19.2).

A similar study in South Africa (Bennett and Attwood 1991) showed a temporal increase of fish abundance (estimated by catch per unit effort methods) following closure of fishing in the De Hoop Nature Reserve. Abundances increased until they were similar to those in a nearby private fishing reserve, suggesting that protection against fishing led to increased fish densities over the six years of the study. Similarly, Kenyan reefs protected for 25 years showed dramatic differences in fish numbers, size, and density (McClanahan 1994). After establishment of a new Kenyan marine reserve in 1991, the biomass of fish inside the reserve increased fivefold in three years. A nearby site at which traditional net, trap, and line fishing was allowed showed no significant increase in the same period (McClanahan and Kaunda-Arara 1996).

These trends are apparent in many other studies of marine protected areas: heavily fished species often increase in abundance or size. Cole et al. (1990) found larger abundances of lobster, snapper, and red moki inside reserves in New Zealand. Both fish species increased with time after reserve establishment, although control sites were not examined over the same time frame. In addition, snappers were larger inside than outside the reserve. Goatfish appeared to be more abundant outside the reserve than inside, although Cole et al. (1990) record no fishing pressure on this species in these areas. As in some of the Caribbean studies described previously, not all target species responded to protection: eight other species

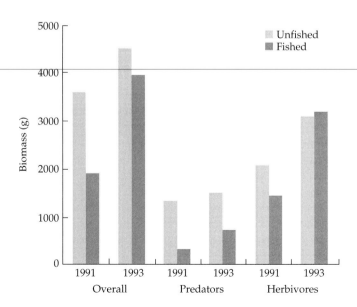

Figure 19.2 Changes in biomass in the Saba Island marine reserve between 1991 and 1993 for predatory fish (groupers, grunts, and snappers), herbivores (parrotfish and surgeonfish), and all five families combined. (After Roberts 1995.)

TABLE 19.2 Some examples of fisheries enhancement MPAs designed for local effect on abundance or biomass of fish or invertebrates. Establishment of these reserves has generally been by legislation, although two examples are given of reserves established on the basis of community management of local resources.

Area	Positive effect?[a]	Control	Size	Time frame	Target taxa	Reference
Mediterranean	Y	Spatial	1 km	9 yr.	Fish	Bell 1983
Mediterranean	Y***	Spatial	<1 km	6 yr.	Fish	Garcia-Rubies and Zabala 1990
Philippines	Y	Spatial		10 yr.	Fish	Russ 1985
Australia	Y	Spatial			Fish	Ayling and Ayling 1986
Kenya	Y***	Spatial			Fish	Samoilys 1988
Philippines	Y***	Temporal		3 yr.	Fish	Alcala 1988
Philippines	Y*	Spatial/temporal		3 yr.	Fish	Russ and Alcala 1989
Africa	Y*	Spatial			Fish	Buxton and Smale 1989
Florida Keys	Y**	Temporal		2 yr.	Fish	Clark et al. 1989
Kenya reefs	Y***	Spatial			Fish	McClanahan and Shafir 1990
Caribbean	Y**	Spatial	1 km	4 yr.	Fish	Polunin and Roberts 1993
Belize	Y**	Spatial	4 km	4 yr.	Fish Conch Lobsters	Polunin and Roberts 1993
Africa	Y***	Spatial/temporal	46 km	2–5 yr.	Fish	Bennett and Attwood 1991
Florida Keys	Y***	Spatial	>100 km	20 yr.	Fish	Bohnsack 1982
Red Sea	Y***	Spatial		15 yr.	Fish	Roberts and Polunin 1993
Chile	Y*	Spatial/temporal	1.5 km	3 yr.	Snails	Duran and Castilla 1989
Chile	Y*	Spatial/temporal	1.5 km	3 yr.	Limpets	Oliva and Castilla 1986
Japan	Y	Temporal			Crabs	Yamasaki and Kuwahara 1990
Kenya reefs	Y*	Spatial/temporal		25 yr.	Fish	McClanahan 1994
Kenya reefs	Y*	Spatial/temporal		1–3 yr.	Fish	McClanahan 1995
Kenya reefs	Y	Spatial		25 yr.	Snails	McClanahan 1989
Florida Keys	Y	Spatial		2 yr.	Shrimp	Klima et al. 1986
Caribbean	Y**	Spatial		1–3 yr.	Urchins	Smith and Berkes 1991
Puget Sound	Y**	Spatial	1–2 km	4–27 yr.	Fish	Palsson and Pacunski 1995
Central CA	Y	Spatial	1–6 km	4–37 yr.	Fish	Paddock 1996
Florida Keys	Y	Spatial			Lobsters	Davis 1977
Caribbean	Y	Spatial			Conch	Weil and Laughlin 1984
Palau	Y	Spatial			Snails	Hesilnga et al. 1984
New Jersey	Y	Spatial			Clams	McCay 1988
Australia	Y	Spatial			Abalone	Shepherd 1990
COMMUNITY-BASED PROTECTION:						
Caribbean	Y**	Spatial	Traditional		Urchins	Smith and Berkes 1991
Fiji	Y**	Spatial	Traditional		Fish	Jennings and Polunin 1997

[a]Asterisks represent statistical power (***$p < 0.001$, **$p < 0.01$, * $p < 0.05$)

of fish and one species of sea urchin showed no significant change between reserve and nonreserve sites.

Fisheries reserves for invertebrates have been studied less often than for fish, but when a heavily exploited invertebrate species is protected from harvest, and when recruitment from outside the reserve can import larvae, then populations typically increase after protection (Table 19.2). Careful studies by Castilla and colleagues have shown such increases among three species of harvested intertidal gastropods after protection from human collection (Castilla and Duran 1985). Likewise, Keough et al. (1993) showed increases in size or abundance of four species of harvested intertidal molluscs compared to protected areas in Australia. White spined sea urchins in St. Lucia are an order of magnitude more abundant in a harvesting reserve than outside, where there is no fishing management (Smith and Berkes 1991). In this case, community control of harvesting has also been shown to be effective. Areas in which the local urchins are harvested by a single village that controls access to the resource have maintained urchin densities similar to those in the reserve (Smith and Berkes 1991).

Ocean scallops increased dramatically on Georges Bank after areas were protected from trawling, although the purpose of this protection was actually to enhance cod stocks (Murawski 1999). Intertidal and subtidal gastropods have increased due to protection in temperate and tropical habitats (references in Dugan and Davis 1993). Heavily fished surf clams were more dense (and grew more slowly) in a no-dredging area (Weinberg 1998). Other invertebrates like urchins and clams have shown variable responses to temporary fishing reserves (Dugan and Davis 1993).

SUMMARY OF LOCAL FISHERIES MPAs. The number of MPAs monitored for local effects on fish density or abundance is growing rapidly, and there is more information about the impact of this type of MPA than any other. In general, biomass tends to increase more quickly than abundance in such reserves (Roberts 1995), but changes in size and number of heavily fished species when they are protected in reserves is very common (Table 19.2). Even small reserves (ca. 0.1 sq. km) appear to have a beneficial effect (Halpern et al., in press) if adults are fairly sedentary and recruitment of larvae from the rest of the ecosystem can supply settlers in the reserve.

Ecosystem Reserves with Local Effects

An ecosystem reserve with only local goals might be successfully implemented by protecting a small stretch of coastline. Although there are few reserves (especially in the United States) whose goals are the enhancement of overall marine diversity, no-take reserves established for fisheries management often have an impact on community composition and diversity. Study of fish diversity patterns inside reserves indicates that protection may have an effect on overall community richness, but that the major changes are in the species previously hunted. In Fiji, large piscivorous fish are much less abundant on more heavily fished reefs, but abundance and species richness of other fish is unaffected (Jennings and Polunin 1997). In the Mediterranean, the total number of fish species was 43 inside and 44 outside a fishing reserve in the northwest Mediterranean, although mean species richness per sampling station was significantly higher inside than outside the reserve (Garcia-Rubies and Zabala 1990). Cole et al. (1990) showed overall increases in fish diversity in MPAs in New Zealand, although the differences are slight (Figure 19.3). In Australia, small seagrass beds harbored fewer species than large ones, but a combination of several small seagrass beds had a higher total of species diversity than did a larger bed of equal area (McNeill and Fairweather 1993). Artificial beds had increased diversity after 10 weeks, but the diversity in several small artificial beds did not exceed that in a large artificial bed.

MPAs established to control physical disturbance caused by fishing methods like dredging or trawling often have important secondary effects on marine community structure. Trawling destroys the biological component of bottom topography (Watling and Norse 1998) and can result in mud/sand barrens that are distinctly different from normal seafloor communities. Dynamite fishing on coral reefs and dredging on oyster bars reduces spatial heterogeneity and collapses community diversity (Lenihan and Peterson 1998). MPAs set up to restrict trawling or other physically damaging fishing methods have resulted in changes in community composition that go far beyond the original fished species (Murawski 1999). Less-invasive methods can also have an impact: along temperate, exposed beaches in Uruguay, hunting for yellow clams negatively impacts abundance of other co-occurring bivalves (Defeo and De Alva 1995).

Such dramatic community-wide effects are not always documented, and ecosystem changes within reserves can be subtle. For example, mollusc community composition did not differ strongly in Kenyan reefs protected from fishing or collecting. McClanahan (1989) surveyed protected and unprotected reefs in Kenya for gastropod diversity. There were only a few clear changes in abundance in this study—densities were low for all species regardless of protected status, and differences among different reef types were larger than

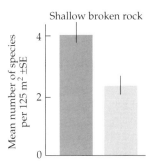
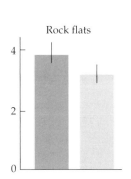
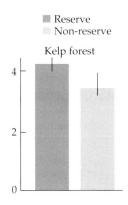

Figure 19.3 Average number of fish species counted within (darkly shaded) and outside (lightly shaded) marine reserves in New Zealand. Error bars are standard errors of the mean for three habitats. (After Cole et al. 1990.)

differences due to protection. Despite this difficulty, 12 of 15 commercially exploited species were more common on protected reefs (although only 5 were significantly so). By contrast only 7 of 15 nonexploited species were more abundant on protected reefs. Thus, fishing protection may have had an effect on molluscan communities, but the variation among reef sites for rare species makes this pattern difficult to demonstrate conclusively.

In the Florida Keys Marine Sanctuary, two years of protection from fishing has had an effect on harvested species, but not on overall abundance of live coral cover or gorgonians. Likewise, there were few significant increases of corals in the Saba Marine Park between 1991 and 1993 (Roberts et al. 1995). Such time frames are too short for responses from long-lived, slow-growing, poorly recruiting taxa like corals, seagrasses, and many sponges. Unfortunately, these taxa tend to provide the biological framework on which other highly diverse communities depend, and so recovery of these framework species is crucial to success of a biodiversity MPA. Indicator organisms with more appropriate life histories (e.g., amphipods, polychaetes, algae that recruit more heavily and grow more quickly) are rarely sampled in MPA studies, but would provide an important view of the changing communities within MPAs.

The Las Cruces Marine Reserve in the intertidal of Chile was designed to test the impact of human predation on ecological patterns among intertidal space occupiers. Along a 1.4 km stretch of coastline, complete fencing and armed guards prevented access by local fishers, with the startling result that the dominant space occupiers along the shore shifted within a period of only a few years from mussels to barnacles and macroalgae (Castilla and Duran 1985; Oliva and Castilla 1986; Castilla and Bustamante 1989). The abundance of a dominant intertidal invertebrate predator, *Concholepas concholepas*, increased by a factor of 2–3, causing the decline of its preferred prey (intertidal mussels) and replacement with a "normal" intertidal community of barnacles and algae that is rarely seen in Chile because of widespread *Concholepas* overharvesting (Castilla and Duran 1985).

In another study of the community level effects of MPAs, McClanahan and coworkers (McClanahan 1994, 1995; McClanahan and Kaunda-Arara 1996) showed that protection from fishing led to an increase in predation on urchins by triggerfish and a reduction in sea urchin overpopulation (McClanahan and Kaunda-Arara 1996). Protection from fishing also led to changes in algal density and in some cases to changes in diversity. The dramatic changes in community structure seen in these reserves underscore the role MPAs can play in diversity management and show how ecological interactions within reserves must be understood as a major part of reserve design strategy.

SUMMARY OF LOCAL BIODIVERSITY RESERVES. Protection of marine communities from exploitation almost always results in dramatic changes in patterns of body size and abundance, and these changes often have a profound effect on communi-

ty composition. Even within the boundaries of small reserves, community composition can be greatly altered by reduced exploitation. However, the relationship between protection and diversity is complex. In some cases, species richness increases inside reserves. In others, the major impact of reserve status is a dramatic shift in which species are present, without necessarily an increase in overall species numbers. Species with strong recruitment, fast generations, and large growth rates are most likely to show increases in short periods of time after reserve establishment. More slowly growing species or those with low recruitment take much longer to show a reserve effect. Although there is ample evidence that reserve status has a marked impact on overall community composition, there is relatively little attention given to noncommercial species within biodiversity reserves and little understanding of the complicated ecological cascades produced by major shifts in exploitation.

Fisheries Reserves with Regional Effects

Few fisheries reserves are established with purely local goals. Usually, a fisheries closure or a protected area is established to augment overall populations and to increase (or stabilize) fisheries yields. In general, regional effects of fisheries reserves are more difficult to demonstrate than local effects. For example, the success of MPAs in increasing fish biomass and abundance (Table 19.2) is due largely to studies of populations within reserves. Fewer studies have examined the impact of an MPA on surrounding areas where fishing is allowed.

McClanahan and Kaunda-Arara (1996) reported that catch-per-unit-effort (CPUE) just outside a newly established Kenyan reef MPA increased for all eight categories of fished species. Traps were moved by local fishers within a year so that most were clustered within 250 m of the MPA boundary. A fishing beach further away from the park had lower CPUE for seven of eight fishing categories, and McClanahan and Kaunda-Arara (1996) suggested that intense edge-fishing was enough to collect all the export from the MPA. Russ and Alcala (1989) studied fishing yields in the Philippines before and after the collapse of the Sumilon Island reserve. They report that fishing was 25% more productive when the reserve was in place than after locals destroyed the reserve by fishing within it. This is indirect evidence that the MPA increased fishing yields, but many more detailed studies need to be done before the overall benefit of MPAs to fishing yields are as firmly established as the local benefits of reserves (Table 19.2).

Theoretical treatments of MPA regional effects suggest that under circumstances where fishing pressure is high, MPAs can increase regional fishing yields. Hastings and Botsford (1999) showed that MPAs provided the same degree of fishery management power as did control of fishing effort. Their model redistributed fishing effort from reserves to the rest of the fishery, thereby increasing fishing pressure outside of reserves. Increased yields require augmentation of regional fish supplies through a common larval pool connecting reserve and nonreserve populations.

DeMartini (1993) and Polacheck (1990) both showed that MPAs could increase fisheries yields under certain circumstances in which outside fishing pressure was high and transport or fish or larvae outside of the MPAs was likely. Low dispersal between MPA and the surrounding habitats severely limits the ability of an MPA to enhance productivity in the overall fishery, because extra eggs, larvae, or adults are trapped inside the protected area (DeMartini 1993). On the other extreme, infinite movement of adults from MPAs to surrounding, fished zones severely reduces their effectiveness at allowing local buildup of populations (for example, for small MPAs and very migratory adults; Armstrong et al. 1993). Moderate movement of adults can result in overall positive impact of MPAs on fishery production (Attwood and Bennett 1995). Thus, the theoretical treatments have all agreed that increased regional yields from MPAs occur over a set of biological parameters that depend largely on the movement of individuals into and out of reserves. For a particular MPA configuration, some species may respond, but others may not. Which species fall into these categories is a critical question for future research.

These theoretical treatments also emphasize that the value of fishery MPAs may not lie solely in their impact on fish biomass (Hastings and Botsford 1999). By providing a refuge for adult fish and a stockpile of large spawners that can produce many eggs and larvae, MPAs may help fisheries recover when other conventional fishery management schemes fail. For cod in the western Atlantic, large spawning aggregations have been rare after the collapse of these historically fished populations (Smedbol et al. 1998), and broad closures along the coast of New England are hoped to enhance the buildup of new spawning populations. If such populations already existed, protected by reserve "banks," commercial recovery might be much faster.

A second value of MPAs may be to reduce recruitment variation. Some fisheries species are characterized by complete recruitment failure for many years. The surf clam population (*Spisula spp.*) along the U.S. eastern seaboard is heavily harvested, but commercial take relies on the progeny from a single age class that recruited heavily in the late 1970s (Weinberg 1998). Similarly, in 1989, Jamieson et al. (1989) reported that there had been no substantial recruitment of the Dungeness crab (*Cancer magister*) near Tofino British Columbia since 1985. Large adult populations within MPAs may provide steady interannual sources for recruits of such commercially important species.

SUMMARY OF REGIONAL EFFECTS OF FISHERIES RESERVES.   Fishery MPAs will function as an important management tool only if they contribute enough to regional ecosystems (in biomass or recruits) to make them worth the cost of restricting fishing. There is emerging evidence that this may be true, but at this time there are simply not enough powerful studies to allow us to understand the regional effects of MPAs on fisheries populations. The local effects of fishery MPAs are clear

(see previous sections), so it is the connection between these local successes and regional ecosystem impact that is terribly unclear. Understanding connectivity in marine populations on a regional scale has long been a difficult challenge in marine ecology. Facing this challenge is now a critical priority in both basic and applied ecology.

Biodiversity Effects on a Regional Scale

Although most fishery MPAs are implemented in order for them to have a regional effect, many biodiversity reserves are designed to have effects only within the reserve. These local biodiversity reserves might be designed to enhance coral diversity for tourism or otherwise protect marine life at a single site. Ecosystem diversity reserves may need to be placed very carefully to have a regional effect. To preserve a substantial fraction of regional marine biological diversity, a series of reserves has been implemented for the coast of South Africa (Attwood et al. 1997). Each of these reserves may function separately to enhance the abundance of exploited taxa or overall species richness, but their placement in different biogeographic provinces allows the system as a whole to preserve a greater fraction of the region's marine diversity (Hockey and Branch 1994).

However, some MPAs may be designed to enhance ecosystem diversity on a larger scale. Here, local effects within the reserve may be expected to be exported to the rest of an unprotected ecosystem through larval dispersal or adult movement outside of the reserve. In the Las Cruces MPA, larval traps have recently been deployed to document any differences in settlement between reserves and surrounding areas. Species with very low dispersal potential like kelp had higher settlement within the reserve, where kelp is denser (Castilla, pers. comm.). Species with larger dispersal potentials had less-obvious differences in and outside the reserve (Castilla and Varas 1998). Although biodiversity reserves might function generally to increase the species representation of marine communities beyond the reserve borders, transport outside reserves is especially poorly documented for nonfisheries species.

SUMMARY OF EFFECTS OF BIODIVERSITY RESERVES ON REGIONAL SCALES.   Less is known about this type of MPA than any other. This is partly because there are relatively few MPAs designed for biodiversity enhancement (especially in the United States) and partly because the MPAs that may function in this regard (e.g., no-take fishery MPAs) are seldom adequately monitored for their impact on regional biodiversity. Surveys of species numbers in areas adjacent to no-take MPAs could test this possibility, but I know of no such studies.

Partial Closures and Attempts
to Protect Particular Life Stages

The previous four sections have reviewed our knowledge about the functioning of two types of reserves in two different contexts. A third major type of reserve focuses on special features of a particular marine habitat (e.g., a geological formation or an artificial reef), or it focuses on a particular life stage of a species through protecting an area crucial to this life stage. Such protection has been shown to be an important component of marine population management for two very different reasons.

First, protecting an area from destructive fishing practices often has striking effects on habitat complexity and on local species diversity (Dayton et al. 1995; Watling and Norse 1998). In addition, trawling for one species often impacts many others because of by-catch of nontarget species. For example, red snapper by-catch in the Gulf of Mexico during shrimp trawling is thought to be the most important source of mortality for this species, making recovery efforts that focus on adult fish extremely difficult (Hendrickson and Griffin 1993). In areas of high by-catch or sensitive spawning grounds, trawling closures have been implemented to increase stocks. One such case is the trawling closure in the eastern Bering Sea. Designed to reduce by-catch on a series of benthic species of fish and invertebrates, the closure is centered over spawning grounds of the red King Crab (Armstrong et al. 1993).

Trawlable and nontrawlable areas have sometimes been compared in order to assess the impacts of fishing method on community structure and fishing yields. However, recent work has shown that such areas are not necessarily comparable, and that the differences in bottom topography that result in differential access by trawling gear may be an important agent of community structure. For example, trawlable and nontrawlable areas off the northwest corner of Vancouver Island, British Columbia, differ substantially in bottom topography: nontrawlable areas are steeper and have 1–3 m thick bedrock spikes that damage trawls, whereas trawlable areas have a bottom of mudstone, are more gradually sloped, and have no protruding rock formations (Matthews and Richards 1991). nontrawlable areas are dominated by red-banded or shapchin rockfish, whereas the trawlable areas are dominated by two other species—Pacific Ocean Perch and Greenstriped rockfish (Matthews and Richards 1991). These surveys suggest nontrawlable areas cannot be the source of recruitment into heavily fished trawlable areas and also cast doubt on the ability of natural barriers to trawling to serve as MPAs representative of trawlable zones.

Second, efforts to protect particularly vulnerable life stages have helped augment populations and have increased numbers in even highly mobile, pelagic species. Perhaps the most familiar example is the recovery of some marine turtle species following decades of protection of turtle-nesting beaches around the world (Bowen and Avise 1996). Although turtles face many perils in the open ocean, especially from net fishing far from their natal beaches (Bowen and Avise 1996), protection of egg-laying areas has helped increase supply of young. Another example is the protection of grouper spawning aggregations. Off the Atlantic coast of Florida, rock pinnacles festooned with the deep water coral *Oculina varicosa* have

served as the site of spawning aggregation of gag groupers. Intense dredging of spawning animals has not only reduced grouper populations, but it has also leveled the coral cover. A 92 sq. km area has been designated as a Research Reserve and is being replanted to attempt to hasten coral recovery.

This strategy of protecting areas of particularly vulnerable life history stages assumes the products of these spawning animals or the protected juveniles will augment populations of adults in the future. This strategy has seemed perfectly logical, but it depends on the connectivity of spawning grounds and juvenile nursery areas with adult populations. Little or no information is available on the efficacy of such management schemes, although protection of turtle-nesting beaches has been a successful strategy in increasing numbers of these previously overfished species.

Overall Summary of Effects of MPAs

The previous sections show that of the six major types of MPAs (Table 19.3), ample evidence exists to evaluate only the local effects of fisheries reserves. In this case, the evidence is overwhelming that MPAs allow the increase of biomass and abundance of many species that are overfished. Such benefits accrue in local areas for finfish and invertebrates. Changes in biomass can be obvious after only a period of several years. Increases in abundance may occur more slowly, but have been visible in numerous species that can recruit from a regional larval pool. Similarly, MPAs are known to have a strong local effect on community structure. When fishing pressure is relaxed, a number of studies have shown large-scale changes in prey species abundances. In such cases, the "natural" community may in fact be an artificial one maintained by human predation on an important ecological element (Jackson 1997). Effects of natural predators or grazers, once they increase in abundance after relaxation of fishing, can ripple through communities and promote dramatic shifts in community composition (Duran et al. 1987). A distinct type of local effect is the protection of an area from disturbance caused by fishing (e.g., dynamite or trawling). In cases where community structure may be altered by the physical activity of fishing, recovery may be rapid or may require the centuries-long rebuilding of complex benthic biological topography.

Information about the function of MPAs on a regional scale is much less complete. A few examples exist showing an effect of a local fishery MPA on wider-scale fishery yields. Most analytical or simulation studies of the fishery impacts of MPAs have shown positive effects on overfished stocks, but more empirical studies are required to fill in the picture of the regional value of fishery MPAs. Even less well understood is the potential of local biodiversity MPAs to export diversity value to surrounding communities. This is partially because few MPA studies focus on broad-scale biological diversity and partially because of the overall poor understanding of how this biological diversity could affect surrounding areas. Do complex communities with complicated trophic interactions somehow stabilize diversity over a scale beyond

TABLE 19.3   Summary of levels of evidence of the impact of different types of marine protected areas.

	Local Effect?	Regional Effect?
Fishery MPA	Many studies show increases in biomass or abundance of heavily fished species. Most MPA studies fall into this category.	Only two studies have examined and found regional effects. Many models suggest regional effects are possible depending on connectivity.
Biodiversity MPA	Several studies show strong impact of MPAs on marine community characteristics. But species diversity and ecological cascades show complicated responses to protection.	Extremely little is known.
Special feature	n/a	Success in augmenting some threatened species like turtles by protecting nursery grounds, but otherwise there are few comprehensive studies.

their geographic borders—perhaps by serving as a source population for colonization elsewhere? This aspect of MPA function is virtually unexplored empirically or theoretically.

Some Cautionary Tales

The success of MPAs in augmenting local population sizes and in providing enhanced egg and larval production will not by themselves solve all of the problems faced by coastal ecosystems, because overfishing is but one of the environmental problems known to dramatically affect marine habitats. For example, invasive species have swept through many well-studied marine communities, particularly in estuarine habitats near major industrial ports with the result that whole marine communities have been overturned (Carlton and Geller 1993; Geller 1996; Geller et al. 1997). Environmental changes such as increased sedimentation and nutrient runoff in the Black Sea, increased seawater temperature and its impact on coral bleaching (Rowan et al. 1997), or marine diseases outbreaks (Harvell et al. 1999) will not heed the boundaries of marine reserves.

In addition, the monitoring and enforcement of marine reserves is a critically important facet of their potential success, as shown most dramatically by the rapid decay of population abundance in Philippine reserves after their local enforcement evaporated (Russ and Alcala 1989; Alcala and Russ 1990).

In addition, there may well be cases in which traditional fisheries management is more successful at single-species control than reserves. Hastings and Botsford (1999) showed that the fishery effect of reserves was the same in principle as an equivalent degree of control in fishing effort. A case study

of the difference between marine reserve control of overfishing and traditional methods for two species of California rockfish showed that an accidental consequence of reserve establishment would be a large increase in fishing effort outside of reserves (Parrish 1999), with potentially severe impacts on bottom communities due to increased trawling rates. In addition, species that are highly mobile as adults may not respond as well to reserve establishment and may fail to increase in population size or individual size, as is typically the case for more sedentary species (Attwood and Bennett 1994; Parrish 1999).

What Is Needed Now

A consolidation of information about the six different types of MPAs in Figure 19.1 shows that current knowledge is extremely unbalanced (Table 19.3). We know a great deal about the local effects of fishery MPAs and something about local biodiversity reserves. Within local reserves, information about fish abundances and size is common. Information about other taxa and detailed investigations of how ecological interactions are altered in MPAs is much less available. This latter aspect of MPA research could benefit greatly from the long history of experimental ecology in marine habitats, but little attention has been given to human effects on marine ecosystems (Castilla 1999). The other area of critical ignorance is the connectivity of local populations into regional, multispecies ecosystems. The function of MPAs depends on such connectivity, but little direct information is available that can be used to better understand marine populations or improve MPA designs.

In the rest of this chapter, I will try to summarize the state of information about these two broad areas—human impacts on the ecology of marine ecosystems and what is known about marine connectivity in order to provide a springboard for future work on MPA implementation. Neither section is comprehensive, but the goal is to provide a sense of the important issues linking basic marine ecological research to the emerging field of MPA management.

THE FUNCTION OF MPAS: THE IMPORTANCE OF ECOLOGICAL INTERACTIONS

Marine protected areas can be considered ecological experiments on a large scale. They involve profound changes in the species composition of a particular area—perhaps bringing it closer to the original—but also changing it with respect to the "normal" exploited habitats of the modern oceans. But even the smallest MPAs are bigger than most ecological experiments, except for the few MPAs that actually ARE ecological experiments. These few careful studies of ecological interactions within MPAs show how profound and widespread the community alterations can be when intense human exploitation of coastlines is reduced. In some cases, contemporary communities may be nothing like historical ones (Jackson 1997). Yet, we know very little about the changes human predation in the sea has wrought.

Human Impact

The human exclusion experiment at Las Cruces, Chile, shows not only how chronic coastal exploitation can reduce the abundance of important food species, but also how removal of only a few economically important species can affect the structure of the local community. The normal zonation patterns on the intertidal shorelines of central Chile include a wide band of the mussel *Perumytilus purpuratus* and associated predators (Paine et al. 1985). The mussel is the dominant space occupier, outcompeting barnacles and taking space from benthic, foliose algae. A widespread, but rare, predator on *P. purpuratus* is the muricid gastropod *Concholepas concholepas*. There has long been a small local market for *C. concholepas*, and intertidal harvesting is commonplace. Castilla (cited in Castilla and Duran 1985) noted decreased mussel beds and increased *C. concholepas* populations along shorelines with limited human perturbation, suggesting the possibility that the normal mussel-dominated zonation pattern was due to widespread predation by humans on *C. concholepas* and the subsequent cascade of trophic changes that resulted from the removal of a dominant predator.

Along a 1.4 km stretch of the Chilean shoreline, Castilla restricted access by human collectors using fencing and armed guards. *C. concholepas* increased quickly to levels seldom seen except in the most inaccessible shorelines. Within a few years, other dramatic changes had taken place. In high wave impact areas, mussels declined in abundance. Mussels in low wave impact areas followed suit in a few more years. Barnacle cover increased in the extra space at first and then declined as

C. concholepas consumed them as well. Keyhole limpets also increased due to release from human predation, and algal cover declined. These dramatic results underscore the complex impact that humans have on shorelines and demonstrate that no-take marine protected areas can be remarkably different in community structure. The species that responded to this change in management were many more than the few that are actively harvested. Instead, the depth of the community change is due to interactions between harvested species, their prey, and competitors.

Studies of the impact of fishing on Kenyan reefs have also emphasized the interactions among trophic levels. Heavy fish predation has reduced fish population sizes along many Kenyan reefs (McClanahan 1994), including those species like trigger fish that prey on sea urchins. Predation rates on sea urchins are very low on fished reefs, but are high on protected reefs in several marine parks (McClanahan and Shafir 1990). Urchin population sizes are also very different on these reefs, with a population explosion on fished reefs that McClanahan ascribes to the effects of removal of predatory fish. Bioerosion from these reef-burrowing urchins may have increased to the point where framework erosion is faster than framework construction, threatening the physical integrity of these reefs (McClanahan and Shafir 1990).

Intertidal collecting or other human activities can have a strong effect on species composition and abundance. The frequency of overturned rocks increased with increased human activity along a shoreline near San Diego, California (Addessi 1994), correlating with a decrease in algal cover. Macroinvertebrates were much rarer (especially large herbivores and predators) where human activity was highest (Addessi 1994). Although these studies do not experimentally demonstrate the importance of human disturbance as has been done in Chile, it seems likely that marine communities in areas of high human use are dramatically different than they would be otherwise. Similarly, human predation on temperate intertidal reefs in Australia has been shown to change the abundance of targeted species (Keough et al. 1993; Edgar and Barrett 1997).

Research within MPAs shows that human impact is dramatic in many cases. However, Ruckelshaus and Hayes (1998) noted that the effects of MPAs varied considerably whether or not overall fish abundance, density, or diversity were monitored. A summary of some well-cited examples for MPA effects showed general increases in occurrence of harvested species in reserves, but in many of these cases there was no overall shift in density. These results probably reflect the complex nature of ecosystem recovery inside MPAs. Top predators may increase in size in reserves (see Roberts 1995 and many other examples), but may also decrease in density. Likewise, higher predation by a larger population of keystone species may increase the diversity of species at lower trophic levels. By contrast, increased predation of nonkeystone species may lower overall prey diversity. On coral reefs, protection from fishing has resulted in increases in some nonfished species, but not others (Russ and Alcala 1989). Lastly, MPA effects on highly migratory species may be low (e.g., pelagic fish). As a result, the ecological impacts of MPAs on these mobile predators are uncertain, and subsequent changes in their impact on local prey may be difficult to predict (e.g., the effects of orcas on coastal sea otters (Estes et al. 1998).

The Role of Experimental Controls in MPA Studies

Many of these ecological studies of reserves suffer from the lack of perfect controls for spatial variation. MPAs by their very nature are unique habitats, and situations in which multiple replicated MPAs have been studied in detail are few. Most studies report differences between unique MPAs and adjacent control areas in which fishing is allowed. Such controls provide valuable information, but might be criticized for lack of replication (e.g., Osenberg et al. 1994).

For example, the well-known Polunin and Roberts (1993) study of MPAs in the Caribbean was uncontrolled in that abundances of fish prior to the establishment of the marine reserve are unknown. Differences between fished and unfished areas could be due to habitat effects. Even before fishing was halted, the site of the eventual reserve might have had higher overall fish abundances (Polunin and Roberts 1993). Other studies have examined fish densities before and after reserve establishment. In South Africa, Bennett and Attwood used such temporal controls to study the de Hoop reserve (Bennett and Attwood 1991). Although temporal sampling of this study was well done, there was no spatial control. That is, sampling was entirely within the reserve except for the last set of samples, during which both the De Hoop and a private reserve outside the public area were sampled. Thus, it is possible that the apparent increase in fish in the reserve was due to an overall increase in fish populations along the coastline. Such an overall increase of fish abundance was seen in Kenyan reefs during a survey of unprotected and protected sites (McClanahan 1995) in which fish abundance increased twofold at fished and nonfished sites.

These problems with controls may affect generalizations that can be made from a single study. However, the large numbers of similar studies conducted in many habitats and many coastlines for many different types of fished species combine to create an ability to generalize from the entire set of studies. These ecological experiments may be poorly controlled in the classic sense, but in combination, they reveal a great deal about the structure of communities with and without human intervention.

DISPERSAL, CONNECTIVITY OF REGIONAL ECOSYSTEMS, AND RESERVE FUNCTION

Many MPAs are envisioned to play a role in enhancing, stabilizing, or preserving marine ecosystems on a scale larger than the reserve boundaries. This is especially true of fisheries reserves, whose economic value depends on export of individuals into regions where fishing is allowed, but it can also be a feature of biodiversity reserves. The functioning of reserves

in an ecosystem context has been one of the most difficult aspects of MPA impact to understand (Table 19.3). In fact, understanding the coupling of local habitats into regional ecosystems has long been a challenge in marine ecology. The connections between populations in different parts of a species range and how those populations respond to common environmental attributes like nutrients and climate has received little attention because the questions require such a broad experimental approach. The advent of MPAs as an ecological and environmental research tool simultaneously invites and requires increased understanding of the connectivity of marine populations at both fine and coarse scales. What is currently known about marine connectivity, and how does it help guide future work in MPA ecology?

Why Connectivity Is Important

The functioning of MPAs in a regional context requires that organisms protected within the reserve have an impact outside the reserve. Export from reserves or from any geographically defined marine population can take two forms: movement of adults and juveniles into adjacent regions and production of enhanced supplies of eggs and larvae inside reserves, creating a greater larval bank to drive recruitment outside reserves. Leakage of adults and juveniles outside of reserves is fairly well known for a few studies of fish and for lobsters. In a system of South African reserves, Attwood and Bennett (1994) recorded that 17% of fish tagged inside a reserve were recovered outside and suggested that this rate of transfer out of reserves would enhance adjacent fisheries. Different species have different movement rates, with some being characterized as sedentary and some showing relatively high exchange (Attwood and Bennett 1995). Tagged lobsters in the part of Florida Bay protected by the Everglades National Park are known to migrate into surrounding waters of the Florida Keys (Davis 1977). Tagging data on migratory fish (Attwood and Bennett 1994) showed that long-distance movement for some of these species is the norm and that populations cannot be well defined geographically. These tagging identification studies have been done for many species of fisheries interest, but fewer data sets are available on mobile, nonexploited fish or invertebrates.

One of the major values of marine reserves is thought to be the dispersal of larvae to nonprotected habitats, but there are few hard data that can be used to estimate the exchange of larvae among local populations. For American lobsters in the northwest Atlantic, several closed grounds and offshore habitats have been thought to produce the bulk of eggs and larvae for the onshore lobster traps of Nova Scotia and the Bay of Fundy. This expectation is due to the high annual fishing mortality (up to 95%) and the fact that legal size of lobsters is slightly below the size of first egg production in most populations (Campbell and Pezzack 1986). Where lobsters are heavily fished, only 5–15% of females have been recorded with eggs. By contrast, in deeper waters of the Georges Bank or the Browns Bank Closure, many more females are trapped carrying eggs. These areas, although they make up only about 10% of the populations in this part of Canada, contribute about 50% of the eggs and larvae produced. About 300,000 adults in these regions produced an estimated 2–10 billion eggs. By contrast, across the heavily fished zones, 5 million adults produced only 2–5 billion eggs (Campbell and Pezzack 1986). These differences are largely due to the expansion of egg production with size, but are also a reflection of the lack of opportunity to reproduce in populations with high fishing mortality. High numbers in some exploited inshore populations allow them to contribute significantly to current reproductive potential, but a disproportionate amount of reproduction is due to populations protected by law or (in the case of offshore populations) by difficult access (Campbell and Pezzack 1986).

Clearly, adults that live in a reserve will contribute offspring to the population as a whole, and protecting a large number of large adults will increase overall availability of eggs and larvae to the next generation. But, if larvae travel long distances, the immense dilution potential of the sea could make the contribution from a small reserve negligible. Cod abundances in the northwest Atlantic have declined tremendously due to overfishing and poor management (Walters and Maguire 1996; Myers et al. 1997) to the point where large spawning aggregations are rare. One such aggregation was recently discovered and has been suggested to be responsible for increases in egg density in local waters (Smedbol et al. 1998). Although this suggests local retention of eggs, subsequent larval recruitment was not enhanced, suggesting that during development, the cloud of larval cod dispersed beyond the limits of detection (Smedbol et al. 1998). Likewise, dilution during dispersal has been suggested to reduce crab larval availability such that out of 100,000 crab larvae that are near shore when they are 30 days of age, only 1 will be near shore when ready to settle 4 months later (Botsford et al. 1998). Such loss is likely to increase with increasing time in the plankton unless larvae are able to control current-mediated dispersal.

WHAT DO WE KNOW ABOUT MARINE CONNECTIVITY?

Although little direct evidence exists to show the impact of MPAs on regional ecosystems, there is a large and diverse body of literature that addresses issues of connectivity among marine populations. This literature allows a first glimpse at the range of connectivities exhibited by different parts of marine communities, but does not allow firm quantification of the degree to which marine connectivity is maintained by year-to-year demographic exchange. This is because much of the information we have about connectivity is indirect (Levin et al. 1993; Anastasia et al. 1998) and gives contradictory answers. Some information suggests long-distance dispersal is common, but other emerging information suggests the opposite. Exploring the data available for these two disparate points of view provides a good backdrop for the challenges that need to be faced in order to understand the connectivity of marine populations, and helps define the role of MPAs in regional ecosystems.

Why Marine Dispersal Might Be High

Many species of invertebrates, and most species of fish, have larval forms with long planktonic duration. These planktonic periods have been thought to increase the regional scale over which populations of marine species disperse. Marine larvae of coastal species are commonly observed in midocean plankton, showing that offshore transport of larvae is an ongoing process (Scheltema 1986). Larvae have been observed at the interfaces of coastal fronts, between the zones of upwelled water moving away from the coast and the zone of water moving shoreward. When upwelling relaxes, these fronts move back to shore and bring the larvae of coastal species with them (Gaines et al. 1985). If larvae generally travel kilometers from shore towards oceanic fronts, and then return, they are unlikely to settle very near their parents. Botsford et al. (1997) estimated mean dispersal distance of about 50 km for crab larvae based on their offshore/onshore migration patterns and the correlations of recruitment variation along the western coast of the United States. Even in nonupwelling areas, turbulent mixing and advective currents are common and could potentially move larvae many kilometers during a planktonic period of weeks of months.

The marine invertebrate fauna of isolated oceanic islands tends to be dominated by species with long-distance dispersal, showing that long-distance larvae can be successful colonists (Kay and Palumbi 1987). Moreover, genetic data from marine species with long-distance dispersal often show little population structure except over large spatial scales (Palumbi 1996), suggesting that such long-distance migration may be common (at least over evolutionary time frames). Data consistently suggest that dispersal is higher for species with planktonic phases than those with demersal or direct-developing larvae. Isolated reefs often show a preponderance of coral species with brooded larvae (Harriott and Banks 1995), and genetic structure is often higher for species with low dispersal potential (McMillan et al. 1992).

Direct observations of high marine dispersal come from the rapidity with which some marine species can invade new habitats. In most cases, expanding populations increase 10–100s of km a year. Recently, the green crab *Carcinus mineas* has spread up the west coast of the United States from an invasion originally detected in San Francisco Bay (Geller 1996). Other invasions have also been rapid, including the spread of marine diseases. For example, a fatal disease of black spined sea urchins swept throughout the Caribbean Sea in about a year (Lessios 1995). The best-studied invasion remains the spread of the barnacle *Elminius* in Great Britain. In this case, the advancing population spread at about 20–50 km per year (Geller 1994). Although it is not clear whether these maximal spreading distances should be equated with the average dispersal distance of species (animal, plant, or microbial) that are not invading new territory, data show that the seas offer few barriers to movement and great opportunity for demographic connectivity,

Why Larval Transport Might Be Low

LESSONS FROM OCEANOGRAPHY. Despite evidence of widespread larval movement from plankton tows (Scheltema 1986), oceanographic extrapolations, and genetics, there are increasing signs that average larval dispersal in marine systems often might be low, and that long-distance dispersal may be ecologically rare. Simulation studies of movement of larvae as passive particles have shown that larval transport may be affected strongly by local eddies and current reversals. For example, small-scale (<10 km) eddies spin off of the swift Florida Current as it moves past the Florida Keys (Lee et al. 1994). These eddies affect distribution of larval fishes and result in both eastward and westward movement of larvae (Limouzy-Paris et al. 1997). Lee et al. (1994) showed that passive current drifters could be caught in gyres along the Florida Current and kept near their release points for weeks or months. Similarly, simulations of current patterns along the southern Australia coast suggest that larvae that settle within seven days will in general recruit to within 10 km of their release point. Larval dispersal simulations in reef habitats have shown that local retention on the natal reef is 10 times more likely than transport to downstream reef sites unless the spacing between reefs is about the same as the reef diameter (Black 1993). Overall, passive particle simulations or oceanographic models have shown that larval retention on natal reefs or within a few tens of km along coastlines can be very likely (McShane et al. 1988). These few studies suggest that local current patterns are critical in determining actual movement of larvae, and that long-term average current flows may explain only a small fraction of larval movement patterns over short or long temporal scales (Shulman and Bermingham 1995).

LESSONS FROM LARVAE. Abalone represent a heavily fished species that may show local population dynamics and low larval exchange among even nearby populations. To test the ability of local populations in southern California to produce local recruits, Tegner (1992) transplanted 4453 abalone (*Haliotis fulgens*) to two overfished coastal areas with high retention probability. Recruitment subsequent to the transplant was variable: one site showed the highest settlement in the study, the other area showed the lowest recruitment. The experiment was ruined by poaching of the transplanted animals and has never been repeated. The genetic patchwork in other abalone species (Shepherd and Brown 1993) and the scales over which adult and recruitment abundances are correlated (Tegner 1993) both suggested that average dispersal ranges were on the order of 1–5 km. Simulations of larval transport for southern Australia abalone supports this general result (Black 1993). Availability of methods of attracting abalone lar-

vae to artificial collectors (Nash et al. 1995) may make more detailed surveys of larval settlement patterns possible.

Peterson and colleagues used the local crash of a population of bay scallops after a red tide episode to study the spatial dynamics of larval transport in estuaries in North Carolina (Peterson and Summerson 1992). They found a positive relationship between adult densities and recruitment across a series of different populations, suggesting limited larval movement. Failure of local populations to be augmented by recruitment from elsewhere led to slow recovery from the red tide effects. Later work (Peterson et al. 1996) tested the hypothesis of recruitment limitation by transplanting 100,000–150,000 adults into populations reduced by red tide. Local recruitment at these sites increased two- to sixfold, although monitoring of larval and spat densities gave equivocal results. These studies suggest that effective movement of scallop larvae is relatively low, resulting in viscous population structure that does not lend itself to rapid recovery by larval immigration, although the lack of correspondence between recruitment and larval abundance may mean that there are substantial adult-settler interactions that may need to be taken into account.

This pattern may also be visible in recruitment data outside reserves. Hockey and Branch (1994) measured limpet recruitment by counting juveniles at varying distance from a marine protected area in Tenerife, Canary Islands, and showed an exponential decline of juveniles outside a refuge, with an average movement of about 1.5 km. Increased juvenile abundance appeared to extend about 4 km from the refuge boundaries (Figure 19.4). Although these studies of abalone, scallops, and limpets are not controlled for the impact of changed benthic conditions in habitats with larger numbers of adults, they both suggest that invertebrates with free spawned eggs and sperm and a planktonic larval phase may show substantial re-

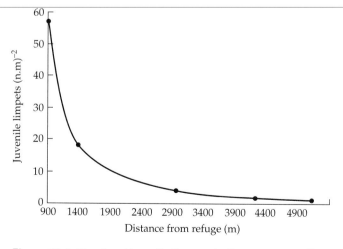

Figure 19.4 Density of juvenile limpets declines exponentially away from the boundaries of a marine refuge in the Canary Islands, suggesting spillover of larvae is occurring. (After Hockey and Branch 1994.)

tention even within small kilometer scale MPAs, and thus show substantial export "seed shadows" into nonfished areas.

Larval behavior may also play a critical role. Although larvae may spend weeks or months in the plankton, larval swimming, especially when it allows depth regulation, has been shown to enhance dispersal and affect settlement patterns (Grosberg 1982). Postlarval lobsters are much more common in nearshore habitats in New England, whereas early larval stages are most abundant offshore. Katz et al. (1994) suggested this pattern was generated by a combination of wind-driven surface currents and directional larval swimming. Deeper, average current measurements were very poor predictors of this phenomenon. Black et al. (1991) used a three-dimensional model of larval dispersal on Davies Reef to show that retention of larvae on the reef was 10 times more likely for a demersal larva than for larvae near the surface, and was 100 times more likely than for larvae that stationed themselves at mid-depth where currents were fastest. Other studies have shown that depth regulation sometimes allows retention of larvae in tidal estuaries (Cronin and Forward 1986; Tankersley et al. 1995), but can also be responsible for rapid emigration from estuaries to the open ocean (Christy and Morgan 1998). Larval behavior can also help place offshore larvae into currents that might bring them back towards coastlines (Forward et al. 1997; Botsford et al. 1998). Limouzy-Paris et al. (1997) showed that larvae of coastal spawning pelagic fish and pelagic spawning reef fishes have very different distributions throughout a local eddy, perhaps related to the behavior of larvae of fish with different adult habitats.

Recently, two studies of reef fish larvae suggest that local retention may be more common than previously thought. Swearer et al. (1999) measured the elemental content of otoliths collected from settling wrasse larvae in the U.S. Virgin Islands to estimate where larvae had drifted. The key surprise in these results is that many larvae—up to 50% in some collections—had otolith chemistries indicating retention of larvae in nearshore waters. These larvae developed without a long open ocean voyage, and so they must have settled on the reefs of their natal island.

Jones et al. (1999) tagged 10 million damselfish larvae around Lizard Island on the Great Barrier Reef using a dilute solution of tetracycline as a fluorescent dye. The tetracycline was incorporated into the calcareous matrix of larval otoliths and could be visualized as a glowing ring under UV light. Capture of settling larvae with light traps showed that up to 33–66% of the tagged larvae were retained bear Lizard Island for the entire three-week planktonic period.

LESSONS FROM GENETICS. The spatial scale of genetic structure tends to be larger for species with long-distance dispersal potential (McMillan et al. 1992; Bohonak 1999), and populations of marine species with lengthy planktonic phases tend to show few genetic differences over large spatial scales (Doherty et al. 1995). These results have been used to suggest that larval dispersal is generally high. However, the genetic conclusions are best interpreted on an evolutionary time scale and

address issues of long-term genetic exchange across a species' range (Palumbi 1994). But what do these results tell us about short-term ecological exchange between marine populations? Do they prove that marine populations are demographically open? Application of genetic data to questions of short-term demographic exchange is difficult because of the difference between evolutionary time scales inherent in the genetic data and the ecological or management time scales that determine the utility of MPAs. But in general, many emerging genetic studies suggest that dispersal over ecological time scales may be more limited than thought previously.

The major reason for this discrepancy is that genetic studies can easily measure gene flow only when it is very small. Genetic exchange is monitored in terms of the average number of migrants that move between populations and become breeding adults every generation. This value is a product of the average population size (N) and the average fraction of each population that are immigrants (m). When Nm is much smaller than 1.0, then genetic structure evolves readily, and different populations are essentially on different evolutionary trajectories (see Slatkin 1987 for review). If Nm is between 1 and about 5, then genetic differentiation of populations can occur, but there is enough genetic exchange to prevent wholesale genetic divergence. If Nm is greater than 5–10, then little geographic genetic structure will be apparent. Such high values of gene flow are typically seen in marine organisms with long-distance larval exchange (Doherty et al. 1995).

However, even in these cases, the amount of demographic exchange may be minor. For sea urchins along the west coast of the United States (*Strongylocentrotus purpuratus*), gene flow was estimated to be high along 2500 km from Seattle to Los Angeles (Palumbi 1996). F_{ST} values, the approximate proportion of genetic variability that is distributed geographically (see (Wright 1978), were on the order of 0.01, with Nm estimated to be on the order of 20–50. Although these values are easily interpreted in a genetic and evolutionary context—the populations are not diverging—even high values of genetic exchange actually might represent a very low fraction of migrants into any one population. For example, migration of 20–50 individuals per generation must be compared with the number of individuals that do not migrate. In *S. purpuratus*, population size has been estimated in the billions, and genetically effective population size (breeding adults averaged over a large number of generations) is on the order of 500,000 to 1,000,000 (Palumbi and Wilson 1990). Thus, the proportion of migrants in each population per generation (Nm/N) is estimated to be about one in 100,000. As a result, for this highly dispersive marine species, less than a hundredth of a percent of individuals are estimated to be immigrants in every generation. Clearly such low demographic exchange will have negligible effects on local population dynamics, even though migration is still high in evolutionary terms.

This disparity between ecological and genetic views of marine populations is illustrated by a simulation of the genetic consequences of different types of larval dispersal. A stepping-stone model of larval exchange among adjacent, coastal populations was constructed to test the impact of different dispersal scenarios on genetic structure (Palumbi 2001). Local populations were 10 km wide and were arrayed continuously along a 2000 km coastline. Populations 500 km apart were monitored for genetic homogeneity by simulating gene flow and random genetic drift at a single nuclear locus under a wide variety of dispersal regimes. Overall, unless 98% of the larvae settled within 20 km of their origins (Figure 19.5A), there was no genetic structure. Even structure so slight that only 1% of the genetic variation is distributed geographically (e.g., $F_{ST} = 0.01$) required this restricted larval dispersal (Figure 19.5B). Although these conclusions are sensitive to assumptions about local population size, they suggest that even low levels of genetic differentiation are a signal of ecologically limited larval exchange.

Such signals of high gene flow but low demographic exchange may be visible in studies of several species of coastal marine invertebrates with nominally high dispersal abilities. In western Australia, for example, four studies of coastal invertebrates have shown significant gene frequency differ-

ences between larval cohorts or adult year classes or populations separated by short distances (Johnson and Black 1982; Johnson and Black 1984; Watts et al. 1990; Johnson et al. 1993). In Australia and California, abalone are now known to have significant genetic structure over spatial scales of kilometers, despite a larval period of 5–10 days (Shepherd and Brown 1993). The Australian crown-of-thorns starfish shows low but significant genetic structure across the Great Barrier Reef (Benzie and Stoddart 1992). These results are inconsistent with panmixia of marine populations with high larval dispersal. Instead, they suggest that average larval dispersal may be low. Two possible explanations are that selection is acting on some loci to increase genetic differentiation (e.g., Edmands et al. 1996), or that the fraction of migrants into a marine population from outside may be very small. A third possibility is that minor departures from neutral expectations may be artifacts of measurement error at low values of F_{ST}, and thus be entirely consistent with high dispersal and settlement of larvae far from their parents. Only if the geography of genetic differentiation of marine species is measured very

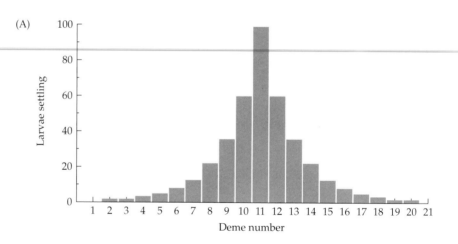

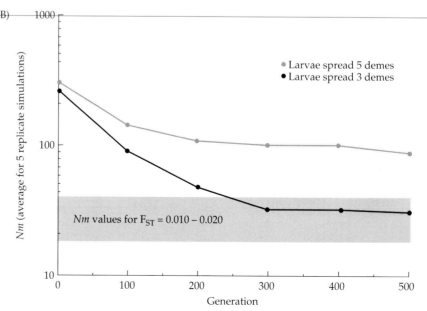

Figure 19.5 Simulation model showing that even slight genetic structure suggests limited larval exchange in marine species. (A) Dispersal shadow for a stepping-stone model of coastal marine populations. In this scheme, a larval spread of 5 demes means that 98% of the larvae stay within 5 demes of their origin. (B) Estimated gene flow along a stepping-stone array of demes in which dispersal varies from a larval spread of 5 demes (open circles) to 2 demes (closed circles). These simulations start with an even distribution of gene frequencies and a very high inferred level of gene flow (depicted here as Nm). As the populations reach an equilibrium between drift and migration, estimated Nm declines. Values of Nm as low as 20–50 (corresponding to an F_{ST} of 0.01–0.02 and 1–2% of the genetic variation structured geographically) are observed only with larval spread of 2 demes. A larval spread of 5 demes is too wide for the buildup of even 1–2% geographic structure. (Based on Palumbi 2001 and Palumbi, unpublished data.)

carefully and precisely can a low but significant F_{ST} be distinguished from zero (Waples 1998).

WHEN GENETICS SPEAKS LOUDLY. There are, in addition, an increasingly large number of studies of that show quite high genetic differentiation in marine species with potentially high dispersal. In these cases, the genetic implications are quite clear: very little ecological exchange is occurring. The genetic break of marine invertebrates and fish along the southeast coast of the United States (reviewed in Avise 1992) may represent surprisingly little gene flow in some widespread marine species. First recognized in horseshoe crabs, similar genetic breaks have been recorded for American oysters and several species of marine fish (Avise 1992). Horseshoe crabs have a swimming benthic "trilobite" larva with a development time of about two weeks. Oysters also have a two-week planktonic phase, and genetic breaks are seen between adjacent inshore marine lagoons currently separated by land. Strong gene frequency changes in these invertebrates and fish show either large-scale selection across many loci, or low realized genetic exchange between populations. If gene flow is low by evolutionary standards, it is miniscule by ecological criteria, and these populations can be considered to be demographically segregated.

Likewise, populations of marine invertebrates and fish separated by the Indonesian Archipelago often show strong gene frequency differences. Populations of mantis shrimp separated by only 300–400 km show strong genetic breaks, despite strong currents flowing between them (Figure 19.6; Barber et al. 2000). In addition, tiger shrimp, sea stars, coconut crabs, and several species of reef fish show major genetic differences between the Indian and Pacific Oceans (Lavery et al. 1996; Palumbi 1997; Williams and Benzie 1997; Duda and Palumbi 1999). These studies show the existence of sharp genetic and ecological discontinuities and suggest that dispersal between oceans has clearly been low over recent evolutionary time scales.

IS LONG DISTANCE DISPERSAL RARE? The blending of genetic results with emerging ecological data is not complete, but a possibility is that successful long-distance dispersal is relatively rare for many marine species. Long-distance gene flow for species with planktonic phases may occur often enough over evolutionary time scales that genetic uniformity is maintained. However, the paucity of studies of realized dispersal distances of marine larvae in natural settings, except for those with extremely low dispersal like ascidians (Olson 1985), means that it is extremely difficult to be confident about dispersal over ecological time scales for most species. Thus, the functional linkages of marine populations over ecological time scales is severely in doubt until more direct measurements of average larval dispersal are made, and the possibility of larval retention in local areas is more fully understood.

This uncertainty makes it difficult to understand completely how MPAs might function on a regional scale. If larval dispersal outside of reserves is moderate for some species, then the major benefit of fishery reserves—enhancement of fishing outside small reserves—may be likely for those species. The dispersal rate of larvae from particular marine protected areas needs to be understood in order to understand the impact of a reserve in a particular place on a particular species and to understand the likely importance of an MPA on the surrounding community. Because different species have such different potentials for dispersal, it may be

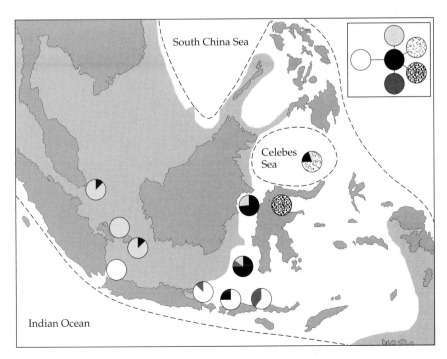

Figure 19.6 Strong genetic structure in Indonesian mantis shrimp shows that connectivity among populations is low despite strong currents. The pie diagrams represent frequencies of six major mtDNA haplotypes found in the stomatopod *Haptosquilla pulchella*. Distinct haplotype frequency differences show that populations as close as 300–400 km are genetically distinct, implying lack of connectivity. Because small Indonesian marine reserves are scattered across the archipelago, these genetic results suggest that reserves are not necessarily highly connected even by strong oceanic currents that flow between them. Lightly shaded areas represent seabed exposed during low sea level periods. (After Barber et al. 2000.)

that no single MPA size is appropriate for an entire marine community. Alternatively, it may be that MPAs need to be designed to accommodate the species with the highest dispersal capacity and that species with lower larval dispersal will also prosper in these conditions. This is currently one of the critical missing links in marine ecological and MPA research. Connectivity among MPAs cannot be evaluated completely until the average dispersal distances of marine larvae are available for a number of marine ecosystems and a number of ecologically important taxa.

DESIGN OF MARINE PROTECTED AREAS

Uncertainties about marine connectivity has not halted implementation of marine reserves, and in fact some of the pioneers of MPA design regard networks of marine protected areas as the only realistic political and economic solution to multiple use needs of marine coastal habitats (Ballantine 1991). Others point to the strong relationship between MPA function and the life history of a particular species (including whether adults are mobile, juveniles disperse a long distance, commercial exploitation is high, etc) and suggest that no single network design will be optimal for all the species in a marine community (Roberts and Polunin 1991).

Discussion of MPA design frequently focuses on two major issues: How big should individual no-take zones be? and How much area overall should be included in no-take zones? No-take zones that are too small will not retain a local reproductive population of species with high adult or larval movement (Attwood and Bennett 1995), and recent models suggest that MPAs should be about the same size as average dispersal distance per generation to provide the greatest benefit (A. Hastings and L. Botsford, in preparation). Two obvious problems with this approach are that we know little about average larval dispersal for particular species (see previous) and that a community has a huge variety of dispersal strategies. One possible solution is to scale MPAs to the size required for species with typical planktonic periods of a month or so and hope that these are larger than required for most other species in the community. However, typical planktonic dispersal averages of 20–50 km per generation (Palumbi 2001) may suggest MPAs that are too large to be politically practical: there is not a single marine no-take zone this size in the entire United States. Smaller no-take zones can be effective and may be more desirable for enhancement of recruitment to overfished species, but only if they are numerous enough and close enough to allow hopscotching between them (Hastings and Botsford 2001).

The other major MPA battleground is the amount of coastal habitat that should be in no-take reserves. Fisheries models suggest that complete control of fish population sizes will only be achieved with MPA fractions of 50% or more in many cases (Polacheck 1990; DeMartini 1993; Roberts 1997; Guénette et al. 1998; Lauck et al. 1998), but if this amount of area is set aside from fishing, then fisheries yields will tend to decline even if overall fish population sizes increase (Botsford

et al. 1999). At the other extreme, the tiny fraction of marine habitat currently in no-take marine reserves in the United States is estimated to be only on the order of 0.1% (McArdle 1997; Agardy 1999), and although this is enough for local population enhancement (Table 19.2), this is obviously too small to produce a substantial effect on overall marine ecosystems (Bohnsack 1994; Ballantine 1997).

Is there a reserve area between 0.1% and 50% that will provide substantial fisheries and biodiversity benefits, enough to outweigh the economic and political costs of establishing protected areas? Mace and Sissenwine (1993) suggested that preserving 20% of a reproductive population may be enough to prevent recruitment overfishing, the point where recruitment begins to falter because of low numbers of reproductive adults. Botsford et al. (1999) point out that the balance between enhanced fisheries production due to reserve protection and declines in fisheries access due to restricted fishing opportunities occurs at about 15–20% of habitable area, depending on the number of recruits per adult female . Roberts (2001) calculated that connectivity is enhanced when 10–35% of an area is split into many small reserves. Some advocates of marine protected areas have used these figures as a starting place, suggesting that 20% of each type of marine habitat be placed in reserve (Bohnsack 1994; Roberts 2001). Although this may seem too high a figure, it has been approached in other countries besides the United States: Bermuda has declared 20% of its continental shelf fully protected; South Africa protects 17% of its coastline, with a third of this being fully protected; Belize fully protects 19% of its reefs in marine parks (Roberts 2001).

Because even 20% protection is clearly not enough to provide optimal fishery benefits in most cases, this degree of habitat protection actually may represent a minimum level at which MPAs provide both diversity and fisheries benefits. Even at this level, MPAs cannot be the only fisheries management tool, but must be augmented by other effort controls. The impact on an entire ecosystem of protecting 10%, 20%, or 50% of the area from fishing is currently unknown because empirical tests have not been accomplished. Evidence suggests that MPAs on this order of scale will have an effect, but demonstrating this without a real example remains elusive.

Perhaps the most logical course is to establish research reserves with this degree of protection, and use this system as a clinical trial to verify or refute MPAs as a prescription for biodiversity and fisheries protection. In other realms, such as pharmaceutical development, clinical trials are recognized as costly but necessary; however, the patients are not required to foot the bill. A parallel construction would be to set up research reserves without passing the costs on to local fishers before the benefits of the reserves could be shown.

CONCLUSIONS

There is a variety of different goals for marine protected areas that can be categorized into efforts to enhance fishing, biodiversity, or protection of vulnerable life history stages. The scale of desired impact of an MPA also varies from those that focus on effects within the MPA boundary to those that depend on the MPA having an impact on the surrounding marine ecosystem. Marine protected areas show strong and consistent differences from adjacent, exploited habitats, but the best evidence is for fisheries reserves with local effects. MPA studies of biodiversity lag far behind those on fisheries, primarily because attention is focused, even in no-take reserves, on the monitoring of fish. MPA effects on regional ecosystems are even less well understood, primarily because the connectivity of populations within MPAs to those outside is poorly known.

Careful studies of the impact of current MPAs on surrounding ecosystems may allow such information to be collected in ways not possible before and may demonstrate the conditions under which a small unexploited population may enhance regional ecosystem diversity or productivity. The complicated trophic interactions within marine communities are reflected in dramatic changes when human exploitation is manipulated. Most marine communities are probably very deeply affected by current levels of human predation, and ecological studies should take this into account.

Three lines of evidence about marine connectivity—from oceanography, larval biology, and genetics—give contradictory answers about the degree to which larvae usually disperse long distances. Measuring the average dispersal distance of marine species remains a critical challenge in marine ecology and MPA design.

MPA research combines a basic desire to understand marine ecological interactions with a practical need to manage global marine resources more carefully. MPAs not only represent important reservoirs for populations under increasing exploitative demands, but they also represent valuable research sites for untangling the ecological interactions between humans and the rest of marine communities.

LITERATURE CITED

Addessi, L. 1994. Human disturbance and long-term changes on a rocky intertidal community. *Ecol. Appl.* 4: 786–797.

Agardy, M. T. 1994. Closed areas: a tool to complement other forms of fisheries management. In K. L. Gimbel (ed.), *Limiting Access to Marine Fisheries: Keeping the Focus on Conservation*. Center for Marine Conservation and World Wildlife Fund, Washington, DC.

Agardy, T. 1999. Creating havens for marine life. *Issues Sci. Tech.* 16: 37–44.

Alcala, A. C. 1988. Effects of marine reserves on coral fish abundances and yields of Philippine coral reefs. *Ambio* 17: 194–199.

Alcala, A. C. and G. R. Russ. 1990. A direct test of the effects of protective management on abundance and yield of tropical marine resources. *J. Conseil* 46: 40–47.

Anastasia, J. R., S. G. Morgan and N. S. Fisher. 1998. Tagging crustacea larvae: Assimilation and retention of trace elements. *Limn. Oceangr.* 43: 362–368.

Armstrong, D. A., T. C. Wainwright, G. C. Jensen, P. A. Dinnel and H. B. Anderson. 1993. Taking refuge from bycatch issues: Red king crab (*Paralithodes camtschaticus*) and trawl fisheries in the eastern Bering Sea. *Can. J. Fish. Aquat. Sci.* 50: 1993–2000.

Attwood, C. G. and B. A. Bennett. 1994. Variation in dispersal of galjoen (*Coracinus capensis*) (Teleostei: Coracinidae) from a marine reserve. *Can. J. Fish. Aquat. Sci.* 51: 1247–1257.

Attwood, C. G. and B. A. Bennett. 1995. Modeling the effect of marine reserves on the recreational shore-fishery of the South-Western Cape, South Africa. *S. African J. Mar. Sci.* 16: 227–240.

Attwood, C. G., J. M. Harris and A. J. Williams. 1997. International experience of marine protected areas and their relevance to South Africa. *S. African J. Mar. Sci.* 18: 311–332.

Avise, J. C. 1992. Molecular population structure and biogeographic history of a regional fauna: A case history with lessons for conservation and biology. *Oikos* 63: 62–76.

Ayling, A. M. and A. L. Ayling. 1986. Unpublished report to Great Barrier Reef Marine Park, cited in Roberts and Polunin, Are marine reserves effective in management of reef fisheries? *Rev. Fish Biol. Fish.* 1: 65–91.

Ballantine, W. J. 1991. Marine reserves: The need for networks. *New Zealand J. Mar. Freshw. Res.* 25: 115–116.

Ballantine, W. J. 1997. Design principles for systems of "no-take" marine reserves. In *The Design and Monitoring of Marine Reserves*. Fisheries Center, University of British Columbia, Vancouver.

Barber, P. H., S. R. Palumbi, N. V. Erdmann and M. K. Moosa. 2000. A marine Wallace's line? *Nature* 406: 692693.

Bell, J. D. 1983. Effects of depth and marine reserve fishing restrictions on the structure of a rocky reef fish assemblage in the northwestern Mediterranean Sea. *J. Appl. Ecol.* 20: 357–369.

Bennett, B. A. and C. B. Attwood. 1991. Evidence for recovery of a surf-zone fish assemblage following the establishment of a marine reserve on the southern coast of South Africa. *Mar. Ecol. Prog. Ser.* 75: 173–181.

Benzie, J. H. A. and J. Stoddart. 1992. Genetic structure of crown-of-thorns starfish (*Acanthaster planci*) in Australia. *Mar. Biol.* 112: 631–639.

Black, K. P. 1993. The relative importance of local retention and inter-reef dispersal of neutrally buoyant material on coral reefs. *Coral Reefs* 12: 43–53.

Black, K. P., P. J. Moran and L. S. Hammond. 1991. Numerical models show coral reefs can be self-seeding. *Mar. Ecol. Prog. Ser.* 74: 1–11.

Bohnsack, J. A. 1982. Effects of piscivorous predator removal on coral reef fish community structure. In G. M. Caillet and C. A. Simenstad (eds.), *Gutshop 1981: Fish Food Habits and Studies*. Washington Seagrant Publishers, Seattle.

Bohnsack, J. A. 1994. How marine fishery reserves can improve reef fisheries. *Proc. Gulf Caribbean Fish. Inst.* 43: 217–241.

Bohonak, A. J. 1999. Dispersal, gene flow, and population structure. *Q. Rev. Biol.* 74: 21–45.

Botsford, L. W., J. C. Castilla and C. H. Peterson. 1997. The management of fisheries and marine ecosystems. *Science* 277: 509–515.

Botsford, L. W., C. L. Moloney, J. L. Largier and A. Hastings. 1998. Metapopulation dynamics of meroplanktonic invertebrates: The Dungeness crab (*Cancer magister*) as an example. *Can. Spec. Publ. Fish. Aquat. Sci.* 125: 295–306.

Botsford, L. W., L. E. Morgan, D. R. Lockwood and J. Wilen, R. 1999. Marine reserves and management of the California red sea urchin fishery. *Cal. COFI Reports* 40: 87–93.

Bowen, B. and J. C. Avise. 1996. Conservation genetics of marine turtles. In J. C. Avise and J. L. Hamrick (eds.), *Conservation Genetics: Case Histories from Nature*, pp. 190–237. Chapman and Hall, New York.

Buxton, C. D. and M. J. Smale. 1989. Abundance and distribution patterns of three temperate marine reef fish (Teleostei: Sparidae) in exploited and unexploited areas off the southern cape coast. *J. Appl. Ecol.* 26: 441–452.

Campbell, A. and D. S. Pezzack. 1986. Relative egg production and abundance of berried Lobsters, *Homarus americanus*, in the Bay of Fundy and off Southwestern Nova Scotia. *Can. J. Fish. Aquat. Sci.* 43: 2190–2196.

Carlton, J. T. and J. B. Geller. 1993. Ecological roulette: The global transport of non-indigenous marine organisms. *Science* 261: 78–82.

Castilla, J. C. 1999. Coastal marine communities: trends and perspectives from human exclusion experiments. *Trends Ecol. Evol.* 14: 280-283.

Castilla, J. C. and R. H. Bustamante. 1989. Human exclusion from rocky intertidal of Las Cruces, central Chile: Effects on *Durvillaea antarctica* (Phaeophyta, Durvilleales). *Mar. Ecol. Prog. Ser.* 50: 203–214.

Castilla, J. C. and R. Duran. 1985. Human exclusion from the rocky intertidal zone of central Chile: the effects on *Concholepas* (Gastropoda). *Oikos* 45: 391–399.

Castilla, J. C. and M. A. Varas. 1998. A plankton trap for exposed rocky intertidal shores. *Mar. Biol. Prog. Ser.* 175: 299–305.

Christy, J. H. and S. G. Morgan. 1998. Estuarine immigration by crab postlarvae: mechanisms, reliability and adaptive significance. *Mar. Ecol. Prog. Ser.* 174: 51–65.

Clark, J. R., B. Causey and J. A. Bohnsack. 1989. Benefits from coral reef protection: Looe Key Reef, Florida. In O. T. Magoon, H. Converse, D. Miner, L. T. Tobin and J. R. Clark (eds.), *Proc. 6th Symp. Coastal and Ocean Management*, (Charleston, NC, July 11-14, 1989), pp. 3076-3086.

Cole, R. G., T. M. Ayling and R. G. Creese. 1990. Effects of marine reserve protection at Goat Island, northern New Zealand. *New Zealand J. Mar. Freshwat. Res.* 24: 197–210,.

Cronin, T. W. and R. B. Forward. 1986. Vertical migration cycles of crab larvae and their role in larval dispersal. *Bull. Mar. Sci.* 39: 192–201.

Davis, G. E. 1977. Effects of recreational harvest on a spiny lobster, *Panulirus argus*, population. *Bull. Mar. Sci.* 27(2): 223–236.

Dayton, P. K., S. F. Thrush, M. T. Agardy and R. J. Hofman. 1995. Environmental effects of marine fishing. *Aquat. Conserv. Mar. Freshw. Ecosyst.* 5: 205–232.

Defeo, O. and A. De Alva. 1995. Effects of human activities on long-term trends in sandy beach populations: The wedge clam *Donax hanleyanus* in Uruguay. *Mar. Ecol. Prog. Ser.* 123: 73–82.

DeMartini, E. E. 1993. Modeling the potential of fishery reserves for managing Pacific coral reef fishes. *Fish. Bull.* 91: 414–427.

Doherty, P. J., S. Planes and P. Mather. 1995. Gene flow and larval duration in 7 species of fish from the Great Barrier Reef. *Ecology* 76: 2373–2391.

Duda, T. F. and S. R. Palumbi. 1999. Population structure of the black Tiger Prawn, *Penaeus monodon*, among western Indian Ocean and Western Pacific Populations. *Mar. Biol.* 134: 705-710.

Dugan, J. E. and G. E. Davis. 1993. Applications of marine refugia to coastal fisheries management. *Can. J. Fish. Aquat. Sci.* 50: 2029–2042.

Duran, L. R. and J. C. Castilla. 1989. Variation and persistence of the middle rocky internal community of central Chile, with and without harvesting. *Mar. Biol.* 103: 555–562.

Duran, L. R., J. C. Castilla and D. Oliva. 1987. Intensity of human predation on rocky shores at Las Cruces in Central Chile. *Environ. Conserv.* 14: 143–149.

Edmands, S., P. Moberg and R. S. Burton. 1996. Allozyme and mitochondrial DNA evidence of population subdivision in the purple sea urchin *Strongylocentrotus purpuratus*. *Mar. Biol.* 126: 443–450.

Edgar, G. J. and N. S. Barrett. 1997. Short term monitoring of biotic change in Tasmanian marine reserves. *J. Exp. Mar. Biol. Ecol.* 213: 261–279.

Estes, J. A., M. T. Tinker, T. M. Williams and D. F. Doak. 1998. Killer whale predation on sea otters linking oceanic and nearshore ecosystems. *Science* 282: 473–476.

Forward, R. B., J. Swanson, R. A. Tankerse;y and J. M. Welch. 1997. Endogenous swimming rhythms of blue crab, *Callinectes sapidus*, megalopae: Effects of offshore and estuarine cues. *Mar. Biol.* 127: 621–628.

Gaines, S., S. Brown and J. Roughgarden. 1985. Spatial variation in larval concentrations as a cause of spatial variation in settlement for the barnacle, *Balanus glandula*. *Oecologia* 67: 267–272.

Garcia-Rubies, A. and M. Zabala. 1990. Effects of total fishing prohibition on the rocky fish assemblages of Medes Islands marine reserve (Northwest Mediterranean). *Scientia Marina* 54: 317–328.

Geller, J. 1996. Molecular approaches to the study of marine biological invasions. In J. D. Ferraris and S. R. Palumbi (eds.), *Molecular Zoology: Advances, Strategies, and Protocols*, pp. 119–132. Wiley-Liss, New York.

Geller, J. B. 1994. Marine biological invasions as models of dispersal: Tracking secondary spread and introgressive gene flow. *Calif. Coop. Oceanic Fish. Inv. Rep.* 35: 68–72.

Geller, J. B., E. D. Walton, E. D. Grosholz and G. M. Ruiz. 1997. Cryptic invasions of the crab *Carcinus* detected by molecular phylogeography. *Molec. Ecol.* 6: 256–261.

Grosberg, R. K. 1982. Intertidal zonation of barnacles: The influence of planktonic zonation of larvae on the vertical distribution of adults. *Ecology* 63: 894–899.

Guénette, S., T. Lauck, and C. Clark. 1998. Marine reserves: from Beverton and Holt to the present. *Rev. Fish Biol. Behav.* 8: 251–272.

Halpern, B. 2001. The impact of marine reserves: Do reserves work and does reserve size matter? *Ecol. Appl.* in press.

Harriott, V. J. and S. A. Banks. 1995. Recruitment of scleractinian corals in the Solitary Islands Marine Reserve, a high latitude coral-dominated community in Eastern Australia. *Mar. Ecol. Prog. Ser.* 123: 155–161.

Harvell, C. D., K. Kim, J. Burkholder, R. Colwell, P. Epstein, D. Grimes, E. Hofmann, E. Lipp, A. Osterhaus, R. Overstreet, J. Porter, G. Smith and G. Vasta. 1999. Emerging marine diseases—Climate links and anthropogenic factors. *Science* 285: 1505–1510.

Hastings, A. and L. W. Botsford. 1999. Equivalence in yield from marine reserves and traditional fisheries management. *Science* 284: 1537–1541.

Hastings, A. and L. W. Botsford. 2001. Are marine reserves for fisheries and biodiversiry compatible? *Ecol. Appl.* submitted.

Hendrickson, H. M. and W. L. Griffin. 1993. An analysis of management policies for reducing shrimp by-catch in the Gulf of Mexico. *N. Amer. J. Fish. Man.* 13: 686–697.

Heslinga, G. A., O. Orak and M. Ngiramengior. 1984. Coral reef sanctuaries for trochus shells. *Mar. Fish. Rev.* 46: 73-80.

Hockey, P. A. and G. M. Branch. 1994. Conserving marine biodiversity on the African coast: implications of a terrestrial perspective. *Aquat. Conserv.: Mar. Freshw. Ecosyst.* 4: 345–362.

Hutchings, J. A. 1995. Seasonal marine protected areas within the context of spatio-temporal variation in the northern cod fishery. In N. Shackell and J. H. M. Willison (eds.), *Marine Protected Areas and Sustainable Fisheries*, pp. 39–47. SAMPAA, Wolfville, Nova Scotia.

Jackson, J. B. C. 1997. Reefs since Columbus. *Coral Reefs* 16: S23-S32.

Jamieson, G. S., A. C. Phillips and W. S. Hugget. 1989. Effects of ocean variability on the abundance of Dungeness crab (*Cancer magister*) megalope. *Can. Spec. Publ. Fish. Aquat. Sci.* 108: 305-325.

Jennings, S. and N. V. C. Polunin. 1997. Impacts of predator depletion by fishing on the biomass and diversity of non-target reef fish communities. *Coral Reefs* 16: 71–82.

Johnson, M. S. and R. Black. 1982. Chaotic genetic patchiness in an intertidal limpet, *Siphonaria* sp. *Mar. Biol.* 70: 157–164.

Johnson, M. S. and R. Black. 1984. Pattern between the chaos: The effect of recruitment on genetic patchiness in an intertidal limpet. *Evolution* 38: 1371–1383.

Johnson, M. S., K. Holborn and R. Black. 1993. Fine-scale patchiness and genetic heterogeneity of recruits of the carallivorous gastropod *Drupella cornus*. *Mar. Biol.* 117: 91–96.

Jones, G. P., M. J. Milicich, M. J. Emslie and C. Lunow. 1999. Self-recruitment in a coral reef fish population. *Nature* 402: 802-804

Katz, C. H., J. S. Cobb and M. Spaulding. 1994. Larval behavior, hydrodynamic transport, and potential offshore-to-inshore recruitment in the American lobster *Homarus americanus*. *Mar. Ecol. Prog. Ser.* 103: 265–273.

Kay, A. E. and S. R. Palumbi. 1987. Endemism and evolution in Hawaiian marine invertebrates. *Trends Ecol. Evol.* 2: 183–186.

Kelleher, G. and C. Recchia. 1998. Editorial: Lessons from marine protected areas around the world. PARKS, *Internatl. J. Protected Area Man.* 8: 1–4.

Keough, M. J., G. P. Quinn and A. King. 1993. Correlations between human collecting and intertidal Mollusc populations on rocky shores. *Conserv. Biol.* 7: 378–390.

Klima, E. F., G. A. Matthews and F. J. Patella. 1986. Abundance and distribution of pink shrimp in and around the Tortugas Sanctuary, 1981–1983. *N. Amer. J. Fish. Man.* 6: 301–310.

Lauck, T., C. W. Clarke, M. Mangel and G. R. Munro. 1998. Implementing the precautionary principles in fisheries management through marine reserves. Ecol. Appl. 8 (Supp.): S72-S78.

Lavery, S., C. Moritz and D. R. Fielder. 1996. Indo-Pacific population structure and evolutionary history of the coconut crab *Birgus latro*. *Molec. Ecol.* 5: 557–570.

Lee, T. N., M. E. Clarke, E. Williams, A. F. Szmant and T. Berger. 1994. Evolution of the
Tortugas Gyre and its influence on recruitment in the Florida Keys. *Bull. Mar. Sci.* 54:
621–646.

Lenihan, H. S. and C. H. Peterson. 1998. How
habitat degradation through fishery disturbance enhances impacts of hypoxia on oyster reefs. *Ecol. Appl.* 8: 128–140.

Lessios, H. A. 1995. *Diadema antillarumi* 10
years after mass mortality: Still rare, despite
help from a competitor. *Proc. Roy. Soc. Lond*
B 259: 331–337.

Levin, L. A., D. Huggett, P. Myers, T. Bridges
and J. Weaver. 1993. Rare-earth tagging
methods for the study of larval dispersal by
marine-invertebrates. *Limnol. Oceanogr.* 38:
246–360.

Limouzy-Paris, C. B., H. C. Graber, D. L. Jones,
A. W. Ropke and Richards. 1997. Translocation of larval coral reef fishes via sub-
mesoscale spin-off eddies from the Florida
current. *Bull. Mar. Sci.* 60: 966–983.

Lubchenco, J. 1998. Entering the century of the
environment: A new social contract for science. *Science* 279: 491–497.

Mace, P. M. and M. P. Sissenwine. 1993. How
much spawning per recruit is enough? *Can.
Spec. Publ. Fish. Aquat. Sci.* 120: 101–118.

Matthews, K. R. and L. Richards. 1991. Rockfish (Scorpaenidae) assemblages of
trawlable and untrawlable habitats off Van-
cover Island, British Columbia. *N. Amer. J.
Fish. Manag.* 11: 312–318.

McArdle, D. A. 1997. The status of California
marine protected areas. In D. A. McArdle
(ed.), *Marine Protected Areas of California: A
Summary of a Conference Session*, pp. 13–24.
University of California, Santa Barbara.

McCay. 1988. Muddling through the clam
beds: Cooperative management of New Jersey's hard clam spawner sanctuaries. *J.
Shellfish Res.* 7: 327–340.

McClanahan, T. 1989. Kenyan coral reef-associated gastropod fauna—a comparison between protected and unprotected reefs. *Mar.
Ecol. Prog. Ser.* 53: 11–20.

McClanahan, T. R. 1994. Kenyan coral reef lagoon fish: Effects of fishing, substrate complexity, and sea urchins. *Coral Reefs* 13:
231–241.

McClanahan, T. R. 1995. A coral reef ecosys-
tem-fisheries model: Impacts of fishing intensity and catch selection on reef structure
and processes. *Ecol. Modeling* 80: 1–19.

McClanahan, T. R. and B. Kaunda-Arara. 1996.
Fishery recovery in a coral-reef marine park
and its effect on the adjacent fishery. *Conserv. Biol.* 10: 1187–1199.

McClanahan, T. R. and S. H. Shafir. 1990. Causes and consequences of sea urchin abundance and diversity in Kenyan coral reef lagoons. *Oecologia* 83: 362–370.

McMillan, W. O., R. A. Raff and S. R. Palumbi.
1992. Population genetic consequences of
developmental evolution in sea urchins
(Genus *Heliocidaris*). *Evolution* 46:
1299–1312.

McNeill, S. E. and P. G. Fairweather. 1993. Single large or several small marine reserves?

An experimental approach with seagrass
fauna. *J. Biogeog.* 20: 429–440.

McShane, P. E., K. P. Black and M. G. Smith.
1988. Recruitment processes in *Haliotis rubra*
(Mollusca Gastropoda) and regional hydrodynamics in southeastern Australia imply
localized dispersal of larvae. *J. Exp. Mar.
Biol. Ecol.* 124: 175–204.

Murawski, S. A., R. Brown, H.-L. Lai, P. J. Rago
and L. Hendrickson. 2000. Large-scale
closed areas as a fishery-management tool
in temperate marine systems: The Georges
Bank experience. *Bull. Mar. Sci.* 66: 775-798.

Myers, R. A., J. A. Hutchings and N. J. Barrow-
man. 1997. Why do fish stocks collapse? The
example of cod in Atlantic Canada. *Ecol.
Appl.* 7: 91–106.

Nash, W. J., J. C. Sanderson, J. Bridley, S. Dick-
son and B. Hislop. 1995. Post-larval recruitment of blacklip abalone (*Haliotis rubra*) on
artificial collectors in Southern Tasmania.
Mar. Freshw. Res. 46: 531–538.

Oliva, D. and J. C. Castilla. 1986. The effect of
human exclusion on the population structure of key-hole limpets *Fissurella crassa* and
F. limbata on the coast of central Chile. *Mar.
Ecol.* 7: 201–217.

Olson, R. 1985. The consequences of short-distance larval dispersal in a sessile marine invertebrate. *Ecology* 66: 30–39.

Osenberg, C. W., R. Schmidtt, S. Hollbrook, S.
K. E. Abu and A. R. Flegal. 1994. Detection
of environmental impacts: Natural variability, effect size, and power analysis. *Ecol.
Appl.* 4: 16–30.

Paddock, M. J. 1996. The influence of marine
reserves upon rockfish populations in central California kelp forests. MS Thesis, University of California, Santa Cruz.

Paine, R. T. 1984. Ecological determinism in
the competition for space. *Ecology* 65:
1339–1348.

Paine, R. T. 1992. Food-web analysis through
field measurements of per capita interaction
strength. *Nature* 355: 73–75.

Paine, R. T., J. C. Castilla and J. Cancino. 1985.
Perturbation and recovery patterns of
starfish-dominated intertidal assemblages
in Chile, New Zealand and Washington
state. *Amer. Nat.* 125: 679–691.

Paine, R. T., J. L. Ruesink, A. Sun, E. L.
Soulanille, M. J. Wonham, C. D. G. Harley,
D. R. Brumbaugh and D. L. Secord. 1996.
Trouble on oiled waters: Lessons from the
Exxon Valdez oil spill. *Annu. Rev. Ecol. Syst.*
27: 197–236.

Palsson, W. A. and R. E. Pacunski. 1995. The
response of rocky reef fishes to harvest refugia, In *Puget Sound Research '95.* Puget
Sound Water Quality Authority, Olympia,
WA.

Palumbi, S. R. 1994. Genetic divergence, reproductive isolation, and marine speciation.
Annu. Rev. Ecol. Syst. 25: 547–572.

Palumbi, S. R. 1996. What can molecular genetics contribute to marine biogeography?
An urchin's tale. *J. Exp. Mar. Biol. Ecol.* 203:
75–92.

Palumbi, S. R. 1997. Molecular biogeography
of the Pacific. *Coral Reefs* 15: S47–52.

Palumbi, S. R. 2001. Population genetics, demographic connectivity and the design of
marine reserves. *Ecol. Appl.* in press.

Palumbi, S. R. and A. C. Wilson. 1990. Mitochondrial DNA diversity in the sea urchins
Strongylocentrotus purpuratus and *S. droebachiensis*. *Evolution* 44: 403–415.

Parrish, R. 1999. Marine reserves for fisheries
management: Why not? *CalCOFI Reports* 40:
77–86.

Pauly, D., V. Christensen, J. Dalsgaard, R.
Froese and F. Torres. 1998. Fishing down
marine food webs. *Science* 279: 860–863.

Peterson, C. H. and H. C. Summerson. 1992.
Basin-scale coherence of population dynamics of an exploited marine invertebrate, the
bay scallop: Implications of recruitment limitations. *Mar. Ecol. Prog. Ser.* 90: 257–272.

Peterson, C. H., H. C. Summerson and R. A. J.
Leuttich. 1996. Response of bay scallops to
spawner transplants: A test of recruitment
limitation. *Mar. Ecol. Prog. Ser.* 132: 93–107.

Polacheck, T. 1990. Year round closed areas as
a management tool. *Nat. Resource Modeling*
4: 327–354.

Polunin, N. V. C. and C. M. Roberts. 1993.
Greater biomass and value of target coral-
reef fishes in two small Caribbean marine
reserves. *Mar. Ecol. Prog. Ser.* 100: 167–176.

Roberts, C. M. 1995. Rapid build-up of fish
biomass in a Caribbean marine reserve.
Conserv. Biol. 9: 815–826.

Roberts, C. M. 1997. Ecological advice for the
global fisheries crisis. *Trends Evol. Ecol.* 12:
35–38.

Roberts, C. M. 2001. How much of the sea
should be in marine reserves? *Ecol. Appl.* in
press:

Roberts, C. M. and N. V. Polunin. 1991. Are
marine reserves effective in management of
reef fisheries? *Rev. Fish Biol. Fish.* 1: 65–91.

Roberts, C. M. and N. V. Polunin. 1993. Effects
of marine reservation protection on northern Red Sea fish populations. In *Proc. 7th Internatl. Coral Reef Symp.*, pp. 969-977. University of Guam Press, Mangilao.

Roberts, C. M., W. J. Ballantine, C. D. Buxton,
P. Dayton, L. B. Crowder, W. Milon, M. K.
Orback, D. Pauly, J. Trexler and C. J. Walters. 1995. Review of the use of marine fishery reserves in the U.S. southeastern Atlantic. National Oceanic and Atmospheric
Administration (NOAA) Technical Memorandum NMFS-SEFSC-376, Miami, FL.

Rowan, R., N. Knowlton, A. Baker and J. Jara.
1997. Landscape ecology of algal symbionts
creates variation in episodes of coral bleaching. *Nature* 388: 265–269.

Ruckelshaus, M. H. and C. G. Hayes. 1998.
Conservation and management of species in
the sea. In P. Fiedler and P. Kareiva (eds.),
Conservation Biology for the Coming Decade,
pp. 110-156. Chapman and Hall, London.

Russ, G. 1985. Effects of protective management of coral reef fishes in the central
Philippines. *Moorea* 4: 219–224.

Russ, G. R. and A. C. Alcala. 1989. Effects of intense fishing pressure on an assemblage of
coral reef fishes. *Mar. Ecol. Prog. Ser.* 56:
13–28.

Ruth, M. and J. Lindholm. 1996. Dynamic modeling of multispecies fisheries for consensus building and management. *Environ. Conserv.* 23: 332–342.

Samoilys, M. 1988. Abundance and species richness of coral reef fish on the Kenyan coast: The effects of protective management and fishing. *Proc. 6th Internatl. Coral Reef Symp.* 2: 261–266.

Scheltema, R. S. 1986. On dispersal and planktonic larvae of benthic invertebrates: An eclectic overview and summary of problems. *Bull. Mar. Sci.* 39: 290–322.

Shepherd, S. A. 1990. Studies on the Southern Australia abalone (genus *Haliotis*) XII: Long-term recruitment and mortality dynamics of an unfished population. *Austral. J. Mar. Freshw. Res.* 41: 475–492:

Shepherd, S. A. and L. D. Brown. 1993. What is an abalone stock: Implications for the role of refugia in conservation. *Can. J. Fish. Aquat. Sci.* 50: 2001–2009.

Shulman, M. J. and E. Bermingham. 1995. Early life histories, ocean currents, and the population genetics of Caribbean reef fishes. *Evolution* 49: 897–910.

Slatkin, M. 1987. Gene flow and the geographic structure of natural populations. *Science* 236: 787–792.

Smedbol, R. K., D. C. Schneider, J. S. Wroblewski and D. A. Methven. 1998. Outcome of an inshore spawning event by northern cod (*Gadus morhua*) at a low stock level. *Can. J. Fish. Aquat. Sci.* 55: 2283–2291.

Smith, A. H. and F. Berkes. 1991. Solutions to the "tragedy of the commons": Sea urchin management in St. Lucia, West Indies. *Environ. Conserv.* 18: 131–136.

Swearer, S. E., J. E. Caselle, D. W. Lea and R. R. Warner. 1999. Larval retention and recruitment in an island population of a coral reef fish. *Nature* 402: 799-802.

Tankersley, R. A., L. M. McKelvey and R. B. Forward. 1995. Responses of estuarine crab megalopae to pressure, salinity and light: Implications for flood-tide transport. *Mar. Biol.* 122: 391–400.

Tegner, M. J. 1989. The feasibility of enhancing red sea urchin, *Strongylocentrotus franciscanus*, stocks in California: An analysis of options. *Mar. Fish. Rev.* 51: 1–22.

Tegner, M. J. 1992. Brood-stock transplants as an approach to abalone stock enhancement. In S. A. Shepherd, M. J. Tegner and S. A. Guzman del Proo (eds.), *Abalone of the World: Their Biology, Fisheries and Culture,* pp. 504-517. Blackwell Scientific Publications, Oxford, U.K.

Tegner, M. J. 1993. Southern California abalones: Can stocks be rebuilt using marine harvest refugia? *Can. J. Fish. Aquat. Sci.* 50: 2010–2018.

Tilman, D. and J. A. Downing. 1994. Biodiversity and stability in grasslands. *Nature* 367: 363–365.

Walters, C. J. and J. J. Maguire. 1996. Lessons for stock assessment from the Northern Cod collapse. *Rev. Fish Biol. Fish.* 6: 125–137.

Waples, R. S. 1998. Separating the wheat from the chaff: Patterns of genetic differentiation in high gene flow species. *J. Hered.* 89: 438–450.

Watling, L. and E. A. Norse. 1998. Disturbance of the seabed by mobile fishing gear: A comparison to forest clearcutting. *Conserv. Biol.* 12: 1180–1197.

Watts, R. J., M. S. Johnson and R. Black. 1990. Effects of recruitment on genetic patchiness in the urchin *Echinometra mathaei* in Western Australia. *Mar. Biol.* 105: 145–151.

Weil, E. M. and G. Laughlin. 1984. Biology, population dynamics and reproduction of the queen conch *Strombus gigas* Linne in the Archipelago De Los Roques National Park. *J. Shellfish Res.* 4: 45–62.

Weinberg, J. R. 1998. Density-dependent growth in the Atlantic surfclam, *Spisula solidissima*, off the coast of the Delmarva Peninsula, USA. *Mar. Biol.* 130: 621–630.

Williams, S. and J. A. Benzie. 1997. Indo-West Pacific patterns of genetic differentiation in the high dispersal starfish, *Linkia laevigata*. *Molec. Ecol.* 6: 559–573.

Wright, S. 1978. *Evolution and the Genetics of Populations* (4 vol.): Vol. 4: *Variability within and among Natural Populations*. University of Chicago Press, Chicago.

Yamasaki, A. and A. Kuwahara. 1990. Preserved areas do effect recovery of overfished Zuwai crab stocks of Kyoto Prefecture. In Proc. Internatl. Symp. King and Tanner Crabs, pp. 575–578. Alaska Sea Grant, Fairbanks.

Illustration Credits

Index

Numbers in italics are references to illustrations.